DORLING KINDERSLEY

ULTIMATE
VISUAL
DICTIONARY

EXTERNAL FEATURES
OF A BUTTERFLY

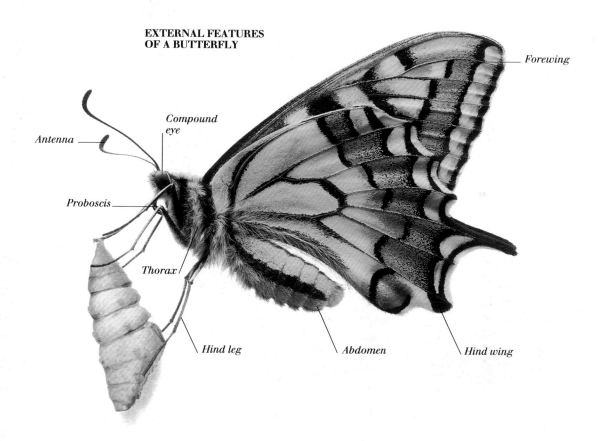

Forewing

Compound
eye

Antenna

Proboscis

Thorax

Hind leg

Abdomen

Hind wing

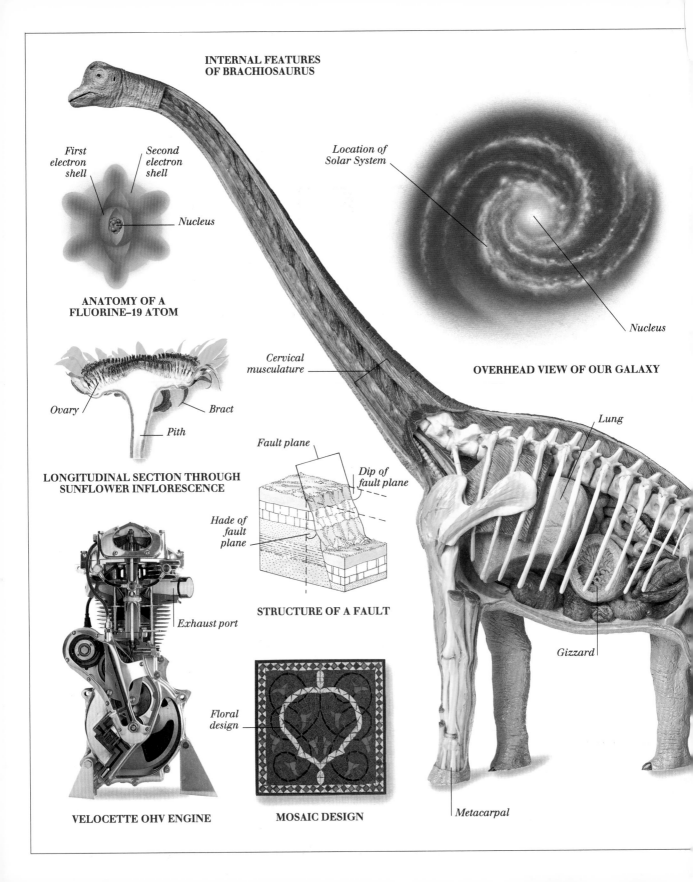

**INTERNAL FEATURES
OF BRACHIOSAURUS**

*First
electron
shell*

*Second
electron
shell*

Nucleus

**ANATOMY OF A
FLUORINE–19 ATOM**

*Location of
Solar System*

Nucleus

OVERHEAD VIEW OF OUR GALAXY

Ovary

Bract

Pith

*Cervical
musculature*

Lung

**LONGITUDINAL SECTION THROUGH
SUNFLOWER INFLORESCENCE**

Fault plane

*Dip of
fault plane*

*Hade of
fault
plane*

STRUCTURE OF A FAULT

Exhaust port

Gizzard

*Floral
design*

VELOCETTE OHV ENGINE

MOSAIC DESIGN

Metacarpal

ULTIMATE
VISUAL
DICTIONARY

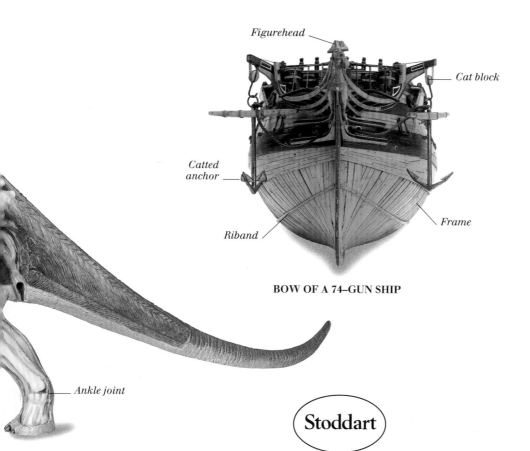

Figurehead

Cat block

Catted
anchor

Frame

Riband

BOW OF A 74–GUN SHIP

Ankle joint

Stoddart

A DORLING KINDERSLEY BOOK

PROJECT ART EDITORS HEATHER McCARRY, JOHNNY PAU, CHRIS WALKER, KEVIN WILLIAMS
DESIGNER SIMON MURRELL

PROJECT EDITORS LUISA CARUSO, PETER JONES, JANE MASON, GEOFFREY STALKER
EDITOR JO EVANS

DTP DESIGNER ZIRRINIA AUSTIN
PICTURE RESEARCHER CHARLOTTE BUSH

MANAGING ART EDITOR TONI KAY
SENIOR EDITOR ROGER TRITTON
MANAGING EDITOR SEAN MOORE

PRODUCTION MANAGER HILARY STEPHENS

ANATOMICAL AND BOTANICAL MODELS SUPPLIED BY SOMSO MODELLE, COBURG, GERMANY

Sound-hole

Hollow body

Bridge

Headstock

ACOUSTIC GUITAR

PUBLISHED IN CANADA IN 1994 BY STODDART PUBLISHING CO. LIMITED
34 LESMILL ROAD, TORONTO, CANADA, M3B 2T6

FIRST PUBLISHED IN GREAT BRITAIN IN 1994
BY DORLING KINDERSLEY LIMITED, 9 HENRIETTA STREET, COVENT GARDEN, LONDON WC2E 8PS

CANADIAN CATALOGUING IN PUBLICATION DATA
MAIN ENTRY UNDER TITLE:
ULTIMATE VISUAL DICTIONARY
INCLUDES INDEX.
ISBN 0-7737-2823-6
1. PICTURE DICTIONARIES, ENGLISH.

PE1629.U58 1994   423'.1   C94-931562-1

REPRODUCED BY COLOURSCAN, SINGAPORE

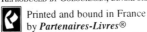

Printed and bound in France
by *Partenaires-Livres*®

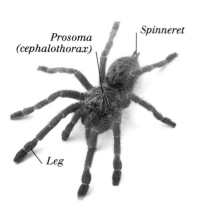

Prosoma (cephalothorax)

Spinneret

Leg

EXTERNAL FEATURES OF A SPIDER

Canopy

Fin

G-BNHB

Main landing gear

SIDE VIEW OF ARV SUPER 2 AIRPLANE

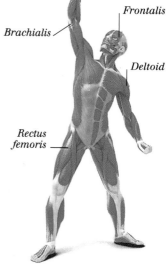

Frontalis

Brachialis

Deltoid

Rectus femoris

SUPERFICIAL SKELETAL MUSCLES

CONTENTS

Barrel

Permanent black ink

FOUNTAIN PEN AND INK

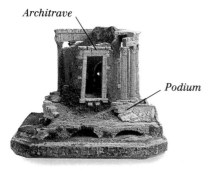

Architrave

Podium

TEMPLE OF VESTA, TIVOLI, ITALY, c.80 bc

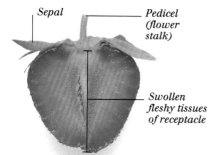

Sepal

Pedicel (flower stalk)

Swollen fleshy tissues of receptacle

LONGITUDINAL SECTION THROUGH A STRAWBERRY

INTRODUCTION 6

THE UNIVERSE 8

PREHISTORIC EARTH 54

PLANTS 110

ANIMALS 164

THE HUMAN BODY 208

GEOLOGY, GEOGRAPHY, AND METEOROLOGY 262

PHYSICS AND CHEMISTRY 304

RAIL AND ROAD 322

SEA AND AIR 370

THE VISUAL ARTS 428

ARCHITECTURE 456

MUSIC 500

SPORTS 522

EVERYDAY THINGS 564

APPENDIX: USEFUL DATA 590

INDEX 592

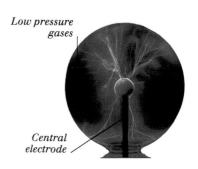

Low pressure gases

Central electrode

BALL CONTAINING HIGH TEMPERATURE GAS (PLASMA)

Nonbreakable plastic

Shock absorber

FOOTBALL HELMET

Introduction

THE ULTIMATE VISUAL DICTIONARY is a completely new kind of reference book. It provides a link between pictures and words in a way that no ordinary dictionary ever has. Most dictionaries simply tell you what a word means, but the ULTIMATE VISUAL DICTIONARY shows you —through a combination of detailed annotations, explicit photographs, and illustrations. In the ULTIMATE VISUAL DICTIONARY, pictures define the annotations around them. You do not read definitions of the annotated words, you see them. The highly accessible format of the ULTIMATE VISUAL DICTIONARY, the thoroughness of its annotations, and the range of its subject matter make it a unique and helpful reference tool.

How to use the ULTIMATE VISUAL DICTIONARY
You will find the ULTIMATE VISUAL DICTIONARY simple to use. It is divided by subject into 14 sections— THE UNIVERSE, PREHISTORIC EARTH, PLANTS, ANIMALS, THE HUMAN BODY, etc. Each section begins with a table of contents listing the major entries within that section. For example, THE VISUAL ARTS section contains entries on *Drawing*, *Tempera*, *Fresco*, *Oils*, *Watercolor*, *Pastels*, *Acrylics*, *Calligraphy*, *Printmaking*, *Mosaic*, and *Sculpture*. Every entry includes a short introduction explaining the purpose of the photographs and illustrations, and the significance of the annotations.

If you know what something looks like, but don't know its name, turn to the annotations surrounding the pictures; if you know a word, but don't know what it refers to, use the comprehensive index to direct you to the appropriate page.

Suppose you want to know what the bone at the end of your little finger is called. With a standard dictionary, you wouldn't know where to begin. But with the ULTIMATE VISUAL DICTIONARY you simply turn to the entry called *Hands*—within THE HUMAN BODY section—and you will find four fully annotated color photographs showing the skin, muscles, and bones of the human hand. In this entry you will quickly find that the bone you are searching for is called the distal phalanx. In addition, you will discover that it is attached to the middle phalanx by the distal interphalangeal joint.

Perhaps you want to know what a catalytic converter looks like. If you look up "catalytic converter" in an ordinary dictionary, you will be told what it is and possibly what it does—but you will not be able to tell what shape it is or what it is made of. However, if you look up "catalytic converter" in the index of the ULTIMATE VISUAL DICTIONARY, you will be directed to the *Modern engines* entry on page 344—where the introduction gives you basic information about what a catalytic converter is—and to page 350—where there is a spectacular exploded-view photograph of the mechanics of a Renault Clio. From these pages you will find out not only what a catalytic converter looks like, but also that it is attached at one end to an exhaust downpipe and at the other to a silencer.

Whatever it is that you want to find a name for, or whatever name you want to find a picture for, you will find it quickly and easily in the ULTIMATE VISUAL DICTIONARY. Perhaps you need to know where the vamp on a shoe is; or how to tell obovate and lanceolate leaves apart; or what a spiral galaxy looks like; or whether birds have nostrils. With the ULTIMATE VISUAL DICTIONARY close by, the answers to each of these questions, and thousands more, are readily available.

The ULTIMATE VISUAL DICTIONARY does not just tell you what the names of the different parts of an object are. The photographs, illustrations, and annotations are all specially arranged to help you understand which parts relate to one another and how objects function.

With the ULTIMATE VISUAL DICTIONARY, in seconds you can find the words or pictures that you are looking for; or you can simply browse. The ULTIMATE VISUAL DICTIONARY is not intended to replace a standard dictionary or encyclopedia, but is instead a stimulating and valuable companion to ordinary reference volumes. Giving you access to the language that is used by astronomers and architects, musicians and mechanics, pilots and professional athletes, it is the ideal reference book for experts and novices of all ages.

Sections of the ULTIMATE VISUAL DICTIONARY
The 14 sections of the *ULTIMATE VISUAL DICTIONARY*
contain a total of more than 30,000 terms,
encompassing a wide range of topics:

• In the first section, THE UNIVERSE, spectacular
photographs and illustrations are used to show
the names of the stars and planets and to explain
the structure of solar systems, galaxies,
nebulae, comets, and black holes.

• PREHISTORIC EARTH tells the story of how
our own planet has evolved since its formation.
It includes examples of prehistoric flora and
fauna, and fascinating dinosaur models—
some with parts of the body stripped away
to show anatomical sections.

• PLANTS covers a huge range of species—
from the familiar to the exotic. In addition to
the color photographs of plants included in
this section, there is a series of micrographic
photographs illustrating plant details—such
as pollen grains, spores, and cross-sections
of stems and roots.

• In the ANIMALS section, skeletons, anatomical
diagrams, and different parts of animals' bodies
have been meticulously annotated. This section
provides a comprehensive guide to the vocabulary
of zoological classification and animal physiology.

• The structure of the human body, its parts,
and its systems are presented in THE HUMAN BODY.
The section includes lifelike, three-dimensional
models and the latest false-color images.
Clear and authoritative annotations
indicate the correct anatomical terms.

• GEOLOGY, GEOGRAPHY, AND METEOROLOGY
describes the structure of the Earth—from the
inner core to the exosphere—and the physical
phenomena, such as volcanoes, rivers, glaciers,
and climate, that shape its surface.

• PHYSICS AND CHEMISTRY is a visual
journey through the fundamental principles
underlying the physical universe, that provides
the essential vocabulary of these sciences.

• In RAIL AND ROAD, a wide range of
trains, trolleys and buses, cars, bicycles,
and motorcycles are described. Exploded-
view photographs show mechanical
details with striking clarity.

• SEA AND AIR illustrates hundreds of parts of
ships and airplanes. The section includes civil
and fighting craft, both historical and modern.

• THE VISUAL ARTS shows the equipment and
materials used by painters, sculptors, printers,
and other artists. Well-known compositions
have been chosen to illustrate specific
artistic techniques and effects.

• ARCHITECTURE includes photographs
of exemplary architectural models and
illustrates dozens of additional features
such as columns, domes, and arches.

• MUSIC provides a visual introduction to
the special language of music and musical
instruments. It includes clearly annotated
photographs of each of the major groups of
traditional instruments—brass, woodwind,
strings, and percussion—together with
modern electronic instruments.

• The SPORTS section is a guide to the playing
areas, formations, equipment, and techniques
needed for many of today's most popular sports.

• In EVERYDAY THINGS, familiar objects,
such as shoes, clocks, and toasters, are taken
apart—down to the very last screw or length
of thread—to show their inner workings and
to give a special insight into the language
that is used by their manufacturers.

THE UNIVERSE

ANATOMY OF THE UNIVERSE · · · · · · · · · 10

GALAXIES · · · · · · · · · · · · · · · 12

THE MILKY WAY · · · · · · · · · · · 14

NEBULAE AND STAR CLUSTERS · · · · 16

STARS OF NORTHERN SKIES · · · · · · 18

STARS OF SOUTHERN SKIES · · · · · 20

STARS · · · · · · · · · · · · · · · · 22

SMALL STARS · · · · · · · · · · · · 24

MASSIVE STARS · · · · · · · · · · · 26

NEUTRON STARS AND BLACK HOLES · · · 28

THE SOLAR SYSTEM · · · · · · · · · 30

THE SUN · · · · · · · · · · · · · · · 32

MERCURY · · · · · · · · · · · · · · 34

VENUS · · · · · · · · · · · · · · · · 36

THE EARTH · · · · · · · · · · · · · · 38

THE MOON · · · · · · · · · · · · · · 40

MARS · · · · · · · · · · · · · · · · · 42

JUPITER · · · · · · · · · · · · · · · · 44

SATURN · · · · · · · · · · · · · · · · 46

URANUS · · · · · · · · · · · · · · · · 48

NEPTUNE AND PLUTO · · · · · · · · · 50

ASTEROIDS, COMETS, AND METEOROIDS · · · 52

Anatomy of the Universe

Fireball of rapidly expanding, extremely hot gas lasting about one million years

THE UNIVERSE CONTAINS EVERYTHING that exists, from the tiniest subatomic particles to galactic superclusters (the largest structures known). Nobody knows how big the Universe is, but astronomers estimate that it contains about 100 billion galaxies, each comprising an average of 100 billion stars. The most widely accepted theory about the origin of the Universe is the Big Bang theory, which states that the Universe came into being in a huge explosion—the Big Bang—that took place between 10 and 20 billion years ago. The Universe initially consisted of a very hot, dense fireball of expanding, cooling gas. After about one million years, the gas probably began to condense into localized clumps called protogalaxies. During the next five billion years, the protogalaxies continued condensing, forming galaxies in which stars were being born. Today, billions of years later, the Universe as a whole is still expanding, although there are localized areas in which objects are held together by gravity; for example, many galaxies are found in clusters. The Big Bang theory is supported by the discovery of faint, cool background radiation coming evenly from all directions. This radiation is believed to be the remnant of the radiation produced by the Big Bang. Small "ripples" in the temperature of the cosmic background radiation are thought to be evidence of slight fluctuations in the density of the early Universe, which resulted in the formation of galaxies. Astronomers do not yet know if the Universe is "closed," which means it will eventually stop expanding and begin to contract, or if it is "open," which means it will continue expanding forever.

COMPUTER-ENHANCED MICROWAVE MAP OF COSMIC BACKGROUND RADIATION

Pink indicates "warm ripples" in background radiation

Pale blue indicates "cool ripples" in background radiation

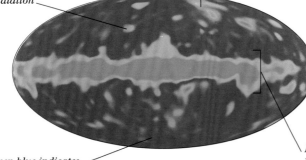

Deep blue indicates background radiation corresponding to -454.5°F (remnant of the Big Bang)

Low-energy microwave radiation corresponding to about -454°F

Red and pink band indicates radiation from our galaxy

High-energy gamma radiation corresponding to about 5,400°F

ORIGIN AND EXPANSION OF THE UNIVERSE

Quasar (probably the center of a galaxy containing a massive black hole)

Universe one to five billion years after Big Bang

Protogalaxy (condensing gas cloud)

Galaxy spinning and flattening to become spiral shaped

Dark cloud (dust and gas condensing to form a protogalaxy)

Elliptical galaxy in which stars form rapidly

Universe today (10–20 billion years after Big Bang)

Cluster of galaxies held together by gravity

Elliptical galaxy containing old stars and little gas and dust

Irregular galaxy

Spiral galaxy containing gas, dust, and young stars

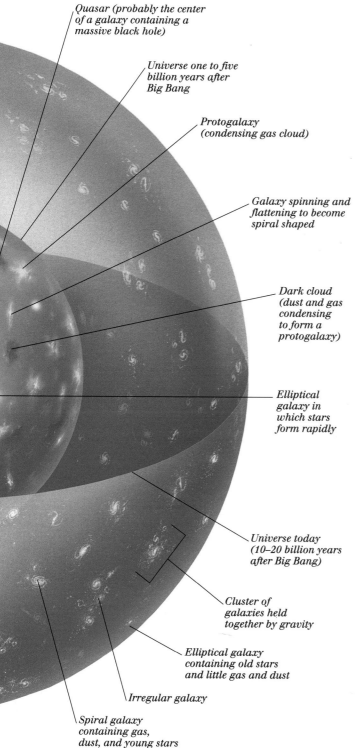

OBJECTS IN THE UNIVERSE

CLUSTER OF GALAXIES IN VIRGO

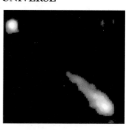

COLOR-ENHANCED IMAGE OF 3C273 (QUASAR)

NGC 4406 (ELLIPTICAL GALAXY)

NGC 5236 (SPIRAL GALAXY)

NGC 6822 (IRREGULAR GALAXY)

THE ROSETTE NEBULA (EMISSION NEBULA)

THE JEWEL BOX (STAR CLUSTER)

THE SUN (MAIN SEQUENCE STAR)

EARTH

THE MOON

Galaxies

SOMBRERO,
A SPIRAL GALAXY

A GALAXY IS A HUGE MASS OF STARS, nebulae, and interstellar material. The smallest galaxies contain about 100,000 stars, while the largest contain up to 3,000 billion stars. There are three main types of galaxy, classified according to their shape: elliptical, which are oval shaped; spiral, which have arms spiraling outward from a central bulge; and irregular, which have no obvious shape. Sometimes, the shape of a galaxy is distorted by a collision with another galaxy. Quasars (quasi-stellar objects) are thought to be galactic nuclei but are so far away that their exact nature is still uncertain. They are compact, highly luminous objects in the outer reaches of the known Universe; while the farthest known "ordinary" galaxies are about 10 billion light-years away, the farthest known quasar is about 15 billion light-years away. Active galaxies, such as Seyfert galaxies and radio galaxies, emit intense radiation. In a Seyfert galaxy, this radiation comes from the galactic nucleus; in a radio galaxy, it also comes from huge lobes on either side of the galaxy. The radiation from active galaxies and quasars is thought to be caused by black holes (see pp. 28-29).

OPTICAL IMAGE OF NGC 4486 (ELLIPTICAL GALAXY)

Globular cluster containing very old red giants

Central region containing old red giants

Less densely populated region

Neighboring galaxy

OPTICAL IMAGE OF LARGE MAGELLANIC CLOUD (IRREGULAR GALAXY)

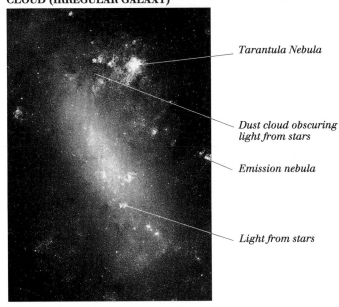

Tarantula Nebula

Dust cloud obscuring light from stars

Emission nebula

Light from stars

OPTICAL IMAGE OF NGC 2997 (SPIRAL GALAXY)

Glowing nebula in spiral arm

Spiral arm containing young stars

Galactic nucleus containing old stars

Dust in spiral arm reflecting blue light from hot young stars

Hot, ionized hydrogen gas emitting red light

Dust lane

OPTICAL IMAGE OF CENTAURUS A (RADIO GALAXY)

Dust lane crossing elliptical galaxy

Galactic nucleus containing powerful source of radiation

Light from old stars

COLOR-ENHANCED RADIO IMAGE OF CENTAURUS A

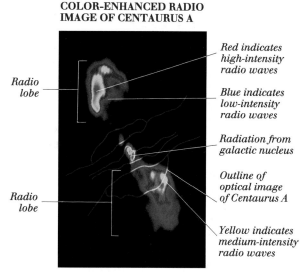

Red indicates high-intensity radio waves

Blue indicates low-intensity radio waves

Radiation from galactic nucleus

Outline of optical image of Centaurus A

Yellow indicates medium-intensity radio waves

Radio lobe

Radio lobe

COLOR-ENHANCED RADIO IMAGE OF 3C273 (QUASAR)

Radiation from jet of high-energy particles moving away from quasar

Blue indicates low-intensity radio waves

Quasar nucleus

White indicates high-intensity radio waves

OPTICAL IMAGE OF NGC 1566 (SEYFERT GALAXY)

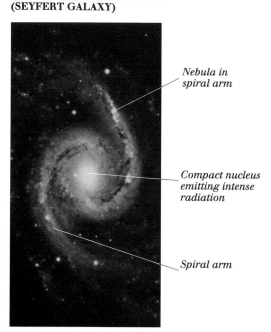

Nebula in spiral arm

Compact nucleus emitting intense radiation

Spiral arm

COLOR-ENHANCED OPTICAL IMAGE OF NGC 5754 (TWO COLLIDING GALAXIES)

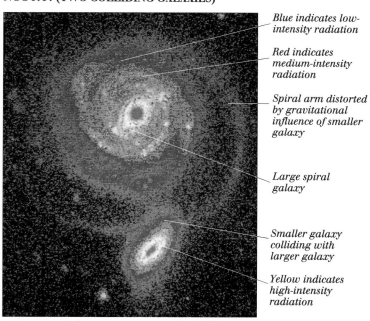

Blue indicates low-intensity radiation

Red indicates medium-intensity radiation

Spiral arm distorted by gravitational influence of smaller galaxy

Large spiral galaxy

Smaller galaxy colliding with larger galaxy

Yellow indicates high-intensity radiation

The Milky Way

VIEW TOWARD GALACTIC CENTER

THE MILKY WAY IS THE NAME GIVEN TO THE FAINT BAND OF LIGHT that stretches across the night sky. This light comes from stars and nebulae in our galaxy, known as the Milky Way Galaxy or simply as "the Galaxy." The Galaxy is shaped like a spiral, with a dense central bulge that is encircled by four arms spiraling outward and surrounded by a less dense halo. We cannot see the spiral shape because our Solar System is in one of the spiral arms, the Orion Arm (also called the Local Arm). From our position, the center of the Galaxy is completely obscured by dust clouds; as a result, optical maps give only a limited view of the Galaxy. However, a more complete picture can be obtained by studying radio, infrared, and other radiation. The central bulge of the Galaxy is a relatively small, dense sphere that contains mainly older red and yellow stars. The halo is a less dense region in which the oldest stars are situated; some of these stars may be as old as the Galaxy itself (possibly 15 billion years). The spiral arms contain mainly hot, young, blue stars, as well as nebulae (clouds of dust and gas, inside which stars are born). The Galaxy is vast—about 100,000 light-years across (a light-year is about 5,879 billion miles); in comparison, the Solar System seems small, at about 12 light-hours across (about 8 billion miles). The entire Galaxy is rotating in space, although the inner stars travel faster than those further out. The Sun, which is about two-thirds out from the center, completes one lap of the Galaxy about every 220 million years.

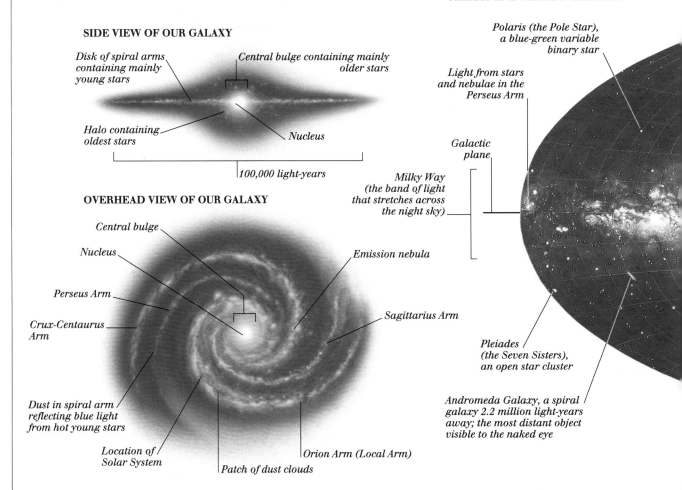

SIDE VIEW OF OUR GALAXY

Disk of spiral arms containing mainly young stars

Central bulge containing mainly older stars

Halo containing oldest stars

Nucleus

100,000 light-years

OVERHEAD VIEW OF OUR GALAXY

Central bulge

Nucleus

Perseus Arm

Crux-Centaurus Arm

Dust in spiral arm reflecting blue light from hot young stars

Location of Solar System

Patch of dust clouds

Orion Arm (Local Arm)

Sagittarius Arm

Emission nebula

PANORAMIC OPTICAL MAP OF OUR GALAXY AND NEARBY GALAXIES

Polaris (the Pole Star), a blue-green variable binary star

Light from stars and nebulae in the Perseus Arm

Galactic plane

Milky Way (the band of light that stretches across the night sky)

Pleiades (the Seven Sisters), an open star cluster

Andromeda Galaxy, a spiral galaxy 2.2 million light-years away; the most distant object visible to the naked eye

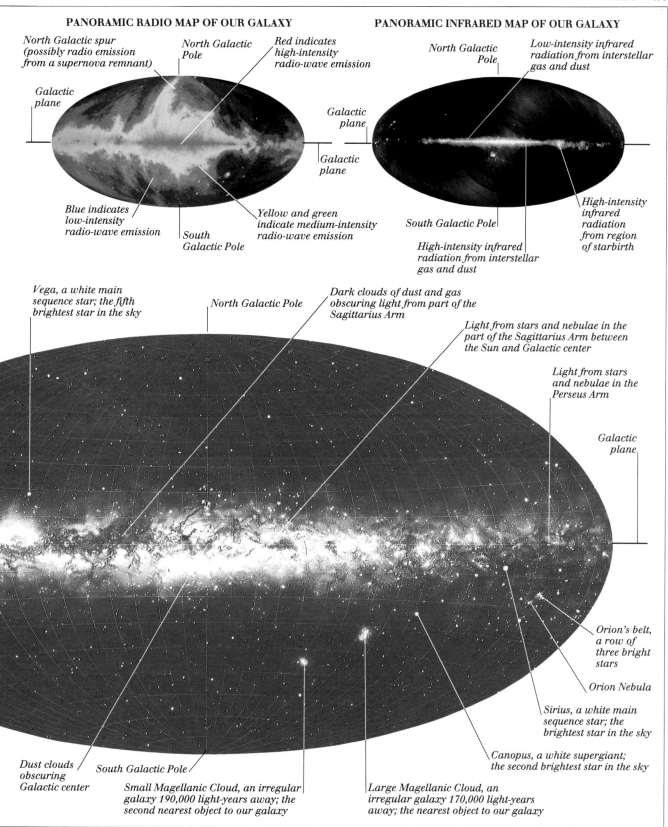

PANORAMIC RADIO MAP OF OUR GALAXY

North Galactic spur (possibly radio emission from a supernova remnant)

North Galactic Pole

Red indicates high-intensity radio-wave emission

Galactic plane

Blue indicates low-intensity radio-wave emission

South Galactic Pole

Yellow and green indicate medium-intensity radio-wave emission

PANORAMIC INFRARED MAP OF OUR GALAXY

North Galactic Pole

Low-intensity infrared radiation from interstellar gas and dust

Galactic plane

Galactic plane

South Galactic Pole

High-intensity infrared radiation from interstellar gas and dust

High-intensity infrared radiation from region of starbirth

Vega, a white main sequence star; the fifth brightest star in the sky

North Galactic Pole

Dark clouds of dust and gas obscuring light from part of the Sagittarius Arm

Light from stars and nebulae in the part of the Sagittarius Arm between the Sun and Galactic center

Light from stars and nebulae in the Perseus Arm

Galactic plane

Orion's belt, a row of three bright stars

Orion Nebula

Sirius, a white main sequence star; the brightest star in the sky

Canopus, a white supergiant; the second brightest star in the sky

Dust clouds obscuring Galactic center

South Galactic Pole

Small Magellanic Cloud, an irregular galaxy 190,000 light-years away; the second nearest object to our galaxy

Large Magellanic Cloud, an irregular galaxy 170,000 light-years away; the nearest object to our galaxy

15

Nebulae and star clusters

**HODGE 11, A
GLOBULAR CLUSTER**

A NEBULA IS A CLOUD OF DUST AND GAS inside a galaxy. Nebulae become visible if the gas glows or if the cloud reflects starlight or obscures light from more distant objects. Emission nebulae shine because their gas emits light when it is stimulated by radiation from hot young stars. Reflection nebulae shine because their dust reflects light from stars in or around the nebula. Dark nebulae appear as silhouettes because they block light from shining nebulae or stars behind them. Two types of nebula are associated with dying stars: planetary nebulae and supernova remnants. Both consist of expanding shells of gas that were once the outer layers of a star. A planetary nebula is a gas shell drifting away from a dying stellar core. A supernova remnant is a gas shell moving away from a stellar core at great speed following a violent explosion called a supernova (see pp. 26-27). Stars are often found in groups known as clusters. Open clusters are loose groups of a few thousand young stars that were born in the same cloud and are drifting apart. Globular clusters are densely packed, roughly spherical groups of hundreds of thousands of older stars.

TRIFID NEBULA (EMISSION NEBULA)

Reflection nebula

Emission nebula

Dust lane

Starbirth region (area in which dust and gas combine to form stars)

**PLEIADES (OPEN STAR CLUSTER)
WITH A REFLECTION NEBULA**

Wisps of dust and hydrogen gas remaining from cloud in which stars formed

Young star in an open cluster of 300–500 stars

Reflection nebula

HORSEHEAD NEBULA (DARK NEBULA)

Glowing filament of hot, ionized hydrogen gas

Alnitak (star in Orion's belt)

Dust lane

Emission nebula

Star near southern end of Orion's belt

Emission nebula

Horsehead Nebula

Reflection nebula

Dark nebula obscuring light from distant stars

ORION NEBULA (DIFFUSE EMISSION NEBULA)

Glowing cloud of dust and hydrogen gas forming part of Orion Nebula

Dust cloud

Trapezium (group of four young stars)

Red light from hot, ionized hydrogen gas

Gas cloud emitting light because of ultraviolet radiation from the four young Trapezium stars

Green light from hot, ionized oxygen gas

Glowing filament of hot, ionized hydrogen gas

HELIX NEBULA (PLANETARY NEBULA)

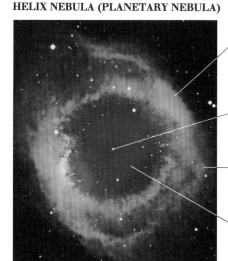

Planetary nebula (gas shell expanding outward from dying stellar core)

Stellar core at a temperature of about 180,000°F

Red light from hot, ionized hydrogen gas

Blue-green light from hot, ionized oxygen and nitrogen gases

VELA SUPERNOVA REMNANT

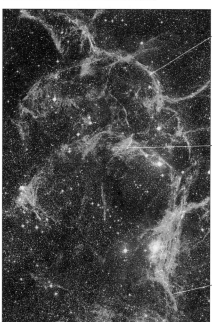

Supernova remnant (gas shell consisting of outer layers of star thrown off in supernova explosion)

Hydrogen gas emitting red light due to being heated by supernova explosion

Glowing filament of hot, ionized hydrogen gas

Stars of northern skies

WHEN YOU LOOK AT THE NORTHERN SKY, you look away from the densely populated Galactic center, so the northern sky generally appears less bright than the southern sky (see pp. 20-21). Among the best-known sights in the northern sky are the constellations Ursa Major (the Great Bear) and Orion. Some ancient civilizations believed that the stars were fixed to a celestial sphere surrounding the Earth, and modern maps of the sky are based on a similar idea. The North and South Poles of this imaginary celestial sphere are directly above the North and South Poles of the Earth, at the points where the Earth's axis of rotation intersects the sphere. The celestial North Pole is at the center of the map shown here, and Polaris (the Pole Star) lies very close to it. The celestial equator marks a projection of the Earth's equator on the sphere. The ecliptic marks the path of the Sun across the sky as the Earth orbits the Sun. The Moon and planets move against the background of the stars because the stars are much more distant; the nearest star outside the Solar System (Proxima Centauri) is more than 50,000 times farther away than the planet Jupiter.

ORION

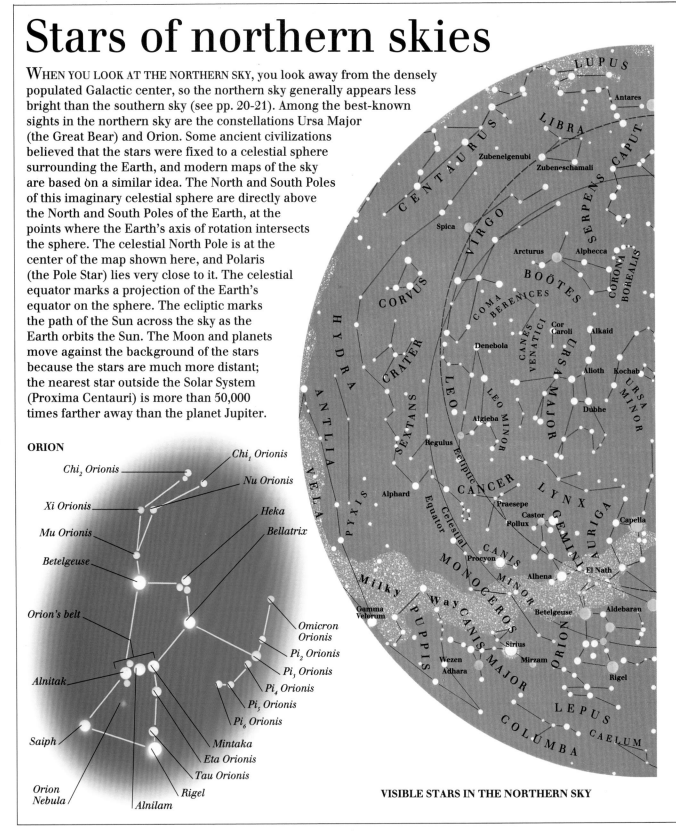

VISIBLE STARS IN THE NORTHERN SKY

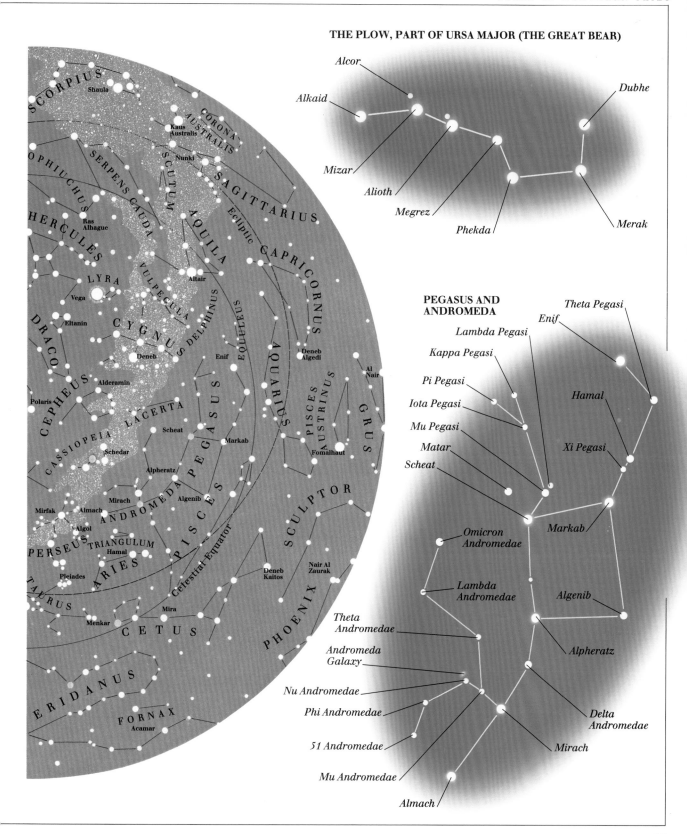

THE PLOW, PART OF URSA MAJOR (THE GREAT BEAR)

Alcor
Alkaid
Mizar
Alioth
Megrez
Phekda
Dubhe
Merak

PEGASUS AND ANDROMEDA

Theta Pegasi
Enif
Lambda Pegasi
Kappa Pegasi
Pi Pegasi
Iota Pegasi
Mu Pegasi
Matar
Scheat
Omicron Andromedae
Lambda Andromedae
Theta Andromedae
Andromeda Galaxy
Nu Andromedae
Phi Andromedae
51 Andromedae
Mu Andromedae
Almach
Hamal
Xi Pegasi
Markab
Algenib
Alpheratz
Delta Andromedae
Mirach

SCORPIUS
Shaula
CORONA AUSTRALIS
Kaus Australis
OPHIUCHUS
SERPENS CAUDA
Ras Alhague
HERCULES
Nunki
SAGITTARIUS
SCUTUM
AQUILA
Ecliptic
CAPRICORNUS
LYRA
Vega
VULPECULA
Altair
Eltanin
DRACO
CYGNUS
DELPHINUS
Deneb
AQUARIUS
Enif
EQUULEUS
Deneb Algedi
Al Nair
Polaris
CEPHEUS
Alderamin
LACERTA
Scheat
PEGASUS
Markab
PISCES AUSTRINUS
GRUS
Fomalhaut
CASSIOPEIA
Schedar
Alpheratz
Algenib
Mirfak
Mirach
Almach
ANDROMEDA
Algol
PISCES
SCULPTOR
Celestial Equator
PERSEUS
TRIANGULUM
Hamal
ARIES
Deneb Kaitos
Nair Al Zaurak
Pleiades
Mira
PHOENIX
TAURUS
Menkar
CETUS
ERIDANUS
FORNAX
Acamar

Stars of southern skies

WHEN YOU LOOK AT THE SOUTHERN SKY, you look toward the Galactic center, which has a huge population of stars. As a result, the Milky Way appears brighter in the southern sky than in the northern sky (see pp. 18-19). The southern sky is rich in nebulae and star clusters. It contains the Large and Small Magellanic Clouds, which are the two nearest galaxies to our own. Stars make fixed patterns in the sky called constellations. The constellations, however, are only apparent groupings of stars, because the distances to the stars in a constellation may vary enormously. The shapes of constellations may change over many thousands of years because of the relative motions of stars. The apparent movement of entire constellations across the sky is due to the Earth's motion in space. The daily rotation of the Earth causes the constellations to move across the sky from east to west, and the orbit of the Earth around the Sun causes different areas of sky to be visible in different seasons. The visibility of areas of sky also depends on the location of the observer. For instance, stars near the celestial equator may be seen from either hemisphere at some time during the year, while stars close to the celestial poles (the celestial South Pole is at the center of the map shown here) can never be seen from the opposite hemisphere.

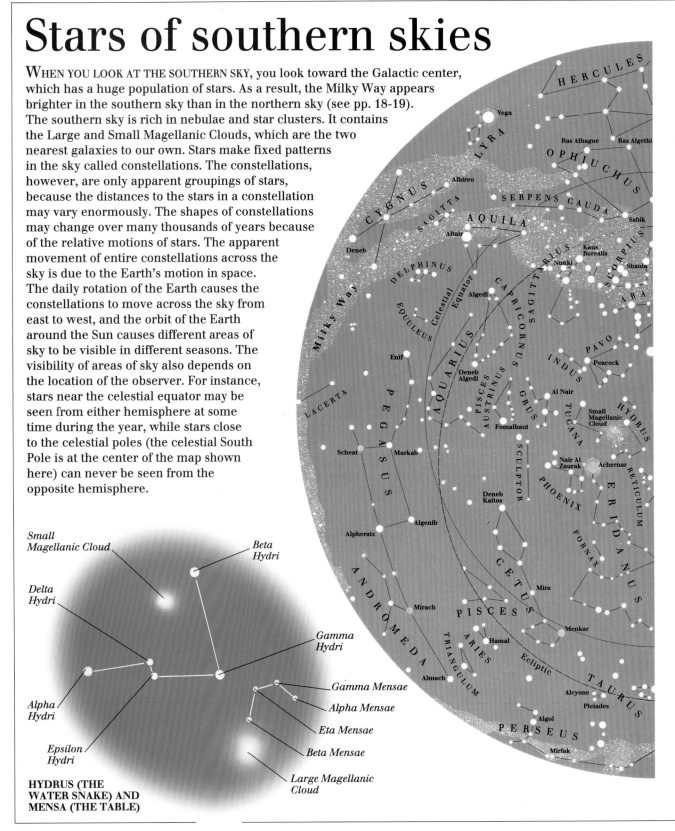

HYDRUS (THE WATER SNAKE) AND MENSA (THE TABLE)

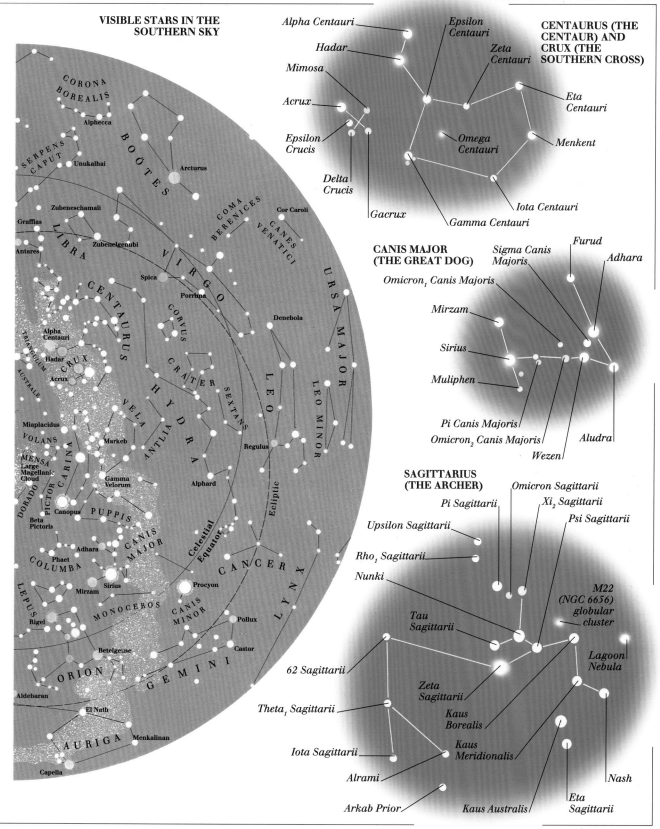

VISIBLE STARS IN THE SOUTHERN SKY

CORONA
BOREALIS
Alphecca
SERPENS
CAPUT
Unukalhai
BOÖTES
Arcturus
Zubeneschamali
Graffias
Antares
LIBRA
Zubenelgenubi
COMA
BERENICES
VIRGO
Spica
Porrima
CANES
VENATICI
Cor Caroli
Denebola
URSA
MAJOR
CENTAURUS
Alpha
Centauri
Hadar
Acrux
CRUX
TRIANGULUM
AUSTRALE
HYDRA
CORVUS
CRATER
SEXTANS
LEO
LEO MINOR
VELA
ANTLIA
Regulus
Ecliptic
Miaplacidus
VOLANS
MENSA
Large
Magellanic
Cloud
DORADO
PICTOR
CARINA
Markeb
Gamma
Velorum
PUPPIS
Alphard
Celestial
Equator
CANCER
LYNX
Canopus
Beta
Pictoris
Adhara
CANIS
MAJOR
Procyon
CANIS
MINOR
Pollux
COLUMBA
Phaet
Mirzam
Sirius
MONOCEROS
Castor
LEPUS
Rigel
Betelgeuse
ORION
GEMINI
Aldebaran
El Nath
AURIGA
Menkalinan
Capella

CENTAURUS (THE CENTAUR) AND CRUX (THE SOUTHERN CROSS)

Alpha Centauri
Hadar
Mimosa
Acrux
Epsilon Crucis
Delta Crucis
Gacrux
Epsilon Centauri
Zeta Centauri
Eta Centauri
Omega Centauri
Menkent
Iota Centauri
Gamma Centauri

CANIS MAJOR (THE GREAT DOG)

Sigma Canis Majoris
Furud
Adhara
Omicron$_1$ Canis Majoris
Mirzam
Sirius
Muliphen
Pi Canis Majoris
Omicron$_2$ Canis Majoris
Wezen
Aludra

SAGITTARIUS (THE ARCHER)

Pi Sagittarii
Upsilon Sagittarii
Rho$_1$ Sagittarii
Nunki
Tau Sagittarii
62 Sagittarii
Theta$_1$ Sagittarii
Iota Sagittarii
Alrami
Arkab Prior
Omicron Sagittarii
Xi$_2$ Sagittarii
Psi Sagittarii
M22 (NGC 6656) globular cluster
Lagoon Nebula
Zeta Sagittarii
Kaus Borealis
Kaus Meridionalis
Kaus Australis
Eta Sagittarii
Nash

Stars

**OPEN STAR CLUSTER
AND DUST CLOUD**

STARS ARE BODIES of hot glowing gas that are born in nebulae (see pp. 24-27). They vary enormously in size, mass, and temperature: diameters range from about 450 times smaller to over 1,000 times bigger than that of the Sun; masses range from about a twentieth to over 50 solar masses; and surface temperatures range from about 5,500°F to over 90,000°F. The color of a star is determined by its temperature: the hottest stars are blue and the coolest are red. The Sun, with a surface temperature of 10,000°F, is between these extremes and appears yellow. The energy emitted by a shining star is produced by nuclear fusion in the star's core. The brightness of a star is measured in magnitudes—the brighter the star, the lower its magnitude. There are two types of magnitude: apparent magnitude, which is the brightness seen from Earth, and absolute magnitude, which is the brightness that would be seen from a standard distance of 10 parsecs (32.6 light-years). The light emitted by a star may be split to form a spectrum containing a series of dark lines (absorption lines). The patterns of lines indicate the presence of particular chemical elements, enabling astronomers to deduce the composition of the star's atmosphere. The magnitude and spectral type (color) of stars may be plotted on a graph called a Hertzsprung-Russell diagram, which shows that stars tend to fall into several well-defined groups. The principal groups are main sequence stars (those which are fusing hydrogen to form helium), giants, supergiants, and white dwarfs.

STAR SIZES

Red giant (diameters between about 10 million and 100 million miles)

The Sun (main sequence star with diameter about 870,000 miles)

White dwarf (diameters between about 2,000 and 30,000 miles)

ENERGY EMISSION FROM THE SUN

Nuclear fusion in core produces gamma rays and neutrinos

Neutrinos travel to Earth directly from Sun's core in about 8 minutes

Lower-energy radiation travels to Earth in about 8 minutes

Earth

Sun

High-energy radiation (gamma rays) loses energy while traveling to surface over 2 million years

Lower-energy radiation (mainly ultraviolet, infrared, and light rays) leaves surface

STAR MAGNITUDES

APPARENT MAGNITUDE

ABSOLUTE MAGNITUDE

Brighter stars

-9

0

+9

Sirius: apparent magnitude of -1.46

Rigel: apparent magnitude of +0.12

Objects of magnitude higher than about +5.5 cannot be seen by the naked eye

Fainter stars

Rigel: absolute magnitude of -7.1

Sirius: absolute magnitude of +1.4

NUCLEAR FUSION IN MAIN SEQUENCE STARS LIKE THE SUN

Positron

Deuterium nucleus

Proton

Neutron

Proton (hydrogen nucleus)

Neutrino

Gamma rays

Helium-3 nucleus

Helium-4 nucleus

HERTZSPRUNG-RUSSELL DIAGRAM

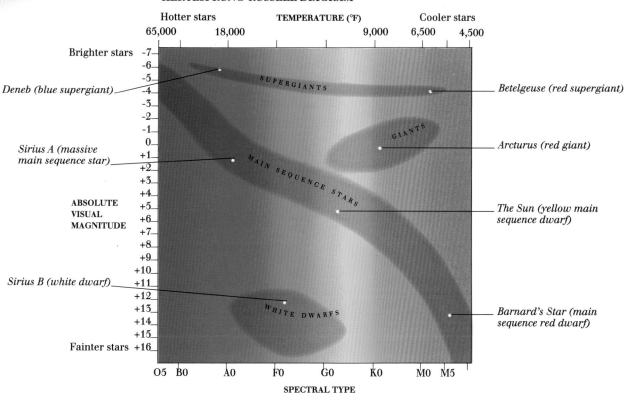

Hotter stars   **TEMPERATURE (°F)**   Cooler stars

65,000   18,000   9,000   6,500   4,500

Brighter stars   −7

−6

Deneb (blue supergiant)   −5   SUPERGIANTS   Betelgeuse (red supergiant)
−4
−3
−2
−1
0
Sirius A (massive   +1   GIANTS   Arcturus (red giant)
main sequence star)   +2   MAIN SEQUENCE STARS
+3
+4
ABSOLUTE   +5
VISUAL   +6   The Sun (yellow main
MAGNITUDE   +7   sequence dwarf)
+8
+9
+10
Sirius B (white dwarf)   +11
+12
+13   WHITE DWARFS
+14
+15   Barnard's Star (main
Fainter stars   +16   sequence red dwarf)

O5   B0   A0   F0   G0   K0   M0   M5

SPECTRAL TYPE

STELLAR SPECTRAL ABSORPTION LINES

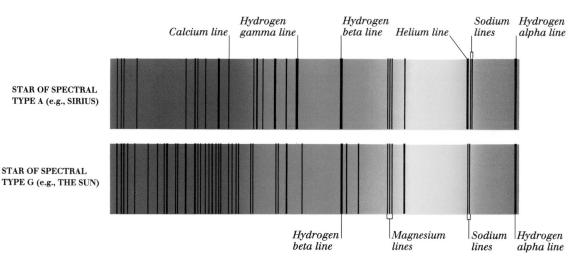

Calcium line   Hydrogen gamma line   Hydrogen beta line   Helium line   Sodium lines   Hydrogen alpha line

STAR OF SPECTRAL TYPE A (e.g., SIRIUS)

STAR OF SPECTRAL TYPE G (e.g., THE SUN)

Hydrogen beta line   Magnesium lines   Sodium lines   Hydrogen alpha line

Small stars

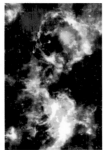

REGION OF STAR FORMATION IN ORION

SMALL STARS HAVE A MASS of up to about one and a half times that of the Sun. They begin to form when a region of higher density in a nebula condenses into a huge globule of gas and dust that contracts under its own gravity. Within a globule, regions of condensing matter heat up and begin to glow, forming protostars. If a protostar contains enough matter, the central temperature reaches about 27 million °F. At this temperature, nuclear reactions in which hydrogen fuses to form helium can start. This process releases energy, which prevents the star from contracting further, and also causes it to shine; it is now a main sequence star. A star of about one solar mass remains in the main sequence for about 10 billion years, until the hydrogen in the star's core has been converted into helium. The helium core then contracts again, and nuclear reactions continue in a shell around the core. The core becomes hot enough for helium to fuse to form carbon, while the outer layers of the star expand, cool, and shine less brightly. The expanding star is known as a red giant. When the helium in the core runs out, the outer layers of the star may drift off as an expanding gas shell called a planetary nebula. The remaining core (about 80 percent of the original star) is now in its final stages. It becomes a white dwarf star that gradually cools and dims. When it finally stops shining altogether, the dead star will become a black dwarf.

STRUCTURE OF A MAIN SEQUENCE STAR

Core containing hydrogen fusing to form helium

Radiative zone

Convective zone

Surface temperature about 10,000°F

Core temperature about 27 million °F

STRUCTURE OF A NEBULA

Young main sequence star

Dense region of dust and gas (mainly hydrogen) condensing under gravity to form globules

Hot, ionized hydrogen gas emitting red light due to stimulation by radiation from hot young stars

Dark globule of dust and gas (mainly hydrogen) contracting to form protostars

LIFE OF A SMALL STAR OF ABOUT ONE SOLAR MASS

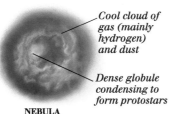

Cool cloud of gas (mainly hydrogen) and dust

Dense globule condensing to form protostars

NEBULA

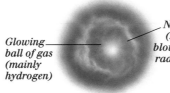

Glowing ball of gas (mainly hydrogen)

Natal cocoon (shell of dust blown away by radiation from protostar)

PROTOSTAR
Duration: 50 million years

About 870,000 miles

Star producing energy by nuclear fusion in core

MAIN SEQUENCE STAR
Duration: 10 billion years

STRUCTURE OF A RED GIANT

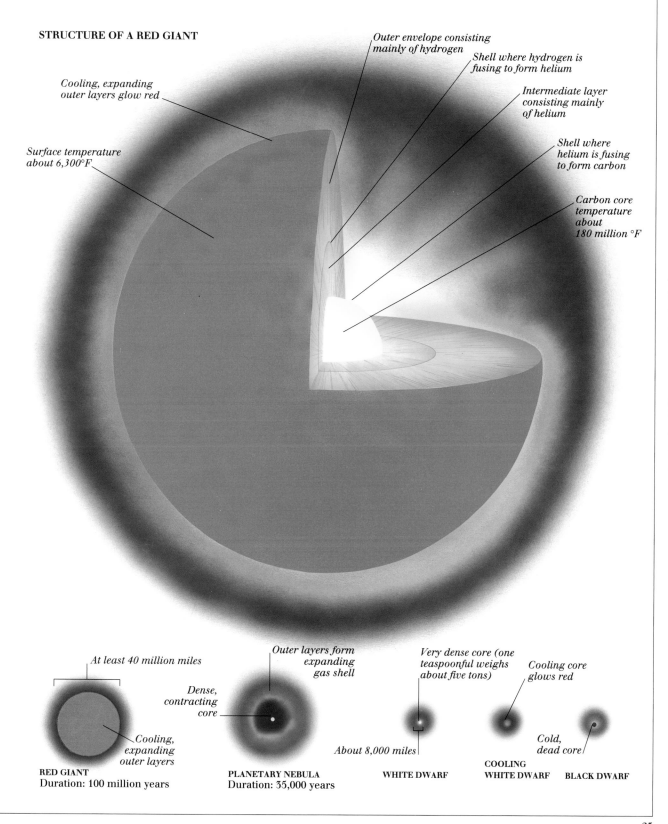

Cooling, expanding outer layers glow red

Surface temperature about 6,300°F

Outer envelope consisting mainly of hydrogen

Shell where hydrogen is fusing to form helium

Intermediate layer consisting mainly of helium

Shell where helium is fusing to form carbon

Carbon core temperature about 180 million °F

At least 40 million miles

Cooling, expanding outer layers

RED GIANT
Duration: 100 million years

Dense, contracting core

Outer layers form expanding gas shell

PLANETARY NEBULA
Duration: 35,000 years

Very dense core (one teaspoonful weighs about five tons)

About 8,000 miles

WHITE DWARF

Cooling core glows red

Cold, dead core

COOLING WHITE DWARF

BLACK DWARF

Massive stars

MASSIVE STARS HAVE A MASS AT LEAST THREE TIMES that of the Sun, and some stars are as massive as about 50 Suns. A massive star evolves in a similar way to a small star until it reaches the main sequence stage (see pp. 24-25). During the main sequence, a star shines steadily until the hydrogen in its core has fused to form helium. This process takes billions of years in a small star, but only millions of years in a massive star. A massive star then becomes a red supergiant, which initially consists of a helium core surrounded by outer layers of cooling, expanding gas. Over the next few million years, a series of nuclear reactions form different elements in shells around an iron core. The core eventually collapses in less than a second, causing a massive explosion called a supernova, in which a shock wave blows away the outer layers of the star. Supernovae shine brighter than an entire galaxy for a short time. Sometimes, the core survives the supernova explosion. If the surviving core is between about one and a half and three solar masses, it contracts to become a tiny, dense neutron star. If the core is considerably greater than three solar masses, it contracts to become a black hole (see pp. 28-29).

SUPERNOVA

TARANTULA NEBULA BEFORE
SUPERNOVA

**STRUCTURE
OF A RED SUPERGIANT**

*Outer envelope consisting
mainly of hydrogen*

*Layer consisting
mainly of helium*

*Layer consisting
mainly of carbon*

*Layer consisting
mainly of oxygen*

*Layer consisting
mainly of silicon*

*Shell of hydrogen
fusing to form
helium*

*Shell of helium
fusing to form
carbon*

*Shell of carbon
fusing to form
oxygen*

*Shell of oxygen fusing
to form silicon*

*Shell of silicon fusing
to form iron core*

*Surface temperature
about 5,500°F*

*Cooling, expanding
outer layers glow red*

*Core of mainly iron at a
temperature of 5.4–9 billion °F*

**LIFE OF A MASSIVE STAR OF
ABOUT 10 SOLAR MASSES**

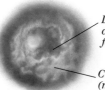

*Dense globule
condensing to
form protostars*

*Cool cloud of gas
(mainly hydrogen)
and dust*

NEBULA

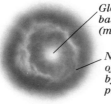

*Glowing
ball of gas
(mainly hydrogen)*

*Natal cocoon (shell
of dust blown away
by radiation from
protostar)*

PROTOSTAR
Duration: a few hundred
thousand years

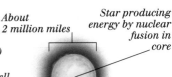

*About
2 million miles*

*Star producing
energy by nuclear
fusion in
core*

MAIN SEQUENCE STAR
Duration: 10 million years

FEATURES OF A SUPERNOVA

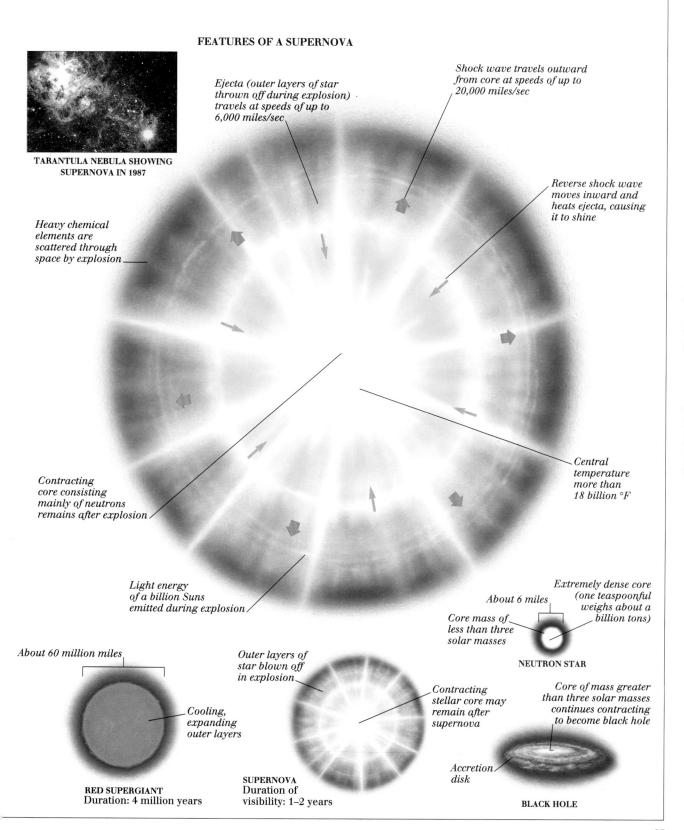

TARANTULA NEBULA SHOWING SUPERNOVA IN 1987

Ejecta (outer layers of star thrown off during explosion) travels at speeds of up to 6,000 miles/sec

Shock wave travels outward from core at speeds of up to 20,000 miles/sec

Reverse shock wave moves inward and heats ejecta, causing it to shine

Heavy chemical elements are scattered through space by explosion

Contracting core consisting mainly of neutrons remains after explosion

Central temperature more than 18 billion °F

Light energy of a billion Suns emitted during explosion

About 60 million miles

Cooling, expanding outer layers

RED SUPERGIANT
Duration: 4 million years

Outer layers of star blown off in explosion

Contracting stellar core may remain after supernova

SUPERNOVA
Duration of visibility: 1–2 years

About 6 miles

Core mass of less than three solar masses

Extremely dense core (one teaspoonful weighs about a billion tons)

NEUTRON STAR

Core of mass greater than three solar masses continues contracting to become black hole

Accretion disk

BLACK HOLE

Neutron stars and black holes

NEUTRON STARS AND BLACK HOLES form from the stellar cores that remain after stars have exploded as supernovae (see pp. 26-27). If the remaining core is between about one and a half and three solar masses, it contracts to form a neutron star. If the remaining core is considerably greater than about three solar masses, it contracts to form a black hole. Neutron stars are typically only about six miles in diameter and consist almost entirely of subatomic particles called neutrons. These stars are so dense that a teaspoonful would weigh about a billion tons. Neutron stars are observed as pulsars, so-called because they rotate rapidly and emit two beams of radio waves, which sweep across the sky and are detected as short pulses. Black holes are characterized by their extremely strong gravity, which is so powerful that not even light can escape; as a result, black holes are invisible. However, they may be detected if they have a close companion star. The gravity of the black hole pulls gas from the other star, forming an accretion disk that spirals around the black hole at high speed, heating up and emitting radiation. Eventually, the matter spirals in to cross the event horizon (the boundary of the black hole), finally disappearing from the visible Universe.

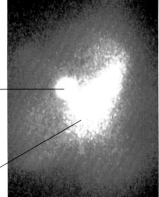

X-ray emission from pulsar (neutron star rotating 30 times each second)

X-ray emission from center of nebula

X-RAY IMAGE OF THE CRAB NEBULA (SUPERNOVA REMNANT)

PULSAR (ROTATING NEUTRON STAR)

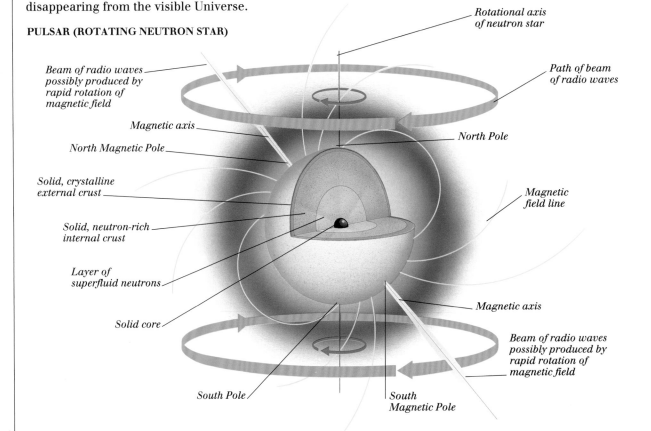

Rotational axis of neutron star

Beam of radio waves possibly produced by rapid rotation of magnetic field

Path of beam of radio waves

Magnetic axis

North Magnetic Pole

North Pole

Solid, crystalline external crust

Magnetic field line

Solid, neutron-rich internal crust

Layer of superfluid neutrons

Magnetic axis

Solid core

Beam of radio waves possibly produced by rapid rotation of magnetic field

South Pole

South Magnetic Pole

STELLAR BLACK HOLE

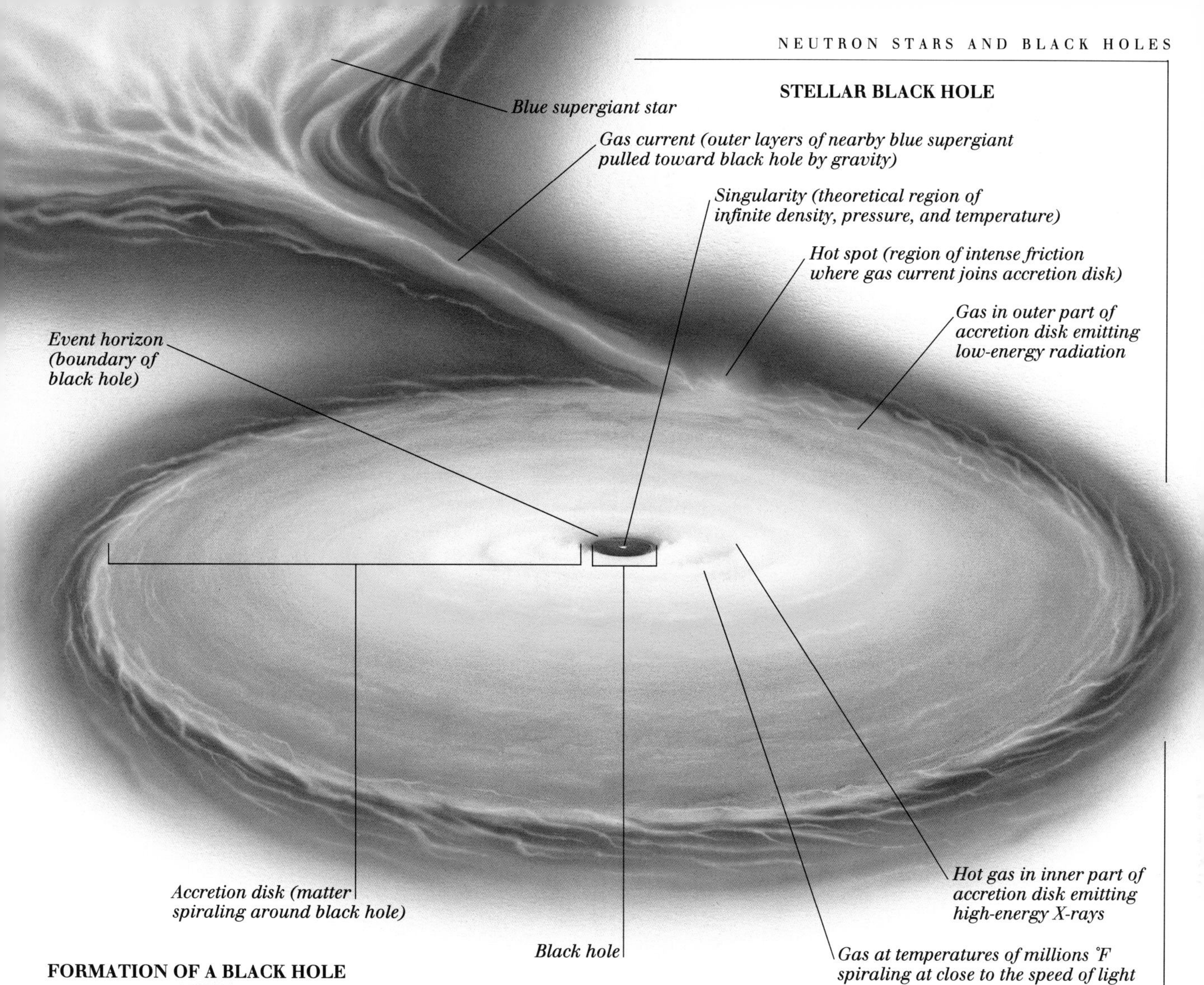

Blue supergiant star

Gas current (outer layers of nearby blue supergiant pulled toward black hole by gravity)

Singularity (theoretical region of infinite density, pressure, and temperature)

Hot spot (region of intense friction where gas current joins accretion disk)

Gas in outer part of accretion disk emitting low-energy radiation

Event horizon (boundary of black hole)

Hot gas in inner part of accretion disk emitting high-energy X-rays

Accretion disk (matter spiraling around black hole)

Black hole

Gas at temperatures of millions °F spiraling at close to the speed of light

FORMATION OF A BLACK HOLE

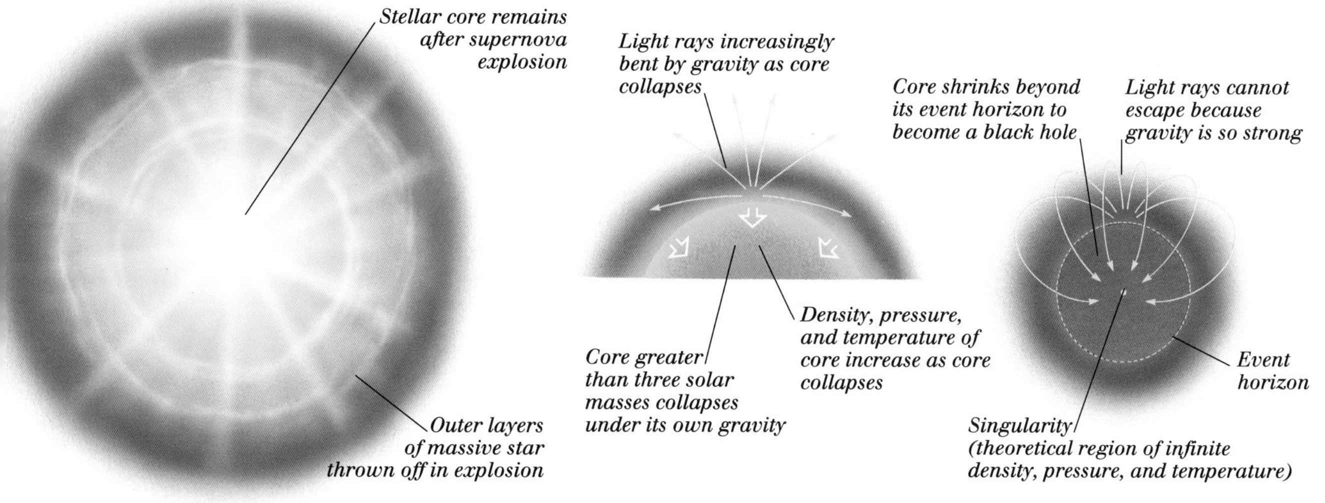

Stellar core remains after supernova explosion

Light rays increasingly bent by gravity as core collapses

Core shrinks beyond its event horizon to become a black hole

Light rays cannot escape because gravity is so strong

Density, pressure, and temperature of core increase as core collapses

Core greater than three solar masses collapses under its own gravity

Outer layers of massive star thrown off in explosion

Event horizon

Singularity (theoretical region of infinite density, pressure, and temperature)

SUPERNOVA

COLLAPSING STELLAR CORE

BLACK HOLE

The Solar System

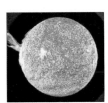

THE SUN

THE SOLAR SYSTEM consists of a central star (the Sun) and the bodies that orbit it. These bodies include nine planets and their 61 known moons, asteroids, comets, and meteoroids. The Solar System also contains interplanetary gas and dust. Most of the planets fall into two groups: four small rocky planets near the Sun (Mercury, Venus, Earth, and Mars), and four planets farther out, the gas giants (Jupiter, Saturn, Uranus, and Neptune). Pluto belongs to neither group—it is very small, solid, and icy. Pluto is the outermost planet, except when it passes briefly inside Neptune's orbit. Between the rocky planets and gas giants is the asteroid belt, which contains thousands of chunks of rock orbiting the Sun. Most of the bodies in the Solar System move around the Sun in elliptical orbits located in a thin disk around the Sun's equator. All the planets orbit the Sun in the same direction (counterclockwise when viewed from above) and all but Venus, Uranus, and Pluto also spin around their axes in this direction. Moons also spin as they, in turn, orbit their planets. The entire Solar System orbits the center of our galaxy, the Milky Way (see pp. 14-15).

PLANETARY ORBIT

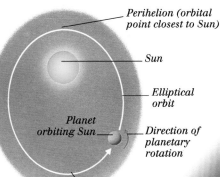

Perihelion (orbital point closest to Sun)

Sun

Elliptical orbit

Planet orbiting Sun

Direction of planetary rotation

Aphelion (orbital point farthest from Sun)

Aphelion of Neptune: 2,819 million miles

ORBITS OF INNER PLANETS

Perihelion of Mercury: 28.5 million miles

Perihelion of Venus: 66.7 million miles

Perihelion of Earth: 91.4 million miles

Mercury

Average orbital speed of Venus: 21.8 miles/sec

Average orbital speed of Mercury: 29.8 miles/sec

Average orbital speed of Earth: 18.5 miles/sec

Average orbital speed of Mars: 15 miles/sec

Mars

Perihelion of Mars: 128.4 million miles

Earth

Venus

Sun

Aphelion of Mercury: 43.3 million miles

Asteroid belt

Aphelion of Venus: 67.7 million miles

Aphelion of Earth: 94.5 million miles

Aphelion of Mars: 154.8 million miles

Aphelion of Pluto: 4,583 million miles

MERCURY
Year: 87.97 Earth days
Mass: 0.055 Earth masses
Diameter: 3,031 miles

VENUS
Year: 224.7 Earth days
Mass: 0.81 Earth masses
Diameter: 7,521 miles

EARTH
Year: 365.26 days
Mass: 1 Earth mass
Diameter: 7,926 miles

MARS
Year: 1.88 Earth years
Mass: 0.11 Earth masses
Diameter: 4,217 miles

JUPITER
Year: 11.86 Earth years
Mass: 318 Earth masses
Diameter: 88,850 miles

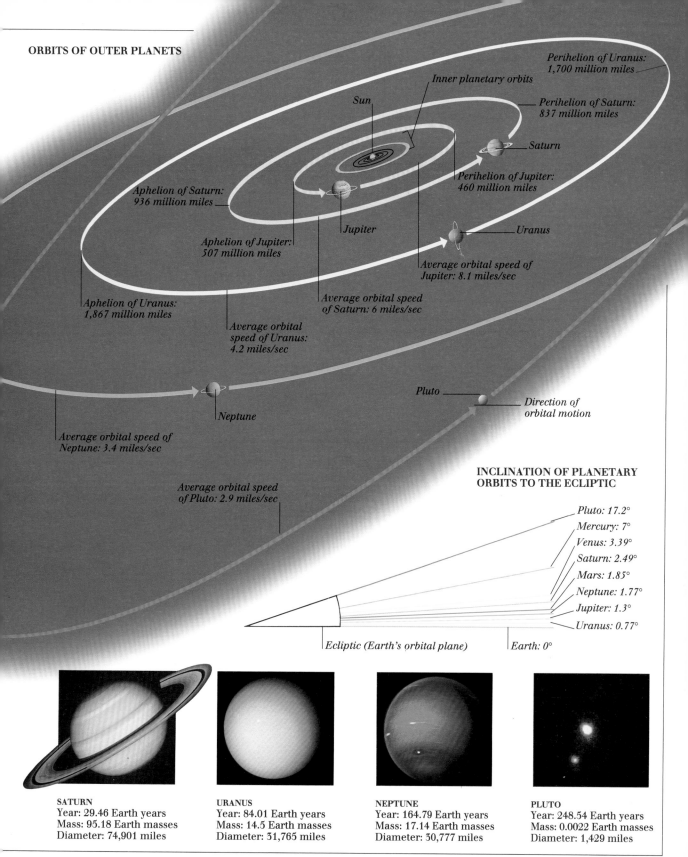

ORBITS OF OUTER PLANETS

Perihelion of Uranus:
1,700 million miles

Inner planetary orbits

Perihelion of Saturn:
837 million miles

Sun

Saturn

Perihelion of Jupiter:
460 million miles

Aphelion of Saturn:
936 million miles

Jupiter

Uranus

Aphelion of Jupiter:
507 million miles

Average orbital speed of
Jupiter: 8.1 miles/sec

Average orbital speed
of Saturn: 6 miles/sec

Aphelion of Uranus:
1,867 million miles

Average orbital
speed of Uranus:
4.2 miles/sec

Pluto

Direction of
orbital motion

Neptune

Average orbital speed of
Neptune: 3.4 miles/sec

**INCLINATION OF PLANETARY
ORBITS TO THE ECLIPTIC**

Average orbital speed
of Pluto: 2.9 miles/sec

Pluto: 17.2°
Mercury: 7°
Venus: 3.39°
Saturn: 2.49°
Mars: 1.85°
Neptune: 1.77°
Jupiter: 1.3°
Uranus: 0.77°

Ecliptic (Earth's orbital plane)   Earth: 0°

SATURN
Year: 29.46 Earth years
Mass: 95.18 Earth masses
Diameter: 74,901 miles

URANUS
Year: 84.01 Earth years
Mass: 14.5 Earth masses
Diameter: 31,765 miles

NEPTUNE
Year: 164.79 Earth years
Mass: 17.14 Earth masses
Diameter: 30,777 miles

PLUTO
Year: 248.54 Earth years
Mass: 0.0022 Earth masses
Diameter: 1,429 miles

The Sun

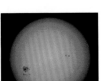

SOLAR PHOTOSPHERE

THE SUN IS THE STAR AT THE CENTER of our Solar System. It is about five billion years old and will probably continue to shine as it does now for about another five billion years. The Sun is a yellow main sequence star (see pp. 22-23) about 870,000 miles in diameter. It consists almost entirely of hydrogen and helium. In the Sun's core, hydrogen is converted to helium by nuclear fusion, releasing energy in the process. The energy travels from the core through the radiative and convective zones to the photosphere (visible surface), where it leaves the Sun in the form of heat and light. On the photosphere there are often dark, relatively cool areas called sunspots. These usually appear in pairs or groups and are thought to be caused by magnetic fields. Other types of solar activity are flares, which are usually associated with sunspots, and prominences. Flares are sudden discharges of high-energy radiation and atomic particles. Prominences are huge loops or filaments of gas extending into the solar atmosphere; some last for hours, others for months. Beyond the photosphere is the chromosphere (inner atmosphere) and the extremely rarified corona (outer atmosphere), which extends millions of miles into space. Tiny particles that escape from the corona give rise to the solar wind, which streams through space at hundreds of miles per second. The chromosphere and corona can be seen from Earth when the Sun is totally eclipsed by the Moon.

HOW A SOLAR ECLIPSE OCCURS

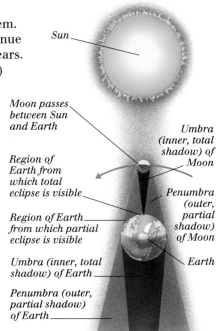

Sun

Moon passes between Sun and Earth

Umbra (inner, total shadow) of Moon

Region of Earth from which total eclipse is visible

Region of Earth from which partial eclipse is visible

Penumbra (outer, partial shadow) of Moon

Umbra (inner, total shadow) of Earth

Earth

Penumbra (outer, partial shadow) of Earth

SURFACE FEATURES

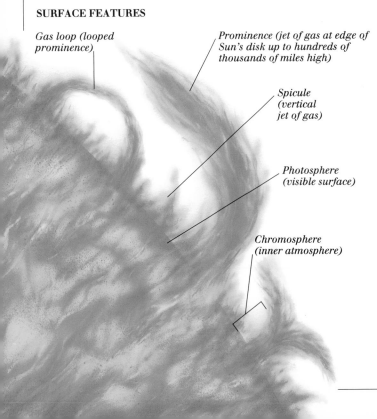

Gas loop (looped prominence)

Prominence (jet of gas at edge of Sun's disk up to hundreds of thousands of miles high)

Spicule (vertical jet of gas)

Photosphere (visible surface)

Chromosphere (inner atmosphere)

TOTAL SOLAR ECLIPSE

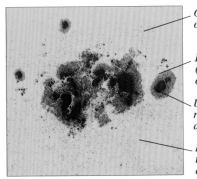

Corona (outer atmosphere of extremely hot diffuse gas)

Moon covers Sun's disk

SUNSPOTS

Granulated surface of Sun

Penumbra (lighter, outer region) containing radial fibrils

Umbra (darker, inner region) temperature about 7,200°F

Photosphere temperature about 9,900°F

**EXTERNAL FEATURES AND
INTERNAL STRUCTURE OF THE SUN**

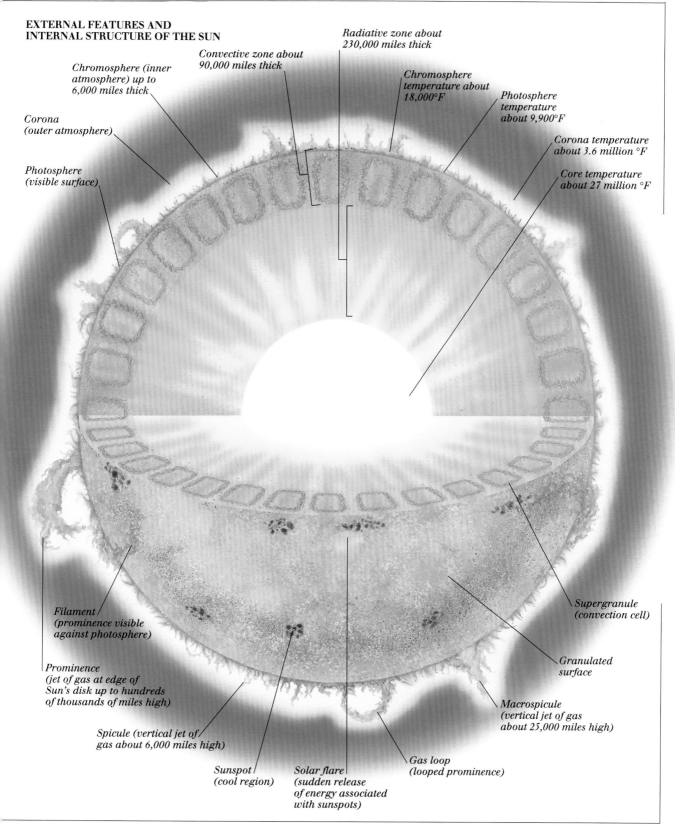

*Radiative zone about
230,000 miles thick*

*Chromosphere (inner
atmosphere) up to
6,000 miles thick*

*Convective zone about
90,000 miles thick*

*Chromosphere
temperature about
18,000°F*

*Photosphere
temperature
about 9,900°F*

*Corona
(outer atmosphere)*

*Corona temperature
about 3.6 million °F*

*Core temperature
about 27 million °F*

*Photosphere
(visible surface)*

*Supergranule
(convection cell)*

*Filament
(prominence visible
against photosphere)*

*Granulated
surface*

*Prominence
(jet of gas at edge of
Sun's disk up to hundreds
of thousands of miles high)*

*Macrospicule
(vertical jet of gas
about 25,000 miles high)*

*Spicule (vertical jet of
gas about 6,000 miles high)*

*Sunspot
(cool region)*

*Solar flare
(sudden release
of energy associated
with sunspots)*

*Gas loop
(looped prominence)*

Mercury

MERCURY

MERCURY IS THE NEAREST PLANET to the Sun, orbiting at an average distance of about 36 million miles. Because Mercury is the closest planet to the Sun, it moves faster than any other planet, traveling at an average speed of nearly 30 miles per second and completing an orbit in just under 88 days. Mercury is very small (only Pluto is smaller) and rocky. Most of the surface has been heavily cratered by the impact of meteorites, although there are also smooth, sparsely cratered plains. The Caloris Basin is the largest crater, measuring about 800 miles across. It is thought to have been formed when a rock the size of an asteroid hit the planet and is surrounded by concentric rings of mountains thrown up by the impact. The surface also has many ridges, called rupes, that are thought to have been formed when the hot core of the young planet cooled and shrank about four billion years ago, buckling the planet's surface in the process. The planet rotates about its axis very slowly, taking nearly 59 Earth days to complete one rotation. As a result, a solar day (sunrise to sunrise) on Mercury is about 176 Earth days—twice as long as the 88-day Mercurian year. Mercury has extreme surface temperatures, ranging from a maximum of 800°F on the sunlit side to -270°F on the dark side. At nightfall, the temperature drops very quickly because the planet's atmosphere is almost nonexistent. It consists only of minute amounts of helium and hydrogen captured from the solar wind, plus traces of other gases.

TILT AND ROTATION OF MERCURY

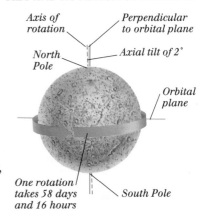

Axis of rotation

Perpendicular to orbital plane

North Pole

Axial tilt of 2°

Orbital plane

One rotation takes 58 days and 16 hours

South Pole

DEGAS AND BRONTË (RAY CRATERS)

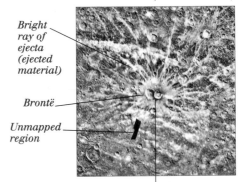

Bright ray of ejecta (ejected material)

Brontë

Unmapped region

Degas with central peak

FORMATION OF A RAY CRATER

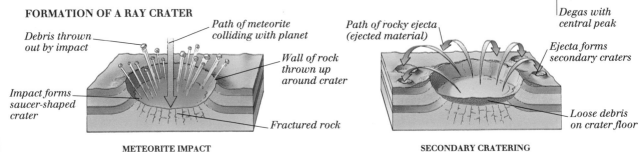

Debris thrown out by impact

Path of meteorite colliding with planet

Wall of rock thrown up around crater

Impact forms saucer-shaped crater

Fractured rock

METEORITE IMPACT

Path of rocky ejecta (ejected material)

Ejecta forms secondary craters

Loose debris on crater floor

SECONDARY CRATERING

Wall of rock forms ring of mountains

Ray of ejecta (ejected material)

Small secondary crater

Loose ejected rock

Central mountain rings form if floor of large crater recoils from meteorite impact

Falling debris forms ridges on side of wall

RAY CRATER

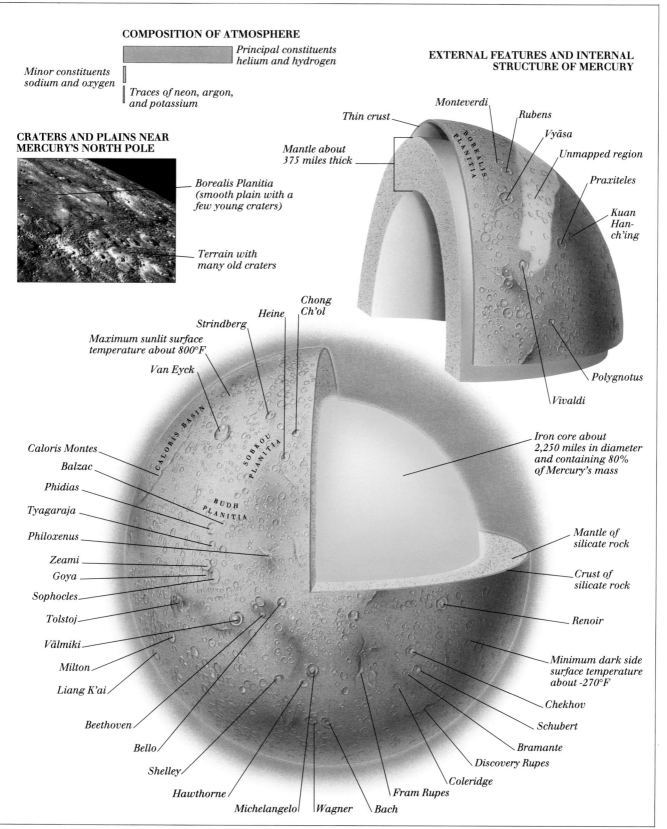

COMPOSITION OF ATMOSPHERE

Principal constituents
helium and hydrogen

Minor constituents
sodium and oxygen

Traces of neon, argon,
and potassium

**EXTERNAL FEATURES AND INTERNAL
STRUCTURE OF MERCURY**

Monteverdi

Rubens

Vyāsa

Unmapped region

Praxiteles

Kuan
Han-
ch'ing

Thin crust

Mantle about
375 miles thick

BOREALIS
PLANITIA

Polygnotus

Vivaldi

**CRATERS AND PLAINS NEAR
MERCURY'S NORTH POLE**

Borealis Planitia
(smooth plain with a
few young craters)

Terrain with
many old craters

Chong
Ch'ol

Heine

Strindberg

Maximum sunlit surface
temperature about 800°F

Van Eyck

Caloris Montes

Balzac

Phidias

Tyagaraja

Philoxenus

Zeami

Goya

Sophocles

Tolstoj

Vālmiki

Milton

Liang K'ai

Beethoven

Bello

Shelley

Hawthorne

Michelangelo

Wagner

Bach

Fram Rupes

Coleridge

Discovery Rupes

Bramante

Schubert

Chekhov

Minimum dark side
surface temperature
about -270°F

Renoir

Crust of
silicate rock

Mantle of
silicate rock

Iron core about
2,250 miles in diameter
and containing 80%
of Mercury's mass

CALORIS BASIN

SOBKOU
PLANITIA

BUDH
PLANITIA

35

Venus

RADAR IMAGE OF VENUS

VENUS IS A ROCKY PLANET and the second planet from the Sun. Venus spins slowly backward as it orbits the Sun, causing its rotational period to be the longest in the Solar System, at about 243 Earth days. It is slightly smaller than Earth and probably has a similar internal structure, consisting of a semisolid metal core surrounded by a rocky mantle and crust. Venus is the brightest object in the sky after the Sun and Moon because its atmosphere reflects sunlight strongly. The main component of the atmosphere is carbon dioxide, which traps heat in a greenhouse effect far stronger than that on Earth. As a result, Venus is the hottest planet, with a maximum surface temperature of about 900°F. The thick cloud layers contain droplets of sulfuric acid and are driven around the planet by winds at speeds of up to 220 miles per hour. Although the planet takes 243 Earth days to rotate once, the high-speed winds cause the clouds to circle the planet in only four Earth days. The high temperature, acidic clouds, and enormous atmospheric pressure (about 90 times greater at the surface than that on Earth) make the environment extremely hostile. However, orbiting satellites have managed to land on Venus and photograph its dry, dusty surface. The Venusian surface has also been mapped by probes with radar equipment that can "see" through the cloud layers. Such radar maps reveal a terrain with craters, mountains, volcanoes, and areas where craters have been covered by plains of solidified volcanic lava. There are two large highland regions called Aphrodite Terra and Ishtar Terra.

TILT AND ROTATION OF VENUS

Axis of rotation

Perpendicular to orbital plane

North Pole

Axial tilt of 2°

Orbital plane

One rotation takes 243 days and 14 minutes

South Pole

CLOUD FEATURES

Polar hood

Dark, mid-latitude band

Cloud features swept around planet by winds of up to 220 mph

Dirty yellow hue due to sulfuric acid in atmosphere

Bright polar band

VENUSIAN CRATERS

Danilova

Ejecta (ejected material)

Central peak

Howe

COMPUTER-ENHANCED RADAR MAP OF THE SURFACE OF VENUS

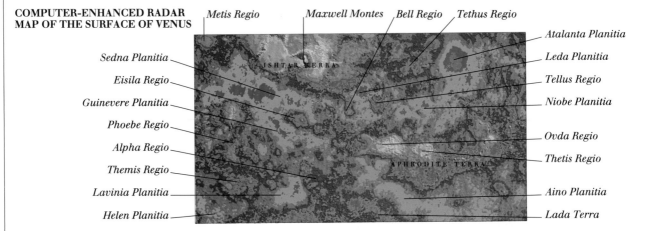

Metis Regio

Maxwell Montes

Bell Regio

Tethus Regio

Atalanta Planitia

Sedna Planitia

Leda Planitia

Eisila Regio

Tellus Regio

Guinevere Planitia

Niobe Planitia

Phoebe Regio

Alpha Regio

Ovda Regio

Themis Regio

Thetis Regio

Lavinia Planitia

Aino Planitia

Helen Planitia

Lada Terra

ISHTAR TERRA

APHRODITE TERRA

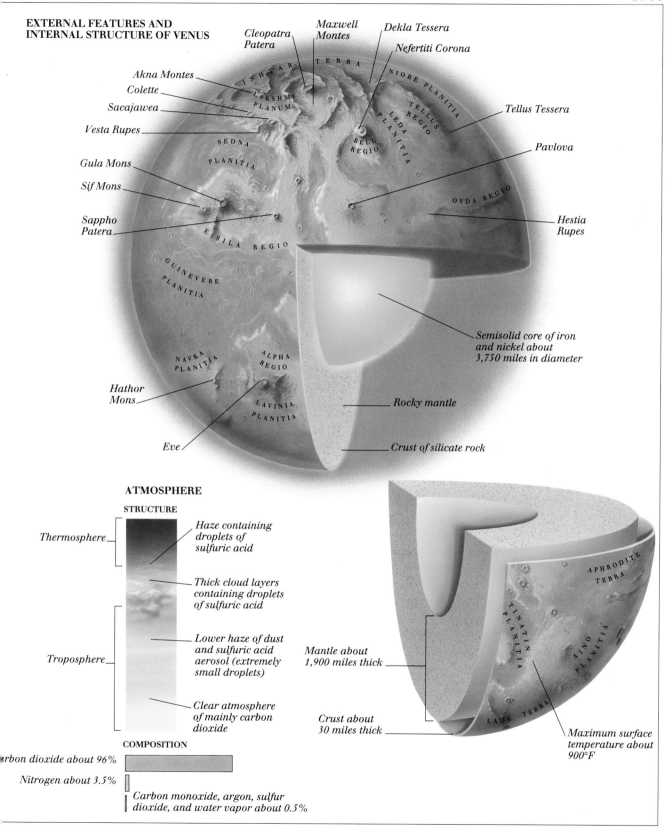

EXTERNAL FEATURES AND INTERNAL STRUCTURE OF VENUS

Cleopatra Patera
Maxwell Montes
Dekla Tessera
Nefertiti Corona
Akna Montes
Colette
Sacajawea
Vesta Rupes
Gula Mons
Sif Mons
Sappho Patera
Hathor Mons
Eve

ISHTAR TERRA
NIOBE PLANITIA
LAKSHMI PLANUM
TELLUS REGIO
LEDA PLANITIA
BELL REGIO
SEDNA PLANITIA
EISILA REGIO
GUINEVERE PLANITIA
OVDA REGIO
NAVKA PLANITIA
ALPHA REGIO
LAVINIA PLANITIA

Tellus Tessera
Pavlova
Hestia Rupes

Semisolid core of iron and nickel about 3,750 miles in diameter

Rocky mantle

Crust of silicate rock

ATMOSPHERE

STRUCTURE

Thermosphere

Troposphere

Haze containing droplets of sulfuric acid

Thick cloud layers containing droplets of sulfuric acid

Lower haze of dust and sulfuric acid aerosol (extremely small droplets)

Clear atmosphere of mainly carbon dioxide

COMPOSITION

Carbon dioxide about 96%

Nitrogen about 3.5%

Carbon monoxide, argon, sulfur dioxide, and water vapor about 0.5%

Mantle about 1,900 miles thick

Crust about 30 miles thick

APHRODITE TERRA
TINATIN PLANITIA
AINO PLANITIA
LADA TERRA

Maximum surface temperature about 900°F

The Earth

THE EARTH

THE EARTH IS THE THIRD of the nine planets that orbit the Sun. It is the largest and densest rocky planet, and the only one known to support life. About 70 percent of the Earth's surface is covered by water, which is not found in liquid form on the surface of any other planet. There are four main layers: the inner core, the outer core, the mantle, and the crust. At the heart of the planet the solid inner core has a temperature of about 7,230°F. The heat from this inner core causes material in the molten outer core and mantle to circulate in convection currents. It is thought that these convection currents generate the Earth's magnetic field, which extends into space as the magnetosphere. The Earth's atmosphere helps screen out some of the harmful radiation from the Sun, stops meteorites from reaching the planet's surface, and traps enough heat to prevent extremes of cold. The Earth has one natural satellite, the Moon, which is large enough for both bodies to be considered a double-planet system.

TILT AND ROTATION OF THE EARTH

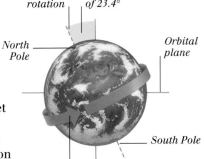

Axis of rotation

Axial tilt of 23.4°

North Pole

Orbital plane

South Pole

One rotation takes 23 hours and 56 minutes

Perpendicular to orbital plane

THE FORMATION OF THE EARTH

The heat of the collisions caused the planet to glow red

The cloud broke up into particles of ice and rock, which stuck together to form planets

Microorganisms began to photosynthesize, creating a supply of oxygen

4,600 MILLION YEARS AGO, THE SOLAR SYSTEM FORMED FROM A CLOUD OF GAS AND DUST

THE EARTH WAS FORMED FROM COLLIDING ROCKS

4,500 MILLION YEARS AGO THE SURFACE COOLED TO FORM THE CRUST

THE CONTINENTS BROKE UP AND REFORMED, GRADUALLY TAKING THEIR PRESENT POSITIONS

Solar wind enters atmosphere and produces aurora

Magnetosphere (magnetic field)

Solar wind (stream of electrically charged particles)

THE EARTH'S MAGNETOSPHERE

Van Allen radiation belt

Earth

Axis of geographic poles

Axis of magnetic poles

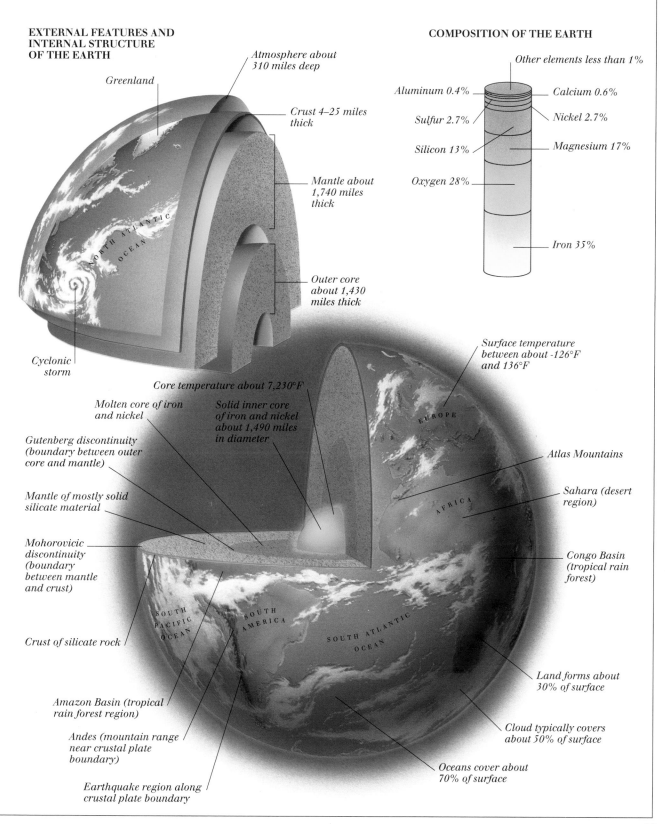

**EXTERNAL FEATURES AND
INTERNAL STRUCTURE
OF THE EARTH**

Greenland

Atmosphere about
310 miles deep

Crust 4–25 miles
thick

Mantle about
1,740 miles
thick

NORTH ATLANTIC
OCEAN

Outer core
about 1,430
miles thick

Cyclonic
storm

COMPOSITION OF THE EARTH

Other elements less than 1%

Aluminum 0.4%

Calcium 0.6%

Sulfur 2.7%

Nickel 2.7%

Silicon 13%

Magnesium 17%

Oxygen 28%

Iron 35%

Surface temperature
between about -126°F
and 136°F

Core temperature about 7,230°F

Molten core of iron
and nickel

Solid inner core
of iron and nickel
about 1,490 miles
in diameter

EUROPE

Gutenberg discontinuity
(boundary between outer
core and mantle)

Atlas Mountains

AFRICA

Sahara (desert
region)

Mantle of mostly solid
silicate material

Mohorovicic
discontinuity
(boundary
between mantle
and crust)

Congo Basin
(tropical rain
forest)

SOUTH
PACIFIC
OCEAN

SOUTH
AMERICA

SOUTH ATLANTIC
OCEAN

Crust of silicate rock

Land forms about
30% of surface

Amazon Basin (tropical
rain forest region)

Cloud typically covers
about 50% of surface

Andes (mountain range
near crustal plate
boundary)

Oceans cover about
70% of surface

Earthquake region along
crustal plate boundary

The Moon

THE MOON FROM EARTH

THE MOON IS THE EARTH'S only natural satellite. It is relatively large for a moon, with a diameter of about 2,155 miles—just over a quarter that of the Earth. The Moon takes the same time to rotate on its axis as it takes to orbit the Earth (27.3 days), and so the same side (the near side) always faces us. However, the amount of the surface we can see—the phase of the Moon—depends on how much of the near side is in sunlight. The Moon is dry and barren, with no atmosphere or water. It consists mainly of solid rock, although its core may contain molten rock or iron. The surface is dusty, with highlands covered in craters caused by meteorite impacts, and lowlands in which large craters have been filled by solidified lava to form dark areas called maria or "seas." Maria occur mainly on the near side, which has a thinner crust than the far side. Many of the craters are rimmed by mountain ranges that form the crater walls and can be thousands of feet high.

TILT AND ROTATION OF THE MOON

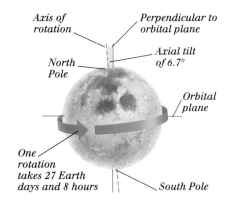

- Axis of rotation
- Perpendicular to orbital plane
- North Pole
- Axial tilt of 6.7°
- Orbital plane
- One rotation takes 27 Earth days and 8 hours
- South Pole

CRATERS ON OCEANUS PROCELLARUM

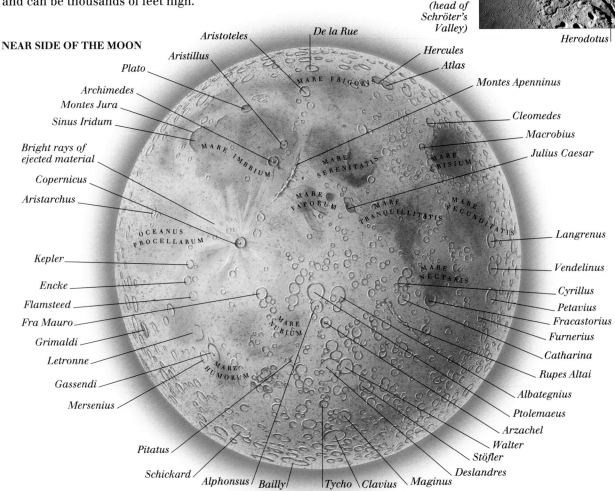

- Aristarchus
- Cobra Head (head of Schröter's Valley)
- Herodotus

NEAR SIDE OF THE MOON

- Aristoteles
- De la Rue
- Aristillus
- Hercules
- Plato
- Atlas
- Archimedes
- Montes Apenninus
- Montes Jura
- Cleomedes
- Sinus Iridum
- Macrobius
- Bright rays of ejected material
- Julius Caesar
- Copernicus
- Aristarchus
- Langrenus
- Kepler
- Vendelinus
- Encke
- Cyrillus
- Flamsteed
- Petavius
- Fra Mauro
- Fracastorius
- Grimaldi
- Furnerius
- Letronne
- Catharina
- Gassendi
- Rupes Altai
- Mersenius
- Albategnius
- Ptolemaeus
- Arzachel
- Walter
- Stöfler
- Pitatus
- Deslandres
- Schickard
- Alphonsus
- Bailly
- Tycho
- Clavius
- Maginus

Mare labels on map: MARE FRIGORIS, MARE IMBRIUM, MARE SERENITATIS, MARE CRISIUM, MARE VAPORUM, MARE TRANQUILLITATIS, MARE FECUNDITATIS, MARE NECTARIS, OCEANUS PROCELLARUM, MARE NUBIUM, MARE HUMORUM

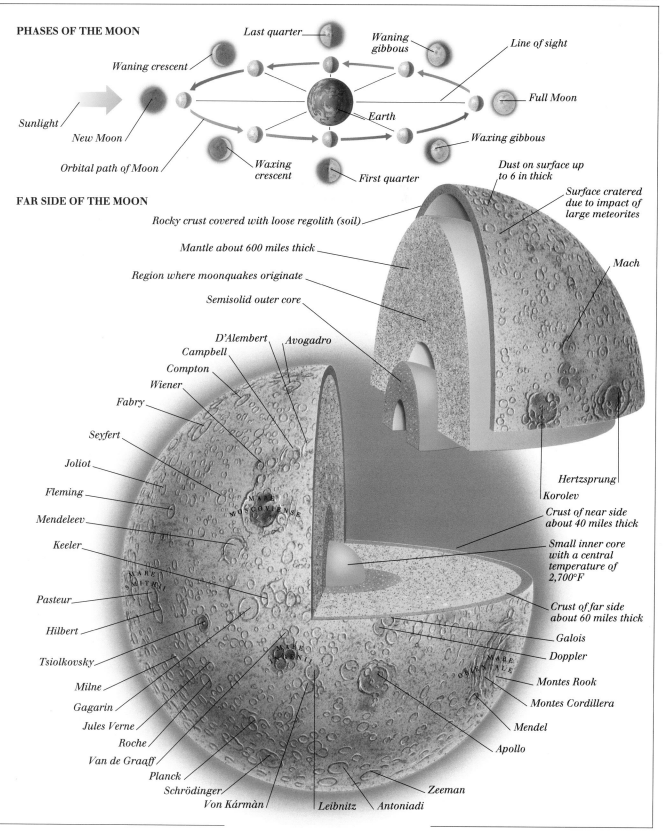

PHASES OF THE MOON

Last quarter

Waning gibbous

Line of sight

Waning crescent

Sunlight

New Moon

Full Moon

Earth

Orbital path of Moon

Waxing gibbous

Waxing crescent

First quarter

Dust on surface up to 6 in thick

Surface cratered due to impact of large meteorites

FAR SIDE OF THE MOON

Rocky crust covered with loose regolith (soil)

Mantle about 600 miles thick

Region where moonquakes originate

Semisolid outer core

Mach

D'Alembert

Avogadro

Campbell

Compton

Wiener

Fabry

Seyfert

Joliot

Fleming

Mendeleev

Keeler

Pasteur

Hilbert

Tsiolkovsky

Milne

Gagarin

Jules Verne

Roche

Van de Graaff

Planck

Schrödinger

Von Kármàn

Leibnitz

Antoniadi

Zeeman

Apollo

Mendel

Montes Cordillera

Montes Rook

Doppler

Galois

Crust of far side about 60 miles thick

Small inner core with a central temperature of 2,700°F

Crust of near side about 40 miles thick

Korolev

Hertzsprung

MARE MOSCOVIENSE

MARE SMITHII

MARE INGENII

MARE ORIENTALE

Mars

MARS

MARS, KNOWN AS THE RED PLANET, is the fourth planet from the Sun and the outermost rocky planet. In the 19th century, astronomers first observed what were thought to be signs of life on Mars. These signs included apparent canal-like markings on the surface, and dark patches that were thought to be vegetation. It is now known that the canals are an optical illusion and the dark patches are areas where the red dust that covers most of the planet has blown away. The fine dust particles are often whipped up by winds into dust storms that occasionally obscure almost all Mars's surface. Residual dust in the atmosphere gives the Martian sky a pinkish hue. The northern hemisphere of Mars has many large plains formed of solidified volcanic lava, while the southern hemisphere has many craters and large impact basins. There are also several huge, extinct volcanoes, including Olympus Mons, which at 370 miles wide and 15 miles high is the largest known volcano in the Solar System. The surface also has many canyons and branching channels. The canyons were formed by movements of the surface crust, but the channels are thought to have been formed by flowing water that has now vaporized almost completely and escaped from the atmosphere. The Martian atmosphere is much thinner than Earth's, with only a few clouds and morning mists. Mars has two tiny irregularly shaped moons, Phobos and Deimos. Their small size indicates that they may be asteroids that have been captured by the gravity of Mars.

TILT AND ROTATION OF MARS

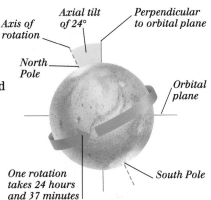

Axis of rotation

Axial tilt of 24°

Perpendicular to orbital plane

North Pole

Orbital plane

One rotation takes 24 hours and 37 minutes

South Pole

SURFACE FEATURES OF MARS

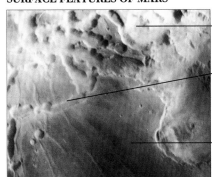

Bright water-ice fog

Fog in canyon about 12 miles wide at end of Valles Marineris

Syria Planum

NOCTIS LABYRINTHUS (CANYON SYSTEM)

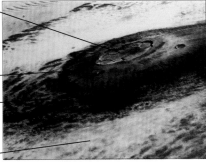

Summit caldera consisting of overlapping collapsed volcanic craters

Crater

Gentle slope produced by lava flow

Cloud formation

OLYMPUS MONS (EXTINCT SHIELD VOLCANO)

THE SURFACE OF MARS

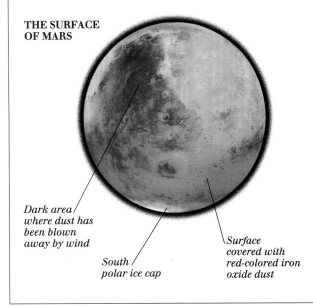

Dark area where dust has been blown away by wind

South polar ice cap

Surface covered with red-colored iron oxide dust

MOONS OF MARS

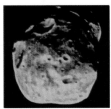

PHOBOS
Average diameter: 14 miles
Average distance from planet: 5,800 miles

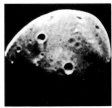

DEIMOS
Average diameter: 8 miles
Average distance from planet: 14,600 miles

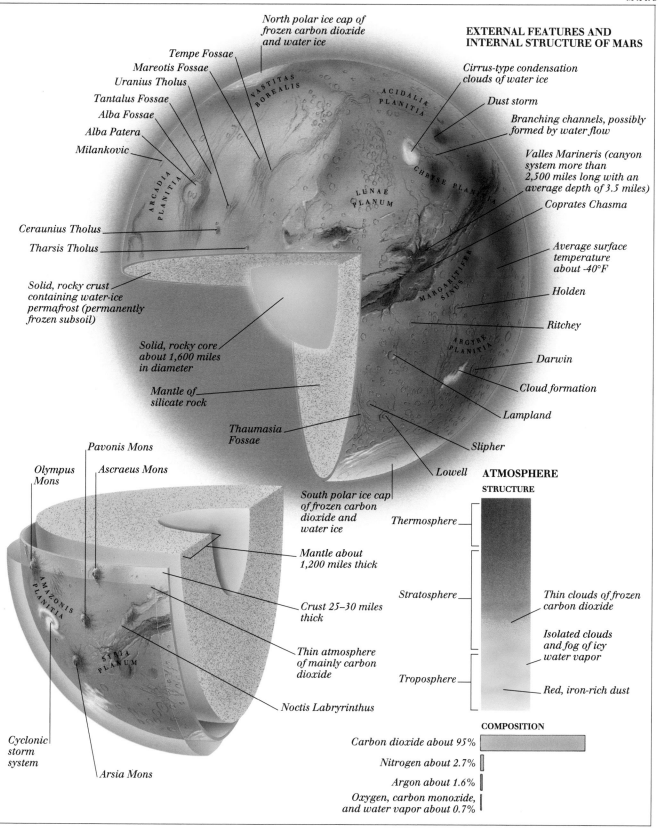

North polar ice cap of frozen carbon dioxide and water ice

Tempe Fossae

Mareotis Fossae

Uranius Tholus

Tantalus Fossae

Alba Fossae

Alba Patera

Milankovic

Ceraunius Tholus

Tharsis Tholus

Solid, rocky crust containing water-ice permafrost (permanently frozen subsoil)

Solid, rocky core about 1,600 miles in diameter

Mantle of silicate rock

Thaumasia Fossae

VASTITAS BOREALIS

ARCADIA PLANITIA

ACIDALIA PLANITIA

CHRYSE PLANITIA

LUNAE PLANUM

MARGARITIFER SINUS

ARGYRE PLANITIA

EXTERNAL FEATURES AND INTERNAL STRUCTURE OF MARS

Cirrus-type condensation clouds of water ice

Dust storm

Branching channels, possibly formed by water flow

Valles Marineris (canyon system more than 2,500 miles long with an average depth of 3.5 miles)

Coprates Chasma

Average surface temperature about -40°F

Holden

Ritchey

Darwin

Cloud formation

Lampland

Slipher

Lowell

South polar ice cap of frozen carbon dioxide and water ice

Mantle about 1,200 miles thick

Crust 25–30 miles thick

Thin atmosphere of mainly carbon dioxide

Noctis Labryrinthus

Olympus Mons

Pavonis Mons

Ascraeus Mons

Cyclonic storm system

Arsia Mons

AMAZONIS PLANITIA

SYRIA PLANUM

ATMOSPHERE

STRUCTURE

Thermosphere

Stratosphere

Troposphere

Thin clouds of frozen carbon dioxide

Isolated clouds and fog of icy water vapor

Red, iron-rich dust

COMPOSITION

Carbon dioxide about 95%

Nitrogen about 2.7%

Argon about 1.6%

Oxygen, carbon monoxide, and water vapor about 0.7%

Jupiter

JUPITER

JUPITER IS THE FIFTH PLANET from the Sun and the first of the four gas giants. It is the largest and the most massive planet, with a diameter about 11 times that of the Earth and a mass about 2.5 times the combined mass of the eight other planets. Jupiter is thought to have a small rocky core surrounded by an inner mantle of metallic hydrogen (liquid hydrogen that acts like a metal). Outside the inner mantle is an outer mantle of liquid hydrogen and helium that merges into the gaseous atmosphere. Jupiter's rapid rate of rotation causes the clouds in its atmosphere to form belts and zones that encircle the planet parallel to the equator. Belts are dark, low-lying, relatively warm cloud layers. Zones are bright, high-altitude, cooler cloud layers. Within the belts and zones, turbulence causes the formation of cloud features such as white ovals and red spots, both of which are huge storm systems. The most prominent cloud feature is a storm called the Great Red Spot, which consists of a spiraling column of clouds three times wider than the Earth that rises about five miles above the upper cloud layer. Jupiter has one thin, faint, main ring, inside of which is a halo ring of tiny particles extending toward the planet. There are 16 known Jovian moons. The four largest moons (called the Galileans) are Ganymede, Callisto, Io, and Europa. Ganymede and Callisto are cratered and probably icy. Europa is smooth and icy and may contain water. Io is covered in bright red, orange, and yellow splotches. This coloring is caused by sulfurous material from active volcanoes that shoot plumes of lava hundreds of miles above the surface.

RINGS OF JUPITER

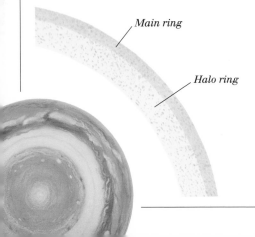

Main ring

Halo ring

TILT AND ROTATION OF JUPITER

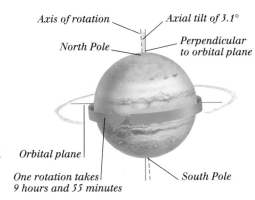

Axis of rotation

Axial tilt of 3.1°

North Pole

Perpendicular to orbital plane

Orbital plane

One rotation takes 9 hours and 55 minutes

South Pole

GREAT RED SPOT AND WHITE OVAL

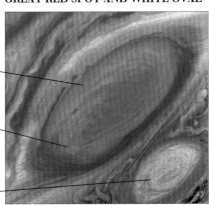

Great Red Spot (anticyclonic storm system)

Red color probably due to phosphorus

White oval (temporary anticyclonic storm system)

GALILEAN MOONS OF JUPITER

EUROPA
Diameter: 1,950 miles
Average distance from planet: 416,900 miles

CALLISTO
Diameter: 2,983 miles
Average distance from planet: 1,168,200 miles

GANYMEDE
Diameter: 3,270 miles
Average distance from planet: 664,900 miles

IO
Diameter: 2,263 miles
Average distance from planet: 262,100 miles

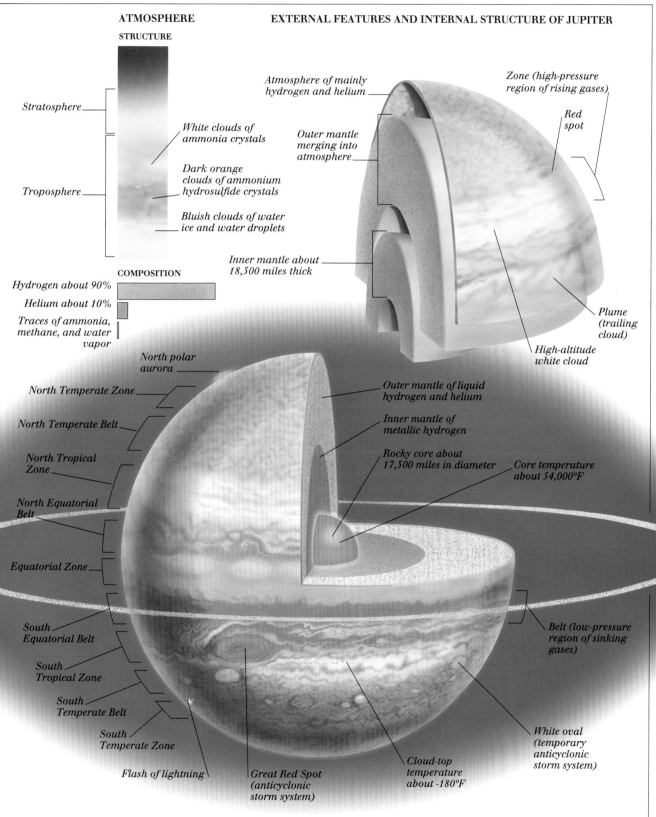

Saturn

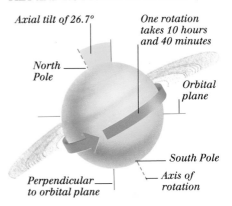

TILT AND ROTATION OF SATURN

Axial tilt of 26.7°

One rotation takes 10 hours and 40 minutes

North Pole

Orbital plane

South Pole

Axis of rotation

Perpendicular to orbital plane

SATURN IS THE SIXTH PLANET from the Sun. It is a gas giant almost as big as Jupiter, with an equatorial diameter of about 74,900 miles. Saturn is thought to consist of a small core of rock and ice surrounded by an inner mantle of metallic hydrogen (liquid hydrogen that acts like a metal). Outside the inner mantle is an outer mantle of liquid hydrogen that merges into a gaseous atmosphere. Saturn's clouds form belts and zones similar to those on Jupiter, but obscured by overlying haze. Storms and eddies, seen as red or white ovals, occur in the clouds. Saturn has an extremely thin but wide system of rings that is less than one mile thick but extends outward to about 260,000 miles from the planet's surface. The main rings comprise thousands of narrow ringlets, each made of icy lumps that range in size from tiny particles to chunks several yards across. The D, E, and G rings are very faint, the F ring is brighter, and the A, B, and C rings are bright enough to be seen from Earth with binoculars. Saturn has 18 known moons, some of which orbit inside the rings and are thought to exert a gravitational influence on the shapes of the rings. Unusually, seven of the moons are co-orbital—they share an orbit with another moon. Astronomers believe that such co-orbital moons may have originated from a single satellite that broke up.

COLOR-ENHANCED IMAGE OF SATURN

COLOR-ENHANCED IMAGE OF SATURN'S CLOUD FEATURES

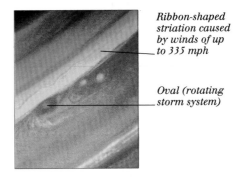

Ribbon-shaped striation caused by winds of up to 335 mph

Oval (rotating storm system)

INNER RINGS OF SATURN

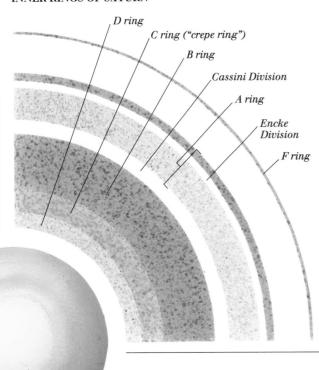

D ring

C ring ("crepe ring")

B ring

Cassini Division

A ring

Encke Division

F ring

MOONS OF SATURN

ENCELADUS
Diameter: 309 miles
Average distance from planet: 148,000 miles

TETHYS
Diameter: 652 miles
Average distance from planet: 183,000 miles

DIONE
Diameter: 695 miles
Average distance from planet: 234,000 miles

MIMAS
Diameter: 247 miles
Average distance from planet: 115,600 miles

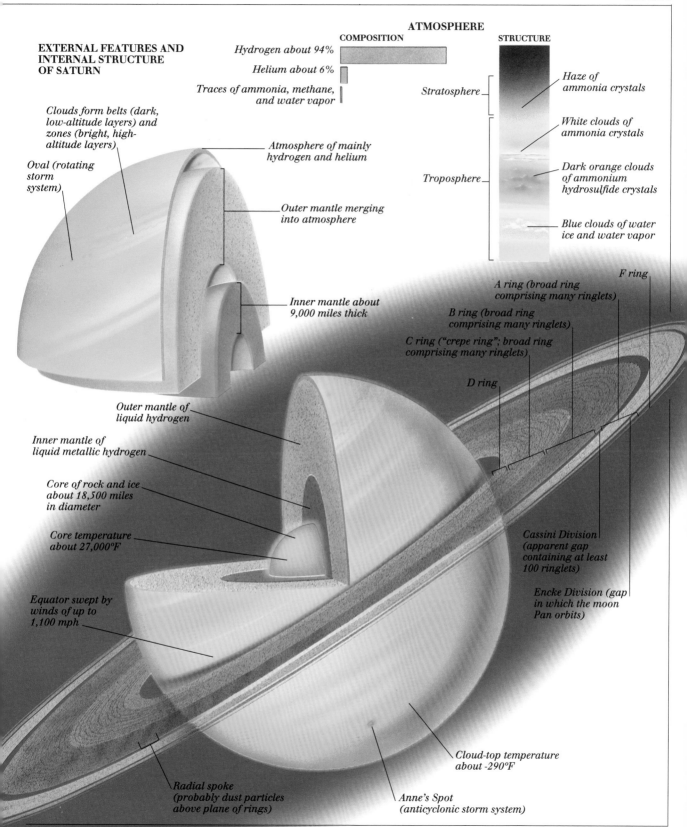

**EXTERNAL FEATURES AND
INTERNAL STRUCTURE
OF SATURN**

ATMOSPHERE

COMPOSITION

Hydrogen about 94%

Helium about 6%

Traces of ammonia, methane,
and water vapor

STRUCTURE

Stratosphere

Troposphere

Haze of
ammonia crystals

White clouds of
ammonia crystals

Dark orange clouds
of ammonium
hydrosulfide crystals

Blue clouds of water
ice and water vapor

Clouds form belts (dark,
low-altitude layers) and
zones (bright, high-
altitude layers)

Oval (rotating
storm
system)

Atmosphere of mainly
hydrogen and helium

Outer mantle merging
into atmosphere

Inner mantle about
9,000 miles thick

Outer mantle of
liquid hydrogen

Inner mantle of
liquid metallic hydrogen

Core of rock and ice
about 18,500 miles
in diameter

Core temperature
about 27,000°F

Equator swept by
winds of up to
1,100 mph

F ring

A ring (broad ring
comprising many ringlets)

B ring (broad ring
comprising many ringlets)

C ring ("crepe ring"; broad ring
comprising many ringlets)

D ring

Cassini Division
(apparent gap
containing at least
100 ringlets)

Encke Division (gap
in which the moon
Pan orbits)

Cloud-top temperature
about -290°F

Radial spoke
(probably dust particles
above plane of rings)

Anne's Spot
(anticyclonic storm system)

47

Uranus

COLOR-ENHANCED IMAGE OF URANUS

URANUS IS THE SEVENTH PLANET from the Sun and the third largest, with a diameter of about 32,000 miles. It is thought to consist of a dense mixture of different types of ice and gas around a solid core. Its atmosphere contains traces of methane, giving the planet a blue-green hue, and the temperature at the cloud tops is about -350°F. Uranus is the most featureless planet to have been closely observed: only a few icy clouds of methane have been seen so far. Uranus is unique among the planets in that its axis of rotation lies close to its orbital plane. As a result of its strongly tilted rotational axis, Uranus rolls on its side along its orbital path around the Sun, while other planets spin more or less upright. Uranus is encircled by 11 rings that consist of rocks interspersed with dust lanes. The rings contain some of the darkest matter in the Solar System. They are extremely narrow, making them difficult to detect: nine of them are less than six miles wide, whereas most of Saturn's rings are thousands of miles in width. There are 15 known Uranian moons, all of which are icy and most of which are farther out than the rings. The 10 inner moons are small and dark, with diameters of less than 100 miles, and the five outer moons are between about 290 and 1,000 miles in diameter. The outer moons have a wide variety of surface features. Miranda has the most varied surface, with cratered areas broken up by huge ridges and cliffs 12 miles high.

TILT AND ROTATION OF URANUS

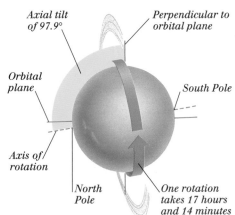

Axial tilt of 97.9°

Perpendicular to orbital plane

Orbital plane

South Pole

Axis of rotation

North Pole

One rotation takes 17 hours and 14 minutes

OUTER MOONS

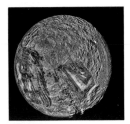

MIRANDA
Diameter: 293 miles
Average distance from planet: 80,700 miles

TITANIA
Diameter: 981 miles
Average distance from planet: 270,900 miles

OBERON
Diameter: 946 miles
Average distance from planet: 362,000 miles

RINGS OF URANUS

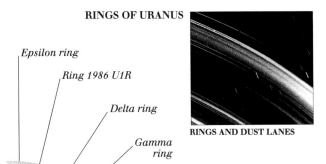

RINGS AND DUST LANES

Epsilon ring

Ring 1986 U1R

Delta ring

Gamma ring

Eta ring

Beta ring

Alpha ring

Rings 4 and 5

Ring 6

Ring 1986 U2R

ARIEL
Diameter: 720 miles
Average distance from planet: 118,800 miles

UMBRIEL
Diameter: 726 miles
Average distance from planet: 165,300 miles

**EXTERNAL FEATURES AND
INTERNAL STRUCTURE
OF URANUS**

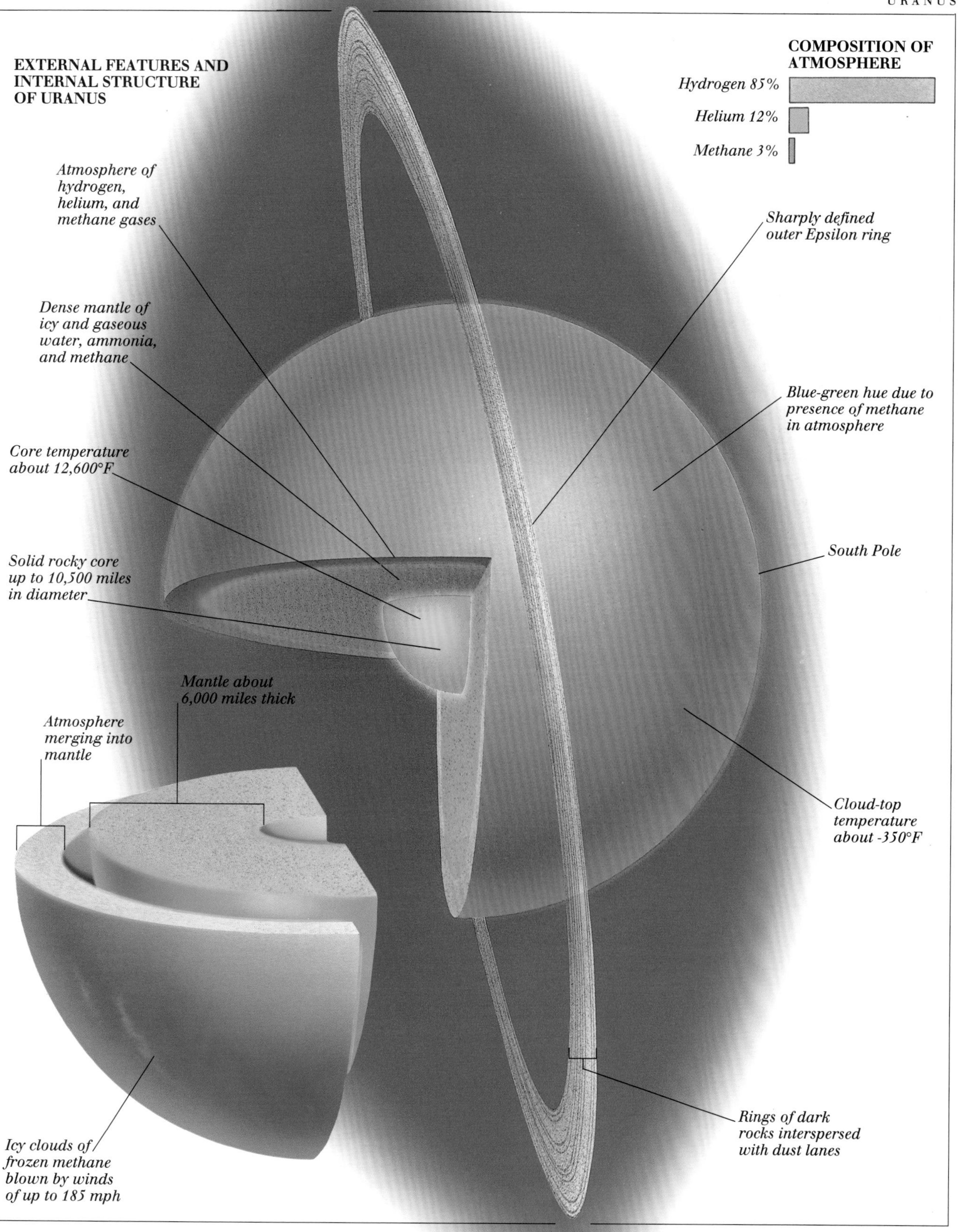

**COMPOSITION OF
ATMOSPHERE**

Hydrogen 85%

Helium 12%

Methane 3%

Atmosphere of
hydrogen,
helium, and
methane gases

Dense mantle of
icy and gaseous
water, ammonia,
and methane

Core temperature
about 12,600°F

Solid rocky core
up to 10,500 miles
in diameter

Mantle about
6,000 miles thick

Atmosphere
merging into
mantle

Sharply defined
outer Epsilon ring

Blue-green hue due to
presence of methane
in atmosphere

South Pole

Cloud-top
temperature
about -350°F

Rings of dark
rocks interspersed
with dust lanes

Icy clouds of
frozen methane
blown by winds
of up to 185 mph

49

Neptune and Pluto

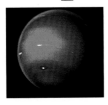

COLOR-ENHANCED IMAGE OF NEPTUNE

NEPTUNE AND PLUTO are the two farthest planets from the Sun, at an average distance of about 2,800 million miles and 3,700 million miles, respectively. Neptune is a gas giant and is thought to consist of a small rocky core surrounded by a mixture of liquids and gases. The atmosphere contains several prominent cloud features. The largest of these are the Great Dark Spot, which is as wide as the Earth, the Small Dark Spot, and the Scooter. The Great and Small Dark Spots are huge storms that are swept around the planet by winds of about 1,200 miles per hour. The Scooter is a large area of cirrus cloud. Neptune has four tenuous rings and eight known moons. Triton is the largest Neptunian moon and the coldest object in the Solar System, with a temperature of -391°F. Unlike most moons in the Solar System, Triton orbits its mother planet in the opposite direction to the planet's rotation. Pluto is usually the outermost planet, but its elliptical orbit causes it to pass inside the orbit of Neptune for 20 years of its 248-year orbit. Pluto is so small and distant that little is known about it. It is a rocky planet, probably covered with ice and frozen methane. Pluto's only known moon, Charon, is large for a moon, at half the size of its parent planet. Because of the small difference in their sizes, Pluto and Charon are sometimes considered to be a double-planet system.

TILT AND ROTATION OF NEPTUNE

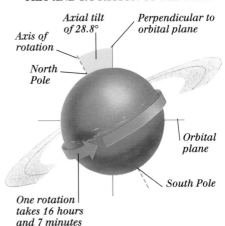

Axis of rotation

Axial tilt of 28.8°

Perpendicular to orbital plane

North Pole

Orbital plane

South Pole

One rotation takes 16 hours and 7 minutes

CLOUD FEATURES OF NEPTUNE

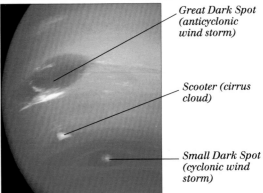

Great Dark Spot (anticyclonic wind storm)

Scooter (cirrus cloud)

Small Dark Spot (cyclonic wind storm)

HIGH-ALTITUDE CLOUDS

Methane cirrus clouds 25 miles above main cloud deck

Cloud shadow

Main cloud deck blown by winds at speeds of about 1,200 mph

RINGS OF NEPTUNE

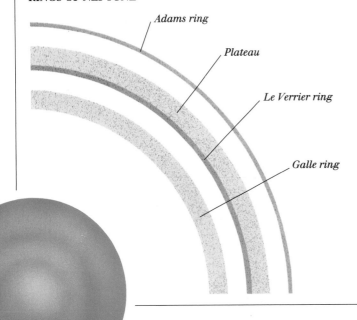

Adams ring

Plateau

Le Verrier ring

Galle ring

MOONS OF NEPTUNE

TRITON
Diameter: 1,681 miles
Average distance from planet: 220,500 miles

PROTEUS
Diameter: 259 miles
Average distance from planet: 73,100 miles

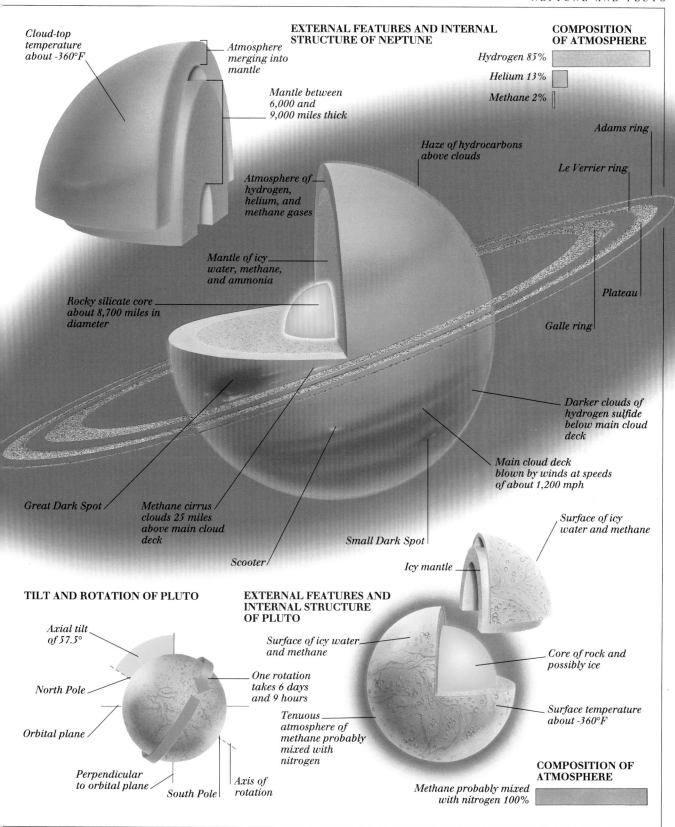

Cloud-top temperature about -360°F

EXTERNAL FEATURES AND INTERNAL STRUCTURE OF NEPTUNE

COMPOSITION OF ATMOSPHERE

Hydrogen 85%

Helium 13%

Methane 2%

Atmosphere merging into mantle

Mantle between 6,000 and 9,000 miles thick

Haze of hydrocarbons above clouds

Adams ring

Le Verrier ring

Atmosphere of hydrogen, helium, and methane gases

Mantle of icy water, methane, and ammonia

Plateau

Rocky silicate core about 8,700 miles in diameter

Galle ring

Darker clouds of hydrogen sulfide below main cloud deck

Main cloud deck blown by winds at speeds of about 1,200 mph

Great Dark Spot

Methane cirrus clouds 25 miles above main cloud deck

Scooter

Small Dark Spot

Surface of icy water and methane

Icy mantle

TILT AND ROTATION OF PLUTO

EXTERNAL FEATURES AND INTERNAL STRUCTURE OF PLUTO

Axial tilt of 57.5°

Surface of icy water and methane

Core of rock and possibly ice

North Pole

One rotation takes 6 days and 9 hours

Orbital plane

Tenuous atmosphere of methane probably mixed with nitrogen

Surface temperature about -360°F

Perpendicular to orbital plane

South Pole

Axis of rotation

COMPOSITION OF ATMOSPHERE

Methane probably mixed with nitrogen 100%

51

Asteroids, comets, and meteoroids

ASTEROID 951 GASPRA

ASTEROIDS, COMETS, AND METEOROIDS are all debris remaining from the nebula in which the Solar System formed 4.6 billion years ago. Asteroids are rocky bodies up to several hundred miles in diameter, although most are much smaller. Most of them orbit the Sun in the asteroid belt, which lies between the orbits of Mars and Jupiter. Comets may originate in a huge cloud, called the Oort Cloud, that is thought to surround the Solar System. They are made of frozen gases and dust, and are a few miles in diameter. Occasionally, a comet is deflected from the Oort Cloud to orbit the Sun in a long, elliptical path. As the comet approaches the Sun, the comet's surface starts to vaporize in the heat, producing a brightly shining coma (a huge sphere of gas and dust around the nucleus), a gas tail, and a dust tail. Meteoroids are small chunks of stone or stone and iron, some of which are fragments of asteroids or comets. Meteoroids range in size from tiny dust particles to objects tens of yards across. If a meteoroid enters the Earth's atmosphere, it is heated by friction and appears as a glowing streak of light called a meteor (also known as a shooting star). Meteor showers occur when the Earth passes through the trail of dust particles left by a comet. Most meteors burn up in the atmosphere. The few that are large enough to reach the Earth's surface are termed meteorites.

COLOR-ENHANCED IMAGE OF HALLEY'S COMET

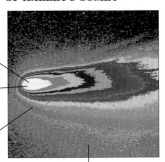

High-intensity light emission

Nucleus

Medium-intensity light emission

Low-intensity light emission

COLOR-ENHANCED IMAGE OF A LEONID METEOR SHOWER

METEORITES

DEVELOPMENT OF COMET TAILS

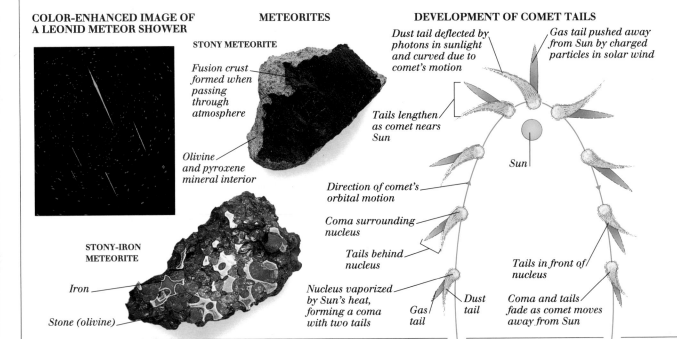

STONY METEORITE

Fusion crust formed when passing through atmosphere

Olivine and pyroxene mineral interior

STONY-IRON METEORITE

Iron

Stone (olivine)

Dust tail deflected by photons in sunlight and curved due to comet's motion

Gas tail pushed away from Sun by charged particles in solar wind

Tails lengthen as comet nears Sun

Sun

Direction of comet's orbital motion

Coma surrounding nucleus

Tails behind nucleus

Nucleus vaporized by Sun's heat, forming a coma with two tails

Gas tail

Dust tail

Tails in front of nucleus

Coma and tails fade as comet moves away from Sun

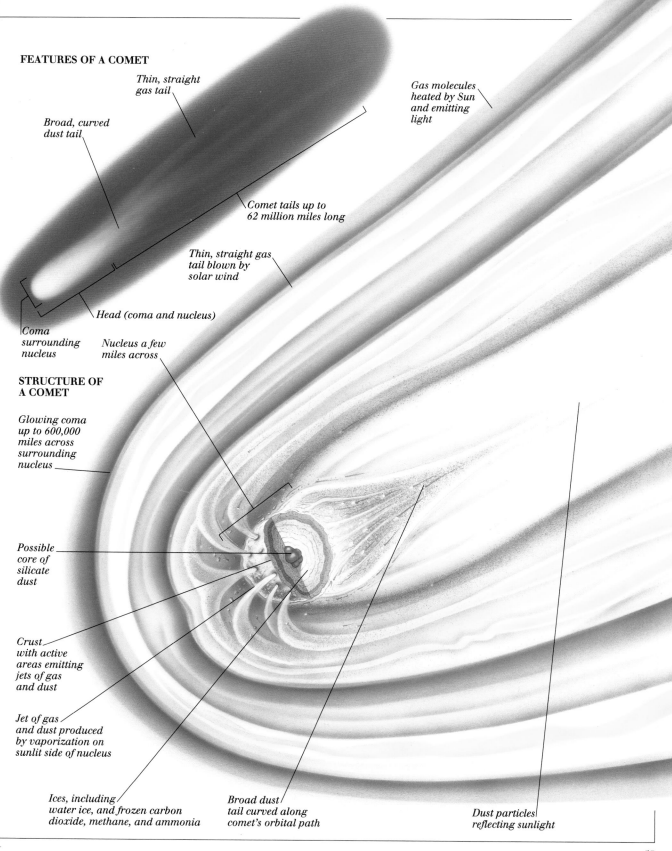

FEATURES OF A COMET

Thin, straight
gas tail

Broad, curved
dust tail

Gas molecules
heated by Sun
and emitting
light

Comet tails up to
62 million miles long

Thin, straight gas
tail blown by
solar wind

Head (coma and nucleus)

Coma
surrounding
nucleus

Nucleus a few
miles across

**STRUCTURE OF
A COMET**

Glowing coma
up to 600,000
miles across
surrounding
nucleus

Possible
core of
silicate
dust

Crust
with active
areas emitting
jets of gas
and dust

Jet of gas
and dust produced
by vaporization on
sunlit side of nucleus

Ices, including
water ice, and frozen carbon
dioxide, methane, and ammonia

Broad dust
tail curved along
comet's orbital path

Dust particles
reflecting sunlight

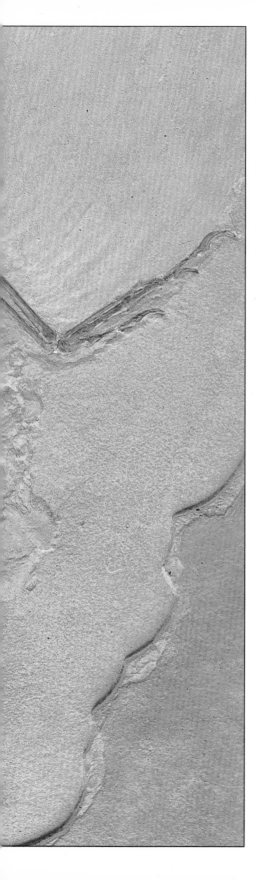

Prehistoric Earth

THE CHANGING EARTH · · · · · · · · · 56

THE EARTH'S CRUST · · · · · · · · · 58

FAULTS AND FOLDS · · · · · · · · · 60

MOUNTAIN BUILDING · · · · · · · · · 62

PRECAMBRIAN TO DEVONIAN PERIOD · · · 64

CARBONIFEROUS TO PERMIAN PERIOD · · · 66

TRIASSIC PERIOD · · · · · · · · · 68

JURASSIC PERIOD · · · · · · · · · 70

CRETACEOUS PERIOD · · · · · · · · · 72

TERTIARY PERIOD · · · · · · · · · 74

QUATERNARY PERIOD · · · · · · · · · 76

EARLY SIGNS OF LIFE · · · · · · · · · 78

AMPHIBIANS AND REPTILES · · · · · · · 80

THE DINOSAURS · · · · · · · · · 82

THEROPODS 1 · · · · · · · · · 84

THEROPODS 2 · · · · · · · · · 86

SAUROPODOMORPHS 1 · · · · · · · · · 88

SAUROPODOMORPHS 2 · · · · · · · · · 90

THYREOPHORANS 1 · · · · · · · · · 92

THYREOPHORANS 2 · · · · · · · · · 94

ORNITHOPODS 1 · · · · · · · · · 96

ORNITHOPODS 2 · · · · · · · · · 98

MARGINOCEPHALIANS 1 · · · · · · · · · 100

MARGINOCEPHALIANS 2 · · · · · · · · · 102

MAMMALS 1 · · · · · · · · · 104

MAMMALS 2 · · · · · · · · · 106

THE FIRST HOMINIDS · · · · · · · · · 108

The changing Earth

THE EARTH FORMED FROM A CLOUD OF DUST and gas drifting through space about 4,600 million years ago. Dense minerals sank to the center while lighter ones formed a thin rocky crust. However, the first known life forms—bacteria and blue-green algae—did not appear until about 3,400 million years ago, and it was only about 700 million years ago that more complex plants and animals began to develop. Since then, thousands of animal and plant species have evolved. Some, such as the dinosaurs, survived for millions of years, while others died out quickly. The Earth itself is continually changing. Although continents neared their present locations about 50 million years ago, they are still drifting slowly over the planet's surface, and mountain ranges such as the Himalayas—which began to form 40 million years ago—are continually being built up and worn away. Climate is also subject to change: the Earth has undergone a series of ice ages interspersed with warmer periods (the most recent ice age was at its height about 20,000 years ago).

Small mammals appeared (e.g., Crusafontia)

Dinosaurs became extinct

Global mountain building occurred

CRETACEOU

Multicellular soft-bodied animals appeared (e.g., worms and jellyfish)

Shelled invertebrates appeared (e.g., trilobites)

Marine plants flourished

Land plants appeared (e.g., Cooksonia)

ORDOVICIAN

CAMBRIAN

PRECAMBRIAN TIME

SILURIAN

DEVONIAN

Unicellular organisms appeared (e.g., blue-green algae)

Earth formed

Coral reefs appeared

Vertebrates appeared (e.g., Hemicyclaspis)

More complex types of algae appeared

Amphibians appeared (e.g., Ichthyostega)

GEOLOGICAL TIMESCALE

MILLIONS OF
YEARS AGO (MYA)

4,600	570	510	439	409	363	323	290

PRECAMBRIAN TIME	CAMBRIAN	ORDOVICIAN	SILURIAN	DEVONIAN	MISSISSIPPIAN (NORTH AMERICA)	PENNSYLVANIAN (NORTH AMERICA)
					CARBONIFEROUS	
	PALEOZOIC					

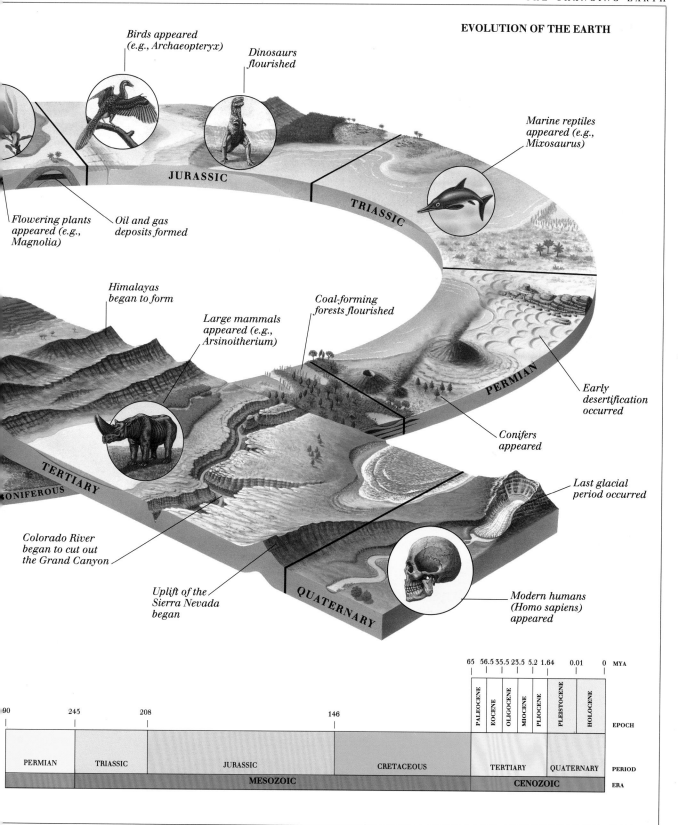

EVOLUTION OF THE EARTH

Birds appeared
(e.g., Archaeopteryx)

Dinosaurs
flourished

Marine reptiles
appeared (e.g.,
Mixosaurus)

JURASSIC

TRIASSIC

Flowering plants
appeared (e.g.,
Magnolia)

Oil and gas
deposits formed

Himalayas
began to form

Large mammals
appeared (e.g.,
Arsinoitherium)

Coal-forming
forests flourished

PERMIAN

Early
desertification
occurred

Conifers
appeared

TERTIARY

ONIFEROUS

Last glacial
period occurred

Colorado River
began to cut out
the Grand Canyon

Uplift of the
Sierra Nevada
began

QUATERNARY

Modern humans
(Homo sapiens)
appeared

	65	56.5	35.5	23.5	5.2	1.64	0.01	0	MYA
	PALEOCENE	EOCENE	OLIGOCENE	MIOCENE	PLIOCENE	PLEISTOCENE	HOLOCENE		EPOCH

90	245	208	146				

PERMIAN	TRIASSIC	JURASSIC	CRETACEOUS	TERTIARY	QUATERNARY	PERIOD
		MESOZOIC		CENOZOIC		ERA

57

The Earth's crust

THE EARTH'S CRUST IS THE SOLID outer shell of the Earth. It includes continental crust (about 25 miles thick) and oceanic crust (about four miles thick). The crust and the topmost layer of the mantle form the lithosphere. The lithosphere consists of semi-rigid plates that move relative to each other on the underlying asthenosphere (a partly molten layer of the mantle). This movement is known as plate tectonics and helps explain continental drift. Where two plates move apart, there are rifts in the crust. In mid-ocean, this movement results in seafloor spreading and the formation of ocean ridges; on continents, crustal spreading can form rift valleys. When plates move toward each other, one may be subducted beneath (forced under) the other. In mid-ocean, this causes ocean trenches, seismic activity, and arcs of volcanic islands. Where oceanic crust is subducted beneath continental crust or where continents collide, land may be uplifted and mountains formed (see pp. 62–63). Plates may also slide past each other—along the San Andreas fault, for example. Crustal movement on continents may result in earthquakes, while movement under the seabed can lead to tidal waves.

ELEMENTS IN THE EARTH'S CRUST

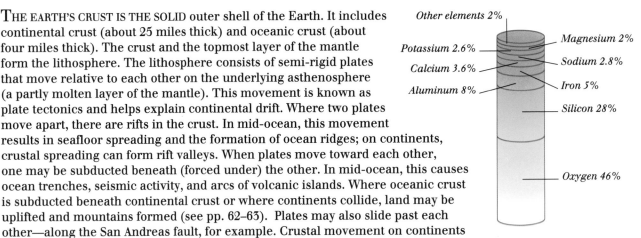

Other elements 2%
Potassium 2.6%
Calcium 3.6%
Aluminum 8%
Magnesium 2%
Sodium 2.8%
Iron 5%
Silicon 28%
Oxygen 46%

FEATURES OF PLATE MOVEMENTS

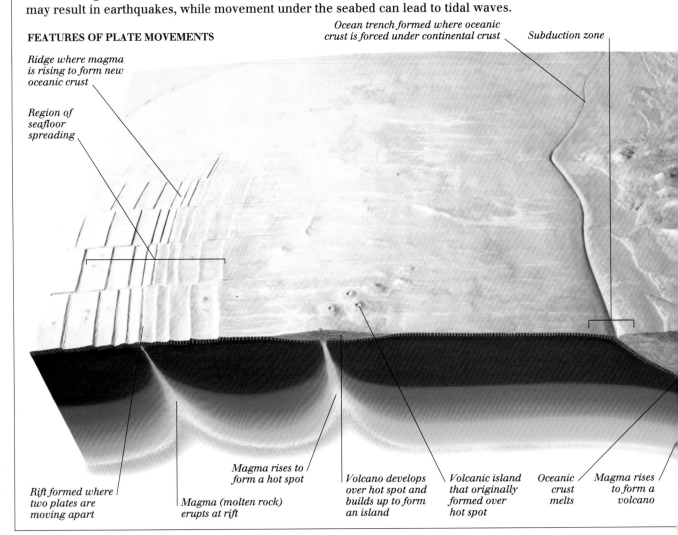

Ridge where magma is rising to form new oceanic crust

Region of seafloor spreading

Ocean trench formed where oceanic crust is forced under continental crust

Subduction zone

Rift formed where two plates are moving apart

Magma (molten rock) erupts at rift

Magma rises to form a hot spot

Volcano develops over hot spot and builds up to form an island

Volcanic island that originally formed over hot spot

Oceanic crust melts

Magma rises to form a volcano

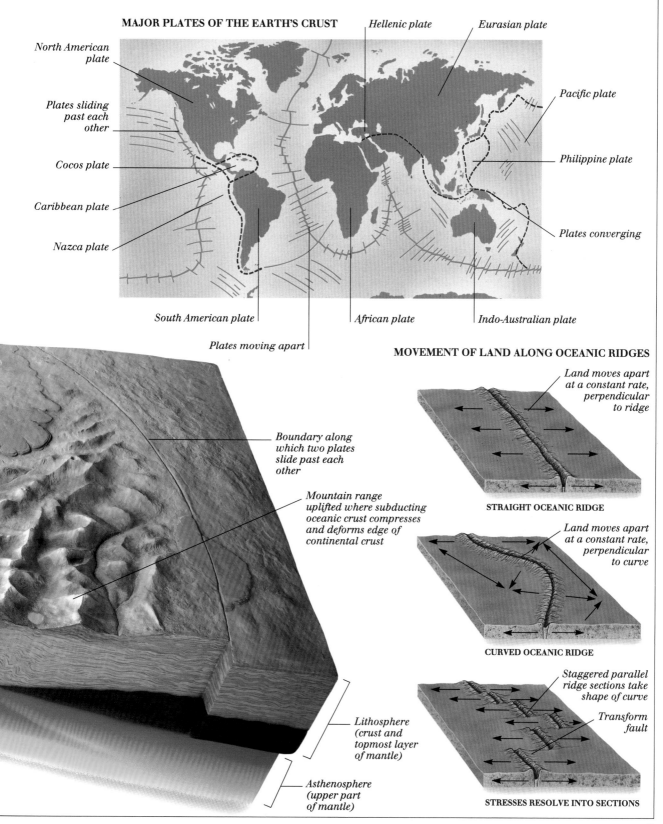

MAJOR PLATES OF THE EARTH'S CRUST

North American plate

Hellenic plate

Eurasian plate

Plates sliding past each other

Pacific plate

Cocos plate

Philippine plate

Caribbean plate

Plates converging

Nazca plate

South American plate

African plate

Indo-Australian plate

Plates moving apart

Boundary along which two plates slide past each other

Mountain range uplifted where subducting oceanic crust compresses and deforms edge of continental crust

Lithosphere (crust and topmost layer of mantle)

Asthenosphere (upper part of mantle)

MOVEMENT OF LAND ALONG OCEANIC RIDGES

Land moves apart at a constant rate, perpendicular to ridge

STRAIGHT OCEANIC RIDGE

Land moves apart at a constant rate, perpendicular to curve

CURVED OCEANIC RIDGE

Staggered parallel ridge sections take shape of curve

Transform fault

STRESSES RESOLVE INTO SECTIONS

Faults and folds

THE CONTINUOUS MOVEMENT of the Earth's crustal plates (see pp. 58–59) can squeeze, stretch, or break rock strata, deforming them and producing faults and folds. A fault is a fracture in a rock along which there is movement of one side relative to the other. The movement can be vertical, horizontal, or oblique (vertical and horizontal). Faults develop when rocks are subjected to compression or tension. They tend to occur in hard, rigid rocks, which are more likely to break than bend. The smallest faults occur in single mineral crystals and are microscopically small, while the largest —the Great Rift Valley in Africa, which formed between 5 million and 100,000 years ago—is more than 6,000 miles long. A fold is a bend in a rock layer caused by compression. Folds occur in elastic rocks, which tend to bend rather than break. The two main types of fold are anticlines (upfolds) and synclines (downfolds). Folds vary in size from a few millimeters long to folded mountain ranges hundreds of miles long, such as the Himalayas (see pp. 62–63) and the Alps, which are repeatedly folding. In addition to faults and folds, other features associated with rock deformations include boudins, mullions, and *en échelon* fractures.

STRUCTURE OF A FOLD

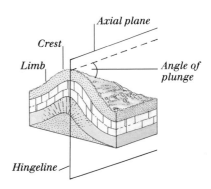

Axial plane

Crest

Limb

Angle of plunge

Hingeline

STRUCTURE OF A FAULT

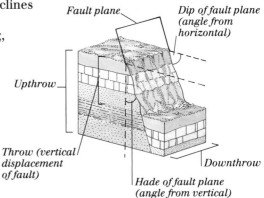

Fault plane

Dip of fault plane (angle from horizontal)

Upthrow

Throw (vertical displacement of fault)

Downthrow

Hade of fault plane (angle from vertical)

STRUCTURE OF A SLOPE

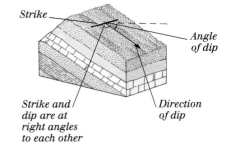

Strike

Angle of dip

Strike and dip are at right angles to each other

Direction of dip

FOLDED ROCK

Crest of anticline

Plunge

Steeply dipping limbs

SECTION THROUGH FOLDED ROCK STRATA THAT HAVE BEEN ERODED

Dipping bed

Anticlinal fold

Monoclinal fold

Mineral-filled fault

Upper Carboniferous Millstone Grit

Lower Carboniferous Limestone

EXAMPLES OF FOLDS

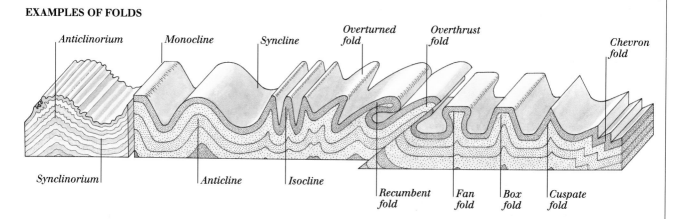

Anticlinorium
Monocline
Syncline
Overturned fold
Overthrust fold
Chevron fold
Synclinorium
Anticline
Isocline
Recumbent fold
Fan fold
Box fold
Cuspate fold

EXAMPLES OF FAULTS

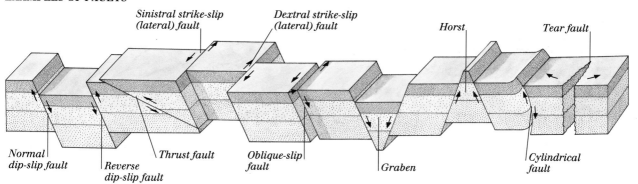

Sinistral strike-slip (lateral) fault
Dextral strike-slip (lateral) fault
Horst
Tear fault
Normal dip-slip fault
Reverse dip-slip fault
Thrust fault
Oblique-slip fault
Graben
Cylindrical fault

SMALL-SCALE ROCK DEFORMATIONS

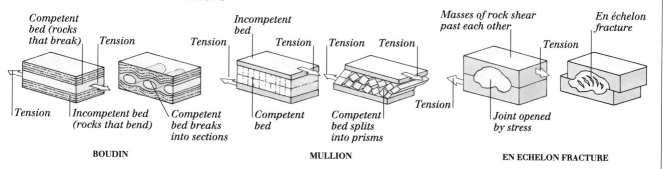

Competent bed (rocks that break)
Tension
Tension
Incompetent bed (rocks that bend)
Competent bed breaks into sections
Incompetent bed
Tension
Tension
Tension
Competent bed
Competent bed splits into prisms
Masses of rock shear past each other
Tension
Joint opened by stress
En échelon fracture

BOUDIN
MULLION
EN ECHELON FRACTURE

Mineral-filled fault
Dipping bed
Gently folded bed
Horizontal bed
Mineral-filled fault
Dipping bed
Upper Carboniferous Millstone Grit
Upper Carboniferous Coal Measures

Mountain building

THE PROCESSES INVOLVED in mountain building—termed orogenesis—occur as a result of the movement of the Earth's crustal plates (see pp. 58-59). There are three main types of mountains: volcanic mountains, fold mountains, and block mountains. Most volcanic mountains have been formed along plate boundaries where plates have come together or moved apart and lava and other debris have been ejected onto the Earth's surface. The lava and debris may have built up to form a dome around the vent of a volcano. Fold mountains are formed where plates push together and cause the rock to buckle upward. Where oceanic crust meets less dense continental crust, the oceanic crust is forced under the continental crust. The continental crust is buckled by the impact. This is how folded mountain ranges, such as the Appalachian Mountains in North America, were formed. Fold mountains are also formed where two areas of continental crust meet. The Himalayas, for example, began to form when India collided with Asia, buckling the sediments and parts of the oceanic crust between them. Block mountains are formed when a block of land is uplifted between two faults as a result of compression or tension in the Earth's crust (see pp. 60-61). Often, the movement along faults has taken place gradually over millions of years. However, two plates may cause an earthquake by suddenly sliding past each other along a faultline.

BHAGIRATHI PARBAT, HIMALAYAS

FORMATION OF THE HIMALAYAS

Asia

Himalayas formed by buckling of sediment and part of the oceanic crust between two colliding continents

India moves north

India collides with Asia about 40 million years ago

EXAMPLES OF MOUNTAINS

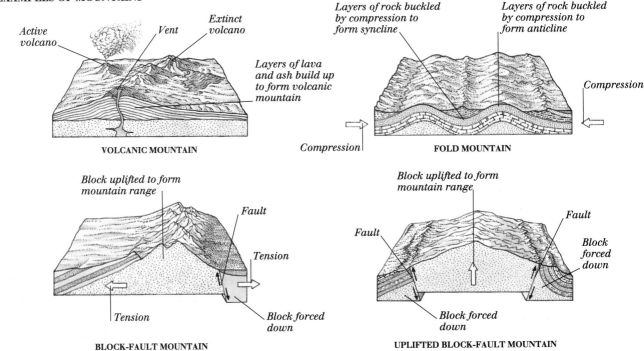

Active volcano

Vent

Extinct volcano

Layers of lava and ash build up to form volcanic mountain

VOLCANIC MOUNTAIN

Layers of rock buckled by compression to form syncline

Layers of rock buckled by compression to form anticline

Compression

Compression

FOLD MOUNTAIN

Block uplifted to form mountain range

Fault

Tension

Tension

Block forced down

BLOCK-FAULT MOUNTAIN

Block uplifted to form mountain range

Fault

Fault

Block forced down

Block forced down

UPLIFTED BLOCK-FAULT MOUNTAIN

STAGES IN THE FORMATION OF THE HIMALAYAS

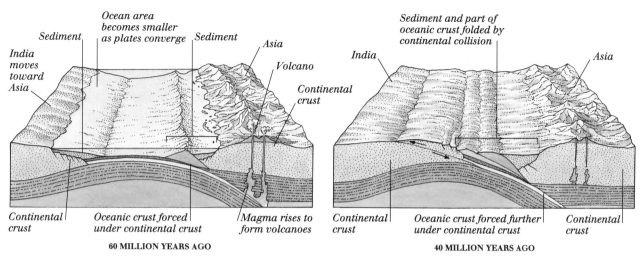

Sediment

India moves toward Asia

Ocean area becomes smaller as plates converge

Sediment

Asia

Volcano

Continental crust

Continental crust

Oceanic crust forced under continental crust

Magma rises to form volcanoes

60 MILLION YEARS AGO

India

Sediment and part of oceanic crust folded by continental collision

Asia

Continental crust

Oceanic crust forced further under continental crust

Continental crust

40 MILLION YEARS AGO

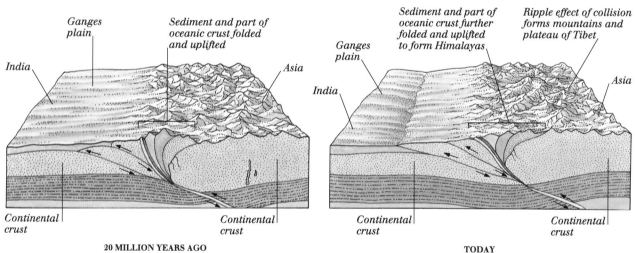

Ganges plain

India

Sediment and part of oceanic crust folded and uplifted

Asia

Continental crust

Continental crust

20 MILLION YEARS AGO

Ganges plain

India

Sediment and part of oceanic crust further folded and uplifted to form Himalayas

Ripple effect of collision forms mountains and plateau of Tibet

Asia

Continental crust

Continental crust

TODAY

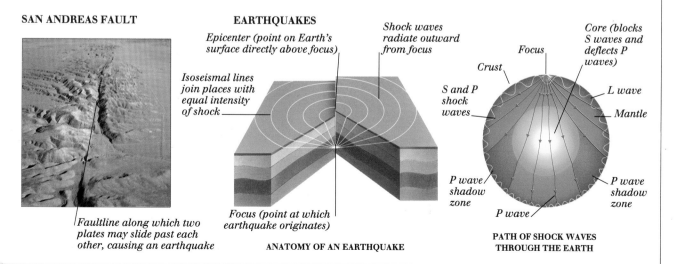

SAN ANDREAS FAULT

Faultline along which two plates may slide past each other, causing an earthquake

EARTHQUAKES

Epicenter (point on Earth's surface directly above focus)

Isoseismal lines join places with equal intensity of shock

Shock waves radiate outward from focus

Focus (point at which earthquake originates)

ANATOMY OF AN EARTHQUAKE

Focus

Crust

S and P shock waves

P wave shadow zone

P wave

Core (blocks S waves and deflects P waves)

L wave

Mantle

P wave shadow zone

PATH OF SHOCK WAVES THROUGH THE EARTH

Precambrian to Devonian periods

WHEN THE EARTH FORMED about 4,600 million years ago, its atmosphere consisted of volcanic gases with little oxygen, making it hostile to most forms of life. One large supercontinent, Gondwanaland, was situated over the southern polar region, while other smaller continents were spread over the rest of the world. Constant movement of the earth's crustal plates carried continents across the earth's surface. The first primitive life-forms emerged around 3,400 million years ago in shallow, warm seas. The build up of oxygen began to form a shield of ozone around the earth, protecting living organisms from the sun's harmful rays and helping to establish an atmosphere in which life could sustain itself. The first vertebrates appeared about 470 million years ago, during the Ordovician period (510–439 million years ago), the first land plants appeared around 400 million years ago during the Devonian period (409–363 million years ago), and the first land animals about 30 million years later.

MIDDLE ORDOVICIAN POSITIONS OF PRESENT-DAY LANDMASSES

North America · Greenland · China · Australia · South America · South Africa · Africa · Scandinavia · Europe · Siberia · India · North East Africa · Central Asia

EXAMPLES OF PRECAMBRIAN TO DEVONIAN PLANT GROUPS

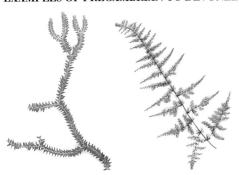

A PRESENT-DAY CLUBMOSS
(Lycopodium sp.)

A PRESENT-DAY LAND PLANT
(Asparagus setaceous)

FOSSIL OF AN EXTINCT LAND PLANT
(Cooksonia hemisphaerica)

FOSSIL OF AN EXTINCT SWAMP PLANT
(Zosterophyllum llanoveranum)

EXAMPLES OF PRECAMBRIAN TO DEVONIAN TRILOBITES

ACADAGNOSTUS
Family: Agnostidae
Length: 1/3 in (8 mm)

PHACOPS
Family: Phacopidae
Length: 1 3/4 in (4.5 cm)

OLENELLUS
Family: Olenellidae
Length: 2 1/2 in (6 cm)

ELRATHIA
Family: Ptychopariidae
Length: 3/4 in (2 cm)

THE EARTH DURING THE MIDDLE ORDOVICIAN PERIOD

EXAMPLES OF EARLY MARINE INVERTEBRATES

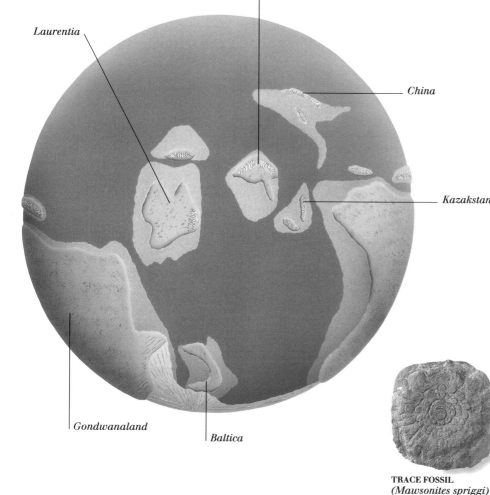

Siberia

Laurentia

China

Kazakstania

Gondwanaland

Baltica

FOSSIL NAUTILOID
(*Estonioceras perforatum*)

FOSSIL BRACHIOPOD
(*Dicoelosia bilobata*)

TRACE FOSSIL
(*Mawsonites spriggi*)

FOSSIL GRAPTOLITE
(*Monograptus convolutus*)

EXAMPLES OF DEVONIAN FISH

RHAMPHODOPSIS
Family: Ptyctodontidae
Length: 6 in (15 cm)

PTERASPIS
Family: Pteraspidae
Length: 10 in (25 cm)

COCCOSTEUS
Family: Coccosteidae
Length: 14 in (35 cm)

BOTHRIOLEPIS
Family: Bothriolepidae
Length: 16 in (40 cm)

CHEIRACANTHUS
Family: Acanthodidae
Length: 12 in (30 cm)

PTERICHTHYODES
Family: Asterolepidae
Length: 6 in (15 cm)

CHEIROLEPIS
Family: Cheirolepidae
Length: 6¾ in (17 cm)

CEPHALASPIS
Family: Cephalaspidae
Length: 8¾ in (22 cm)

Carboniferous to Permian periods

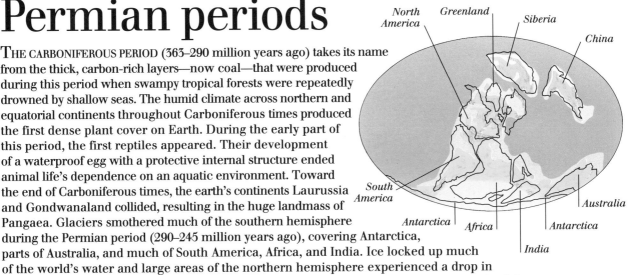

THE CARBONIFEROUS PERIOD (363–290 million years ago) takes its name from the thick, carbon-rich layers—now coal—that were produced during this period when swampy tropical forests were repeatedly drowned by shallow seas. The humid climate across northern and equatorial continents throughout Carboniferous times produced the first dense plant cover on Earth. During the early part of this period, the first reptiles appeared. Their development of a waterproof egg with a protective internal structure ended animal life's dependence on an aquatic environment. Toward the end of Carboniferous times, the earth's continents Laurussia and Gondwanaland collided, resulting in the huge landmass of Pangaea. Glaciers smothered much of the southern hemisphere during the Permian period (290–245 million years ago), covering Antarctica, parts of Australia, and much of South America, Africa, and India. Ice locked up much of the world's water and large areas of the northern hemisphere experienced a drop in sea-level. Away from the poles, deserts and a hot dry climate predominated. As a result of these conditions, the Permian period ended with the greatest mass extinction of life on earth ever.

EXAMPLES OF CARBONIFEROUS AND PERMIAN PLANT GROUPS

A PRESENT-DAY FIR
(Abies concolor)

FOSSIL OF AN EXTINCT FERN
(Zeilleria frenzlii)

**FOSSIL OF AN
EXTINCT HORSETAIL**
(Equisetites sp.)

**FOSSIL OF AN
EXTINCT CLUBMOSS**
(Lepidodendron sp.)

EXAMPLES OF CARBONIFEROUS AND PERMIAN TREES

PECOPTERIS
Family: Marattiaceae
Height: 13 ft (4 m)

PARIPTERIS
Family: Medullosaceae
Height: 16 ft 6 in (5 m)

MARIOPTERIS
Family: Unclassified
Height: 16 ft 6 in (5 m)

MEDULLOSA
Family: Medullosaceae
Height: 16 ft 6 in (5 m)

THE EARTH DURING THE LATE CARBONIFEROUS PERIOD

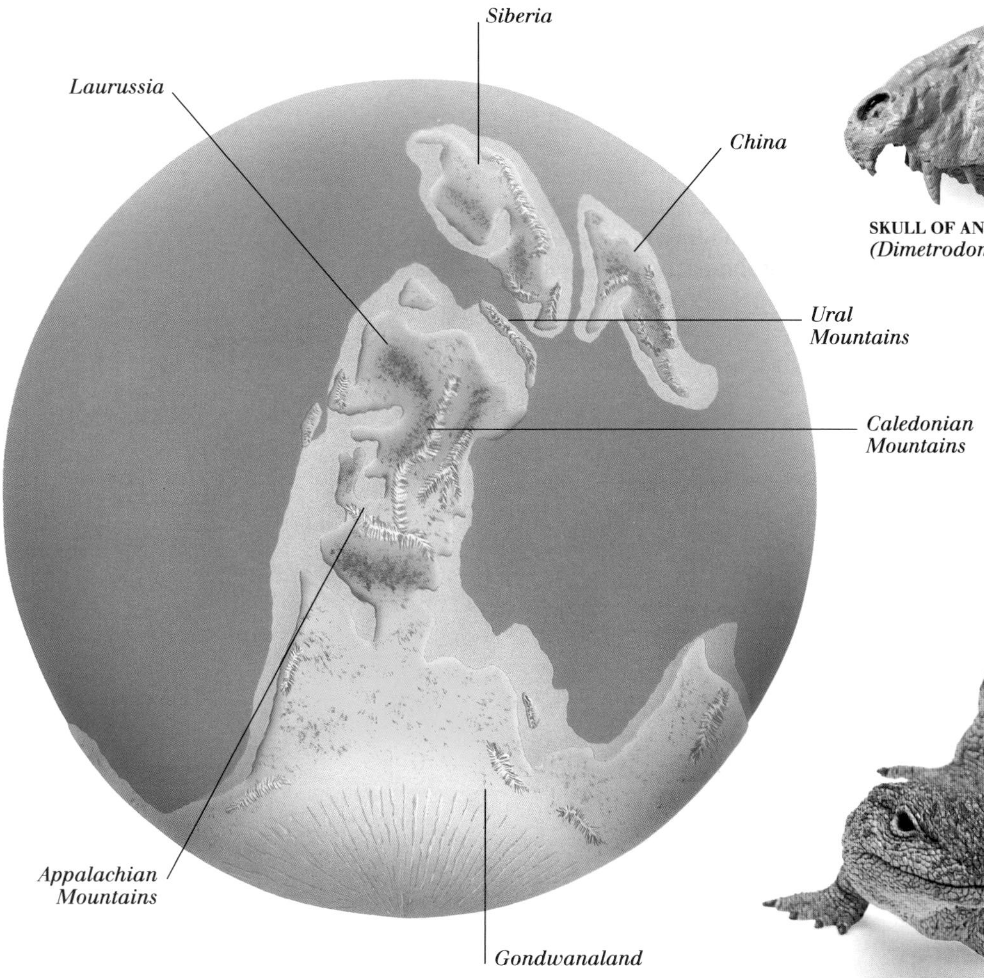

Siberia

Laurussia

China

Ural Mountains

Caledonian Mountains

Appalachian Mountains

Gondwanaland

EXAMPLES OF CARBONIFEROUS AND PERMIAN ANIMALS

SKULL OF AN EXTINCT SYNAPSID REPTILE
(*Dimetrodon loomisi*)

**FOSSIL TEETH OF
AN EXTINCT SHARK**
(*Helicoprion bessonowi*)

**MODEL OF AN EXTINCT
CARBONIFEROUS REPTILE**
(*Westlothiana lizziae*)

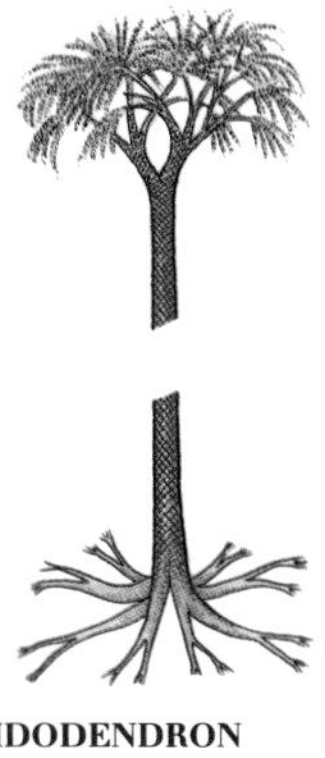

LEPIDODENDRON
Family: Lepidodendraceae
Height: 100 ft (30 m)

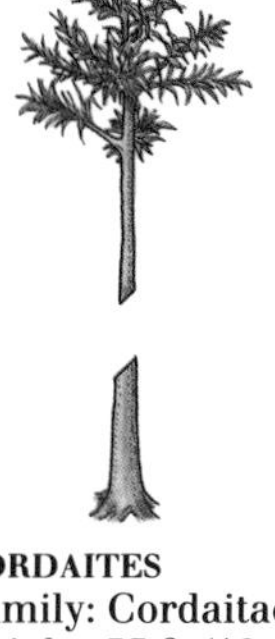

CORDAITES
Family: Cordaitacea
Height: 33 ft (10 m)

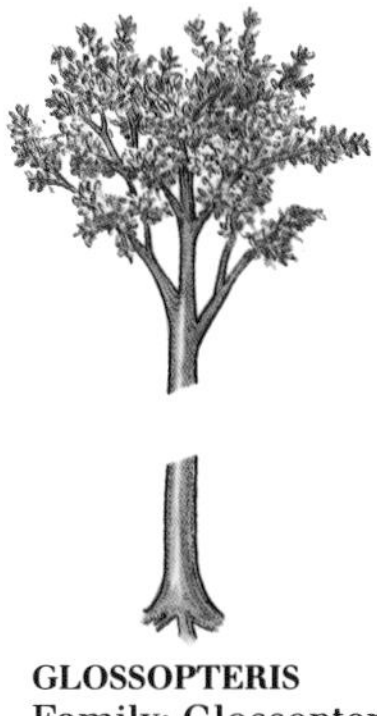

GLOSSOPTERIS
Family: Glossopteridaceae
Height: 26 ft (8 m)

ALETHOPTERIS
Family Medullosaceae
Height: 16 ft 6 in (5 m)

Triassic period

THE TRIASSIC PERIOD (245–208 million years ago) marked the beginning of what is known as the Age of the Dinosaurs (the Mesozoic era). During this period, the present-day continents were massed together, forming one huge continent known as Pangaea. This landmass experienced extremes of climate, with lush green areas around the coast or by lakes and rivers, and arid deserts in the interior. The only forms of plant life were nonflowering plants, such as conifers, ferns, cycads, and ginkgos; flowering plants had not yet evolved. The principal forms of animal life included primitive amphibians, rhynchosaurs ("beaked lizards"), and primitive crocodilians. Dinosaurs first appeared about 230 million years ago, at the beginning of the Late Triassic period. The earliest known dinosaurs were the carnivorous (flesh-eating) herrerasaurids and staurikosaurids, such as *Herrerasaurus* and *Staurikosaurus*. Early herbivorous (plant-eating) dinosaurs first appeared in Late Triassic times and included *Plateosaurus* and *Technosaurus*. By the end of the Triassic period, dinosaurs dominated Pangaea, possibly contributing to the extinction of many other reptiles.

TRIASSIC POSITIONS OF PRESENT-DAY LANDMASSES

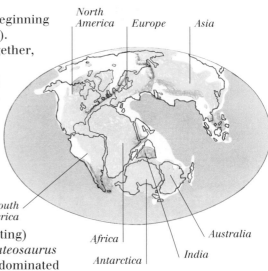

North America

Europe

Asia

South America

Africa

Antarctica

India

Australia

EXAMPLES OF TRIASSIC PLANT GROUPS

A PRESENT-DAY CYCAD
(*Cycas revoluta*)

A PRESENT-DAY GINKGO
(*Ginkgo biloba*)

A PRESENT-DAY CONIFER
(*Araucaria araucana*)

FOSSIL OF AN EXTINCT FERN
(*Pachypteris* sp.)

FOSSIL LEAF OF AN EXTINCT CYCAD
(*Cycas* sp.)

EXAMPLES OF TRIASSIC DINOSAURS

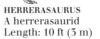

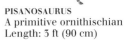

MELANOROSAURUS
A melanorosaurid
Length: 40 ft (12.2 m)

MUSSAURUS
A plateosaurid
Length: 6 ft 6 in–10 ft (2–3 m)

HERRERASAURUS
A herrerasaurid
Length: 10 ft (3 m)

PISANOSAURUS
A primitive ornithischian
Length: 3 ft (90 cm)

THE EARTH DURING THE TRIASSIC PERIOD

EXAMPLES OF TRIASSIC ANIMALS

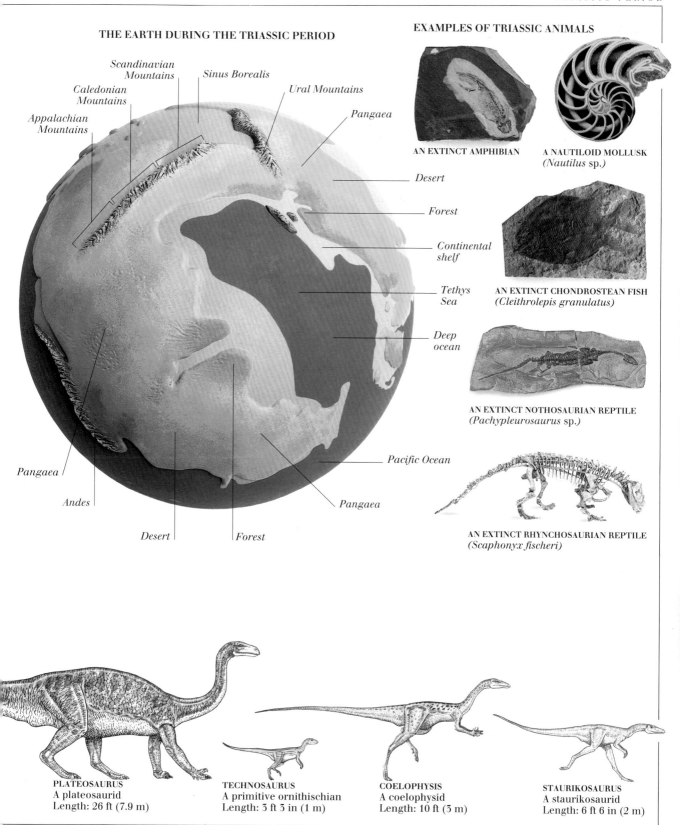

Scandinavian
Mountains

Caledonian
Mountains

Sinus Borealis

Ural Mountains

Appalachian
Mountains

Pangaea

Desert

Forest

Continental
shelf

Tethys
Sea

Deep
ocean

Pangaea

Andes

Pacific Ocean

Desert

Forest

Pangaea

AN EXTINCT AMPHIBIAN

A NAUTILOID MOLLUSK
(*Nautilus* sp.)

AN EXTINCT CHONDROSTEAN FISH
(*Cleithrolepis granulatus*)

AN EXTINCT NOTHOSAURIAN REPTILE
(*Pachypleurosaurus* sp.)

AN EXTINCT RHYNCHOSAURIAN REPTILE
(*Scaphonyx fischeri*)

PLATEOSAURUS
A plateosaurid
Length: 26 ft (7.9 m)

TECHNOSAURUS
A primitive ornithischian
Length: 3 ft 3 in (1 m)

COELOPHYSIS
A coelophysid
Length: 10 ft (3 m)

STAURIKOSAURUS
A staurikosaurid
Length: 6 ft 6 in (2 m)

Jurassic period

THE JURASSIC PERIOD, the middle part of the Mesozoic era, lasted from 208 to 146 million years ago. During the Jurassic period, the landmass of Pangaea broke up into the continents of Gondwanaland and Laurasia, and sea-levels rose, flooding areas of lower land. The Jurassic climate was warm and moist. Plants such as ginkgos, horsetails, and conifers thrived, and giant redwood trees appeared, as did the first flowering plants. The abundance of plant food coincided with the proliferation of herbivorous (plant-eating) dinosaurs, such as the large sauropods (e.g., *Diplodocus*) and stegosaurs (e.g., *Stegosaurus*). Carnivorous (flesh-eating) dinosaurs, such as *Compsognathus* and *Allosaurus*, also flourished by hunting the many animals that existed—among them other dinosaurs. Further Jurassic animals included shrewlike mammals, and pterosaurs (flying reptiles), as well as plesiosaurs and ichthyosaurs (both marine reptiles).

JURASSIC POSITIONS OF PRESENT-DAY LANDMASSES

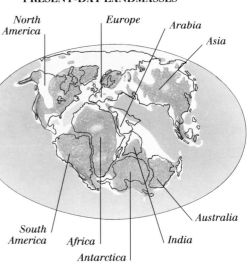

North America
Europe
Arabia
Asia
South America
Africa
Antarctica
India
Australia

EXAMPLES OF JURASSIC PLANT GROUPS

A PRESENT-DAY FERN
(*Dicksonia antarctica*)

A PRESENT-DAY HORSETAIL
(*Equisetum arvense*)

A PRESENT-DAY CONIFER
(*Taxus baccata*)

FOSSIL LEAF OF AN EXTINCT CONIFER
(*Taxus sp.*)

FOSSIL LEAF OF AN EXTINCT REDWOOD
(*Sequoiadendron affinis*)

EXAMPLES OF JURASSIC DINOSAURS

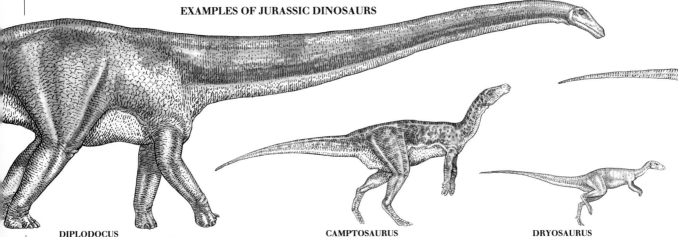

DIPLODOCUS
A diplodocid
Length: 88 ft (26.8 m)

CAMPTOSAURUS
A camptosaurid
Length: 16–23 ft (4.9–7 m)

DRYOSAURUS
A dryosaurid
Length: 10–13 ft (3–4 m)

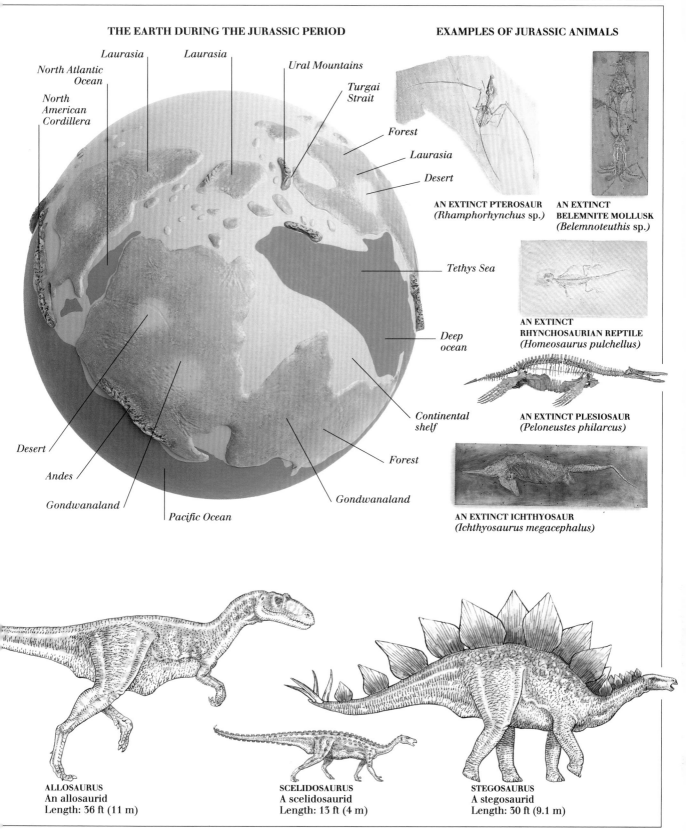

THE EARTH DURING THE JURASSIC PERIOD

North Atlantic
Ocean

Laurasia

Laurasia

Ural Mountains

North
American
Cordillera

Turgai
Strait

Forest

Laurasia

Desert

Tethys Sea

Deep
ocean

Continental
shelf

Forest

Desert

Andes

Gondwanaland

Pacific Ocean

Gondwanaland

EXAMPLES OF JURASSIC ANIMALS

AN EXTINCT PTEROSAUR
(*Rhamphorhynchus* sp.)

**AN EXTINCT
BELEMNITE MOLLUSK**
(*Belemnoteuthis* sp.)

**AN EXTINCT
RHYNCHOSAURIAN REPTILE**
(*Homeosaurus pulchellus*)

AN EXTINCT PLESIOSAUR
(*Peloneustes philarcus*)

AN EXTINCT ICHTHYOSAUR
(*Ichthyosaurus megacephalus*)

ALLOSAURUS
An allosaurid
Length: 36 ft (11 m)

SCELIDOSAURUS
A scelidosaurid
Length: 13 ft (4 m)

STEGOSAURUS
A stegosaurid
Length: 30 ft (9.1 m)

Cretaceous period

THE MESOZOIC ERA ENDED WITH the Cretaceous period, which lasted from 146 to 65 million years ago. During this period, Gondwanaland and Laurasia were breaking up into smaller landmasses that more closely resembled those of the modern continents. The climate remained mild and moist, but the seasons became more marked. Flowering plants, including deciduous trees, replaced many cycads, seed ferns, and conifers. Animal species became more varied, with the evolution of new mammals, insects, fish, crustaceans, and turtles. Dinosaurs evolved into a wide variety of species during Cretaceous times; more than half of all known dinosaurs—including *Iguanodon, Deinonychus, Tyrannosaurus,* and *Hypsilophodon* —lived during this period. At the end of the Cretaceous period, however, large dinosaurs became extinct. The reason for this mass extinction is unknown but it is thought to have been caused by climatic changes due to either a catastrophic meteor impact with the Earth or extensive volcanic eruptions.

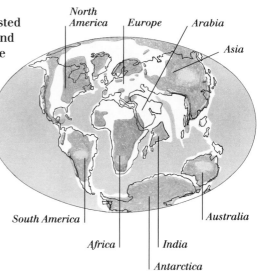

North America
Europe
Arabia
Asia
South America
Africa
India
Antarctica
Australia

EXAMPLES OF CRETACEOUS PLANT GROUPS

A PRESENT-DAY CONIFER
(Pinus muricata)

A PRESENT-DAY DECIDUOUS TREE
(Magnolia sp.)

FOSSIL OF AN EXTINCT FERN
(Sphenopteris latiloba)

FOSSIL OF AN EXTINCT GINKGO
(Ginkgo pluripartita)

FOSSIL LEAVES OF AN EXTINCT DECIDUOUS TREE
(Cercidyphyllum sp.)

EXAMPLES OF CRETACEOUS DINOSAURS

SALTASAURUS
A titanosaurid
Length: 40 ft (12.2 m)

TOROSAURUS
A ceratopsid
Length: 25 ft (7.6 m)

HYPSILOPHODON
A hypsilophodontid
Length: 4 ft 6 in–7 ft 6 in (1.4–2.3 m)

THE EARTH DURING THE CRETACEOUS PERIOD

EXAMPLES OF CRETACEOUS ANIMALS

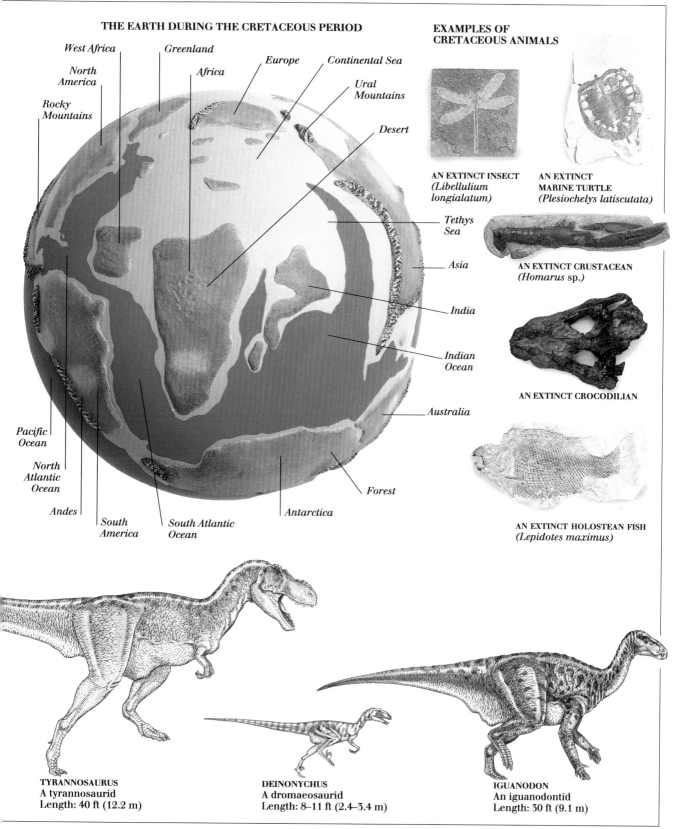

West Africa

Greenland

North America

Africa

Europe

Continental Sea

Ural Mountains

Rocky Mountains

Desert

Tethys Sea

Asia

India

Indian Ocean

Pacific Ocean

North Atlantic Ocean

Andes

South America

South Atlantic Ocean

Antarctica

Forest

Australia

AN EXTINCT INSECT
(Libellulium longialatum)

AN EXTINCT MARINE TURTLE
(Plesiochelys latiscutata)

AN EXTINCT CRUSTACEAN
(Homarus sp.)

AN EXTINCT CROCODILIAN

AN EXTINCT HOLOSTEAN FISH
(Lepidotes maximus)

TYRANNOSAURUS
A tyrannosaurid
Length: 40 ft (12.2 m)

DEINONYCHUS
A dromaeosaurid
Length: 8–11 ft (2.4–3.4 m)

IGUANODON
An iguanodontid
Length: 30 ft (9.1 m)

73

Tertiary period

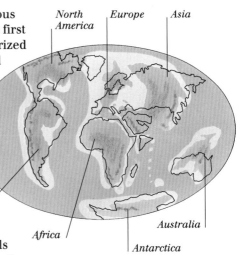

FOLLOWING THE DEMISE OF THE DINOSAURS at the end of the Cretaceous period, the Tertiary period (65–1.6 million years ago), which formed the first part of the Cenozoic era (65 million years ago–present), was characterized by a huge expansion of mammal life. Placental mammals nourish and maintain their young in the mother's uterus; only three orders of placental mammals existed during Cretaceous times, compared with 25 orders during the Tertiary period. One of these 25 included the first hominid (see pp.108–109), *Australopithecus*, which appeared in Africa. By the beginning of the Tertiary period, the continents had almost reached their present position. The Tethys Sea, which had separated the northern continents from Africa and India, began to close up, forming the Mediterranean Sea and allowing the migration of terrestrial animals between Africa and western Europe. India's collision with Asia led to the formation of the Himalayas. During the middle part of the Tertiary period, the forest-dwelling and browsing mammals were replaced by mammals such as the horse, better suited to grazing the open savannahs that began to dominate. Repeated cool periods throughout the Tertiary period established the Antarctic as an icy island continent.

EXAMPLES OF TERTIARY PLANT GROUPS

A PRESENT-DAY OAK
(Quercus palustris)

A PRESENT-DAY BIRCH
(Betula grossa)

**FOSSIL LEAF OF AN
EXTINCT BIRCH**
(Betulites sp.)

**FOSSIL STEM OF AN
EXTINCT PALM**
(Palmoxylon)

EXAMPLES OF TERTIARY
ANIMAL GROUPS

HYAENODON
An hyaenodontid
Length: 6 ft 6 in (2 m)

TITANOHYRAX
A pliohyracid
Length: 6 ft 6 in (2 m)

PHORUSRHACUS
A phorusrhacid
Length: 5 ft (1.5 m)

SAMOTHERIUM
A giraffid
Length: 10 ft (3 m)

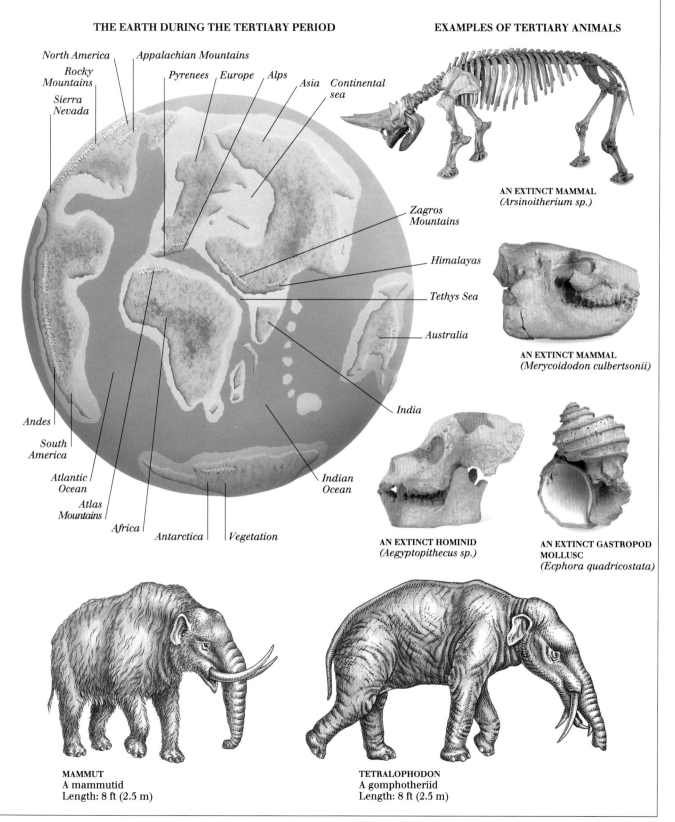

THE EARTH DURING THE TERTIARY PERIOD

North America

Rocky Mountains

Sierra Nevada

Appalachian Mountains

Pyrenees

Europe

Alps

Asia

Continental sea

Zagros Mountains

Himalayas

Tethys Sea

Australia

India

Andes

South America

Atlantic Ocean

Atlas Mountains

Africa

Antarctica

Vegetation

Indian Ocean

EXAMPLES OF TERTIARY ANIMALS

AN EXTINCT MAMMAL
(*Arsinoitherium sp.*)

AN EXTINCT MAMMAL
(*Merycoidodon culbertsonii*)

AN EXTINCT HOMINID
(*Aegyptopithecus sp.*)

AN EXTINCT GASTROPOD MOLLUSC
(*Ecphora quadricostata*)

MAMMUT
A mammutid
Length: 8 ft (2.5 m)

TETRALOPHODON
A gomphotheriid
Length: 8 ft (2.5 m)

Quaternary period

QUATERNARY POSITIONS OF PRESENT-DAY LANDMASSES

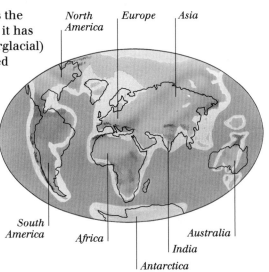

North America
Europe
Asia
South America
Africa
Australia
India
Antarctica

THE QUATERNARY PERIOD (1.6 million years ago–present) forms the second part of the Cenozoic era (65 million years ago–present): it has been characterized by alternating cold (glacial) and warm (interglacial) periods. During cold periods, ice sheets and glaciers have formed repeatedly on northern and southern continents. The cold environments in North America and Eurasia, and to a lesser extent in southern South America and parts of Australia, have caused the migration of many life forms toward the Equator. Only the specialized ice-age mammals such as *Mammuthus* and *Coelodonta*, with their thick wool and fat insulation, were suited to life in very cold climates. Humans developed throughout the Pleistocene period (1.6 million–10,000 years ago) in Africa and migrated northward into Europe and Asia. Modern humans, *Homo sapiens*, lived on the cold European continent 30,000 years ago and hunted mammals. The end of the last ice age and the climatic changes that occurred about 10,000 years ago brought extinction to many Pleistocene mammals, but enabled humans to flourish.

EXAMPLES OF QUATERNARY PLANT GROUPS

A PRESENT-DAY BIRCH
(*Betula lenta*)

A PRESENT-DAY SWEEETGUM
(*Liquidambar styraciflua*)

FOSSIL LEAF OF A SWEETGUM
(*Liquidambar europeanum*)

FOSSIL LEAF OF A BIRCH
(*Betula sp.*)

EXAMPLES OF QUATERNARY ANIMAL GROUPS

PROCOPTODON
A macropodid
Length: 10 ft (3 m)

DIPROTODON
A diprotodontid
Length: 10 ft (3 m)

TOXODON
A toxodontid
Length: 10 ft (3 m)

MAMMUTHUS
An elephantid
Length: 10 ft (3 m)

THE EARTH DURING THE QUATERNARY PERIOD

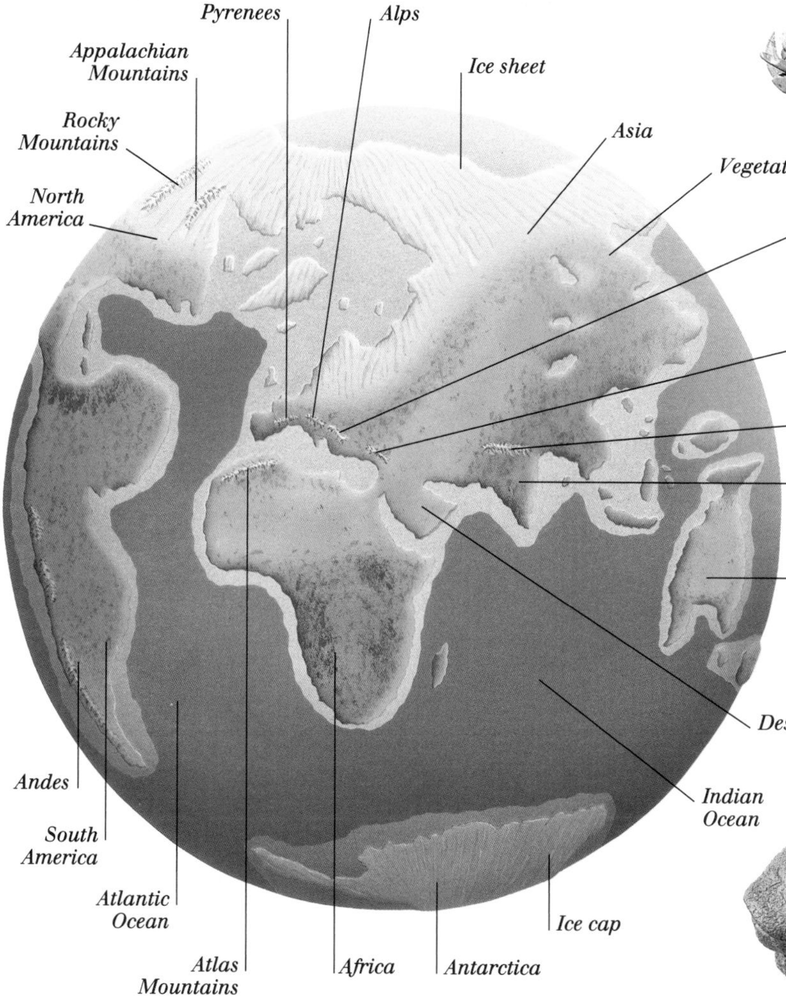

Pyrenees
Alps
Appalachian Mountains
Ice sheet
Rocky Mountains
North America
Asia
Vegetation
Carpathian Mountains
Taurus Mountains
Himalayas
India
Australia
Desert
Indian Ocean
Andes
South America
Atlantic Ocean
Atlas Mountains
Africa
Antarctica
Ice cap

EXAMPLES OF QUATERNARY ANIMALS

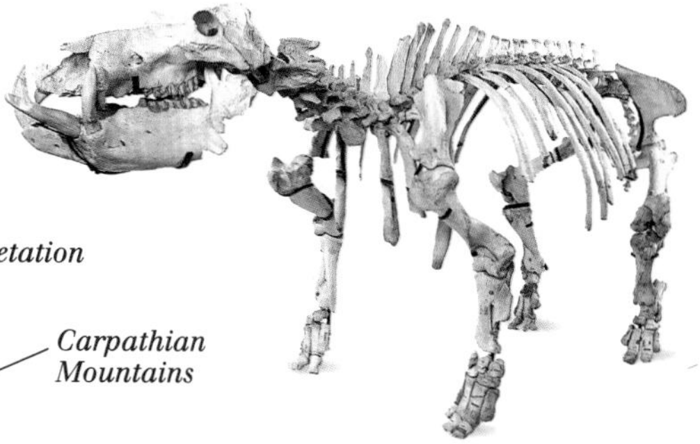

A MAMMAL SKELETON
(Hippopotamus amphibius)

SKULL OF AN EXTINCT CAVE BEAR
(Ursus spelaeus)

SKULL OF AN EXTINCT TORTOISE
(Meiolania platyceps)

A MAMMOTH TOOTH
(Mammuthus primigenius)

DEINOTHERIUM
A deinotheriid
Length: 13 ft (4 m)

COELODONTA
A rhinocerotid
Length: 13 ft (4 m)

AUSTRALOPITHECUS
A hominid
Length: 4 ft (1.2 m)

Early signs of life

FOR ALMOST A THOUSAND MILLION YEARS after its formation, there was no known life on Earth. The first simple, sea-dwelling organic structures appeared about 3,400 years ago; they may have formed when certain chemical molecules joined together. Prokaryotes, single-celled micro-organisms such as blue-green algae, were able to photosynthesize (see pp. 138–139), and thus produce oxygen. A thousand million years later, sufficient oxygen had built up in the earth's atmosphere to allow multicellular organisms to proliferate in the Precambrian seas (before 570 million years ago). Soft-bodied jellyfish, corals, and seaworms flourished about 700 million years ago. Trilobites, the first animals with hard body frames, developed during the Cambrian period (570–510 million years ago). However, it was not until the beginning of the Devonian period (409–363 million years ago) that early land plants, such as *Asteroxylon*, formed a water-retaining cuticle, which ended their dependence on an aquatic environment. About 363 million years ago, the first amphibians (see pp. 80–81) crawled onto the land, although they still returned to the water to lay their soft eggs. Not until the emergence of the first reptiles would animals appear that were not dependent on water in this way.

STROMATOLITIC LIMESTONE

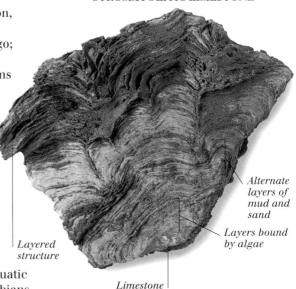

Alternate layers of mud and sand

Layers bound by algae

Layered structure

Limestone

Long, beaklike snout

Growth line

Dorsal plate

Fixed lateral plate

Dorsal spine base

Bony dorsal shield

FOSSILIZED JAWLESS FISH

Glabella

Eye

Thoracic pleurae

Tail shield

Tail area

FOSSILIZED TRILOBITE

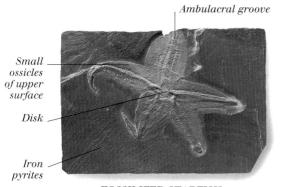

Ambulacral groove

Small ossicles of upper surface

Disk

Iron pyrites

FOSSILIZED STARFISH

Row of ossicles

Broad disk

Row of ossicles

Short arm

UPPER SURFACE OF FOSSILIZED STARFISH

LOWER SURFACE OF FOSSILIZED STARFISH

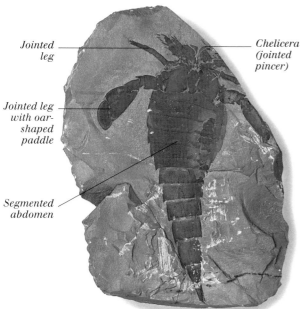

Jointed leg

Chelicera (jointed pincer)

Jointed leg with oar-shaped paddle

Segmented abdomen

UNDERSIDE OF FOSSILIZED EURYPTERID

Telson (tail spine)

Shell contains eight somites (thoracic segments)

Abdominal segments

Hingeless, bivalved shell

FOSSIL OF AN EXTINCT SHRIMP

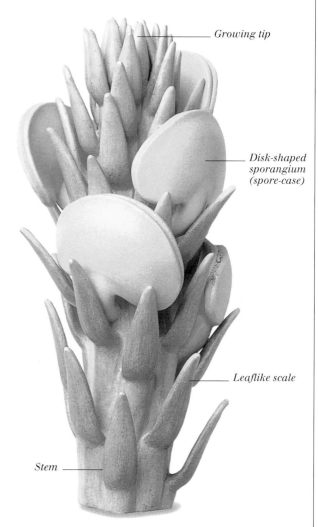

Growing tip

Disk-shaped sporangium (spore-case)

Leaflike scale

Stem

RECONSTRUCTION OF ASTEROXYLON

Amphibians and reptiles

THE EARLIEST KNOWN AMPHIBIANS, such as *Acanthostega* and *Ichthyostega*, lived about 363 million years ago at the end of the Devonian period (409–363 million years ago). Their limbs may have evolved from the muscular fins of lungfish. These fish can use their fins to push themselves along the bottom of lakes and some can breathe at the water's surface. While amphibians (see pp. 182–183) can exist on land, they are dependent on a wet environment because their skin does not retain moisture and they must return to the water to lay their eggs. Evolving from amphibians, reptiles (see pp. 184–187) first appeared during the Carboniferous period (363–290 million years ago): *Westlothiana*, the earliest known reptile, lived on land 338 million years ago. The development of the amniotic egg, with an embryo enclosed in its own wet environment (the amnion) and protected by a waterproof shell, freed reptiles from the amphibian's dependence on a wet habitat. A scaly skin protected the reptile from desiccation on land and enabled it to exploit ways of life closed to its amphibian ancestors. Reptiles include the dinosaurs, which came to dominate life on land during the Mesozoic era (245–65 million years ago).

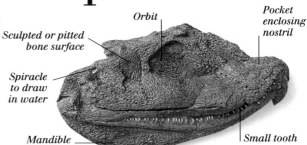

Orbit

Sculpted or pitted bone surface

Pocket enclosing nostril

Spiracle to draw in water

Mandible

Small tooth

FOSSIL SKULL OF ACANTHOSTEGA

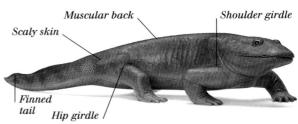

Muscular back

Scaly skin

Shoulder girdle

Finned tail

Hip girdle

MODEL OF ICHTHYOSTEGA

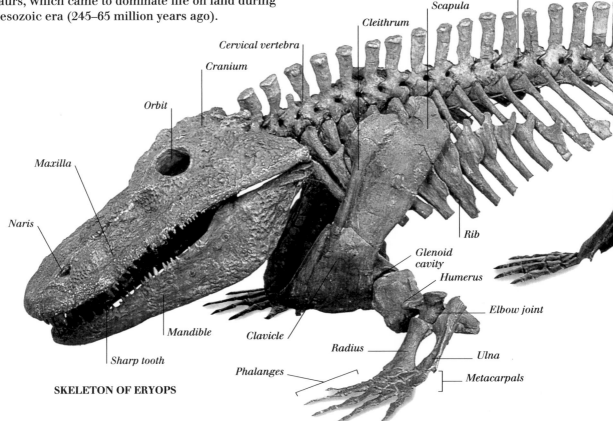

Dorsal vertebra

Scapula

Cleithrum

Cervical vertebra

Cranium

Orbit

Maxilla

Naris

Rib

Glenoid cavity

Humerus

Elbow joint

Mandible

Clavicle

Radius

Ulna

Phalanges

Metacarpals

Sharp tooth

SKELETON OF ERYOPS

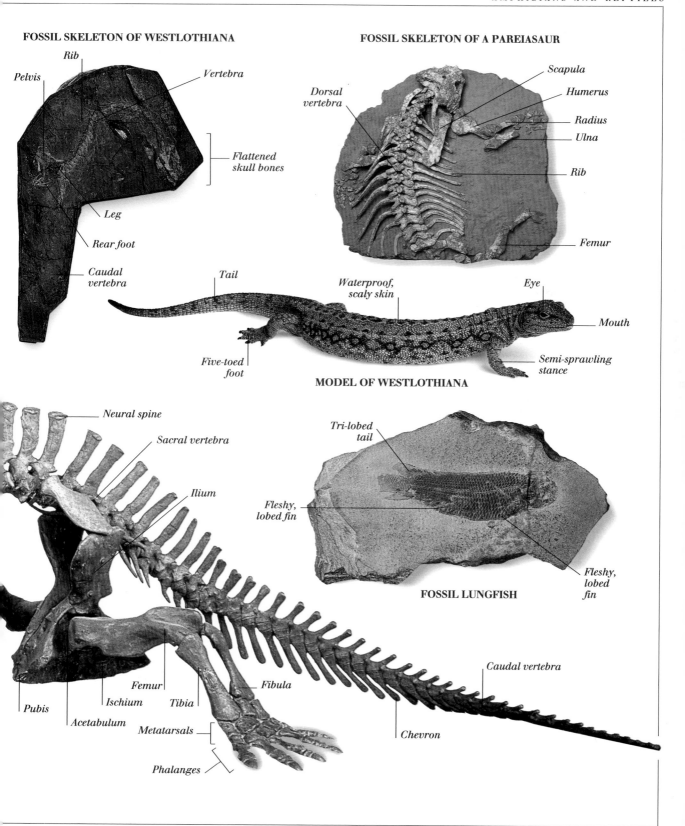

FOSSIL SKELETON OF WESTLOTHIANA

Rib

Vertebra

Pelvis

Flattened
skull bones

Leg

Rear foot

Caudal
vertebra

FOSSIL SKELETON OF A PAREIASAUR

Scapula

Humerus

Dorsal
vertebra

Radius

Ulna

Rib

Femur

Tail

Waterproof,
scaly skin

Eye

Mouth

Five-toed
foot

Semi-sprawling
stance

MODEL OF WESTLOTHIANA

Neural spine

Sacral vertebra

Ilium

Tri-lobed
tail

Fleshy,
lobed fin

Fleshy,
lobed
fin

FOSSIL LUNGFISH

Femur

Fibula

Pubis

Ischium

Tibia

Caudal vertebra

Acetabulum

Metatarsals

Chevron

Phalanges

The dinosaurs

THE DINOSAURS WERE A LARGE GROUP of reptiles that were the dominant land vertebrates (animals with backbones) for most of the Mesozoic era (245–65 million years ago). They appeared some 230 million years ago and were distinguished from other scaly, egg-laying reptiles by an important feature: dinosaurs had an erect limb stance. This enabled them to keep their bodies well above the ground, unlike the sprawling and semi-sprawling stance of other reptiles. The head of the dinosaur's femur (thighbone) fits into a socket in its pelvis (hipbone), producing efficient and mobile locomotion. Dinosaurs are categorized into two groups according to the structure of their pelvis: saurischian (lizard-hipped) and ornithischian (bird-hipped) dinosaurs. In the case of most saurischians, the pubis (part of the pelvis) jutted forward, while in ornithischians it slanted back, parallel to the ischium (another part of the pelvis). The enormous variety of dinosaur species equals that of mammals. The Dinosauria were the most successful land vertebrates ever, and survived for 165 million years, until their extinction 65 million years ago.

STRUCTURE OF SAURISCHIAN PELVIS

Ilium

Hook of preacetabular process

Postacetabular process

Ilio-pubic joint

Acetabulum

Pubis

Ilio-ischial joint

Pubic foot

Ischium

GALLIMIMUS
A saurischian dinosaur

POSITION OF PELVIS IN A SAURISCHIAN DINOSAUR

STRUCTURE OF ORNTHISCHIAN PELVIS

Ilium

Preacetabular process

Postacetabular process

Ilio-pubic joint

Ilio-ischial joint

Prepubis

Acetabulum

Pubis

Ischium

HYPSILOPHODON
An ornithischian dinosaur

POSITION OF PELVIS IN AN ORNITHISCHIAN DINOSAUR

BAROSAURUS
A saurischian dinosaur

COMPARISON OF ANIMAL STANCES

SPRAWLING STANCE
The thighs and upper arms project straight out from the body so that the knees and elbows are bent at right angles.

COMMON IGUANA
(*Iguana iguana*)
A present-day reptile

ERECT STANCE
The thighs and upper arms project straight down from the body so that the knees and elbows are straight.

SEMI-SPRAWLING STANCE
The thighs and upper arms project downward and outward so that the knees and elbows are slightly bent.

DWARF CROCODILE
(*Osteolaemus tetraspis*)
A present-day reptile

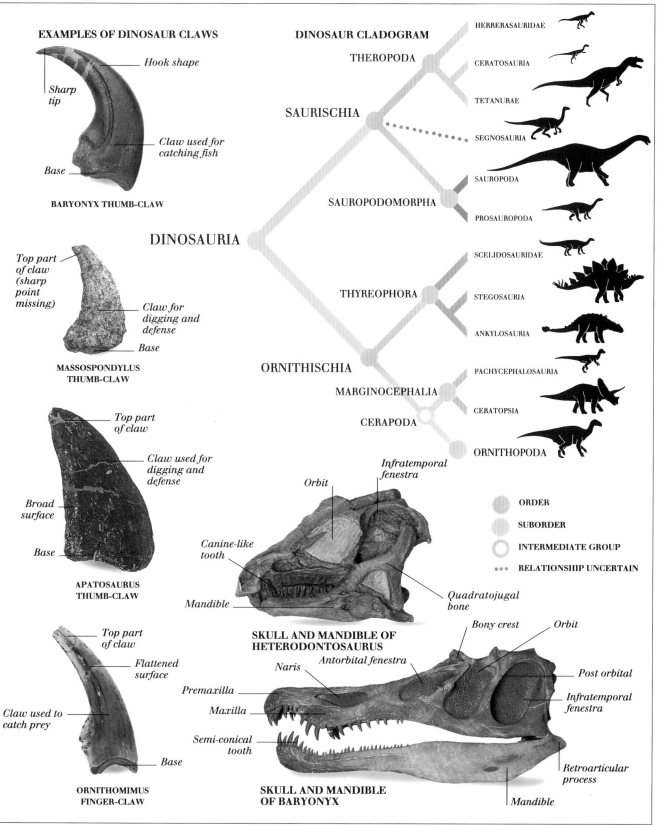

EXAMPLES OF DINOSAUR CLAWS

Hook shape

Sharp tip

Claw used for catching fish

Base

BARYONYX THUMB-CLAW

Top part of claw (sharp point missing)

Claw for digging and defense

Base

MASSOSPONDYLUS THUMB-CLAW

Top part of claw

Claw used for digging and defense

Broad surface

Base

APATOSAURUS THUMB-CLAW

Top part of claw

Flattened surface

Claw used to catch prey

Base

ORNITHOMIMUS FINGER-CLAW

DINOSAUR CLADOGRAM

HERRERASAURIDAE

THEROPODA

CERATOSAURIA

SAURISCHIA

TETANURAE

SEGNOSAURIA

SAUROPODA

SAUROPODOMORPHA

PROSAUROPODA

DINOSAURIA

SCELIDOSAURIDAE

THYREOPHORA

STEGOSAURIA

ANKYLOSAURIA

PACHYCEPHALOSAURIA

ORNITHISCHIA

MARGINOCEPHALIA

CERATOPSIA

CERAPODA

ORNITHOPODA

- ORDER
- SUBORDER
- INTERMEDIATE GROUP
- ••• RELATIONSHIP UNCERTAIN

Infratemporal fenestra

Orbit

Canine-like tooth

Mandible

Quadratojugal bone

SKULL AND MANDIBLE OF HETERODONTOSAURUS

Bony crest

Orbit

Naris

Antorbital fenestra

Post orbital

Premaxilla

Infratemporal fenestra

Maxilla

Semi-conical tooth

Retroarticular process

Mandible

SKULL AND MANDIBLE OF BARYONYX

Theropods 1

AN ENORMOUSLY SUCCESSFUL SUBORDER of the Saurischia, the bipedal (two-footed) theropods ("beast feet") emerged 230 million years ago in Late Triassic times; the oldest known example comes from South America. Theropods spanned the whole of the Age of the Dinosaurs (230–65 million years ago) and included most known predatory dinosaurs. The typical theropod had small arms with sharp, clawed fingers; powerful jaws lined with sharp teeth; an S-shaped neck; long, muscular hind limbs; and clawed, usually four-toed feet. Many theropods may have been warm-blooded; most were exclusively carnivorous. Theropods ranged from animals no larger than a chicken to huge creatures, such as *Tyrannosaurus* and *Baryonyx*. The group also included ostrichlike omnivores and herbivores with toothless beaks, such as *Struthiomimus* and *Gallimimus*. Many scientists believe that birds are the closest living relatives to the dinosaurs, and share a common ancestor with the theropods. *Archaeopteryx*, small and feathered, was the first known bird and lived alongside its dinosaur relatives.

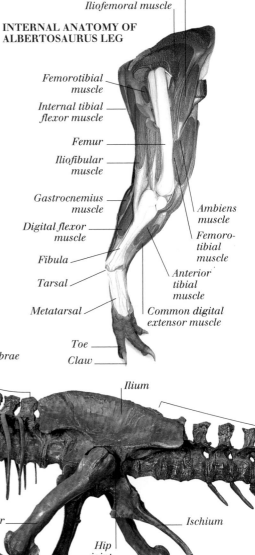

INTERNAL ANATOMY OF ALBERTOSAURUS LEG

Iliotibial muscle
Iliofemoral muscle
Femorotibial muscle
Internal tibial flexor muscle
Femur
Iliofibular muscle
Gastrocnemius muscle
Digital flexor muscle
Fibula
Tarsal
Metatarsal
Ambiens muscle
Femoro-tibial muscle
Anterior tibial muscle
Common digital extensor muscle
Toe
Claw

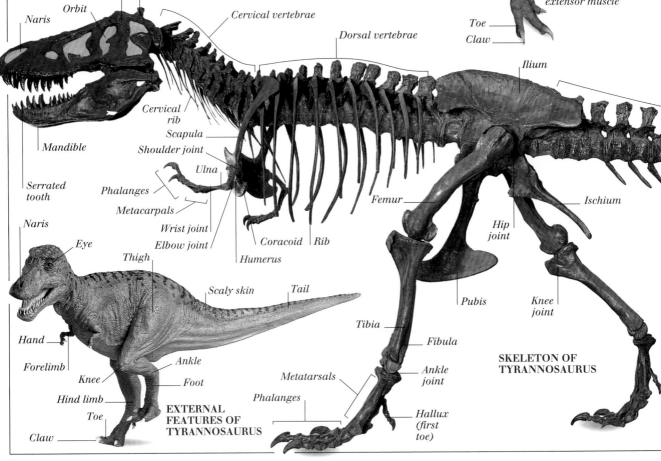

Cranium
Supraoccipital crest
Orbit
Naris
Cervical vertebrae
Dorsal vertebrae
Ilium
Cervical rib
Scapula
Shoulder joint
Ulna
Phalanges
Metacarpals
Wrist joint
Elbow joint
Coracoid
Rib
Humerus
Femur
Ischium
Hip joint
Knee joint
Mandible
Serrated tooth
Naris
Eye
Thigh
Scaly skin
Tail
Pubis
Tibia
Fibula
Hand
Forelimb
Knee
Foot
Ankle
Metatarsals
Phalanges
Ankle joint
Hind limb
Toe
Claw

SKELETON OF TYRANNOSAURUS

EXTERNAL FEATURES OF TYRANNOSAURUS

Hallux (first toe)

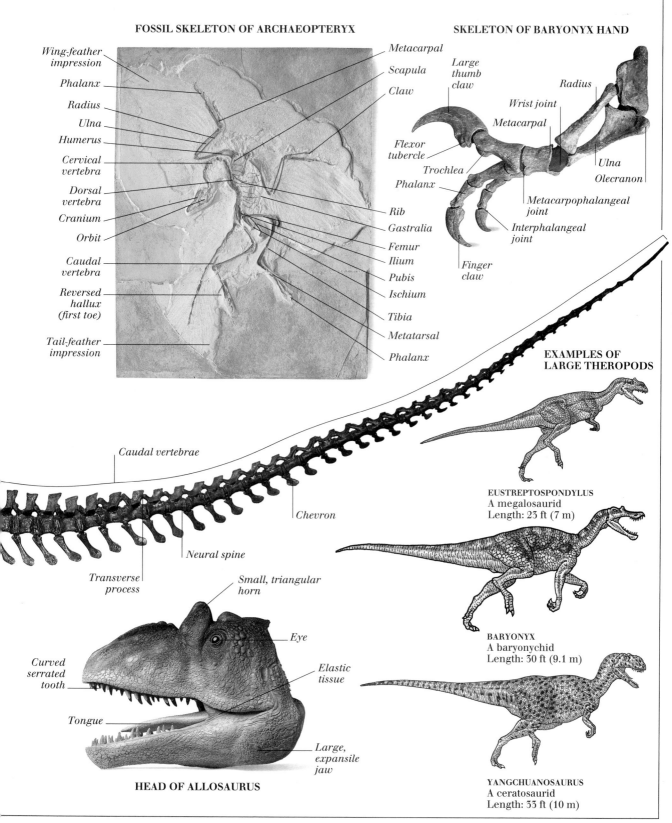

FOSSIL SKELETON OF ARCHAEOPTERYX

Wing-feather impression
Phalanx
Radius
Ulna
Humerus
Cervical vertebra
Dorsal vertebra
Cranium
Orbit
Caudal vertebra
Reversed hallux (first toe)
Tail-feather impression

Metacarpal
Scapula
Claw

Rib
Gastralia
Femur
Ilium
Pubis
Ischium
Tibia
Metatarsal
Phalanx

SKELETON OF BARYONYX HAND

Large thumb claw
Flexor tubercle
Trochlea
Phalanx
Finger claw

Radius
Wrist joint
Metacarpal
Ulna
Olecranon
Metacarpophalangeal joint
Interphalangeal joint

EXAMPLES OF LARGE THEROPODS

Caudal vertebrae
Chevron
Neural spine
Transverse process

EUSTREPTOSPONDYLUS
A megalosaurid
Length: 23 ft (7 m)

BARYONYX
A baryonychid
Length: 30 ft (9.1 m)

Small, triangular horn
Eye
Elastic tissue
Curved serrated tooth
Tongue
Large, expansile jaw

HEAD OF ALLOSAURUS

YANGCHUANOSAURUS
A ceratosaurid
Length: 33 ft (10 m)

Theropods 2

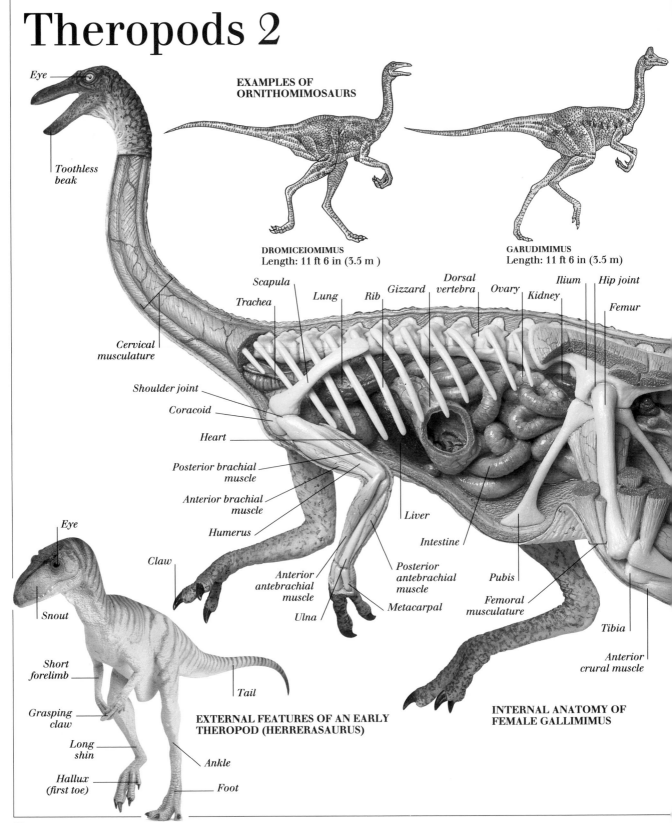

Eye

Toothless beak

EXAMPLES OF ORNITHOMIMOSAURS

Cervical musculature

Scapula

Trachea

Lung

Rib

Gizzard

Dorsal vertebra

Ovary

Kidney

Ilium

Hip joint

Femur

DROMICEIOMIMUS
Length: 11 ft 6 in (3.5 m)

GARUDIMIMUS
Length: 11 ft 6 in (3.5 m)

Shoulder joint

Coracoid

Heart

Posterior brachial muscle

Anterior brachial muscle

Humerus

Liver

Intestine

Claw

Anterior antebrachial muscle

Ulna

Posterior antebrachial muscle

Metacarpal

Pubis

Femoral musculature

Tibia

Anterior crural muscle

Eye

Snout

Short forelimb

Grasping claw

Long shin

Hallux (first toe)

Tail

Ankle

Foot

EXTERNAL FEATURES OF AN EARLY THEROPOD (HERRERASAURUS)

INTERNAL ANATOMY OF FEMALE GALLIMIMUS

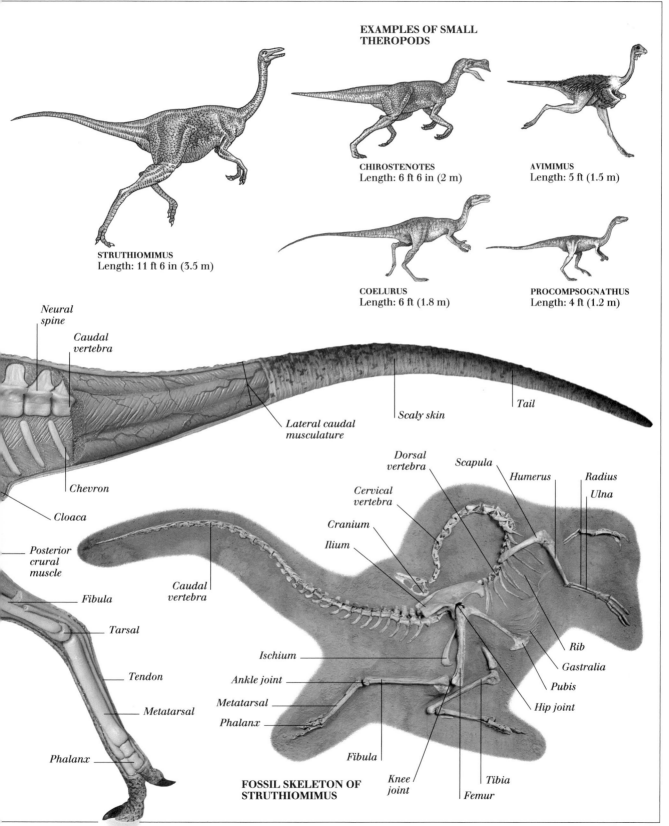

**EXAMPLES OF SMALL
THEROPODS**

CHIROSTENOTES
Length: 6 ft 6 in (2 m)

AVIMIMUS
Length: 5 ft (1.5 m)

STRUTHIOMIMUS
Length: 11 ft 6 in (3.5 m)

COELURUS
Length: 6 ft (1.8 m)

PROCOMPSOGNATHUS
Length: 4 ft (1.2 m)

Neural
spine

Caudal
vertebra

Scaly skin

Tail

Lateral caudal
musculature

Chevron

Cloaca

Posterior
crural
muscle

Fibula

Tarsal

Tendon

Metatarsal

Phalanx

Caudal
vertebra

Dorsal
vertebra

Scapula

Humerus

Radius

Ulna

Cervical
vertebra

Cranium

Ilium

Rib

Gastralia

Pubis

Hip joint

Ischium

Ankle joint

Metatarsal

Phalanx

Fibula

Knee
joint

Femur

Tibia

**FOSSIL SKELETON OF
STRUTHIOMIMUS**

Sauropodomorphs 1

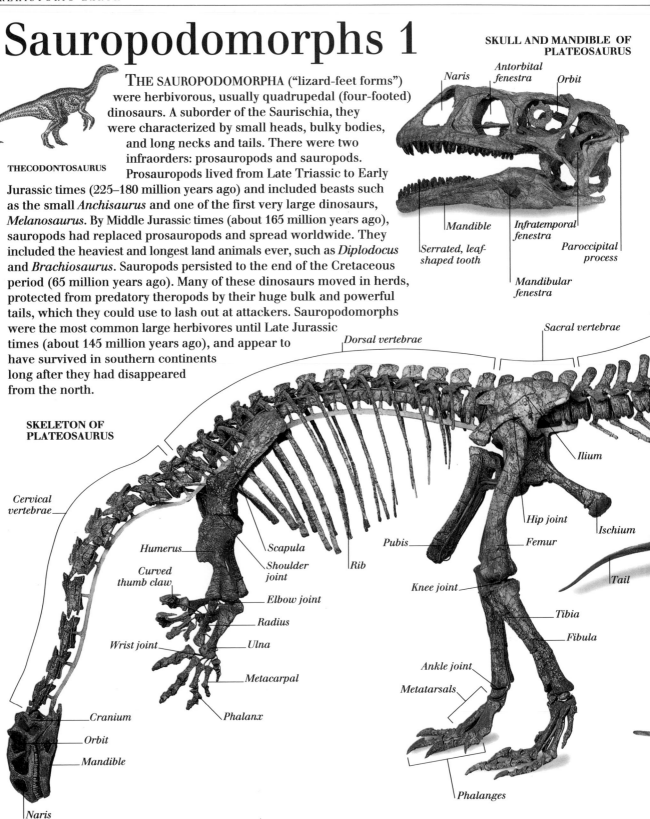

THECODONTOSAURUS

THE SAUROPODOMORPHA ("lizard-feet forms") were herbivorous, usually quadrupedal (four-footed) dinosaurs. A suborder of the Saurischia, they were characterized by small heads, bulky bodies, and long necks and tails. There were two infraorders: prosauropods and sauropods. Prosauropods lived from Late Triassic to Early Jurassic times (225–180 million years ago) and included beasts such as the small *Anchisaurus* and one of the first very large dinosaurs, *Melanosaurus*. By Middle Jurassic times (about 165 million years ago), sauropods had replaced prosauropods and spread worldwide. They included the heaviest and longest land animals ever, such as *Diplodocus* and *Brachiosaurus*. Sauropods persisted to the end of the Cretaceous period (65 million years ago). Many of these dinosaurs moved in herds, protected from predatory theropods by their huge bulk and powerful tails, which they could use to lash out at attackers. Sauropodomorphs were the most common large herbivores until Late Jurassic times (about 145 million years ago), and appear to have survived in southern continents long after they had disappeared from the north.

SKULL AND MANDIBLE OF PLATEOSAURUS

Naris

Antorbital fenestra

Orbit

Mandible

Infratemporal fenestra

Paroccipital process

Serrated, leaf-shaped tooth

Mandibular fenestra

SKELETON OF PLATEOSAURUS

Sacral vertebrae

Dorsal vertebrae

Cervical vertebrae

Ilium

Hip joint

Ischium

Tail

Humerus

Scapula

Rib

Pubis

Femur

Shoulder joint

Curved thumb claw

Knee joint

Elbow joint

Radius

Tibia

Fibula

Wrist joint

Ulna

Metacarpal

Ankle joint

Metatarsals

Cranium

Phalanx

Orbit

Mandible

Phalanges

Naris

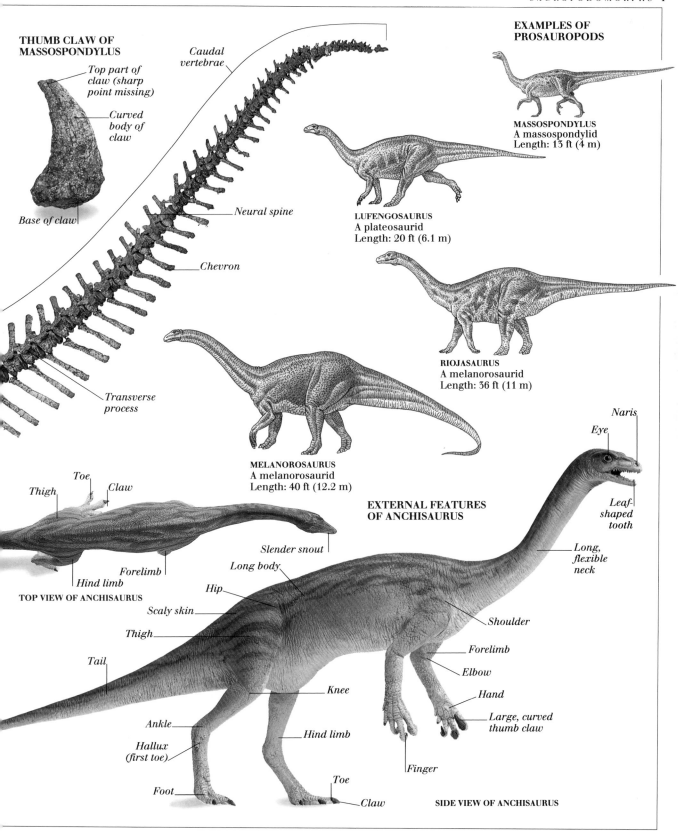

THUMB CLAW OF MASSOSPONDYLUS

Top part of claw (sharp point missing)

Curved body of claw

Base of claw

Caudal vertebrae

Neural spine

Chevron

Transverse process

EXAMPLES OF PROSAUROPODS

MASSOSPONDYLUS
A massospondylid
Length: 13 ft (4 m)

LUFENGOSAURUS
A plateosaurid
Length: 20 ft (6.1 m)

RIOJASAURUS
A melanorosaurid
Length: 36 ft (11 m)

MELANOROSAURUS
A melanorosaurid
Length: 40 ft (12.2 m)

EXTERNAL FEATURES OF ANCHISAURUS

Naris

Eye

Leaf-shaped tooth

Long, flexible neck

Shoulder

Forelimb

Elbow

Hand

Large, curved thumb claw

Finger

Toe

Claw

SIDE VIEW OF ANCHISAURUS

Slender snout

Long body

Hip

Scaly skin

Thigh

Tail

Knee

Ankle

Hallux (first toe)

Hind limb

Foot

Thigh

Toe

Claw

Forelimb

Hind limb

TOP VIEW OF ANCHISAURUS

Sauropodomorphs 2

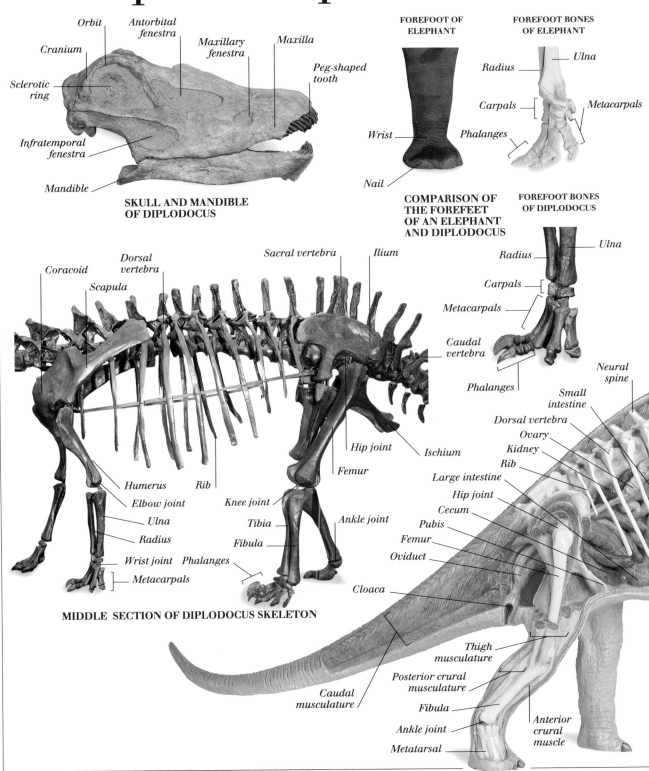

Orbit

Antorbital
fenestra

Cranium

Maxillary
fenestra

Maxilla

Sclerotic
ring

Peg-shaped
tooth

Infratemporal
fenestra

Mandible

**SKULL AND MANDIBLE
OF DIPLODOCUS**

FOREFOOT OF
ELEPHANT

FOREFOOT BONES
OF ELEPHANT

Radius

Ulna

Carpals

Metacarpals

Phalanges

Wrist

Nail

**COMPARISON OF
THE FOREFEET
OF AN ELEPHANT
AND DIPLODOCUS**

FOREFOOT BONES
OF DIPLODOCUS

Radius

Ulna

Carpals

Metacarpals

Phalanges

Coracoid

Dorsal
vertebra

Sacral vertebra

Ilium

Scapula

Caudal
vertebra

Neural
spine

Small
intestine

Dorsal vertebra

Ovary

Kidney

Rib

Large intestine

Hip joint

Cecum

Pubis

Femur

Oviduct

Hip joint

Ischium

Femur

Humerus

Rib

Elbow joint

Knee joint

Ankle joint

Ulna

Tibia

Radius

Fibula

Wrist joint

Phalanges

Metacarpals

Cloaca

MIDDLE SECTION OF DIPLODOCUS SKELETON

Thigh
musculature

Caudal
musculature

Posterior crural
musculature

Fibula

Anterior
crural
muscle

Ankle joint

Metatarsal

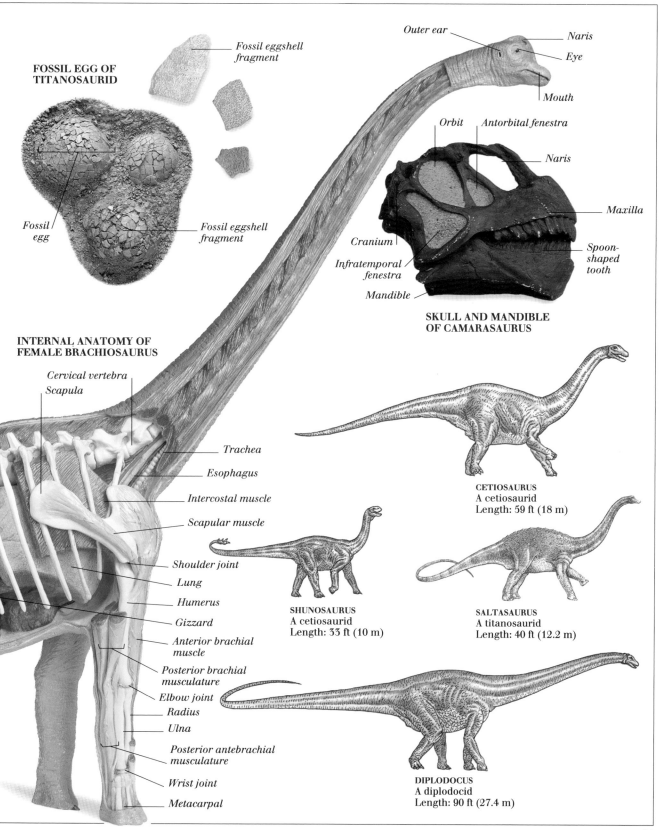

FOSSIL EGG OF TITANOSAURID

Fossil eggshell fragment

Fossil egg

Fossil eggshell fragment

Outer ear

Naris

Eye

Mouth

Orbit

Antorbital fenestra

Naris

Cranium

Maxilla

Infratemporal fenestra

Spoon-shaped tooth

Mandible

SKULL AND MANDIBLE OF CAMARASAURUS

INTERNAL ANATOMY OF FEMALE BRACHIOSAURUS

Cervical vertebra

Scapula

Trachea

Esophagus

Intercostal muscle

Scapular muscle

Shoulder joint

Lung

Humerus

Gizzard

Anterior brachial muscle

Posterior brachial musculature

Elbow joint

Radius

Ulna

Posterior antebrachial musculature

Wrist joint

Metacarpal

CETIOSAURUS
A cetiosaurid
Length: 59 ft (18 m)

SHUNOSAURUS
A cetiosaurid
Length: 33 ft (10 m)

SALTASAURUS
A titanosaurid
Length: 40 ft (12.2 m)

DIPLODOCUS
A diplodocid
Length: 90 ft (27.4 m)

Thyreophorans 1

THYREOPHORANS ("SHIELD BEARERS") were a group of quadrupedal armored dinosaurs. A suborder of the Ornithischia (bird-hipped dinosaurs), they were characterized by rows of bony studs, plates, or spikes along the back, which protected some from predators and may have helped others regulate body temperature. Up to 30ft (9m) long, with a small head and small cheek teeth, Thyreophorans had shorter forelimbs than hind limbs and probably browsed on low-level vegetation. The earliest thyreophorans were small and lived in Early Jurassic times (about 200 million years ago) in Europe, North America, and China. Stegosaurs, such as *Stegosaurus* and *Kentrosaurus*, replaced these older forms. The earliest stegosaur remains come from England and China. Several genera of stegosaurs survived into the Early Cretaceous period (146–100 million years ago), but only in India did they persist into Late Cretaceous times (97–65 million years ago). Ankylosaurs, with their toothless beaks and cheek teeth adapted for cropping vegetation, appeared later than stegosaurs. They originated in the Late Jurassic period (155 million years ago) and in North America survived until the extinction of the dinosaurs, 65 million years ago.

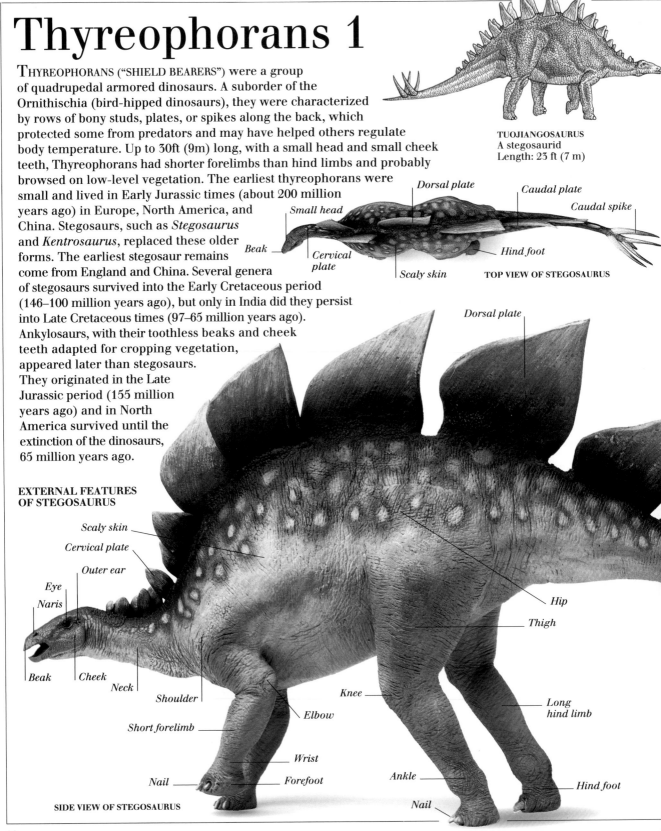

TUOJIANGOSAURUS
A stegosaurid
Length: 23 ft (7 m)

Dorsal plate

Caudal plate

Caudal spike

Small head

Beak

Cervical plate

Hind foot

Scaly skin

TOP VIEW OF STEGOSAURUS

Dorsal plate

**EXTERNAL FEATURES
OF STEGOSAURUS**

Scaly skin

Cervical plate

Outer ear

Eye

Naris

Hip

Thigh

Beak

Cheek

Neck

Shoulder

Elbow

Knee

Long hind limb

Short forelimb

Wrist

Nail

Forefoot

Ankle

Hind foot

Nail

SIDE VIEW OF STEGOSAURUS

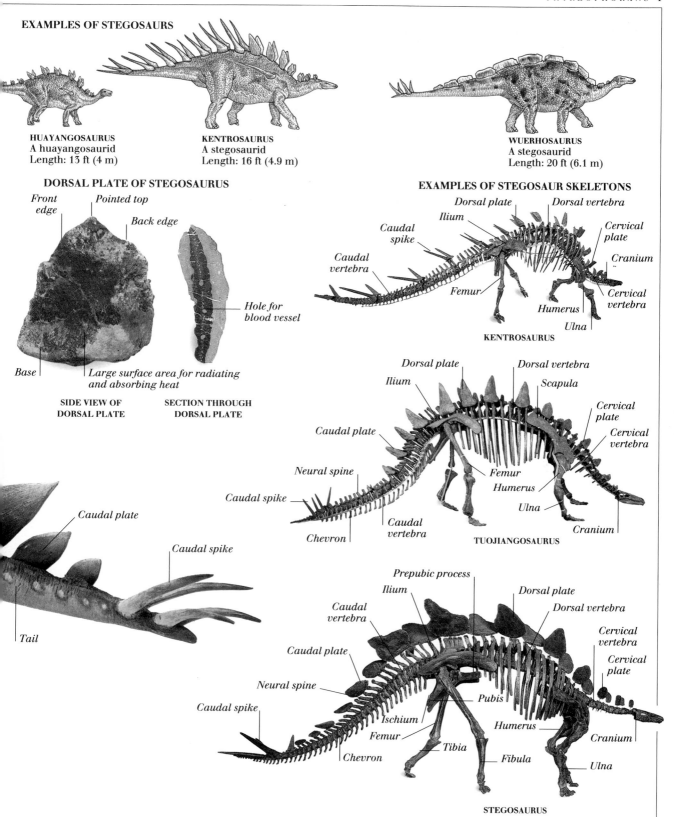

EXAMPLES OF STEGOSAURS

HUAYANGOSAURUS
A huayangosaurid
Length: 13 ft (4 m)

KENTROSAURUS
A stegosaurid
Length: 16 ft (4.9 m)

WUERHOSAURUS
A stegosaurid
Length: 20 ft (6.1 m)

DORSAL PLATE OF STEGOSAURUS

Front edge

Pointed top

Back edge

Hole for blood vessel

Base

Large surface area for radiating and absorbing heat

SIDE VIEW OF DORSAL PLATE

SECTION THROUGH DORSAL PLATE

Caudal plate

Caudal spike

Tail

EXAMPLES OF STEGOSAUR SKELETONS

Dorsal plate

Dorsal vertebra

Ilium

Cervical plate

Caudal spike

Cranium

Caudal vertebra

Femur

Cervical vertebra

Humerus

Ulna

KENTROSAURUS

Dorsal plate

Dorsal vertebra

Ilium

Scapula

Cervical plate

Caudal plate

Cervical vertebra

Neural spine

Femur

Caudal spike

Humerus

Chevron

Caudal vertebra

Ulna

Cranium

TUOJIANGOSAURUS

Prepubic process

Ilium

Dorsal plate

Caudal vertebra

Dorsal vertebra

Caudal plate

Cervical vertebra

Neural spine

Cervical plate

Pubis

Caudal spike

Ischium

Humerus

Femur

Tibia

Cranium

Chevron

Fibula

Ulna

STEGOSAURUS

93

Thyreophorans 2

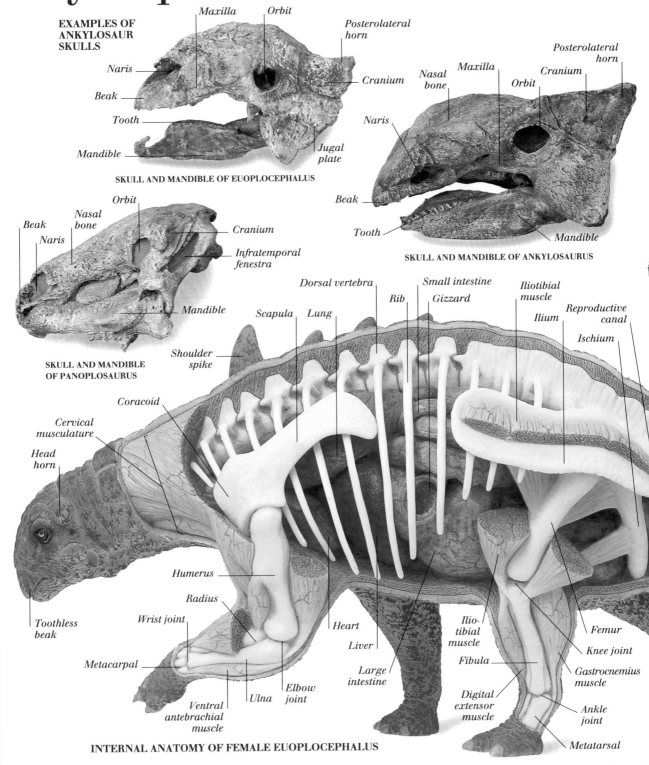

EXAMPLES OF ANKYLOSAUR SKULLS

Maxilla

Orbit

Posterolateral horn

Naris

Beak

Cranium

Tooth

Mandible

Jugal plate

SKULL AND MANDIBLE OF EUOPLOCEPHALUS

Posterolateral horn

Nasal bone

Maxilla

Orbit

Cranium

Naris

Beak

Tooth

Mandible

SKULL AND MANDIBLE OF ANKYLOSAURUS

Beak

Nasal bone

Orbit

Naris

Cranium

Infratemporal fenestra

Mandible

SKULL AND MANDIBLE OF PANOPLOSAURUS

Dorsal vertebra

Small intestine

Rib

Gizzard

Iliotibial muscle

Ilium

Reproductive canal

Ischium

Scapula

Lung

Shoulder spike

Coracoid

Cervical musculature

Head horn

Humerus

Radius

Wrist joint

Metacarpal

Toothless beak

Ventral antebrachial muscle

Ulna

Elbow joint

Heart

Liver

Large intestine

Ilio-tibial muscle

Digital extensor muscle

Fibula

Femur

Knee joint

Gastrocnemius muscle

Ankle joint

Metatarsal

INTERNAL ANATOMY OF FEMALE EUOPLOCEPHALUS

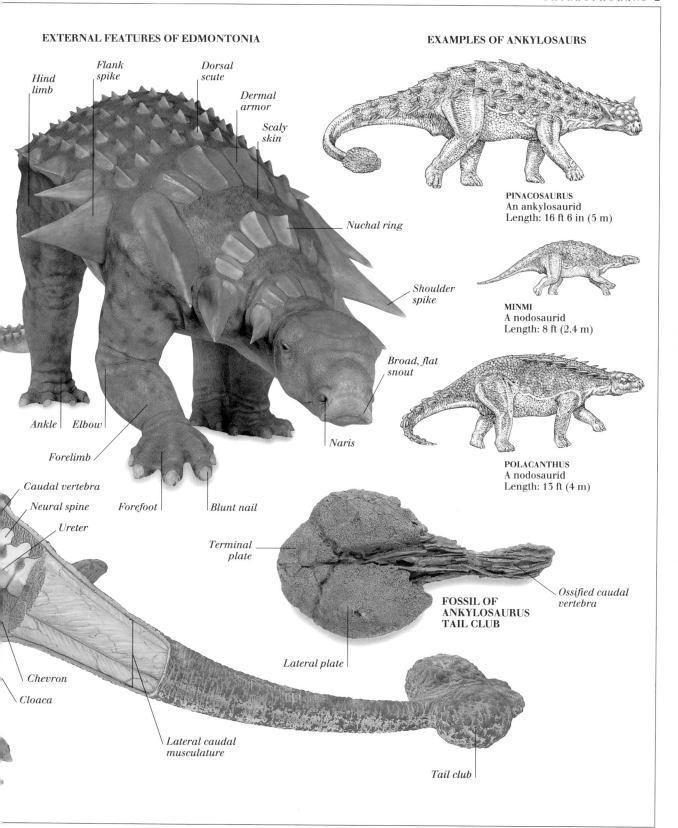

EXTERNAL FEATURES OF EDMONTONIA

Hind
limb

Flank
spike

Dorsal
scute

Dermal
armor

Scaly
skin

Nuchal ring

Shoulder
spike

Broad, flat
snout

Ankle | Elbow

Naris

Forelimb

Caudal vertebra

Neural spine

Ureter

Forefoot

Blunt nail

Terminal
plate

Lateral plate

Chevron

Cloaca

Lateral caudal
musculature

Tail club

EXAMPLES OF ANKYLOSAURS

PINACOSAURUS
An ankylosaurid
Length: 16 ft 6 in (5 m)

MINMI
A nodosaurid
Length: 8 ft (2.4 m)

POLACANTHUS
A nodosaurid
Length: 13 ft (4 m)

Ossified caudal
vertebra

**FOSSIL OF
ANKYLOSAURUS
TAIL CLUB**

Ornithopods 1

IGUANODON TOOTH

ORNITHOPODS ("BIRD FEET") were a group of ornithischian ("bird-hipped") dinosaurs. These bipedal and quadrupedal herbivores had a horny beak, plant-cutting or grinding cheek teeth, and a pelvic and tail region stiffened by bony tendons. They evolved teeth and jaws adapted to pulping vegetation and flourished from the Middle Jurassic to the Late Cretaceous period (165–65 million years ago) in North America, Europe, Africa, China, Australia, and Antarctica. Some ornithopods were no larger than a dog, while others were immense creatures up to 49 ft (15 m) long. Iguanodonts, an ornithopod group, had a broad, toothless beak at the end of a long snout, large jaws with long rows of ridged, closely packed teeth for grinding vegetation, a bulky body, and a heavy tail. *Iguanodon* and some other iguanodonts had large thumb-spikes that were strong enough to stab attackers. Another group, the hadrosaurs, such as *Gryposaurus* and *Hadrosaurus*, lived in Late Cretaceous times (97–65 million years ago) and with their broad beaks are sometimes known as "duckbills." They were characterized by their deep skulls and closely packed rows of teeth, while some, such as *Corythosaurus* and *Lambeosaurus*, had tall, hollow, bony head crests.

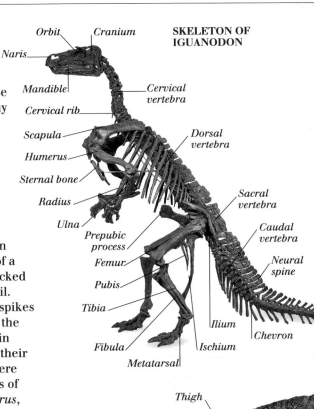

SKELETON OF IGUANODON

Orbit
Cranium
Naris
Mandible
Cervical vertebra
Cervical rib
Scapula
Dorsal vertebra
Humerus
Sternal bone
Radius
Sacral vertebra
Ulna
Prepubic process
Caudal vertebra
Femur
Pubis
Neural spine
Tibia
Ilium
Chevron
Fibula
Ischium
Metatarsal

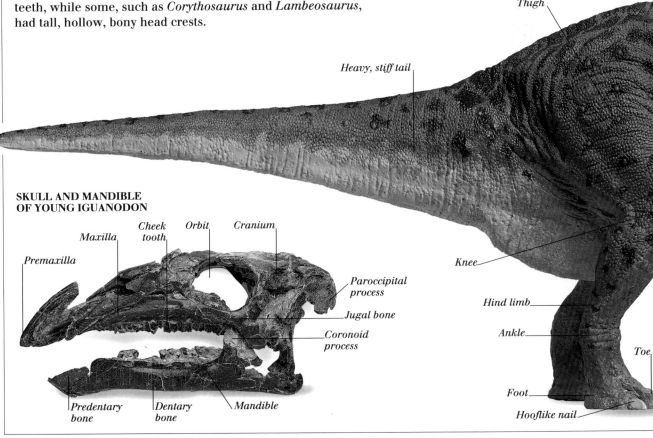

SKULL AND MANDIBLE OF YOUNG IGUANODON

Maxilla
Cheek tooth
Orbit
Cranium
Premaxilla
Paroccipital process
Jugal bone
Coronoid process
Predentary bone
Dentary bone
Mandible

Thigh
Heavy, stiff tail
Knee
Hind limb
Ankle
Toe
Foot
Hooflike nail

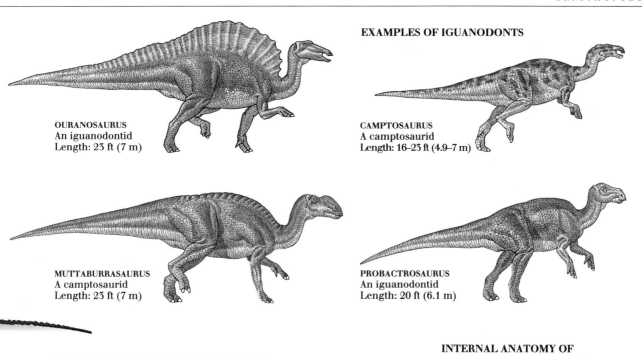

EXAMPLES OF IGUANODONTS

OURANOSAURUS
An iguanodontid
Length: 23 ft (7 m)

CAMPTOSAURUS
A camptosaurid
Length: 16–23 ft (4.9–7 m)

MUTTABURRASAURUS
A camptosaurid
Length: 23 ft (7 m)

PROBACTROSAURUS
An iguanodontid
Length: 20 ft (6.1 m)

EXTERNAL FEATURES OF IGUANODON

Eye

Naris

Shoulder

Neck

Tongue

Beak

Scaly skin

Forelimb

Elbow

Thumb-spike

Wrist

Hand

Finger

Hooflike nail

**INTERNAL ANATOMY OF
HIND LEG OF IGUANODON**

Iliofemoral
muscle

Ilium

Iliotibial
muscle

Ambiens
muscle

Short
caudo-
femoral
muscle

External pubo-ischio-
femoral muscle

Tibial flexor
muscle

Femur

Iliofibular
muscle

Common digital
extensor muscle

Gastrocnemius
muscle

Anterior tibial
muscle

Tibia

Fibula

Tarsal

Metatarsal

Toe

Hooflike nail

Ornithopods 2

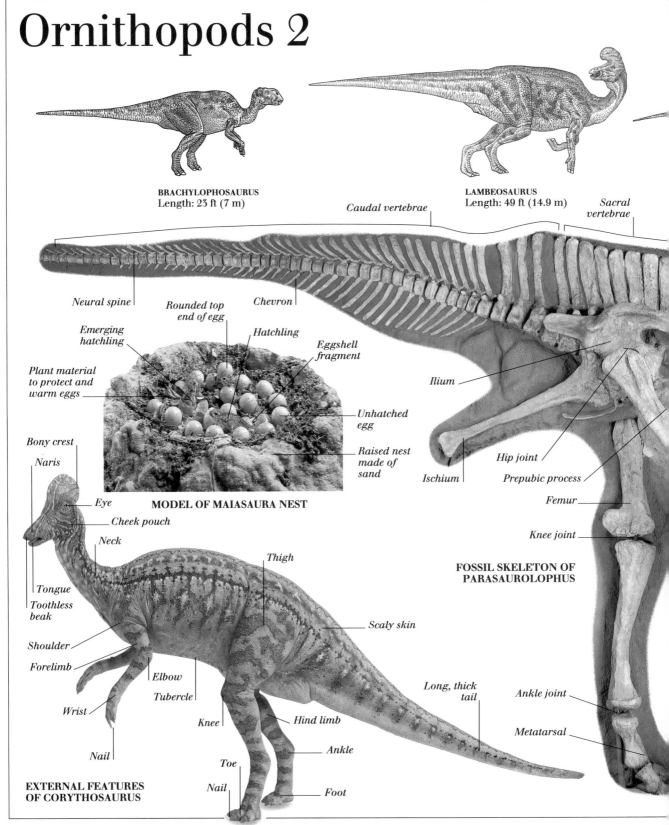

BRACHYLOPHOSAURUS
Length: 23 ft (7 m)

LAMBEOSAURUS
Length: 49 ft (14.9 m)

Caudal vertebrae

Sacral vertebrae

Neural spine

Chevron

Rounded top end of egg

Emerging hatchling

Hatchling

Eggshell fragment

Plant material to protect and warm eggs

Ilium

Unhatched egg

Ischium

Hip joint

Prepubic process

Raised nest made of sand

Femur

Bony crest

Naris

MODEL OF MAIASAURA NEST

Eye

Knee joint

Cheek pouch

Neck

Thigh

FOSSIL SKELETON OF PARASAUROLOPHUS

Tongue

Toothless beak

Scaly skin

Shoulder

Forelimb

Elbow

Tubercle

Long, thick tail

Ankle joint

Wrist

Knee

Hind limb

Metatarsal

Nail

Ankle

Toe

EXTERNAL FEATURES OF CORYTHOSAURUS

Nail

Foot

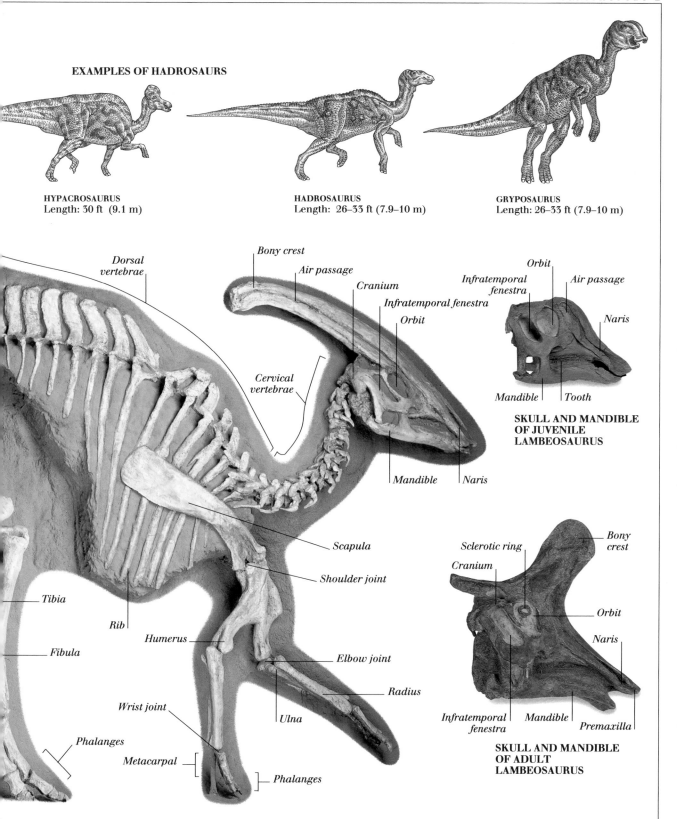

EXAMPLES OF HADROSAURS

HYPACROSAURUS
Length: 30 ft (9.1 m)

HADROSAURUS
Length: 26–33 ft (7.9–10 m)

GRYPOSAURUS
Length: 26–33 ft (7.9–10 m)

Dorsal vertebrae

Bony crest

Air passage

Cranium

Infratemporal fenestra

Orbit

Cervical vertebrae

Mandible

Naris

Scapula

Shoulder joint

Tibia

Rib

Humerus

Fibula

Elbow joint

Radius

Wrist joint

Ulna

Phalanges

Metacarpal

Phalanges

Orbit

Infratemporal fenestra

Air passage

Naris

Mandible

Tooth

**SKULL AND MANDIBLE
OF JUVENILE
LAMBEOSAURUS**

Sclerotic ring

Bony crest

Cranium

Orbit

Naris

Infratemporal fenestra

Mandible

Premaxilla

**SKULL AND MANDIBLE
OF ADULT
LAMBEOSAURUS**

Marginocephalians 1

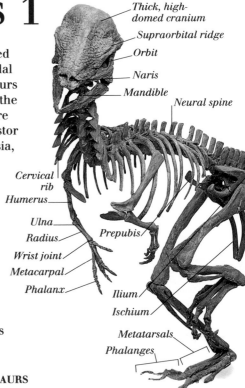

Thick, high-domed cranium
Supraorbital ridge
Orbit
Naris
Mandible
Neural spine
Cervical rib
Humerus
Ulna
Radius
Wrist joint
Metacarpal
Phalanx
Prepubis
Ilium
Ischium
Metatarsals
Phalanges

HEAD-BUTTING PRENOCEPHALES

MARGINOCEPHALIA ("margined heads") were a group of bipedal and quadrupedal ornithischian dinosaurs with a narrow shelf or deep, bony frill at the back of the skull. Marginocephalians were probably descended from the same ancestor as the ornithopods and lived in what are now North America, Africa, Asia, and Europe during the Cretaceous period (146–65 million years ago). They were divided into two infraorders: Pachycephalosauria ("thick-headed lizards"), such as *Pachycephalosaurus* and *Stegoceras*, and Ceratopsia ("horned faces"), such as *Triceratops* and *Psittacosaurus*. The thick skulls of Pachycephalosauria protected their brains during head-butting contests fought to win territory and mates; their hips and spines were also strengthened to withstand the shock. The bony frill of Ceratopsia would have added to their frightening appearance when charging; the neck was strengthened for impact and to support the huge head, with its snipping beak and powerful slicing toothed jaws. A charging ceratops would have been a formidable opponent for even the largest predators. Ceratopsia were among the most abundant herbivorous dinosaurs of the Late Cretaceous period (97–65 million years ago).

EXAMPLES OF SKULLS OF PACHYCEPHALOSAURS

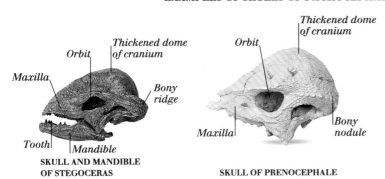

Orbit
Thickened dome of cranium
Maxilla
Bony ridge
Tooth
Mandible

SKULL AND MANDIBLE
OF STEGOCERAS

Thickened dome of cranium
Orbit
Bony nodule
Maxilla

SKULL OF PRENOCEPHALE

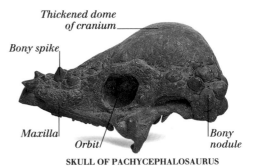

Thickened dome of cranium
Bony spike
Maxilla
Orbit
Bony nodule

SKULL OF PACHYCEPHALOSAURUS

EXTERNAL FEATURES OF PACHYCEPHALOSAURUS

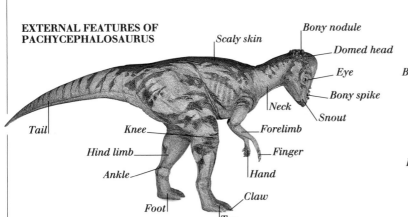

Scaly skin
Bony nodule
Domed head
Eye
Bony spike
Neck
Snout
Tail
Knee
Forelimb
Finger
Hind limb
Hand
Ankle
Foot
Claw
Toe

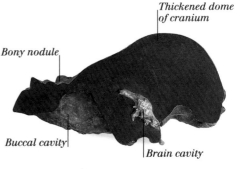

Thickened dome of cranium
Bony nodule
Buccal cavity
Brain cavity

SECTION THROUGH SKULL OF
PACHYCEPHALOSAURUS

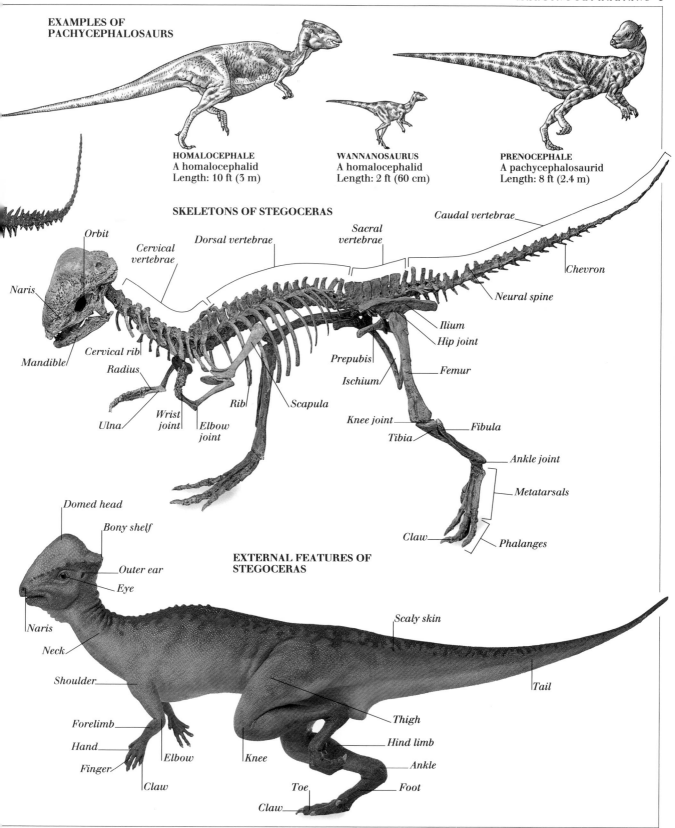

EXAMPLES OF
PACHYCEPHALOSAURS

HOMALOCEPHALE
A homalocephalid
Length: 10 ft (3 m)

WANNANOSAURUS
A homalocephalid
Length: 2 ft (60 cm)

PRENOCEPHALE
A pachycephalosaurid
Length: 8 ft (2.4 m)

SKELETONS OF STEGOCERAS

Orbit

Cervical
vertebrae

Dorsal vertebrae

Sacral
vertebrae

Caudal vertebrae

Chevron

Naris

Neural spine

Ilium

Hip joint

Mandible

Cervical rib

Radius

Prepubis

Femur

Ischium

Ulna

Wrist
joint

Elbow
joint

Rib

Scapula

Knee joint

Fibula

Tibia

Ankle joint

Metatarsals

Claw

Phalanges

Domed head

Bony shelf

EXTERNAL FEATURES OF
STEGOCERAS

Outer ear

Eye

Scaly skin

Naris

Neck

Tail

Shoulder

Thigh

Forelimb

Hind limb

Hand

Elbow

Knee

Ankle

Finger

Foot

Claw

Toe

Claw

Marginocephalians 2

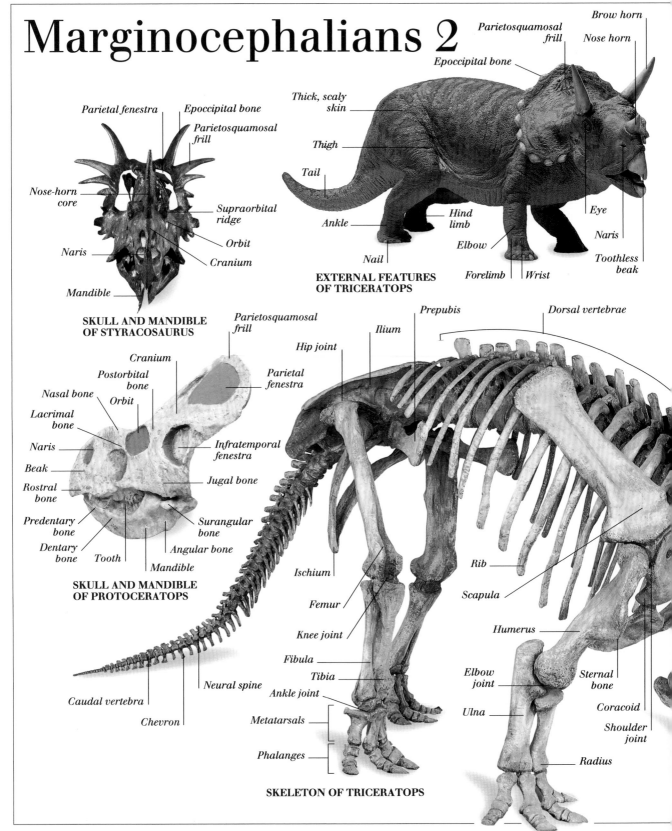

Parietosquamosal frill

Brow horn

Nose horn

Epoccipital bone

Thick, scaly skin

Thigh

Tail

Ankle

Hind limb

Elbow

Nail

Forelimb

Wrist

Eye

Naris

Toothless beak

EXTERNAL FEATURES OF TRICERATOPS

Parietal fenestra

Epoccipital bone

Parietosquamosal frill

Nose-horn core

Supraorbital ridge

Orbit

Naris

Cranium

Mandible

SKULL AND MANDIBLE OF STYRACOSAURUS

Parietosquamosal frill

Cranium

Postorbital bone

Nasal bone

Orbit

Lacrimal bone

Naris

Beak

Rostral bone

Predentary bone

Dentary bone

Tooth

Mandible

Angular bone

Surangular bone

Jugal bone

Infratemporal fenestra

Parietal fenestra

SKULL AND MANDIBLE OF PROTOCERATOPS

Prepubis

Ilium

Hip joint

Dorsal vertebrae

Ischium

Femur

Knee joint

Fibula

Tibia

Ankle joint

Metatarsals

Phalanges

Caudal vertebra

Chevron

Neural spine

Rib

Scapula

Humerus

Elbow joint

Ulna

Sternal bone

Coracoid

Shoulder joint

Radius

SKELETON OF TRICERATOPS

**EXTERNAL FEATURES
OF PSITTACOSAURUS**

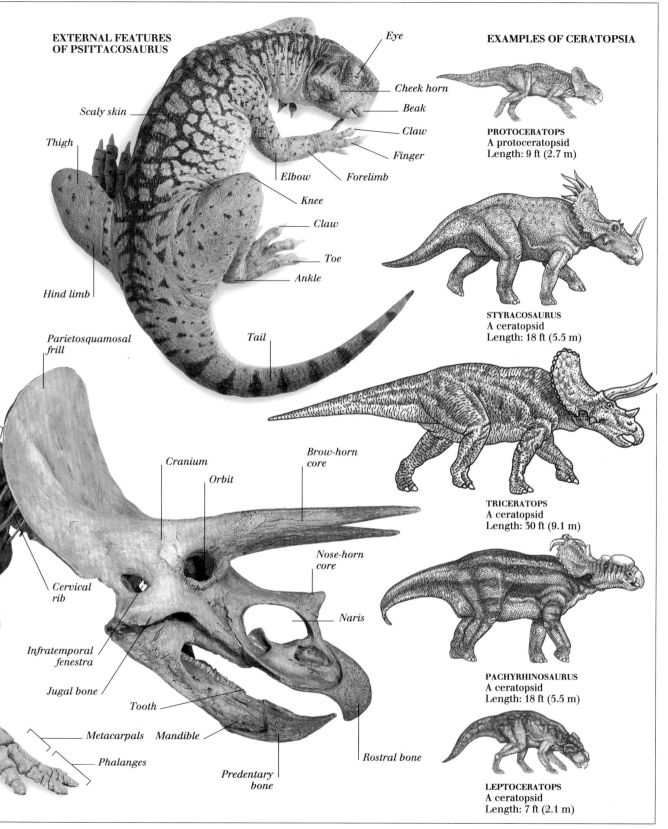

Eye

Cheek horn

Beak

Claw

Finger

Scaly skin

Thigh

Forelimb

Elbow

Knee

Claw

Toe

Ankle

Hind limb

*Parietosquamosal
frill*

Tail

Cranium

Orbit

*Brow-horn
core*

*Nose-horn
core*

*Cervical
rib*

Naris

*Infratemporal
fenestra*

Jugal bone

Tooth

Metacarpals *Mandible*

Phalanges

*Predentary
bone*

Rostral bone

EXAMPLES OF CERATOPSIA

PROTOCERATOPS
A protoceratopsid
Length: 9 ft (2.7 m)

STYRACOSAURUS
A ceratopsid
Length: 18 ft (5.5 m)

TRICERATOPS
A ceratopsid
Length: 30 ft (9.1 m)

PACHYRHINOSAURUS
A ceratopsid
Length: 18 ft (5.5 m)

LEPTOCERATOPS
A ceratopsid
Length: 7 ft (2.1 m)

Mammals 1

**TETRALOPHODON
CHEEK TEETH**

SINCE THE EXTINCTION of the dinosaurs 65 million years ago, mammals have been the dominant vertebrates on Earth and include terrestrial, aerial, and aquatic forms. Having developed from the reptilian Therapsids, the first true mammals—small, nocturnal, rodentlike creatures, such as *Megazostrodon*—appeared over 200 million years ago during the Triassic period (245–208 million years ago). Mammals had several features that improved on those of their reptilian ancestors: an efficient four-chambered heart allowed these warm-blooded animals to sustain high levels of activity; a covering of hair helped them maintain a constant body temperature; an improved limb structure gave them more efficient locomotion; and the birth of live young and the immediate supply of food from the mother's milk aided their rapid growth. Since the end of the Mesozoic era (65 million years ago), the number of different mammal orders and the abundance of species in each order have varied dramatically. For example, the Perissodactyla (the order that includes *Coelodonta* and modern horses) was the most common group during the Early Tertiary period (about 54 million years ago). Today, the mammalian orders with the most populous species are the Rodentia (rats and mice), the Carnivora (bears, cats, and dogs), and the Artiodactyla (cattle, deer, and pigs), while the Proboscidea order, which included many genera, such as *Phiomia, Moeritherium, Tetralophodon,* and *Mammuthus,* now has only one member: the modern elephant. In Australia and South America, millions of years of continental isolation led to the development of the marsupials, a group of mammals distinct from the placentals (see p. 74) that existed elsewhere.

**MODEL OF A
MEGAZOSTRODON**

*Long tail aids
balance*

*Insulating
hair*

*Neural
spine*

Scapula

*Cervical
vertebra*

Humerus

Nasal horn

Naris

Orbit

Mandible

*Predentary
bone*

Radius

Ulna

*Chisel-edged
molar*

Metacarpal

Phalanx

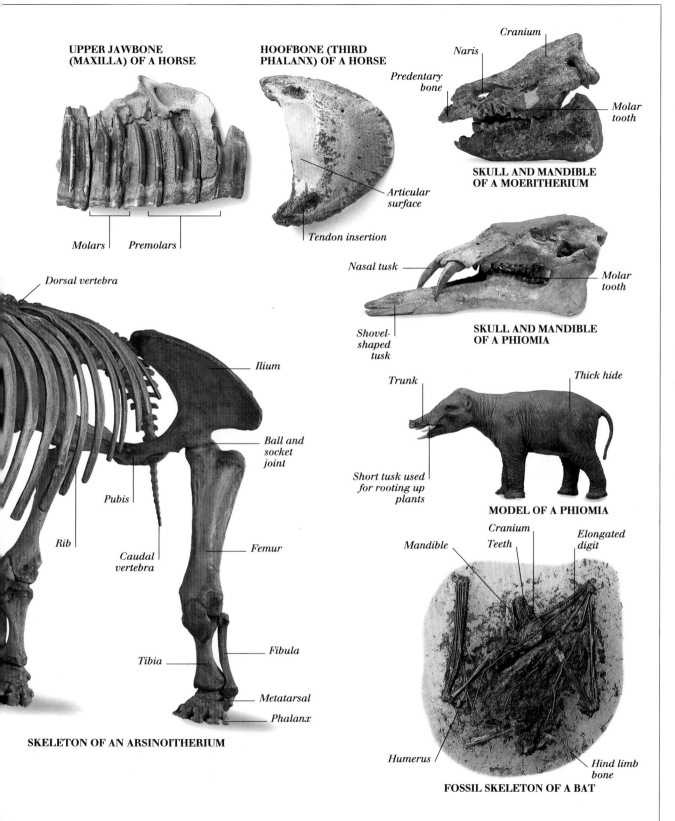

UPPER JAWBONE (MAXILLA) OF A HORSE

Molars Premolars

HOOFBONE (THIRD PHALANX) OF A HORSE

Articular surface

Tendon insertion

Cranium

Naris

Predentary bone

Molar tooth

SKULL AND MANDIBLE OF A MOERITHERIUM

Nasal tusk

Molar tooth

Shovel-shaped tusk

SKULL AND MANDIBLE OF A PHIOMIA

Trunk

Thick hide

Short tusk used for rooting up plants

MODEL OF A PHIOMIA

Dorsal vertebra

Ilium

Ball and socket joint

Pubis

Rib

Caudal vertebra

Femur

Tibia

Fibula

Metatarsal

Phalanx

SKELETON OF AN ARSINOITHERIUM

Cranium

Mandible

Teeth

Elongated digit

Humerus

Hind limb bone

FOSSIL SKELETON OF A BAT

105

Mammals 2

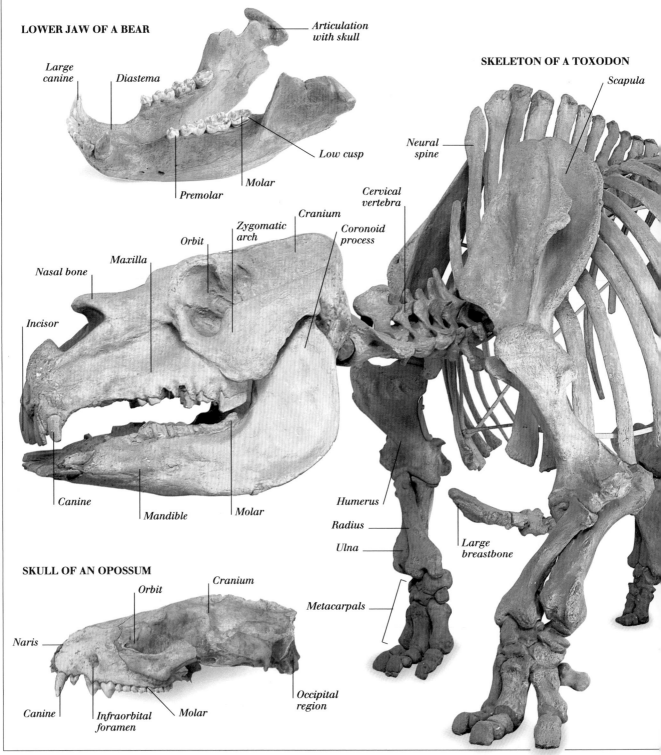

LOWER JAW OF A BEAR

Articulation with skull

Large canine

Diastema

Low cusp

Molar

Premolar

Cranium

Zygomatic arch

Orbit

Coronoid process

Cervical vertebra

Maxilla

Nasal bone

Incisor

Canine

Mandible

Molar

Humerus

Radius

Ulna

Large breastbone

SKELETON OF A TOXODON

Scapula

Neural spine

Metacarpals

SKULL OF AN OPOSSUM

Orbit

Cranium

Naris

Canine

Infraorbital foramen

Molar

Occipital region

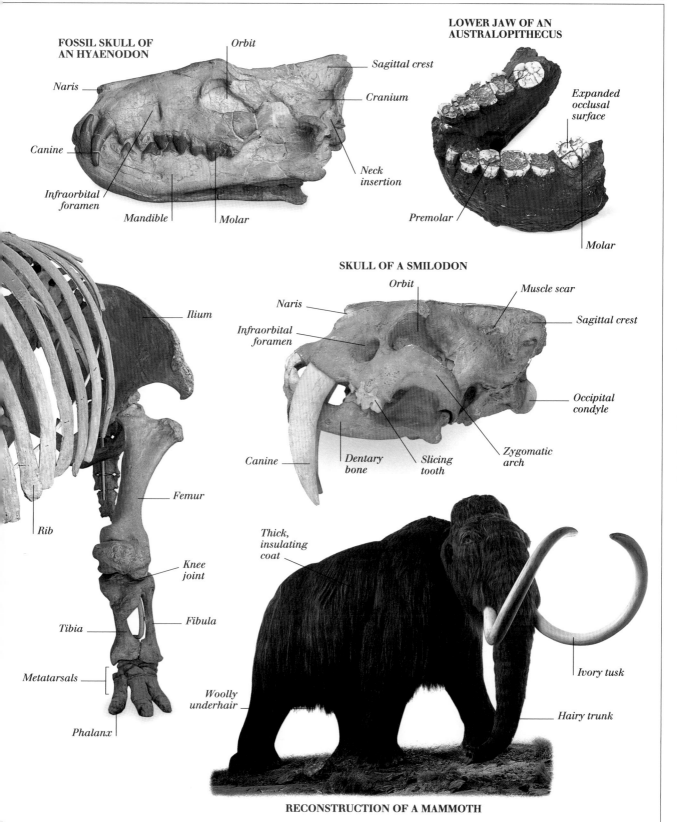

FOSSIL SKULL OF AN HYAENODON

Orbit

Sagittal crest

Naris

Cranium

Canine

Neck insertion

Infraorbital foramen

Mandible

Molar

LOWER JAW OF AN AUSTRALOPITHECUS

Expanded occlusal surface

Premolar

Molar

SKULL OF A SMILODON

Orbit

Muscle scar

Naris

Sagittal crest

Infraorbital foramen

Occipital condyle

Canine

Dentary bone

Slicing tooth

Zygomatic arch

Ilium

Femur

Rib

Knee joint

Tibia

Fibula

Metatarsals

Phalanx

Thick, insulating coat

Woolly underhair

Ivory tusk

Hairy trunk

RECONSTRUCTION OF A MAMMOTH

The first hominids

MODERN HUMANS BELONG TO THE MAMMALIAN order of primates
(see pp. 202–203), which originated about 55 million years ago; they
comprise the only extant hominid species. The earliest hominid was
Australopithecus ("southern ape"), a small-brained intermediate between
apes and humans that was capable of standing and walking upright. *Homo
habilis*, the first known human appeared at least 2 million years ago. This
larger-brained "handy man" began making tools for hunting. *Homo erectus*
first appeared in Africa about 1.8 million years ago and spread into Asia about
800,000 years later. Smaller toothed than *Homo habilis*, it developed fire as a
tool, which enabled it to cook food. Neanderthals, a near relative of modern
humans, originated about 200,000 years ago, and *Homo sapiens* (modern humans)
appeared in Africa about 100,000 years later. The two coexisted for thousands of
years, but by 30,000 years ago, *Homo sapiens* had become dominant and the
Neanderthals had died out. Classification of *Homo sapiens* in relation to its ancestors
is enormously problematic: modern humans must be classified not only by bone structure,
but also by specific behavior—the ability to plan future action; to follow traditions;
and to use symbolic communication, including complex language and the
ability to use and recognize symbols.

**JAWBONE OF AUSTRALOPITHECUS
(SOUTHERN APE)**

*Larger jawbone
than modern
human*

*Large back
tooth*

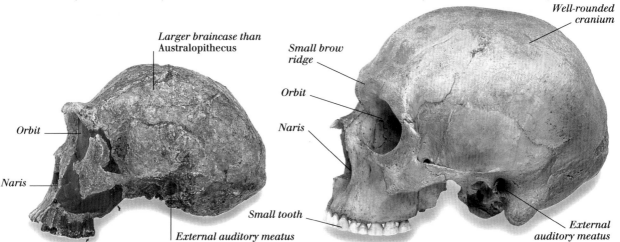

*Jutting brow
ridge*

Cranium

Orbit

Naris

*Jutting
jawbone*

**SKULL OF AUSTRALOPITHECUS
(SOUTHERN APE)**

Orbit

Naris

**SKULL OF HOMO HABILIS
(FIRST KNOWN HUMAN)**

*Well-rounded
cranium*

*Larger braincase than
Australopithecus*

*Small brow
ridge*

Orbit

Orbit

Naris

Naris

Small tooth

External auditory meatus

*External
auditory meatus*

SKULL OF HOMO ERECTUS (UPRIGHT MAN)

SKULL OF HOMO SAPIENS (MODERN HUMAN)

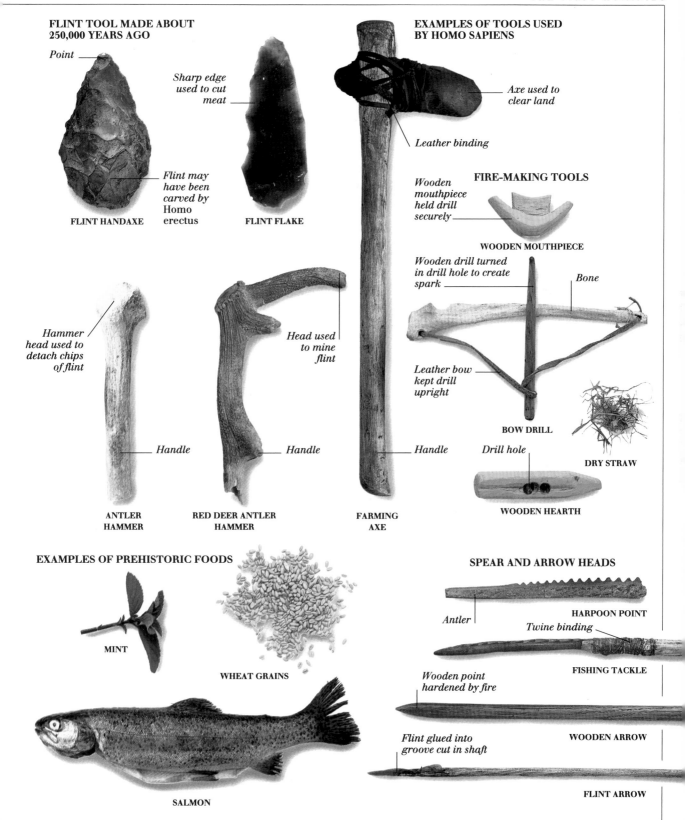

FLINT TOOL MADE ABOUT 250,000 YEARS AGO

Point

Sharp edge used to cut meat

Flint may have been carved by Homo erectus

FLINT HANDAXE

FLINT FLAKE

Hammer head used to detach chips of flint

Handle

ANTLER HAMMER

Head used to mine flint

Handle

RED DEER ANTLER HAMMER

Handle

FARMING AXE

EXAMPLES OF TOOLS USED BY HOMO SAPIENS

Axe used to clear land

Leather binding

FIRE-MAKING TOOLS

Wooden mouthpiece held drill securely

WOODEN MOUTHPIECE

Wooden drill turned in drill hole to create spark

Bone

Leather bow kept drill upright

BOW DRILL

Drill hole

DRY STRAW

WOODEN HEARTH

EXAMPLES OF PREHISTORIC FOODS

MINT

WHEAT GRAINS

SALMON

SPEAR AND ARROW HEADS

Antler

HARPOON POINT

Twine binding

FISHING TACKLE

Wooden point hardened by fire

WOODEN ARROW

Flint glued into groove cut in shaft

FLINT ARROW

PLANTS

PLANT VARIETIES 112
FUNGI AND LICHENS 114
ALGAE AND SEAWEED 116
LIVERWORTS AND MOSSES 118
HORSETAILS, CLUB MOSSES, AND FERNS 120
GYMNOSPERMS 1 122
GYMNOSPERMS 2 124
MONOCOTYLEDONS AND DICOTYLEDONS . . . 126
HERBACEOUS FLOWERING PLANTS 128
WOODY FLOWERING PLANTS 130
ROOTS 132
STEMS 134
LEAVES 136
PHOTOSYNTHESIS 138
FLOWERS 1 140
FLOWERS 2 142
POLLINATION 144
FERTILIZATION 146
SUCCULENT FRUITS 148
DRY FRUITS 150
GERMINATION 152
VEGETATIVE REPRODUCTION 154
DRYLAND PLANTS 156
WETLAND PLANTS 158
CARNIVOROUS PLANTS 160
EPIPHYTIC AND PARASITIC PLANTS 162

Plant varieties

Leaf

THERE ARE MORE THAN 300,000 SPECIES of plants. They
show a wide diversity of forms, ranging from delicate liverworts, adapted for life
in a damp habitat, to cacti, capable of surviving in the desert. The plant kingdom includes
herbaceous plants, such as corn, which completes its life cycle in one year, to the giant redwood tree, which
can live for thousands of years. This diversity reflects the adaptations of plants to survive in a wide range of
habitats. This is seen most clearly in the flowering plants (phylum Angiospermophyta), which are the most
numerous, with over 250,000 species. They are also the most widespread, being found from the tropics to the
arctic. Despite their diversity, plants share certain characteristics. Typically, plants are green, and make their
food by photosynthesis. Most plants live in or on a substrate, such as soil, and do not actively move. Algae
(kingdom Protista) and fungi (kingdom Fungi) have some plantlike characteristics and are
often studied alongside plants, although they are not true plants.

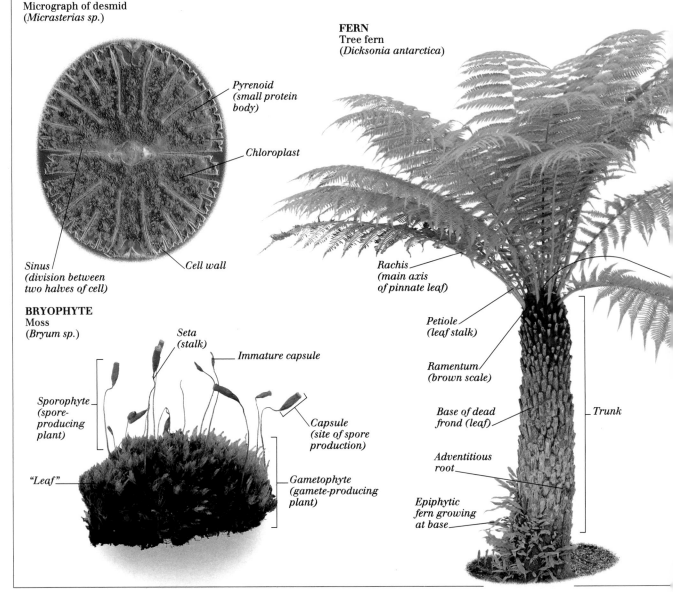

GREEN ALGA
Micrograph of desmid
(*Micrasterias sp.*)

*Pyrenoid
(small protein
body)*

Chloroplast

*Sinus
(division between
two halves of cell)*

Cell wall

FERN
Tree fern
(*Dicksonia antarctica*)

*Rachis
(main axis
of pinnate leaf)*

*Petiole
(leaf stalk)*

*Ramentum
(brown scale)*

*Base of dead
frond (leaf)*

Trunk

*Adventitious
root*

*Epiphytic
fern growing
at base*

BRYOPHYTE
Moss
(*Bryum sp.*)

*Seta
(stalk)*

Immature capsule

*Sporophyte
(spore-
producing
plant)*

*Capsule
(site of spore
production)*

"Leaf"

*Gametophyte
(gamete-producing
plant)*

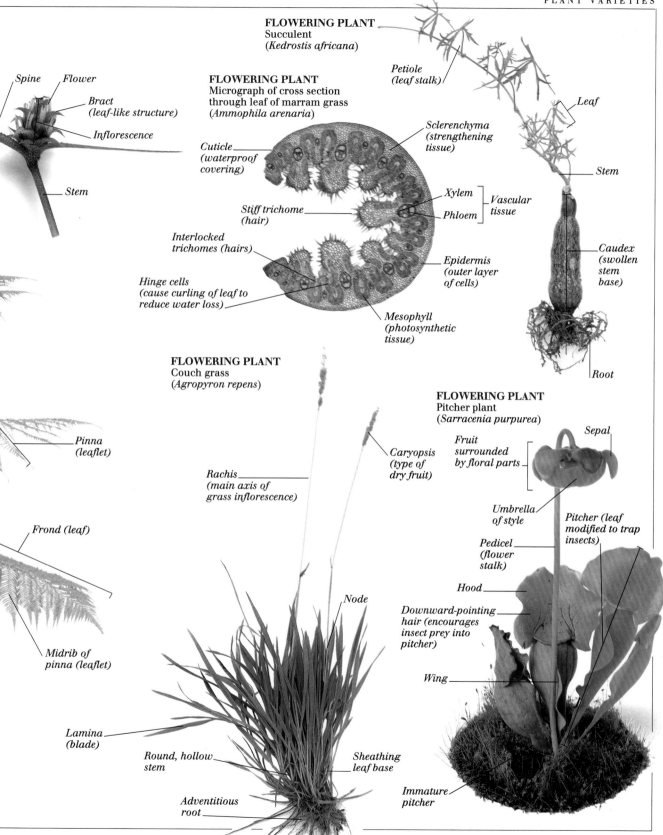

FLOWERING PLANT
Succulent
(*Kedrostis africana*)

*Petiole
(leaf stalk)*

Leaf

Stem

*Caudex
(swollen
stem
base)*

Root

Spine
Flower

Bract
(leaf-like structure)

Inflorescence

Stem

FLOWERING PLANT
Micrograph of cross section
through leaf of marram grass
(*Ammophila arenaria*)

*Cuticle
(waterproof
covering)*

*Sclerenchyma
(strengthening
tissue)*

Xylem

Phloem

*Vascular
tissue*

*Stiff trichome
(hair)*

*Epidermis
(outer layer
of cells)*

*Interlocked
trichomes (hairs)*

*Hinge cells
(cause curling of leaf to
reduce water loss)*

*Mesophyll
(photosynthetic
tissue)*

FLOWERING PLANT
Couch grass
(*Agropyron repens*)

*Caryopsis
(type of
dry fruit)*

*Rachis
(main axis of
grass inflorescence)*

Pinna
(leaflet)

Frond (leaf)

Midrib of
pinna (leaflet)

Node

Lamina
(blade)

Round, hollow
stem

Sheathing
leaf base

Adventitious
root

FLOWERING PLANT
Pitcher plant
(*Sarracenia purpurea*)

Sepal

*Fruit
surrounded
by floral parts*

*Umbrella
of style*

*Pitcher (leaf
modified to trap
insects)*

*Pedicel
(flower
stalk)*

Hood

*Downward-pointing
hair (encourages
insect prey into
pitcher)*

Wing

*Immature
pitcher*

Fungi and lichens

FUNGI WERE ONCE THOUGHT OF AS PLANTS but are now classified as a separate kingdom. This kingdom includes not only the familiar mushrooms, puffballs, stinkhorns, and molds, but also yeasts, smuts, rusts, and lichens. Most fungi are multicellular, consisting of a mass of thread-like hyphae that together form a mycelium. However, the simpler fungi, like yeasts, are microscopic, single-celled organisms. Typically, fungi reproduce by means of spores. Most fungi feed on dead or decaying matter or on living organisms. A few fungi obtain their food from plants or algae, with which they have a symbiotic (mutually advantageous) relationship. Lichens are a symbiotic partnership between algae and fungi. Of the six types of lichens the three most common are crustose (flat and crusty), foliose (leafy), and fruticose (shrub-like). Some lichens (such as *Cladonia floerkeana*) are a combination of types. Lichens reproduce by means of spores or soredia (powdery vegetative fragments).

EXAMPLES OF FUNGI

Emerging sporophore (spore-bearing structure)

Pileus (cap) continuous with stipe (stalk)

Bark of dead beech tree

Inrolled margin of pileus (cap)

Gill (site of spore production)

Sporophore (spore-bearing structure)

Stipe (stalk)

Hyphae (fungal filaments)

OYSTER FUNGUS
(*Pleurotus pulmonarius*)

EXAMPLES OF LICHENS

Secondary fruticose thallus

Branched, hollow stem

Apothecium (spore-producing body)

FRUTICOSE
Cladonia portentosa

Soredia (powdery vegetative fragments) produced at end of lobe

Tree bark

Foliose thallus

FOLIOSE
Hypogymnia physodes

Gleba (spore-producing tissue found in this type of fungus)

Sporophore (spore-bearing structure)

Porous stipe (stalk)

Volva (remains of universal veil)

STINKHORN
(*Phallus impudicus*)

Toothed branchlet

Branch

Sporophore (spore-bearing structure)

Stipe (stalk)

RAMARIA FORMOSA

Soredia (powdery vegetative fragments) released onto surface of squamulose thallus

Apothecium (spore-producing body)

Basal scale of primary squamulose thallus

Podetium (granular stalk) of secondary fruticose thallus

Moss

SQUAMULOSE (SCALY) AND FRUTICOSE THALLUS
Cladonia floerkeana

SECTION THROUGH FOLIOSE LICHEN SHOWING REPRODUCTION BY SOREDIA

Algal cell

Fungal hypha

Soredium (powdery vegetative fragment involved in propagation) released from lichen

Upper cortex

Algal layer

Medulla of fungal hyphae (mycelium)

Lower cortex

Rhizine (bundle of absorptive hyphae)

Soralium (pore in upper surface of thallus)

Upper surface of thallus

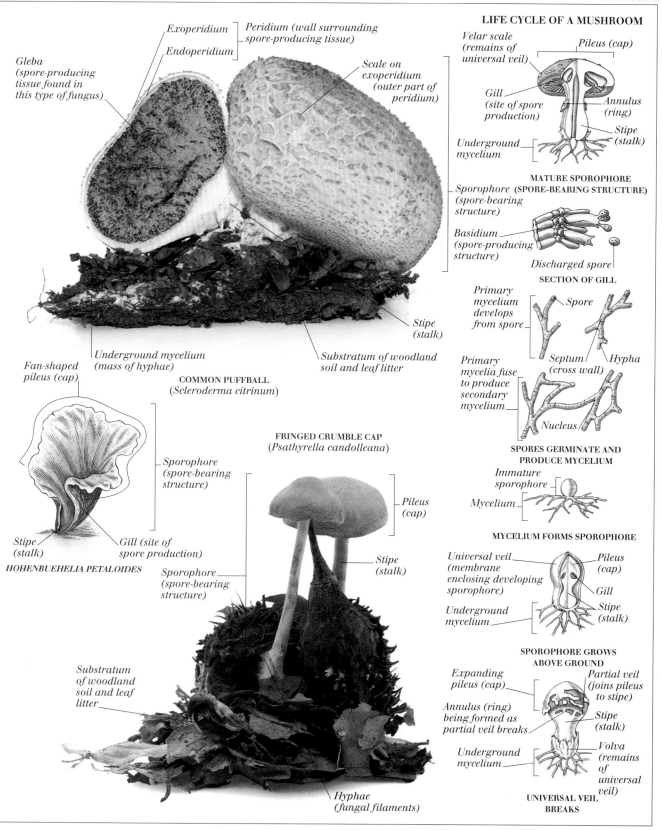

Gleba (spore-producing tissue found in this type of fungus)

Exoperidium

Endoperidium

Peridium (wall surrounding spore-producing tissue)

Scale on exoperidium (outer part of peridium)

Stipe (stalk)

Underground mycelium (mass of hyphae)

Substratum of woodland soil and leaf litter

COMMON PUFFBALL
(Scleroderma citrinum)

Fan-shaped pileus (cap)

Sporophore (spore-bearing structure)

Stipe (stalk)

Gill (site of spore production)

HOHENBUEHELIA PETALOIDES

Sporophore (spore-bearing structure)

FRINGED CRUMBLE CAP
(Psathyrella candolleana)

Pileus (cap)

Stipe (stalk)

Substratum of woodland soil and leaf litter

Hyphae (fungal filaments)

LIFE CYCLE OF A MUSHROOM

Velar scale (remains of universal veil)

Pileus (cap)

Gill (site of spore production)

Annulus (ring)

Stipe (stalk)

Underground mycelium

Sporophore (spore-bearing structure)

Basidium (spore-producing structure)

Discharged spore

MATURE SPOROPHORE
(SPORE-BEARING STRUCTURE)

SECTION OF GILL

Primary mycelium develops from spore

Spore

Septum (cross wall)

Hypha

Primary mycelia fuse to produce secondary mycelium

Nucleus

SPORES GERMINATE AND PRODUCE MYCELIUM

Immature sporophore

Mycelium

MYCELIUM FORMS SPOROPHORE

Universal veil (membrane enclosing developing sporophore)

Pileus (cap)

Gill

Underground mycelium

Stipe (stalk)

SPOROPHORE GROWS ABOVE GROUND

Expanding pileus (cap)

Partial veil (joins pileus to stipe)

Annulus (ring) being formed as partial veil breaks

Stipe (stalk)

Underground mycelium

Volva (remains of universal veil)

UNIVERSAL VEIL BREAKS

Algae and seaweed

ALGAE ARE NOT TRUE PLANTS. They form a diverse group of plantlike organisms that belong to the kingdom Protista. Like plants, algae possess the green pigment chlorophyll and make their own food by photosynthesis (see pp. 138-139). Many algae also possess other pigments by which they can be classified. For example, the brown pigment fucoxanthin is found in brown algae. Some of the ten phyla of algae are exclusively unicellular (single-celled); others also contain aggregates of cells in filaments or colonies. Three phyla— the Chlorophyta (green algae), Rhodophyta (red algae), and Phaeophyta (brown algae)—contain larger, multicellular, thalloid (flat), marine organisms commonly known as seaweed. Most algae can reproduce sexually. For example, in brown seaweed *Fucus vesiculosus*, gametes (sex cells) are produced in conceptacles (chambers) in the receptacles (fertile tips of fronds); after their release into the sea, antherozoids (male gametes) and oospheres (female gametes) fuse. The resulting zygote settles on a rock and develops into a new seaweed.

BROWN SEAWEED
Channeled wrack
(*Pelvetia canaliculata*)

Thallus (plant body)

Receptacle (fertile tip of frond)

Apical notch

Margin of lamina (blade) rolled inwards to form channel

Hapteron (holdfast)

BROWN SEAWEED
Spiral wrack
(*Fucus spiralis*)

Apical notch

Conceptacle (chamber)

Receptacle (fertile tip of frond)

Lamina (blade)

Smooth margin

Midrib

Thallus (plant body)

Hapteron (holdfast)

EXAMPLES OF ALGAE

Reproductive chamber

Cap

Sterile whorl

Cell wall

Stalk

Rhizoid

GREEN ALGA
Acetabularia sp.

Flagellum

Eyespot

Contractile vacuole

Cytoplasm

Nucleus

Cell wall

Chloroplast

Pyrenoid (small protein body)

Starch grain

GREEN ALGA
Chlamydomonas sp.

Coenobium (colony of cells)

Daughter coenobium

Gelatinous sheath

Biflagellate cell

GREEN ALGA
Volvox sp.

Spine

Cytoplasm

Girdle

Vacuole

Nucleus

Plastid (photosynthetic organelle)

DIATOM
Thalassiosira sp.

Apical notch

Receptacle (fertile tip of frond)

Conceptacle (chamber) containing reproductive structures

Lamina (blade)

Midrib

RECEPTACLE
Spiral wrack
(*Fucus spiralis*)

BROWN SEAWEED
Oarweed
(*Laminaria digitata*)

Thallus (plant body)

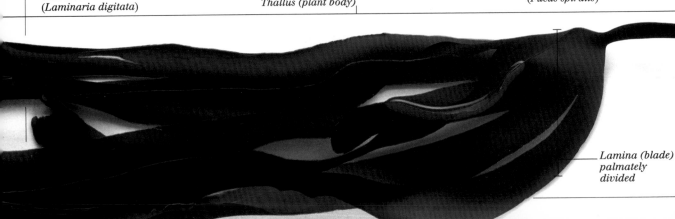

Lamina (blade) palmately divided

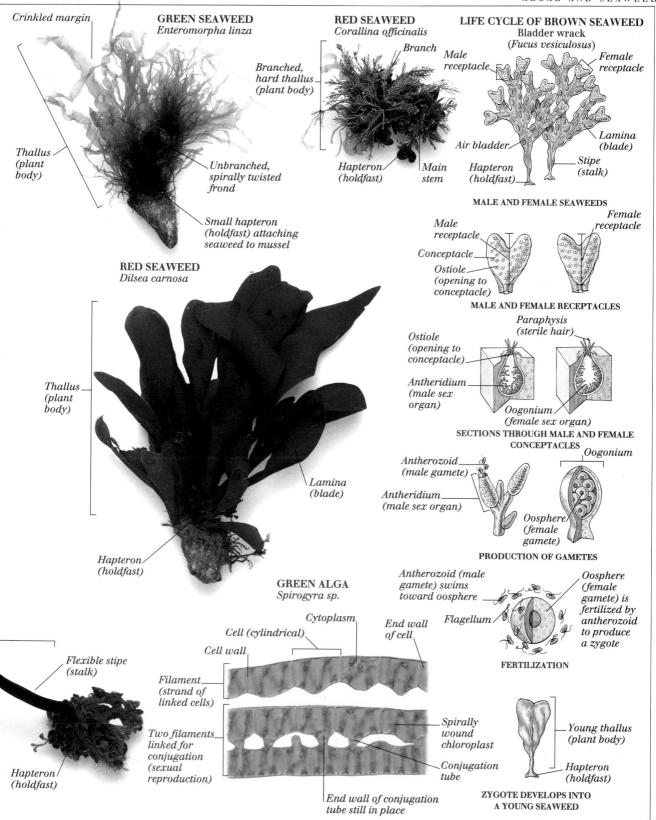

GREEN SEAWEED
Enteromorpha linza

Crinkled margin

Thallus
(plant
body)

Unbranched,
spirally twisted
frond

Small hapteron
(holdfast) attaching
seaweed to mussel

RED SEAWEED
Corallina officinalis

Branch

Branched,
hard thallus
(plant body)

Hapteron
(holdfast)

Main
stem

LIFE CYCLE OF BROWN SEAWEED
Bladder wrack
(*Fucus vesiculosus*)

Male
receptacle

Female
receptacle

Air bladder

Lamina
(blade)

Hapteron
(holdfast)

Stipe
(stalk)

MALE AND FEMALE SEAWEEDS

Male
receptacle

Female
receptacle

Conceptacle

Ostiole
(opening to
conceptacle)

MALE AND FEMALE RECEPTACLES

Paraphysis
(sterile hair)

Ostiole
(opening to
conceptacle)

Antheridium
(male sex
organ)

Oogonium
(female sex organ)

**SECTIONS THROUGH MALE AND FEMALE
CONCEPTACLES**

Antherozoid
(male gamete)

Oogonium

Antheridium
(male sex organ)

Oosphere
(female
gamete)

PRODUCTION OF GAMETES

RED SEAWEED
Dilsea carnosa

Thallus
(plant
body)

Lamina
(blade)

Hapteron
(holdfast)

GREEN ALGA
Spirogyra sp.

Cytoplasm

Cell (cylindrical)

End wall
of cell

Cell wall

Filament
(strand of
linked cells)

Two filaments
linked for
conjugation
(sexual
reproduction)

Spirally
wound
chloroplast

Conjugation
tube

End wall of conjugation
tube still in place

Antherozoid (male
gamete) swims
toward oosphere

Flagellum

Oosphere
(female
gamete) is
fertilized by
antherozoid
to produce
a zygote

FERTILIZATION

Young thallus
(plant body)

Hapteron
(holdfast)

**ZYGOTE DEVELOPS INTO
A YOUNG SEAWEED**

Flexible stipe
(stalk)

Hapteron
(holdfast)

Liverworts and mosses

LIVERWORTS AND MOSSES ARE SMALL, LOW-GROWING PLANTS that belong to the phylum Bryophyta. Bryophytes do not have true stems, leaves, or roots (they are anchored to the ground by rhizoids), nor do they have the vascular tissues (xylem and phloem) that transport water and nutrients in higher plants. With no outer, waterproof cuticle, bryophytes are susceptible to dehydration, and most grow in moist habitats. The bryophyte life cycle has two stages. In stage one, the green plant (gametophyte) produces male and female gametes (sex cells), which fuse to form a zygote. In stage two, the zygote develops into a sporophyte that remains attached to the gametophyte. The sporophyte produces spores, which are released and germinate into new green plants. Liverworts (class Hepaticae) grow horizontally and may be thalloid (flat and ribbon-like) or "leafy." Mosses (class Musci) typically have an upright "stem" with spirally arranged "leaves."

A LEAFY LIVERWORT
Scapania undulata

"Stem"

"Leaf"

Rhizoid

A THALLOID LIVERWORT
Marchantia polymorpha

Gemma cup

Gemma (detachable tissue that produces new plants)

Thallus (plant body)

Toothed margin of cup

DETAIL OF GEMMA CUP

Archegoniophore (stalked structure carrying archegonia)

Disk

Lobe

Stalk

Thallus (plant body)

Rhizoid

FEMALE GAMETOPHYTE

Disk

Lobe

Stalk

SIDE VIEW OF ARCHEGONIOPHORE

Lobe

Disk

Ray (radial groove)

Stalk

ARCHEGONIOPHORE FROM BELOW

Pore

Ray (radial groove)

MICROGRAPH OF LOBE

Apical notch

Gemma cup

Thallus (plant body)

Midrib

Archegoniophore (stalked structure carrying archegonia)

MICROGRAPH OF THALLUS
Conocephalum conicum

Position of air chamber

Pore for exchange of gases

Upper surface

Rhizoid

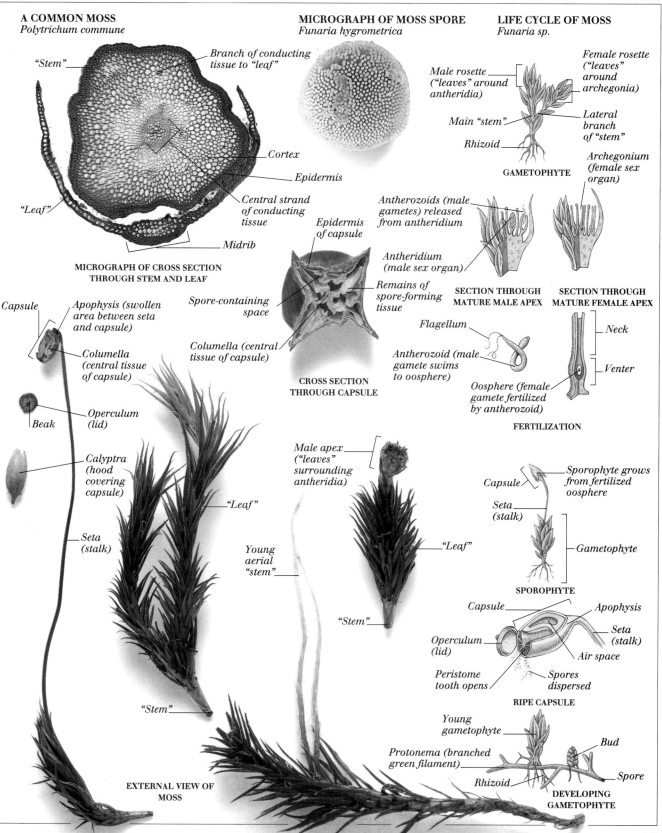

A COMMON MOSS
Polytrichum commune

"Stem"

Branch of conducting tissue to "leaf"

Cortex

Epidermis

Central strand of conducting tissue

"Leaf"

Midrib

MICROGRAPH OF CROSS SECTION THROUGH STEM AND LEAF

MICROGRAPH OF MOSS SPORE
Funaria hygrometrica

LIFE CYCLE OF MOSS
Funaria sp.

Female rosette ("leaves" around archegonia)

Male rosette ("leaves" around antheridia)

Main "stem"

Lateral branch of "stem"

Rhizoid

GAMETOPHYTE

Archegonium (female sex organ)

Antherozoids (male gametes) released from antheridium

Antheridium (male sex organ)

Epidermis of capsule

Spore-containing space

Remains of spore-forming tissue

Columella (central tissue of capsule)

CROSS SECTION THROUGH CAPSULE

SECTION THROUGH MATURE MALE APEX

SECTION THROUGH MATURE FEMALE APEX

Neck

Venter

Flagellum

Antherozoid (male gamete swims to oosphere)

Oosphere (female gamete fertilized by antherozoid)

FERTILIZATION

Capsule

Apophysis (swollen area between seta and capsule)

Columella (central tissue of capsule)

Operculum (lid)

Beak

Calyptra (hood covering capsule)

Seta (stalk)

"Leaf"

Male apex ("leaves" surrounding antheridia)

Young aerial "stem"

"Leaf"

"Stem"

Capsule

Seta (stalk)

Sporophyte grows from fertilized oosphere

Gametophyte

SPOROPHYTE

Capsule

Operculum (lid)

Peristome tooth opens

Apophysis

Seta (stalk)

Air space

Spores dispersed

RIPE CAPSULE

"Stem"

EXTERNAL VIEW OF MOSS

Young gametophyte

Protonema (branched green filament)

Rhizoid

Bud

Spore

DEVELOPING GAMETOPHYTE

119

Horsetails, club mosses, and ferns

HORSETAILS, CLUB MOSSES, AND FERNS are primitive land plants, which, like higher plants, have stems, roots, leaves, and vascular systems that transport water, minerals, and food. Unlike higher plants, however, they do not produce seeds when reproducing. Their life cycles involve two stages. In stage one, the sporophyte (green plant) produces spores in sporangia. In stage two, the spores germinate, developing into small, short-lived gametophyte plants that produce male and female gametes (sex cells). The gametes fuse to form a zygote from which a new sporophyte plant develops. Horsetails (phylum Sphenophyta) have erect green stems with branches arranged in whorls. Some stems are fertile and have a single spore-producing strobilus (group of sporangia) at the tip. Club mosses (phylum Lycopodophyta) typically have small leaves arranged spirally around the stem, with spore-producing strobili at the tip of some stems. Ferns (phylum Filicinophyta) usually have large, pinnate leaves called fronds. Sporangia, grouped together in sori, develop on the underside of fertile fronds.

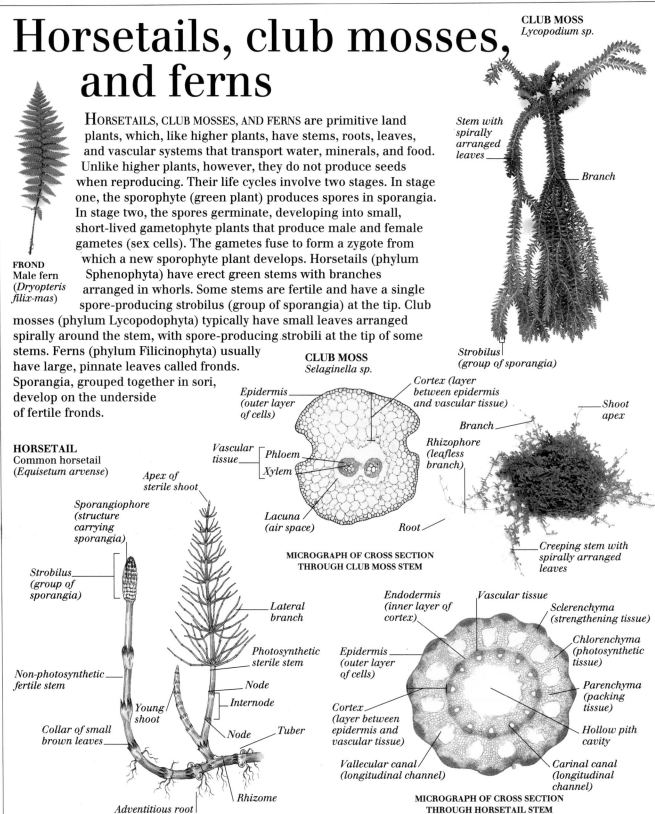

FROND
Male fern
(*Dryopteris filix-mas*)

CLUB MOSS
Lycopodium sp.

Stem with spirally arranged leaves

Branch

Strobilus (group of sporangia)

CLUB MOSS
Selaginella sp.

Epidermis (outer layer of cells)

Cortex (layer between epidermis and vascular tissue)

Vascular tissue
Phloem
Xylem

Lacuna (air space)

Root

Branch

Rhizophore (leafless branch)

Shoot apex

Creeping stem with spirally arranged leaves

MICROGRAPH OF CROSS SECTION THROUGH CLUB MOSS STEM

HORSETAIL
Common horsetail
(*Equisetum arvense*)

Apex of sterile shoot

Sporangiophore (structure carrying sporangia)

Strobilus (group of sporangia)

Non-photosynthetic fertile stem

Collar of small brown leaves

Young shoot

Lateral branch

Photosynthetic sterile stem

Node

Internode

Node

Tuber

Rhizome

Adventitious root

Endodermis (inner layer of cortex)

Vascular tissue

Sclerenchyma (strengthening tissue)

Chlorenchyma (photosynthetic tissue)

Epidermis (outer layer of cells)

Cortex (layer between epidermis and vascular tissue)

Parenchyma (packing tissue)

Hollow pith cavity

Vallecular canal (longitudinal channel)

Carinal canal (longitudinal channel)

MICROGRAPH OF CROSS SECTION THROUGH HORSETAIL STEM

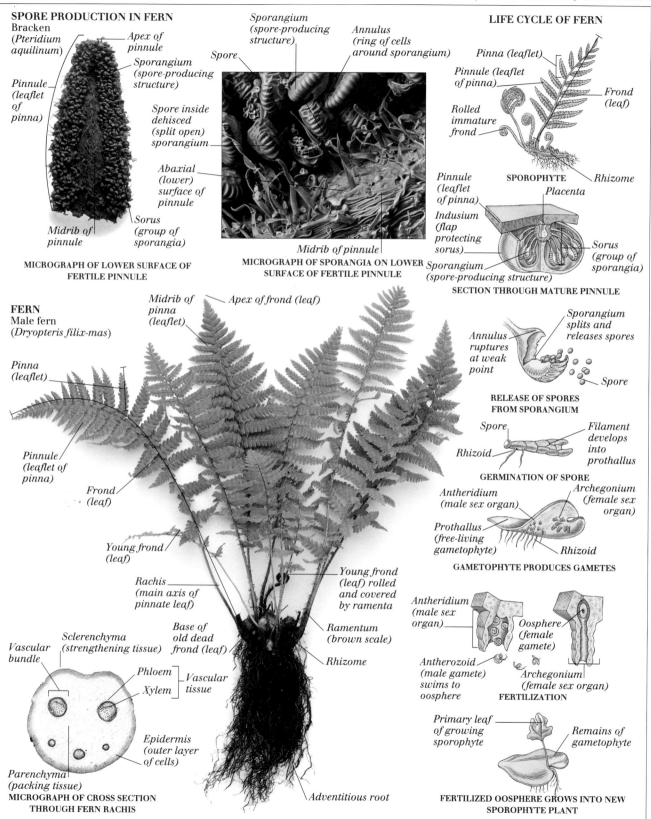

SPORE PRODUCTION IN FERN

Bracken
(*Pteridium aquilinum*)

Apex of pinnule

Sporangium (spore-producing structure)

Pinnule (leaflet of pinna)

Midrib of pinnule

Sorus (group of sporangia)

MICROGRAPH OF LOWER SURFACE OF FERTILE PINNULE

Sporangium (spore-producing structure)

Spore

Annulus (ring of cells around sporangium)

Spore inside dehisced (split open) sporangium

Abaxial (lower) surface of pinnule

Midrib of pinnule

MICROGRAPH OF SPORANGIA ON LOWER SURFACE OF FERTILE PINNULE

LIFE CYCLE OF FERN

Pinna (leaflet)

Pinnule (leaflet of pinna)

Rolled immature frond

Frond (leaf)

SPOROPHYTE

Rhizome

Pinnule (leaflet of pinna)

Placenta

Indusium (flap protecting sorus)

Sporangium (spore-producing structure)

Sorus (group of sporangia)

SECTION THROUGH MATURE PINNULE

Sporangium splits and releases spores

Annulus ruptures at weak point

Spore

RELEASE OF SPORES FROM SPORANGIUM

Spore

Rhizoid

Filament develops into prothallus

GERMINATION OF SPORE

Antheridium (male sex organ)

Archegonium (female sex organ)

Prothallus (free-living gametophyte)

Rhizoid

GAMETOPHYTE PRODUCES GAMETES

Antheridium (male sex organ)

Oosphere (female gamete)

Antherozoid (male gamete) swims to oosphere

Archegonium (female sex organ)

FERTILIZATION

Primary leaf of growing sporophyte

Remains of gametophyte

FERTILIZED OOSPHERE GROWS INTO NEW SPOROPHYTE PLANT

FERN

Male fern
(*Dryopteris filix-mas*)

Midrib of pinna (leaflet)

Apex of frond (leaf)

Pinna (leaflet)

Pinnule (leaflet of pinna)

Frond (leaf)

Young frond (leaf)

Rachis (main axis of pinnate leaf)

Base of old dead frond (leaf)

Young frond (leaf) rolled and covered by ramenta

Ramentum (brown scale)

Rhizome

Vascular bundle

Sclerenchyma (strengthening tissue)

Phloem

Xylem

Vascular tissue

Epidermis (outer layer of cells)

Parenchyma (packing tissue)

MICROGRAPH OF CROSS SECTION THROUGH FERN RACHIS

Adventitious root

121

Gymnosperms 1

THE GYMNOSPERMS ARE FOUR RELATED PHYLA of seed-producing
plants: Their seeds, however, lack the protective outer covering
which surrounds the seeds of flowering plants. Typically,
gymnosperms are woody, perennial shrubs or trees, with stems,
leaves, roots, and a well-developed vascular (transport) system.
The reproductive structures in most gymnosperms are cones. Male
cones produce microspores in which male gametes (sex cells) develop;
female cones produce megaspores in which female gametes develop.
Microspores are blown by the wind to female cones, male and female
gametes fuse during fertilization, and a seed develops. The four
gymnosperm phyla are the conifers (phylum Coniferophyta), mostly
tall trees; cycads (phylum Cycadophyta), small palm-like
trees; the ginkgo or maidenhair tree
(phylum Ginkgophyta), a tall tree with
bilobed leaves; and gnetophytes
(phylum Gnetophyta), a diverse
group of plants, mainly shrubs,
but also including the
horizontally growing
welwitschia.

LIFE CYCLE OF SCOTS PINE
(*Pinus sylvestris*)

Needle
(foliage
leaf)

Cone

Ovuliferous scale
(ovule-/seed-
bearing structure)

MALE CONES   **YOUNG FEMALE CONE**

Pollen grain in micropyle   Ovuliferous
(entrance to ovule)   scale

Pollen
grain

Nucleus

Air sac   Ovule
                             (contains
                             female
                             gamete)

POLLINATION

Integument
(outer part
of ovule)

Pollen tube
(carries male
gamete from
pollen grain
to ovum)

Archegonium
(containing
female
gamete)

FERTILIZATION

Seed

Seed

Wing

Ovuliferous
scale (ovule-/
seed-bearing
structure)

**MATURE FEMALE CONE AND
WINGED SEED**

SCALE AND SEEDS
Pine
(*Pinus sp.*)

Ovuliferous scale
(ovule-/seed-bearing
structure)

Wing of seed
derived from
ovuliferous scale

Wing
scar

Seed

Seed

Point of attachment
to axis of cone

Seed scar

**OVULIFEROUS SCALE FROM
THIRD-YEAR FEMALE CONE**

Microsporangium
(structure in which
pollen grains are
formed)

Microsporophyll
(modified leaf
carrying
microsporangia)

Ovule
(contains
female
gametes)

Bract
scale

Axis
of cone

Scale leaf

Ovuliferous scale
(ovule-/seed-
bearing structure)

Axis
of cone

**MICROGRAPH OF LONGITUDINAL
SECTION THROUGH YOUNG
MALE CONE**

**MICROGRAPH OF LONGITUDINAL
SECTION THROUGH SECOND-YEAR
FEMALE CONE**

Plumule
(embryonic
shoot)

Cotyledon
(seed leaf)

Root

**GERMINATION OF
PINE SEEDLING**

WELWITSCHIA
(*Welwitschia mirabilis*)

Frayed end of leaf

SMOOTH CYPRESS
(*Cupressus glabra*)

Immature female cone

Ovuliferous scale (ovule-/seed-bearing structure)

Mature female cone

Scalelike leaf

Immature male cone

Ovuliferous scale

Ovule (contains female gamete)

CROSS SECTION THROUGH IMMATURE CONE

Ovuliferous scale (ovule-/seed-bearing structure)

Seed

CROSS SECTION THROUGH MATURE CONE

Woody scale

Opening between woody scales through which seeds are released

DISCARDED CONE

YEW
(*Taxus baccata*)

Single ovule (contains female gamete)

Scale

Female "cone"

Scale

Developing seed

Scale

FEMALE "CONES" AT VARIOUS STAGES OF DEVELOPMENT

Seed

Aril (fleshy outgrowth from seed)

Stem

Needle (foliage leaf)

CYCAD
Sago palm
(*Cycas revoluta*)

Pinna (leaflet)

Pinnate leaf

Scale leaf

Old leaf base

Stem covered by scale leaves

GINKGO
(*Ginkgo biloba*)

Stem

Girdle scar

Petiole (leaf stalk)

Bilobed leaf

Continuously growing leaf

Site of cone growth

Adaxial (upper) surface of leaf

Abaxial (lower) surface of leaf

Frayed end of leaf

Immature cone

Stalk scar

Woody stem

Gymnosperms 2

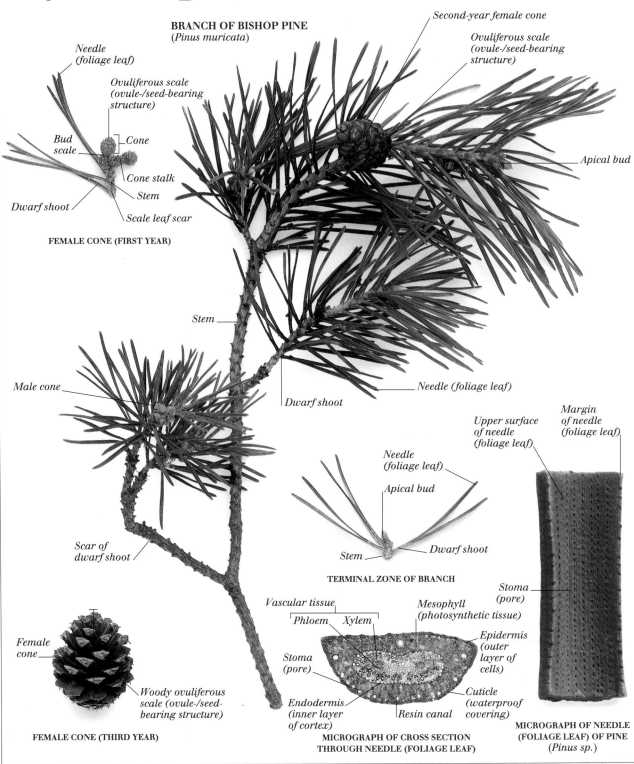

BRANCH OF BISHOP PINE
(*Pinus muricata*)

Needle (foliage leaf)

Ovuliferous scale (ovule-/seed-bearing structure)

Bud scale

Cone

Cone stalk

Stem

Dwarf shoot

Scale leaf scar

FEMALE CONE (FIRST YEAR)

Second-year female cone

Ovuliferous scale (ovule-/seed-bearing structure)

Apical bud

Stem

Male cone

Needle (foliage leaf)

Dwarf shoot

Scar of dwarf shoot

Female cone

Woody ovuliferous scale (ovule-/seed-bearing structure)

FEMALE CONE (THIRD YEAR)

Upper surface of needle (foliage leaf)

Margin of needle (foliage leaf)

Needle (foliage leaf)

Apical bud

Stem

Dwarf shoot

TERMINAL ZONE OF BRANCH

Vascular tissue

Phloem   *Xylem*

Mesophyll (photosynthetic tissue)

Epidermis (outer layer of cells)

Stoma (pore)

Stoma (pore)

Endodermis (inner layer of cortex)

Resin canal

Cuticle (waterproof covering)

MICROGRAPH OF CROSS SECTION THROUGH NEEDLE (FOLIAGE LEAF)

MICROGRAPH OF NEEDLE (FOLIAGE LEAF) OF PINE
(*Pinus sp.*)

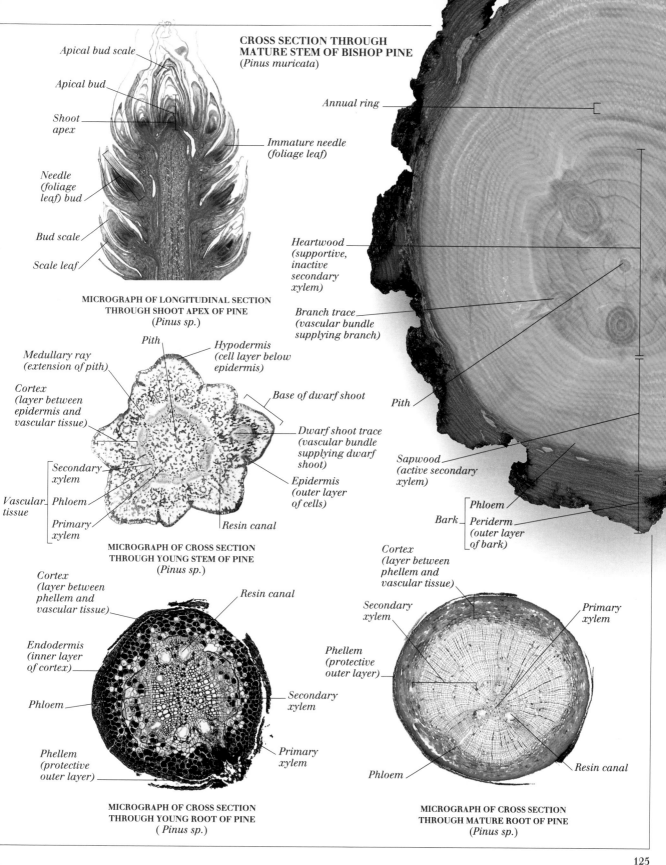

CROSS SECTION THROUGH MATURE STEM OF BISHOP PINE
(*Pinus muricata*)

Apical bud scale

Apical bud

Shoot apex

Immature needle (foliage leaf)

Needle (foliage leaf) bud

Bud scale

Scale leaf

MICROGRAPH OF LONGITUDINAL SECTION THROUGH SHOOT APEX OF PINE
(*Pinus sp.*)

Annual ring

Heartwood (supportive, inactive secondary xylem)

Branch trace (vascular bundle supplying branch)

Pith

Sapwood (active secondary xylem)

Phloem

Bark

Periderm (outer layer of bark)

Medullary ray (extension of pith)

Pith

Hypodermis (cell layer below epidermis)

Cortex (layer between epidermis and vascular tissue)

Base of dwarf shoot

Dwarf shoot trace (vascular bundle supplying dwarf shoot)

Epidermis (outer layer of cells)

Secondary xylem

Phloem

Vascular tissue

Primary xylem

Resin canal

MICROGRAPH OF CROSS SECTION THROUGH YOUNG STEM OF PINE
(*Pinus sp.*)

Cortex (layer between phellem and vascular tissue)

Resin canal

Endodermis (inner layer of cortex)

Phloem

Secondary xylem

Phellem (protective outer layer)

Primary xylem

MICROGRAPH OF CROSS SECTION THROUGH YOUNG ROOT OF PINE
(*Pinus sp.*)

Cortex (layer between phellem and vascular tissue)

Secondary xylem

Phellem (protective outer layer)

Primary xylem

Phloem

Resin canal

MICROGRAPH OF CROSS SECTION THROUGH MATURE ROOT OF PINE
(*Pinus sp.*)

125

Monocotyledons and dicotyledons

FLOWERING PLANTS (PHYLUM ANGIOSPERMOPHYTA) are divided into two classes: monocotyledons (class Monocotyledoneae) and dicotyledons (class Dicotyledoneae). Typically, monocotyledons have seeds with one cotyledon (seed leaf); their foliage leaves are narrow with parallel veins; the flower components occur in multiples of three; sepals and petals are indistinguishable and are known as tepals; vascular (transport) tissues are scattered in random bundles throughout the stem; and, because they lack stem cambium (actively dividing cells that produce wood), most monocotyledons are herbaceous (see pp. 128-129). Dicotyledons have seeds with two cotyledons; leaves are broad with a central midrib and branched veins; flower parts occur in multiples of four or five; sepals are generally small and green; petals are large and colorful; vascular bundles are arranged in a ring around the edge of the stem; and, because many dicotyledons possess wood-producing stem cambium, there are woody forms (see pp. 130-131) as well as herbaceous ones.

CROSS SECTION
THROUGH
MONOCOTYLEDONOUS
LEAF BASES

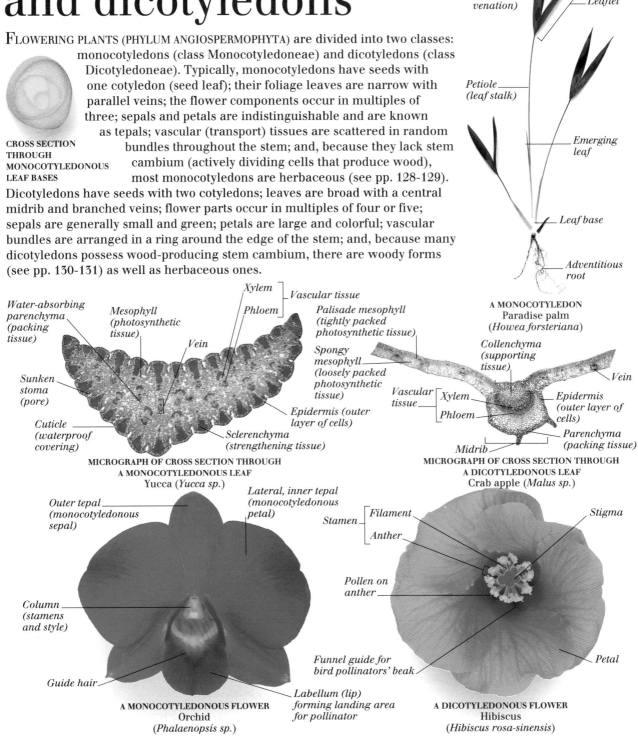

Vein
(parallel
venation)

Leaflet

Petiole
(leaf stalk)

Emerging
leaf

Leaf base

Adventitious
root

A MONOCOTYLEDON
Paradise palm
(*Howea forsteriana*)

Water-absorbing
parenchyma
(packing
tissue)

Mesophyll
(photosynthetic
tissue)

Xylem

Phloem

Vascular tissue

Palisade mesophyll
(tightly packed
photosynthetic tissue)

Vein

Spongy
mesophyll
(loosely packed
photosynthetic
tissue)

Sunken
stoma
(pore)

Vascular
tissue

Xylem

Phloem

Collenchyma
(supporting
tissue)

Vein

Epidermis
(outer layer of
cells)

Cuticle
(waterproof
covering)

Epidermis (outer
layer of cells)

Sclerenchyma
(strengthening tissue)

Parenchyma
(packing tissue)

Midrib

MICROGRAPH OF CROSS SECTION THROUGH
A MONOCOTYLEDONOUS LEAF
Yucca (*Yucca sp.*)

MICROGRAPH OF CROSS SECTION THROUGH
A DICOTYLEDONOUS LEAF
Crab apple (*Malus sp.*)

Outer tepal
(monocotyledonous
sepal)

Lateral, inner tepal
(monocotyledonous
petal)

Stamen

Filament

Anther

Stigma

Column
(stamens
and style)

Pollen on
anther

Guide hair

Funnel guide for
bird pollinators' beak

Petal

Labellum (lip)
forming landing area
for pollinator

A MONOCOTYLEDONOUS FLOWER
Orchid
(*Phalaenopsis sp.*)

A DICOTYLEDONOUS FLOWER
Hibiscus
(*Hibiscus rosa-sinensis*)

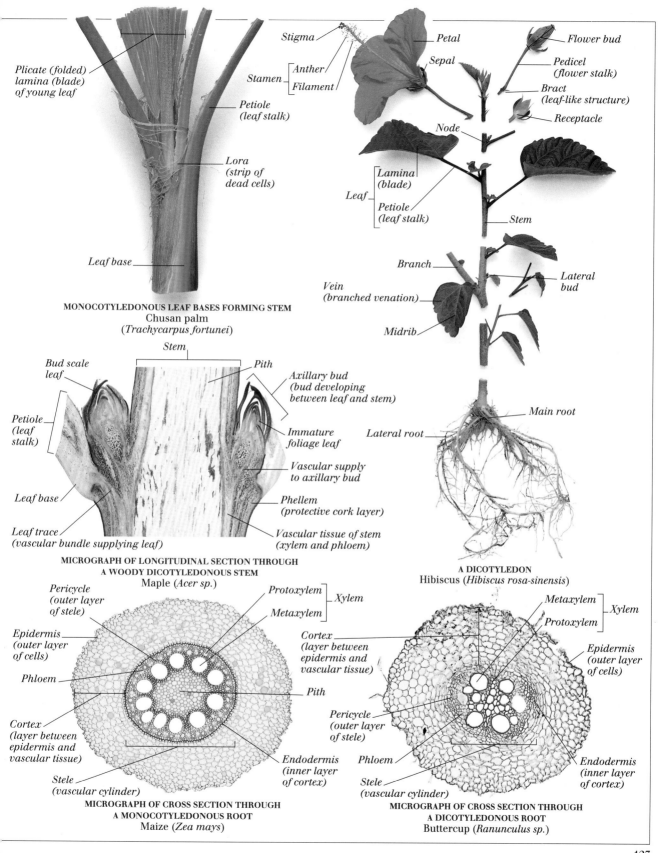

Plicate (folded) lamina (blade) of young leaf

Stigma

Petal

Anther

Sepal

Stamen

Filament

Petiole (leaf stalk)

Node

Lora (strip of dead cells)

Lamina (blade)

Leaf

Petiole (leaf stalk)

Flower bud

Pedicel (flower stalk)

Bract (leaf-like structure)

Receptacle

Stem

Leaf base

Branch

Vein (branched venation)

Midrib

Lateral bud

MONOCOTYLEDONOUS LEAF BASES FORMING STEM
Chusan palm (*Trachycarpus fortunei*)

Stem

Bud scale leaf

Pith

Axillary bud (bud developing between leaf and stem)

Petiole (leaf stalk)

Immature foliage leaf

Vascular supply to axillary bud

Leaf base

Phellem (protective cork layer)

Leaf trace (vascular bundle supplying leaf)

Vascular tissue of stem (xylem and phloem)

MICROGRAPH OF LONGITUDINAL SECTION THROUGH A WOODY DICOTYLEDONOUS STEM
Maple (*Acer sp.*)

Main root

Lateral root

A DICOTYLEDON
Hibiscus (*Hibiscus rosa-sinensis*)

Pericycle (outer layer of stele)

Epidermis (outer layer of cells)

Phloem

Cortex (layer between epidermis and vascular tissue)

Stele (vascular cylinder)

Protoxylem

Metaxylem

Xylem

Pith

Endodermis (inner layer of cortex)

MICROGRAPH OF CROSS SECTION THROUGH A MONOCOTYLEDONOUS ROOT
Maize (*Zea mays*)

Cortex (layer between epidermis and vascular tissue)

Pericycle (outer layer of stele)

Phloem

Stele (vascular cylinder)

Metaxylem

Protoxylem

Xylem

Epidermis (outer layer of cells)

Endodermis (inner layer of cortex)

MICROGRAPH OF CROSS SECTION THROUGH A DICOTYLEDONOUS ROOT
Buttercup (*Ranunculus sp.*)

Herbaceous flowering plants

HERBACEOUS FLOWERING PLANTS TYPICALLY HAVE GREEN NON-WOODY STEMS, and tend to be relatively short-lived. Many herbaceous plants live for only one or two years. Annuals (such as sweet peas) grow from seed, produce flowers and then seeds, and die within a single year. Biennials (like carrots) have a two-year life cycle. In the first year, seeds grow into plants, which produce leaves and store food in underground storage organs; the stems and foliage then die in winter. In the second year, new stems grow from the storage organs, produce leaves, flowers, and seeds, and then die. Some herbaceous plants (such as potatoes) are perennial. They grow back year after year, producing shoots and flowers in spring, storing food in underground tubers or rhizomes during summer, dying in autumn, and surviving underground during winter.

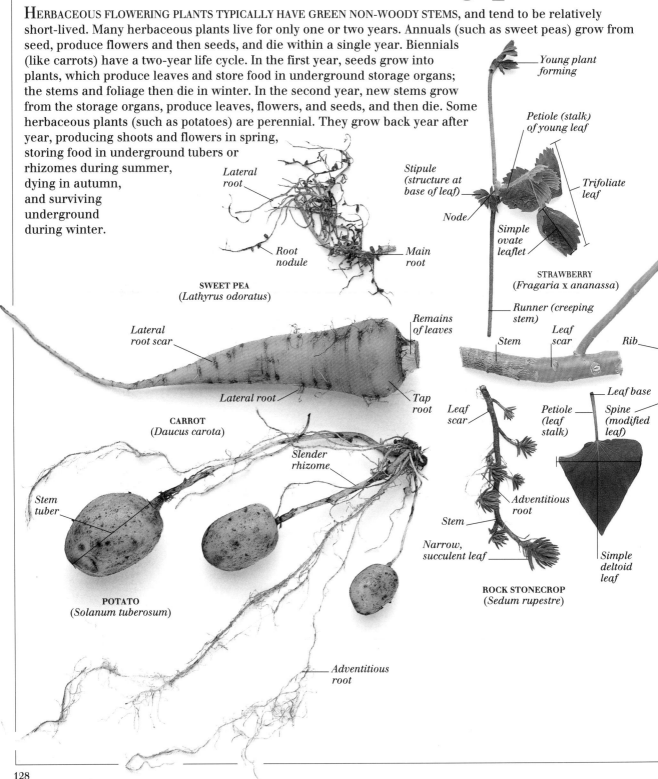

Young plant forming

Petiole (stalk) of young leaf

Trifoliate leaf

Stipule (structure at base of leaf)

Node

Simple ovate leaflet

STRAWBERRY
(*Fragaria* x *ananassa*)

Lateral root

Root nodule

Main root

SWEET PEA
(*Lathyrus odoratus*)

Runner (creeping stem)

Leaf scar

Stem

Rib

Lateral root scar

Remains of leaves

Lateral root

Tap root

CARROT
(*Daucus carota*)

Leaf base

Spine (modified leaf)

Petiole (leaf stalk)

Leaf scar

Slender rhizome

Stem tuber

Adventitious root

Stem

Narrow, succulent leaf

Simple deltoid leaf

ROCK STONECROP
(*Sedum rupestre*)

POTATO
(*Solanum tuberosum*)

Adventitious root

PARTS OF HERBACEOUS FLOWERING PLANTS

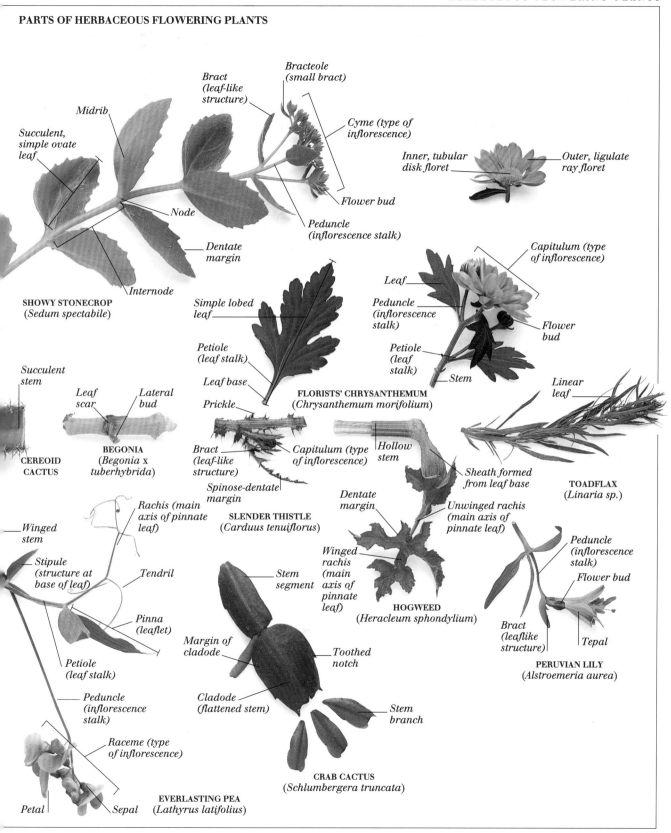

Midrib

Bract (leaf-like structure)

Bracteole (small bract)

Cyme (type of inflorescence)

Succulent, simple ovate leaf

Inner, tubular disk floret

Outer, ligulate ray floret

Node

Flower bud

Dentate margin

Peduncle (inflorescence stalk)

SHOWY STONECROP
(*Sedum spectabile*)

Internode

Capitulum (type of inflorescence)

Leaf

Peduncle (inflorescence stalk)

Flower bud

Simple lobed leaf

Petiole (leaf stalk)

Leaf base

Petiole (leaf stalk)

Stem

Linear leaf

Succulent stem

Leaf scar

Lateral bud

Prickle

FLORISTS' CHRYSANTHEMUM
(*Chrysanthemum morifolium*)

CEREOID CACTUS

BEGONIA
(*Begonia* x *tuberhybrida*)

Bract (leaf-like structure)

Capitulum (type of inflorescence)

Hollow stem

Sheath formed from leaf base

TOADFLAX
(*Linaria* sp.)

Spinose-dentate margin

Dentate margin

Unwinged rachis (main axis of pinnate leaf)

Peduncle (inflorescence stalk)

Rachis (main axis of pinnate leaf)

SLENDER THISTLE
(*Carduus tenuiflorus*)

Flower bud

Winged stem

Tendril

Winged rachis (main axis of pinnate leaf)

Stem segment

Bract (leaflike structure)

Stipule (structure at base of leaf)

Tepal

Pinna (leaflet)

HOGWEED
(*Heracleum sphondylium*)

PERUVIAN LILY
(*Alstroemeria aurea*)

Margin of cladode

Toothed notch

Petiole (leaf stalk)

Peduncle (inflorescence stalk)

Cladode (flattened stem)

Stem branch

Raceme (type of inflorescence)

CRAB CACTUS
(*Schlumbergera truncata*)

Petal

Sepal

EVERLASTING PEA
(*Lathyrus latifolius*)

Woody flowering plants

WOODY FLOWERING PLANTS ARE PERENNIAL: They continue to grow and reproduce for many years. They have one or more permanent stems above ground and numerous smaller branches. The stems and branches have a strong woody core that supports the plant and contains vascular tissue for transporting water and nutrients. Outside the woody core is a layer of tough, protective bark, which has lenticels (tiny pores) to allow gases to pass through. Woody flowering plants may be shrubs, which have several stems rising from the soil; bushes, which are shrubs with dense branching and foliage; or trees, which typically have a single upright stem (the trunk) that bears branches. Deciduous woody plants (like roses) shed all their leaves once a year and remain leafless during winter. Evergreen woody plants (such as holly) shed their leaves gradually, so they retain full leaf cover throughout the year.

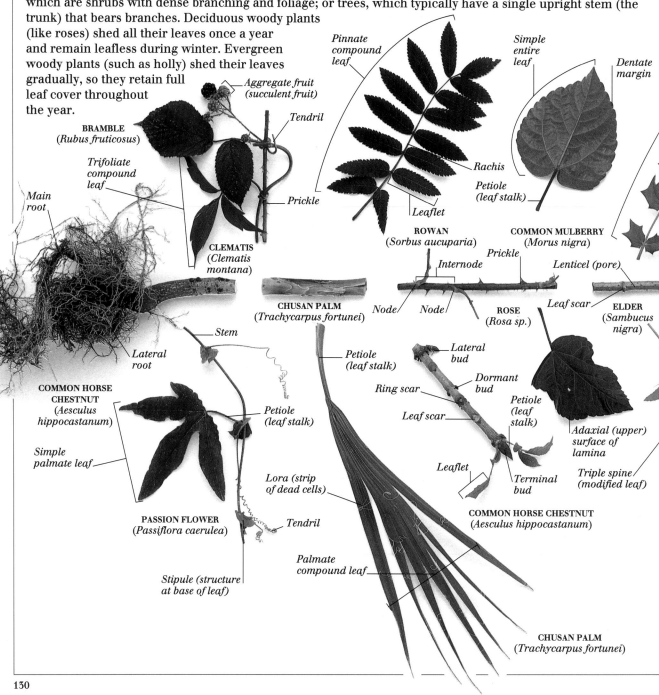

Aggregate fruit (succulent fruit)

Tendril

BRAMBLE
(*Rubus fruticosus*)

Trifoliate compound leaf

Prickle

Main root

CLEMATIS
(*Clematis montana*)

Pinnate compound leaf

Simple entire leaf

Dentate margin

Rachis

Petiole (leaf stalk)

Leaflet

ROWAN
(*Sorbus aucuparia*)

COMMON MULBERRY
(*Morus nigra*)

Prickle

Lenticel (pore)

Internode

Node   Node

ROSE
(*Rosa sp.*)

Leaf scar

ELDER
(*Sambucus nigra*)

CHUSAN PALM
(*Trachycarpus fortunei*)

Lateral root

Stem

Petiole (leaf stalk)

Lateral bud

Dormant bud

Ring scar

Petiole (leaf stalk)

Leaf scar

COMMON HORSE CHESTNUT
(*Aesculus hippocastanum*)

Simple palmate leaf

Petiole (leaf stalk)

Lora (strip of dead cells)

Leaflet

Terminal bud

Adaxial (upper) surface of lamina

Triple spine (modified leaf)

PASSION FLOWER
(*Passiflora caerulea*)

Tendril

COMMON HORSE CHESTNUT
(*Aesculus hippocastanum*)

Stipule (structure at base of leaf)

Palmate compound leaf

CHUSAN PALM
(*Trachycarpus fortunei*)

PARTS OF WOODY FLOWERING PLANTS

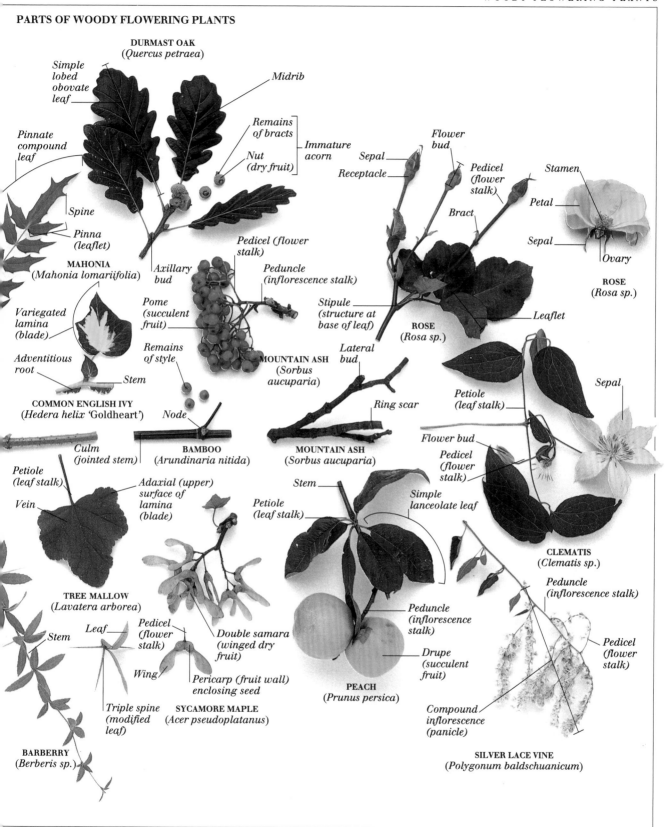

DURMAST OAK
(*Quercus petraea*)

Simple lobed obovate leaf

Midrib

Pinnate compound leaf

Remains of bracts

Nut (dry fruit)

Immature acorn

Spine

Pinna (leaflet)

MAHONIA
(*Mahonia lomariifolia*)

Axillary bud

Pedicel (flower stalk)

Peduncle (inflorescence stalk)

Variegated lamina (blade)

Pome (succulent fruit)

Adventitious root

Remains of style

Stem

COMMON ENGLISH IVY
(*Hedera helix* 'Goldheart')

Node

BAMBOO
(*Arundinaria nitida*)

MOUNTAIN ASH
(*Sorbus aucuparia*)

Culm (jointed stem)

Ring scar

MOUNTAIN ASH
(*Sorbus aucuparia*)

Lateral bud

Stipule (structure at base of leaf)

ROSE
(*Rosa sp.*)

Leaflet

Flower bud

Sepal

Receptacle

Pedicel (flower stalk)

Bract

Stamen

Petal

Sepal

Ovary

ROSE
(*Rosa sp.*)

Sepal

Petiole (leaf stalk)

Flower bud

Pedicel (flower stalk)

CLEMATIS
(*Clematis sp.*)

Petiole (leaf stalk)

Vein

Adaxial (upper) surface of lamina (blade)

TREE MALLOW
(*Lavatera arborea*)

Stem

Leaf

Pedicel (flower stalk)

Wing

Double samara (winged dry fruit)

Pericarp (fruit wall) enclosing seed

Triple spine (modified leaf)

SYCAMORE MAPLE
(*Acer pseudoplatanus*)

BARBERRY
(*Berberis sp.*)

Stem

Petiole (leaf stalk)

Simple lanceolate leaf

Peduncle (inflorescence stalk)

Drupe (succulent fruit)

PEACH
(*Prunus persica*)

Peduncle (inflorescence stalk)

Pedicel (flower stalk)

Compound inflorescence (panicle)

SILVER LACE VINE
(*Polygonum baldschuanicum*)

Roots

ROOTS ARE THE UNDERGROUND PARTS OF PLANTS. They have three main functions. First, they anchor the plant in the soil. Second, they absorb water and minerals from the spaces between soil particles. The roots' absorptive properties are increased by root hairs, which grow behind the root tip, allowing maximum absorption of vital substances. Third, the root is part of the plant's transport system. Xylem carries water and minerals from the roots to the stem and leaves, and phloem carries nutrients from the leaves to all parts of the root system. In addition, some roots (like carrots) are food stores. Roots have an outer epidermis covering a cortex of parenchyma (packing tissue), and a central cylinder of vascular tissue. This arrangement helps the roots resist the forces of compression as they grow through the soil.

MICROGRAPH OF PRIMARY ROOT DEVELOPMENT
Cabbage (*Brassica sp.*)

Split in testa
as seed
germinates

Cotyledon
(seed leaf)

Primary root

Testa
(seed coat)

Root hair

Root tip
(region of
cell division)

CARROT
(*Daucus carota*)

FEATURES OF A TYPICAL ROOT
Buttercup
(*Ranunculus sp.*)

Pericycle
(outer layer
of stele)

Root hair

Air space
(allowing gas
diffusion in
the root)

Stele
(vascular cylinder)

Phloem sieve tube
(through which
nutrients are
transported)

Companion cell
(cell associated
with phloem
sieve tube)

Cortex
(layer between
epidermis and
vascular tissue)

Root hair

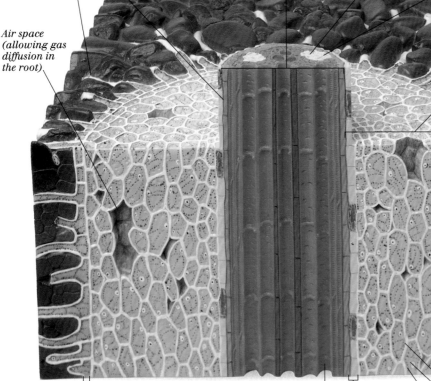

Epidermis
(outer layer
of cells)

Xylem vessel
(through which water
and minerals are transported)

Endodermis
(inner layer
of cortex)

Cell wall

Nucleus

Cytoplasm

Parenchyma
(packing) cell

PRIMARY ROOT AND MICROGRAPHS OF SECTIONS THROUGH ROOTS

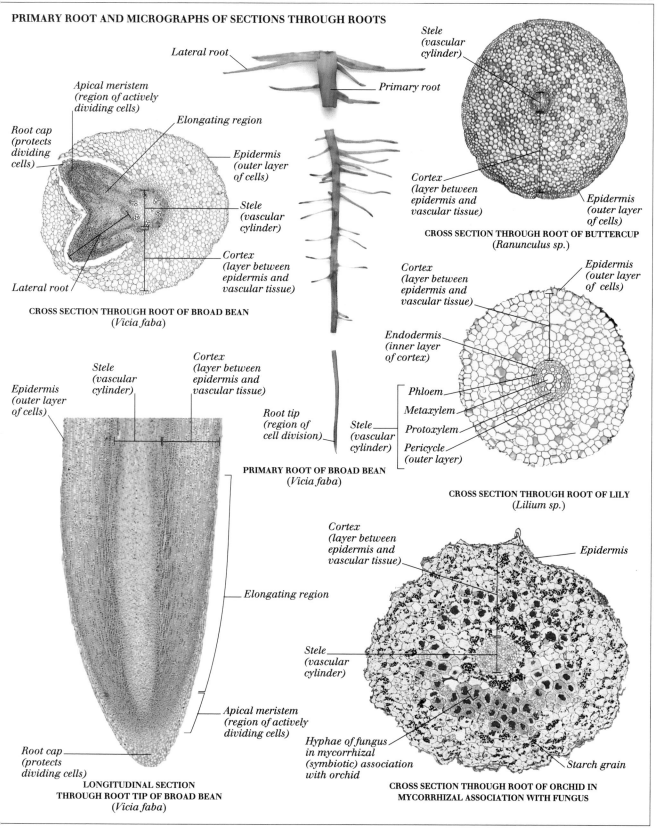

Lateral root

Primary root

Apical meristem
(region of actively
dividing cells)

Elongating region

Root cap
(protects
dividing
cells)

Epidermis
(outer layer
of cells)

Stele
(vascular
cylinder)

Cortex
(layer between
epidermis and
vascular tissue)

Lateral root

CROSS SECTION THROUGH ROOT OF BROAD BEAN
(Vicia faba)

Stele
(vascular
cylinder)

Cortex
(layer between
epidermis and
vascular tissue)

Cortex
(layer between
epidermis and
vascular tissue)

Epidermis
(outer layer
of cells)

CROSS SECTION THROUGH ROOT OF BUTTERCUP
(Ranunculus sp.)

Epidermis
(outer layer
of cells)

Cortex
(layer between
epidermis and
vascular tissue)

Endodermis
(inner layer
of cortex)

Phloem

Metaxylem

Protoxylem

Stele
(vascular
cylinder)

Pericycle
(outer layer)

CROSS SECTION THROUGH ROOT OF LILY
(Lilium sp.)

Epidermis
(outer layer
of cells)

Stele
(vascular
cylinder)

Cortex
(layer between
epidermis and
vascular tissue)

Root tip
(region of
cell division)

Stele
(vascular
cylinder)

PRIMARY ROOT OF BROAD BEAN
(Vicia faba)

Elongating region

Apical meristem
(region of actively
dividing cells)

Root cap
(protects
dividing cells)

LONGITUDINAL SECTION
THROUGH ROOT TIP OF BROAD BEAN
(Vicia faba)

Cortex
(layer between
epidermis and
vascular tissue)

Epidermis

Stele
(vascular
cylinder)

Hyphae of fungus
in mycorrhizal
(symbiotic) association
with orchid

Starch grain

CROSS SECTION THROUGH ROOT OF ORCHID IN
MYCORRHIZAL ASSOCIATION WITH FUNGUS

Stems

THE STEM IS THE MAIN SUPPORTIVE PART OF A PLANT that grows above ground. Stems bear leaves (organs of photosynthesis), which grow at nodes; buds (shoots covered by protective scales), which grow at the stem tip (apical or terminal buds) and in the angle between a leaf and the stem (axillary or lateral buds); and flowers (reproductive structures). The stem forms part of the plant's transport system. Xylem tissue in the stem transports water and minerals from the roots to the aerial parts of the plant, and phloem tissue transports nutrients manufactured in the leaves to other parts of the plant. Stem tissues are also used for storing water and food. Herbaceous (nonwoody) stems have an outer protective epidermis covering a cortex that consists mainly of parenchyma (packing tissue) but also has some collenchyma (supporting tissue). The vascular tissue of such stems is arranged in bundles, each of which consists of xylem, phloem, and sclerenchyma (strengthening tissue). Woody stems have an outer protective layer of tough bark, which is perforated with lenticels (pores) to allow gas exchange. Inside the bark is a ring of secondary phloem, which surrounds an inner core of secondary xylem.

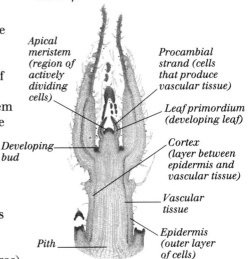

MICROGRAPH OF LONGITUDINAL SECTION THROUGH APEX OF STEM
Coleus sp.

Apical meristem (region of actively dividing cells)

Procambial strand (cells that produce vascular tissue)

Leaf primordium (developing leaf)

Developing bud

Cortex (layer between epidermis and vascular tissue)

Vascular tissue

Epidermis (outer layer of cells)

Pith

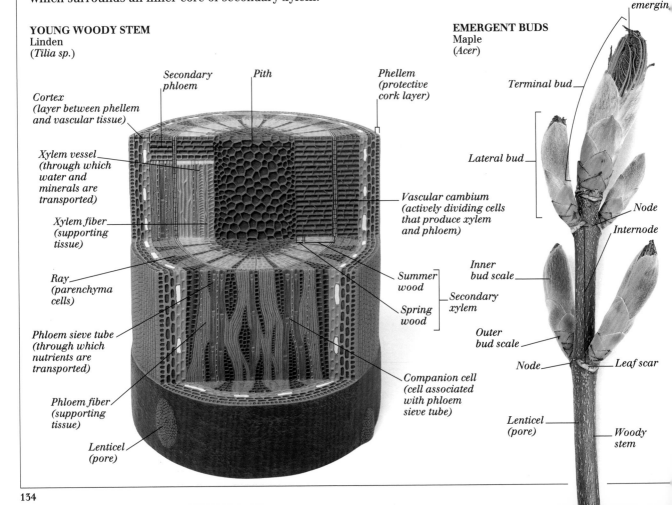

YOUNG WOODY STEM
Linden
(*Tilia sp.*)

Secondary phloem

Pith

Phellem (protective cork layer)

Cortex (layer between phellem and vascular tissue)

Xylem vessel (through which water and minerals are transported)

Xylem fiber (supporting tissue)

Ray (parenchyma cells)

Phloem sieve tube (through which nutrients are transported)

Phloem fiber (supporting tissue)

Lenticel (pore)

Vascular cambium (actively dividing cells that produce xylem and phloem)

Summer wood

Spring wood

Secondary xylem

Companion cell (cell associated with phloem sieve tube)

EMERGENT BUDS
Maple
(*Acer*)

Young leaves emerging

Terminal bud

Lateral bud

Node

Internode

Inner bud scale

Outer bud scale

Node

Leaf scar

Lenticel (pore)

Woody stem

MICROGRAPHS OF CROSS SECTIONS THROUGH VARIOUS STEMS

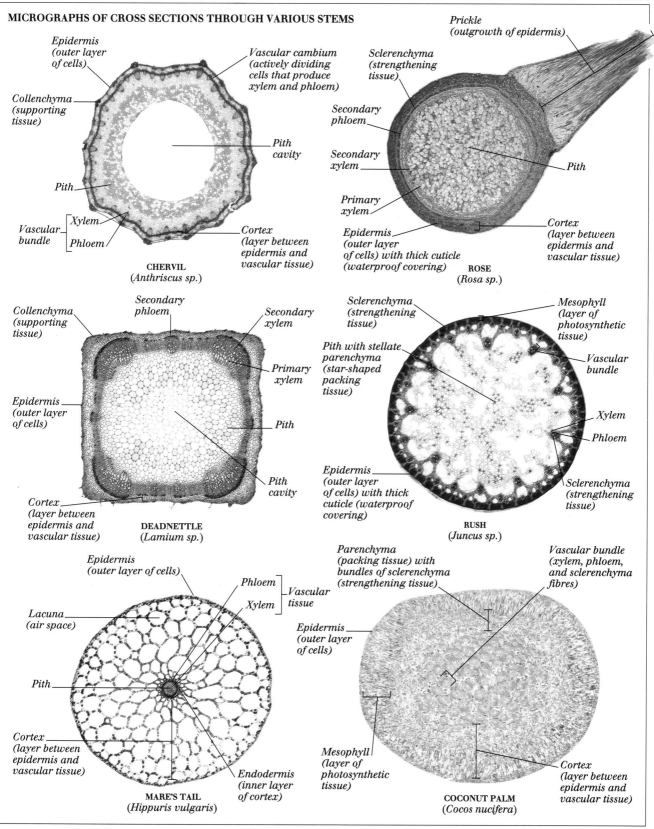

Epidermis (outer layer of cells)

Vascular cambium (actively dividing cells that produce xylem and phloem)

Collenchyma (supporting tissue)

Pith cavity

Pith

Vascular bundle — **Xylem** / **Phloem**

Cortex (layer between epidermis and vascular tissue)

CHERVIL (*Anthriscus sp.*)

Prickle (outgrowth of epidermis)

Sclerenchyma (strengthening tissue)

Secondary phloem

Secondary xylem

Primary xylem

Epidermis (outer layer of cells) with thick cuticle (waterproof covering)

Pith

Cortex (layer between epidermis and vascular tissue)

ROSE (*Rosa sp.*)

Collenchyma (supporting tissue)

Secondary phloem

Secondary xylem

Primary xylem

Epidermis (outer layer of cells)

Pith

Pith cavity

Cortex (layer between epidermis and vascular tissue)

DEADNETTLE (*Lamium sp.*)

Sclerenchyma (strengthening tissue)

Pith with stellate parenchyma (star-shaped packing tissue)

Mesophyll (layer of photosynthetic tissue)

Vascular bundle

Xylem

Phloem

Epidermis (outer layer of cells) with thick cuticle (waterproof covering)

Sclerenchyma (strengthening tissue)

RUSH (*Juncus sp.*)

Epidermis (outer layer of cells)

Phloem

Xylem — **Vascular tissue**

Lacuna (air space)

Pith

Cortex (layer between epidermis and vascular tissue)

Endodermis (inner layer of cortex)

MARE'S TAIL (*Hippuris vulgaris*)

Parenchyma (packing tissue) with bundles of sclerenchyma (strengthening tissue)

Vascular bundle (xylem, phloem, and sclerenchyma fibres)

Epidermis (outer layer of cells)

Mesophyll (layer of photosynthetic tissue)

Cortex (layer between epidermis and vascular tissue)

COCONUT PALM (*Cocos nucifera*)

Leaves

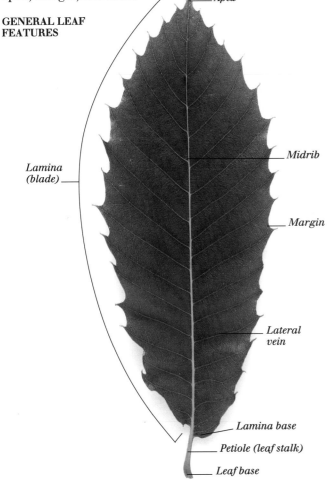

LEAVES ARE THE MAIN SITES OF PHOTOSYNTHESIS (see pp. 138-139) and transpiration (water loss by evaporation) in plants. A typical leaf consists of a thin, flat lamina (blade) supported by a network of veins; a petiole (leaf stalk); and a leaf base, where the petiole joins the stem. Leaves can be classified as simple, in which the lamina is a single unit, or compound, in which the lamina is divided into separate leaflets. Compound leaves may be pinnate, with pinnae (leaflets) on both sides of a rachis (main axis), or palmate, with leaflets arising from a single point at the tip of the petiole. Leaves can be classified further by the overall shape of the lamina, and by the shape of the lamina's apex, margin, and base.

CHECKERBLOOM
(*Sidalcea malviflora*)

SIMPLE LEAF SHAPES

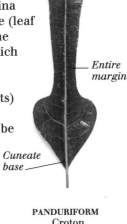

Subacute apex

Entire margin

Cuneate base

PANDURIFORM
Croton
(*Codiaeum variegatum*)

Acuminate apex

Entire margin

Cordate base

LANCEOLATE
Sea buckthorn
(*Hippophae rhamnoides*)

GENERAL LEAF FEATURES

Apex

Lamina (blade)

Midrib

Margin

Lateral vein

Lamina base

Petiole (leaf stalk)

Leaf base

Spanish chestnut
(*Castanea sativa*)

COMPOUND LEAF SHAPES

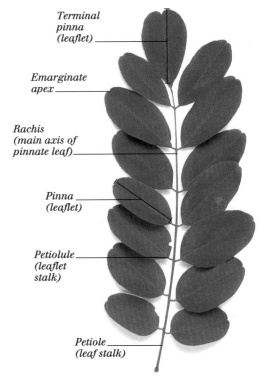

Terminal pinna (leaflet)

Emarginate apex

Rachis (main axis of pinnate leaf)

Pinna (leaflet)

Petiolule (leaflet stalk)

Petiole (leaf stalk)

ODD PINNATE
Black locust
(*Robinia pseudoacacia*)

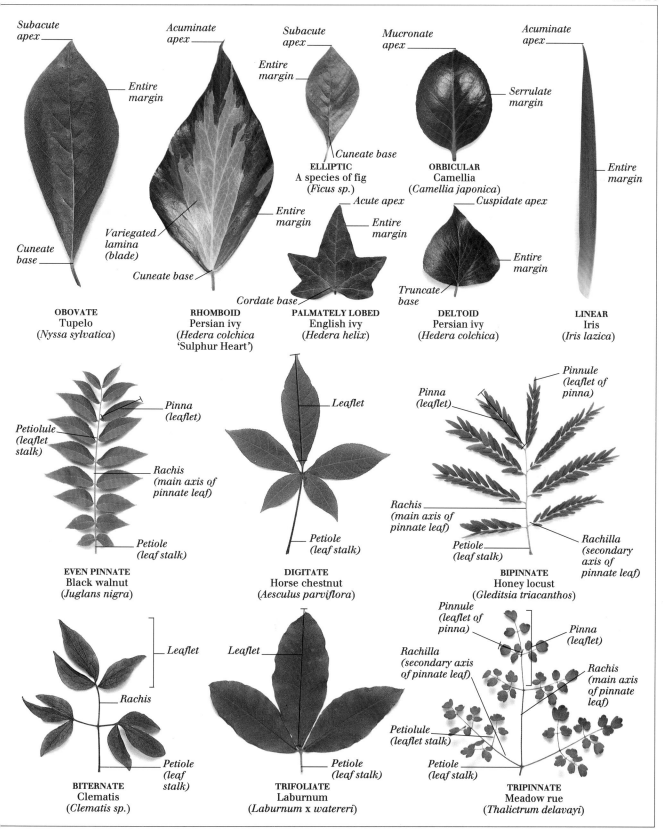

OBOVATE
Tupelo
(*Nyssa sylvatica*)

Subacute apex

Entire margin

Cuneate base

RHOMBOID
Persian ivy
(*Hedera colchica*
'Sulphur Heart')

Acuminate apex

Variegated lamina (blade)

Cuneate base

ELLIPTIC
A species of fig
(*Ficus sp.*)

Subacute apex

Entire margin

Cuneate base

PALMATELY LOBED
English ivy
(*Hedera helix*)

Acute apex

Entire margin

Cordate base

ORBICULAR
Camellia
(*Camellia japonica*)

Mucronate apex

Serrulate margin

DELTOID
Persian ivy
(*Hedera colchica*)

Cuspidate apex

Entire margin

Truncate base

LINEAR
Iris
(*Iris lazica*)

Acuminate apex

Entire margin

EVEN PINNATE
Black walnut
(*Juglans nigra*)

Pinna (leaflet)

Petiolule (leaflet stalk)

Rachis (main axis of pinnate leaf)

Petiole (leaf stalk)

DIGITATE
Horse chestnut
(*Aesculus parviflora*)

Leaflet

Petiole (leaf stalk)

BIPINNATE
Honey locust
(*Gleditsia triacanthos*)

Pinnule (leaflet of pinna)

Pinna (leaflet)

Rachis (main axis of pinnate leaf)

Petiole (leaf stalk)

Rachilla (secondary axis of pinnate leaf)

BITERNATE
Clematis
(*Clematis sp.*)

Leaflet

Rachis

Petiole (leaf stalk)

TRIFOLIATE
Laburnum
(*Laburnum x watereri*)

Leaflet

Petiole (leaf stalk)

TRIPINNATE
Meadow rue
(*Thalictrum delavayi*)

Pinnule (leaflet of pinna)

Pinna (leaflet)

Rachilla (secondary axis of pinnate leaf)

Rachis (main axis of pinnate leaf)

Petiolule (leaflet stalk)

Petiole (leaf stalk)

137

Photosynthesis

PHOTOSYNTHESIS IS THE PROCESS by which plants make their food using sunlight, water, and carbon dioxide. It takes place inside special structures in leaf cells called chloroplasts. The chloroplasts contain chlorophyll, a green pigment that absorbs energy from sunlight. During photosynthesis, the absorbed energy is used to join together carbon dioxide and water to form the sugar glucose, which is the energy source for the whole plant. Oxygen, a waste product, is released into the air. Leaves are the main sites of photosynthesis and have various adaptations for that purpose. Flat laminae (blades) provide a large surface for absorbing sunlight; stomata (pores) in the lower surface of the laminae allow gases (carbon dioxide and oxygen) to pass into and out of the leaves; and an extensive network of veins brings water into the leaves and transports the glucose produced by photosynthesis to the rest of the plant.

MICROGRAPH OF LEAF
Lily (*Lilium sp.*)

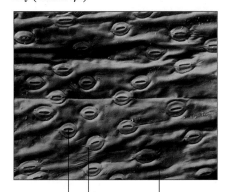

Stoma (pore)

Guard cell (controls opening and closing of stoma)

Lower surface of lamina (blade)

THE PROCESS OF PHOTOSYNTHESIS

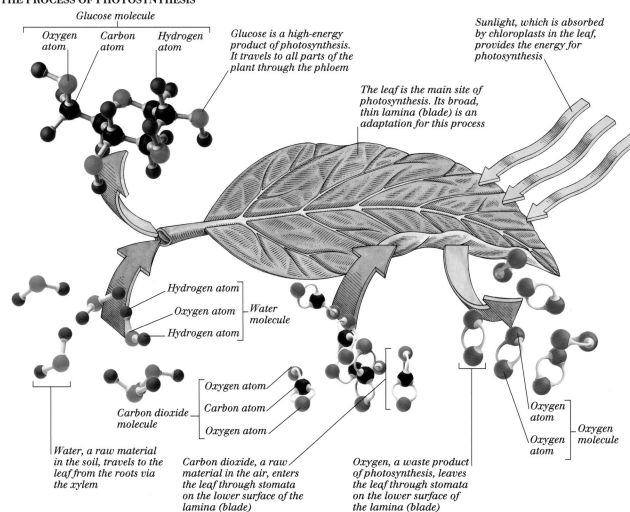

Glucose molecule

Oxygen atom

Carbon atom

Hydrogen atom

Glucose is a high-energy product of photosynthesis. It travels to all parts of the plant through the phloem

Sunlight, which is absorbed by chloroplasts in the leaf, provides the energy for photosynthesis

The leaf is the main site of photosynthesis. Its broad, thin lamina (blade) is an adaptation for this process

Hydrogen atom

Oxygen atom — Water molecule

Hydrogen atom

Carbon dioxide molecule

Oxygen atom

Carbon atom

Oxygen atom

Oxygen atom

Oxygen atom — Oxygen molecule

Water, a raw material in the soil, travels to the leaf from the roots via the xylem

Carbon dioxide, a raw material in the air, enters the leaf through stomata on the lower surface of the lamina (blade)

Oxygen, a waste product of photosynthesis, leaves the leaf through stomata on the lower surface of the lamina (blade)

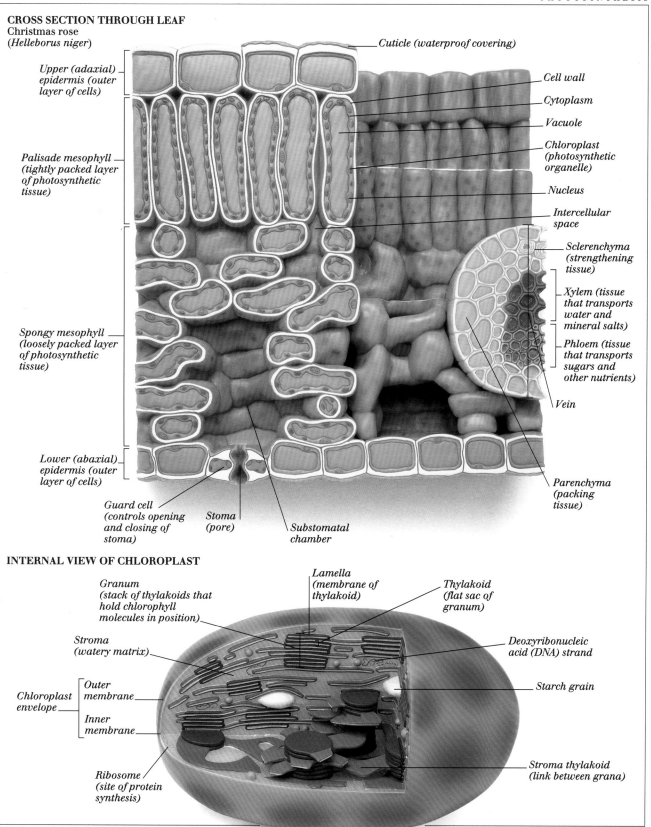

CROSS SECTION THROUGH LEAF
Christmas rose
(*Helleborus niger*)

Cuticle (waterproof covering)

Upper (adaxial) epidermis (outer layer of cells)

Cell wall

Cytoplasm

Vacuole

Chloroplast (photosynthetic organelle)

Palisade mesophyll (tightly packed layer of photosynthetic tissue)

Nucleus

Intercellular space

Sclerenchyma (strengthening tissue)

Xylem (tissue that transports water and mineral salts)

Phloem (tissue that transports sugars and other nutrients)

Spongy mesophyll (loosely packed layer of photosynthetic tissue)

Vein

Lower (abaxial) epidermis (outer layer of cells)

Parenchyma (packing tissue)

Guard cell (controls opening and closing of stoma)

Stoma (pore)

Substomatal chamber

INTERNAL VIEW OF CHLOROPLAST

Granum (stack of thylakoids that hold chlorophyll molecules in position)

Lamella (membrane of thylakoid)

Thylakoid (flat sac of granum)

Stroma (watery matrix)

Deoxyribonucleic acid (DNA) strand

Chloroplast envelope

Outer membrane

Inner membrane

Starch grain

Ribosome (site of protein synthesis)

Stroma thylakoid (link between grana)

139

Flowers 1

FLOWERS ARE THE SITES OF SEXUAL REPRODUCTION in flowering plants. Their component parts are arranged in whorls around the receptacle (tip of the flower stalk). The sepals (collectively called the calyx) are outermost; typically small and green, they protect the developing flower. The petals (collectively called the corolla) are typically large and brightly colored; they are found inside the sepals. In monocotyledonous flowers (see pp. 126-127), sepals and petals are indistinguishable; individually they are called tepals (collectively called the perianth). The petals surround the male and female reproductive structures (androecium and gynoecium). The androecium consists of stamens (male organs); each stamen is made up of a filament (stalk) and anther. The gynoecium has one or more carpels (female organs); each carpel consists of an ovary, style, and stigma. Some flowers (like the lily) occur singly on a pedicel (flower stalk); others (such as elder, sunflower) are arranged in a group (inflorescence) on a peduncle (inflorescence stalk).

A MONOCOTYLEDONOUS FLOWER
Lily
(*Lilium sp.*)

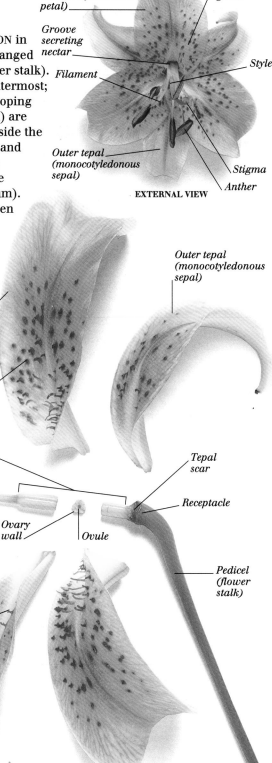

EXTERNAL VIEW

Inner tepal (monocotyledonous petal)

Honey guide

Groove secreting nectar

Filament

Style

Outer tepal (monocotyledonous sepal)

Stigma

Anther

Inner tepal (monocotyledonous petal)

Honey guide

Outer tepal (monocotyledonous sepal)

Tepal scar

Receptacle

Syncarpous (fused carpels) gynoecium

Ovary

Stigma

Style

Stamen

Anther

Filament

Pollen on anther

Ovary wall

Ovule

Pedicel (flower stalk)

Papilla (fleshy hair)

Outer tepal sheath

Style

Folded inner tepal (monocotyledonous petal)

Stigma

Ovary

Receptacle

Anther

Pedicel (flower stalk)

Filament

LONGITUDINAL SECTION THROUGH FLOWER BUD

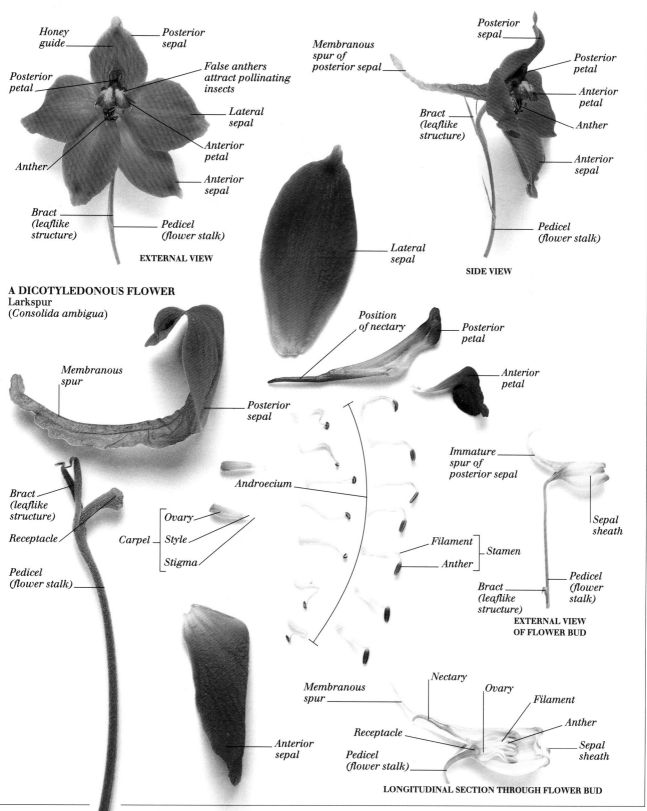

Honey guide
Posterior sepal
Posterior petal
False anthers attract pollinating insects
Lateral sepal
Anterior petal
Anther
Anterior sepal
Bract (leaflike structure)
Pedicel (flower stalk)

EXTERNAL VIEW

Membranous spur of posterior sepal
Posterior sepal
Posterior petal
Anterior petal
Anther
Bract (leaflike structure)
Anterior sepal
Pedicel (flower stalk)

SIDE VIEW

A DICOTYLEDONOUS FLOWER
Larkspur
(*Consolida ambigua*)

Lateral sepal

Membranous spur

Position of nectary
Posterior petal
Anterior petal

Posterior sepal

Bract (leaflike structure)

Receptacle

Androecium

Carpel
Ovary
Style
Stigma

Filament
Anther
Stamen

Immature spur of posterior sepal

Sepal sheath

Pedicel (flower stalk)

Bract (leaflike structure)
Pedicel (flower stalk)

EXTERNAL VIEW OF FLOWER BUD

Anterior sepal

Membranous spur

Nectary
Ovary
Filament
Anther
Sepal sheath
Receptacle
Pedicel (flower stalk)

LONGITUDINAL SECTION THROUGH FLOWER BUD

141

Flowers 2

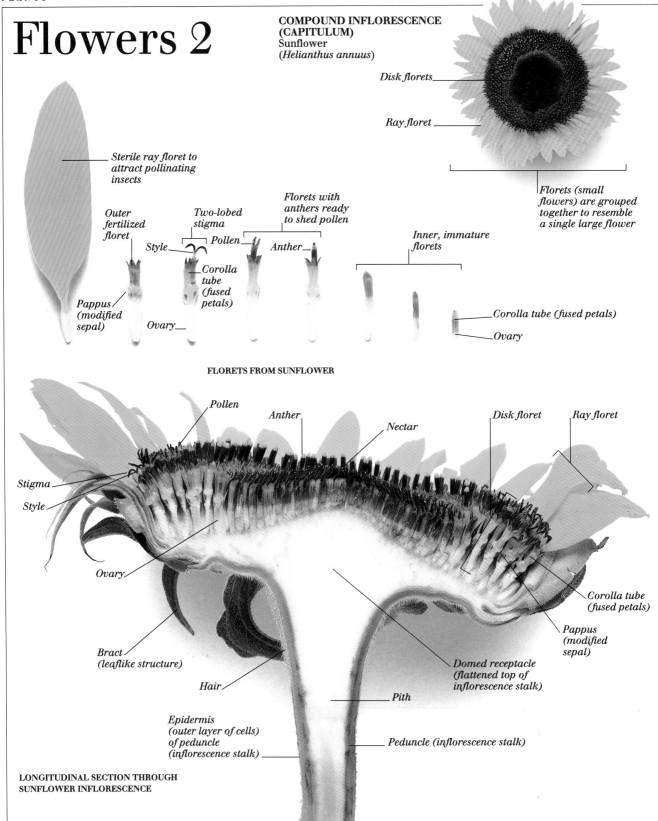

COMPOUND INFLORESCENCE (CAPITULUM)
Sunflower
(*Helianthus annuus*)

Disk florets

Ray floret

Florets (small flowers) are grouped together to resemble a single large flower

Sterile ray floret to attract pollinating insects

Outer fertilized floret

Two-lobed stigma

Florets with anthers ready to shed pollen

Style

Pollen

Anther

Inner, immature florets

Corolla tube (fused petals)

Pappus (modified sepal)

Ovary

Corolla tube (fused petals)

Ovary

FLORETS FROM SUNFLOWER

Pollen

Anther

Nectar

Disk floret

Ray floret

Stigma

Style

Ovary

Corolla tube (fused petals)

Pappus (modified sepal)

Bract (leaflike structure)

Hair

Domed receptacle (flattened top of inflorescence stalk)

Pith

Epidermis (outer layer of cells) of peduncle (inflorescence stalk)

Peduncle (inflorescence stalk)

LONGITUDINAL SECTION THROUGH SUNFLOWER INFLORESCENCE

ARRANGEMENT OF FLOWERS ON STEM

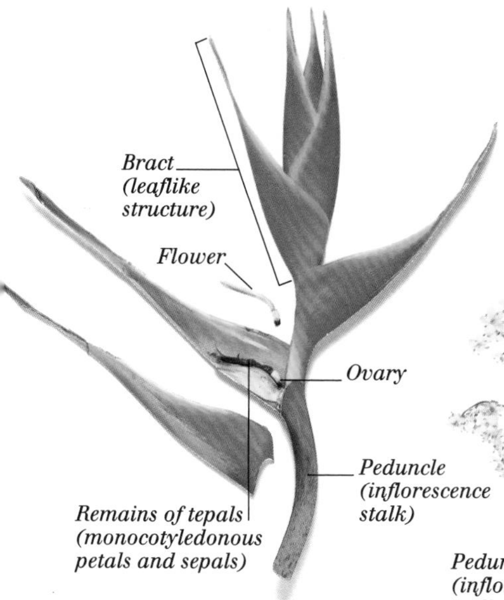

Bract
(leaflike
structure)

Flower

Ovary

Remains of tepals
(monocotyledonous
petals and sepals)

Peduncle
(inflorescence
stalk)

INFLORESCENCE (SPIKE)
Heliconia peruviana

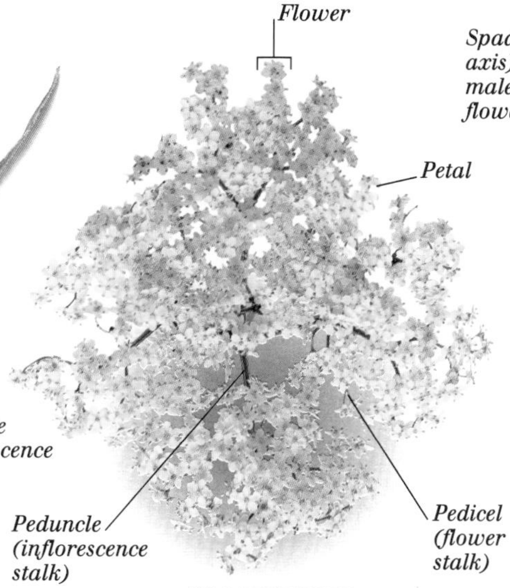

Flower

Petal

Peduncle
(inflorescence
stalk)

Pedicel
(flower
stalk)

**INFLORESCENCE
(COMPOUND UMBEL)**
European elder
(*Sambucus nigra*)

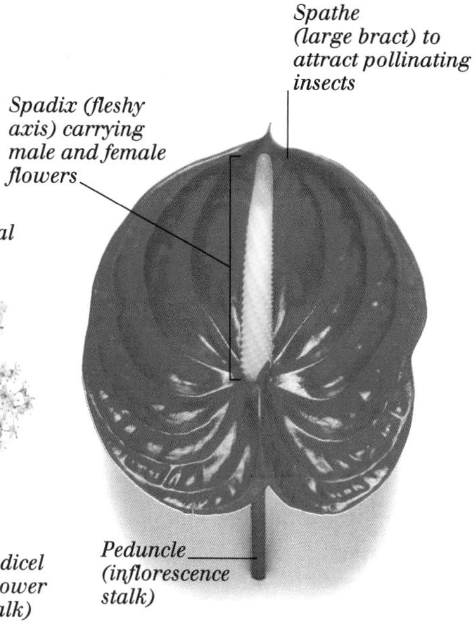

Spathe
(large bract) to
attract pollinating
insects

Spadix (fleshy
axis) carrying
male and female
flowers

Peduncle
(inflorescence
stalk)

INFLORESCENCE (SPADIX)
Flamingo Flower
(*Anthurium andreanum*)

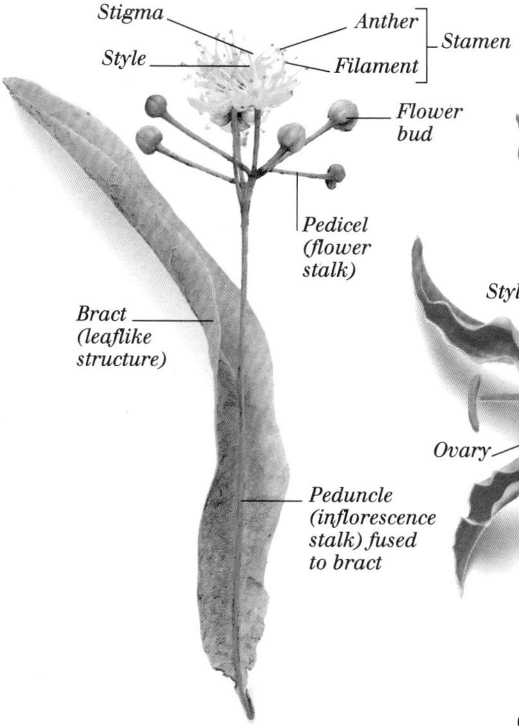

Stigma

Style

Anther

Filament

Stamen

Flower
bud

Pedicel
(flower
stalk)

Bract
(leaflike
structure)

Peduncle
(inflorescence
stalk) fused
to bract

**INFLORESCENCE
(DICHASIAL CYME)**
Common linden
(*Tilia x europaea*)

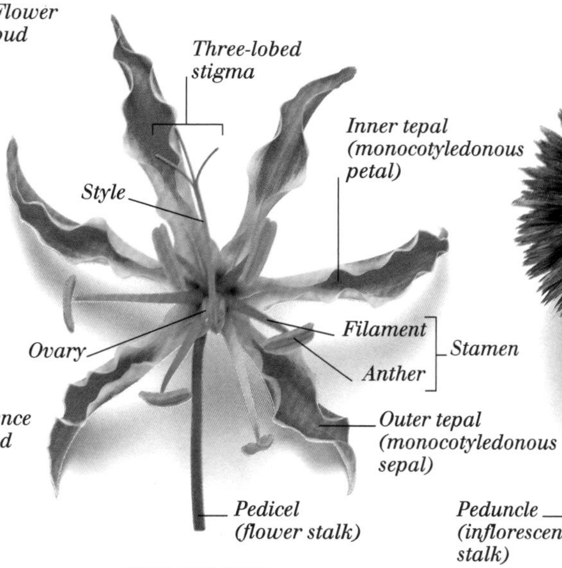

Three-lobed
stigma

Style

Inner tepal
(monocotyledonous
petal)

Ovary

Filament

Anther

Stamen

Outer tepal
(monocotyledonous
sepal)

Pedicel
(flower stalk)

SINGLE FLOWER
Glory lily
(*Gloriosa superba*)

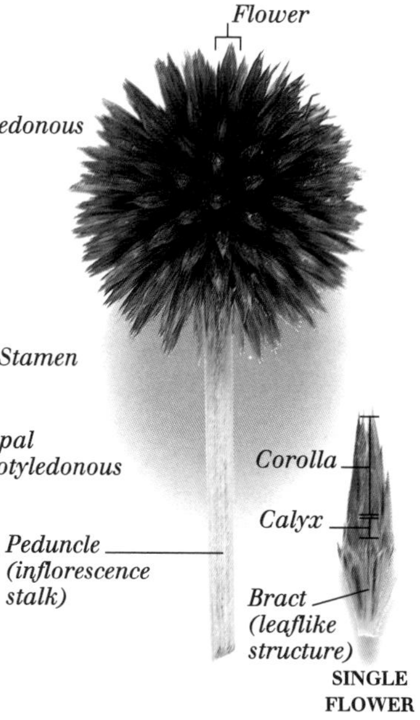

Flower

Corolla

Calyx

Peduncle
(inflorescence
stalk)

Bract
(leaflike
structure)

**SINGLE
FLOWER**

**INFLORESCENCE
(SPHERICAL UMBEL)**
Echinops sp.

Pollination

POLLINATION IS THE TRANSFER OF POLLEN (which contains the male sex cells) from an anther (part of the male reproductive organ) to a stigma (part of the female reproductive organ). This process precedes fertilization (see pp. 146-147). Pollination may occur within the same flower (self-pollination), or between flowers on separate plants of the same species (cross-pollination). In most plants, pollination is carried out either by insects (entomophilous pollination) or by the wind (anemophilous pollination). Less commonly, birds, bats, or water are the agents of pollination. Insect-pollinated flowers are typically scented and brightly colored. They also produce nectar, on which insects feed. Such flowers also tend to have patterns that are visible only in ultraviolet light, which many insects can see but which humans cannot. These features attract insects, which become covered with the sticky pollen grains when they visit one flower, and then transfer the pollen to the next flower they visit. Wind-pollinated flowers are generally small, relatively inconspicuous, and unscented. They produce large quantities of light pollen grains that are easily blown by the wind to other flowers.

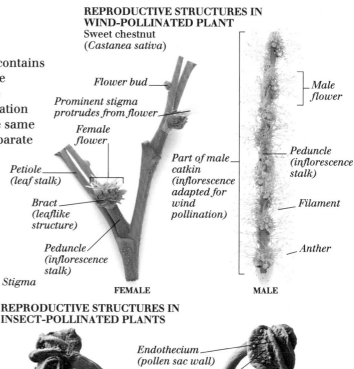

REPRODUCTIVE STRUCTURES IN WIND-POLLINATED PLANT
Sweet chestnut
(*Castanea sativa*)

Flower bud

Prominent stigma protrudes from flower

Female flower

Petiole (leaf stalk)

Bract (leaflike structure)

Peduncle (inflorescence stalk)

Part of male catkin (inflorescence adapted for wind pollination)

Male flower

Peduncle (inflorescence stalk)

Filament

Anther

FEMALE

MALE

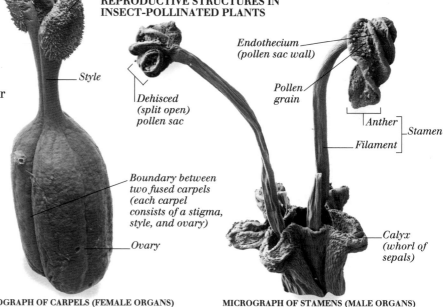

REPRODUCTIVE STRUCTURES IN INSECT-POLLINATED PLANTS

Stigma

Style

Dehisced (split open) pollen sac

Boundary between two fused carpels (each carpel consists of a stigma, style, and ovary)

Ovary

Endothecium (pollen sac wall)

Pollen grain

Anther
Filament
Stamen

Calyx (whorl of sepals)

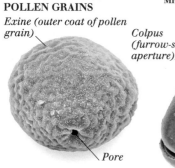

MICROGRAPHS OF POLLEN GRAINS

Exine (outer coat of pollen grain)

Pore

EUROPEAN FIELD ELM
(*Ulmus minor*)

MICROGRAPH OF CARPELS (FEMALE ORGANS)
Yellow-wort
(*Blackstonia perfoliata*)

Colpus (furrow-shaped aperture)

Exine (outer coat of pollen grain)

JUSTICIA AUREA

Exine (outer coat of pollen grain)

Pore

Baculum (rod-shaped structure)

MEADOW CRANESBILL
(*Geranium pratense*)

MICROGRAPH OF STAMENS (MALE ORGANS)
Common centaury
(*Centaurium erythraea*)

Colpus (furrow-shaped aperture)

Exine (outer coat of pollen grain)

Equatorial furrow

BOX-LEAVED MILKWORT
(*Polygala chamaebuxus*)

INSECT POLLINATION OF MEADOW SAGE

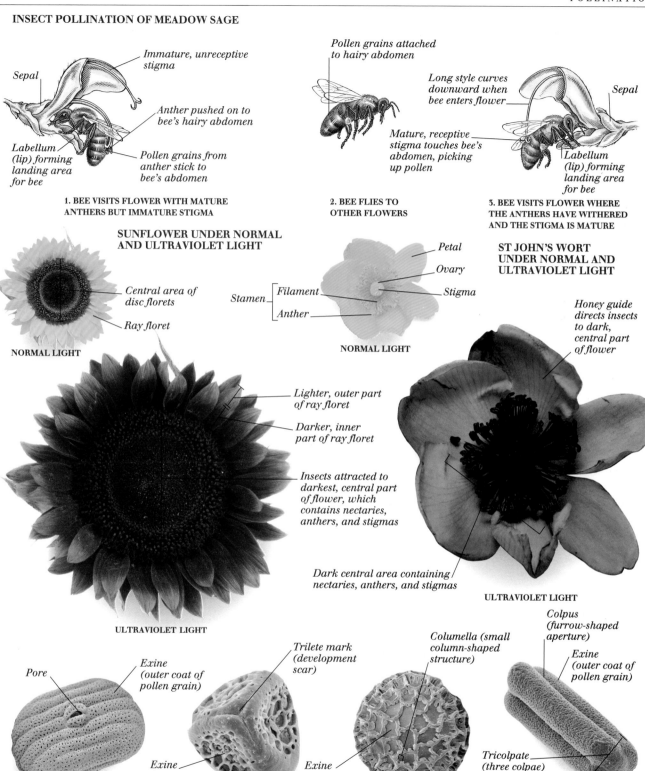

Sepal

Immature, unreceptive stigma

Anther pushed on to bee's hairy abdomen

Labellum (lip) forming landing area for bee

Pollen grains from anther stick to bee's abdomen

Pollen grains attached to hairy abdomen

Long style curves downward when bee enters flower

Mature, receptive stigma touches bee's abdomen, picking up pollen

Sepal

Labellum (lip) forming landing area for bee

1. BEE VISITS FLOWER WITH MATURE ANTHERS BUT IMMATURE STIGMA

2. BEE FLIES TO OTHER FLOWERS

3. BEE VISITS FLOWER WHERE THE ANTHERS HAVE WITHERED AND THE STIGMA IS MATURE

SUNFLOWER UNDER NORMAL AND ULTRAVIOLET LIGHT

Central area of disc florets

Ray floret

NORMAL LIGHT

Petal

Ovary

Stamen — Filament

Anther

Stigma

NORMAL LIGHT

ST JOHN'S WORT UNDER NORMAL AND ULTRAVIOLET LIGHT

Honey guide directs insects to dark, central part of flower

Lighter, outer part of ray floret

Darker, inner part of ray floret

Insects attracted to darkest, central part of flower, which contains nectaries, anthers, and stigmas

Dark central area containing nectaries, anthers, and stigmas

ULTRAVIOLET LIGHT

ULTRAVIOLET LIGHT

Pore

Exine (outer coat of pollen grain)

Trilete mark (development scar)

Columella (small column-shaped structure)

Colpus (furrow-shaped aperture)

Exine (outer coat of pollen grain)

Exine (outer coat of pollen grain)

Exine (outer coat of pollen grain)

Tricolpate (three colpae) pollen grain

MIMULOPSIS SOLMSII

THESIUM ALPINIUM

RUELLIA GRANDIFLORA

CROSSANDRA NILOTICA

Fertilization

FERTILIZATION IS THE FUSION of male and female gametes (sex cells) to produce a zygote (embryo). Following pollination (see pp. 144-145), the pollen grains that contain the male gametes are on the stigma, some distance from the female gamete (ovum) inside the ovule. To enable the gametes to meet, the pollen grain germinates and produces a pollen tube, which grows down and enters the embryo sac (the inner part of the ovule that contains the ovum). Two male gametes, traveling at the tip of the pollen tube, enter the embryo sac. One gamete fuses with the ovum to produce a zygote that will develop into an embryo plant. The other male gamete fuses with two polar nuclei to produce the endosperm, which acts as a food supply for the developing embryo. Fertilization also initiates other changes: the integument (outer part of ovule) forms a testa (seed coat) around the embryo and endosperm; the petals fall off; the stigma and style wither; and the ovary wall forms a layer (called the pericarp) around the seed. Together, the pericarp and seed form the fruit, which may be succulent (see pp. 148-149) or dry (see pp. 150-151). In some species (such as blackberry), apomixis can occur: The seed develops without fertilization of the ovum by a male gamete, but endosperm formation and fruit development take place as in other species.

BANANA
(*Musa 'Lacatan'*)

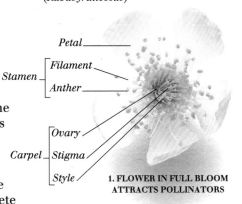

1. FLOWER IN FULL BLOOM
ATTRACTS POLLINATORS

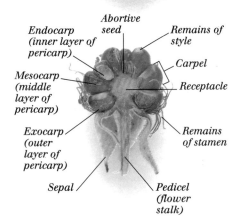

4. PERICARP FORMS
FLESH, SKIN, AND A HARD INNER
LAYER (SHOWN IN CROSS SECTION)

7. MESOCARP (FLESHY PART OF PERICARP)
OF EACH CARPEL STARTS TO
CHANGE COLOR

8. CARPELS MATURE INTO DRUPELETS
(SMALL FLESHY FRUITS WITH SINGLE SEEDS
SURROUNDED BY HARD ENDOCARP)

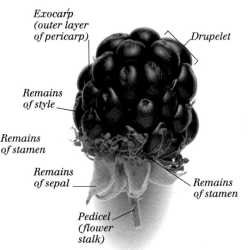

9. MESOCARP OF DRUPELET BECOMES
DARKER AND SWEETER

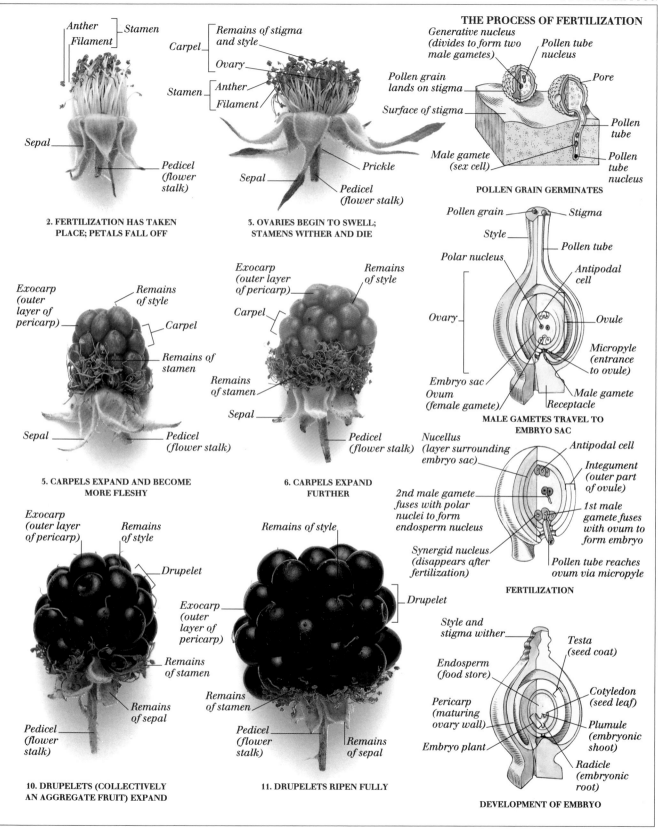

Anther — Stamen
Filament —

Sepal

Pedicel
(flower
stalk)

**2. FERTILIZATION HAS TAKEN
PLACE; PETALS FALL OFF**

Remains of stigma
and style
Carpel
Ovary

Stamen
Anther
Filament

Sepal

Prickle

Pedicel
(flower stalk)

**3. OVARIES BEGIN TO SWELL;
STAMENS WITHER AND DIE**

THE PROCESS OF FERTILIZATION

Generative nucleus
(divides to form two
male gametes)
Pollen tube
nucleus

Pollen grain
lands on stigma

Pore

Surface of stigma

Pollen
tube

Male gamete
(sex cell)

Pollen
tube
nucleus

POLLEN GRAIN GERMINATES

Exocarp
(outer
layer of
pericarp)

Remains of
style

Carpel

Remains of
stamen

Sepal

Pedicel
(flower stalk)

**5. CARPELS EXPAND AND BECOME
MORE FLESHY**

Exocarp
(outer layer
of pericarp)

Remains
of style

Carpel

Remains
of stamen

Sepal

Pedicel
(flower stalk)

**6. CARPELS EXPAND
FURTHER**

Pollen grain
Stigma
Style
Pollen tube
Polar nucleus
Antipodal
cell
Ovary
Ovule
Micropyle
(entrance
to ovule)
Embryo sac
Ovum
(female gamete)
Male gamete
Receptacle

**MALE GAMETES TRAVEL TO
EMBRYO SAC**

Exocarp
(outer layer
of pericarp)

Remains
of style

Drupelet

Remains
of stamen

Remains
of sepal

Pedicel
(flower
stalk)

**10. DRUPELETS (COLLECTIVELY
AN AGGREGATE FRUIT) EXPAND**

Remains of style

Exocarp
(outer
layer of
pericarp)

Drupelet

Remains
of stamen

Pedicel
(flower
stalk)

Remains
of sepal

11. DRUPELETS RIPEN FULLY

Nucellus
(layer surrounding
embryo sac)

Antipodal cell

Integument
(outer part
of ovule)

2nd male gamete
fuses with polar
nuclei to form
endosperm nucleus

1st male
gamete fuses
with ovum to
form embryo

Synergid nucleus
(disappears after
fertilization)

Pollen tube reaches
ovum via micropyle

FERTILIZATION

Style and
stigma wither

Testa
(seed coat)

Endosperm
(food store)

Cotyledon
(seed leaf)

Pericarp
(maturing
ovary wall)

Plumule
(embryonic
shoot)

Embryo plant

Radicle
(embryonic
root)

DEVELOPMENT OF EMBRYO

Succulent fruits

A FRUIT IS A FULLY DEVELOPED and ripened ovary—the seed-producing part of a plant's female reproductive organs. Fruits may be succulent or dry (see pp. 150-151). Succulent fruits are fleshy and brightly colored, making them attractive to animals, which eat them and disperse the seeds away from the parent plant. The wall (pericarp) of a succulent fruit has three layers: an outer exocarp, a middle mesocarp, and an inner endocarp. These three layers vary in thickness and texture in different types of fruits and may blend into each other. Succulent fruits can be classed as simple (derived from one ovary) or compound (derived from several ovaries). Simple succulent fruits include berries, which typically have many seeds, and drupes, which typically have a single stone or pit (such as cherry and peach). Compound succulent fruits include aggregate fruits, which are formed from many ovaries in one flower, and multiple fruits, which develop from the ovaries of many flowers. Some fruits, known as false fruits or pseudocarps, develop from parts of the flower in addition to the ovaries. For example, the flesh of the apple is formed from the receptacle (the upper end of the flower stalk).

BERRY
Cocoa
(*Theobroma cacao*)

HESPERIDIUM (A TYPE OF BERRY)
Lemon
(*Citrus limon*)

Pedicel (flower stalk)
Mesocarp
Endocarp
Pedicel (flower stalk)
Exocarp
Leathery exocarp
Seed
Oil gland
Vesicle (juice sac)
Remains of style
Remains of style
Placenta

EXTERNAL VIEW OF FRUIT

LONGITUDINAL SECTION THROUGH FRUIT

Embryo
Seed
Hilum (point of attachment to ovary)
Carpel wall
Carpel
Testa (seed coat)
Cotyledon (seed leaf)
Placenta

EXTERNAL VIEW AND SECTION THROUGH SEED

CROSS SECTION THROUGH FRUIT

SYCONIUM (A TYPE OF FALSE FRUIT)
Fig
(*Ficus carica*)

Remains of female flowers
Fleshy infolded receptacle
Remains of male flowers
Peduncle (inflorescence stalk)
Pit (seed surrounded by endocarp)
Skin
Pore closed by scales

EXTERNAL VIEW OF FRUIT

LONGITUDINAL SECTION THROUGH FRUIT

FRUIT WITH FLESHY ARIL
Lychee
(*Litchi chinensis*)

Pedicel (flower stalk)
Pedicel (flower stalk)
Seed
Aril (fleshy outgrowth from seed stalk)
Pericarp (fruit wall)
Pericarp (fruit wall)

Remains of style
Endocarp

EXTERNAL VIEW AND SECTION THROUGH PIT

Drupelet
Pit
Pedicel (flower stalk)
Endocarp
Embryo
Testa (seed coat)
Cotyledon (seed leaf)

EXTERNAL VIEW OF FRUIT

LONGITUDINAL SECTION THROUGH FRUIT

REMAINS OF A SINGLE FEMALE FLOWER

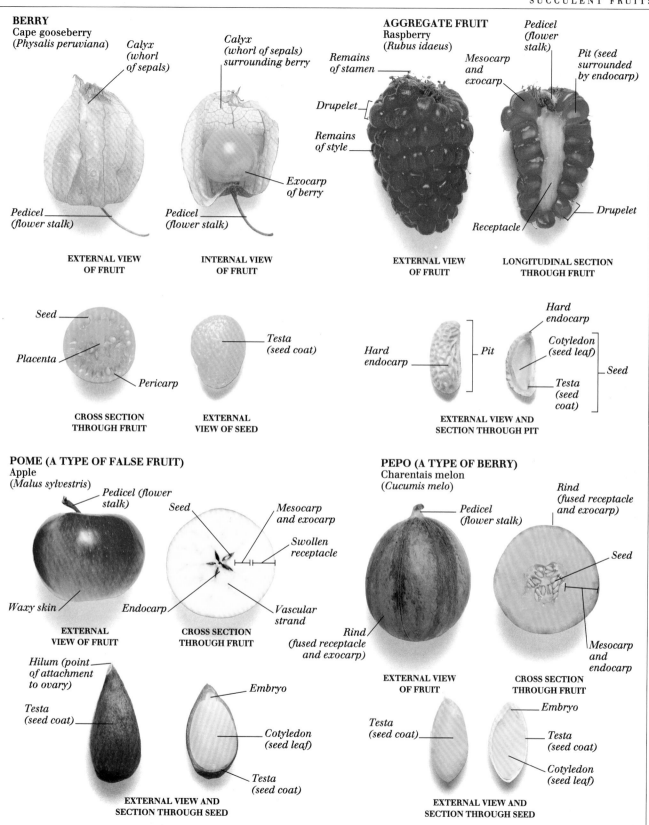

BERRY
Cape gooseberry
(*Physalis peruviana*)

Calyx (whorl of sepals)

Calyx (whorl of sepals) surrounding berry

Exocarp of berry

Pedicel (flower stalk)

Pedicel (flower stalk)

EXTERNAL VIEW OF FRUIT

INTERNAL VIEW OF FRUIT

Seed

Placenta

Pericarp

Testa (seed coat)

CROSS SECTION THROUGH FRUIT

EXTERNAL VIEW OF SEED

AGGREGATE FRUIT
Raspberry
(*Rubus idaeus*)

Remains of stamen

Drupelet

Remains of style

Mesocarp and exocarp

Pedicel (flower stalk)

Pit (seed surrounded by endocarp)

Drupelet

Receptacle

EXTERNAL VIEW OF FRUIT

LONGITUDINAL SECTION THROUGH FRUIT

Hard endocarp

Pit

Hard endocarp

Cotyledon (seed leaf)

Testa (seed coat)

Seed

EXTERNAL VIEW AND SECTION THROUGH PIT

POME (A TYPE OF FALSE FRUIT)
Apple
(*Malus sylvestris*)

Pedicel (flower stalk)

Seed

Mesocarp and exocarp

Swollen receptacle

Waxy skin

Endocarp

Vascular strand

EXTERNAL VIEW OF FRUIT

CROSS SECTION THROUGH FRUIT

Hilum (point of attachment to ovary)

Testa (seed coat)

Embryo

Cotyledon (seed leaf)

Testa (seed coat)

EXTERNAL VIEW AND SECTION THROUGH SEED

PEPO (A TYPE OF BERRY)
Charentais melon
(*Cucumis melo*)

Pedicel (flower stalk)

Rind (fused receptacle and exocarp)

Seed

Rind (fused receptacle and exocarp)

Mesocarp and endocarp

EXTERNAL VIEW OF FRUIT

CROSS SECTION THROUGH FRUIT

Testa (seed coat)

Embryo

Testa (seed coat)

Cotyledon (seed leaf)

EXTERNAL VIEW AND SECTION THROUGH SEED

Dry fruits

DRY FRUITS HAVE A HARD, DRY PERICARP (fruit wall) around their seeds, unlike succulent fruits, which have fleshy pericarps (see pp. 148-149). Dry fruits are divided into three types: dehiscent, in which the pericarp splits open to release the seeds; indehiscent, which do not split open; and schizocarpic, in which the fruit splits but the seeds are not exposed. Dehiscent dry fruits include capsules (for example, love-in-a-mist), follicles (delphinium), legumes (pea), and silicles (honesty). Typically, the seeds of dehiscent fruits are dispersed by the wind. Indehiscent dry fruits include nuts (sweet chestnut), nutlets (goose grass), achenes (strawberry), caryopses (wheat), samaras (elm), and cypselas (dandelion). Some indehiscent dry fruits are dispersed by the wind, assisted by "wings" (elm) or "parachutes" (dandelion); others (goose grass) have hooked pericarps to aid dispersal on animals' fur. Schizocarpic dry fruits include cremocarps (hogweed), and double samaras (sycamore maple); these are dispersed by the wind.

NUTLET
Goose grass
(*Galium aparine*)

LEGUME
Pea
(*Pisum sativum*)

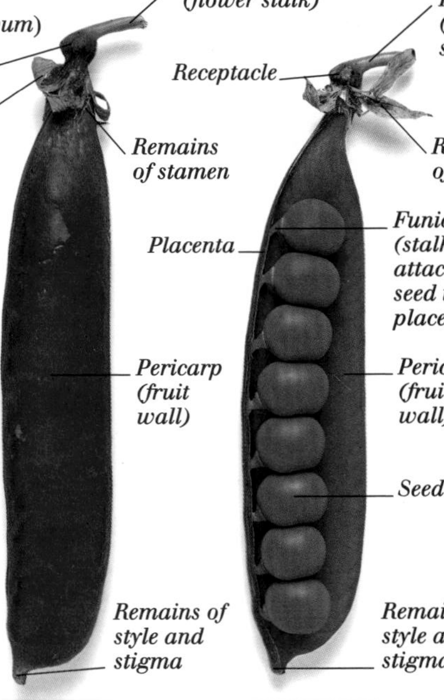

EXTERNAL VIEW
OF FRUIT

INTERNAL VIEW
OF FRUIT

NUT
Spanish chestnut
(*Castanea sativa*)

EXTERNAL VIEW OF FRUIT WITH
SURROUNDING CUPULE

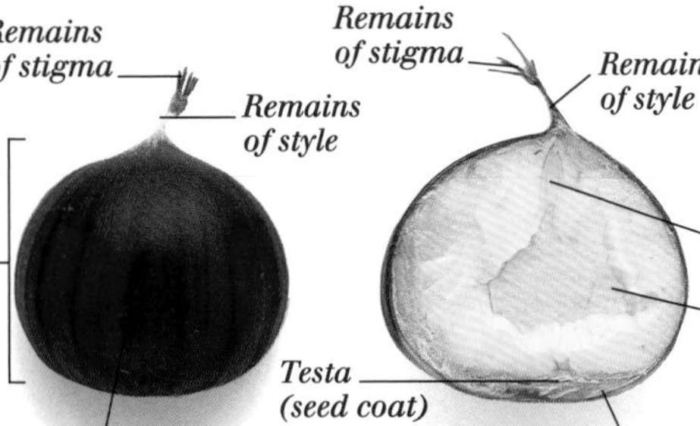

EXTERIOR VIEW AND
SECTION THROUGH SEED

ACHENE
Strawberry
(*Fragaria* x *ananassa*)

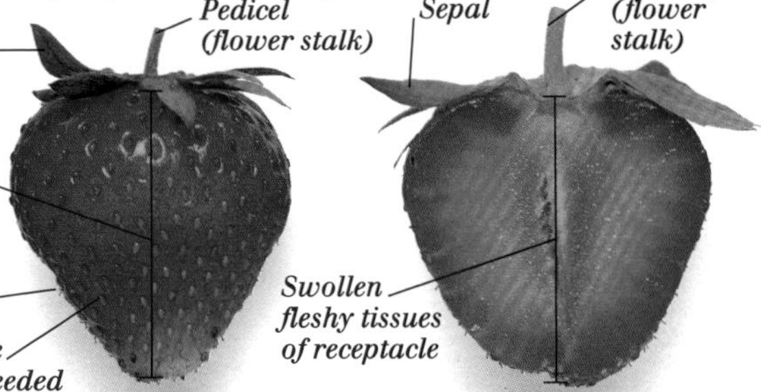

EXTERNAL VIEW
OF FRUIT

LONGITUDINAL SECTION
THROUGH FRUIT

EXTERNAL VIEW AND
SECTION THROUGH FRUIT

EXTERNAL VIEW AND
SECTION THROUGH SEED

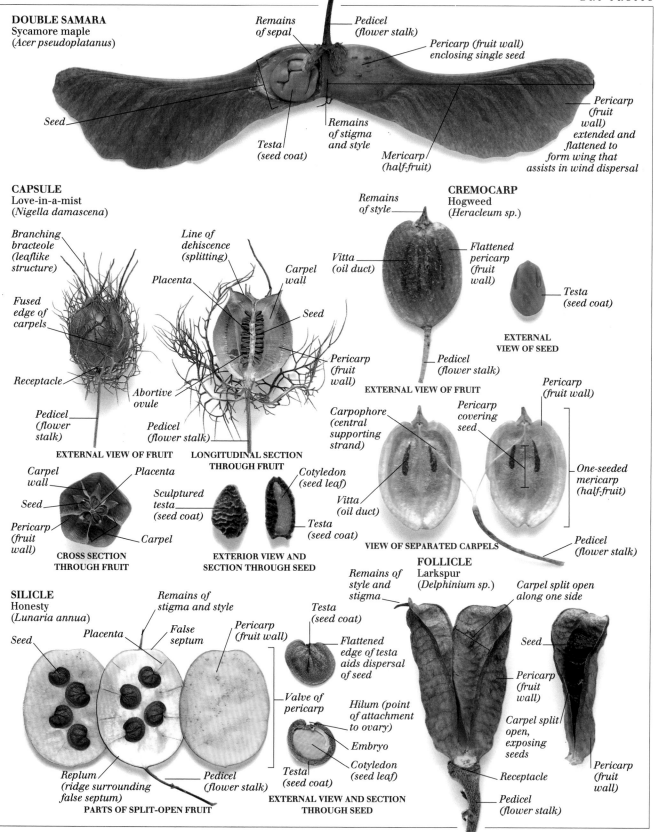

DOUBLE SAMARA
Sycamore maple
(*Acer pseudoplatanus*)

Remains of sepal

Pedicel (flower stalk)

Pericarp (fruit wall) enclosing single seed

Seed

Testa (seed coat)

Remains of stigma and style

Mericarp (half-fruit)

Pericarp (fruit wall) extended and flattened to form wing that assists in wind dispersal

CAPSULE
Love-in-a-mist
(*Nigella damascena*)

Branching bracteole (leaflike structure)

Line of dehiscence (splitting)

Carpel wall

Placenta

Fused edge of carpels

Seed

Receptacle

Pericarp (fruit wall)

Abortive ovule

Pedicel (flower stalk)

Pedicel (flower stalk)

EXTERNAL VIEW OF FRUIT

LONGITUDINAL SECTION THROUGH FRUIT

Carpel wall

Placenta

Seed

Sculptured testa (seed coat)

Cotyledon (seed leaf)

Pericarp (fruit wall)

Carpel

Testa (seed coat)

CROSS SECTION THROUGH FRUIT

EXTERIOR VIEW AND SECTION THROUGH SEED

CREMOCARP
Hogweed
(*Heracleum sp.*)

Remains of style

Vitta (oil duct)

Flattened pericarp (fruit wall)

Testa (seed coat)

EXTERNAL VIEW OF SEED

Pedicel (flower stalk)

EXTERNAL VIEW OF FRUIT

Carpophore (central supporting strand)

Pericarp covering seed

Pericarp (fruit wall)

Vitta (oil duct)

One-seeded mericarp (half-fruit)

VIEW OF SEPARATED CARPELS

Pedicel (flower stalk)

FOLLICLE
Larkspur
(*Delphinium sp.*)

Remains of style and stigma

Carpel split open along one side

SILICLE
Honesty
(*Lunaria annua*)

Remains of stigma and style

False septum

Placenta

Pericarp (fruit wall)

Seed

Testa (seed coat)

Flattened edge of testa aids dispersal of seed

Seed

Pericarp (fruit wall)

Valve of pericarp

Hilum (point of attachment to ovary)

Embryo

Carpel split open, exposing seeds

Replum (ridge surrounding false septum)

Pedicel (flower stalk)

Testa (seed coat)

Cotyledon (seed leaf)

Receptacle

Pericarp (fruit wall)

PARTS OF SPLIT-OPEN FRUIT

EXTERNAL VIEW AND SECTION THROUGH SEED

Pedicel (flower stalk)

Germination

GERMINATION IS THE GROWTH OF SEEDS INTO SEEDLINGS. It starts when seeds become active below ground, and ends when the first foliage leaves appear above ground. A seed consists of an embryo and its food supply, surrounded by a testa (seed coat). The embryo is made up of one or two cotyledons (seed leaves) attached to a central axis. The upper part of the axis consists of an epicotyl, which has a plumule (embryonic shoot) at its tip. The lower part of the axis consists of a hypocotyl and a radicle (embryonic root). After dispersal from the parent plant, the seeds dehydrate and enter a period of dormancy. Germination begins, following this dormant period, as long as the seeds have enough water, oxygen, warmth, and, in some cases, light. In the first stages of germination, the seed takes in water; the embryo starts to use its food store; and the radicle swells, breaks through the testa, and grows downward. Germination then proceeds in one of two ways, depending on the type of seed. In epigeal germination, the hypocotyl lengthens, pulling the plumule and its protective cotyledons out of the soil. In hypogeal germination, the cotyledons remain below ground and the epicotyl lengthens, pushing the plumule upward.

HYPOGEAL GERMINATION
Broad bean
(Vicia faba)

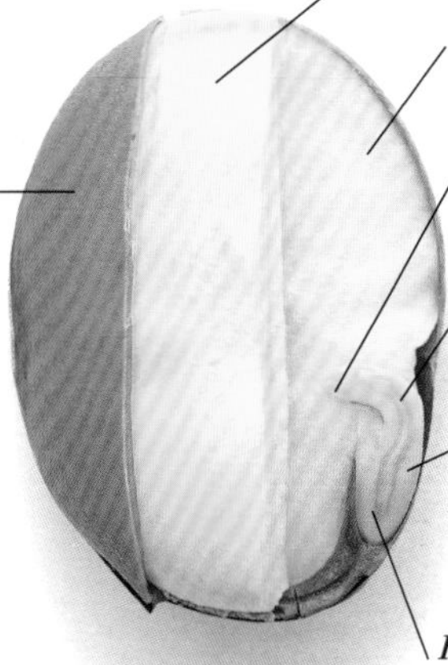

Cotyledon (seed leaf)

Cotyledon (seed leaf)

Testa (seed coat)

Plumule (embryonic shoot)

Epicotyl (upper part of axis)

Hypocotyl (region between epicotyl and radicle)

Radicle (embryonic root)

SEED AT START OF GERMINATION

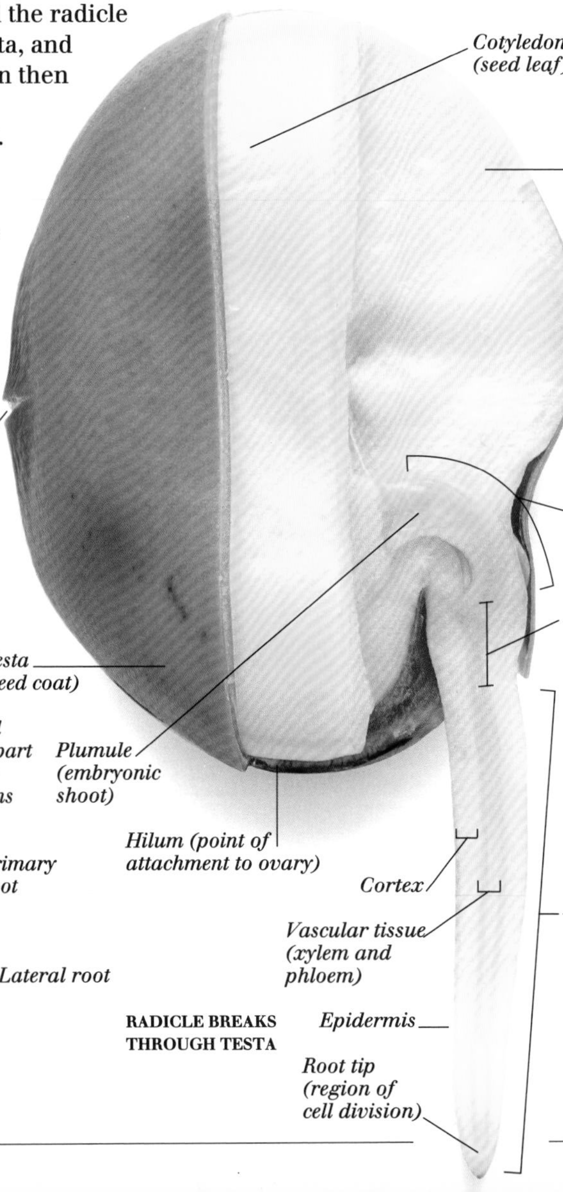

Cotyledon (seed leaf)

Foliage leaf

Cotyledon (seed leaf)

Stipule (structure at base of leaf)

Epicotyl increases in length and turns green

Cataphyll (scale leaf of plumule)

Epicotyl (upper part of axis)

Hypocotyl (region between epicotyl and radicle)

FOLIAGE LEAVES APPEAR

Split in testa (seed coat) due to expanding cotyledons

Young shoot

Cataphyll (scale leaf of plumule)

Cotyledons (seed leaves) remain within testa (seed coat) below soil's surface

Testa (seed coat)

Epicotyl (upper part of axis) lengthens

Plumule (embryonic shoot)

Primary root

Hilum (point of attachment to ovary)

Cortex

Vascular tissue (xylem and phloem)

Epidermis

Root tip (region of cell division)

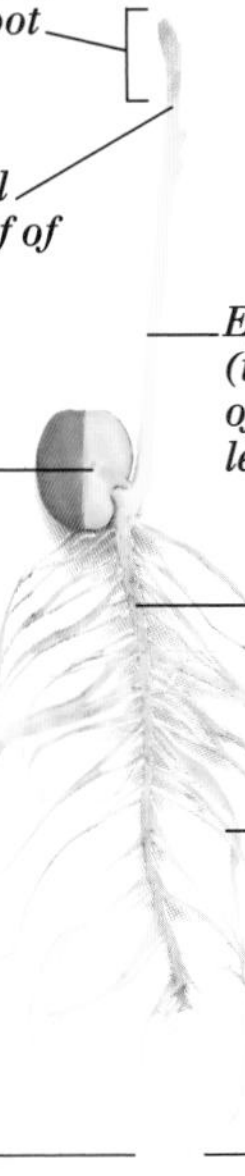

SHOOT APPEARS ABOVE SOIL

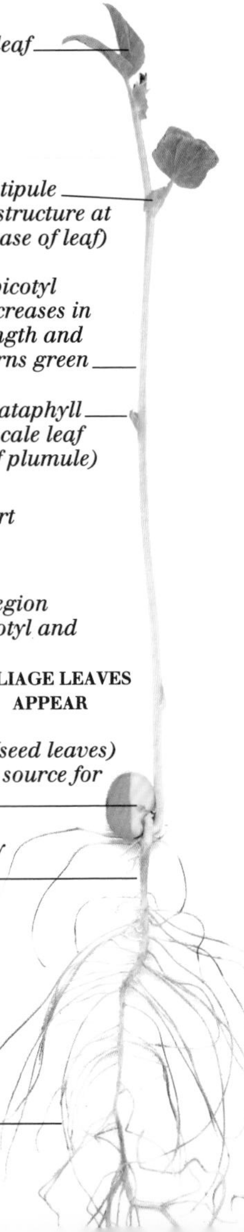

Lateral root

RADICLE BREAKS THROUGH TESTA

Cotyledons (seed leaves) remain food source for the seedling

Primary root

Radicle (embryonic root)

Lateral root system

152

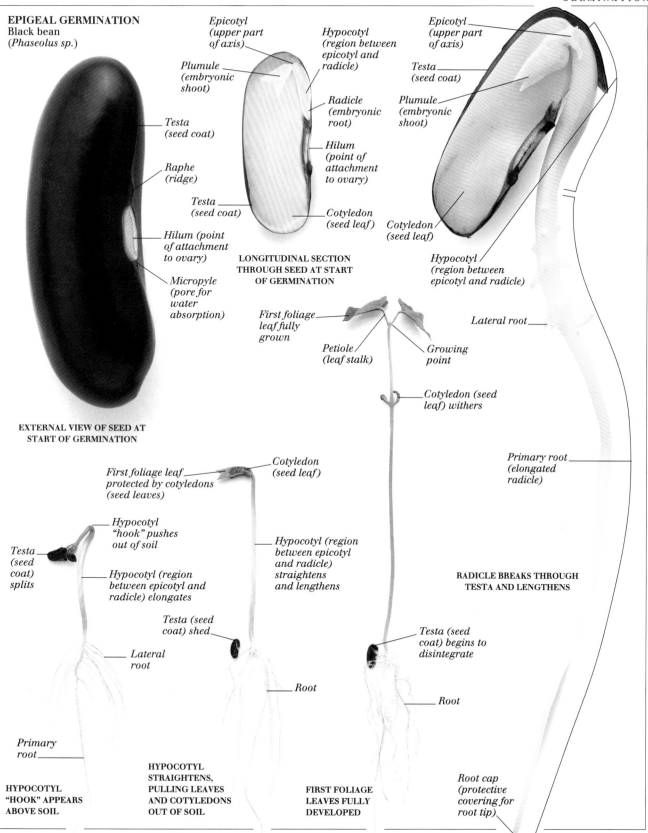

EPIGEAL GERMINATION
Black bean
(*Phaseolus sp.*)

*Testa
(seed coat)*

*Raphe
(ridge)*

*Hilum (point
of attachment
to ovary)*

*Micropyle
(pore for
water
absorption)*

**EXTERNAL VIEW OF SEED AT
START OF GERMINATION**

*Epicotyl
(upper part
of axis)*

*Plumule
(embryonic
shoot)*

*Hypocotyl
(region between
epicotyl and
radicle)*

*Radicle
(embryonic
root)*

*Hilum
(point of
attachment
to ovary)*

*Testa
(seed coat)*

*Cotyledon
(seed leaf)*

**LONGITUDINAL SECTION
THROUGH SEED AT START
OF GERMINATION**

*Epicotyl
(upper part
of axis)*

*Testa
(seed coat)*

*Plumule
(embryonic
shoot)*

*Cotyledon
(seed leaf)*

*Hypocotyl
(region between
epicotyl and
radicle)*

Lateral root

*Primary root
(elongated
radicle)*

**RADICLE BREAKS THROUGH
TESTA AND LENGTHENS**

*First foliage
leaf fully
grown*

*Petiole
(leaf stalk)*

*Growing
point*

*Cotyledon (seed
leaf) withers*

*First foliage leaf
protected by cotyledons
(seed leaves)*

*Cotyledon
(seed leaf)*

*Testa
(seed
coat)
splits*

*Hypocotyl
"hook" pushes
out of soil*

*Hypocotyl (region
between epicotyl
and radicle)
straightens
and lengthens*

*Hypocotyl (region
between epicotyl and
radicle) elongates*

*Testa (seed
coat) shed*

*Lateral
root*

Root

*Testa (seed
coat) begins to
disintegrate*

Root

*Primary
root*

**HYPOCOTYL
"HOOK" APPEARS
ABOVE SOIL**

**HYPOCOTYL
STRAIGHTENS,
PULLING LEAVES
AND COTYLEDONS
OUT OF SOIL**

**FIRST FOLIAGE
LEAVES FULLY
DEVELOPED**

*Root cap
(protective
covering for
root tip)*

Vegetative reproduction

MANY PLANTS CAN PROPAGATE THEMSELVES by vegetative reproduction. In this process, part of a plant separates, takes root, and grows into a new plant. Vegetative reproduction is a type of asexual reproduction; it involves only one parent and there is no fusion of gametes (sex cells). Plants use various structures to reproduce vegetatively. Some plants use underground storage organs. Such organs include rhizomes (horizontal, underground stems), the branches of which produce new plants; bulbs (swollen leaf bases) and corms (swollen stems), which produce daughter bulbs or corms that separate from the parent; and stem tubers (thickened underground stems) and root tubers (swollen adventitious roots), which also separate from the parent. Other propagative structures include runners and stolons, creeping horizontal stems that take root and produce new plants; bulbils, small bulbs that develop on the stem or in the place of flowers, and then drop off and grow into new plants; and adventitious buds, miniature plants that form on leaf margins before dropping to the ground and growing into mature plants.

CORM
Gladiolus
(*Gladiolus sp.*)

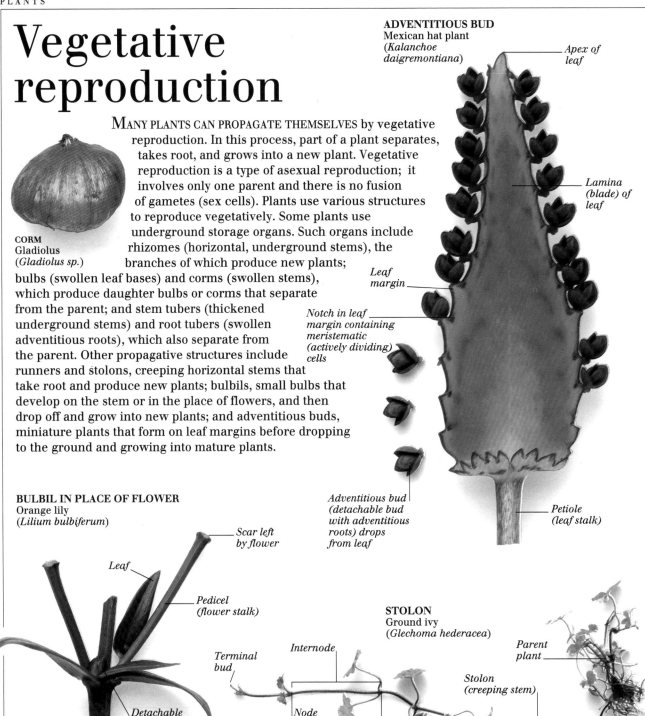

Apex of leaf

Lamina (blade) of leaf

Leaf margin

Notch in leaf margin containing meristematic (actively dividing) cells

Adventitious bud (detachable bud with adventitious roots) drops from leaf

Petiole (leaf stalk)

BULBIL IN PLACE OF FLOWER
Orange lily
(*Lilium bulbiferum*)

Scar left by flower

Leaf

Pedicel (flower stalk)

Detachable bulbil formed in place of flower

Peduncle (inflorescence stalk)

STOLON
Ground ivy
(*Glechoma hederacea*)

Terminal bud

Internode

Node

Node

Parent plant

Stolon (creeping stem)

Adventitious root of daughter plant

Daughter plant developed from lateral bud

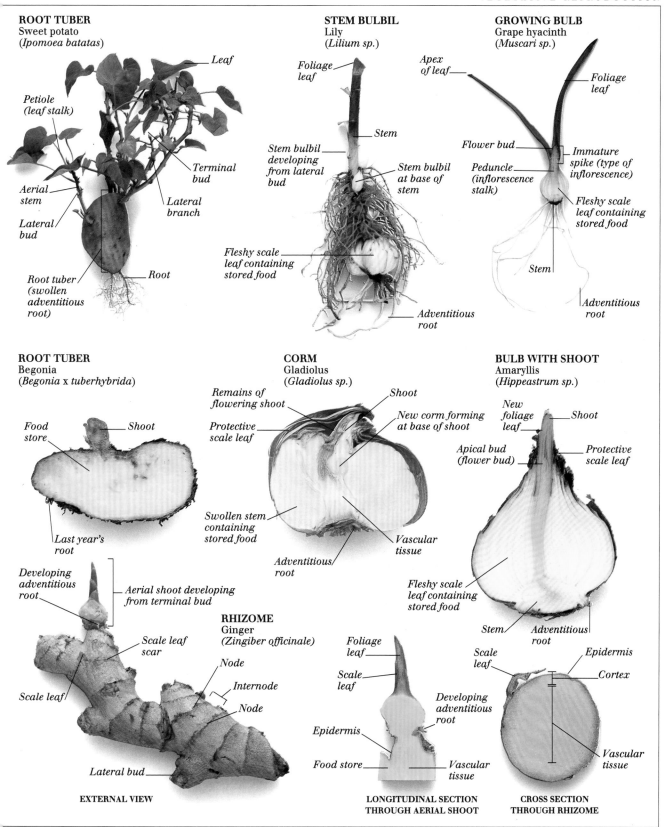

ROOT TUBER
Sweet potato
(*Ipomoea batatas*)

Leaf

Petiole
(leaf stalk)

Terminal
bud

Aerial
stem

Lateral
branch

Lateral
bud

Root tuber
(swollen
adventitious
root)

Root

STEM BULBIL
Lily
(*Lilium sp.*)

Foliage
leaf

Stem

Stem bulbil
developing
from lateral
bud

Stem bulbil
at base of
stem

Fleshy scale
leaf containing
stored food

Adventitious
root

GROWING BULB
Grape hyacinth
(*Muscari sp.*)

Apex
of leaf

Foliage
leaf

Flower bud

Immature
spike (type of
inflorescence)

Peduncle
(inflorescence
stalk)

Fleshy scale
leaf containing
stored food

Stem

Adventitious
root

ROOT TUBER
Begonia
(*Begonia* x *tuberhybrida*)

Food
store

Shoot

Last year's
root

Developing
adventitious
root

Aerial shoot developing
from terminal bud

Scale leaf
scar

Node

Internode

Node

Scale leaf

Lateral bud

EXTERNAL VIEW

CORM
Gladiolus
(*Gladiolus sp.*)

Remains of
flowering shoot

Shoot

Protective
scale leaf

New corm forming
at base of shoot

Swollen stem
containing
stored food

Vascular
tissue

Adventitious
root

RHIZOME
Ginger
(*Zingiber officinale*)

Foliage
leaf

Scale
leaf

Epidermis

Food store

Developing
adventitious
root

Vascular
tissue

**LONGITUDINAL SECTION
THROUGH AERIAL SHOOT**

BULB WITH SHOOT
Amaryllis
(*Hippeastrum sp.*)

New
foliage
leaf

Shoot

Apical bud
(flower bud)

Protective
scale leaf

Fleshy scale
leaf containing
stored food

Stem

Adventitious
root

Scale
leaf

Epidermis

Cortex

Vascular
tissue

**CROSS SECTION
THROUGH RHIZOME**

Dryland plants

DRYLAND PLANTS (XEROPHYTES) are able to survive in unfavorable habitats. All are found in places where little water is available; some live in high temperatures that cause excessive loss of water from the leaves. Xerophytes show a number of adaptations to dry conditions. These include reduced leaf area, rolled leaves, sunken stomata, hairs, spines, and thick cuticles. One group, succulent plants, stores water in specially enlarged spongy tissues found in leaves, roots, or stems. Leaf succulents have enlarged, fleshy, water-storing leaves. Root succulents have a large underground water-storage organ with short-lived stems and leaves above ground. Stem succulents are represented by the cacti (family Cactaceae). Cacti stems are fleshy, green, and photosynthetic. They are typically ribbed or covered by tubercles in rows, with leaves being reduced to spines or entirely absent.

LEAF SUCCULENT *Lithops sp.*

STEM SUCCULENT Golden barrel cactus (*Echinocactus grusonii*)

Areole (modified lateral shoot)

Trichome (hair)

Spine (modified leaf)

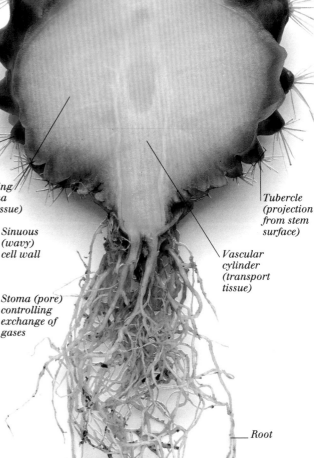

Waxy cuticle (waterproof covering)

Water-storing parenchyma (packing tissue)

Tubercle (projection from stem surface)

Vascular cylinder (transport tissue)

Spine (modified leaf)

Tubercle (projection from stem surface)

Root

Sinuous (wavy) cell wall

Stoma (pore) controlling exchange of gases

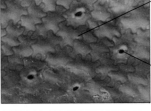

EXTERNAL VIEW

MICROGRAPH OF STEM SURFACE

Root

Spine (modified leaf)

Areole (modified lateral shoot)

Tubercle (projection from stem surface)

Waxy cuticle (waterproof covering)

DETAIL OF STEM SURFACE

LONGITUDINAL SECTION THROUGH STEM

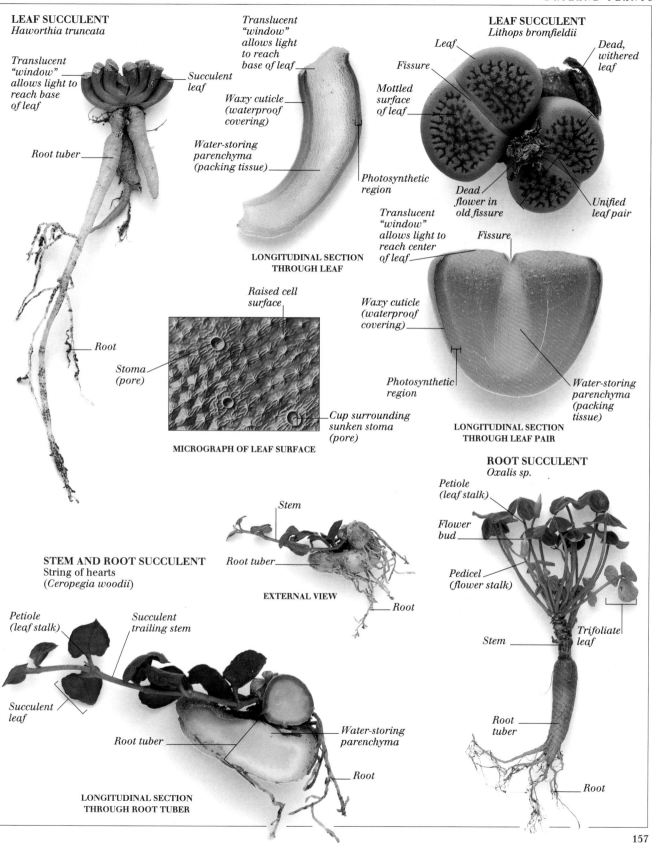

LEAF SUCCULENT
Haworthia truncata

Translucent "window" allows light to reach base of leaf

Succulent leaf

Root tuber

Root

Translucent "window" allows light to reach base of leaf

Waxy cuticle (waterproof covering)

Water-storing parenchyma (packing tissue)

Photosynthetic region

LONGITUDINAL SECTION THROUGH LEAF

Raised cell surface

Stoma (pore)

Cup surrounding sunken stoma (pore)

MICROGRAPH OF LEAF SURFACE

LEAF SUCCULENT
Lithops bromfieldii

Leaf

Fissure

Mottled surface of leaf

Dead, withered leaf

Dead flower in old fissure

Unified leaf pair

Translucent "window" allows light to reach center of leaf

Fissure

Waxy cuticle (waterproof covering)

Photosynthetic region

Water-storing parenchyma (packing tissue)

LONGITUDINAL SECTION THROUGH LEAF PAIR

ROOT SUCCULENT
Oxalis sp.

Petiole (leaf stalk)

Flower bud

Pedicel (flower stalk)

Stem

Trifoliate leaf

Root tuber

Root

Stem

Root tuber

Root

EXTERNAL VIEW

STEM AND ROOT SUCCULENT
String of hearts
(*Ceropegia woodii*)

Petiole (leaf stalk)

Succulent trailing stem

Succulent leaf

Root tuber

Water-storing parenchyma

Root

LONGITUDINAL SECTION THROUGH ROOT TUBER

Wetland plants

WETLAND PLANTS GROW SUBMERGED IN WATER, either partially, like the water hyacinth, or completely, like the pondweeds, and show various adaptations to this habitat. Typically, there are numerous air spaces inside the stems, leaves, and roots; these aid gas exchange and buoyancy. Submerged parts generally have no cuticle (waterproof covering), allowing the plants to absorb minerals and gases directly from the water. Also, because they are supported by the water, wetland plants need little of the supportive tissue found in land plants. Stomata, the gas exchange pores, are absent from plants that are completely submerged. In partially submerged plants with floating leaves, such as water lilies, stomata are found on the upper leaf surfaces, where they cannot be flooded.

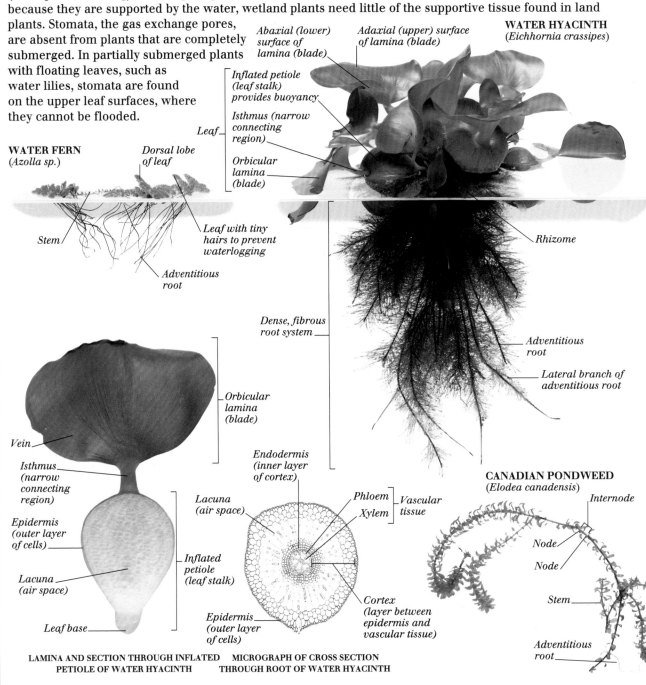

Abaxial (lower) surface of lamina (blade)

Adaxial (upper) surface of lamina (blade)

WATER HYACINTH
(Eichhornia crassipes)

Inflated petiole (leaf stalk) provides buoyancy

Isthmus (narrow connecting region)

Leaf

Orbicular lamina (blade)

WATER FERN
(Azolla sp.)

Dorsal lobe of leaf

Leaf with tiny hairs to prevent waterlogging

Stem

Adventitious root

Rhizome

Dense, fibrous root system

Adventitious root

Lateral branch of adventitious root

Vein

Orbicular lamina (blade)

Isthmus (narrow connecting region)

Endodermis (inner layer of cortex)

CANADIAN PONDWEED
(Elodea canadensis)

Lacuna (air space)

Phloem

Xylem

Vascular tissue

Internode

Epidermis (outer layer of cells)

Node

Node

Lacuna (air space)

Inflated petiole (leaf stalk)

Stem

Leaf base

Epidermis (outer layer of cells)

Cortex (layer between epidermis and vascular tissue)

Adventitious root

LAMINA AND SECTION THROUGH INFLATED PETIOLE OF WATER HYACINTH

MICROGRAPH OF CROSS SECTION THROUGH ROOT OF WATER HYACINTH

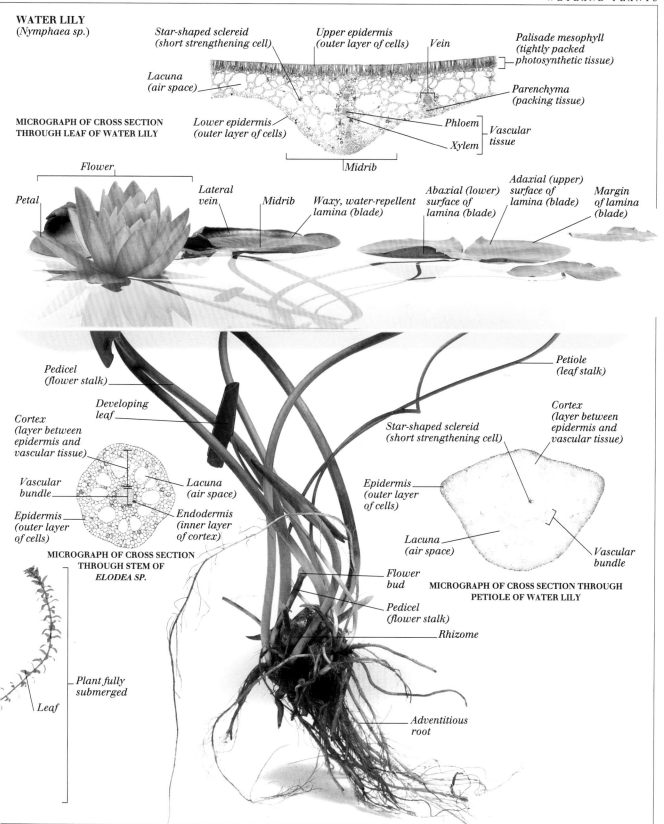

WATER LILY
(*Nymphaea sp.*)

Star-shaped sclereid
(short strengthening cell)

Upper epidermis
(outer layer of cells)

Vein

Palisade mesophyll
(tightly packed
photosynthetic tissue)

Lacuna
(air space)

Parenchyma
(packing tissue)

**MICROGRAPH OF CROSS SECTION
THROUGH LEAF OF WATER LILY**

Lower epidermis
(outer layer of cells)

Phloem

Vascular
tissue

Xylem

Midrib

Flower

Petal

Lateral
vein

Midrib

Waxy, water-repellent
lamina (blade)

Abaxial (lower)
surface of
lamina (blade)

Adaxial (upper)
surface of
lamina (blade)

Margin
of lamina
(blade)

Pedicel
(flower stalk)

Petiole
(leaf stalk)

Developing
leaf

Cortex
(layer between
epidermis and
vascular tissue)

Star-shaped sclereid
(short strengthening cell)

Cortex
(layer between
epidermis and
vascular tissue)

Vascular
bundle

Lacuna
(air space)

Epidermis
(outer layer
of cells)

Epidermis
(outer layer
of cells)

Endodermis
(inner layer
of cortex)

Lacuna
(air space)

Vascular
bundle

**MICROGRAPH OF CROSS SECTION
THROUGH STEM OF
ELODEA SP.**

**MICROGRAPH OF CROSS SECTION THROUGH
PETIOLE OF WATER LILY**

Flower
bud

Pedicel
(flower stalk)

Rhizome

Plant fully
submerged

Leaf

Adventitious
root

Carnivorous plants

CARNIVOROUS (INSECTIVOROUS) PLANTS FEED ON INSECTS and other small animals in addition to producing food in their leaves by photosynthesis. The nutrients absorbed from trapped insects allow carnivorous plants to thrive in acid, boggy soils that lack essential minerals, especially nitrates, where most other plants could not survive. All carnivorous plants have some leaves modified as traps. Many use bright colors and scented nectar to attract prey, and most use enzymes to digest the prey. There are three types of traps. Pitcher plants, such as the monkey cup and cobra lily, have leaves modified as pitcher-shaped pitfall traps, half-filled with water. Once lured inside the mouth of the trap, insects lose their footing on the slippery surface, fall into the liquid, and either decompose or are digested. Venus flytraps use a spring-trap mechanism; when an insect touches trigger hairs on the inner surfaces of the leaves, the two lobes of the trap snap shut. Butterworts and sundews entangle prey by sticky droplets on the leaf surface, while the edges of the leaves slowly curl over to envelop and digest the prey.

A PITCHER PLANT
Cobra lily (*Darlingtonia californica*)

Areola ("window" of transparent tissue)

Fishtail nectary

Wing

Hood

Pitcher

Tubular petiole (leaf stalk)

Areola ("window" of transparent tissue)

Smooth surface

Nectar roll

Dome-shaped hood develops

Fishtail nectary appears

Immature pitcher

Mouth

Wing

Downward-pointing hair

DEVELOPMENT OF MODIFIED LEAF IN COBRA LILY

Immature trap

Interlocked teeth

Closed trap

Red color of trap attracts insects

VENUS FLYTRAP
(*Dionaea muscipula*)

Phyllode (flattened petiole)

Summer petiole (leaf stalk)

Nectary zone (glands secrete nectar)

Digestive zone (glands secrete digestive enzymes)

Tooth

Lobe of trap

Midrib (hinge of trap)

Trigger hair

Spring petiole (leaf stalk)

Trap (twin-lobed leaf blade)

Sensory hinge

Trigger hair

Inner surface of trap

Digestive gland

MICROGRAPH OF LOBE OF VENUS FLYTRAP

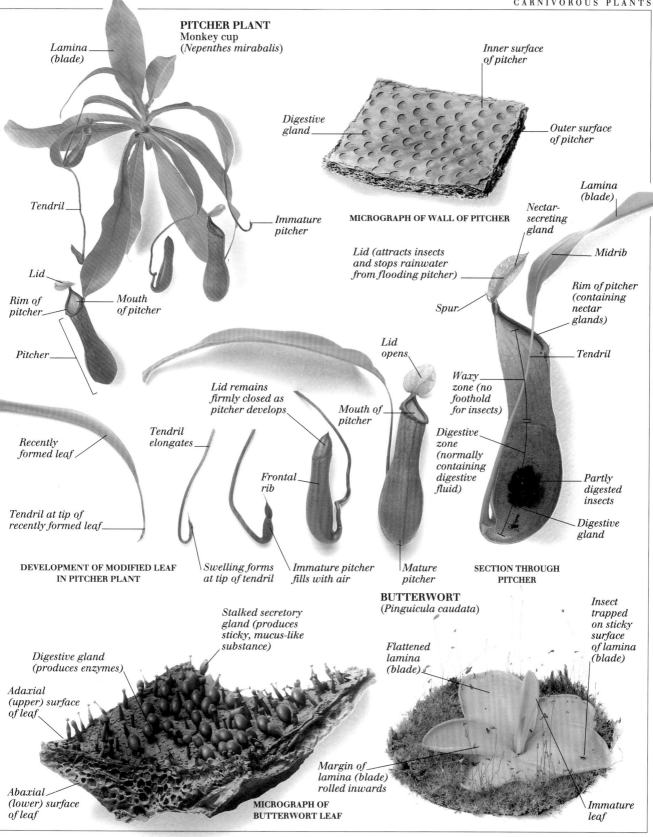

PITCHER PLANT
Monkey cup
(*Nepenthes mirabalis*)

Lamina
(blade)

Tendril

Lid

Rim of
pitcher

Mouth
of pitcher

Pitcher

Immature
pitcher

Inner surface
of pitcher

Digestive
gland

Outer surface
of pitcher

MICROGRAPH OF WALL OF PITCHER

Lamina
(blade)

Nectar-
secreting
gland

Midrib

Lid (attracts insects
and stops rainwater
from flooding pitcher)

Rim of pitcher
(containing
nectar
glands)

Spur

Tendril

Waxy
zone (no
foothold
for insects)

Digestive
zone
(normally
containing
digestive
fluid)

Partly
digested
insects

Digestive
gland

**SECTION THROUGH
PITCHER**

Recently
formed leaf

Tendril
elongates

Lid remains
firmly closed as
pitcher develops

Lid
opens

Mouth of
pitcher

Frontal
rib

Tendril at tip of
recently formed leaf

Swelling forms
at tip of tendril

Immature pitcher
fills with air

Mature
pitcher

**DEVELOPMENT OF MODIFIED LEAF
IN PITCHER PLANT**

BUTTERWORT
(*Pinguicula caudata*)

Stalked secretory
gland (produces
sticky, mucus-like
substance)

Insect
trapped
on sticky
surface
of lamina
(blade)

Flattened
lamina
(blade)

Digestive gland
(produces enzymes)

Adaxial
(upper) surface
of leaf

Margin of
lamina (blade)
rolled inwards

Abaxial
(lower) surface
of leaf

**MICROGRAPH OF
BUTTERWORT LEAF**

Immature
leaf

161

Epiphytic and parasitic plants

EPIPHYTIC AND PARASITIC PLANTS GROW ON OTHER LIVING PLANTS. Typically, epiphytic plants are not rooted in the soil. Instead, they live above ground level on the stems and branches of other plants. Epiphytes obtain water from trapped rainwater and from moisture in the air. They obtain minerals from organic matter that has accumulated on the surface of the plant on which they are growing. Like other green plants, epiphytes produce their food by photosynthesis. Epiphytes include tropical orchids and bromeliads (air plants) and some mosses that live in temperate regions. Parasitic plants obtain all their nutrient requirements from the host plants on which they grow. The parasites produce haustoria, root-like organs that penetrate the stem or roots of the host and grow inward to merge with the host's vascular tissue. These extract water, minerals, and manufactured nutrients. Because they have no need to produce their own food, parasitic plants lack chlorophyll, the green photosynthetic pigment, and they have no foliage leaves. Partial parasitic plants, like mistletoe, obtain water and minerals from the host plant but have green leaves and stems and are therefore able to produce their own food by photosynthesis.

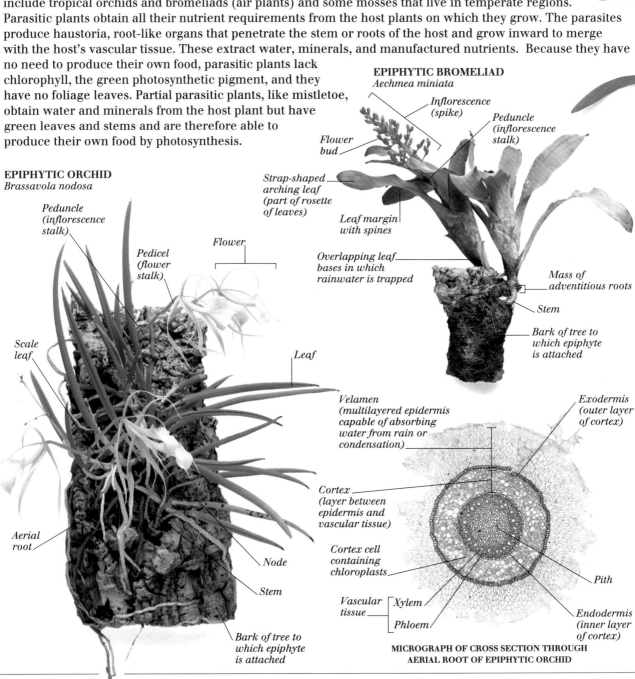

EPIPHYTIC BROMELIAD
Aechmea miniata

Inflorescence (spike)

Peduncle (inflorescence stalk)

Flower bud

Strap-shaped arching leaf (part of rosette of leaves)

Leaf margin with spines

Overlapping leaf bases in which rainwater is trapped

Mass of adventitious roots

Stem

Bark of tree to which epiphyte is attached

EPIPHYTIC ORCHID
Brassavola nodosa

Peduncle (inflorescence stalk)

Pedicel (flower stalk)

Flower

Scale leaf

Leaf

Velamen (multilayered epidermis capable of absorbing water from rain or condensation)

Exodermis (outer layer of cortex)

Cortex (layer between epidermis and vascular tissue)

Cortex cell containing chloroplasts

Pith

Aerial root

Node

Stem

Vascular tissue

Xylem

Phloem

Endodermis (inner layer of cortex)

Bark of tree to which epiphyte is attached

MICROGRAPH OF CROSS SECTION THROUGH AERIAL ROOT OF EPIPHYTIC ORCHID

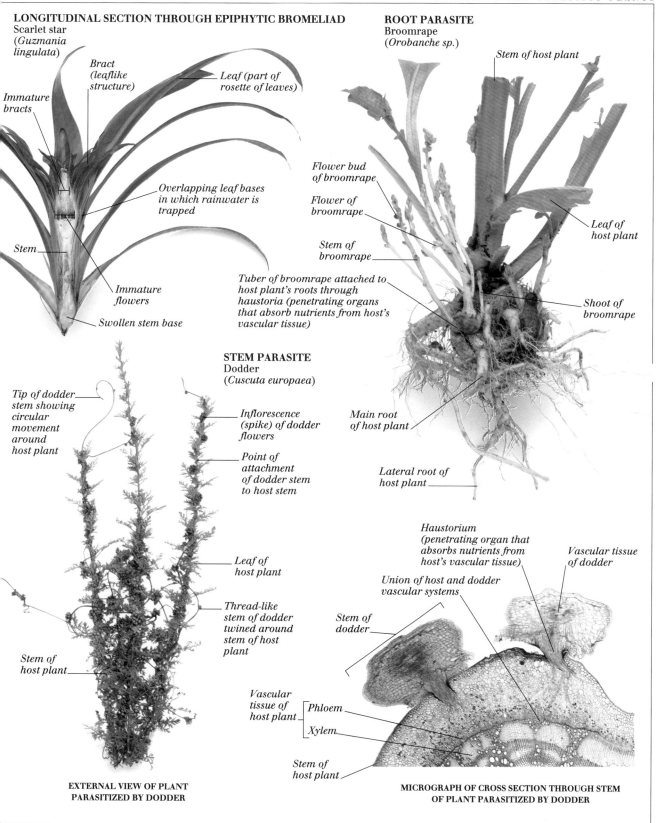

LONGITUDINAL SECTION THROUGH EPIPHYTIC BROMELIAD
Scarlet star
(*Guzmania lingulata*)

Bract (leaflike structure)

Leaf (part of rosette of leaves)

Immature bracts

Overlapping leaf bases in which rainwater is trapped

Stem

Immature flowers

Swollen stem base

ROOT PARASITE
Broomrape
(*Orobanche sp.*)

Stem of host plant

Flower bud of broomrape

Flower of broomrape

Leaf of host plant

Stem of broomrape

Tuber of broomrape attached to host plant's roots through haustoria (penetrating organs that absorb nutrients from host's vascular tissue)

Shoot of broomrape

Main root of host plant

Lateral root of host plant

STEM PARASITE
Dodder
(*Cuscuta europaea*)

Tip of dodder stem showing circular movement around host plant

Inflorescence (spike) of dodder flowers

Point of attachment of dodder stem to host stem

Leaf of host plant

Thread-like stem of dodder twined around stem of host plant

Stem of host plant

EXTERNAL VIEW OF PLANT PARASITIZED BY DODDER

Haustorium (penetrating organ that absorbs nutrients from host's vascular tissue)

Vascular tissue of dodder

Union of host and dodder vascular systems

Stem of dodder

Vascular tissue of host plant

Phloem

Xylem

Stem of host plant

MICROGRAPH OF CROSS SECTION THROUGH STEM OF PLANT PARASITIZED BY DODDER

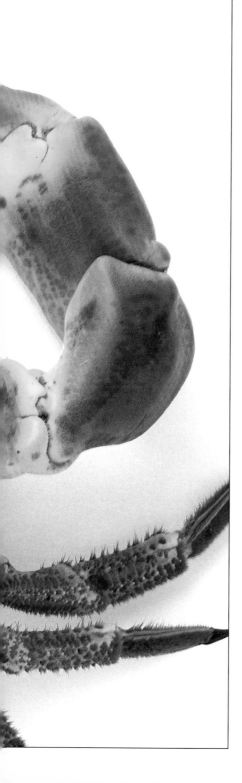

ANIMALS

SPONGES, JELLYFISH, AND SEA ANEMONES   166

INSECTS   168

ARACHNIDS   170

CRUSTACEANS   172

STARFISH AND SEA URCHINS   174

MOLLUSCS   176

SHARKS AND JAWLESS FISH   178

BONY FISH   180

AMPHIBIANS   182

LIZARDS AND SNAKES   184

CROCODILIANS AND TURTLES   186

BIRDS 1   188

BIRDS 2   190

EGGS   192

CARNIVORES   194

RABBITS AND RODENTS   196

UNGULATES   198

ELEPHANTS   200

PRIMATES   202

DOPHINS, WHALES, AND SEALS   204

MARSUPIALS AND MONOTREMES   206

Sponges, jellyfish, and sea anemones

SPONGES ARE MAINLY MARINE animals that make up the phylum Porifera. They are among the simplest of all animals, having no tissues or organs. Their bodies consist of two layers of cells separated by a jelly-like layer (mesohyal) that is strengthened by mineral spicules or protein fibers. The body is perforated by a system of pores and water channels called the aquiferous system. Special cells (choanocytes) with whip-like structures (flagella) draw water through the aquiferous system, thereby bringing tiny food particles to the sponge's cells. Jellyfish (class Scyphozoa), sea anemones (class Anthozoa), and corals (also class Anthozoa) belong to the phylum Cnidaria, also known as Coelenterata. More complex than sponges, coelenterates have simple tissues, such as nervous tissue; a radially symmetrical body; and a mouth surrounded by tentacles with unique stinging cells (cnidocytes).

INTERNAL ANATOMY OF A SPONGE

Amebocyte

Osculum (excurrent pore)

Choanocyte (collar cell)

Ostium (incurrent pore)

Porocyte (pore cell)

Mesohyal

Spongocoel (atrium; paragaster)

Spicule

Pinacocyte (epidermal cell)

Ostium (incurrent pore)

SKELETON OF A SPONGE

Protein matrix

Pore

EXTERNAL FEATURES OF A SEA ANEMONE

Tentacle

EXAMPLES OF SEA ANEMONES

JEWEL ANEMONE
(Corynactis viridis)

PARASITIC ANEMONE
(Calliactis parasitica)

PLUMOSE ANEMONE
(Metridium senile)

MEDITERRANEAN SEA ANEMONE
(Condylactis sp.)

GREEN SNAKELOCK
ANEMONE
(Anemonia viridis)

BEADLET ANEMONE
(Actinia equina)

GHOST ANEMONE
(Actinothoe sphyrodeta)

Sagartia elegans

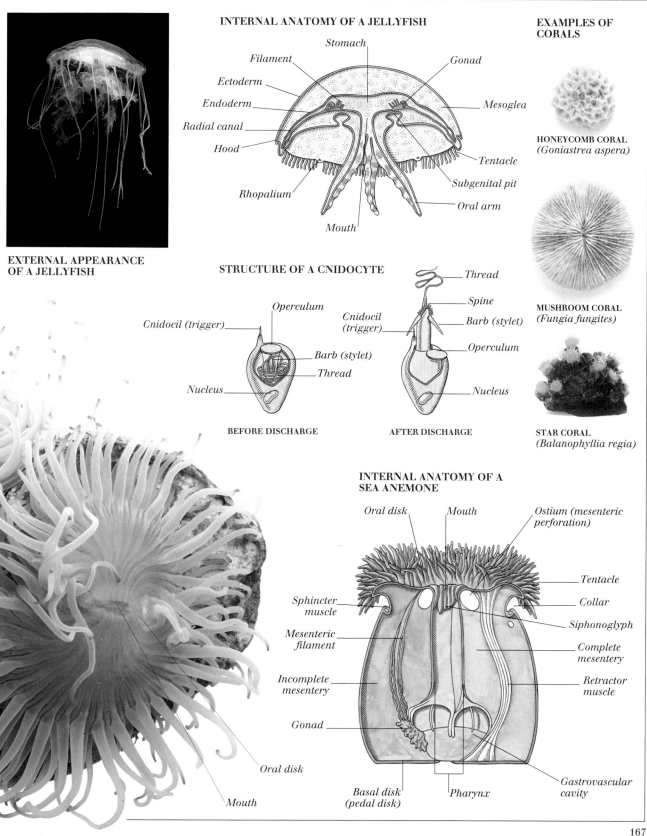

INTERNAL ANATOMY OF A JELLYFISH

Stomach

Filament

Ectoderm

Endoderm

Radial canal

Hood

Gonad

Mesoglea

Tentacle

Subgenital pit

Oral arm

Rhopalium

Mouth

**EXTERNAL APPEARANCE
OF A JELLYFISH**

**EXAMPLES OF
CORALS**

HONEYCOMB CORAL
(*Goniastrea aspera*)

MUSHROOM CORAL
(*Fungia fungites*)

STAR CORAL
(*Balanophyllia regia*)

STRUCTURE OF A CNIDOCYTE

Operculum

Cnidocil (trigger)

Barb (stylet)

Thread

Nucleus

Thread

Spine

Cnidocil
(trigger)

Barb (stylet)

Operculum

Nucleus

BEFORE DISCHARGE

AFTER DISCHARGE

**INTERNAL ANATOMY OF A
SEA ANEMONE**

Oral disk

Mouth

Ostium (mesenteric
perforation)

Sphincter
muscle

Mesenteric
filament

Incomplete
mesentery

Gonad

Tentacle

Collar

Siphonoglyph

Complete
mesentery

Retractor
muscle

Oral disk

Mouth

Basal disk
(pedal disk)

Pharynx

Gastrovascular
cavity

Insects

THE WORD INSECT REFERS to small invertebrate creatures, especially those with bodies divided into sections. Insects, including beetles, ants, bees, butterflies, and moths, belong to various orders in the class Insecta, which is a division of the phylum Arthropoda. Features common to all insects are an exoskeleton (external skeleton); three pairs of jointed legs; three body sections (head, thorax, and abdomen); and one pair of sensory antennae. Beetles (order Coleoptera) are the biggest group of insects, with about 300,000 species (about 30 percent of all known insects). They have a pair of hard elytra (wing cases), which are modified front wings. The principal function of the elytra is to protect the hind wings, which are used for flying. Ants, together with bees and wasps, form the order Hymenoptera, which contains about 200,000 species. This group is characterized by a marked narrowing between the thorax and abdomen. Butterflies and moths form the order Lepidoptera, which has about 150,000 species. They have wings covered with tiny scales, hence the name of their order (Lepidoptera means "scale wings"). The separation of lepidopterans into butterflies and moths is largely artificial as there are no features that categorically distinguish one group from the other. In general, however, most butterflies fly by day, whereas most moths are night flyers. Some insects, including butterflies and moths, undergo complete metamorphosis (transformation) during their life cycle. A butterfly metamorphoses from an egg to a larva (caterpillar), then to a pupa (chrysalis), and finally to an imago (adult).

PUPA (CHRYSALIS)

EXAMPLES OF INSECTS

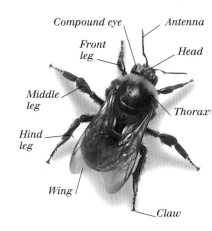

BUMBLEBEE

Compound eye
Antenna
Front leg
Head
Middle leg
Thorax
Hind leg
Wing
Claw

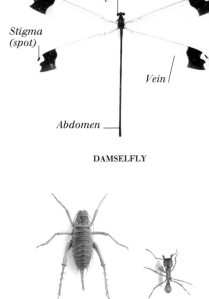

DAMSELFLY

Compound eye
Stigma (spot)
Vein
Abdomen

EXTERNAL FEATURES OF A BEETLE

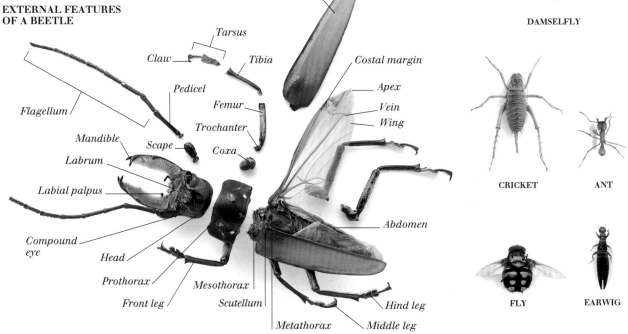

Elytron
Tarsus
Claw
Tibia
Costal margin
Pedicel
Apex
Femur
Vein
Flagellum
Wing
Trochanter
Mandible
Scape
Coxa
Labrum
Labial palpus
Abdomen
Compound eye
Head
Prothorax
Mesothorax
Front leg
Scutellum
Hind leg
Metathorax
Middle leg

CRICKET

ANT

FLY

EARWIG

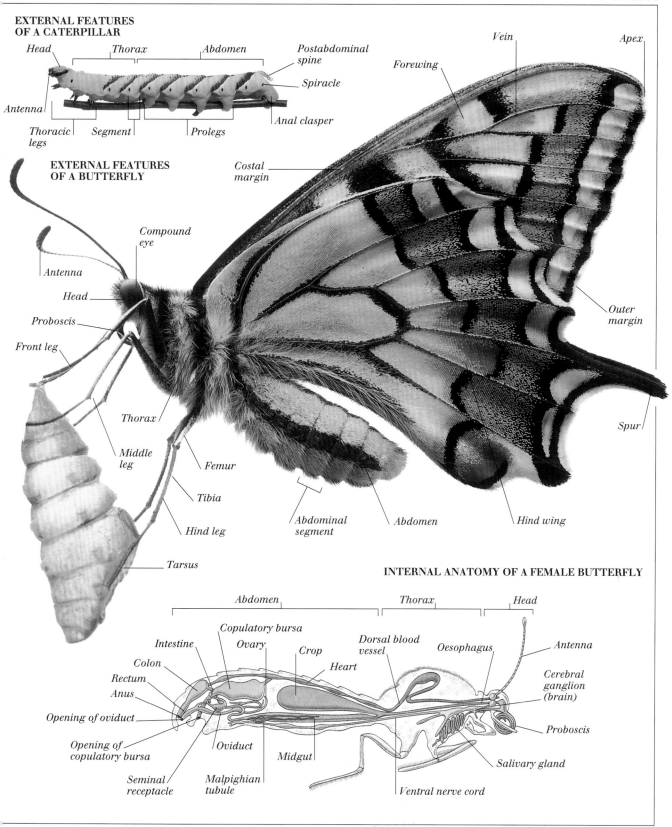

EXTERNAL FEATURES OF A CATERPILLAR

Head
Thorax
Abdomen
Postabdominal spine
Spiracle
Antenna
Anal clasper
Thoracic legs
Segment
Prolegs

EXTERNAL FEATURES OF A BUTTERFLY

Vein
Apex
Forewing
Costal margin
Compound eye
Antenna
Head
Proboscis
Front leg
Outer margin
Thorax
Middle leg
Femur
Tibia
Hind leg
Abdominal segment
Abdomen
Hind wing
Spur
Tarsus

INTERNAL ANATOMY OF A FEMALE BUTTERFLY

Abdomen
Thorax
Head
Copulatory bursa
Dorsal blood vessel
Intestine
Ovary
Crop
Oesophagus
Antenna
Colon
Heart
Cerebral ganglion (brain)
Rectum
Anus
Opening of oviduct
Proboscis
Opening of copulatory bursa
Oviduct
Midgut
Salivary gland
Seminal receptacle
Malpighian tubule
Ventral nerve cord

Arachnids

THE CLASS ARACHNIDA INCLUDES SPIDERS (order Araneae) and scorpions (order Scorpiones). The class is part of the phylum Arthropoda, which also includes insects and crustaceans.

Spiders and scorpions are characterized by having four pairs of walking legs; a pair of pincer-like mouthparts called chelicerae; another pair of frontal appendages called pedipalps, which are sensory in spiders but used for grasping in scorpions; and a body divided into two sections (a combined head and thorax called a cephalothorax, or prosoma, and an abdomen, or opisthosoma). Unlike other arthropods, spiders and scorpions lack antennae. Spiders and scorpions are carnivorous. Spiders poison prey by biting with the fanged chelicerae, scorpions by stinging with the end of the metasoma (tail).

MEXICAN TRUE RED-LEGGED TARANTULA
(Euathlus emilia)

INTERNAL ANATOMY OF A FEMALE SPIDER

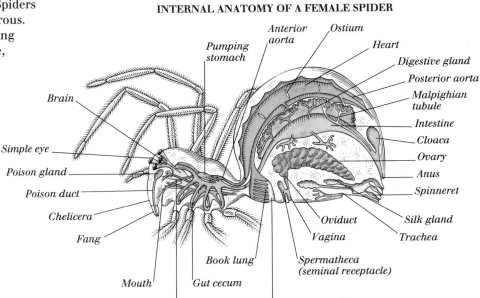

Anterior aorta
Ostium
Heart
Pumping stomach
Digestive gland
Posterior aorta
Malpighian tubule
Intestine
Cloaca
Ovary
Anus
Spinneret
Silk gland
Trachea
Oviduct
Vagina
Spermatheca (seminal receptacle)
Spiracle
Book lung
Gut cecum
Esophagus
Mouth
Fang
Chelicera
Poison duct
Poison gland
Simple eye
Brain

EXTERNAL FEATURES OF A SCORPION

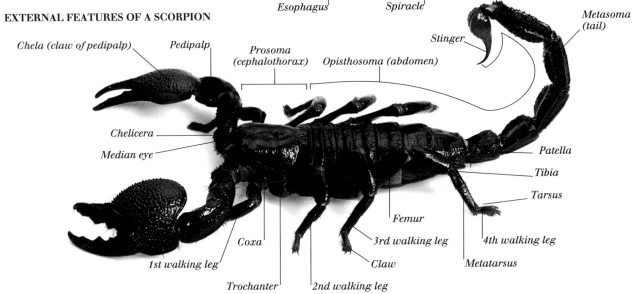

Chela (claw of pedipalp)
Pedipalp
Prosoma (cephalothorax)
Opisthosoma (abdomen)
Stinger
Metasoma (tail)
Chelicera
Median eye
Patella
Tibia
Tarsus
Femur
Coxa
3rd walking leg
4th walking leg
1st walking leg
Claw
Metatarsus
Trochanter
2nd walking leg

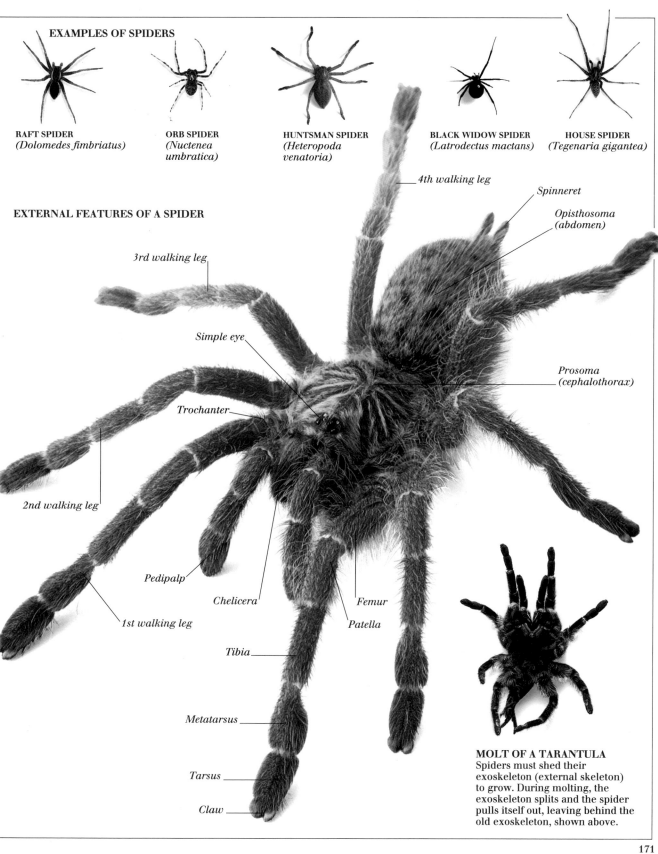

EXAMPLES OF SPIDERS

RAFT SPIDER
(Dolomedes fimbriatus)

ORB SPIDER
(Nuctenea umbratica)

HUNTSMAN SPIDER
(Heteropoda venatoria)

BLACK WIDOW SPIDER
(Latrodectus mactans)

HOUSE SPIDER
(Tegenaria gigantea)

EXTERNAL FEATURES OF A SPIDER

4th walking leg

Spinneret

Opisthosoma (abdomen)

3rd walking leg

Simple eye

Prosoma (cephalothorax)

Trochanter

2nd walking leg

Pedipalp

Chelicera

Femur

1st walking leg

Patella

Tibia

Metatarsus

Tarsus

Claw

MOLT OF A TARANTULA
Spiders must shed their exoskeleton (external skeleton) to grow. During molting, the exoskeleton splits and the spider pulls itself out, leaving behind the old exoskeleton, shown above.

Crustaceans

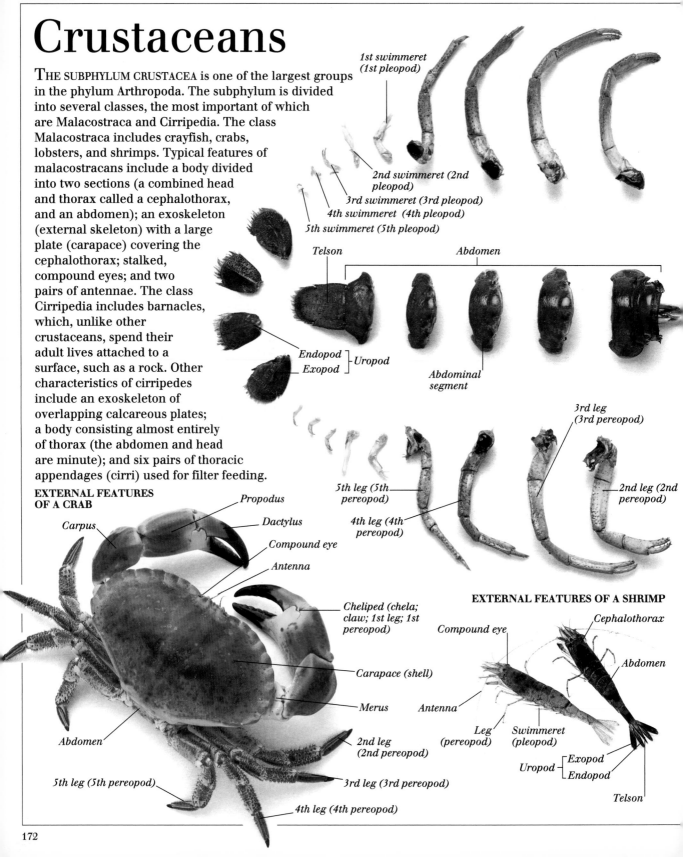

THE SUBPHYLUM CRUSTACEA is one of the largest groups in the phylum Arthropoda. The subphylum is divided into several classes, the most important of which are Malacostraca and Cirripedia. The class Malacostraca includes crayfish, crabs, lobsters, and shrimps. Typical features of malacostracans include a body divided into two sections (a combined head and thorax called a cephalothorax, and an abdomen); an exoskeleton (external skeleton) with a large plate (carapace) covering the cephalothorax; stalked, compound eyes; and two pairs of antennae. The class Cirripedia includes barnacles, which, unlike other crustaceans, spend their adult lives attached to a surface, such as a rock. Other characteristics of cirripedes include an exoskeleton of overlapping calcareous plates; a body consisting almost entirely of thorax (the abdomen and head are minute); and six pairs of thoracic appendages (cirri) used for filter feeding.

1st swimmeret (1st pleopod)

2nd swimmeret (2nd pleopod)

3rd swimmeret (3rd pleopod)

4th swimmeret (4th pleopod)

5th swimmeret (5th pleopod)

Telson

Abdomen

Endopod
Exopod — Uropod

Abdominal segment

3rd leg (3rd pereopod)

5th leg (5th pereopod)

4th leg (4th pereopod)

2nd leg (2nd pereopod)

EXTERNAL FEATURES OF A CRAB

Propodus

Carpus

Dactylus

Compound eye

Antenna

Cheliped (chela; claw; 1st leg; 1st pereopod)

Carapace (shell)

Merus

Abdomen

2nd leg (2nd pereopod)

5th leg (5th pereopod)

3rd leg (3rd pereopod)

4th leg (4th pereopod)

EXTERNAL FEATURES OF A SHRIMP

Compound eye

Cephalothorax

Abdomen

Antenna

Leg (pereopod)

Swimmeret (pleopod)

Uropod — Exopod / Endopod

Telson

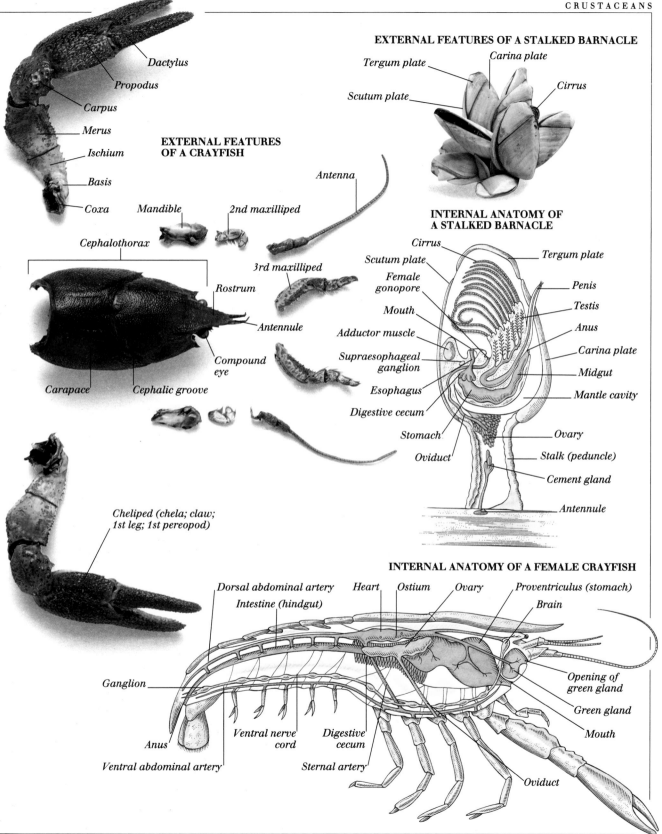

EXTERNAL FEATURES OF A STALKED BARNACLE

Tergum plate
Carina plate
Scutum plate
Cirrus

Dactylus
Propodus
Carpus
Merus
Ischium
Basis
Coxa

EXTERNAL FEATURES OF A CRAYFISH

Antenna
Mandible
2nd maxilliped
Cephalothorax
3rd maxilliped
Rostrum
Antennule
Compound eye
Carapace
Cephalic groove

INTERNAL ANATOMY OF A STALKED BARNACLE

Cirrus
Scutum plate
Female gonopore
Mouth
Adductor muscle
Supraesophageal ganglion
Esophagus
Digestive cecum
Stomach
Oviduct

Tergum plate
Penis
Testis
Anus
Carina plate
Midgut
Mantle cavity
Ovary
Stalk (peduncle)
Cement gland
Antennule

Cheliped (chela; claw; 1st leg; 1st pereopod)

INTERNAL ANATOMY OF A FEMALE CRAYFISH

Dorsal abdominal artery
Heart
Ostium
Ovary
Proventriculus (stomach)
Intestine (hindgut)
Brain
Ganglion
Opening of green gland
Green gland
Mouth
Anus
Ventral nerve cord
Digestive cecum
Oviduct
Ventral abdominal artery
Sternal artery

Starfish and sea urchins

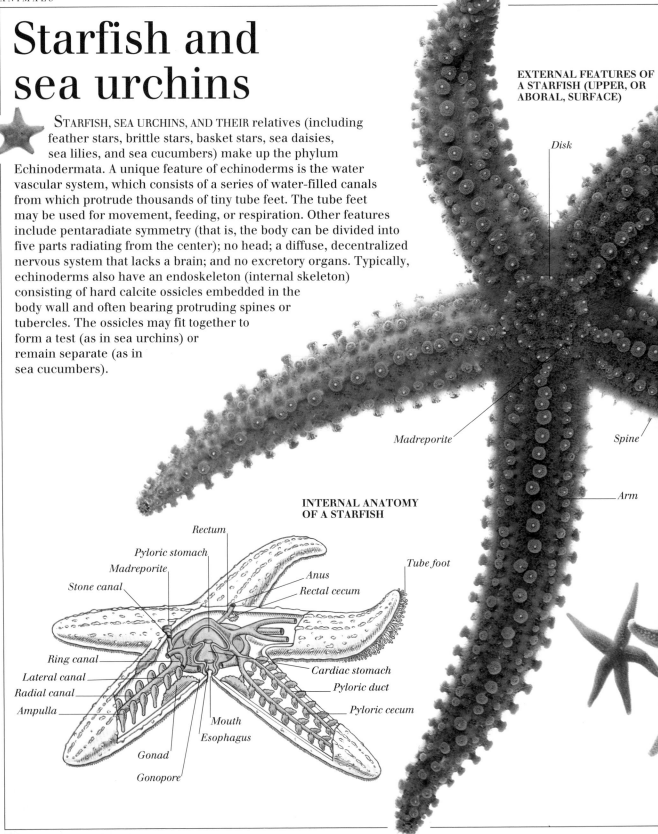

STARFISH, SEA URCHINS, AND THEIR relatives (including feather stars, brittle stars, basket stars, sea daisies, sea lilies, and sea cucumbers) make up the phylum Echinodermata. A unique feature of echinoderms is the water vascular system, which consists of a series of water-filled canals from which protrude thousands of tiny tube feet. The tube feet may be used for movement, feeding, or respiration. Other features include pentaradiate symmetry (that is, the body can be divided into five parts radiating from the center); no head; a diffuse, decentralized nervous system that lacks a brain; and no excretory organs. Typically, echinoderms also have an endoskeleton (internal skeleton) consisting of hard calcite ossicles embedded in the body wall and often bearing protruding spines or tubercles. The ossicles may fit together to form a test (as in sea urchins) or remain separate (as in sea cucumbers).

EXTERNAL FEATURES OF A STARFISH (UPPER, OR ABORAL, SURFACE)

Disk

Madreporite

Spine

Arm

INTERNAL ANATOMY OF A STARFISH

Rectum

Pyloric stomach

Madreporite

Stone canal

Ring canal

Lateral canal

Radial canal

Ampulla

Gonad

Gonopore

Mouth

Esophagus

Anus

Rectal cecum

Tube foot

Cardiac stomach

Pyloric duct

Pyloric cecum

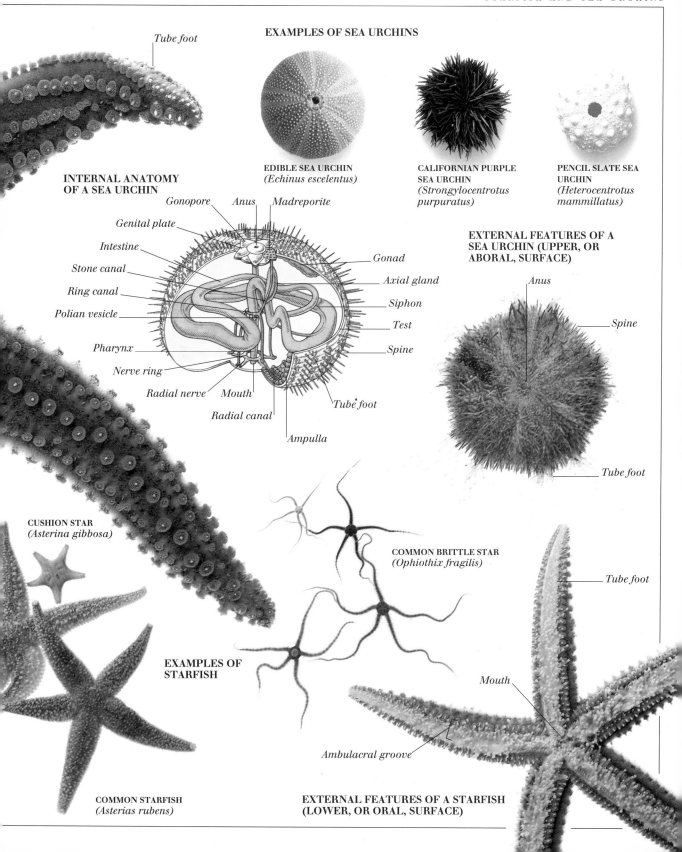

Tube foot

EXAMPLES OF SEA URCHINS

EDIBLE SEA URCHIN
(Echinus escelentus)

**CALIFORNIAN PURPLE
SEA URCHIN**
*(Strongylocentrotus
purpuratus)*

**PENCIL SLATE SEA
URCHIN**
*(Heterocentrotus
mammillatus)*

**INTERNAL ANATOMY
OF A SEA URCHIN**

Gonopore   *Anus*   *Madreporite*

Genital plate

Intestine

Stone canal

Ring canal

Polian vesicle

Pharynx

Nerve ring

Radial nerve   *Mouth*

Radial canal

Ampulla

Gonad

Axial gland

Siphon

Test

Spine

Tube foot

**EXTERNAL FEATURES OF A
SEA URCHIN (UPPER, OR
ABORAL, SURFACE)**

Anus

Spine

Tube foot

CUSHION STAR
(Asterina gibbosa)

COMMON BRITTLE STAR
(Ophiothix fragilis)

Tube foot

Mouth

**EXAMPLES OF
STARFISH**

Ambulacral groove

COMMON STARFISH
(Asterias rubens)

**EXTERNAL FEATURES OF A STARFISH
(LOWER, OR ORAL, SURFACE)**

Mollusks

THE PHYLUM MOLLUSCA (MOLLUSKS) is a large group of animals that includes octopuses, snails, and scallops. Octopuses and their relatives —including squid and cuttlefish—form the class Cephalopoda. Cephalopods typically have a head with a radula (a file-like feeding organ) and beak; a well-developed nervous system; sucker-bearing tentacles; a muscular mantle (part of the body wall) that can expel water through the siphon, enabling movement by jet propulsion; and a small shell or no shell. Snails and their relatives—including slugs, limpets, and abalones—make up the class Gastropoda. Gastropods typically have a coiled external shell, although some, such as slugs, have a small internal shell or no shell; a flat foot; and a head with tentacles and a radula. Scallops and their relatives—including clams, mussels, and oysters—make up the class Bivalvia (also called Pelecypoda). Features of bivalves include a shell with two halves (valves); large gills that are used for breathing and filter feeding; and no radula.

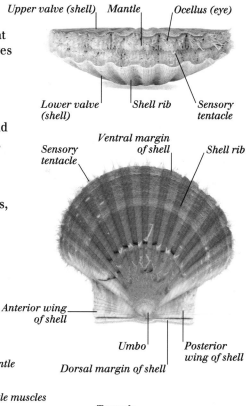

EXTERNAL FEATURES OF A SCALLOP

Upper valve (shell) Mantle Ocellus (eye)

Lower valve (shell) Shell rib Sensory tentacle

Sensory tentacle Ventral margin of shell Shell rib

Anterior wing of shell

Umbo Posterior wing of shell

Dorsal margin of shell

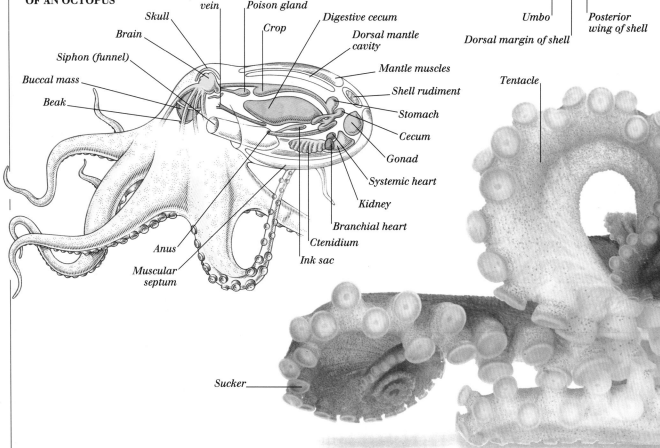

INTERNAL ANATOMY OF AN OCTOPUS

Cephalic vein
Poison gland
Skull
Crop
Digestive cecum
Brain
Dorsal mantle cavity
Siphon (funnel)
Mantle muscles
Buccal mass
Shell rudiment
Beak
Stomach
Cecum
Gonad
Systemic heart
Kidney
Branchial heart
Anus
Ctenidium
Muscular septum
Ink sac

Tentacle

Sucker

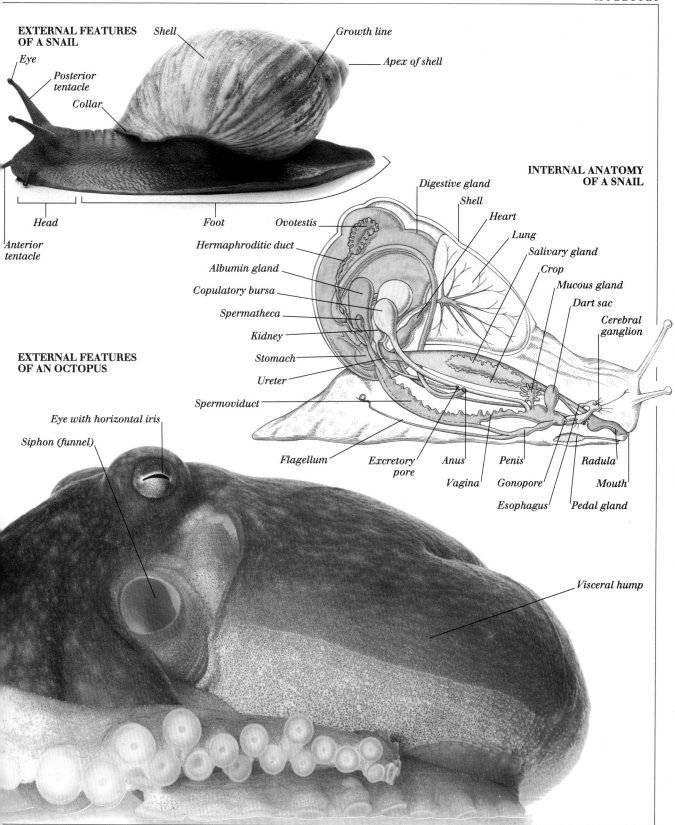

EXTERNAL FEATURES OF A SNAIL

Eye

Posterior tentacle

Collar

Shell

Growth line

Apex of shell

Head

Foot

Anterior tentacle

INTERNAL ANATOMY OF A SNAIL

Digestive gland

Shell

Heart

Lung

Salivary gland

Crop

Mucous gland

Dart sac

Cerebral ganglion

Ovotestis

Hermaphroditic duct

Albumin gland

Copulatory bursa

Spermatheca

Kidney

Stomach

Ureter

Spermoviduct

Flagellum

Excretory pore

Anus

Penis

Radula

Vagina

Gonopore

Mouth

Esophagus

Pedal gland

EXTERNAL FEATURES OF AN OCTOPUS

Eye with horizontal iris

Siphon (funnel)

Visceral hump

Sharks and jawless fish

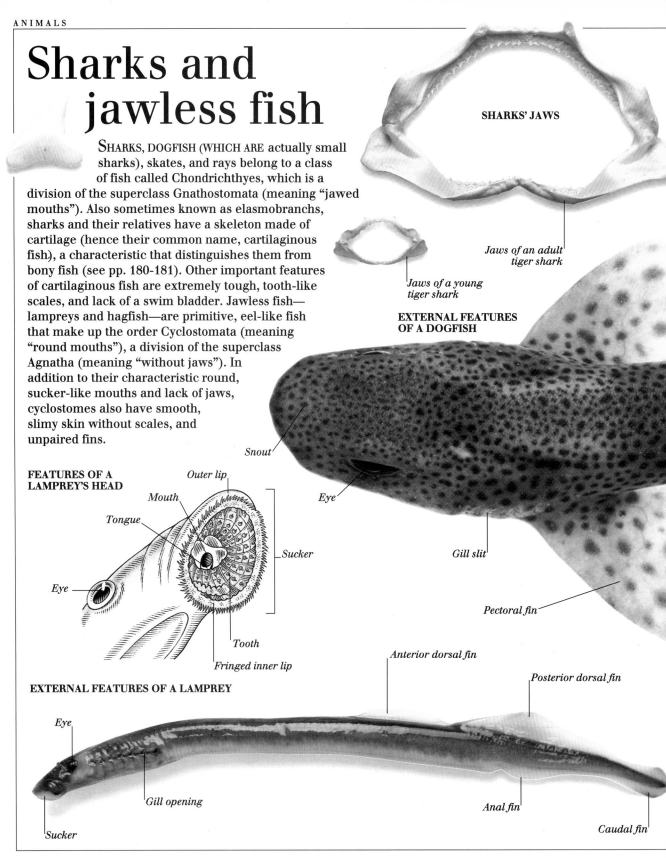

SHARKS, DOGFISH (WHICH ARE actually small sharks), skates, and rays belong to a class of fish called Chondrichthyes, which is a division of the superclass Gnathostomata (meaning "jawed mouths"). Also sometimes known as elasmobranchs, sharks and their relatives have a skeleton made of cartilage (hence their common name, cartilaginous fish), a characteristic that distinguishes them from bony fish (see pp. 180-181). Other important features of cartilaginous fish are extremely tough, tooth-like scales, and lack of a swim bladder. Jawless fish—lampreys and hagfish—are primitive, eel-like fish that make up the order Cyclostomata (meaning "round mouths"), a division of the superclass Agnatha (meaning "without jaws"). In addition to their characteristic round, sucker-like mouths and lack of jaws, cyclostomes also have smooth, slimy skin without scales, and unpaired fins.

SHARKS' JAWS

Jaws of an adult tiger shark

Jaws of a young tiger shark

EXTERNAL FEATURES OF A DOGFISH

Snout

Eye

Gill slit

Pectoral fin

FEATURES OF A LAMPREY'S HEAD

Outer lip

Mouth

Tongue

Sucker

Eye

Tooth

Fringed inner lip

EXTERNAL FEATURES OF A LAMPREY

Eye

Gill opening

Sucker

Anterior dorsal fin

Posterior dorsal fin

Anal fin

Caudal fin

EXAMPLES OF CARTILAGINOUS FISH

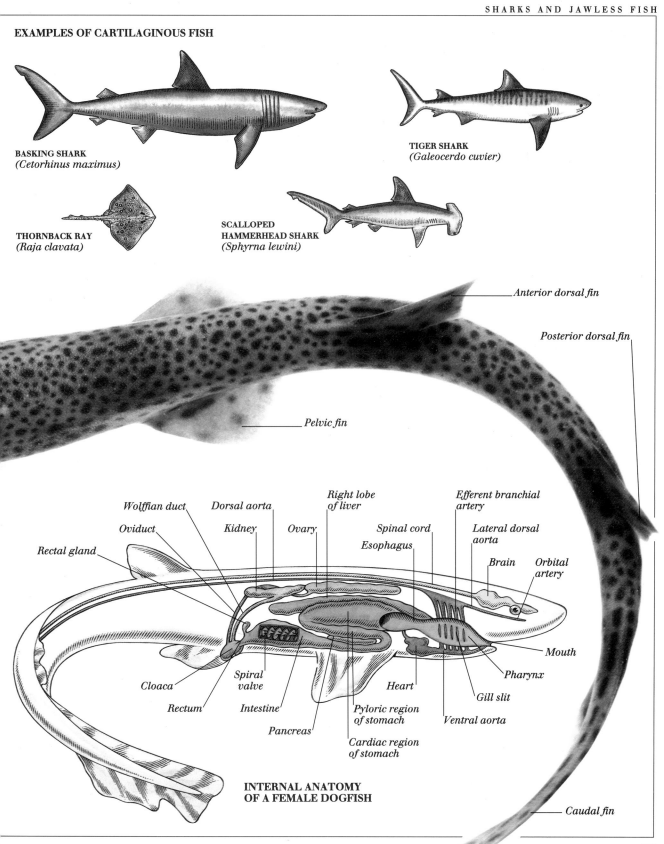

BASKING SHARK
(*Cetorhinus maximus*)

TIGER SHARK
(*Galeocerdo cuvier*)

THORNBACK RAY
(*Raja clavata*)

**SCALLOPED
HAMMERHEAD SHARK**
(*Sphyrna lewini*)

Anterior dorsal fin

Posterior dorsal fin

Pelvic fin

Wolffian duct

Oviduct

Kidney

Ovary

Dorsal aorta

*Right lobe
of liver*

Spinal cord

Esophagus

*Efferent branchial
artery*

*Lateral dorsal
aorta*

Brain

*Orbital
artery*

Rectal gland

Cloaca

Rectum

*Spiral
valve*

Intestine

Pancreas

*Pyloric region
of stomach*

*Cardiac region
of stomach*

Heart

Ventral aorta

Gill slit

Pharynx

Mouth

**INTERNAL ANATOMY
OF A FEMALE DOGFISH**

Caudal fin

Bony fish

BONY FISH, SUCH AS CARP, TROUT, SALMON, perch, and cod, are by far the best known and largest group of fish, with more than 20,000 species (over 95 percent of all known fish). As their name suggests, bony fish have skeletons made of bone, in contrast to the cartilaginous skeletons of sharks, jawless fish, and their relatives (see pp. 178-179). Other typical features of bony fish include a swim bladder, which functions as a variable-buoyancy organ, enabling a fish to remain effortlessly at whatever depth it is swimming; relatively thin, bone-like scales; a flap (called an operculum) covering the gills; and paired pelvic and pectoral fins. Scientifically, bony fish belong to the class Osteichthyes, which is a division of the superclass Gnathostomata (meaning "jawed mouths").

HOW FISH BREATHE

Fish "breathe" by extracting oxygen from water through their gills. Water is sucked in through the mouth; simultaneously, the opercula close to prevent the water from escaping. The mouth is then closed, and muscles in the walls of the mouth, pharynx, and opercular cavity contract to pump the water inside over the gills and out through the opercula. Some fish rely on swimming with their mouths open to keep water flowing over the gills.

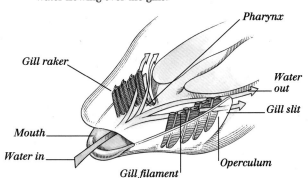

Gill raker

Pharynx

Water out

Gill slit

Mouth

Water in

Gill filament

Operculum

EXAMPLES OF BONY FISH

MANDARINFISH
(*Synchiropus splendidus*)

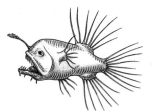

ANGLERFISH
(*Caulophryne jordani*)

LIONFISH
(*Pterois volitans*)

OCEANIC SEAHORSE
(*Hippocampus kuda*)

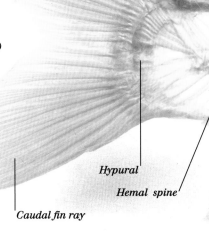

Vertebra

Neural spine

Hypural

Hemal spine

Caudal fin ray

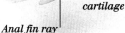

Radial cartilage

Anal fin ray

STURGEON
(*Acipenser sturio*)

SNOWFLAKE MORAY EEL
(*Echidna nebulosa*)

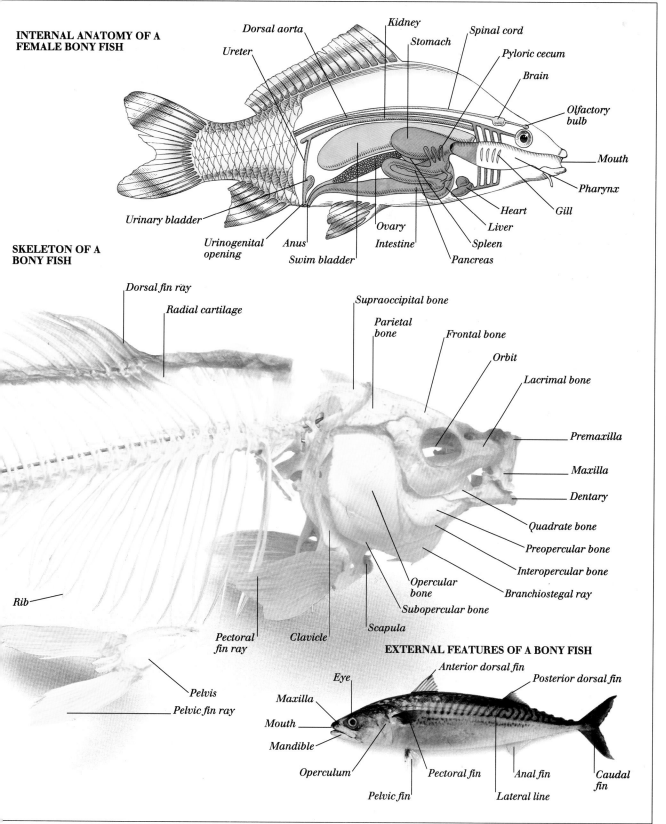

INTERNAL ANATOMY OF A FEMALE BONY FISH

Dorsal aorta

Ureter

Kidney

Stomach

Spinal cord

Pyloric cecum

Brain

Olfactory bulb

Mouth

Pharynx

Gill

Heart

Liver

Spleen

Pancreas

Intestine

Ovary

Swim bladder

Anus

Urinogenital opening

Urinary bladder

SKELETON OF A BONY FISH

Dorsal fin ray

Radial cartilage

Supraoccipital bone

Parietal bone

Frontal bone

Orbit

Lacrimal bone

Premaxilla

Maxilla

Dentary

Quadrate bone

Preopercular bone

Interopercular bone

Branchiostegal ray

Opercular bone

Subopercular bone

Scapula

Clavicle

Pectoral fin ray

Rib

Pelvis

Pelvic fin ray

EXTERNAL FEATURES OF A BONY FISH

Anterior dorsal fin

Posterior dorsal fin

Eye

Maxilla

Mouth

Mandible

Operculum

Pelvic fin

Pectoral fin

Anal fin

Lateral line

Caudal fin

Amphibians

THE CLASS AMPHIBIA INCLUDES FROGS and toads (which make up the order Anura) and newts and salamanders (which make up the order Urodela). Amphibians typically have moist, scaleless, hairless skin; lungs; and are cold-blooded. They also undergo complete metamorphosis, from eggs laid in water through various water-living larval stages (such as the tadpole stage) to land-living adults. Typical features of adult frogs and toads include a squat body with no tail; long, powerful hind legs; and large, often bulging, eyes. Adult newts and salamanders typically have a long body with a well-developed tail; and relatively short legs of equal size. However, newts and salamanders show considerable variation; for example, in some species the adults have minute legs, external gills rather than lungs, and spend their entire lives in water.

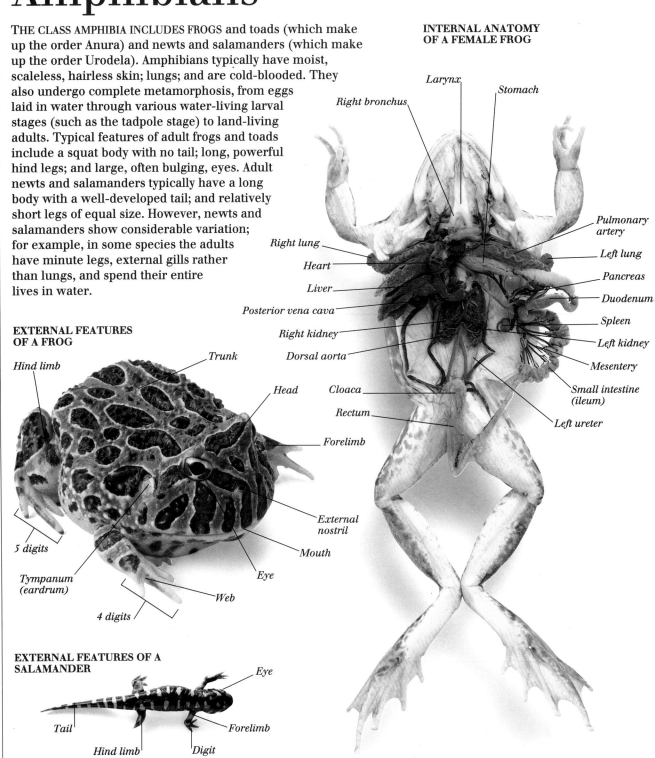

INTERNAL ANATOMY OF A FEMALE FROG

Larynx

Stomach

Right bronchus

Right lung

Heart

Liver

Posterior vena cava

Right kidney

Dorsal aorta

Cloaca

Rectum

Pulmonary artery

Left lung

Pancreas

Duodenum

Spleen

Left kidney

Mesentery

Small intestine (ileum)

Left ureter

EXTERNAL FEATURES OF A FROG

Hind limb

Trunk

Head

Forelimb

External nostril

Mouth

Eye

Web

5 digits

Tympanum (eardrum)

4 digits

EXTERNAL FEATURES OF A SALAMANDER

Eye

Tail

Forelimb

Hind limb

Digit

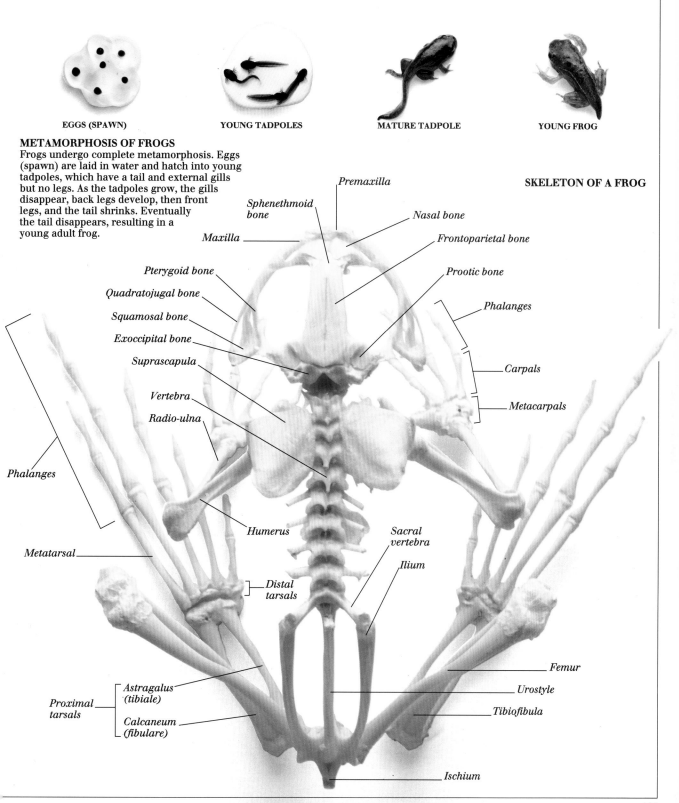

EGGS (SPAWN)

YOUNG TADPOLES

MATURE TADPOLE

YOUNG FROG

METAMORPHOSIS OF FROGS

Frogs undergo complete metamorphosis. Eggs (spawn) are laid in water and hatch into young tadpoles, which have a tail and external gills but no legs. As the tadpoles grow, the gills disappear, back legs develop, then front legs, and the tail shrinks. Eventually the tail disappears, resulting in a young adult frog.

SKELETON OF A FROG

Premaxilla

Sphenethmoid bone

Nasal bone

Maxilla

Frontoparietal bone

Pterygoid bone

Prootic bone

Quadratojugal bone

Phalanges

Squamosal bone

Exoccipital bone

Carpals

Suprascapula

Metacarpals

Vertebra

Radio-ulna

Phalanges

Humerus

Sacral vertebra

Metatarsal

Ilium

Distal tarsals

Femur

Astragalus (tibiale)

Urostyle

Proximal tarsals

Calcaneum (fibulare)

Tibiofibula

Ischium

Lizards and snakes

LIZARDS AND SNAKES BELONG to the order Squamata, a division of the class Reptilia. Characteristic reptilian features include scaly skin, lungs, and cold-bloodedness. Most reptiles lay leathery-shelled eggs, although some hatch the eggs inside their bodies and give birth to live young. Lizards belong to the suborder Lacertilia. Typically, they have long tails, and shed their skin in several pieces. Many lizards can regenerate a tail if it is lost; some can change color; and some are limbless. Snakes make up the suborder Ophidia (also called Serpentes). All snakes have long, limbless bodies; can dislocate their lower jaw to swallow large prey; and have eyelids that are joined together to form a single transparent covering over the front of the eye. Most snakes shed their skin in a single piece. Constrictor snakes kill their prey by squeezing; venomous snakes poison their prey.

EXAMPLES OF SNAKES

MEXICAN MOUNTAIN KING SNAKE (*Lampropeltis triangulum annulata*)

EXTERNAL FEATURES OF A LIZARD

BANDED MILK SNAKE (*Lampropeltis ruthveni*)

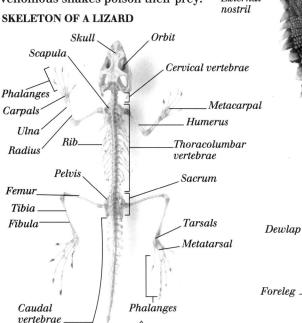

SKELETON OF A LIZARD

- Skull
- Orbit
- Scapula
- Phalanges
- Carpals
- Ulna
- Radius
- Rib
- Cervical vertebrae
- Metacarpal
- Humerus
- Thoracolumbar vertebrae
- Pelvis
- Sacrum
- Femur
- Tibia
- Fibula
- Tarsals
- Metatarsal
- Caudal vertebrae
- Phalanges
- Toe
- Claw

- Eye
- Mouth
- External nostril
- Crest
- Eardrum
- Masseteric scale
- Dorsal scale
- Dewlap
- Foreleg
- Belly
- Ventral scale

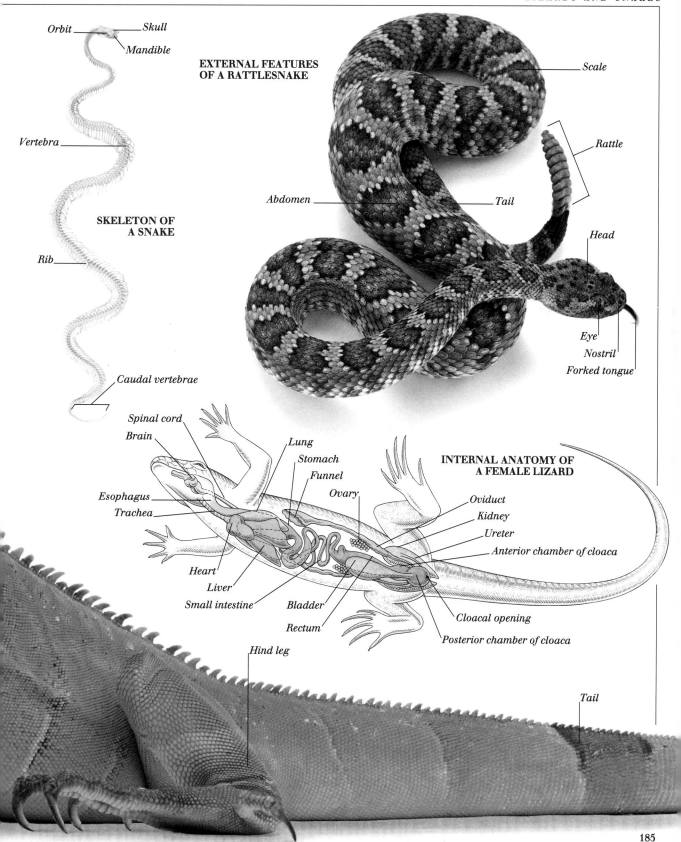

Orbit

Skull

Mandible

EXTERNAL FEATURES OF A RATTLESNAKE

Scale

Vertebra

Rattle

SKELETON OF A SNAKE

Abdomen

Tail

Rib

Head

Caudal vertebrae

Eye

Nostril

Forked tongue

Spinal cord

Brain

Lung

Stomach

Funnel

Ovary

INTERNAL ANATOMY OF A FEMALE LIZARD

Oviduct

Esophagus

Kidney

Trachea

Ureter

Anterior chamber of cloaca

Heart

Liver

Small intestine

Bladder

Cloacal opening

Rectum

Posterior chamber of cloaca

Hind leg

Tail

Crocodilians and turtles

GHARIAL
(Gavialis gangeticus)

NILE CROCODILE
(Crocodylus niloticus)

CROCODILIANS AND TURTLES BELONG to different orders in the class Reptilia. The order Crocodilia includes crocodiles, alligators, caimans, and gharials. Typically, crocodilians are carnivores (flesh-eaters), and have a long snout, sharp teeth for gripping prey, and hard, square scales. All crocodilians are adapted to living on land and in water: they have four strong legs for moving on land; a powerful tail for swimming; and their eyes and nostrils are high on the head so that they stay above water while the rest of the body is submerged. The order Chelonia includes marine turtles, freshwater turtles (terrapins), and land turtles (tortoises). Characteristically, chelonians have a short, broad body encased in a bony shell with an outer horny covering, into which the head and limbs can be withdrawn; and a horny beak instead of teeth.

MISSISSIPPI ALLIGATOR
(Alligator mississippiensis)

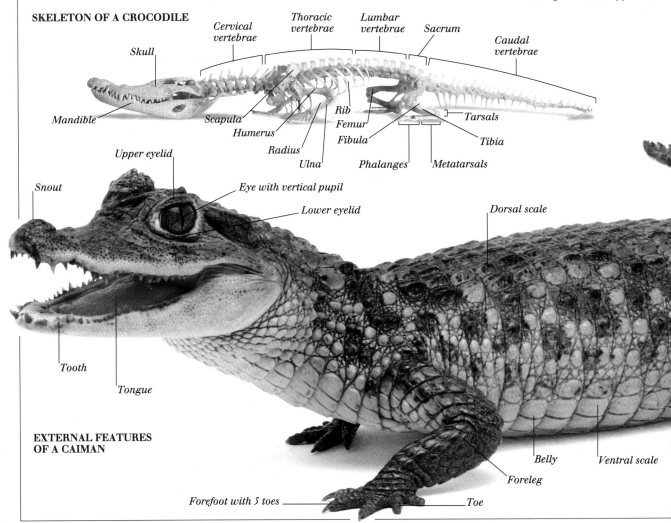

SKELETON OF A CROCODILE

Cervical vertebrae
Thoracic vertebrae
Lumbar vertebrae
Sacrum
Caudal vertebrae
Skull
Mandible
Scapula
Humerus
Radius
Ulna
Rib
Femur
Fibula
Phalanges
Metatarsals
Tarsals
Tibia

Upper eyelid
Eye with vertical pupil
Lower eyelid
Dorsal scale
Snout
Tooth
Tongue

EXTERNAL FEATURES OF A CAIMAN

Belly
Ventral scale
Foreleg
Forefoot with 5 toes
Toe

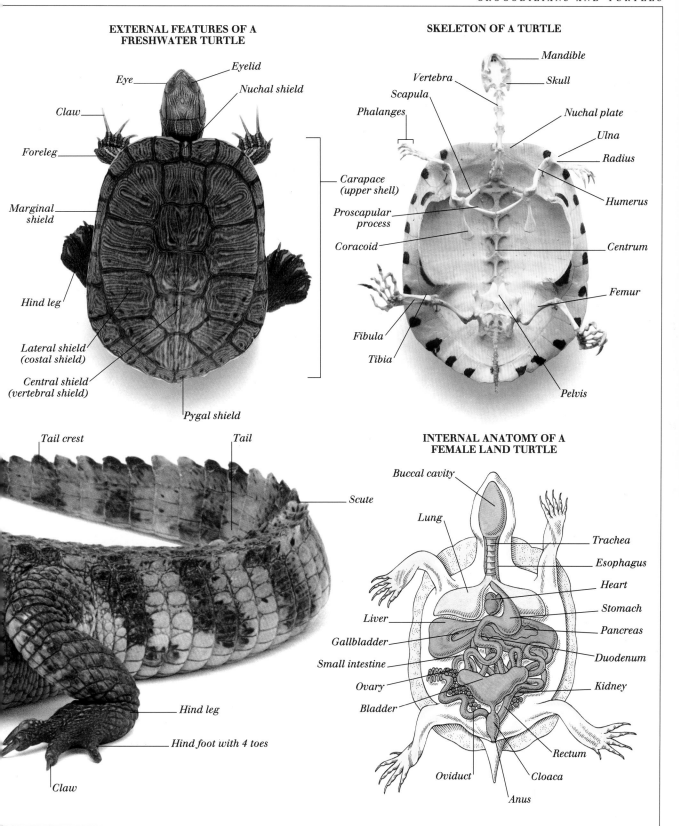

EXTERNAL FEATURES OF A FRESHWATER TURTLE

Eye
Eyelid
Nuchal shield
Claw
Foreleg
Marginal shield
Hind leg
Lateral shield (costal shield)
Central shield (vertebral shield)
Pygal shield
Carapace (upper shell)

SKELETON OF A TURTLE

Mandible
Vertebra
Skull
Scapula
Phalanges
Nuchal plate
Ulna
Radius
Humerus
Proscapular process
Coracoid
Centrum
Femur
Fibula
Tibia
Pelvis

Tail crest
Tail
Scute
Hind leg
Hind foot with 4 toes
Claw

INTERNAL ANATOMY OF A FEMALE LAND TURTLE

Buccal cavity
Lung
Trachea
Esophagus
Heart
Stomach
Pancreas
Duodenum
Kidney
Liver
Gallbladder
Small intestine
Ovary
Bladder
Rectum
Oviduct
Cloaca
Anus

Birds 1

BIRDS MAKE UP THE CLASS AVES. There are more than 9,000 species, almost all of which can fly (the only flightless birds are penguins, ostriches, rheas, cassowaries, and kiwis). The ability to fly is reflected in the typical bird features: forelimbs modified as wings, a streamlined body, and hollow bones to reduce weight. All birds lay hard-shelled eggs, which the parents incubate. Birds' beaks and feet vary according to diet and way of life. Beaks range from general purpose types suitable for a mixed diet (those of thrushes, for example), to types specialized for particular foods (such as the large, curved, sieving beaks of flamingos). Feet range from the webbed "paddles" of ducks, to the talons of birds of prey. Plumage also varies widely, and in many species the male is brightly colored for courtship display whereas the female is drab.

EXTERNAL FEATURES OF A BIRD

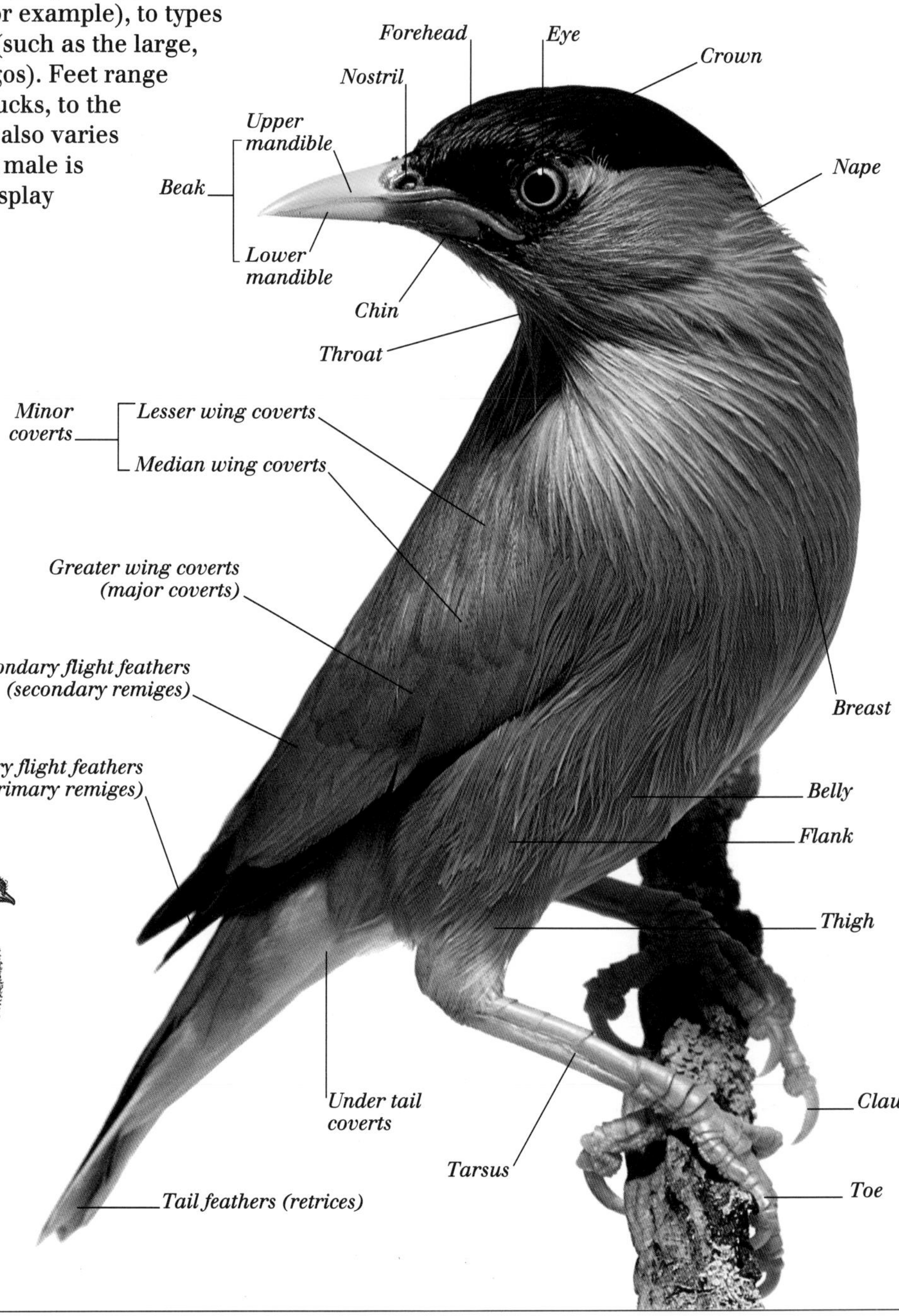

Forehead
Eye
Crown
Nostril
Nape
Upper mandible
Beak
Lower mandible
Chin
Throat
Breast
Belly
Flank
Thigh
Claw
Toe
Tarsus

EXAMPLES OF BIRDS

MALE TUFTED DUCK
(*Aythya fuligula*)

WHITE STORK
(*Ciconia ciconia*)

MALE OSTRICH
(*Struthio camelus*)

Minor coverts
Lesser wing coverts
Median wing coverts

Greater wing coverts
(major coverts)

Secondary flight feathers
(secondary remiges)

Primary flight feathers
(primary remiges)

Under tail coverts

Tail feathers (retrices)

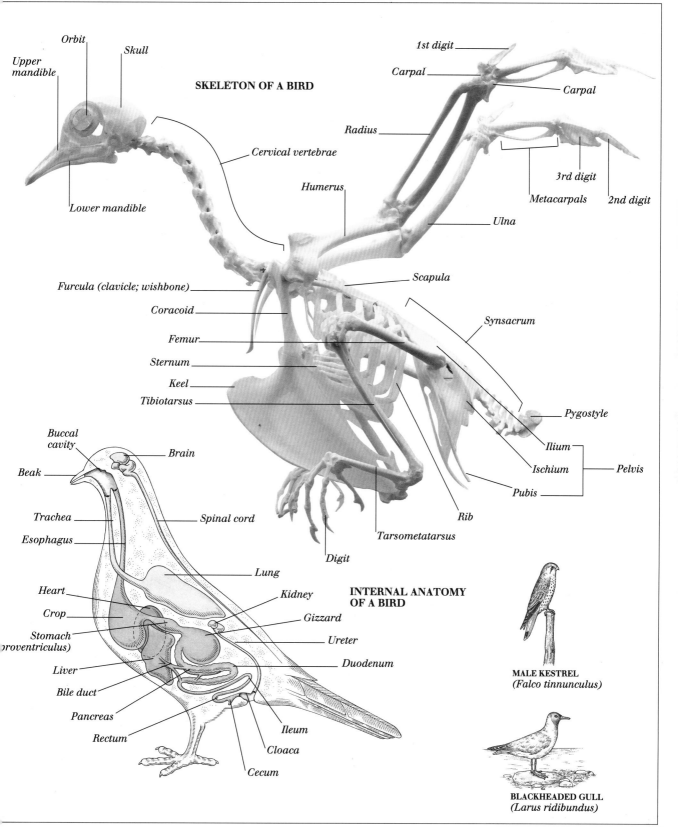

SKELETON OF A BIRD

Upper mandible

Orbit

Skull

1st digit

Carpal

Carpal

Radius

Cervical vertebrae

3rd digit

Metacarpals

2nd digit

Humerus

Lower mandible

Ulna

Scapula

Furcula (clavicle; wishbone)

Synsacrum

Coracoid

Femur

Sternum

Keel

Tibiotarsus

Pygostyle

Ilium

Ischium

Pelvis

Pubis

Rib

Tarsometatarsus

Digit

Buccal cavity

Brain

Beak

Spinal cord

Trachea

INTERNAL ANATOMY OF A BIRD

Esophagus

Lung

Heart

Kidney

Crop

Gizzard

Stomach (proventriculus)

Ureter

Liver

Duodenum

Bile duct

Pancreas

Rectum

Ileum

Cloaca

Cecum

MALE KESTREL
(Falco tinnunculus)

BLACKHEADED GULL
(Larus ridibundus)

Birds 2

EXAMPLES OF BIRDS' FEET

KITTIWAKE
(Rissa tridactyla)
The webbed feet are
adapted for paddling
through water.

LITTLE GREBE
(Tachybaptus ruficollis)
The lobed, flattened feet
are adapted for swimming
underwater.

TAWNY OWL
(Strix aluco)
The clawed feet are adapted
for gripping prey.

EXAMPLES OF BIRDS' BEAKS

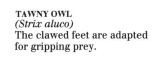

KING VULTURE
(Sarcorhamphus papa)
The hooked beak is adapted
for pulling apart flesh.

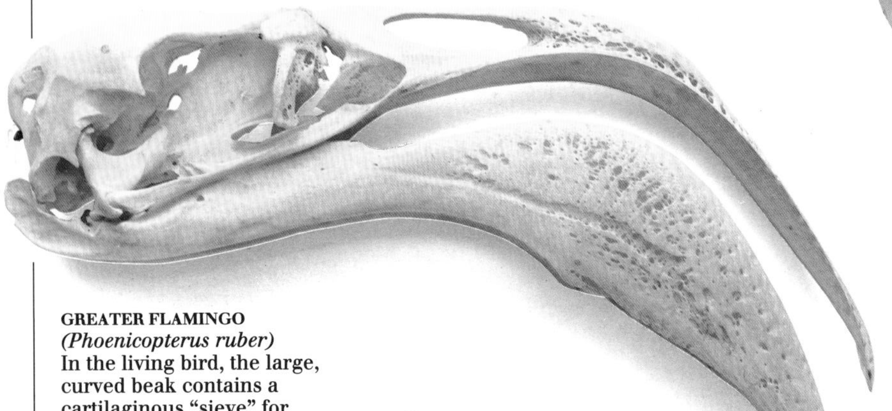

GREATER FLAMINGO
(Phoenicopterus ruber)
In the living bird, the large,
curved beak contains a
cartilaginous "sieve" for
filtering food particles
from water.

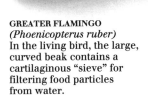

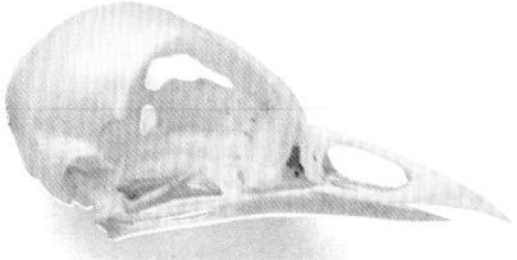

MAVIS, OR MISTLE THRUSH
(Turdus viscivorus)
The all-purpose beak is suitable
for gathering a wide range of
animal and plant foods.

BLUE-AND-YELLOW MACAW
(Ara ararauna)
The broad, powerful, hooked beak
is adapted for crushing seeds and
eating fruit.

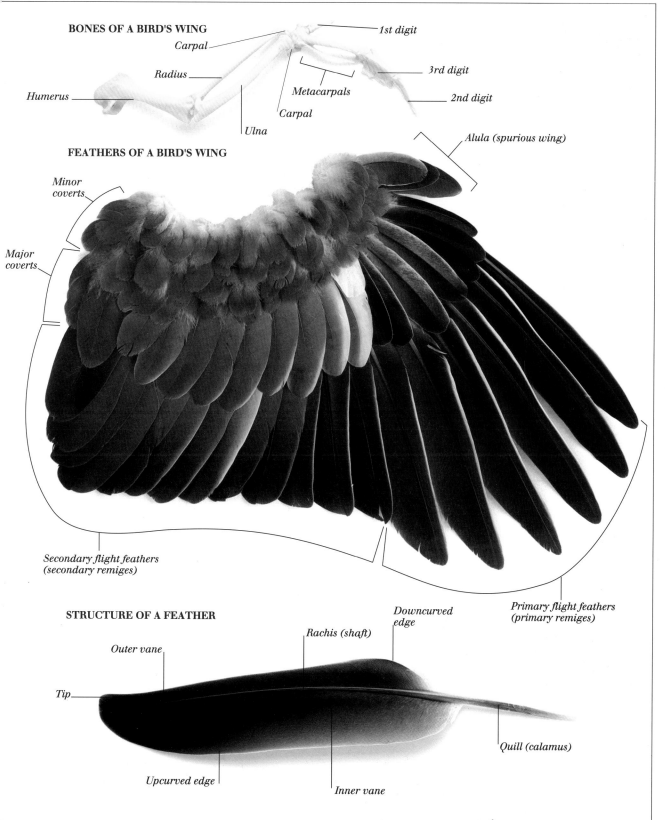

BONES OF A BIRD'S WING

1st digit

Carpal

Radius

3rd digit

Humerus

Metacarpals

2nd digit

Carpal

Ulna

Alula (spurious wing)

FEATHERS OF A BIRD'S WING

Minor
coverts

Major
coverts

Secondary flight feathers
(secondary remiges)

Downcurved
edge

Primary flight feathers
(primary remiges)

STRUCTURE OF A FEATHER

Rachis (shaft)

Outer vane

Tip

Quill (calamus)

Upcurved edge

Inner vane

Eggs

AN EGG IS A SINGLE CELL, produced by the female, with the capacity to develop into a new individual. Development may take place inside the mother's body (as in most mammals) or outside, in which case the egg has a protective covering such as a shell. Egg yolk nourishes the growing young. Eggs developing inside the mother generally have little yolk, because the young are nourished from her body. Eggs developing outside may also have little yolk if they are produced by animals whose young go through a larval stage (such as a caterpillar) that feeds itself while developing into the adult form. The shelled eggs of birds and reptiles contain enough yolk to sustain the young until it hatches into a juvenile version of the adult.

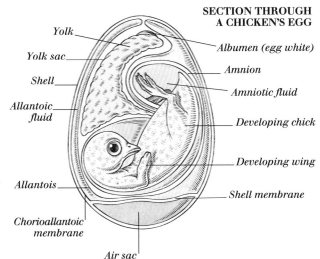

SECTION THROUGH A CHICKEN'S EGG

Yolk
Yolk sac
Shell
Allantoic fluid
Allantois
Chorioallantoic membrane
Air sac
Albumen (egg white)
Amnion
Amniotic fluid
Developing chick
Developing wing
Shell membrane

VARIETY OF EGGS

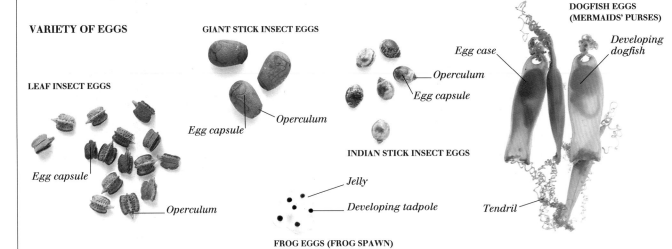

LEAF INSECT EGGS

Egg capsule
Operculum

GIANT STICK INSECT EGGS

Egg capsule
Operculum

INDIAN STICK INSECT EGGS

Operculum
Egg capsule

FROG EGGS (FROG SPAWN)

Jelly
Developing tadpole

DOGFISH EGGS (MERMAIDS' PURSES)

Egg case
Developing dogfish
Tendril

HATCHING OF A QUAIL'S EGG

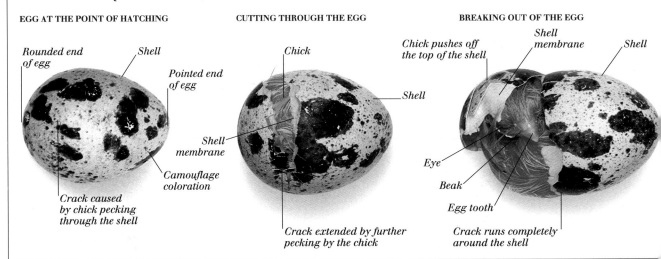

EGG AT THE POINT OF HATCHING

Rounded end of egg
Shell
Pointed end of egg
Shell membrane
Camouflage coloration
Crack caused by chick pecking through the shell

CUTTING THROUGH THE EGG

Chick
Shell
Shell membrane
Crack extended by further pecking by the chick

BREAKING OUT OF THE EGG

Chick pushes off the top of the shell
Shell membrane
Shell
Eye
Beak
Egg tooth
Crack runs completely around the shell

EXAMPLES OF BIRDS' EGGS

BEE HUMMINGBIRD
(*Calypte helenae*)

GREATER BLACKBACKED GULL
(*Larus marinus*)

BALTIMORE ORIOLE
(*Icterus galbula*)

WILLOW GROUSE
(*Lagopus lagopus*)

COMMON TERN
(*Sterna hirundo*)

CARRION CROW
(*Corvus corone*)

CHAFFINCH
(*Fringilla coelebs*)

OSTRICH
(*Struthio camelus*)

EMERGING FROM THE EGG

Eye

Beak

Egg tooth

Chick heaves itself
out of the egg

Tympanum (eardrum)

Shell

Wet down

Remains of egg membranes
(amnion and allantois)

Eye

Beak

Egg tooth

Nostril

THE NEWLY HATCHED CHICK

Tympanum
(eardrum)

Chick is dry
about an hour
after hatching

Dry down

Toe

Claw

Leg

Eggshell

Carnivores

EXTERNAL FEATURES
OF A MALE LION

THE MAMMALIAN ORDER CARNIVORA includes cats, dogs, bears,
raccoons, pandas, weasels, badgers, skunks, otters, civets,
mongooses, and hyenas. The order's name is derived from
the fact that most of its members are carnivores (flesh-
eaters). Typical carnivore features therefore reflect a
hunting lifestyle: speed and agility; sharp claws and
well-developed canine teeth for holding and killing
prey; carnassial teeth (cheek teeth) for cutting flesh;
and forward-facing eyes for good distance judgment.
However, some members of the order—bears,
badgers, and foxes, for example—have a more
mixed diet, and a few are entirely herbivorous
(plant-eating), notably pandas. Such animals
have no carnassial teeth and tend to be slower-
moving than pure flesh-eaters.

SKULL OF A LION

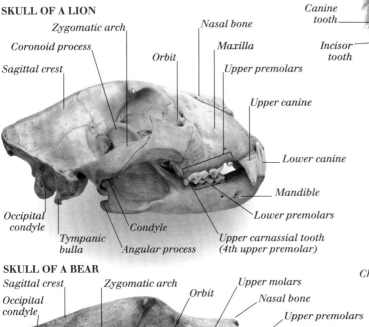

SKULL OF A BEAR

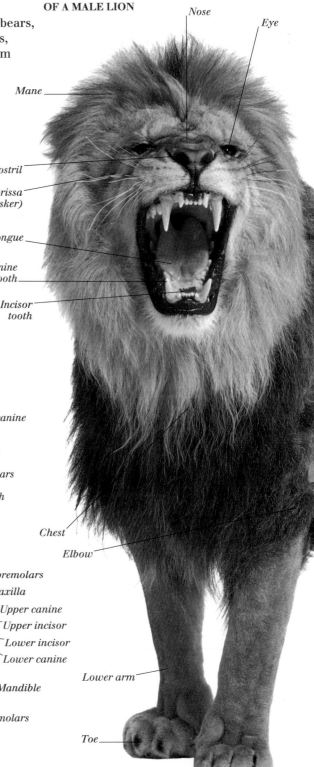

EXAMPLES OF CARNIVORES

GERMAN SHEPHERD DOG
(Canis familiaris)

MANED WOLF
(Chrysocyon brachyurus)

RACCOON
(Procyon lotor)

AMERICAN BLACK BEAR
(Ursus americanus)

SKELETON OF A DOMESTIC CAT

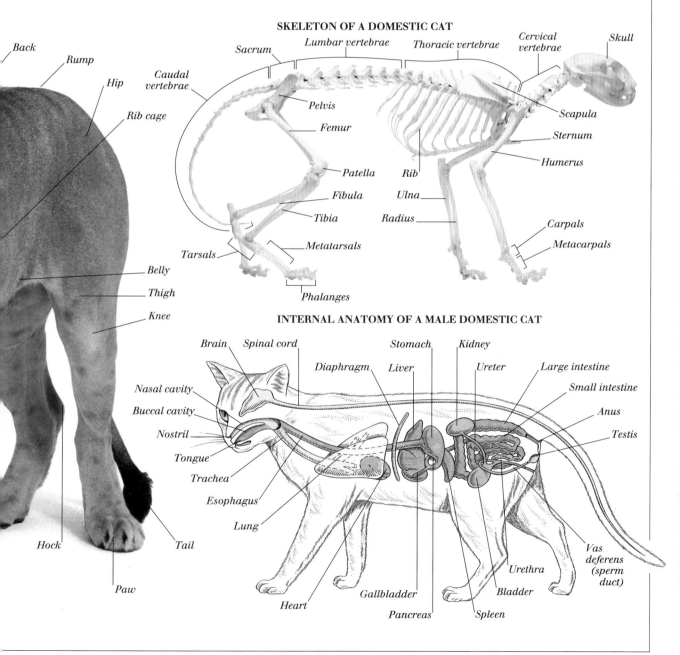

Back

Rump

Hip

Rib cage

Belly

Thigh

Knee

Hock

Paw

Tail

Sacrum

Caudal vertebrae

Lumbar vertebrae

Thoracic vertebrae

Cervical vertebrae

Skull

Pelvis

Femur

Scapula

Sternum

Humerus

Patella

Rib

Fibula

Ulna

Tibia

Radius

Carpals

Metacarpals

Tarsals

Metatarsals

Phalanges

INTERNAL ANATOMY OF A MALE DOMESTIC CAT

Brain

Spinal cord

Stomach

Kidney

Diaphragm

Liver

Ureter

Large intestine

Small intestine

Nasal cavity

Buccal cavity

Anus

Nostril

Testis

Tongue

Trachea

Esophagus

Lung

Vas deferens (sperm duct)

Urethra

Heart

Gallbladder

Bladder

Pancreas

Spleen

Rabbits and rodents

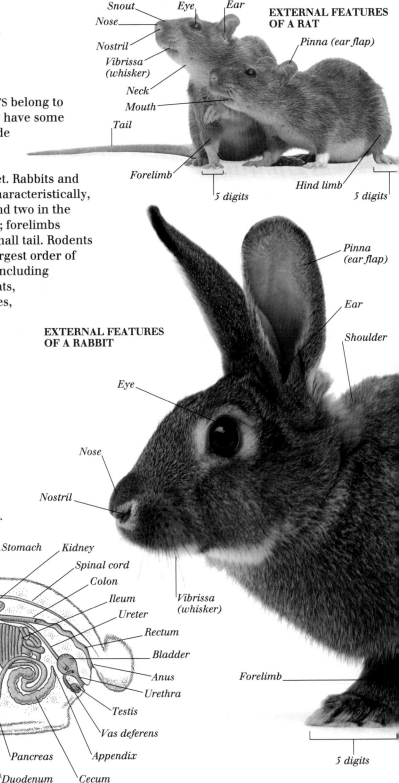

ALTHOUGH RABBITS AND RODENTS belong to different orders of mammals, they have some features in common. These features include chisel-shaped incisor teeth that grow continually, and eating their feces to extract more nutrients from their plant diet. Rabbits and hares belong to the order Lagomorpha. Characteristically, they have four incisors in the upper jaw and two in the lower jaw; powerful hind legs for jumping; forelimbs adapted for burrowing; long ears; and a small tail. Rodents make up the order Rodentia. This is the largest order of mammals, with more than 1,700 species, including squirrels, beavers, chipmunks, gophers, rats, mice, lemmings, gerbils, porcupines, cavies, and the capybara. Typical rodent features include two incisors in each jaw; short forelimbs for manipulating food; and cheek pouches for storing food.

EXTERNAL FEATURES OF A RAT

Snout
Eye
Ear
Nose
Nostril
Vibrissa (whisker)
Neck
Mouth
Tail
Forelimb
Pinna (ear flap)
Hind limb
5 digits
5 digits

EXTERNAL FEATURES OF A RABBIT

Pinna (ear flap)
Ear
Shoulder
Eye
Nose
Nostril
Vibrissa (whisker)
Forelimb
5 digits

INTERNAL ANATOMY OF A MALE RABBIT

Brain
Gallbladder
Liver
Stomach
Kidney
Spinal cord
Colon
Ileum
Ureter
Rectum
Bladder
Anus
Urethra
Testis
Vas deferens
Appendix
Cecum
Duodenum
Pancreas
Diaphragm
Heart
Trachea
Lung
Esophagus
Tongue
Buccal cavity
Mouth
Nasal cavity

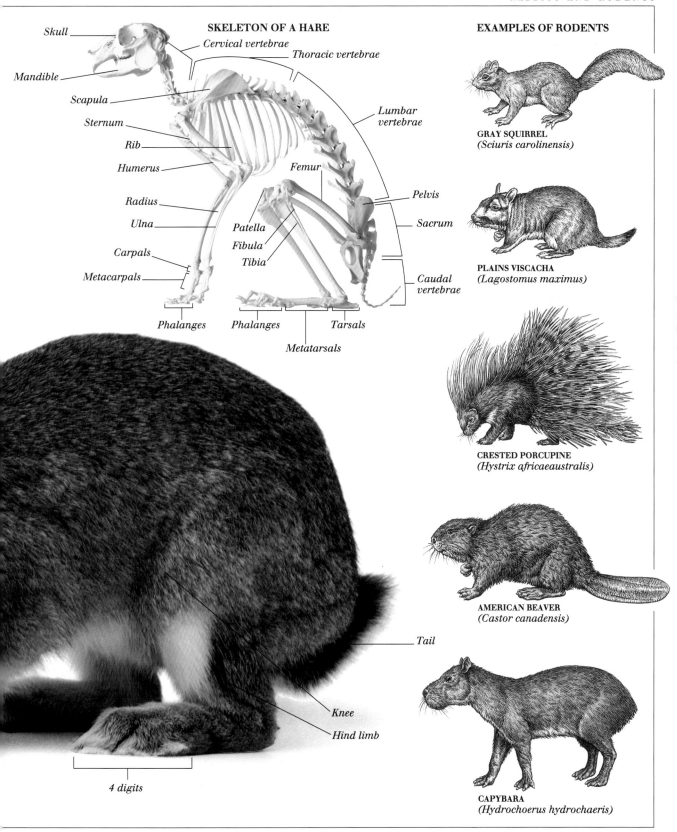

SKELETON OF A HARE

Skull

Mandible

Cervical vertebrae

Thoracic vertebrae

Scapula

Sternum

Rib

Humerus

Radius

Ulna

Carpals

Metacarpals

Lumbar vertebrae

Femur

Pelvis

Sacrum

Patella

Fibula

Tibia

Caudal vertebrae

Phalanges

Phalanges

Tarsals

Metatarsals

4 digits

Tail

Knee

Hind limb

EXAMPLES OF RODENTS

GRAY SQUIRREL
(Sciuris carolinensis)

PLAINS VISCACHA
(Lagostomus maximus)

CRESTED PORCUPINE
(Hystrix africaeaustralis)

AMERICAN BEAVER
(Castor canadensis)

CAPYBARA
(Hydrochoerus hydrochaeris)

Ungulates

UNGULATES IS A GENERAL TERM FOR a large, varied group of mammals that includes horses, cattle, and their relatives. The ungulates are divided into two orders on the basis of the number of toes. Members of the order Perissodactyla (odd-toed ungulates) have one or three toes. Perissodactyls include horses, asses, and zebras (all of which are one-toed), and rhinoceroses and tapirs (which are three-toed). Members of the order Artiodactyla (even-toed ungulates) have two or four toes. Most artiodactyls have two toes, which are typically encased in hooves to give the so-called cloven hoof. Two-toed, cloven-hoofed artiodactyls include cows and other cattle, sheep, goats, antelopes, deer, and giraffes. The other main two-toed artiodactyls are camels and llamas. Most two-toed artiodactyls are ruminants; that is, they have a four-chambered stomach and chew the cud. The principal four-toed artiodactyls are hogs and hippopotamuses.

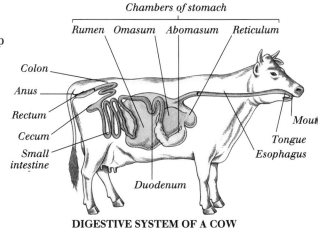

DIGESTIVE SYSTEM OF A COW

COMPARISON OF THE FRONT FEET OF A HORSE AND A COW

SKELETON OF THE LEFT FRONT FOOT OF A HORSE

SKELETON OF THE RIGHT FRONT FOOT OF A COW

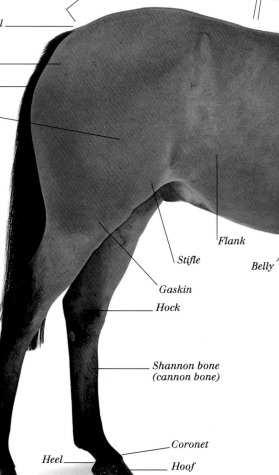

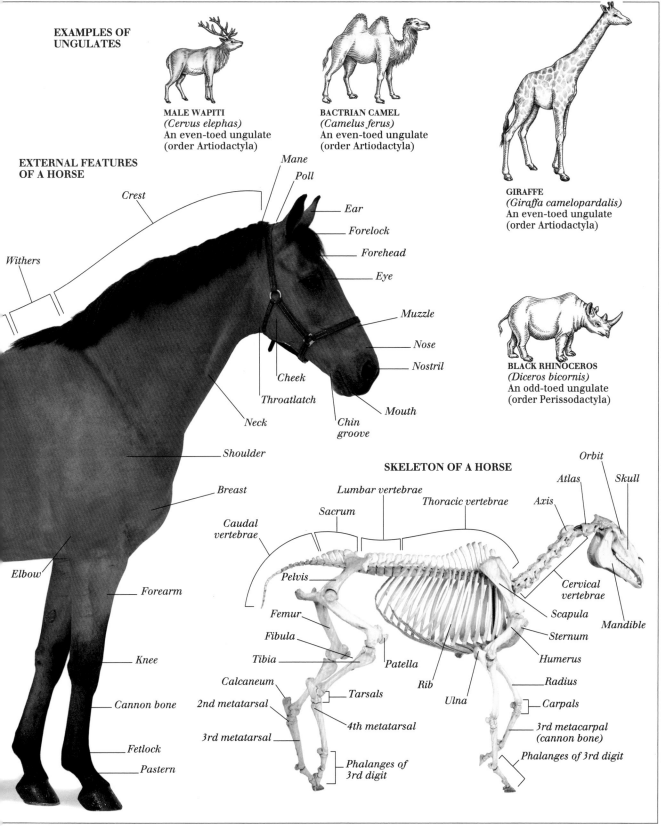

**EXAMPLES OF
UNGULATES**

MALE WAPITI
(Cervus elephas)
An even-toed ungulate
(order Artiodactyla)

BACTRIAN CAMEL
(Camelus ferus)
An even-toed ungulate
(order Artiodactyla)

GIRAFFE
(Giraffa camelopardalis)
An even-toed ungulate
(order Artiodactyla)

**EXTERNAL FEATURES
OF A HORSE**

Mane

Poll

Crest

Ear

Forelock

Forehead

Eye

Withers

Muzzle

Nose

Nostril

Cheek

Throatlatch

Mouth

Neck

Chin
groove

Shoulder

BLACK RHINOCEROS
(Diceros bicornis)
An odd-toed ungulate
(order Perissodactyla)

Breast

SKELETON OF A HORSE

Caudal
vertebrae

Lumbar vertebrae

Sacrum

Thoracic vertebrae

Orbit

Atlas

Skull

Axis

Elbow

Pelvis

Forearm

Femur

Fibula

Tibia

Cervical
vertebrae

Scapula

Mandible

Sternum

Humerus

Knee

Calcaneum

Patella

Rib

Radius

Cannon bone

2nd metatarsal

Tarsals

Ulna

Carpals

4th metatarsal

3rd metatarsal

3rd metacarpal
(cannon bone)

Fetlock

Phalanges of
3rd digit

Phalanges of 3rd digit

Pastern

199

Elephants

THE TWO SPECIES OF elephants—African and Asian—are the only members of the mammalian order Proboscidea. The bigger African elephant is the largest land animal: a fully grown male may be up to 13 ft (4m) tall and weigh as much as 7.7 tons (7 tonnes). A fully grown male Asian elephant may be 11 ft (3.3 m) tall and weigh 6 tons (5.4 tonnes). The muscular trunk—an extension of the nose and upper lip—is the elephant's most obvious feature. It is used for manipulating and lifting, feeding, drinking and spraying water, smelling, touching, and producing trumpeting sounds. Other characteristic features of this mighty plant-eater include a pair of ivory tusks, used for defense and for crushing vegetation; thick, pillar-like legs and broad feet to support the massive body; and large ear flaps that act as radiators to keep the elephant cool.

DIFFERENCES BETWEEN AFRICAN AND ASIAN ELEPHANTS

Flat forehead

Very large ears

2 "lips" at the end of the trunk

Concave back

4 toenails

3 toenails

AFRICAN ELEPHANT
(*Loxodonta africana*)

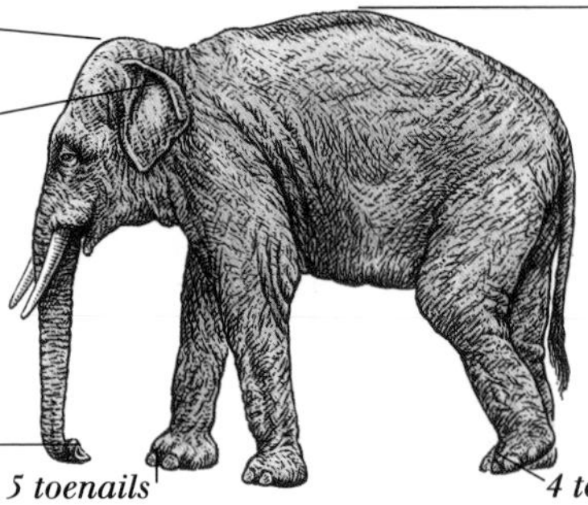

Twin-domed forehead

Smaller ears

1 "lip" at the end of the trunk

Arched back

5 toenails

4 toenails

ASIAN ELEPHANT
(*Elephas maximus*)

INTERNAL ANATOMY OF A FEMALE ELEPHANT

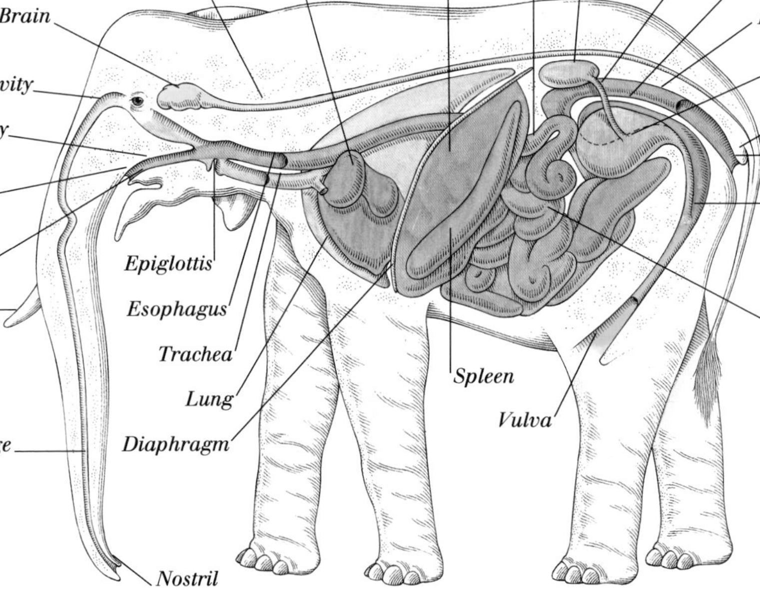

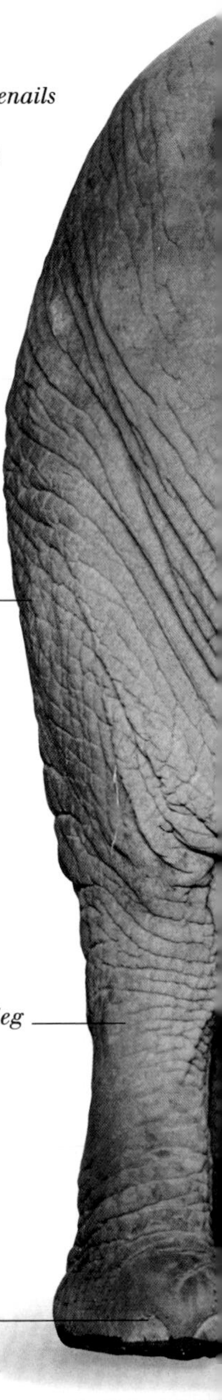

Spinal cord

Heart

Brain

Nasal cavity

Buccal cavity

Mouth

Tongue

Tusk

Epiglottis

Esophagus

Trachea

Lung

Diaphragm

Nasal passage

Nostril

Stomach

Duodenum

Kidney

Ureter

Uterus

Rectum

Bladder

Anal flap

Anus

Vagina

Small intestine

Spleen

Vulva

Rump

Hind leg

Toenail

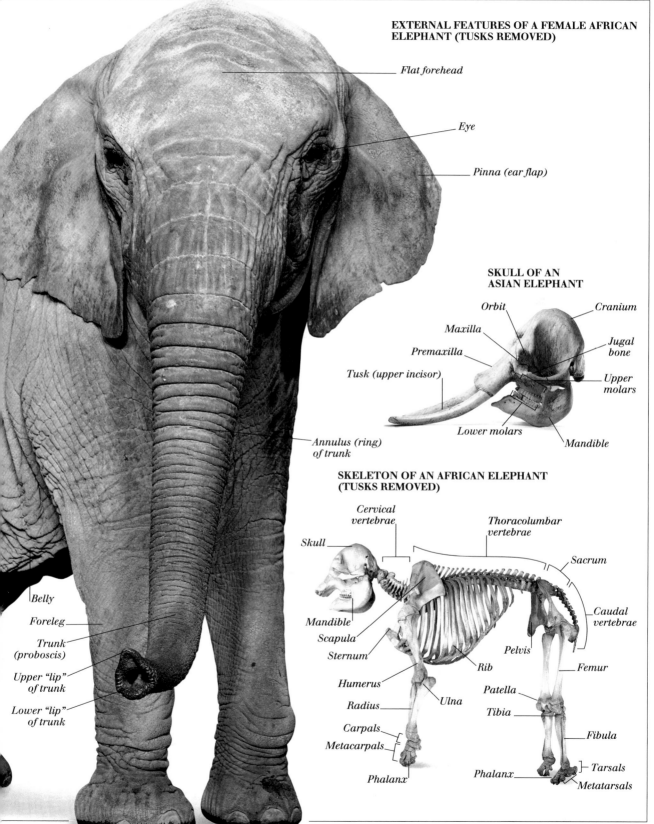

EXTERNAL FEATURES OF A FEMALE AFRICAN ELEPHANT (TUSKS REMOVED)

Flat forehead

Eye

Pinna (ear flap)

Belly

Foreleg

Trunk (proboscis)

Upper "lip" of trunk

Lower "lip" of trunk

Annulus (ring) of trunk

SKULL OF AN ASIAN ELEPHANT

Orbit

Cranium

Maxilla

Jugal bone

Premaxilla

Tusk (upper incisor)

Upper molars

Lower molars

Mandible

SKELETON OF AN AFRICAN ELEPHANT (TUSKS REMOVED)

Cervical vertebrae

Thoracolumbar vertebrae

Skull

Sacrum

Mandible

Scapula

Sternum

Humerus

Radius

Ulna

Carpals

Metacarpals

Phalanx

Caudal vertebrae

Pelvis

Femur

Patella

Tibia

Fibula

Phalanx

Tarsals

Metatarsals

Rib

Primates

THE MAMMALIAN ORDER PRIMATES consists of monkeys, apes, and their relatives (including humans). There are two suborders of primates: Prosimii, the primitive primates, which include lemurs, tarsiers, and lorises; and Anthropoidea, the advanced primates, which include monkeys, apes, and humans. The anthropoids are divided into New World monkeys, Old World monkeys, and hominids. New World monkeys typically have widespread nostrils that open to the side; and long tails, which are prehensile (grasping) in some species. This group of monkeys lives in South America, and includes marmosets, tamarins, and howler monkeys. Old World monkeys typically have close-set nostrils that open forward or downward and nonprehensile tails. This group of monkeys lives in Africa and Asia, and includes langurs, mandrills, macaques, and baboons. Hominids typically have large brains and no tail. This group includes the apes—chimpanzees, gibbons, gorillas, and orangutans—and humans.

INTERNAL ANATOMY OF A FEMALE CHIMPANZEE

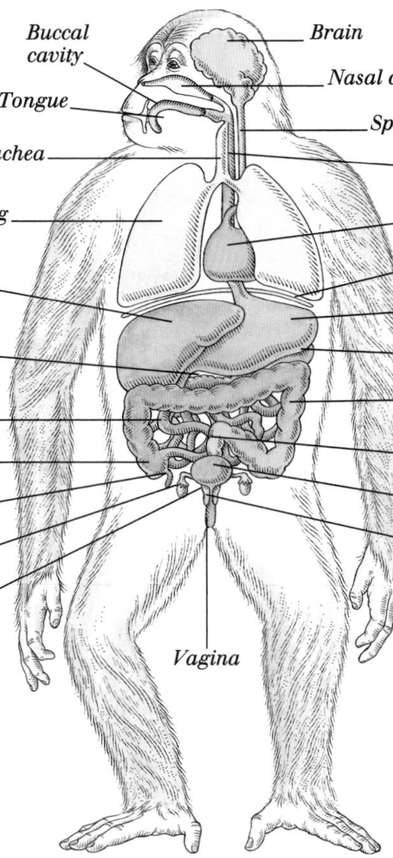

Buccal cavity
Tongue
Trachea
Lung
Liver
Pancreas
Small intestine
Cecum
Appendix
Ovary
Uterus
Brain
Nasal cavity
Spinal cord
Esophagus
Heart
Diaphragm
Stomach
Spleen
Large intestine
Rectum
Bladder
Urethra
Vagina

SKELETON OF A RHESUS MONKEY

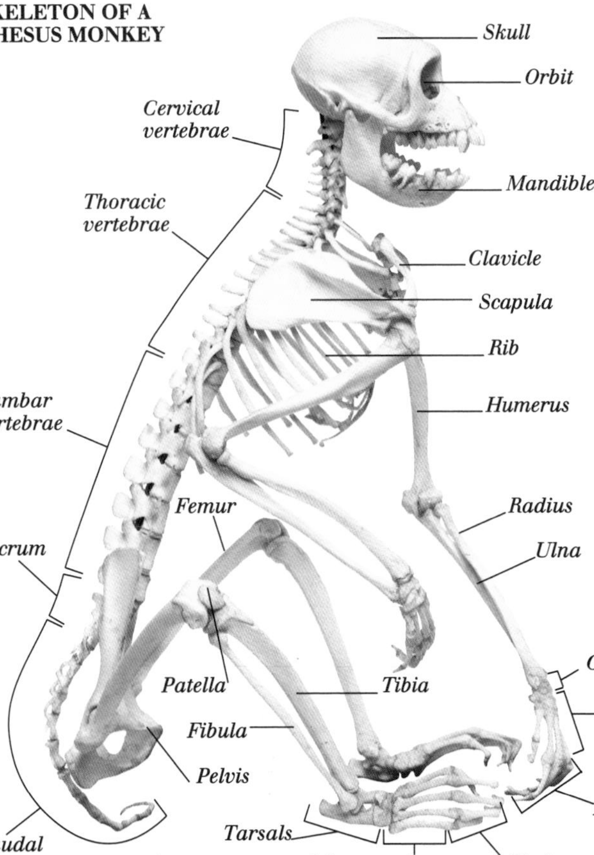

Skull
Orbit
Cervical vertebrae
Mandible
Thoracic vertebrae
Clavicle
Scapula
Rib
Humerus
Lumbar vertebrae
Radius
Ulna
Femur
Sacrum
Carpals
Metacarpals
Patella
Tibia
Fibula
Pelvis
Phalanges
Caudal vertebrae
Tarsals
Metatarsals
Phalanges

SKULL OF A CHIMPANZEE

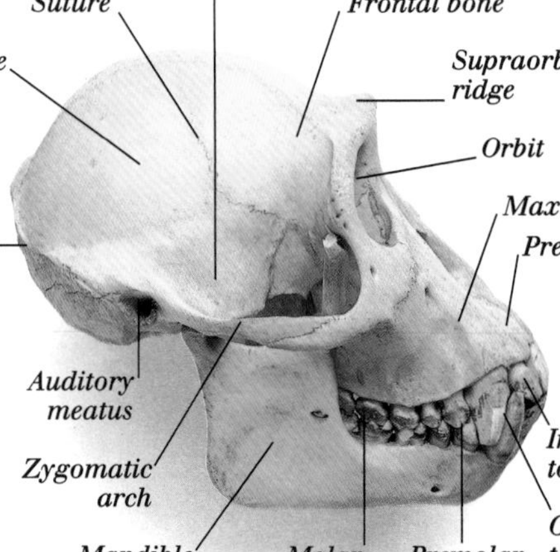

Temporal bone
Suture
Frontal bone
Parietal bone
Supraorbital ridge
Orbit
Maxilla
Premaxilla
Occipital bone
Auditory meatus
Zygomatic arch
Mandible
Incisor tooth
Canine tooth
Molar tooth
Premolar tooth

EXAMPLES OF PRIMATES

RING-TAILED LEMUR
(Lemur catta)
A prosimian

MALE RED HOWLER MONKEY
(Alouatta seniculus)
A New World monkey

MALE MANDRILL
(Mandrillus sphinx)
An Old World monkey

CHIMPANZEE
(Pan troglodytes)
An ape

**EXTERNAL FEATURES OF
A YOUNG GORILLA**

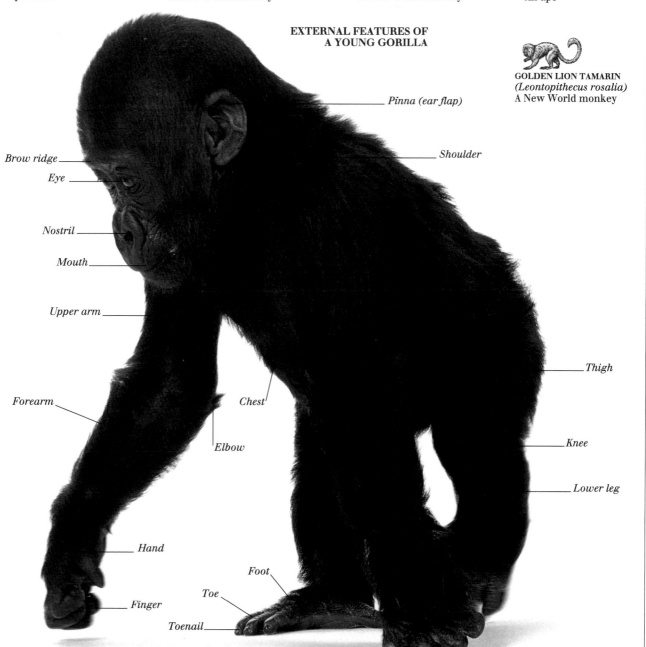

GOLDEN LION TAMARIN
(Leontopithecus rosalia)
A New World monkey

Pinna (ear flap)

Brow ridge

Shoulder

Eye

Nostril

Mouth

Upper arm

Thigh

Chest

Forearm

Elbow

Knee

Lower leg

Hand

Foot

Toe

Finger

Toenail

Dolphins, whales, and seals

DOLPHINS, WHALES, AND SEALS belong to two orders of mammals adapted to living in water. Dolphins and whales make up the order Cetacea. Typical cetacean features include a streamlined, fish-like shape; forelimbs in the form of flippers; no visible hind limbs; a horizontally flattened tail; and thick blubber under the skin. There are two groups of cetaceans: toothed whales, including sperm whales, white whales, beaked whales, dolphins, and porpoises; and the larger whalebone (baleen) whales, including rorquals, gray whales, and right whales. The blue whale—a rorqual—is the largest living animal: an adult may be up to 100 ft (30m) long and weigh 145 tons (130 tonnes). Seals and their relatives—sea lions and walruses—make up the order Pinnipedia. Characteristically, they have a streamlined, torpedo-shaped body; forelimbs and hind limbs modified as flippers; thick blubber; and no external ears.

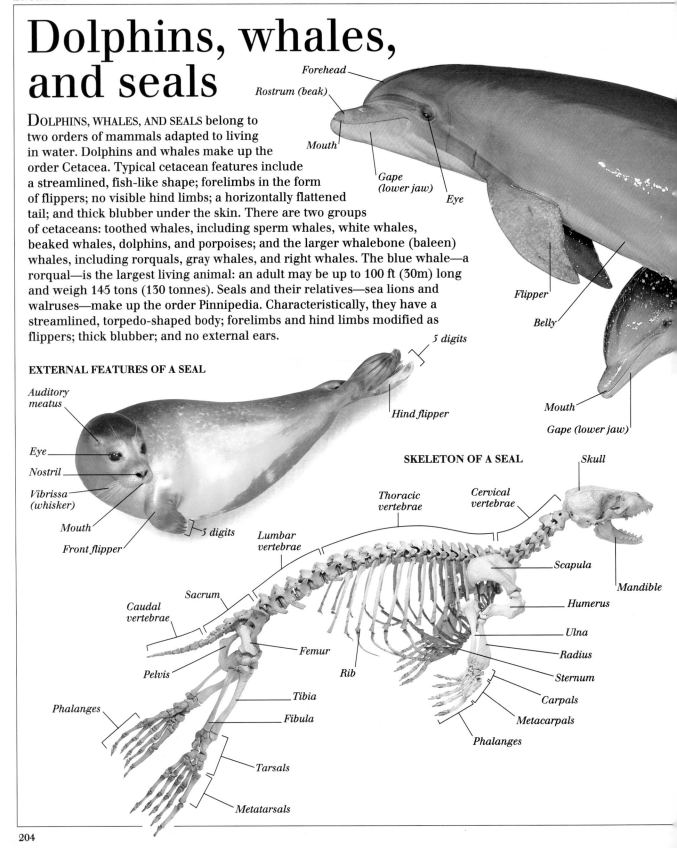

Forehead

Rostrum (beak)

Mouth

Gape (lower jaw)

Eye

Flipper

Belly

Mouth

Gape (lower jaw)

EXTERNAL FEATURES OF A SEAL

Auditory meatus

Eye

Nostril

Vibrissa (whisker)

Mouth

Front flipper

5 digits

Hind flipper

5 digits

SKELETON OF A SEAL

Skull

Thoracic vertebrae

Cervical vertebrae

Mandible

Scapula

Humerus

Lumbar vertebrae

Ulna

Radius

Sternum

Carpals

Metacarpals

Phalanges

Sacrum

Caudal vertebrae

Femur

Rib

Pelvis

Phalanges

Tibia

Fibula

Tarsals

Metatarsals

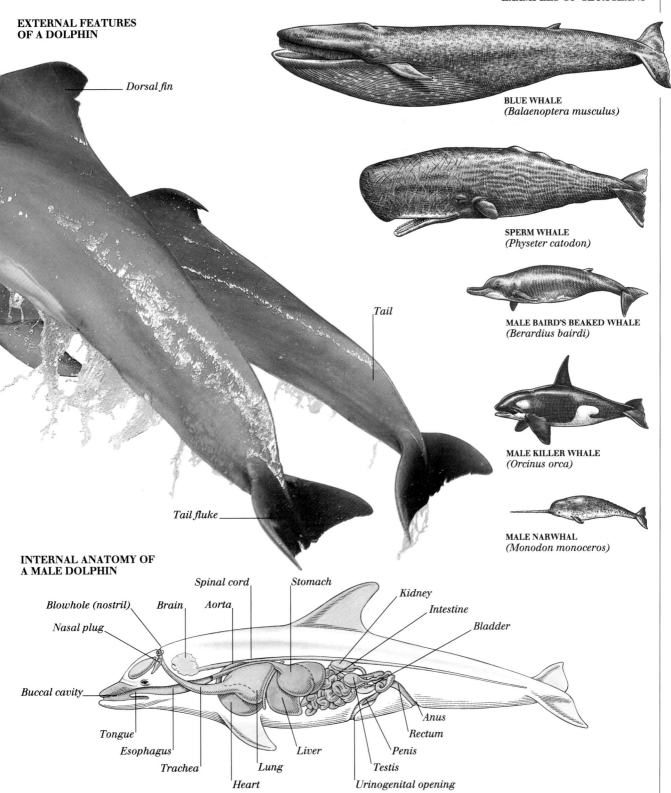

EXAMPLES OF CETACEANS

**EXTERNAL FEATURES
OF A DOLPHIN**

Dorsal fin

BLUE WHALE
(Balaenoptera musculus)

SPERM WHALE
(Physeter catodon)

Tail

MALE BAIRD'S BEAKED WHALE
(Berardius bairdi)

MALE KILLER WHALE
(Orcinus orca)

Tail fluke

MALE NARWHAL
(Monodon monoceros)

**INTERNAL ANATOMY OF
A MALE DOLPHIN**

Spinal cord

Stomach

Blowhole (nostril)

Brain

Aorta

Kidney

Intestine

Nasal plug

Bladder

Buccal cavity

Anus

Rectum

Tongue

Penis

Esophagus

Testis

Trachea

Lung

Liver

Urinogenital opening

Heart

Marsupials and Monotremes

MARSUPIALS AND MONOTREMES are two orders of mammals that differ from other mammalian groups in the ways that their young develop. The order Marsupalia, the pouched mammals, is made up of kangaroos and their relatives. Typically, marsupials give birth to their young at a very early stage of development. The young then crawls to the mother's pouch (which is on the outside of her abdomen), where it attaches itself to a nipple and remains until fully developed. Most marsupials live in Australia, although the opossums—which are classified as marsupials despite not having a pouch—live in the Americas. The order Monotremata is made up of the platypus and its relatives (the echidnas, or spiny anteaters). The monotremes are primitive mammals that lay eggs, which the mother incubates. The monotremes are found only in Australia and New Guinea.

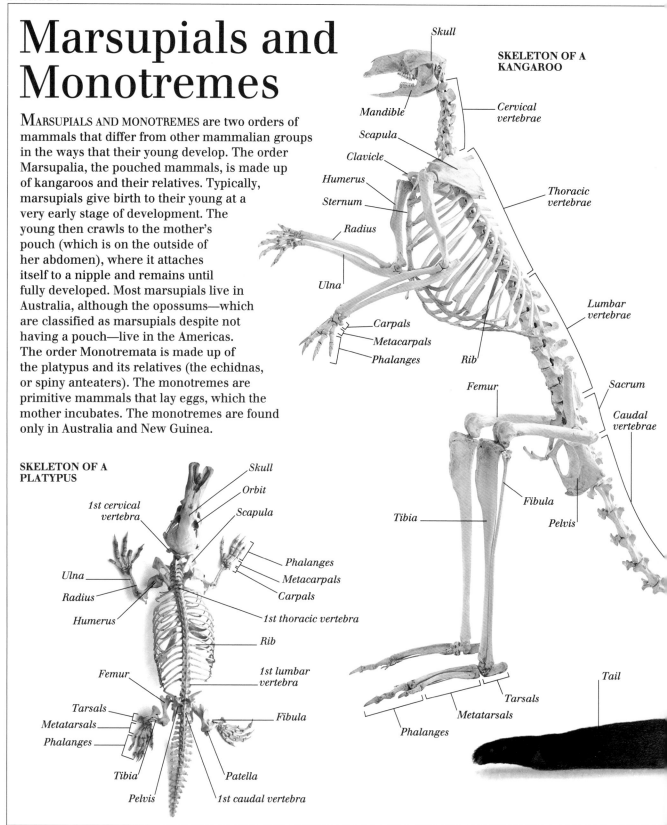

SKELETON OF A KANGAROO

Skull
Mandible
Cervical vertebrae
Scapula
Clavicle
Humerus
Sternum
Radius
Thoracic vertebrae
Ulna
Lumbar vertebrae
Carpals
Metacarpals
Phalanges
Rib
Femur
Sacrum
Caudal vertebrae
Tibia
Fibula
Pelvis
Tail
Tarsals
Metatarsals
Phalanges

SKELETON OF A PLATYPUS

Skull
Orbit
1st cervical vertebra
Scapula
Phalanges
Metacarpals
Carpals
Ulna
Radius
1st thoracic vertebra
Humerus
Rib
Femur
1st lumbar vertebra
Tarsals
Metatarsals
Fibula
Phalanges
Tibia
Patella
Pelvis
1st caudal vertebra

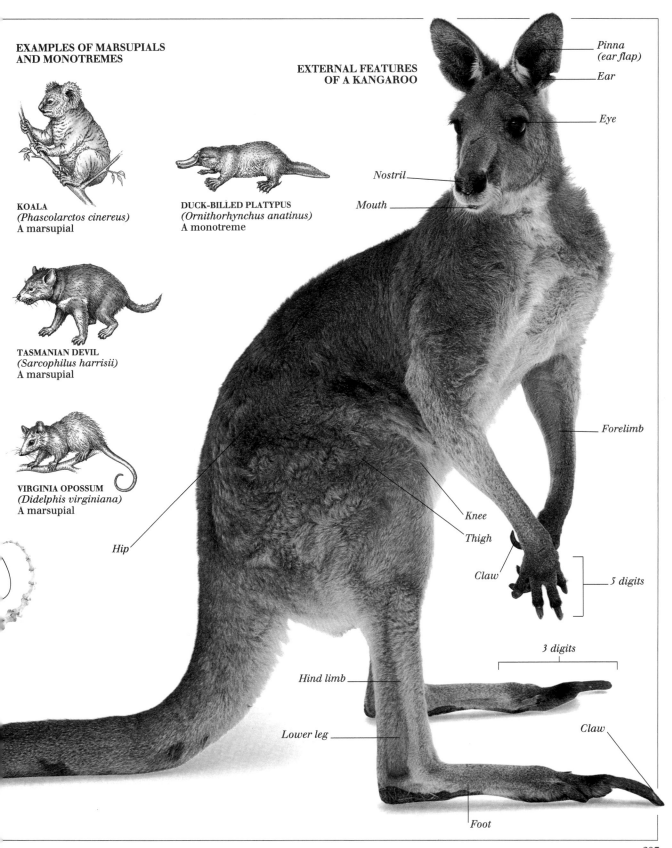

EXAMPLES OF MARSUPIALS
AND MONOTREMES

EXTERNAL FEATURES
OF A KANGAROO

KOALA
(Phascolarctos cinereus)
A marsupial

DUCK-BILLED PLATYPUS
(Ornithorhynchus anatinus)
A monotreme

TASMANIAN DEVIL
(Sarcophilus harrisii)
A marsupial

VIRGINIA OPOSSUM
(Didelphis virginiana)
A marsupial

*Pinna
(ear flap)*

Ear

Eye

Nostril

Mouth

Forelimb

Knee

Thigh

Claw

5 digits

3 digits

Hip

Hind limb

Lower leg

Claw

Foot

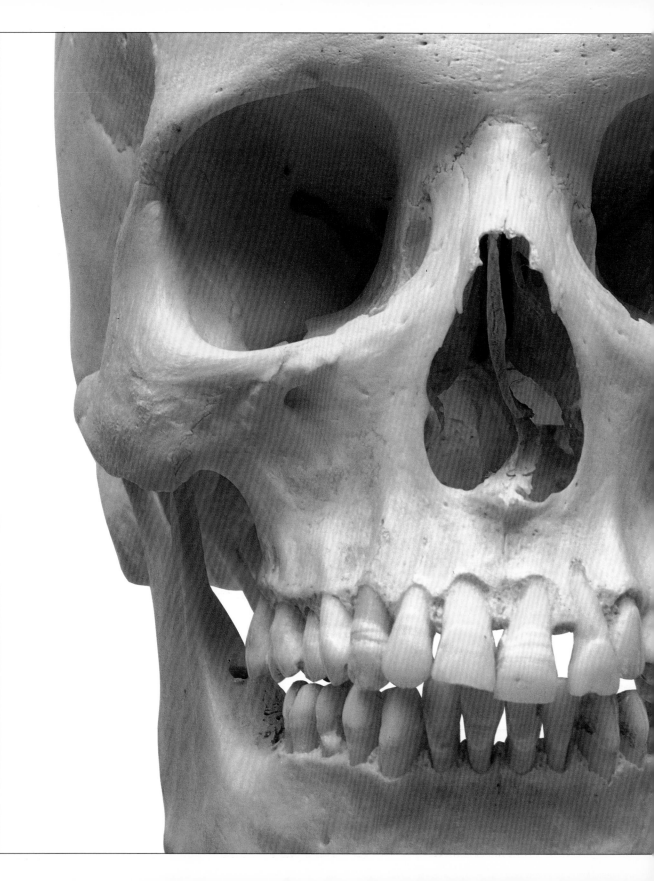

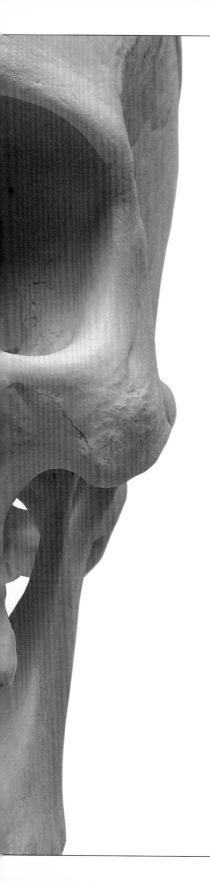

The Human Body

Body Features	210
Head	212
Body Organs	214
Body Cells	216
Skeleton	218
Skull	220
Spine	222
Bones and Joints	224
Muscles 1	226
Muscles 2	228
Hands	230
Feet	232
Skin and Hair	234
Brain	236
Nervous System	238
Eye	240
Ear	242
Nose, Mouth, and Throat	244
Teeth	246
Digestive System	248
Heart	250
Circulatory System	252
Respiratory System	254
Urinary System	256
Reproductive System	258
Development of a Baby	260

Body features

ALTHOUGH THERE IS enormous variation between the external appearances of humans, all bodies contain the same basic features. The outward form of the human body depends on the size of the skeleton, the shape of the muscles, the thickness of the fat layer beneath the skin, the elasticity or sagginess of the skin, and the person's age and gender. Males tend to be taller than females, with broader shoulders, more body hair, and a different pattern of fat deposits under the skin; the female body tends to be less muscular and has a shallower and wider pelvis to allow for childbirth.

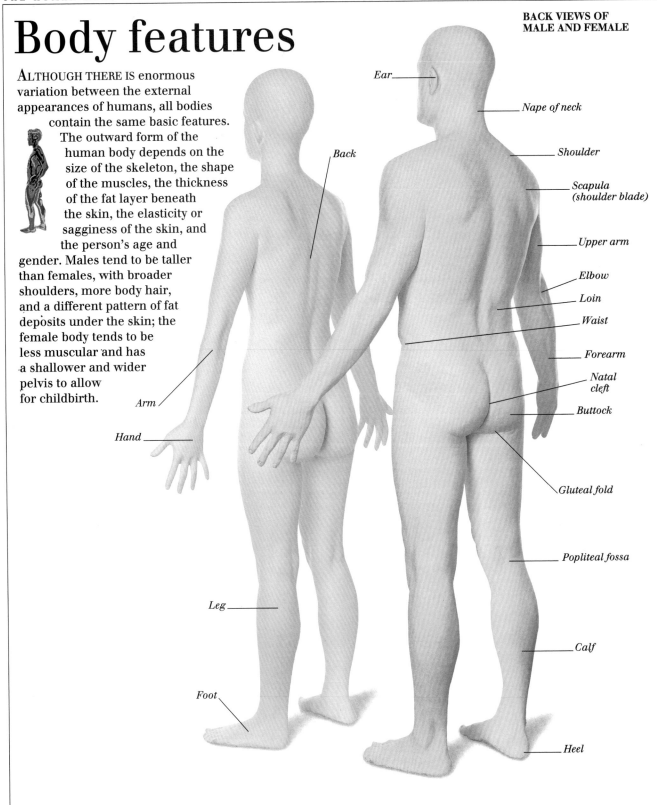

Ear

Nape of neck

Shoulder

Scapula
(shoulder blade)

Upper arm

Elbow

Loin

Waist

Forearm

Natal
cleft

Buttock

Gluteal fold

Popliteal fossa

Calf

Heel

Back

Arm

Hand

Leg

Foot

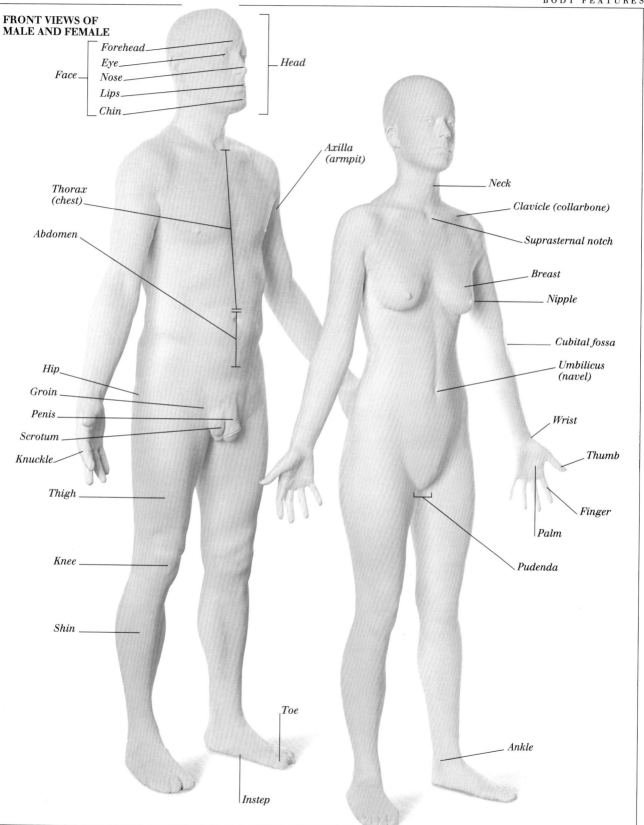

FRONT VIEWS OF MALE AND FEMALE

Face

Forehead

Eye

Nose

Lips

Chin

Head

Thorax (chest)

Abdomen

Hip

Groin

Penis

Scrotum

Knuckle

Thigh

Knee

Shin

Axilla (armpit)

Neck

Clavicle (collarbone)

Suprasternal notch

Breast

Nipple

Cubital fossa

Umbilicus (navel)

Wrist

Thumb

Finger

Palm

Pudenda

Toe

Instep

Ankle

Head

IN A NEWBORN BABY, the head accounts for one quarter of the total body length; by adulthood, the proportion has reduced to one eighth. Contained in the head are the body's main sense organs: eyes, ears, olfactory nerves that detect smells, and the taste buds of the tongue. Signals from these organs pass to the body's great coordination center: the brain, housed in the protective, bony dome of the skull. Hair on the head insulates against heat loss, and adult males also grow thick facial hair. The face has three important openings: two nostrils through which air passes, and the mouth, which takes in nourishment and helps form speech. Although all heads are basically similar, differences in the size, shape, and color of features produce an infinite variety of appearances.

SIDE VIEW OF EXTERNAL FEATURES OF HEAD

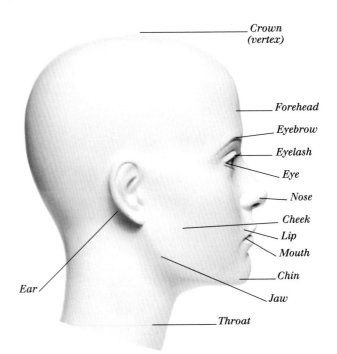

Crown (vertex)

Forehead

Eyebrow

Eyelash

Eye

Nose

Cheek

Lip

Mouth

Chin

Jaw

Throat

Ear

SECTION THROUGH HEAD

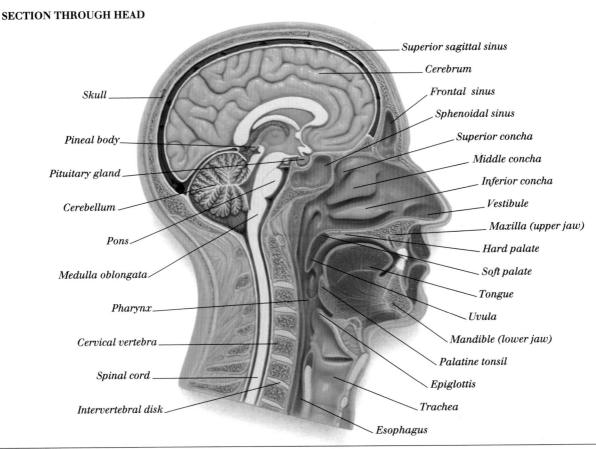

Skull

Pineal body

Pituitary gland

Cerebellum

Pons

Medulla oblongata

Pharynx

Cervical vertebra

Spinal cord

Intervertebral disk

Superior sagittal sinus

Cerebrum

Frontal sinus

Sphenoidal sinus

Superior concha

Middle concha

Inferior concha

Vestibule

Maxilla (upper jaw)

Hard palate

Soft palate

Tongue

Uvula

Mandible (lower jaw)

Palatine tonsil

Epiglottis

Trachea

Esophagus

**FRONT VIEW OF EXTERNAL
FEATURES OF HEAD**

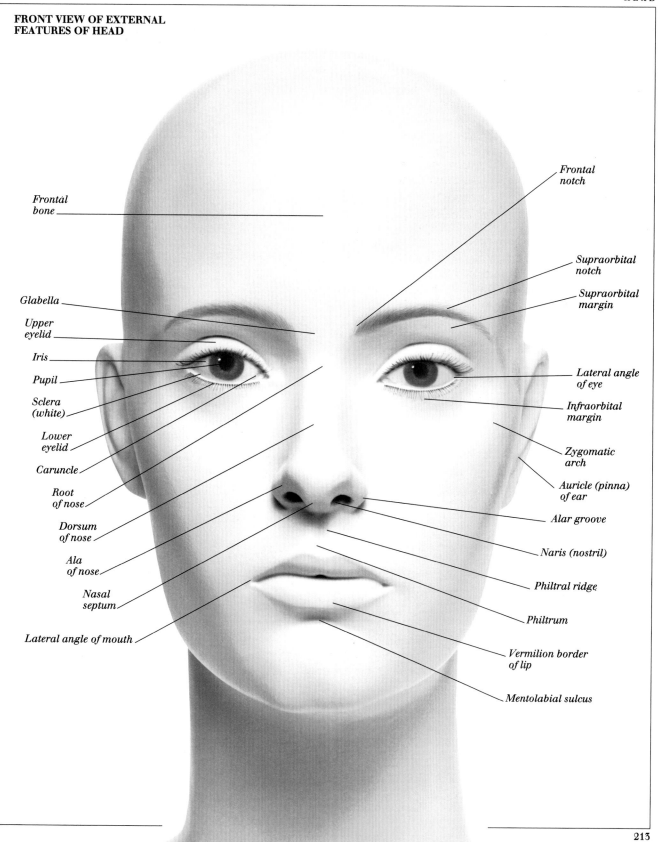

Frontal
notch

Supraorbital
notch

Supraorbital
margin

Frontal
bone

Lateral angle
of eye

Infraorbital
margin

Zygomatic
arch

Auricle (pinna)
of ear

Alar groove

Naris (nostril)

Philtral ridge

Philtrum

Vermilion border
of lip

Mentolabial sulcus

Glabella

Upper
eyelid

Iris

Pupil

Sclera
(white)

Lower
eyelid

Caruncle

Root
of nose

Dorsum
of nose

Ala
of nose

Nasal
septum

Lateral angle of mouth

213

Body organs

ALL THE VITAL BODY ORGANS except for the brain are enclosed within the trunk or torso (the body apart from the head and limbs). The trunk contains two large cavities separated by a muscular sheet called the diaphragm. The upper cavity, known as the thorax or chest cavity, contains the heart and lungs. The lower cavity, called the abdominal cavity, contains the stomach, intestines, liver, and pancreas, which all play a role in digesting food. Also within the trunk are the kidneys and bladder, which are part of the urinary system, and the reproductive organs, which hold the seeds of new human life. Modern imaging techniques, such as contrast X-rays and different types of scans, make it possible to see and study body organs without the need to cut through their protective coverings of skin, fat, muscle, and bone.

MAJOR INTERNAL STRUCTURES

Thyroid gland

Larynx

Heart

Right lung

Left lung

Diaphragm

Liver

Stomach

Large intestine

Small intestine

Greater omentum

IMAGING THE BODY

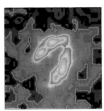

SCINTIGRAM OF HEART CHAMBERS

ANGIOGRAM OF RIGHT LUNG

CONTRAST X-RAY OF GALLBLADDER

SCINTIGRAM OF NERVOUS SYSTEM

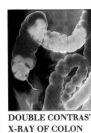

DOUBLE CONTRAST X-RAY OF COLON

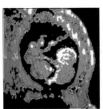

ULTRASOUND SCAN OF TWINS IN UTERUS

ANGIOGRAM OF KIDNEYS

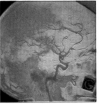

ANGIOGRAM OF ARTERIES OF HEAD

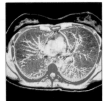

CT SCAN THROUGH FEMALE CHEST

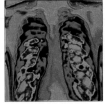

THERMOGRAM OF CHEST REGION

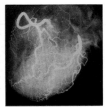

ANGIOGRAM OF ARTERIES OF HEART

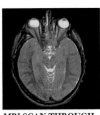

MRI SCAN THROUGH HEAD AT EYE LEVEL

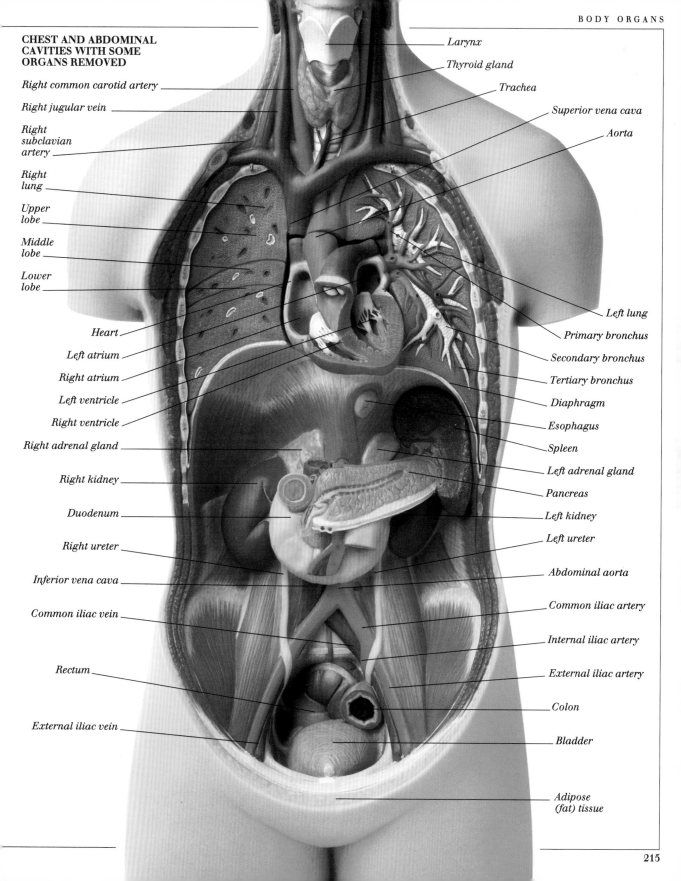

CHEST AND ABDOMINAL CAVITIES WITH SOME ORGANS REMOVED

Right common carotid artery

Right jugular vein

Right subclavian artery

Right lung

Upper lobe

Middle lobe

Lower lobe

Heart

Left atrium

Right atrium

Left ventricle

Right ventricle

Right adrenal gland

Right kidney

Duodenum

Right ureter

Inferior vena cava

Common iliac vein

Rectum

External iliac vein

Larynx

Thyroid gland

Trachea

Superior vena cava

Aorta

Left lung

Primary bronchus

Secondary bronchus

Tertiary bronchus

Diaphragm

Esophagus

Spleen

Left adrenal gland

Pancreas

Left kidney

Left ureter

Abdominal aorta

Common iliac artery

Internal iliac artery

External iliac artery

Colon

Bladder

Adipose (fat) tissue

Body cells

EVERYONE IS MADE UP OF BILLIONS OF CELLS, which are the basic structural units of the body. Bones, muscles, nerves, skin, blood, and all other body tissues are formed from different types of cells. Each cell has a specific function but works with other types of cells to perform the enormous number of tasks needed to sustain life. Most body cells have a similar basic structure. Each cell has an outer layer (called the cell membrane) and contains a fluid material (cytoplasm). Within the cytoplasm are many specialized structures (organelles). The most important organelle is the nucleus, which contains vital genetic material and acts as the cell's control center.

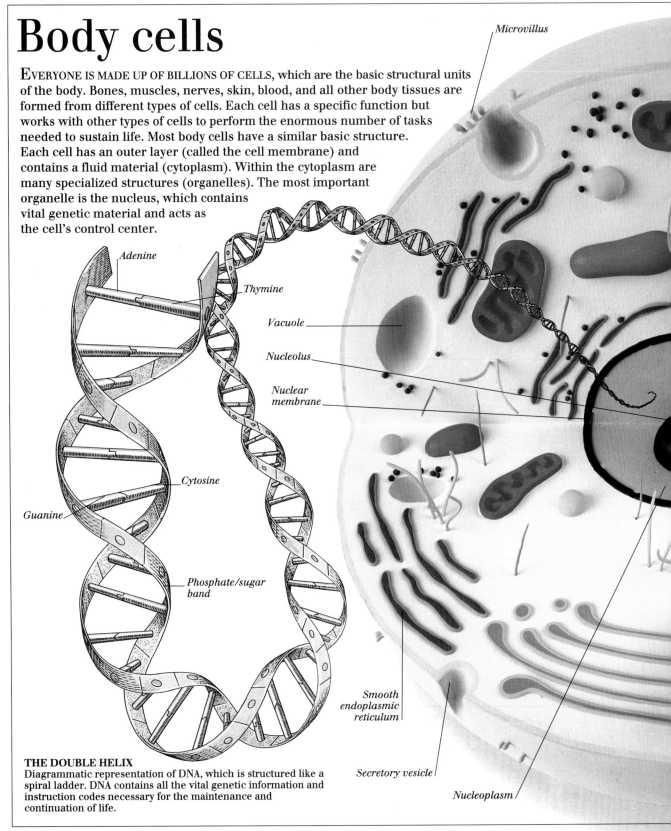

Microvillus

Adenine

Thymine

Vacuole

Nucleolus

Nuclear membrane

Cytosine

Guanine

Phosphate/sugar band

Smooth endoplasmic reticulum

Secretory vesicle

Nucleoplasm

THE DOUBLE HELIX
Diagrammatic representation of DNA, which is structured like a spiral ladder. DNA contains all the vital genetic information and instruction codes necessary for the maintenance and continuation of life.

GENERALIZED HUMAN CELL

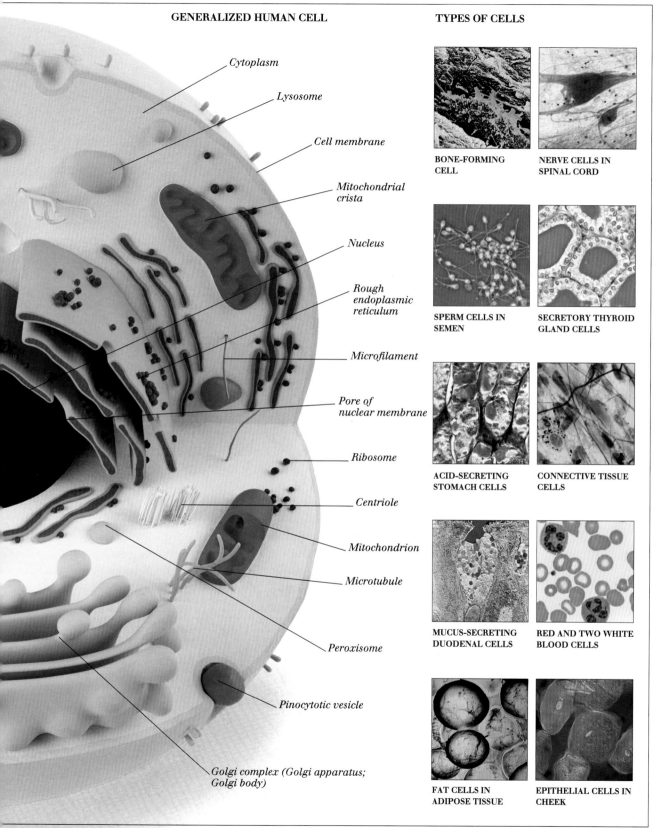

Cytoplasm

Lysosome

Cell membrane

Mitochondrial crista

Nucleus

Rough endoplasmic reticulum

Microfilament

Pore of nuclear membrane

Ribosome

Centriole

Mitochondrion

Microtubule

Peroxisome

Pinocytotic vesicle

Golgi complex (Golgi apparatus; Golgi body)

TYPES OF CELLS

BONE-FORMING CELL

NERVE CELLS IN SPINAL CORD

SPERM CELLS IN SEMEN

SECRETORY THYROID GLAND CELLS

ACID-SECRETING STOMACH CELLS

CONNECTIVE TISSUE CELLS

MUCUS-SECRETING DUODENAL CELLS

RED AND TWO WHITE BLOOD CELLS

FAT CELLS IN ADIPOSE TISSUE

EPITHELIAL CELLS IN CHEEK

Skeleton

THE SKELETON IS A MOBILE FRAMEWORK made up of 206 bones, approximately half of which are in the hands and feet. Although individual bones are rigid, the skeleton as a whole is remarkably flexible and allows the human body a huge range of movement. The skeleton serves as an anchorage for the skeletal muscles, and as a protective cage for the body's internal organs. Female bones are usually smaller and lighter than male bones, and the female pelvis is shallower and has a wider cavity.

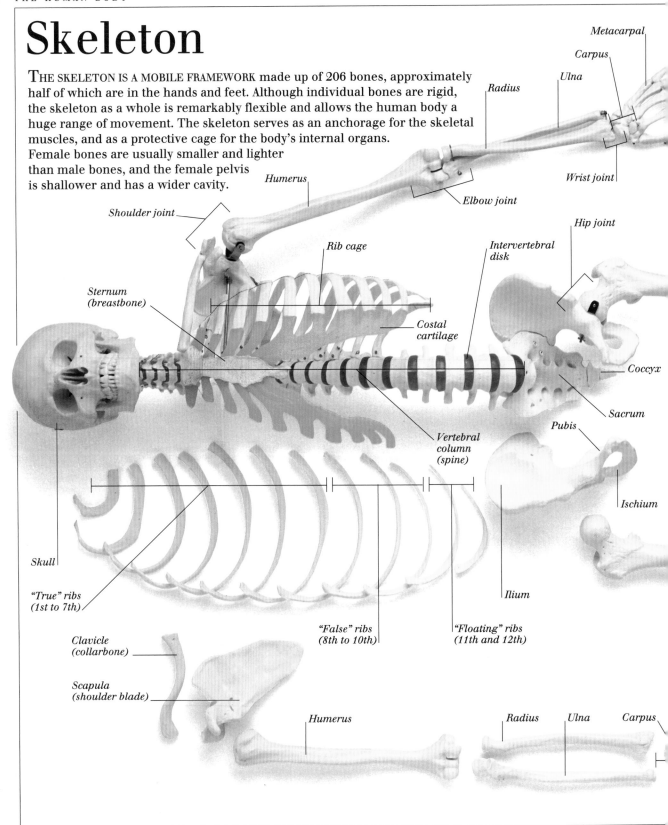

Metacarpal

Carpus

Ulna

Radius

Humerus

Shoulder joint

Wrist joint

Elbow joint

Hip joint

Rib cage

Intervertebral disk

Sternum (breastbone)

Costal cartilage

Coccyx

Sacrum

Pubis

Vertebral column (spine)

Ischium

Skull

Ilium

"True" ribs (1st to 7th)

"False" ribs (8th to 10th)

"Floating" ribs (11th and 12th)

Clavicle (collarbone)

Scapula (shoulder blade)

Humerus

Radius   Ulna   Carpus

Distal phalanx

Middle phalanx

Proximal phalanx

Femur Patella Tibia Fibula Tarsus

Proximal phalanx

Middle phalanx

Distal phalanx

Knee joint

Ankle joint Metatarsal

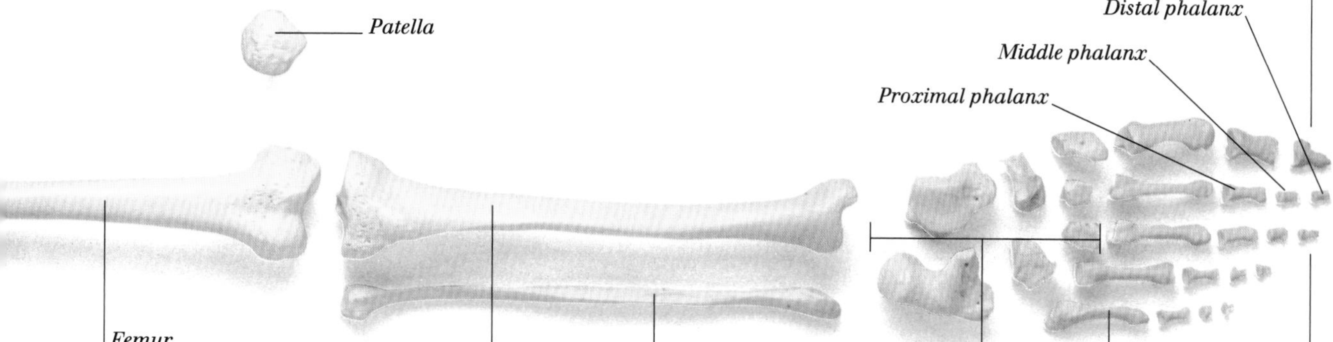

Patella

Distal phalanx

Middle phalanx

Proximal phalanx

Femur

Tibia Fibula

Tarsus Metatarsal

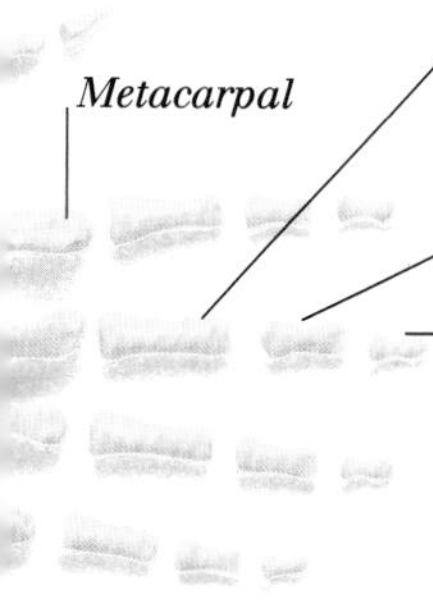

Metacarpal

Proximal phalanx

Middle phalanx

Distal phalanx

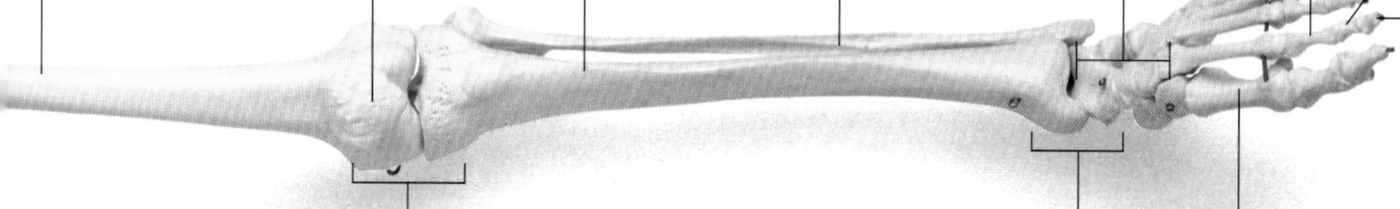

Skull

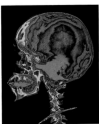

THE SKULL is the most complicated bony structure of the body—but every feature serves a purpose. Internally, the main hollow chamber of the skull has three levels that support the brain, with every bump and hollow corresponding to the shape of the brain. Underneath and toward the back of the skull is a large round hole, called the foramen magnum, through which the spinal cord passes. To the front of this are many smaller openings through which nerves, arteries, and veins pass to and from the brain. The roof of the skull is formed from four thin, curved bones that are firmly fixed together from the age of about two years. At the front of the skull are two orbits, which contain the eyeballs, and a central hole for the airway of the nose. The jawbone hinges on either side of the skull at ear level.

RIGHT SIDE VIEW OF A FETAL SKULL

Anterior fontanelle

Parietal bone

Coronal suture

Frontal bone

Nasal bone

Mental symphysis

Lambdoid suture

Occipital bone

Mastoid fontanelle

External auditory meatus

Sphenoidal fontanelle

RIGHT SIDE VIEW OF SKULL

Greater wing of sphenoid bone

Coronal suture

Frontal bone

Frontozygomatic suture

Parietal bone

Squamous suture

Supraorbital margin

Orbital cavity

Nasal bone

Anterior nasal spine

Maxilla (upper jaw)

Mandible (lower jaw)

Lambdoid suture

Occipital bone

Temporal bone

External auditory meatus

Mastoid process

Condyle

Coronoid process

Zygomatic bone

Styloid process

Mental foramen

VIEW OF SKULL FROM BELOW

External occipital crest

Foramen magnum

Occipital condyle

Carotid canal

Mastoid process

Pharyngeal tubercle

Pterygoid plate

Pterygoid hamulus

Greater palatine foramen

Zygomatic arch

Posterior border of vomer

Concha

Mandible (lower jaw)

Posterior nasal aperture

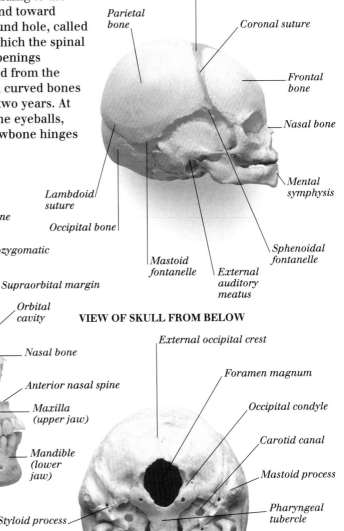

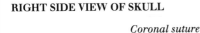

FRONT VIEW OF SKULL

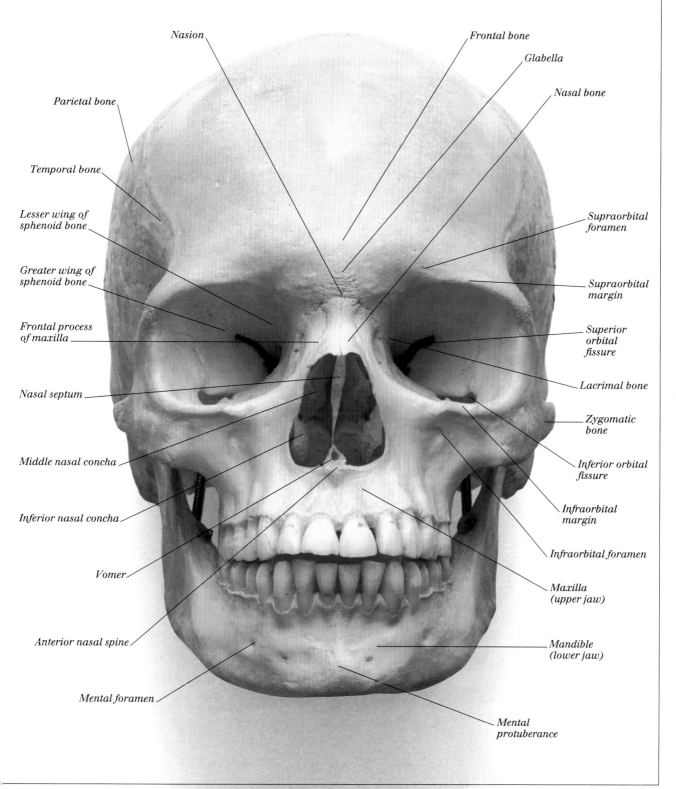

Nasion

Frontal bone

Glabella

Nasal bone

Parietal bone

Temporal bone

Lesser wing of
sphenoid bone

Greater wing of
sphenoid bone

Frontal process
of maxilla

Nasal septum

Middle nasal concha

Inferior nasal concha

Vomer

Anterior nasal spine

Mental foramen

Supraorbital
foramen

Supraorbital
margin

Superior
orbital
fissure

Lacrimal bone

Zygomatic
bone

Inferior orbital
fissure

Infraorbital
margin

Infraorbital foramen

Maxilla
(upper jaw)

Mandible
(lower jaw)

Mental
protuberance

Spine

THE SPINE (OR VERTEBRAL COLUMN) has two main functions: it serves as a protective surrounding for the delicate spinal cord and forms the supporting back bone of the skeleton. The spine consists of 24 separate differently shaped bones (vertebrae) with a curved, triangular bone (the sacrum) at the bottom. The sacrum is made up of fused vertebrae; at its lower end is a small tail-like structure made up of tiny bones collectively called the coccyx. Between each pair of vertebrae is a disc of cartilage that cushions the bones during movement. The top two vertebrae differ in appearance from the others and work as a pair: the first, called the atlas, rotates around a stout vertical peg on the second, the axis. This arrangement allows the skull to move freely up and down, and from side to side.

SPINE DIVIDED INTO VERTEBRAL SECTIONS

FRONT

Cervical vertebrae

Thoracic vertebrae

Lumbar vertebrae

Sacral vertebrae

Coccygeal vertebrae

TYPES OF VERTEBRAE (VIEWED FROM ABOVE)

ATLAS

Anterior arch

Anterior tubercle

Vertebral foramen

Transverse process

Lateral mass with superior articular facet

Posterior arch

Posterior tubercle

Transverse foramen

AXIS

Facet

Dens

Vertebral foramen

Spinous process

Lamina

Transverse process and foramen

CERVICAL VERTEBRA

Body

Anterior tubercle

Posterior tubercle

Superior articular process

Spinous process

Vertebral foramen

Transverse foramen

SKULL AND SPINE

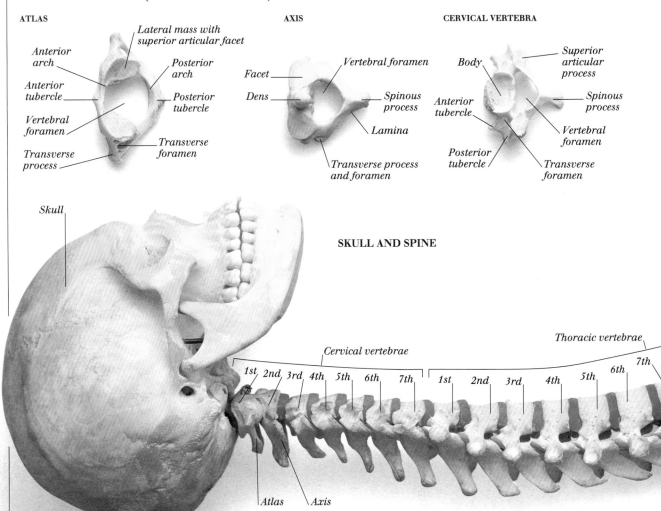

Skull

Cervical vertebrae

1st 2nd 3rd 4th 5th 6th 7th

Atlas   Axis

Thoracic vertebrae

1st 2nd 3rd 4th 5th 6th 7th

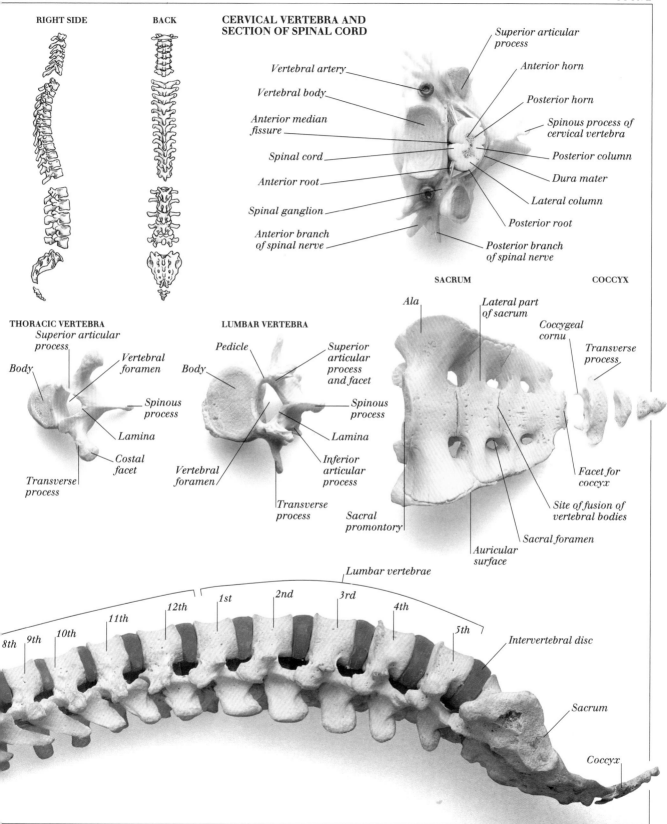

RIGHT SIDE

BACK

**CERVICAL VERTEBRA AND
SECTION OF SPINAL CORD**

Vertebral artery

Vertebral body

Anterior median
fissure

Spinal cord

Anterior root

Spinal ganglion

Anterior branch
of spinal nerve

Superior articular
process

Anterior horn

Posterior horn

Spinous process of
cervical vertebra

Posterior column

Dura mater

Lateral column

Posterior root

Posterior branch
of spinal nerve

THORACIC VERTEBRA

Superior articular
process

Body

Vertebral
foramen

Spinous
process

Lamina

Costal
facet

Transverse
process

LUMBAR VERTEBRA

Pedicle

Body

Superior
articular
process
and facet

Spinous
process

Lamina

Inferior
articular
process

Vertebral
foramen

Transverse
process

Sacral
promontory

SACRUM

Ala

Lateral part
of sacrum

Auricular
surface

Sacral foramen

Site of fusion of
vertebral bodies

COCCYX

Coccygeal
cornu

Transverse
process

Facet for
coccyx

Lumbar vertebrae

1st   2nd   3rd   4th   5th

8th 9th 10th 11th 12th

Intervertebral disc

Sacrum

Coccyx

Bones and joints

BONES FORM the body's hard, strong skeletal framework. Each bone has a hard, compact exterior surrounding a spongy, lighter interior. The long bones of the arms and legs, such as the femur (thigh bone), have a central cavity containing bone marrow. Bones are composed chiefly of calcium, phosphorus, and a fibrous substance known as collagen. Bones meet at joints, which are of several different types. For example, the hip is a ball-and-socket joint that allows the femur a wide range of movement, whereas finger joints are simple hinge joints that allow only bending and straightening. Joints are held in place by bands of tissue called ligaments. Movement of joints is facilitated by the smooth hyaline cartilage that covers the bone ends and by the synovial membrane that lines and lubricates the joint.

LIGAMENTS SURROUNDING HIP JOINT

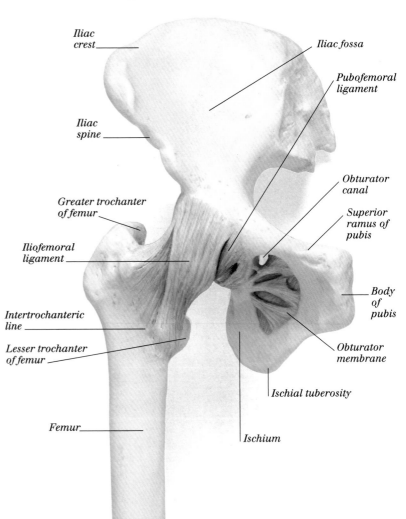

Iliac crest

Iliac fossa

Pubofemoral ligament

Iliac spine

Obturator canal

Greater trochanter of femur

Superior ramus of pubis

Iliofemoral ligament

Body of pubis

Intertrochanteric line

Obturator membrane

Lesser trochanter of femur

Ischial tuberosity

Femur

Ischium

SECTION THROUGH LEFT FEMUR

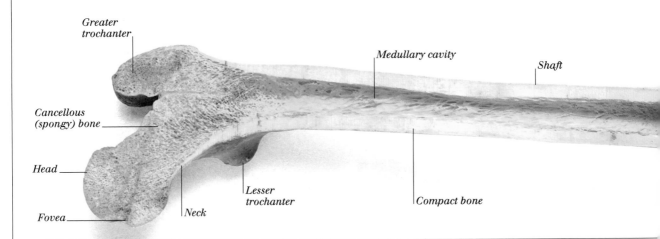

Greater trochanter

Medullary cavity

Shaft

Cancellous (spongy) bone

Head

Lesser trochanter

Compact bone

Fovea

Neck

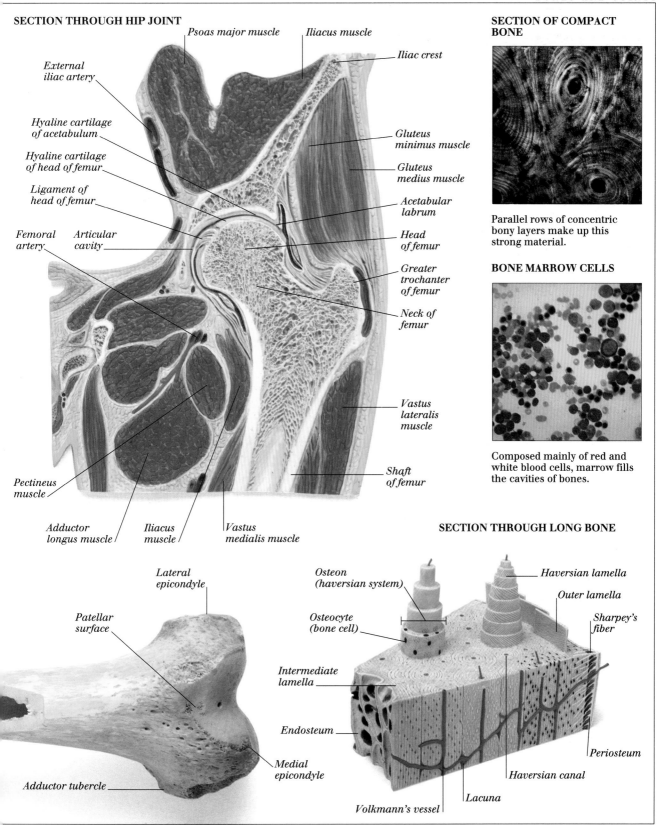

SECTION THROUGH HIP JOINT

Psoas major muscle

Iliacus muscle

External
iliac artery

Iliac crest

Hyaline cartilage
of acetabulum

Gluteus
minimus muscle

Hyaline cartilage
of head of femur

Gluteus
medius muscle

Ligament of
head of femur

Acetabular
labrum

Femoral
artery

Articular
cavity

Head
of femur

Greater
trochanter
of femur

Neck of
femur

Vastus
lateralis
muscle

Pectineus
muscle

Shaft
of femur

Adductor
longus muscle

Iliacus
muscle

Vastus
medialis muscle

**SECTION OF COMPACT
BONE**

Parallel rows of concentric
bony layers make up this
strong material.

BONE MARROW CELLS

Composed mainly of red and
white blood cells, marrow fills
the cavities of bones.

SECTION THROUGH LONG BONE

Lateral
epicondyle

Patellar
surface

Osteon
(haversian system)

Haversian lamella

Outer lamella

Osteocyte
(bone cell)

Sharpey's
fiber

Intermediate
lamella

Endosteum

Periosteum

Medial
epicondyle

Adductor tubercle

Haversian canal

Volkmann's vessel

Lacuna

225

Muscles 1

THERE ARE THREE MAIN TYPES OF MUSCLE: skeletal muscle (also called voluntary muscle because it can be consciously controlled); smooth muscle (also called involuntary muscle because it is not under voluntary control); and the specialized muscle tissue of the heart. Humans have more than 600 skeletal muscles, which differ in size and shape according to the jobs they do. Skeletal muscles are attached either directly or indirectly (via tendons) to bones, and work in opposing pairs (one muscle in the pair contracts while the other relaxes) to produce body movements as diverse as walking, threading a needle, and an array of facial expressions. Smooth muscles occur in the walls of internal body organs and perform actions such as forcing food through the intestines, contracting the uterus (womb) in childbirth, and pumping blood through the blood vessels.

SOME OTHER MUSCLES IN THE BODY

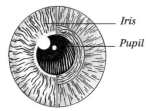

Iris

Pupil

IRIS
The muscle fibers contract and dilate (expand) to alter pupil size.

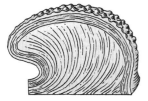

TONGUE
Interlacing layers of muscle allow great mobility.

ILEUM
Opposing muscle layers transport semidigested food.

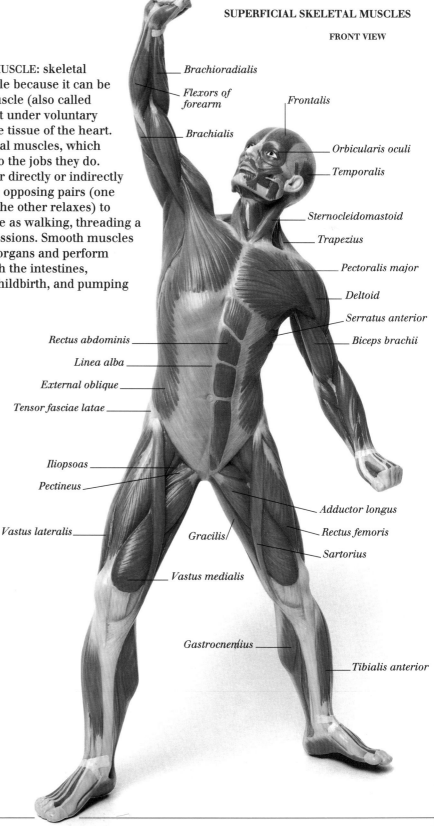

SUPERFICIAL SKELETAL MUSCLES

FRONT VIEW

Brachioradialis

Flexors of forearm

Brachialis

Frontalis

Orbicularis oculi

Temporalis

Sternocleidomastoid

Trapezius

Pectoralis major

Deltoid

Serratus anterior

Biceps brachii

Rectus abdominis

Linea alba

External oblique

Tensor fasciae latae

Iliopsoas

Pectineus

Adductor longus

Rectus femoris

Sartorius

Vastus lateralis

Gracilis

Vastus medialis

Gastrocnemius

Tibialis anterior

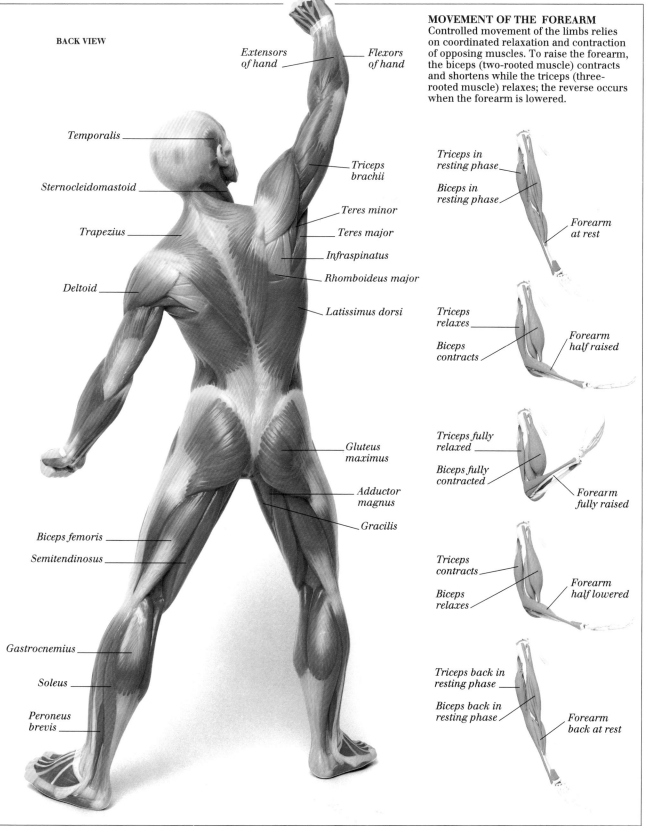

BACK VIEW

MOVEMENT OF THE FOREARM
Controlled movement of the limbs relies on coordinated relaxation and contraction of opposing muscles. To raise the forearm, the biceps (two-rooted muscle) contracts and shortens while the triceps (three-rooted muscle) relaxes; the reverse occurs when the forearm is lowered.

Extensors of hand

Flexors of hand

Temporalis

Sternocleidomastoid

Trapezius

Deltoid

Triceps brachii

Teres minor

Teres major

Infraspinatus

Rhomboideus major

Latissimus dorsi

Gluteus maximus

Adductor magnus

Gracilis

Biceps femoris

Semitendinosus

Gastrocnemius

Soleus

Peroneus brevis

Triceps in resting phase

Biceps in resting phase

Forearm at rest

Triceps relaxes

Biceps contracts

Forearm half raised

Triceps fully relaxed

Biceps fully contracted

Forearm fully raised

Triceps contracts

Biceps relaxes

Forearm half lowered

Triceps back in resting phase

Biceps back in resting phase

Forearm back at rest

Muscles 2

SKELETAL MUSCLE FIBER

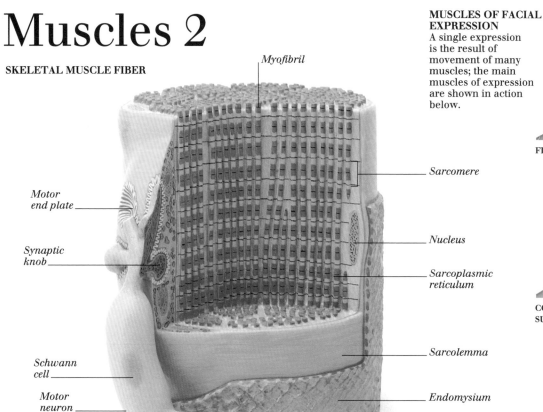

Myofibril

Sarcomere

Motor end plate

Nucleus

Synaptic knob

Sarcoplasmic reticulum

Schwann cell

Sarcolemma

Motor neuron

Endomysium

Node of Ranvier

MUSCLES OF FACIAL EXPRESSION

A single expression is the result of movement of many muscles; the main muscles of expression are shown in action below.

FRONTALIS

CORRUGATOR SUPERCILII

ORBICULARIS ORIS

TYPES OF MUSCLE

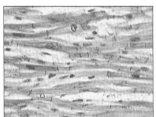

CARDIAC MUSCLE

SKELETAL MUSCLE

SMOOTH MUSCLE

ZYGOMATICUS MAJOR

CONTRACTION OF SKELETAL MUSCLE

RELAXED STATE

CONTRACTED STATE

DEPRESSOR ANGULI ORIS

**MUSCLES OF
HEAD AND NECK**

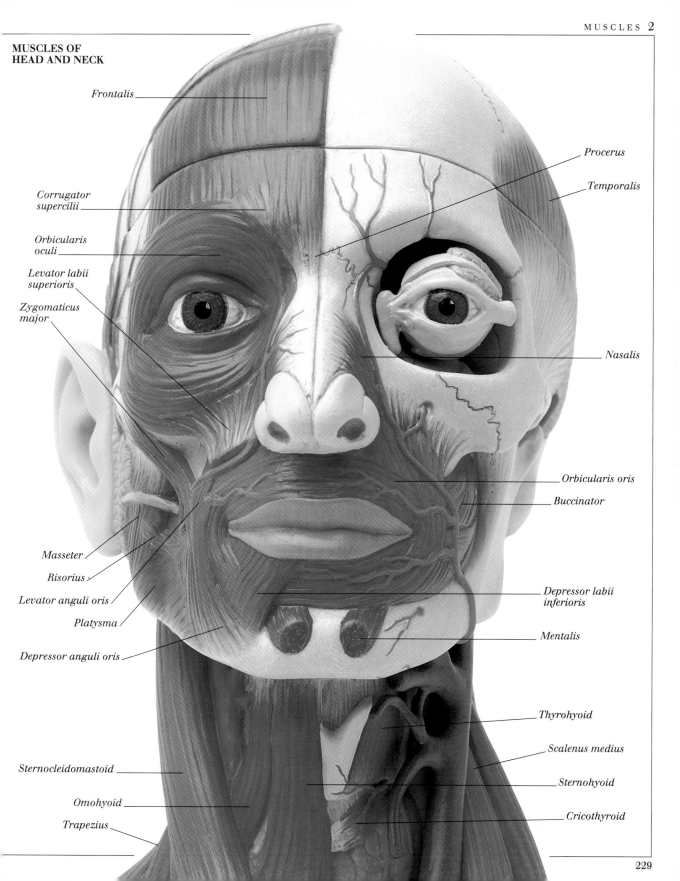

Frontalis

Procerus

Temporalis

Corrugator
supercilii

Orbicularis
oculi

Levator labii
superioris

Zygomaticus
major

Nasalis

Orbicularis oris

Buccinator

Masseter

Risorius

Depressor labii
inferioris

Levator anguli oris

Platysma

Mentalis

Depressor anguli oris

Thyrohyoid

Scalenus medius

Sternocleidomastoid

Sternohyoid

Omohyoid

Cricothyroid

Trapezius

Hands

THE HUMAN HAND is an extremely versatile tool, capable of delicate manipulation as well as powerful gripping actions. The arrangement of its 27 small bones, moved by 37 skeletal muscles that are connected to the bones by tendons, allows a wide range of movements. Our ability to bring the tips of our thumbs and fingers together, combined with the extraordinary sensitivity of our fingertips due to their rich supply of nerve endings, makes our hands uniquely dextrous.

X-RAY OF LEFT HAND OF A YOUNG CHILD

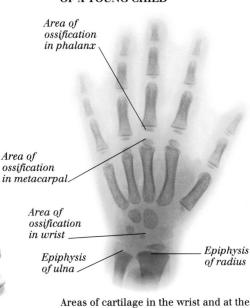

Area of ossification in phalanx

Area of ossification in metacarpal

Area of ossification in wrist

Epiphysis of ulna

Epiphysis of radius

Areas of cartilage in the wrist and at the ends of the finger bones are the sites of growth and have still to ossify.

BONES OF HAND

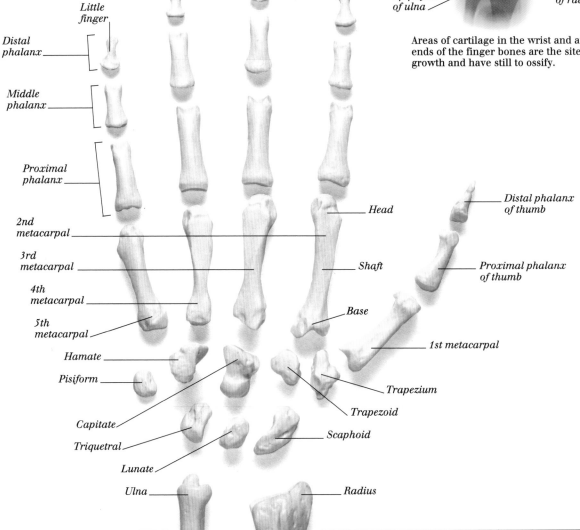

Ring finger

Middle finger

Index finger

Little finger

Distal phalanx

Middle phalanx

Proximal phalanx

2nd metacarpal

3rd metacarpal

4th metacarpal

5th metacarpal

Hamate

Pisiform

Capitate

Triquetral

Lunate

Ulna

Head

Shaft

Base

Trapezium

Trapezoid

Scaphoid

Radius

Distal phalanx of thumb

Proximal phalanx of thumb

1st metacarpal

**STRUCTURES UNDERLYING SKIN
OF PALM OF HAND**

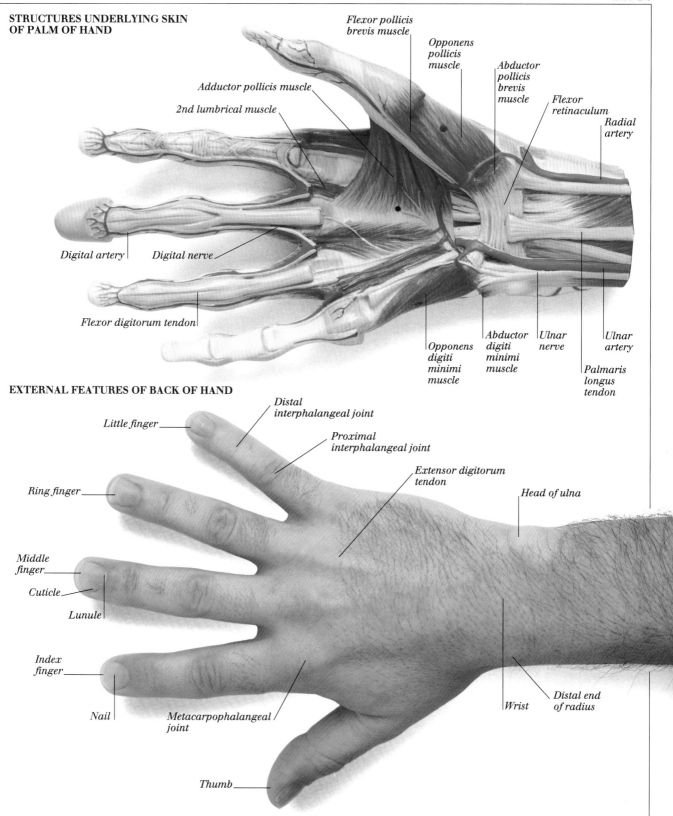

*Flexor pollicis
brevis muscle*

*Opponens
pollicis
muscle*

*Abductor
pollicis
brevis
muscle*

*Flexor
retinaculum*

*Radial
artery*

Adductor pollicis muscle

2nd lumbrical muscle

Digital artery

Digital nerve

Flexor digitorum tendon

*Opponens
digiti
minimi
muscle*

*Abductor
digiti
minimi
muscle*

*Ulnar
nerve*

*Ulnar
artery*

*Palmaris
longus
tendon*

EXTERNAL FEATURES OF BACK OF HAND

Little finger

*Distal
interphalangeal joint*

*Proximal
interphalangeal joint*

*Extensor digitorum
tendon*

Head of ulna

Ring finger

*Middle
finger*

Cuticle

Lunule

*Index
finger*

Nail

*Metacarpophalangeal
joint*

Wrist

*Distal end
of radius*

Thumb

231

Feet

THE FEET AND TOES are essential elements in body movement. They bear and propel the weight of the body during walking and running, and also help to maintain balance during changes of body position. Each foot has 26 bones, more than 100 ligaments, and 33 muscles, some of which are attached to the lower leg. The heel pad and the arch of the foot act as shock absorbers, providing a cushion against the jolts that occur with every step.

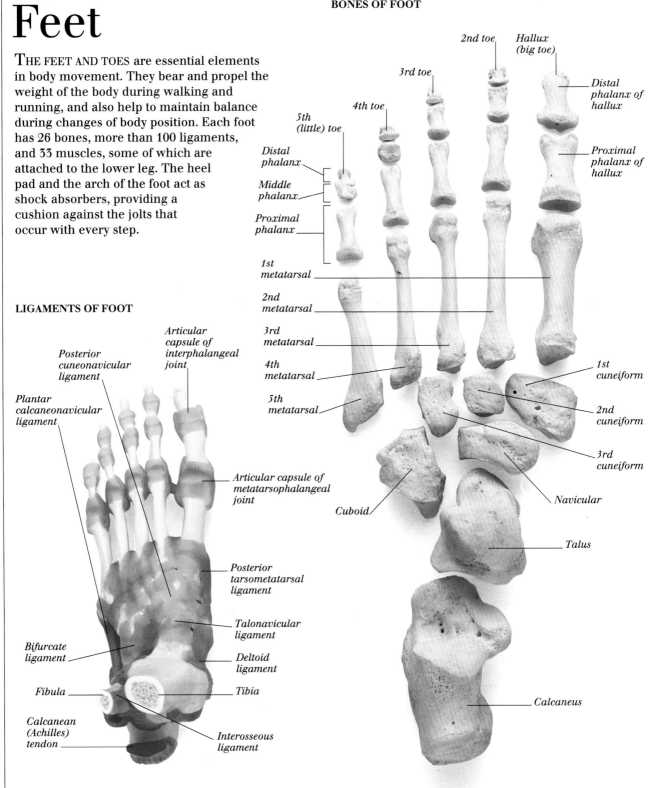

2nd toe

Hallux (big toe)

3rd toe

Distal phalanx of hallux

4th toe

5th (little) toe

Proximal phalanx of hallux

Distal phalanx

Middle phalanx

Proximal phalanx

1st metatarsal

2nd metatarsal

3rd metatarsal

4th metatarsal

5th metatarsal

1st cuneiform

2nd cuneiform

3rd cuneiform

Navicular

Cuboid

Talus

Calcaneus

LIGAMENTS OF FOOT

Articular capsule of interphalangeal joint

Posterior cuneonavicular ligament

Plantar calcaneonavicular ligament

Articular capsule of metatarsophalangeal joint

Posterior tarsometatarsal ligament

Talonavicular ligament

Bifurcate ligament

Deltoid ligament

Fibula

Tibia

Calcanean (Achilles) tendon

Interosseous ligament

STRUCTURES UNDERLYING SKIN OF FOOT

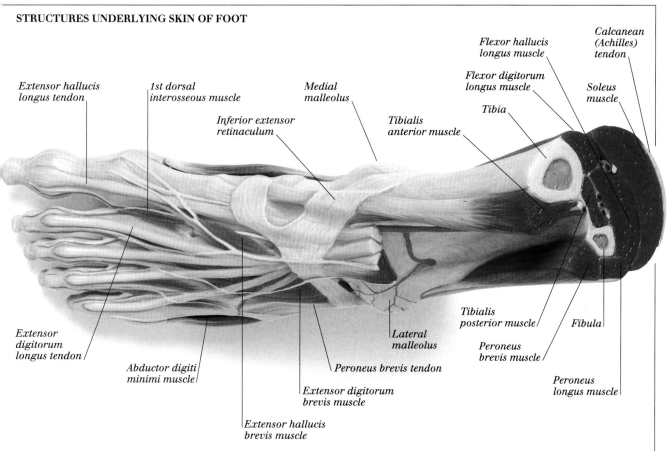

Extensor hallucis longus tendon

1st dorsal interosseous muscle

Medial malleolus

Inferior extensor retinaculum

Tibialis anterior muscle

Flexor hallucis longus muscle

Flexor digitorum longus muscle

Tibia

Calcanean (Achilles) tendon

Soleus muscle

Extensor digitorum longus tendon

Abductor digiti minimi muscle

Extensor hallucis brevis muscle

Extensor digitorum brevis muscle

Peroneus brevis tendon

Lateral malleolus

Tibialis posterior muscle

Peroneus brevis muscle

Fibula

Peroneus longus muscle

EXTERNAL FEATURES OF FOOT

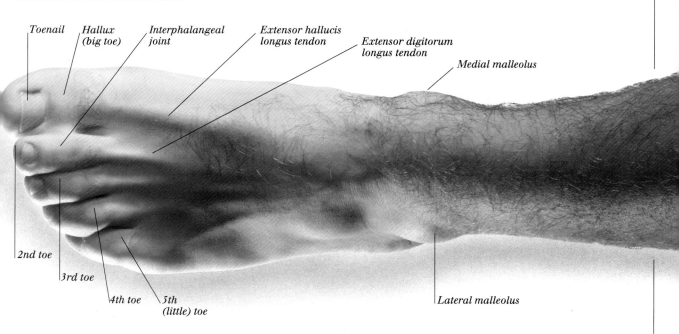

Toenail

Hallux (big toe)

Interphalangeal joint

Extensor hallucis longus tendon

Extensor digitorum longus tendon

Medial malleolus

2nd toe

3rd toe

4th toe

5th (little) toe

Lateral malleolus

Skin and hair

SKIN IS THE BODY'S LARGEST ORGAN, a waterproof barrier that protects the internal organs against infection, injury, and harmful sun rays. The skin is also an important sensory organ and helps to control body temperature. The outer layer of the skin, known as the epidermis, is coated with keratin, a tough, horny protein that is also the chief constituent of hair and nails. Dead cells are shed from the skin's surface and are replaced by new cells from the base of the epidermis, the region that also produces the skin pigment, melanin. The dermis contains most of the skin's living structures, and includes nerve endings, blood vessels, elastic fibers, sweat glands that cool the skin, and sebaceous glands that produce oil to keep the skin supple. Beneath the dermis lies the subcutaneous tissue (hypodermis), which is rich in fat and blood vessels. Hair shafts grow from hair follicles situated in the dermis and subcutaneous tissue. Hair grows on every part of the skin apart from the palms of the hands and soles of the feet.

SECTION OF HAIR

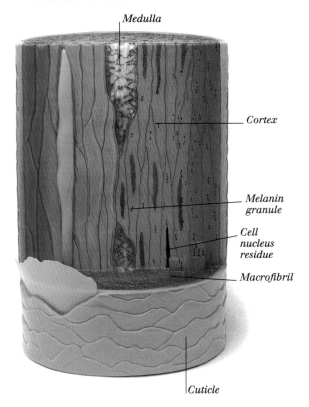

Medulla

Cortex

Melanin granule

Cell nucleus residue

Macrofibril

Cuticle

SECTIONS OF DIFFERENT TYPES OF SKIN

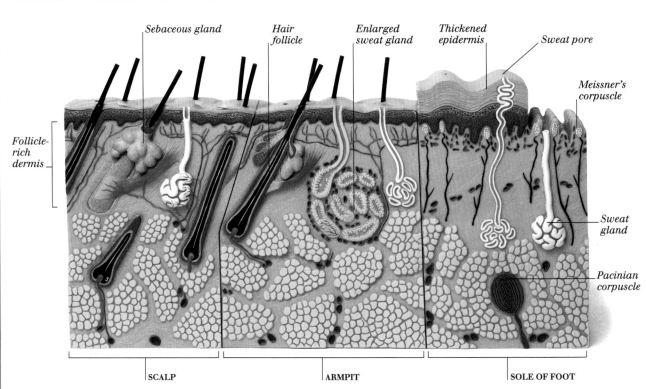

Sebaceous gland

Hair follicle

Enlarged sweat gland

Thickened epidermis

Sweat pore

Meissner's corpuscle

Follicle-rich dermis

Sweat gland

Pacinian corpuscle

SCALP

ARMPIT

SOLE OF FOOT

SECTION OF SKIN

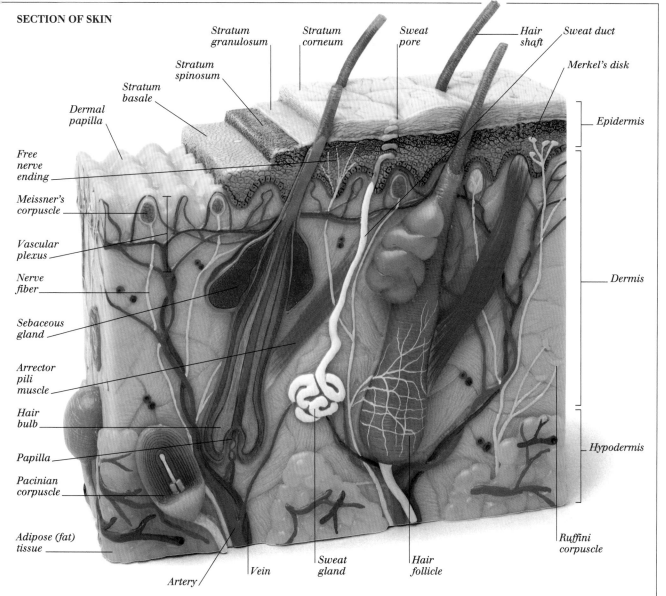

Stratum
granulosum

Stratum
spinosum

Stratum
basale

Stratum
corneum

Sweat
pore

Hair
shaft

Sweat duct

Merkel's disk

Dermal
papilla

Epidermis

Free
nerve
ending

Meissner's
corpuscle

Vascular
plexus

Nerve
fiber

Sebaceous
gland

Arrector
pili
muscle

Dermis

Hair
bulb

Papilla

Pacinian
corpuscle

Hypodermis

Adipose (fat)
tissue

Ruffini
corpuscle

Artery

Vein

Sweat
gland

Hair
follicle

PHOTOMICROGRAPHS OF SKIN AND HAIR

SECTION OF SKIN
The flaky cells at the skin's
surface are shed continuously.

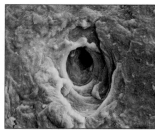

SWEAT PORE
This allows loss of fluid as part
of temperature control.

SKIN HAIR
Two hairs pushing through the
outer layer of skin.

HEAD HAIR
The root and part of the shaft of
a hair from the scalp.

Brain

THE BRAIN IS THE MAJOR ORGAN of the central nervous system and the control center for all the body's voluntary and involuntary activities. It is also responsible for the complexities of thought, memory, emotion, and language. In adults, this complex organ is a mere 3 lb (1.4 kg) in weight, containing over 10 thousand million nerve cells. Three distinct regions can easily be seen—the brainstem, the cerebellum, and the large cerebrum. The brainstem controls vital body functions, such as breathing and digestion. The cerebellum's main functions are the maintenance of posture and the coordination of body movements. The cerebrum, which consists of the right and left cerebral hemispheres joined by the corpus callosum, is the site of most conscious and intelligent activities.

MRI SCAN OF TRANSVERSE SECTION THROUGH BRAIN

White matter
Skull
Scalp
Gray matter
Lateral ventricle
Longitudinal fissure
Sagittal section
Coronal section

SAGITTAL SECTION THROUGH BRAIN

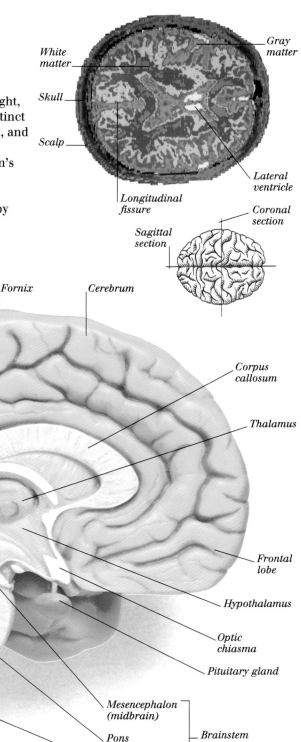

Central sulcus
Fornix
Cerebrum
Parietal lobe
Corpus callosum
Parieto-occipital sulcus
Thalamus
Pineal body
Occipital lobe
Frontal lobe
Aqueduct
Hypothalamus
Cerebellum
Optic chiasma
4th ventricle
Pituitary gland
Mesencephalon (midbrain)
Spinal cord
Pons
Brainstem
Medulla oblongata

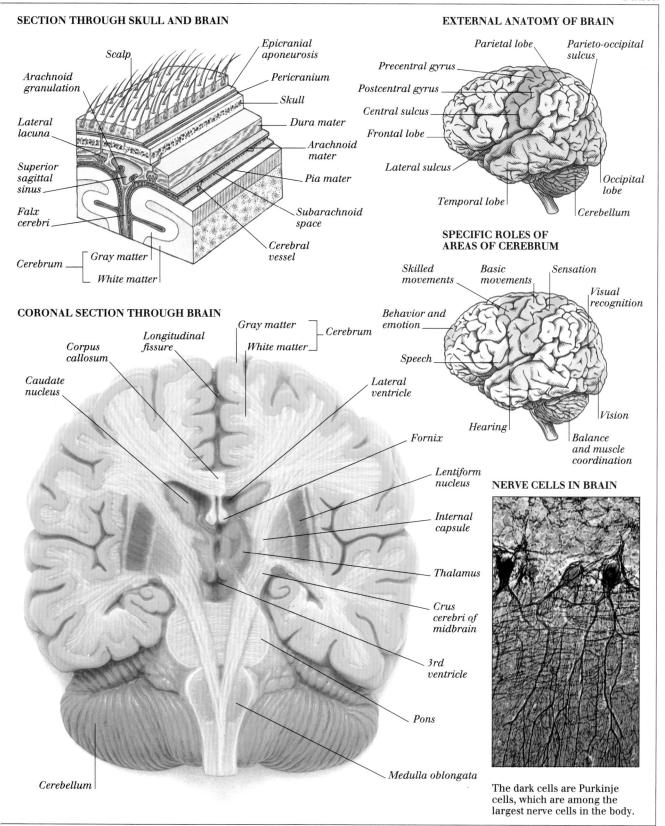

SECTION THROUGH SKULL AND BRAIN

Scalp
Epicranial aponeurosis
Arachnoid granulation
Pericranium
Skull
Lateral lacuna
Dura mater
Arachnoid mater
Superior sagittal sinus
Pia mater
Falx cerebri
Cerebral vessel
Subarachnoid space
Cerebrum
Gray matter
White matter

CORONAL SECTION THROUGH BRAIN

Corpus callosum
Longitudinal fissure
Gray matter
White matter
Cerebrum
Caudate nucleus
Lateral ventricle
Fornix
Lentiform nucleus
Internal capsule
Thalamus
Crus cerebri of midbrain
3rd ventricle
Pons
Medulla oblongata
Cerebellum

EXTERNAL ANATOMY OF BRAIN

Parietal lobe
Parieto-occipital sulcus
Precentral gyrus
Postcentral gyrus
Central sulcus
Frontal lobe
Lateral sulcus
Occipital lobe
Temporal lobe
Cerebellum

SPECIFIC ROLES OF AREAS OF CEREBRUM

Skilled movements
Basic movements
Sensation
Visual recognition
Behavior and emotion
Speech
Hearing
Vision
Balance and muscle coordination

NERVE CELLS IN BRAIN

The dark cells are Purkinje cells, which are among the largest nerve cells in the body.

Nervous system

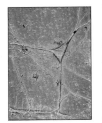

THE NERVOUS SYSTEM IS THE BODY'S internal, electrochemical, communications network. Its main parts are the brain, spinal cord, and nerves. The brain and spinal cord form the central nervous system (CNS), the body's chief controlling and coordinating centers. Billions of long neurons, many grouped as nerves, make up the peripheral nervous system, transmitting nerve impulses between the CNS and other regions of the body. Each neuron has three parts: a cell body, branching dendrites that receive chemical signals from other neurons, and a tube-like axon that conveys these signals as electrical impulses.

CENTRAL AND PERIPHERAL NERVOUS SYSTEMS

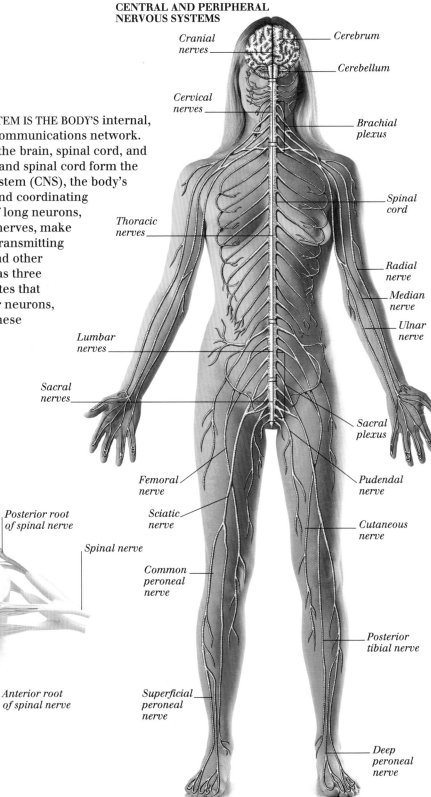

Cranial nerves

Cerebrum

Cerebellum

Cervical nerves

Brachial plexus

Spinal cord

Thoracic nerves

Radial nerve

Median nerve

Ulnar nerve

Lumbar nerves

Sacral nerves

Sacral plexus

Femoral nerve

Pudendal nerve

Sciatic nerve

Cutaneous nerve

Common peroneal nerve

Posterior tibial nerve

Superficial peroneal nerve

Deep peroneal nerve

SECTION THROUGH SPINAL CORD

Spinal ganglion

Gray matter

Central canal

Posterior root of spinal nerve

Spinal nerve

Anterior root of spinal nerve

White matter

Anterior median fissure

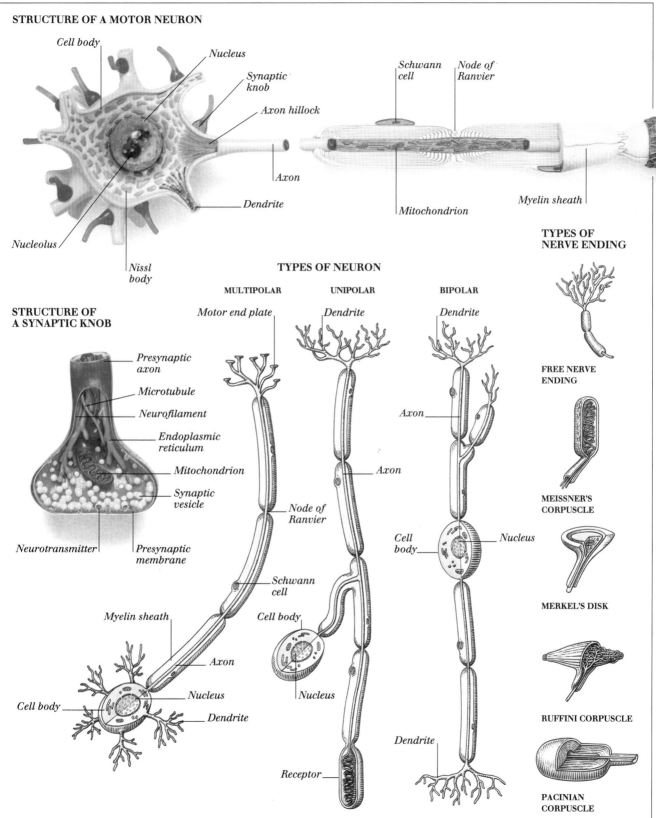

STRUCTURE OF A MOTOR NEURON

Cell body

Nucleus

Synaptic knob

Axon hillock

Axon

Dendrite

Nucleolus

Nissl body

Schwann cell

Node of Ranvier

Mitochondrion

Myelin sheath

TYPES OF NERVE ENDING

TYPES OF NEURON

MULTIPOLAR

UNIPOLAR

BIPOLAR

STRUCTURE OF A SYNAPTIC KNOB

Motor end plate

Dendrite

Dendrite

FREE NERVE ENDING

Presynaptic axon

Microtubule

Neurofilament

Endoplasmic reticulum

Mitochondrion

Synaptic vesicle

Axon

MEISSNER'S CORPUSCLE

Neurotransmitter

Presynaptic membrane

Axon

MERKEL'S DISK

Node of Ranvier

Cell body

Nucleus

Myelin sheath

Schwann cell

Cell body

Nucleus

RUFFINI CORPUSCLE

Axon

Cell body

Nucleus

Dendrite

Nucleus

Dendrite

PACINIAN CORPUSCLE

Receptor

Eye

THE EYE IS THE ORGAN OF SIGHT. The two eyeballs, protected within bony sockets called orbits and on the outside by the eyelids, eyebrows, and tear film, are directly connected to the brain by the optic nerves. Each eye is moved by six muscles, which are attached around the eyeball. Light rays entering the eye through the pupil are focused by the cornea and lens to form an image on the retina. The retina contains millions of light-sensitive cells, called rods and cones, which convert the image into a pattern of nerve impulses. These impulses are transmitted along the optic nerve to the brain. Information from the two optic nerves is processed in the brain to produce a single coordinated image.

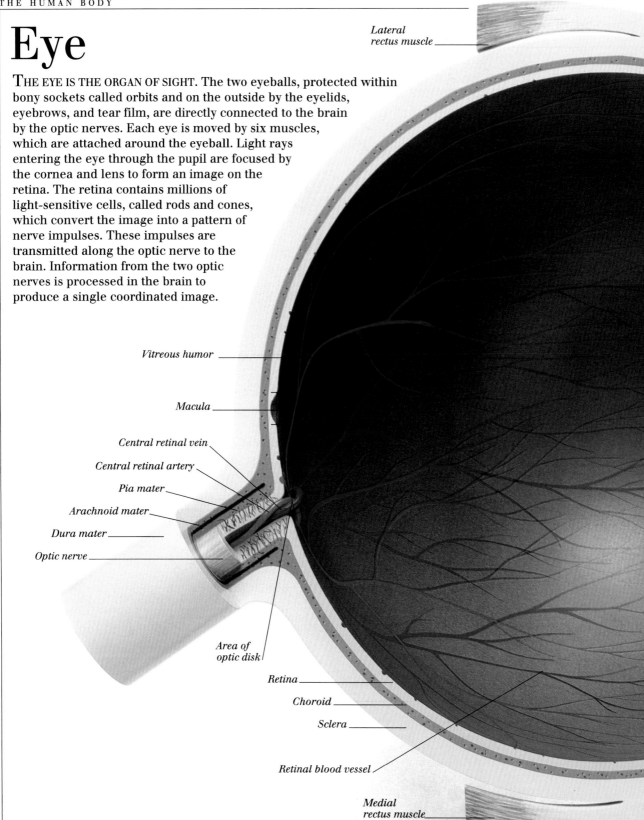

Lateral rectus muscle

Vitreous humor

Macula

Central retinal vein

Central retinal artery

Pia mater

Arachnoid mater

Dura mater

Optic nerve

Area of optic disk

Retina

Choroid

Sclera

Retinal blood vessel

Medial rectus muscle

SECTION THROUGH LEFT EYE

LACRIMAL (TEAR-PRODUCING) APPARATUS

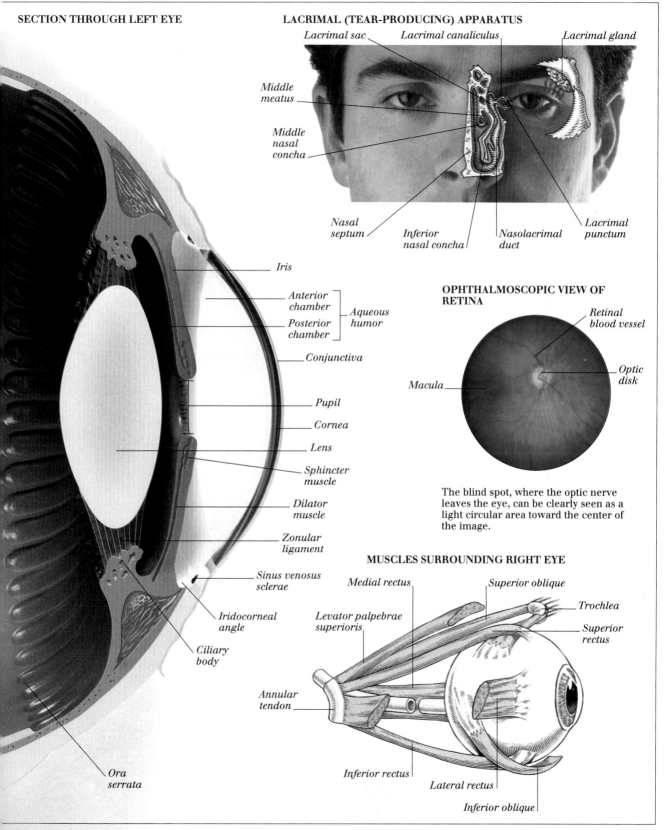

Lacrimal sac

Lacrimal canaliculus

Lacrimal gland

Middle meatus

Middle nasal concha

Nasal septum

Inferior nasal concha

Nasolacrimal duct

Lacrimal punctum

Iris

Anterior chamber

Posterior chamber

Aqueous humor

Conjunctiva

Pupil

Cornea

Lens

Sphincter muscle

Dilator muscle

Zonular ligament

Sinus venosus sclerae

Iridocorneal angle

Ciliary body

Ora serrata

OPHTHALMOSCOPIC VIEW OF RETINA

Retinal blood vessel

Optic disk

Macula

The blind spot, where the optic nerve leaves the eye, can be clearly seen as a light circular area toward the center of the image.

MUSCLES SURROUNDING RIGHT EYE

Medial rectus

Superior oblique

Trochlea

Superior rectus

Levator palpebrae superioris

Annular tendon

Inferior rectus

Lateral rectus

Inferior oblique

Ear

THE EAR IS THE ORGAN OF HEARING AND BALANCE. The outer ear consists of a flap called the auricle or pinna and the auditory canal. The main functional parts—the middle and inner ears—are enclosed within the skull. The middle ear consists of three tiny bones, known as auditory ossicles, and the eustachian tube, which links the ear to the back of the nose. The inner ear consists of the spiral-shaped cochlea, and also the semicircular canals and the vestibule, which are the organs of balance. Sound waves entering the ear travel through the auditory canal to the tympanic membrane (eardrum), where they are converted to vibrations that are transmitted via the ossicles to the cochlea. Here, the vibrations are converted by millions of microscopic hairs into electrical nerve signals to be interpreted by the brain.

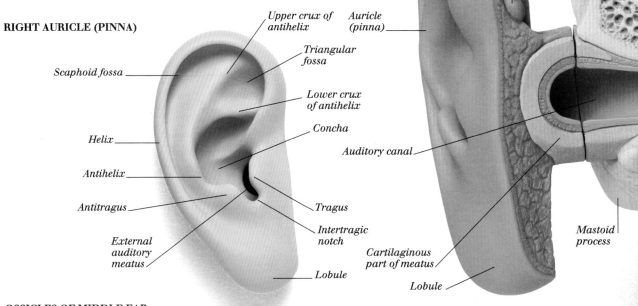

RIGHT AURICLE (PINNA)

Upper crux of antihelix
Auricle (pinna)
Triangular fossa
Scaphoid fossa
Lower crux of antihelix
Concha
Helix
Auditory canal
Antihelix
Antitragus
Tragus
Intertragic notch
External auditory meatus
Cartilaginous part of meatus
Lobule
Lobule

Temporal bone
Cartilage of auricle
Mastoid process

OSSICLES OF MIDDLE EAR

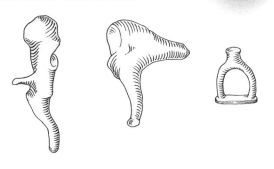

MALLEUS (HAMMER)   INCUS (ANVIL)   STAPES (STIRRUP)

These three tiny bones connect to form a bridge between the tympanic membrane and the oval window. With a system of membranes they convey sound vibrations to the inner ear.

INTERNAL STRUCTURE OF AMPULLA

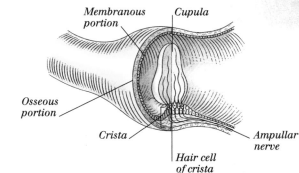

Membranous portion
Cupula
Osseous portion
Crista
Hair cell of crista
Ampullar nerve

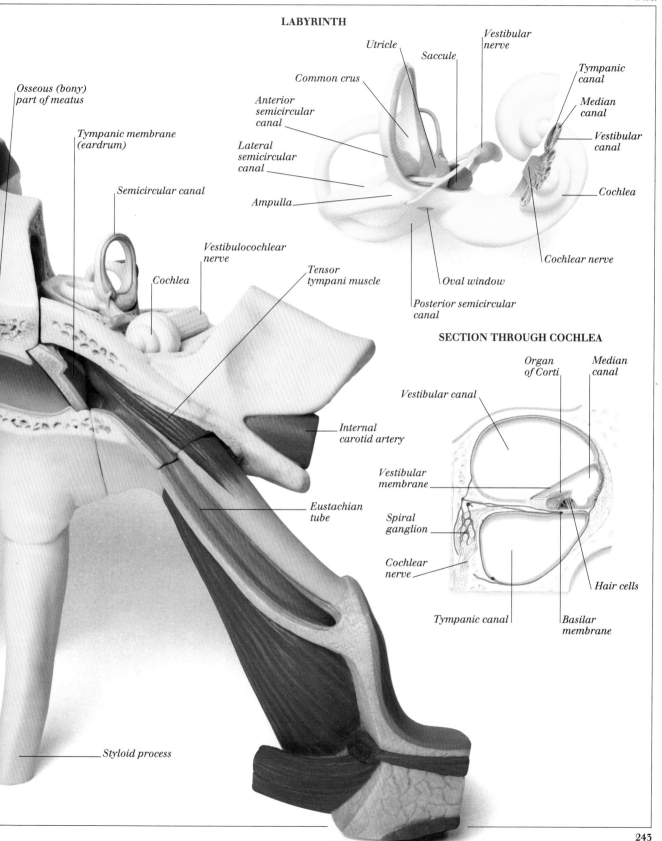

LABYRINTH

Utricle

Saccule

Vestibular nerve

Common crus

Tympanic canal

Anterior semicircular canal

Median canal

Osseous (bony) part of meatus

Vestibular canal

Tympanic membrane (eardrum)

Lateral semicircular canal

Cochlea

Semicircular canal

Ampulla

Vestibulocochlear nerve

Cochlear nerve

Cochlea

Tensor tympani muscle

Oval window

Posterior semicircular canal

SECTION THROUGH COCHLEA

Organ of Corti

Median canal

Vestibular canal

Internal carotid artery

Vestibular membrane

Eustachian tube

Spiral ganglion

Cochlear nerve

Hair cells

Tympanic canal

Basilar membrane

Styloid process

Nose, mouth, and throat

WITH EVERY BREATH, air passes through the nasal cavity down the pharynx (throat), larynx ("voice box"), and trachea (windpipe) to the lungs. The nasal cavity warms and moistens air, and the tiny layers in its lining protect the airway against damage by foreign bodies. During swallowing, the tongue moves up and back, the larynx rises, the epiglottis closes off the entrance to the trachea, and the soft palate separates the nasal cavity from the pharynx. Saliva, secreted from three pairs of salivary glands, lubricates food to make swallowing easier; it also begins the chemical breakdown of food, and helps to produce taste. The senses of taste and smell are closely linked. Both depend on the detection of dissolved molecules by sensory receptors in the olfactory nerve endings of the nose and in the taste buds of the tongue.

STRUCTURE OF TONGUE

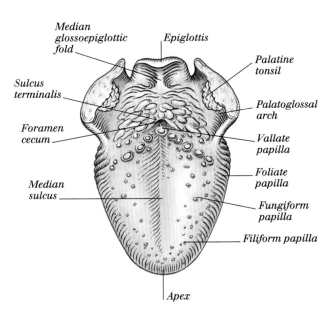

Median glossoepiglottic fold
Epiglottis
Palatine tonsil
Palatoglossal arch
Sulcus terminalis
Vallate papilla
Foramen cecum
Foliate papilla
Median sulcus
Fungiform papilla
Filiform papilla
Apex

TASTE AREAS ON TONGUE

Bitter
Sour
Salt
Sweet

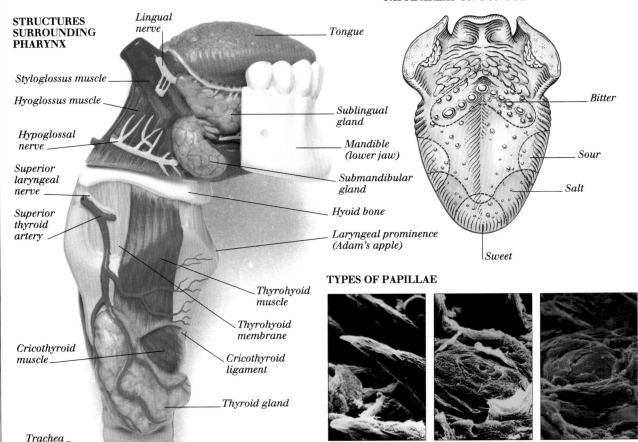

STRUCTURES SURROUNDING PHARYNX

Lingual nerve
Tongue
Styloglossus muscle
Hyoglossus muscle
Sublingual gland
Hypoglossal nerve
Mandible (lower jaw)
Submandibular gland
Superior laryngeal nerve
Hyoid bone
Superior thyroid artery
Laryngeal prominence (Adam's apple)
Thyrohyoid muscle
Thyrohyoid membrane
Cricothyroid muscle
Cricothyroid ligament
Thyroid gland
Trachea

TYPES OF PAPILLAE

FILIFORM PAPILLAE   **FUNGIFORM PAPILLAE**   **VALLATE PAPILLAE**

**SECTION THROUGH NOSE,
MOUTH, AND THROAT**

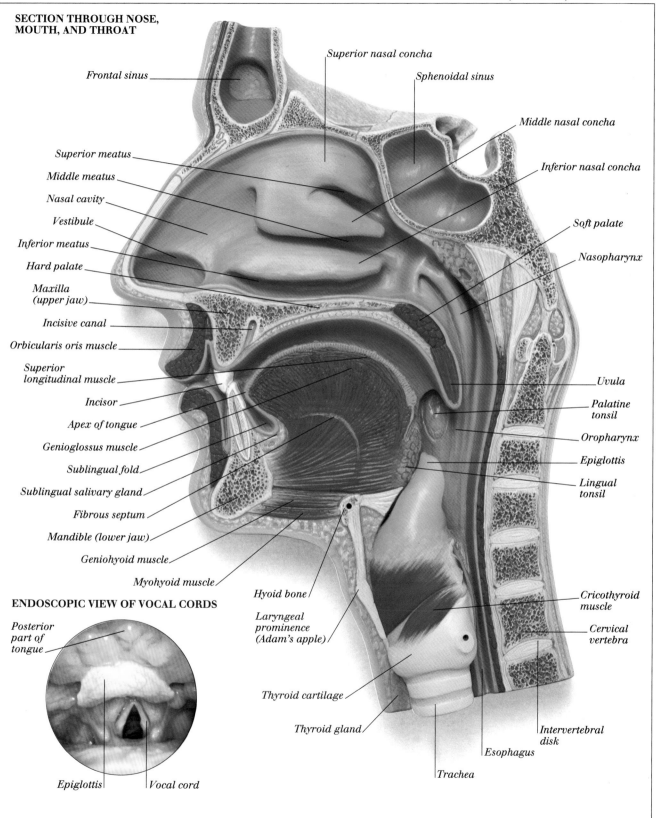

Frontal sinus

Superior nasal concha

Sphenoidal sinus

Middle nasal concha

Inferior nasal concha

Superior meatus

Middle meatus

Nasal cavity

Vestibule

Inferior meatus

Hard palate

Maxilla
(upper jaw)

Incisive canal

Orbicularis oris muscle

Superior
longitudinal muscle

Incisor

Apex of tongue

Genioglossus muscle

Sublingual fold

Sublingual salivary gland

Fibrous septum

Mandible (lower jaw)

Geniohyoid muscle

Myohyoid muscle

Soft palate

Nasopharynx

Uvula

Palatine
tonsil

Oropharynx

Epiglottis

Lingual
tonsil

ENDOSCOPIC VIEW OF VOCAL CORDS

Posterior
part of
tongue

Hyoid bone

Laryngeal
prominence
(Adam's apple)

Cricothyroid
muscle

Cervical
vertebra

Thyroid cartilage

Thyroid gland

Intervertebral
disk

Esophagus

Trachea

Epiglottis

Vocal cord

245

Teeth

THE 20 PRIMARY TEETH (also called deciduous or milk teeth) usually begin to erupt when a baby is about six months old. They start to be replaced by the permanent teeth when the child is about six years old. By the age of 20, most adults have a full set of 32 teeth although the third molars (commonly called wisdom teeth) may never erupt. While teeth help people to speak clearly and give shape to the face, their main function is the chewing of food. Incisors and canines shear and tear the food into pieces; premolars and molars crush and grind it further. Although tooth enamel is the hardest substance in the body, it tends to be eroded and destroyed by acid produced in the mouth during the breakdown of food.

DEVELOPMENT OF TEETH IN A FETUS

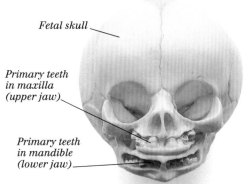

Fetal skull

Primary teeth in maxilla (upper jaw)

Primary teeth in mandible (lower jaw)

FETAL JAWS
By the sixth week of embryonic development areas of thickening occur in each jaw; these areas give rise to tooth buds. By the time the fetus is six months old, enamel has formed on the tooth buds.

DEVELOPMENT OF JAW AND TEETH

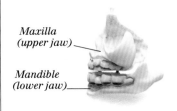

Maxilla (upper jaw)

Mandible (lower jaw)

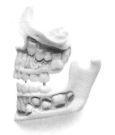

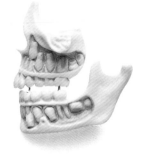

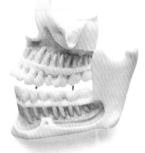

A NEWBORN BABY'S JAWS
The primary teeth can be seen developing in the jawbones; they begin to erupt around the age of six months.

A FIVE-YEAR-OLD CHILD'S TEETH
There is a full set of 20 erupted primary teeth; the permanent teeth can be seen developing in the upper and lower jaws.

A NINE-YEAR-OLD CHILD'S TEETH
Most of the teeth are primary teeth but the permanent incisors and first molars have now emerged.

AN ADULT'S TEETH
By the age of 20, the full set of 32 permanent teeth (including the wisdom teeth) should be in position.

THE PERMANENT TEETH

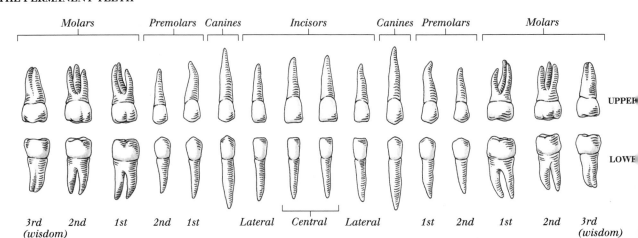

| Molars | Premolars | Canines | Incisors | Canines | Premolars | Molars |

UPPER

LOWER

| 3rd (wisdom) | 2nd | 1st | 2nd | 1st | Lateral | Central | Lateral | 1st | 2nd | 1st | 2nd | 3rd (wisdom) |

STRUCTURE OF A TOOTH

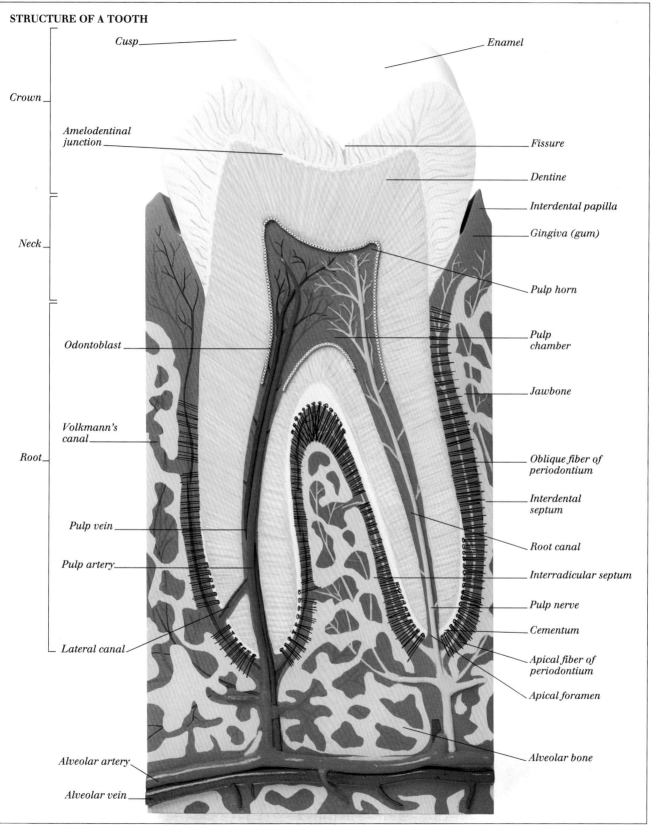

Cusp

Enamel

Crown

Amelodentinal junction

Fissure

Dentine

Interdental papilla

Gingiva (gum)

Neck

Pulp horn

Odontoblast

Pulp chamber

Jawbone

Volkmann's canal

Oblique fiber of periodontium

Root

Interdental septum

Pulp vein

Root canal

Pulp artery

Interradicular septum

Pulp nerve

Cementum

Lateral canal

Apical fiber of periodontium

Apical foramen

Alveolar bone

Alveolar artery

Alveolar vein

Digestive system

THE DIGESTIVE SYSTEM BREAKS DOWN FOOD into particles so tiny that blood can take nourishment to all parts of the body. The system's main part is a 30-foot (9 m) tube from mouth to rectum; muscles in this alimentary canal force food along. Chewed food first travels through the esophagus to the stomach, which churns and liquidizes food before it passes through the duodenum, jejunum, and ileum—the three parts of the long, convoluted small intestine. Here, digestive juices from the gallbladder and pancreas break down food particles; many filter out into the blood through tiny fingerlike villi that line the small intestine's inner wall. Undigested food in the colon forms feces that leave the body through the anus.

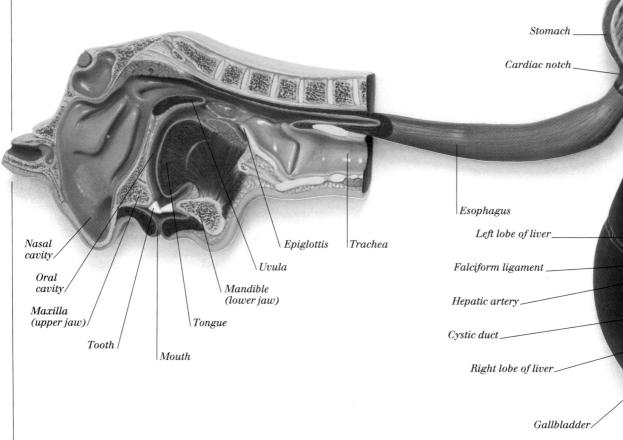

Stomach

Cardiac notch

Nasal cavity

Oral cavity

Maxilla (upper jaw)

Tooth

Mouth

Tongue

Mandible (lower jaw)

Uvula

Epiglottis

Trachea

Esophagus

Left lobe of liver

Falciform ligament

Hepatic artery

Cystic duct

Right lobe of liver

Gallbladder

ENDOSCOPIC VIEWS INSIDE ALIMENTARY CANAL

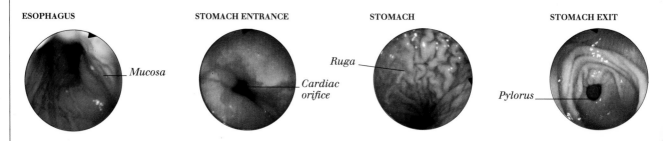

ESOPHAGUS

Mucosa

STOMACH ENTRANCE

Cardiac orifice

STOMACH

Ruga

STOMACH EXIT

Pylorus

ALIMENTARY CANAL

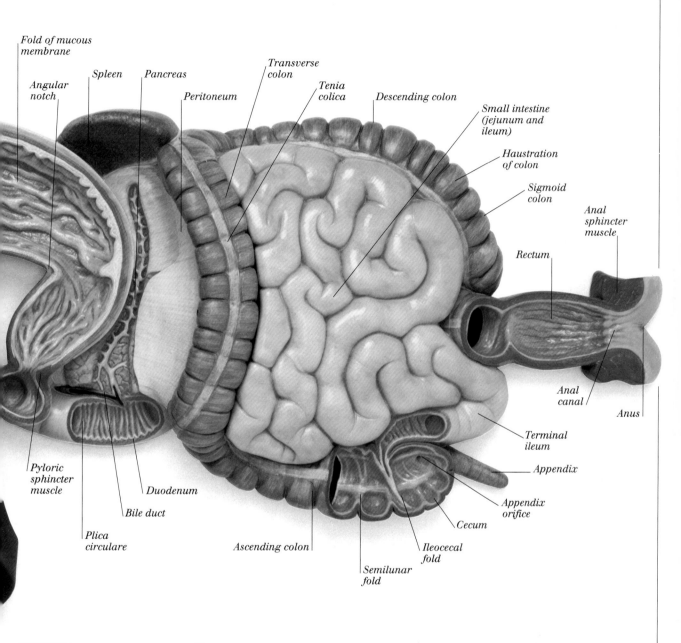

Fold of mucous membrane

Spleen

Pancreas

Angular notch

Peritoneum

Transverse colon

Tenia colica

Descending colon

Small intestine (jejunum and ileum)

Haustration of colon

Sigmoid colon

Anal sphincter muscle

Rectum

Anal canal

Anus

Terminal ileum

Appendix

Appendix orifice

Cecum

Ileocecal fold

Semilunar fold

Ascending colon

Bile duct

Duodenum

Pyloric sphincter muscle

Plica circulare

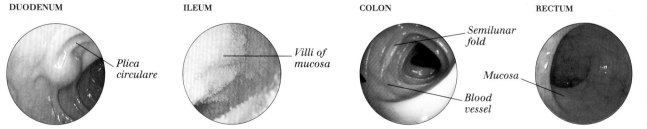

DUODENUM

Plica circulare

ILEUM

Villi of mucosa

COLON

Semilunar fold

Blood vessel

RECTUM

Mucosa

Heart

THE HEART IS A HOLLOW MUSCLE in the middle of the chest that pumps blood around the body, supplying cells with oxygen and nutrients. A muscular wall, called the septum, divides the heart lengthwise into left and right sides. A valve divides each side into two chambers: an upper atrium and a lower ventricle. When the heart muscle contracts, it squeezes blood through the atria and then through the ventricles. Oxygenated blood from the lungs flows from the pulmonary veins into the left atrium, through the left ventricle, and then out via the aorta to all parts of the body. Deoxygenated blood returning from the body flows from the vena cava into the right atrium, through the right ventricle, and then out via the pulmonary artery to the lungs for reoxygenation. At rest the heart beats between 60 and 80 times a minute; during exercise or at times of stress or excitement the rate may increase to 200 beats a minute.

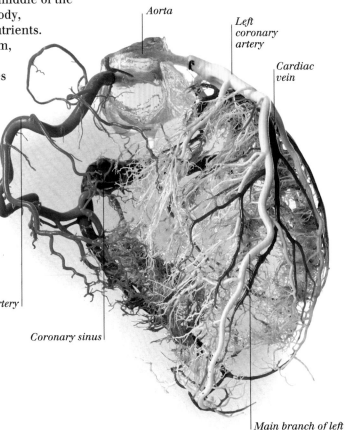

Aorta

Left coronary artery

Cardiac vein

Right coronary artery

Coronary sinus

Main branch of left coronary artery

SECTION THROUGH HEART WALL

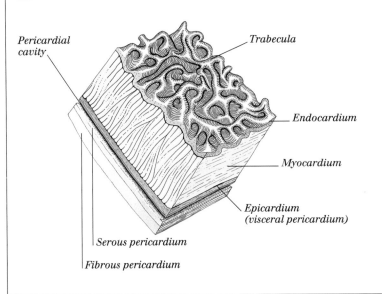

Pericardial cavity

Trabecula

Endocardium

Myocardium

Epicardium (visceral pericardium)

Serous pericardium

Fibrous pericardium

HEARTBEAT SEQUENCE

ATRIAL DIASTOLE

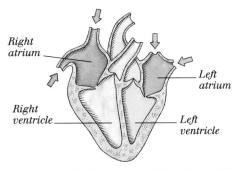

Right atrium

Left atrium

Right ventricle

Left ventricle

Deoxygenated blood enters the right atrium while the left atrium receives oxygenated blood.

STRUCTURE OF HEART

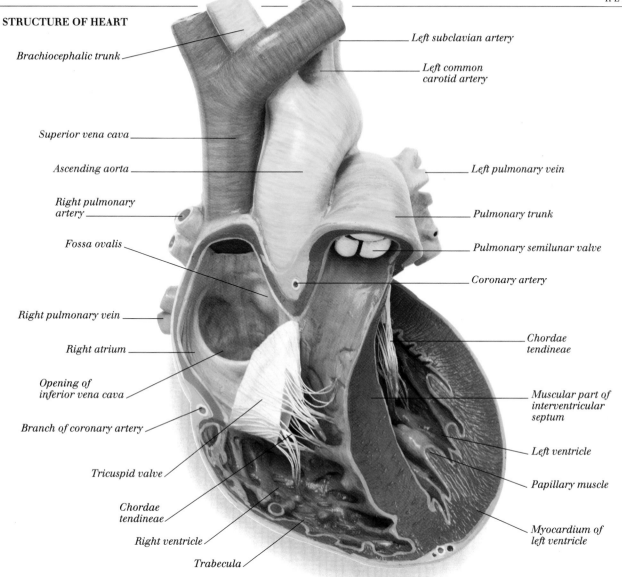

Brachiocephalic trunk

Superior vena cava

Ascending aorta

Right pulmonary artery

Fossa ovalis

Right pulmonary vein

Right atrium

Opening of inferior vena cava

Branch of coronary artery

Tricuspid valve

Chordae tendineae

Right ventricle

Trabecula

Left subclavian artery

Left common carotid artery

Left pulmonary vein

Pulmonary trunk

Pulmonary semilunar valve

Coronary artery

Chordae tendineae

Muscular part of interventricular septum

Left ventricle

Papillary muscle

Myocardium of left ventricle

ATRIAL SYSTOLE (VENTRICULAR DIASTOLE)

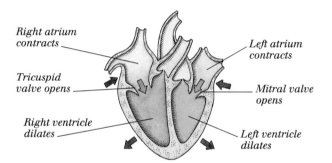

Right atrium contracts

Tricuspid valve opens

Right ventricle dilates

Left atrium contracts

Mitral valve opens

Left ventricle dilates

Left and right atria contract, forcing blood into the relaxed ventricles.

VENTRICULAR SYSTOLE

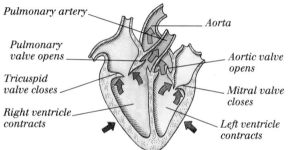

Pulmonary artery

Pulmonary valve opens

Tricuspid valve closes

Right ventricle contracts

Aorta

Aortic valve opens

Mitral valve closes

Left ventricle contracts

Ventricles contract and force blood to the lungs for oxygenation and via the aorta to the rest of the body.

Circulatory system

THE CIRCULATORY SYSTEM consists of the heart and blood vessels, which together maintain a continuous flow of blood around the body. The heart pumps oxygen-rich blood from the lungs to all parts of the body through a network of tubes called arteries, and smaller branches called arterioles. Blood returns to the heart via small vessels called venules, which lead in turn into larger tubes called veins. Arterioles and venules are linked by a network of tiny vessels called capillaries, where the exchange of oxygen and carbon dioxide between blood and body cells takes place. Blood has four main components: red blood cells, white blood cells, platelets, and liquid plasma.

ARTERIAL SYSTEM OF BRAIN

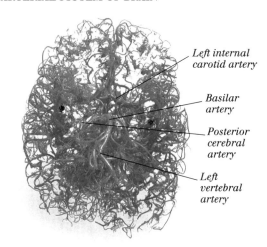

Left internal carotid artery

Basilar artery

Posterior cerebral artery

Left vertebral artery

CIRCULATORY SYSTEM OF LIVER

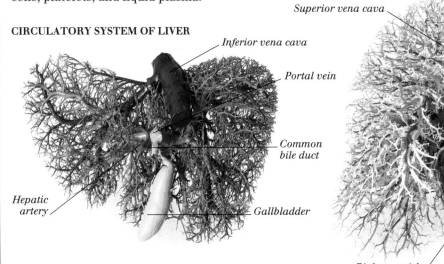

Inferior vena cava

Portal vein

Common bile duct

Hepatic artery

Gallbladder

CIRCULATORY SYSTEM OF HEART AND LUNGS

Superior vena cava

Aorta

Right ventricle

Left ventricle

SECTION OF MAIN ARTERY

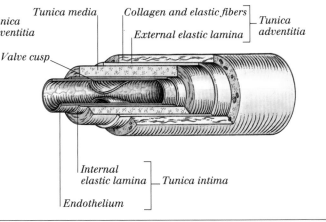

Tunica media

Collagen and elastic fibers

External elastic lamina

Tunica adventitia

Internal elastic lamina

Tunica intima

Endothelium

Arteriole

SECTION OF MAIN VEIN

Tunica media

Collagen and elastic fibers

External elastic lamina

Tunica adventitia

Valve cusp

Internal elastic lamina

Tunica intima

Endothelium

PRINCIPAL ARTERIES AND VEINS OF CIRCULATORY SYSTEM

Internal jugular vein

Common carotid artery

Brachiocephalic vein

Subclavian artery

Subclavian vein

Arch of aorta

Axillary vein

Axillary artery

Cephalic vein

Pulmonary artery

Superior vena cava

Coronary artery

Pulmonary vein

Brachial artery

Basilic vein

Gastric artery

Hepatic portal vein

Hepatic artery

Splenic artery

Median cubital vein

Superior mesenteric artery

Inferior vena cava

Anterior median vein

Radial artery

Gastroepiploic vein

Ulnar artery

Palmar vein

Digital vein

Palmar arch

Inferior mesenteric vein

Digital artery

Superior mesenteric vein

Common iliac artery

Common iliac vein

External iliac artery

Internal iliac artery

External iliac vein

Femoral artery

Internal iliac vein

Popliteal artery

Femoral vein

Peroneal artery

Great saphenous vein

Anterior tibial artery

Short saphenous vein

Posterior tibial artery

Lateral plantar artery

Dorsal metatarsal artery

Dorsal venous arch

Digital vein

TYPES OF BLOOD CELLS

RED BLOOD CELLS
These cells are biconcave in shape to maximize their oxygen-carrying capacity.

WHITE BLOOD CELLS
Lymphocytes are the smallest white blood cells; they form antibodies against disease.

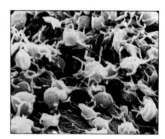

PLATELETS
Tiny cells that are activated whenever blood clotting or repair to vessels is necessary.

BLOOD CLOTTING

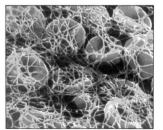

Filaments of fibrin enmesh red blood cells as part of the process of blood clotting.

Respiratory system

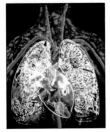

THE RESPIRATORY SYSTEM supplies the oxygen needed by body cells and carries off their carbon dioxide waste. Inhaled air passes via the trachea (windpipe) through two narrower tubes, the bronchi, to the lungs. Each lung comprises many fine, branching tubes called bronchioles that end in tiny clustered chambers called alveoli. Gases cross the thin alveolar walls to and from a network of tiny blood vessels. Intercostal (rib) muscles and the muscular diaphragm below the lungs operate the lungs like bellows, drawing air in and forcing it out at regular intervals.

BRONCHIOLE AND ALVEOLI

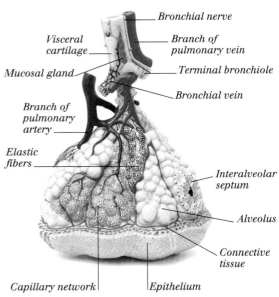

Visceral cartilage
Mucosal gland
Branch of pulmonary artery
Elastic fibers

Bronchial nerve
Branch of pulmonary vein
Terminal bronchiole
Bronchial vein

Interalveolar septum
Alveolus
Connective tissue

Capillary network
Epithelium

SEGMENTS OF BRONCHIAL TREE

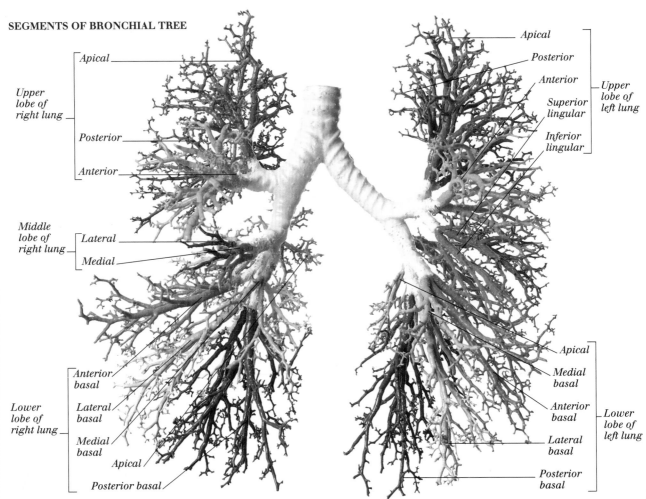

Upper lobe of right lung
Apical
Posterior
Anterior

Middle lobe of right lung
Lateral
Medial

Lower lobe of right lung
Anterior basal
Lateral basal
Medial basal
Apical
Posterior basal

Apical
Posterior
Anterior
Superior lingular
Inferior lingular
Upper lobe of left lung

Apical
Medial basal
Anterior basal
Lateral basal
Posterior basal
Lower lobe of left lung

STRUCTURES OF THORACIC CAVITY

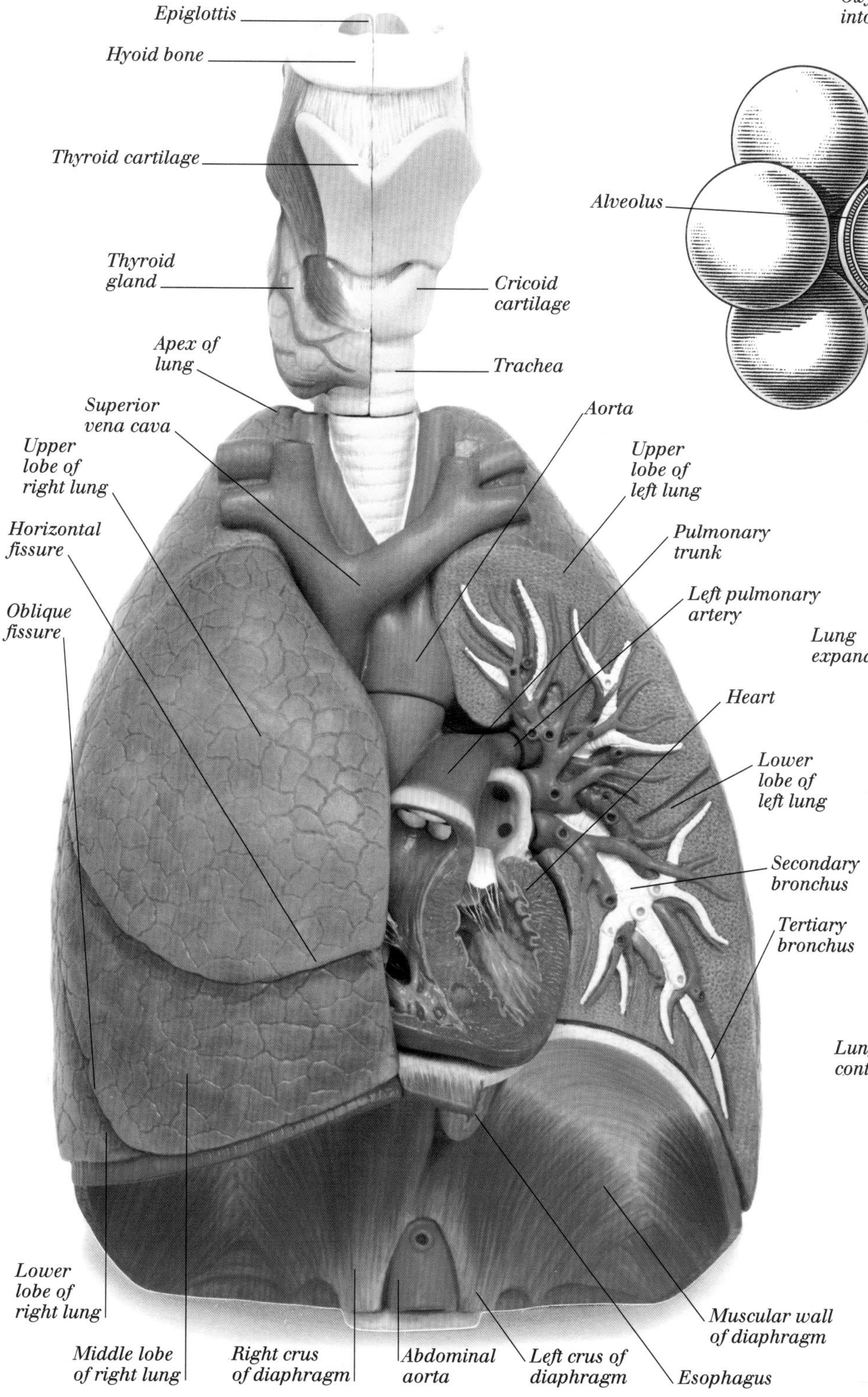

Epiglottis

Hyoid bone

Thyroid cartilage

Thyroid gland

Cricoid cartilage

Apex of lung

Trachea

Superior vena cava

Aorta

Upper lobe of right lung

Upper lobe of left lung

Horizontal fissure

Pulmonary trunk

Oblique fissure

Left pulmonary artery

Heart

Lower lobe of left lung

Secondary bronchus

Tertiary bronchus

Lower lobe of right lung

Middle lobe of right lung

Right crus of diaphragm

Abdominal aorta

Left crus of diaphragm

Esophagus

Muscular wall of diaphragm

GASEOUS EXCHANGE IN ALVEOLUS

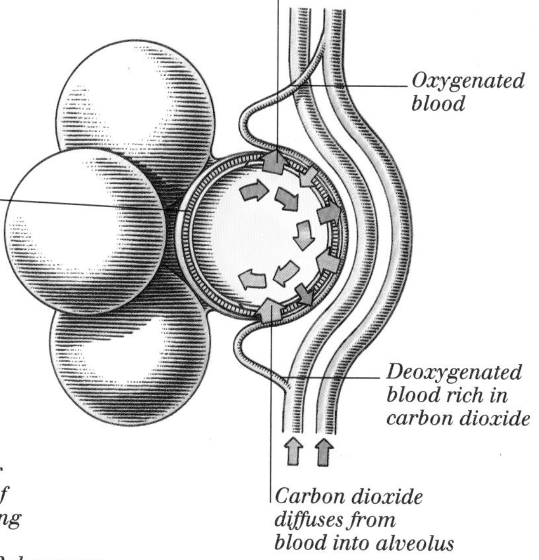

Oxygen diffuses into blood

Oxygenated blood

Alveolus

Deoxygenated blood rich in carbon dioxide

Carbon dioxide diffuses from blood into alveolus

MECHANISM OF RESPIRATION
INSPIRATION

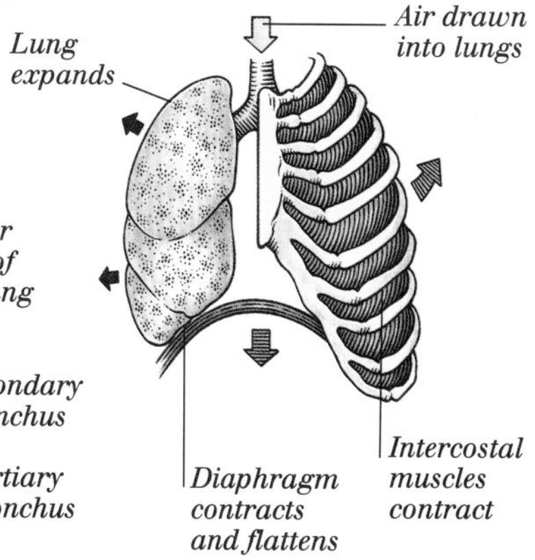

Lung expands

Air drawn into lungs

Diaphragm contracts and flattens

Intercostal muscles contract

EXPIRATION

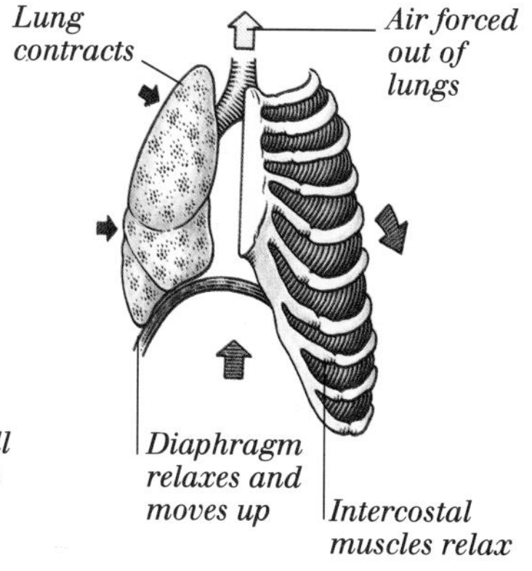

Lung contracts

Air forced out of lungs

Diaphragm relaxes and moves up

Intercostal muscles relax

Urinary system

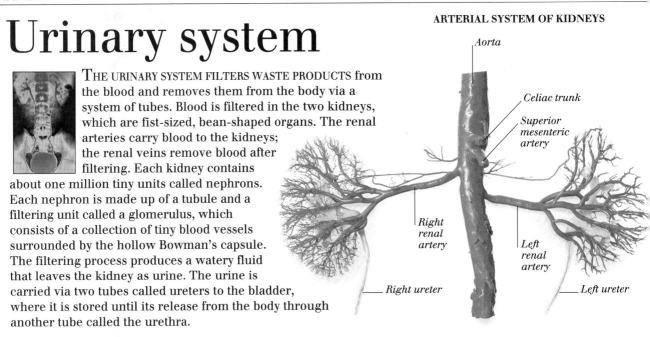

THE URINARY SYSTEM FILTERS WASTE PRODUCTS from the blood and removes them from the body via a system of tubes. Blood is filtered in the two kidneys, which are fist-sized, bean-shaped organs. The renal arteries carry blood to the kidneys; the renal veins remove blood after filtering. Each kidney contains about one million tiny units called nephrons. Each nephron is made up of a tubule and a filtering unit called a glomerulus, which consists of a collection of tiny blood vessels surrounded by the hollow Bowman's capsule. The filtering process produces a watery fluid that leaves the kidney as urine. The urine is carried via two tubes called ureters to the bladder, where it is stored until its release from the body through another tube called the urethra.

ARTERIAL SYSTEM OF KIDNEYS

Aorta

Celiac trunk

Superior mesenteric artery

Right renal artery

Left renal artery

Right ureter

Left ureter

SECTION THROUGH LEFT KIDNEY

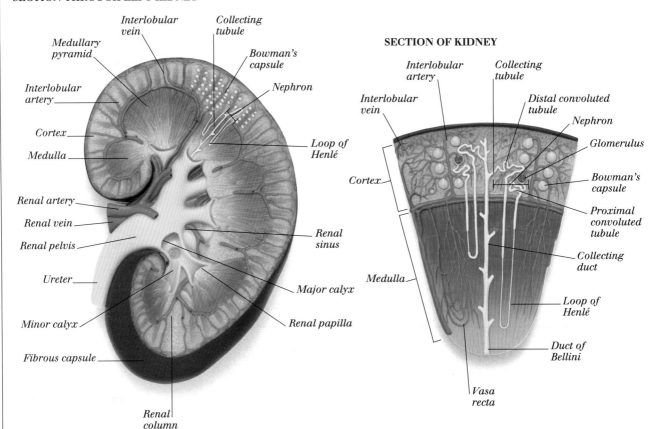

Interlobular vein

Collecting tubule

Medullary pyramid

Bowman's capsule

Interlobular artery

Nephron

Cortex

Medulla

Loop of Henlé

Renal artery

Renal vein

Renal pelvis

Renal sinus

Ureter

Major calyx

Minor calyx

Renal papilla

Fibrous capsule

Renal column

SECTION OF KIDNEY

Interlobular artery

Collecting tubule

Interlobular vein

Distal convoluted tubule

Nephron

Cortex

Glomerulus

Bowman's capsule

Proximal convoluted tubule

Medulla

Collecting duct

Loop of Henlé

Duct of Bellini

Vasa recta

MALE URINARY TRACT

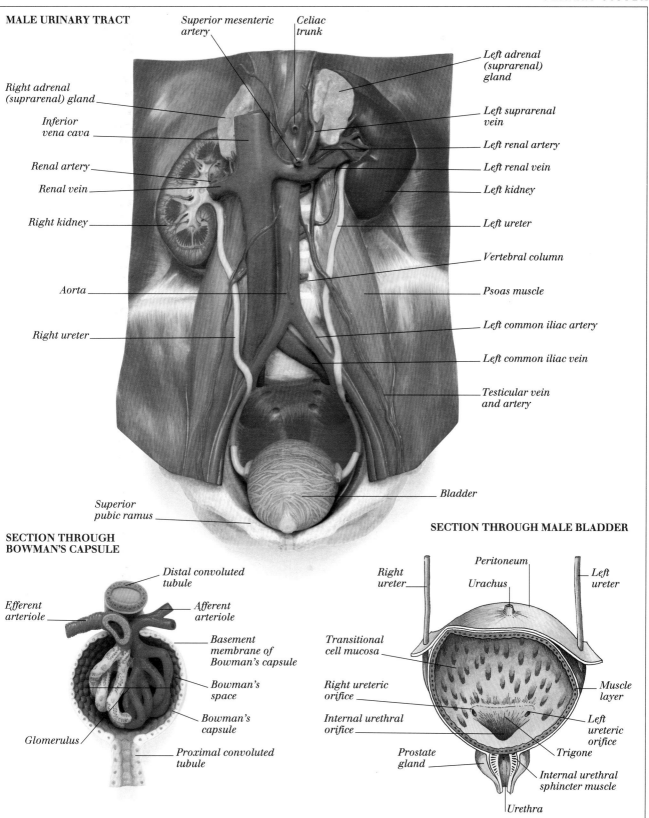

Superior mesenteric artery

Celiac trunk

Left adrenal (suprarenal) gland

Right adrenal (suprarenal) gland

Inferior vena cava

Renal artery

Renal vein

Right kidney

Aorta

Right ureter

Left suprarenal vein

Left renal artery

Left renal vein

Left kidney

Left ureter

Vertebral column

Psoas muscle

Left common iliac artery

Left common iliac vein

Testicular vein and artery

Bladder

Superior pubic ramus

SECTION THROUGH BOWMAN'S CAPSULE

Distal convoluted tubule

Efferent arteriole

Afferent arteriole

Basement membrane of Bowman's capsule

Bowman's space

Bowman's capsule

Glomerulus

Proximal convoluted tubule

SECTION THROUGH MALE BLADDER

Right ureter

Peritoneum

Urachus

Left ureter

Transitional cell mucosa

Right ureteric orifice

Internal urethral orifice

Prostate gland

Urethra

Muscle layer

Left ureteric orifice

Trigone

Internal urethral sphincter muscle

257

Reproductive system

SEX ORGANS LOCATED IN THE PELVIS create new human lives. Each month a ripe egg is released from one of the female's ovaries into a fallopian tube leading to the uterus (womb), a muscular pear-sized organ. A male produces minute tadpole-like sperm in two oval glands called testes. When the male is ready to release sperm into the female's vagina, many millions pass into his urethra and leave his body through the fleshy penis. The sperm travel up through the vagina into the uterus and one sperm may enter and fertilize an egg. The fertilized egg becomes embedded in the uterus wall and starts to grow into a new human being.

SECTION THROUGH OVARY

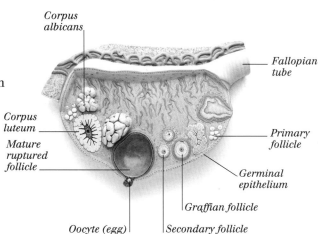

Corpus albicans

Corpus luteum

Mature ruptured follicle

Oocyte (egg)

Secondary follicle

Graffian follicle

Germinal epithelium

Primary follicle

Fallopian tube

SECTION THROUGH FEMALE PELVIC REGION

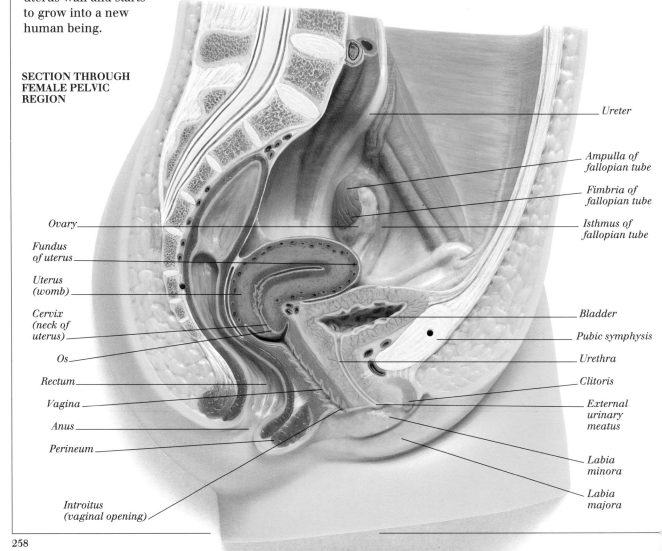

Ovary

Fundus of uterus

Uterus (womb)

Cervix (neck of uterus)

Os

Rectum

Vagina

Anus

Perineum

Introitus (vaginal opening)

Ureter

Ampulla of fallopian tube

Fimbria of fallopian tube

Isthmus of fallopian tube

Bladder

Pubic symphysis

Urethra

Clitoris

External urinary meatus

Labia minora

Labia majora

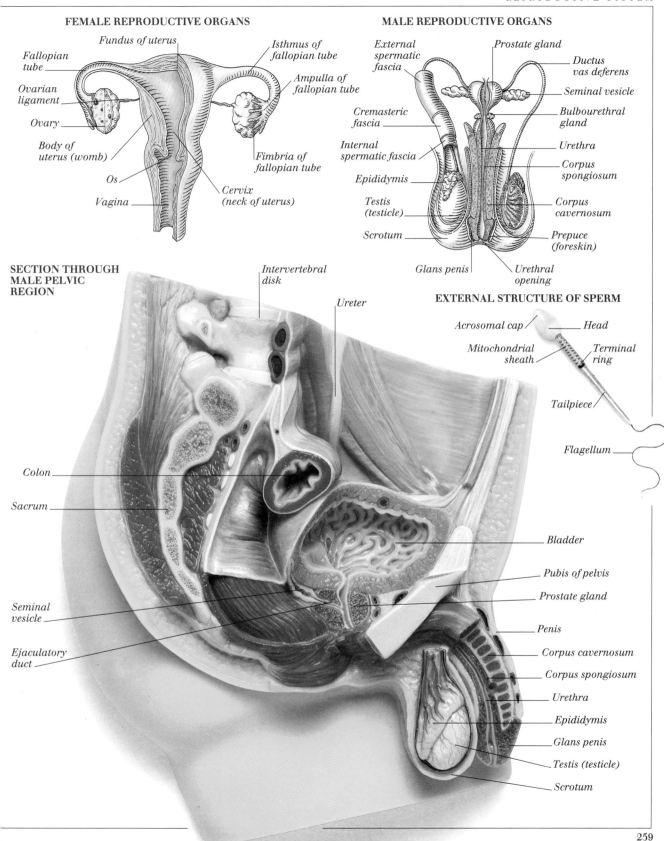

FEMALE REPRODUCTIVE ORGANS

Fallopian tube

Ovarian ligament

Ovary

Body of uterus (womb)

Os

Vagina

Fundus of uterus

Isthmus of fallopian tube

Ampulla of fallopian tube

Fimbria of fallopian tube

Cervix (neck of uterus)

MALE REPRODUCTIVE ORGANS

External spermatic fascia

Cremasteric fascia

Internal spermatic fascia

Epididymis

Testis (testicle)

Scrotum

Glans penis

Prostate gland

Ductus vas deferens

Seminal vesicle

Bulbourethral gland

Urethra

Corpus spongiosum

Corpus cavernosum

Prepuce (foreskin)

Urethral opening

SECTION THROUGH MALE PELVIC REGION

Intervertebral disk

Ureter

Colon

Sacrum

Seminal vesicle

Ejaculatory duct

Bladder

Pubis of pelvis

Prostate gland

Penis

Corpus cavernosum

Corpus spongiosum

Urethra

Epididymis

Glans penis

Testis (testicle)

Scrotum

EXTERNAL STRUCTURE OF SPERM

Acrosomal cap

Mitochondrial sheath

Head

Terminal ring

Tailpiece

Flagellum

Development of a baby

A FERTILIZED EGG IS NOURISHED AND PROTECTED as it
develops into an embryo and then a fetus during the 40
weeks of pregnancy. The placenta, a mass of blood vessels
implanted in the uterus lining, delivers nourishment and
oxygen, and removes waste through the umbilical cord.
Meanwhile, the fetus lies snugly in its amniotic sac, a bag of
fluid that protects it against any sudden jolts. In the last
weeks of the pregnancy, the rapidly growing fetus turns
head down: a baby ready to be born.

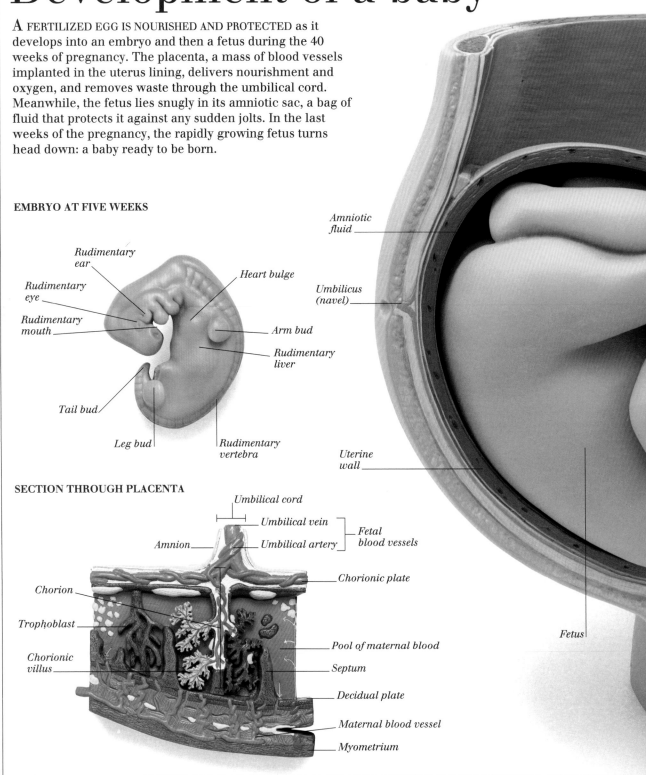

EMBRYO AT FIVE WEEKS

Rudimentary
ear

Rudimentary
eye

Rudimentary
mouth

Heart bulge

Arm bud

Rudimentary
liver

Tail bud

Leg bud

Rudimentary
vertebra

Amniotic
fluid

Umbilicus
(navel)

Uterine
wall

Fetus

SECTION THROUGH PLACENTA

Umbilical cord

Umbilical vein

Amnion

Umbilical artery

Fetal
blood vessels

Chorionic plate

Chorion

Trophoblast

Chorionic
villus

Pool of maternal blood

Septum

Decidual plate

Maternal blood vessel

Myometrium

SECTION THROUGH PELVIS IN NINTH MONTH OF PREGNANCY

THE DEVELOPING FETUS

Uterine wall

Placenta

Fallopian tube

SECOND MONTH
All the internal organs have developed by this stage.

Fetus

Intervertebral disk

Vertebra

Spinal cord

Umbilical cord

THIRD MONTH
The fetus is fully formed and now begins a period of rapid growth.

FIFTH MONTH
Although the fetus here is in breech (bottom down) position, it will probably turn by 180° before birth. By the fifth month the baby is moving actively and responds to sound.

Cervix

Bladder

Cervix

Rectum

SEVENTH MONTH
The internal organs are maturing in preparation for life outside the uterus. The baby has grown to such a size that there is less room for movement within the uterus.

Anus

Pubic bone

Placenta

Vagina

Urethra

GEOLOGY, GEOGRAPHY, AND METEOROLGY

EARTH'S PHYSICAL FEATURES · · · · · · · · 264

THE ROCK CYCLE · · · · · · · 266

MINERALS · · · · · · · · 268

MINRERAL FEATURES · · · · · · · 270

VOLCANOES · · · · · · · · 272

IGNEOUS AND METAMORPHIC ROCKS · · · · 274

SEDIMENTARY ROCKS · · · · · · 276

FOSSILS · · · · · · · · · 278

MINERAL RESOURCES · · · · · · · 280

WEATHERING AND EROSION · · · · · · 282

CAVES · · · · · · · · · 284

GLACIERS · · · · · · · · 286

RIVERS · · · · · · · · · 288

RIVER FEATURES · · · · · · · · 290

LAKES AND GROUNDWATER · · · · · · 292

COASTLINES · · · · · · · · 294

OCEANS AND SEAS · · · · · · · 296

THE OCEAN FLOOR · · · · · · · 298

THE ATMOSPHERE · · · · · · · 300

WEATHER · · · · · · · · 302

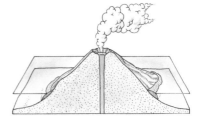

Earth's physical features

MOST OF THE EARTH'S SURFACE (about 70 percent) is covered with water. The largest single body of water, the Pacific Ocean, alone covers about 30 percent of the surface. Most of the land is distributed as seven continents; these are (from largest to smallest) Asia, Africa, North America, South America, Antarctica, Europe, and Australasia. The physical features of the land are remarkably varied. Among the most notable are mountain ranges, rivers, and deserts. The largest mountain ranges—the Himalayas in Asia and the Andes in South America—extend for thousands of miles. The Himalayas include the world's highest mountain, Mount Everest (29,029 feet). The longest rivers are the River Nile in Africa (4,160 miles) and the Amazon River in South America (4,000 miles). Deserts cover about 20 percent of the total land area. The largest is the Sahara, which covers nearly a third of Africa. The Earth's surface features can be represented in various ways. Only a globe can correctly represent areas, shapes, sizes, and directions, because there is always distortion when a spherical surface like the Earth's is projected onto the flat surface of a map. Each map projection is therefore a compromise: some aspects of global features are shown accurately by allowing others to be distorted. Even satellite mapping does not produce completely accurate maps, although they can show physical features with great clarity.

EXAMPLES OF MAP PROJECTIONS

CYLINDRICAL
PROJECTION

CYLINDRICAL-
PROJECTION MAP

SATELLITE MAPPING OF THE EARTH

Satellite takes photographs of the Earth

Solar panel

Earth's rotation

Antenna

Earth

Polar orbit of satellite

Area of Earth's surface on each photograph

Composite picture of Earth created from thousands of separate images

180° 160°

120°

80°

Great Slave Lake

Great Bear Lake

Lake Superior

Greenland

Mackenzie-Peace River

Bering Sea

NORTH AMERICA

Hudson Bay

Baffin Island

Rocky Mountains

Mississippi-Missouri River

Lake Huron
Lake Ontario
Lake Erie
Lake Michigan

Sonoran Desert

Appalachian Mountains

ATLANTIC
OCEAN

Sierra Madre

Gulf of Mexico

Chihuahuan Desert

Caribbean Sea

Guiana Highlands

Ama Rive

PACIFIC
OCEAN

Braz High

Andes

Atacama Desert

Gran Chaco

Ma Gr

Parana River

Pampas

Patagonia

180° 160°

120°

80°

WEST OF GREENW
MERIDIAN

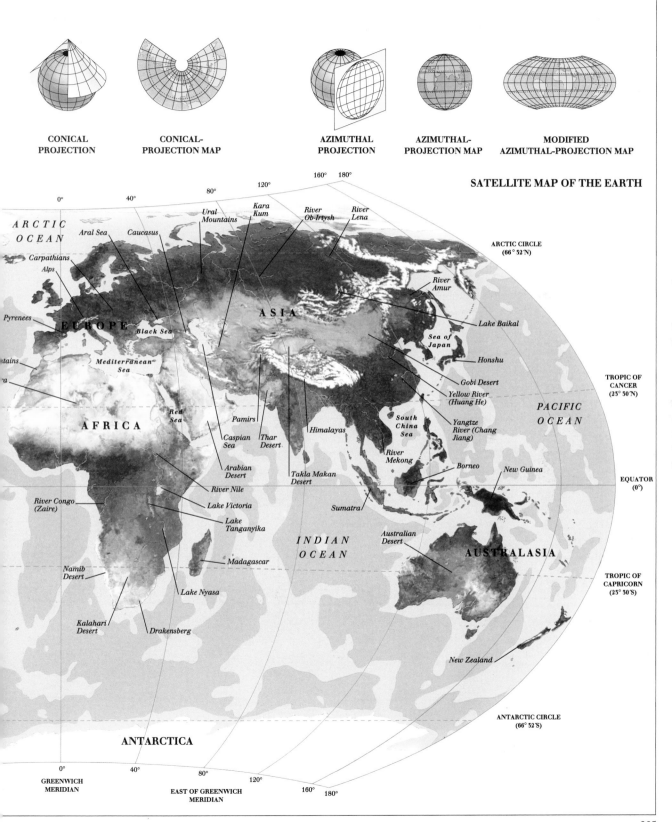

CONICAL PROJECTION

CONICAL-PROJECTION MAP

AZIMUTHAL PROJECTION

AZIMUTHAL-PROJECTION MAP

MODIFIED AZIMUTHAL-PROJECTION MAP

SATELLITE MAP OF THE EARTH

160° 180°

120°

80°

40°

0°

ARCTIC CIRCLE
(66° 32'N)

ARCTIC OCEAN

Aral Sea

Caucasus

Ural Mountains

Kara Kum

River Ob-Irtysh

River Lena

Carpathians

Alps

River Amur

Pyrenees

EUROPE

ASIA

Lake Baikal

Black Sea

Sea of Japan

Mediterranean Sea

Honshu

tains

TROPIC OF CANCER
(23° 30'N)

a

Red Sea

Pamirs

Himalayas

Gobi Desert

Yellow River (Huang He)

PACIFIC OCEAN

AFRICA

Caspian Sea

Thar Desert

Yangtze River (Chang Jiang)

Arabian Desert

Takla Makan Desert

South China Sea

River Mekong

River Nile

Borneo

New Guinea

EQUATOR
(0°)

River Congo (Zaire)

Lake Victoria

Sumatra

Lake Tanganyika

Australian Desert

AUSTRALASIA

INDIAN OCEAN

Namib Desert

Madagascar

TROPIC OF CAPRICORN
(23° 30'S)

Kalahari Desert

Lake Nyasa

Drakensberg

New Zealand

ANTARCTIC CIRCLE
(66° 32'S)

ANTARCTICA

0°

40°

80°

120°

160° 180°

GREENWICH MERIDIAN

EAST OF GREENWICH MERIDIAN

265

The rock cycle

THE ROCK CYCLE IS A CONTINUOUS PROCESS through which old rocks are transformed into new ones. Rocks can be divided into three main groups: igneous, sedimentary, and metamorphic. Igneous rocks are formed when magma (molten rock) from the Earth's interior cools and solidifies (see pp. 274-275). Sedimentary rocks are formed when sediment (rock particles, for example) becomes compressed and cemented together in a process known as lithification (see pp. 276-277). Metamorphic rocks are formed when igneous, sedimentary, or other metamorphic rocks are changed by heat or pressure (see pp. 274-275). Rocks are added to the Earth's surface by crustal movements and volcanic activity. Once exposed on the surface, the rocks are broken down into rock particles by weathering (see pp. 282-283). The particles are then transported by glaciers, rivers, and wind and are deposited as sediment in lakes, deltas, deserts, and on the ocean floor. Some of this sediment undergoes lithification and forms sedimentary rock. This rock may be thrust back to the surface by crustal movements or forced deeper into the Earth's interior, where heat and pressure transform it into metamorphic rock. The metamorphic rock in turn may be pushed up to the surface or may be melted to form magma. Eventually, the magma cools and solidifies—below or on the surface—forming igneous rock. When the sedimentary, igneous, and metamorphic rocks are exposed once more on the Earth's surface, the cycle begins again.

HEXAGONAL BASALT COLUMNS, ICELAND

STAGES IN THE ROCK CYCLE

Magma extruded as lava, which solidifies to form igneous rock

Lava flow

Vent

Main conduit

Secondary conduit

Lava

Ash

THE ROCK CYCLE

Igneous rock

Weathering, transport, and deposition

Sediment

Cooling and solidification (crystallization)

Heat and pressure (metamorphism)

Weathering, transport, and deposition

Weathering, transport, and deposition

Compression and cementation (lithification)

Magma

Melting

Heat and pressure (metamorphism)

Metamorphic rock

Sedimentary rock

Rock surrounding magma changed by heat to form metamorphic rock

Sedimentary rock crushed and folded to form metamorphic rock

Intense heat of rising magma melts some of the surrounding rock

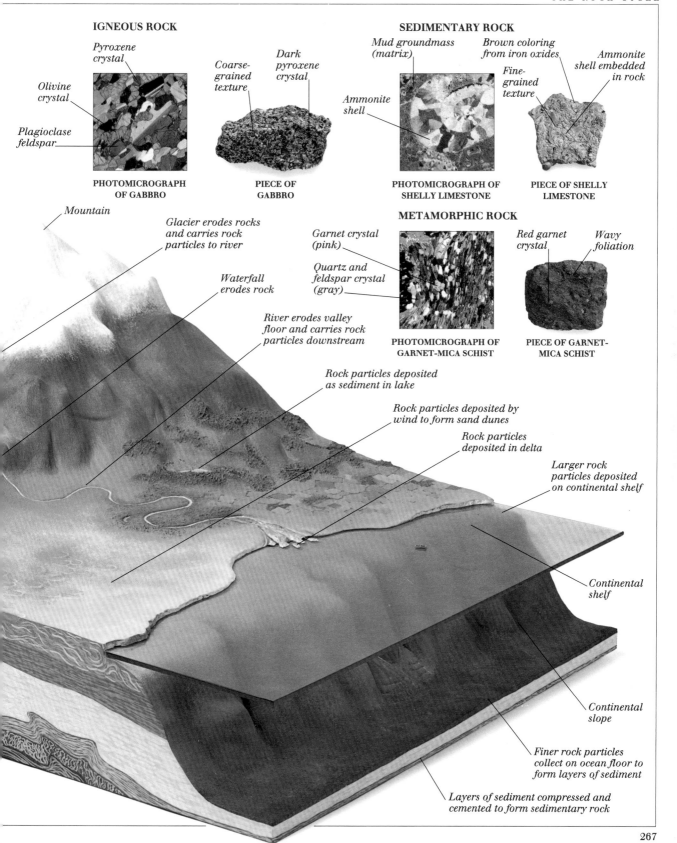

IGNEOUS ROCK

Pyroxene crystal

Olivine crystal

Plagioclase feldspar

Coarse-grained texture

Dark pyroxene crystal

PHOTOMICROGRAPH OF GABBRO

PIECE OF GABBRO

SEDIMENTARY ROCK

Mud groundmass (matrix)

Brown coloring from iron oxides

Ammonite shell

Fine-grained texture

Ammonite shell embedded in rock

PHOTOMICROGRAPH OF SHELLY LIMESTONE

PIECE OF SHELLY LIMESTONE

METAMORPHIC ROCK

Garnet crystal (pink)

Quartz and feldspar crystal (gray)

Red garnet crystal

Wavy foliation

PHOTOMICROGRAPH OF GARNET-MICA SCHIST

PIECE OF GARNET-MICA SCHIST

Mountain

Glacier erodes rocks and carries rock particles to river

Waterfall erodes rock

River erodes valley floor and carries rock particles downstream

Rock particles deposited as sediment in lake

Rock particles deposited by wind to form sand dunes

Rock particles deposited in delta

Larger rock particles deposited on continental shelf

Continental shelf

Continental slope

Finer rock particles collect on ocean floor to form layers of sediment

Layers of sediment compressed and cemented to form sedimentary rock

Minerals

A MINERAL IS A NATURALLY OCCURRING SUBSTANCE that has a characteristic chemical composition and specific physical properties, such as habit and streak (see pp. 270-271). A rock, by comparison, is an aggregate of minerals and need not have a specific chemical composition. Minerals are made up of elements (substances that cannot be broken down chemically into simpler substances), each of which can be represented by a chemical symbol. Minerals can be divided into two main groups: native elements and compounds. Native elements are made up of a pure element. Examples include gold (chemical symbol Au), silver (Ag), copper (Cu), and carbon (C); carbon occurs as a native element in two forms, diamond and graphite. Compounds are combinations of two or more elements. For example, sulfides are compounds of sulfur (S) and one or more other elements, such as lead (Pb) in the mineral galena, or antimony (Sb) in the mineral stibnite.

NATIVE ELEMENTS

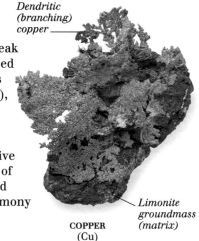

Dendritic (branching) copper

Limonite groundmass (matrix)

COPPER
(Cu)

SULFIDES

Cubic galena crystal

GALENA
(PbS)

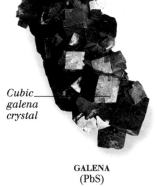

Prismatic stibnite crystal

Quartz groundmass (matrix)

STIBNITE
(Sb₂S₃)

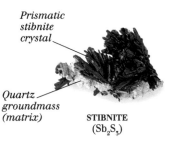

Perfect octahedral pyrites crystal

Quartz crystal

PYRITES
(FeS₂)

Dendritic (branching) gold

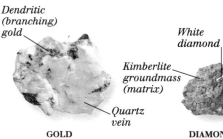

Quartz vein

GOLD
(Au)

White diamond

Kimberlite groundmass (matrix)

DIAMOND
(C)

Hexagonal graphite crystal

GRAPHITE
(C)

OXIDES/HYDROXIDES

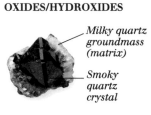

Milky quartz groundmass (matrix)

Smoky quartz crystal

SMOKY QUARTZ
(SiO₂)

Rounded bauxite grains in groundmass (matrix)

Mass of specular hematite crystals

SPECULAR HEMATITE
(Fe₂O₃)

BAUXITE
(FeO(OH) and Al₂O₃.2H₂O)

Parallel bands of onyx

ONYX
(SiO₂)

Kidney ore hematite

Specular crystals of hematite

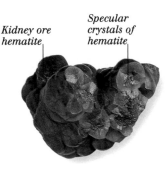

KIDNEY ORE HEMATITE
(Fe₂O₃)

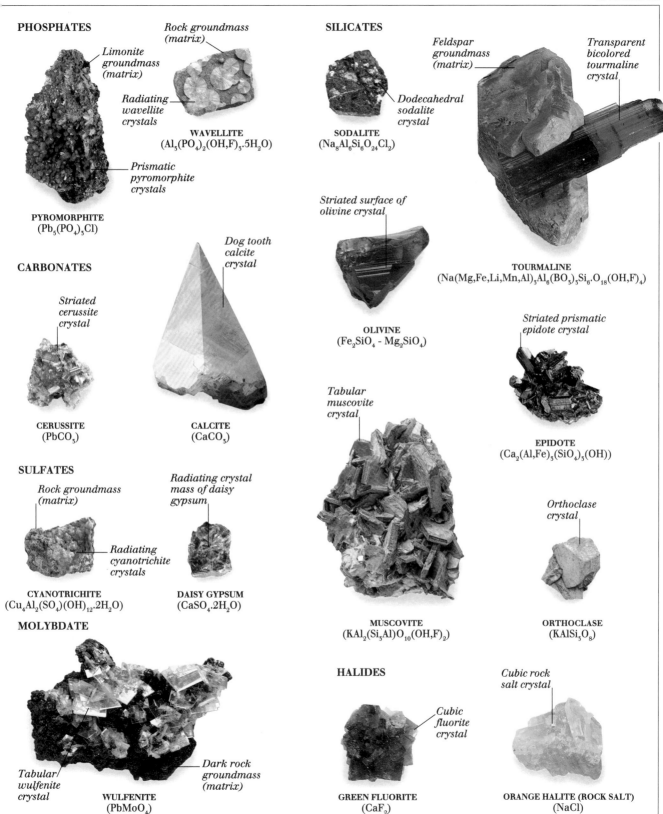

PHOSPHATES

Limonite groundmass (matrix)

Rock groundmass (matrix)

Radiating wavellite crystals

WAVELLITE
$(Al_5(PO_4)_2(OH,F)_5.5H_2O)$

Prismatic pyromorphite crystals

PYROMORPHITE
$(Pb_5(PO_4)_3Cl)$

SILICATES

Feldspar groundmass (matrix)

Transparent bicolored tourmaline crystal

Dodecahedral sodalite crystal

SODALITE
$(Na_8Al_6Si_6O_{24}Cl_2)$

Striated surface of olivine crystal

TOURMALINE
$(Na(Mg,Fe,Li,Mn,Al)_3Al_6(BO_3)_3Si_6.O_{18}(OH,F)_4)$

OLIVINE
$(Fe_2SiO_4 - Mg_2SiO_4)$

CARBONATES

Striated cerussite crystal

Dog tooth calcite crystal

CERUSSITE
$(PbCO_3)$

CALCITE
$(CaCO_3)$

Striated prismatic epidote crystal

EPIDOTE
$(Ca_2(Al,Fe)_3(SiO_4)_3(OH))$

Tabular muscovite crystal

SULFATES

Rock groundmass (matrix)

Radiating crystal mass of daisy gypsum

Radiating cyanotrichite crystals

CYANOTRICHITE
$(Cu_4Al_2(SO_4)(OH)_{12}.2H_2O)$

DAISY GYPSUM
$(CaSO_4.2H_2O)$

Orthoclase crystal

MUSCOVITE
$(KAl_2(Si_3Al)O_{10}(OH,F)_2)$

ORTHOCLASE
$(KAlSi_3O_8)$

MOLYBDATE

HALIDES

Cubic rock salt crystal

Cubic fluorite crystal

Tabular wulfenite crystal

Dark rock groundmass (matrix)

WULFENITE
$(PbMoO_4)$

GREEN FLUORITE
(CaF_2)

ORANGE HALITE (ROCK SALT)
$(NaCl)$

Mineral features

MINERALS CAN BE IDENTIFIED BY STUDYING features such as fracture, cleavage, crystal system, habit, hardness, color, and streak. Minerals can break in different ways. If a mineral breaks in an irregular way, leaving rough surfaces, it possesses fracture. If a mineral breaks along well-defined planes of weakness, it possesses cleavage. Specific minerals have distinctive patterns of cleavage. For example, mica cleaves along one plane. Most minerals form crystals that can be categorized into crystal systems according to their symmetry and number of faces. Within each system, several different but related forms of crystal are possible; for example, a cubic crystal can have six, eight, or twelve sides. A mineral's habit is the typical form taken by an aggregate of its crystals. Examples of habit include botryoidal (like a bunch of grapes) and massive (no definite form). The relative hardness of a mineral may be assessed by testing its resistance to scratching. This property is usually measured using Mohs' scale, which increases in hardness from 1 (talc) to 10 (diamond). The color of a mineral is not a dependable guide to its identity as some minerals have a range of colors. Streak (the color the powdered mineral makes when rubbed across an unglazed tile) is a more reliable indicator.

CLEAVAGE

Cleavage in one direction

CLEAVAGE ALONG ONE PLANE

Cleavage in three directions, forming a block cube

CLEAVAGE ALONG THREE PLANES

Horizontal cleavage

Vertical cleavage

CLEAVAGE ALONG TWO PLANES

Cleavage in four directions, forming a double-pyramid crystal

CLEAVAGE ALONG FOUR PLANES

CRYSTAL SYSTEMS

Cubic iron pyrites crystal

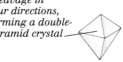

Tetragonal idocrase crystal

Representation of tetragonal system

TETRAGONAL SYSTEM

CUBIC SYSTEM

Representation of cubic system

Hexagonal beryl crystal

Representation of hexagonal/trigonal system

HEXAGONAL/TRIGONAL SYSTEM

Orthorhombic barite crystal

Representation of orthorhombic system

ORTHORHOMBIC SYSTEM

FRACTURE

Fire opal with conchoidal (shell-like) fracture

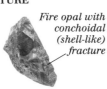

Nickel-iron with hackly (jagged) fracture

CONCHOIDAL FRACTURE

HACKLY FRACTURE

Orpiment with uneven fracture

Garnierite with splintery fracture

UNEVEN FRACTURE

SPLINTERY FRACTURE

Monoclinic selenite crystal

Representation of monoclinic system

MONOCLINIC SYSTEM

Representation of triclinic system

Triclinic axinite crystal

TRICLINIC SYSTEM

HABIT

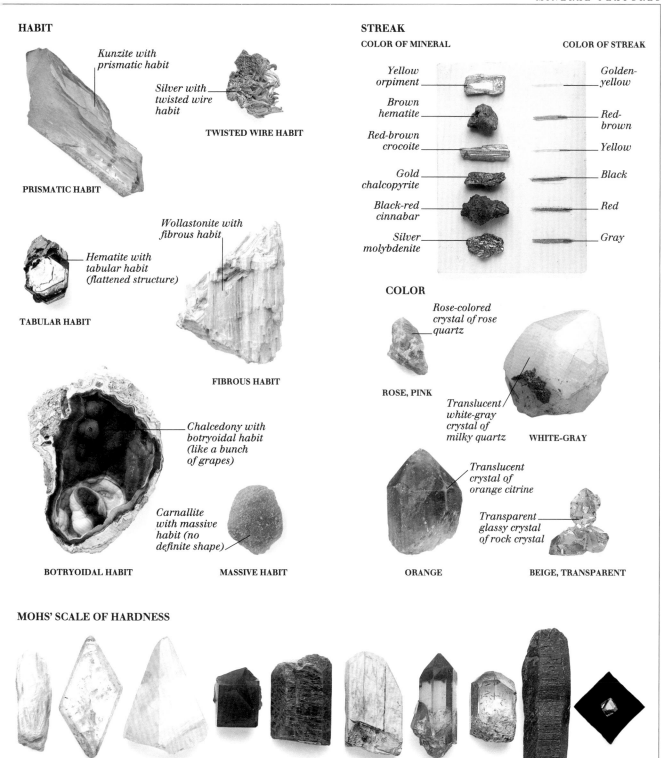

Kunzite with prismatic habit

Silver with twisted wire habit

TWISTED WIRE HABIT

PRISMATIC HABIT

Wollastonite with fibrous habit

Hematite with tabular habit (flattened structure)

TABULAR HABIT

FIBROUS HABIT

Chalcedony with botryoidal habit (like a bunch of grapes)

Carnallite with massive habit (no definite shape)

BOTRYOIDAL HABIT

MASSIVE HABIT

STREAK

COLOR OF MINERAL		COLOR OF STREAK
Yellow orpiment		*Golden-yellow*
Brown hematite		*Red-brown*
Red-brown crocoite		*Yellow*
Gold chalcopyrite		*Black*
Black-red cinnabar		*Red*
Silver molybdenite		*Gray*

COLOR

Rose-colored crystal of rose quartz

ROSE, PINK

Translucent white-gray crystal of milky quartz

WHITE-GRAY

Translucent crystal of orange citrine

Transparent glassy crystal of rock crystal

ORANGE

BEIGE, TRANSPARENT

MOHS' SCALE OF HARDNESS

| TALC 1 | GYPSUM 2 | CALCITE 3 | FLUORITE 4 | APATITE 5 | ORTHOCLASE 6 | QUARTZ 7 | TOPAZ 8 | CORUNDUM 9 | DIAMOND 10 |

Volcanoes

VOLCANOES ARE VENTS OR FISSURES IN THE EARTH'S crust through which magma (molten rock that originates from deep beneath the crust) is forced onto the surface as lava. They occur most commonly along the boundaries of crustal plates; most volcanoes lie in a belt called the "Ring of Fire," which runs along the edge of the Pacific Ocean. Volcanoes can be classified according to the violence and frequency of their eruptions.

Nonexplosive volcanic eruptions generally occur where crustal plates pull apart. These eruptions produce runny basaltic lava that spreads quickly over a wide area to form relatively flat cones. The most violent eruptions take place where plates collide. Such eruptions produce thick rhyolitic lava and may also blast out clouds of dust and pyroclasts (lava fragments). The lava does not flow far before cooling and therefore builds up steep-sided, conical volcanoes. Some volcanoes produce lava and ash eruptions, which build up composite volcanic cones. Volcanoes that erupt frequently are described as active, those that erupt rarely are termed dormant, and those that have stopped erupting altogether are termed extinct. Besides the volcanoes themselves, other features associated with volcanic regions include geysers, hot mineral springs, solfataras, fumaroles, and bubbling mud pools.

HORU GEYSER, NEW ZEALAND

Folded, rope-like surface

PAHOEHOE (ROPY LAVA)

VOLCANO TYPES

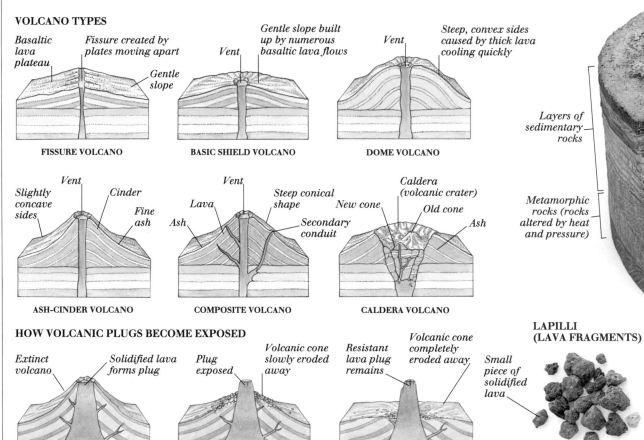

Basaltic lava plateau
Fissure created by plates moving apart
Gentle slope

FISSURE VOLCANO

Gentle slope built up by numerous basaltic lava flows
Vent

BASIC SHIELD VOLCANO

Steep, convex sides caused by thick lava cooling quickly
Vent

DOME VOLCANO

Layers of sedimentary rocks

Metamorphic rocks (rocks altered by heat and pressure)

Slightly concave sides
Vent
Cinder
Fine ash

ASH-CINDER VOLCANO

Vent
Lava
Steep conical shape
Ash
Secondary conduit

COMPOSITE VOLCANO

Caldera (volcanic crater)
New cone
Old cone
Ash

CALDERA VOLCANO

LAPILLI (LAVA FRAGMENTS)

Small piece of solidified lava

HOW VOLCANIC PLUGS BECOME EXPOSED

Extinct volcano
Solidified lava forms plug

PLUG FORMATION

Plug exposed
Volcanic cone slowly eroded away

INITIAL EROSION AROUND PLUG

Resistant lava plug remains
Volcanic cone completely eroded away

COMPLETE DENUDATION OF PLUG

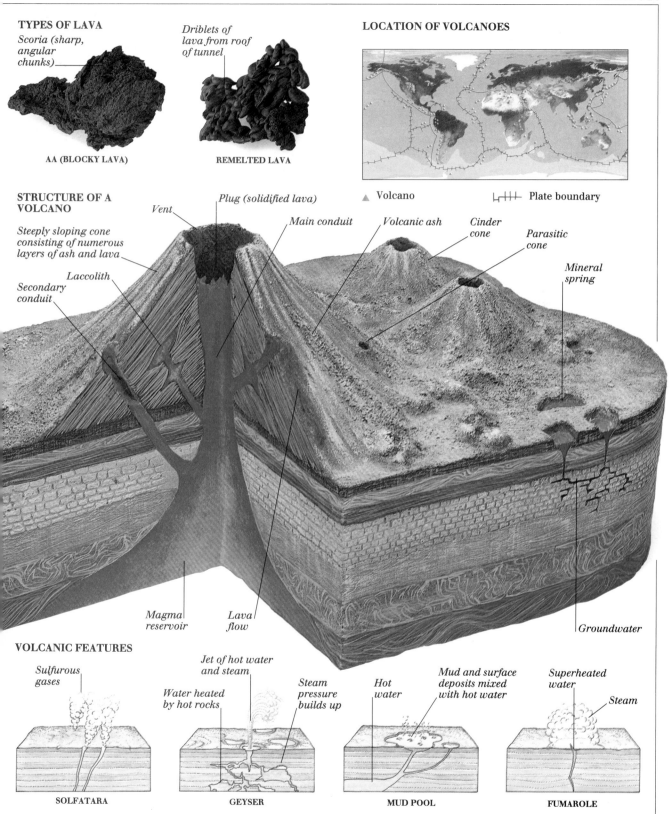

TYPES OF LAVA

Scoria (sharp, angular chunks)

Driblets of lava from roof of tunnel

AA (BLOCKY LAVA)

REMELTED LAVA

LOCATION OF VOLCANOES

▲ Volcano

⊢⊢⊦⊦ Plate boundary

STRUCTURE OF A VOLCANO

Steeply sloping cone consisting of numerous layers of ash and lava

Laccolith

Secondary conduit

Vent

Plug (solidified lava)

Main conduit

Volcanic ash

Cinder cone

Parasitic cone

Mineral spring

Magma reservoir

Lava flow

Groundwater

VOLCANIC FEATURES

Sulfurous gases

Water heated by hot rocks

Jet of hot water and steam

Steam pressure builds up

Hot water

Mud and surface deposits mixed with hot water

Superheated water

Steam

SOLFATARA

GEYSER

MUD POOL

FUMAROLE

Igneous and metamorphic rocks

BASALT COLUMNS

IGNEOUS ROCKS ARE FORMED WHEN MAGMA (molten rock that originates from deep beneath the Earth's crust) cools and solidifies. There are two main types of igneous rock: intrusive and extrusive. Intrusive rocks are formed deep underground, where magma is forced into cracks or between rock layers to form structures including sills, dikes, and batholiths. The magma cools slowly to form coarse-grained rocks such as gabbro and pegmatite. Extrusive rocks are formed above the Earth's surface from lava (magma that has been ejected in a volcanic eruption). The molten lava cools quickly, producing fine-grained rocks such as rhyolite and basalt. Metamorphic rocks are those that have been altered by intense heat (contact metamorphism) or extreme pressure (regional metamorphism). Contact metamorphism occurs when rocks are changed by heat from, for example, an igneous intrusion or lava flow. Regional metamorphism occurs when rock is crushed in the middle of a folding mountain range. Metamorphic rocks can be formed from igneous rocks, sedimentary rocks, or even other metamorphic rocks.

Cinder cone
Large eroded lava flow
Cedar tree laccolith
Butte
Plug

Cone sheet
Ring dike
Batholith
Dike
Sill
Dike swarm
Lopolith

IGNEOUS ROCK STRUCTURES

CONTACT METAMORPHISM

Metamorphic aureole (region where contact metamorphism occurs)

Hot igneous intrusion
Limestone
Shale

Marble (metamorphosed limestone)
Slate (metamorphosed shale)

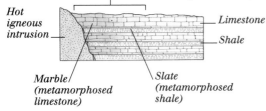

REGIONAL METAMORPHISM

Mountain range
Slate, formed under low pressure and temperature
Compression
Compression
Crust
Mantle
Magma
Schist, formed under medium pressure and temperature
Gneiss, formed under high pressure and temperature

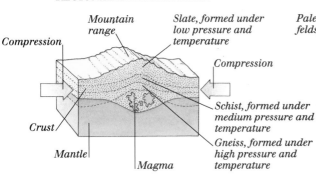

EXAMPLES OF METAMORPHIC ROCKS

Pale feldspar
Dark mica
Dark mineral band
Pale calcite

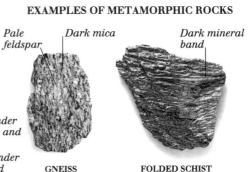

GNEISS   **FOLDED SCHIST**   **SKARN**

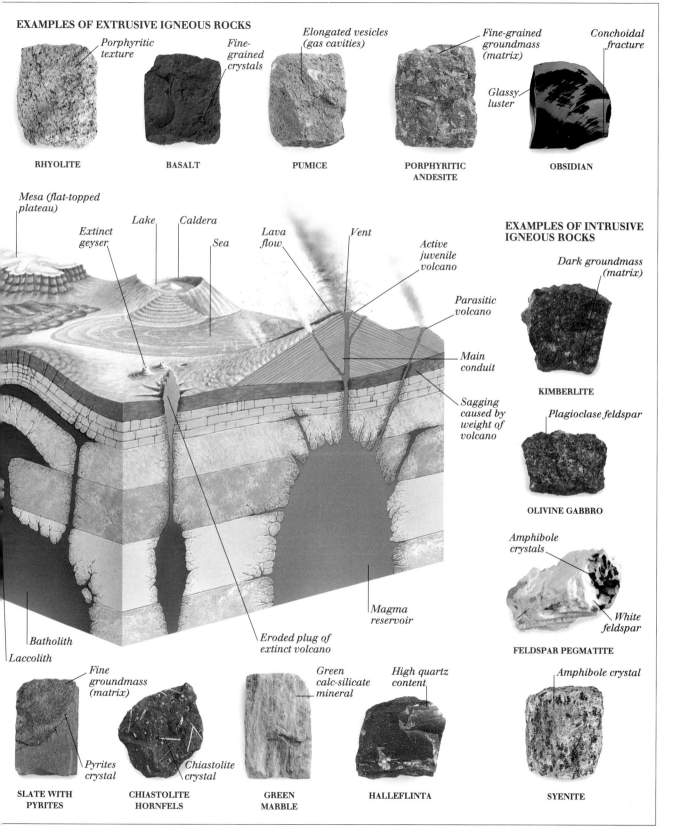

EXAMPLES OF EXTRUSIVE IGNEOUS ROCKS

Porphyritic texture

Fine-grained crystals

Elongated vesicles (gas cavities)

Fine-grained groundmass (matrix)

Conchoidal fracture

Glassy luster

RHYOLITE

BASALT

PUMICE

PORPHYRITIC ANDESITE

OBSIDIAN

Mesa (flat-topped plateau)

Extinct geyser

Lake

Caldera

Sea

Lava flow

Vent

Active juvenile volcano

Parasitic volcano

Main conduit

Sagging caused by weight of volcano

Magma reservoir

Eroded plug of extinct volcano

Batholith

Laccolith

EXAMPLES OF INTRUSIVE IGNEOUS ROCKS

Dark groundmass (matrix)

KIMBERLITE

Plagioclase feldspar

OLIVINE GABBRO

Amphibole crystals

White feldspar

FELDSPAR PEGMATITE

Amphibole crystal

SYENITE

Fine groundmass (matrix)

Pyrites crystal

SLATE WITH PYRITES

Chiastolite crystal

CHIASTOLITE HORNFELS

Green calc-silicate mineral

GREEN MARBLE

High quartz content

HALLEFLINTA

275

Sedimentary rocks

SEDIMENTARY ROCKS ARE FORMED BY THE ACCUMULATION and consolidation of sediments (see pp. 266-267). There are three main types of sedimentary rock: clastic sedimentary rocks, such as breccia or sandstone, are formed from other rocks that have been broken down into fragments by weathering (see pp. 282-283), which have then been transported and deposited elsewhere; organic sedimentary rocks, such as coal (see pp. 280-281), are derived from plant and animal remains; and chemical sedimentary rocks are formed by chemical processes. For example, rock salt is formed when salt dissolved in water is deposited as the water evaporates. Sedimentary rocks are laid down in layers called beds, or strata. Each new layer is laid down horizontally over older ones. There are usually some gaps in the sequence, called unconformities. These represent periods in which no new sediments were being laid down, or when earlier sedimentary layers were raised above sea level and eroded away.

THE GRAND CANYON, U.S.A.

EXAMPLES OF UNCONFORMITIES

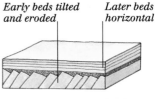

Early beds tilted and eroded

Later beds horizontal

ANGULAR UNCONFORMITY

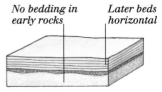

No bedding in early rocks

Later beds horizontal

NONCONFORMITY

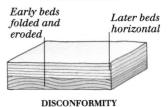

Early beds folded and eroded

Later beds horizontal

DISCONFORMITY

SEDIMENTARY LAYERS OF THE GRAND CANYON REGION

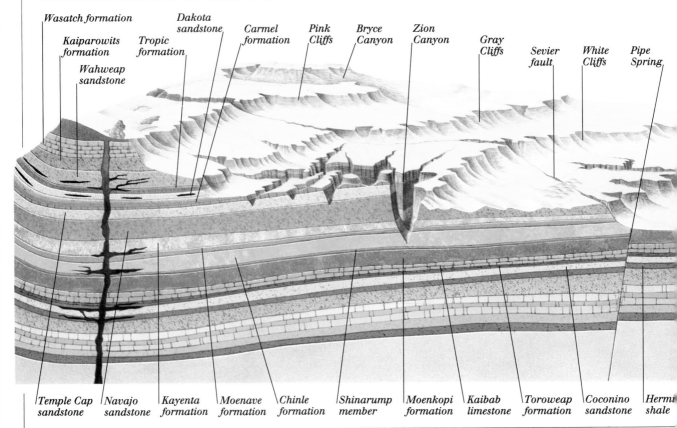

Wasatch formation

Kaiparowits formation

Wahweap sandstone

Tropic formation

Dakota sandstone

Carmel formation

Pink Cliffs

Bryce Canyon

Zion Canyon

Gray Cliffs

Sevier fault

White Cliffs

Pipe Spring

Temple Cap sandstone

Navajo sandstone

Kayenta formation

Moenave formation

Chinle formation

Shinarump member

Moenkopi formation

Kaibab limestone

Toroweap formation

Coconino sandstone

Hermit shale

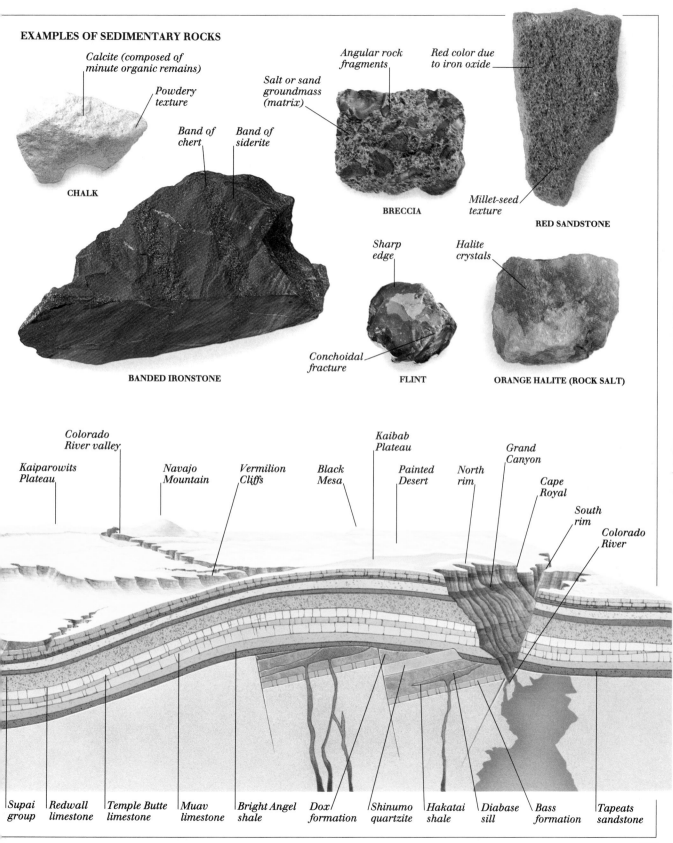

EXAMPLES OF SEDIMENTARY ROCKS

Calcite (composed of
minute organic remains)

Powdery
texture

CHALK

Band of
chert

Band of
siderite

BANDED IRONSTONE

Angular rock
fragments

Salt or sand
groundmass
(matrix)

Red color due
to iron oxide

BRECCIA

Millet-seed
texture

RED SANDSTONE

Sharp
edge

Halite
crystals

Conchoidal
fracture

FLINT

ORANGE HALITE (ROCK SALT)

Kaiparowits
Plateau

Colorado
River valley

Navajo
Mountain

Vermilion
Cliffs

Black
Mesa

Kaibab
Plateau

Painted
Desert

North
rim

Grand
Canyon

Cape
Royal

South
rim

Colorado
River

Supai
group

Redwall
limestone

Temple Butte
limestone

Muav
limestone

Bright Angel
shale

Dox
formation

Shinumo
quartzite

Hakatai
shale

Diabase
sill

Bass
formation

Tapeats
sandstone

Fossils

FOSSILS ARE THE REMAINS of plants and animals that have been preserved in rock. A fossil may be the preserved remains of an organism itself, an impression of it in rock, or preserved traces (known as trace fossils) left by an organism while it was alive, such as organic carbon outlines, fossilized footprints, or droppings. Most dead organisms soon rot away or are eaten by scavengers. For fossilization to occur, rapid burial by sediment is necessary. The organism decays, but the harder parts—bones, teeth, and shells, for example—may be preserved and hardened by minerals from the surrounding sediment. Fossilization may also occur even when the hard parts of an organism are dissolved away to leave an impression called a mold. The mold is filled by minerals, thereby creating a cast of the organism. The study of fossils (paleontology) not only can show how living things have evolved, but can also help reveal the Earth's geological history—for example, by aiding in the dating of rock strata.

PROCESS OF FOSSILIZATION

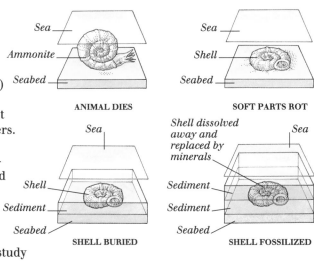

Sea
Ammonite
Seabed
ANIMAL DIES

Sea
Shell
Seabed
SOFT PARTS ROT

Sea
Shell
Sediment
Seabed
SHELL BURIED

Shell dissolved away and replaced by minerals
Sea
Sediment
Sediment
Seabed
SHELL FOSSILIZED

EXAMPLES OF FOSSILS

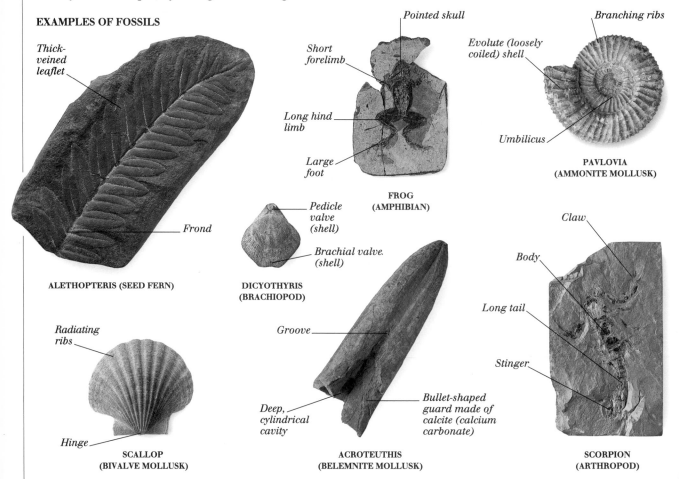

Thick-veined leaflet

Frond

ALETHOPTERIS (SEED FERN)

Pedicle valve (shell)

Brachial valve (shell)

DICYOTHYRIS (BRACHIOPOD)

Radiating ribs

Hinge

SCALLOP (BIVALVE MOLLUSK)

Pointed skull

Short forelimb

Long hind limb

Large foot

FROG (AMPHIBIAN)

Groove

Deep, cylindrical cavity

Bullet-shaped guard made of calcite (calcium carbonate)

ACROTEUTHIS (BELEMNITE MOLLUSK)

Branching ribs

Evolute (loosely coiled) shell

Umbilicus

PAVLOVIA (AMMONITE MOLLUSK)

Claw

Body

Long tail

Stinger

SCORPION (ARTHROPOD)

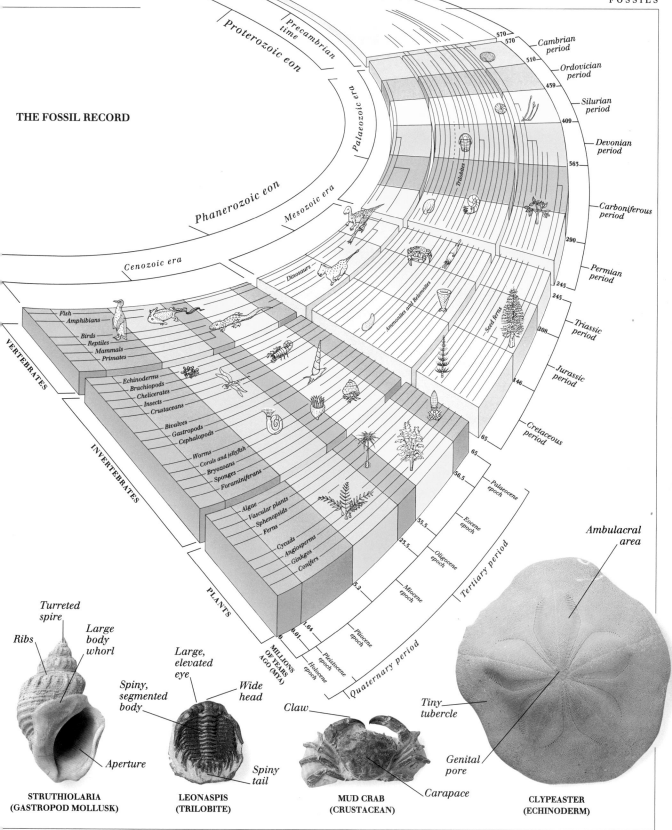

THE FOSSIL RECORD

Precambrian time

Proterozoic eon

Palaeozoic era

Phanerozoic eon

Mesozoic era

Cenozoic era

570 — Cambrian period

510 — Ordovician period

439 — Silurian period

409 — Devonian period

363 — Carboniferous period

290 — Permian period

245 — Permian period

245 — Triassic period

208 — Jurassic period

146 — Cretaceous period

65 —

56.5 — Palaeocene epoch

35.5 — Eocene epoch

23.5 — Oligocene epoch

5.2 — Miocene epoch

1.64 — Pliocene epoch

0.01 — Pleistocene epoch

Holocene epoch

Tertiary period

Quaternary period

Trilobites

Dinosaurs

Ammonites and Belemnites

Seed ferns

VERTEBRATES
- Fish
- Amphibians
- Birds
- Reptiles
- Mammals
- Primates

INVERTEBRATES
- Echinoderms
- Brachiopods
- Chelicerates
- Insects
- Crustaceans
- Bivalves
- Gastropods
- Cephalopods
- Worms
- Corals and jellyfish
- Bryozoans
- Sponges
- Foraminiferans

PLANTS
- Algae
- Vascular plants
- Sphenopsids
- Ferns
- Cycads
- Angiosperms
- Ginkgos
- Conifers

MILLIONS OF YEARS AGO (MYA)

Ambulacral area

Turreted spire

Ribs

Large body whorl

Aperture

STRUTHIOLARIA (GASTROPOD MOLLUSK)

Large, elevated eye

Spiny, segmented body

Wide head

Spiny tail

LEONASPIS (TRILOBITE)

Claw

Carapace

MUD CRAB (CRUSTACEAN)

Tiny tubercle

Genital pore

CLYPEASTER (ECHINODERM)

Mineral resources

Stalk

Leaf

PLANT MATTER

MINERAL RESOURCES CAN BE DEFINED AS naturally occurring substances that can be extracted from the Earth and are useful as fuels and raw materials. Coal, oil, and gas—collectively called fossil fuels—are commonly included in this group, but are not strictly minerals, because they are of organic origin. Coal formation begins when vegetation is buried and partly decomposed to form peat. Overlying sediments compress the peat and transform it into lignite (soft brown coal). As the overlying sediments accumulate, increasing pressure and temperature eventually transform the lignite into bituminous and hard anthracite coals. Oil and gas are usually formed from organic molecules that were deposited in marine sediments. Under the effects of heat and pressure, the compressed organic molecules undergo complex chemical changes to form oil and gas. The oil and gas percolate upward through water-saturated permeable rocks. They may rise to the Earth's surface, or accumulate below an impermeable layer of rock that has been folded or faulted to form a trap—an anticline (upfold) trap, for example. Minerals are inorganic substances that may consist of a single chemical element, such as gold, silver, or copper, or combinations of elements (see pp. 268-269). Some minerals are concentrated in mineralization zones in rock associated with crustal movements or volcanic activity. Others may be found in sediments as placer deposits—accumulations of high-density minerals that have been weathered out of rocks, transported, and deposited (on riverbeds, for example).

OIL RIG, NORTH SEA

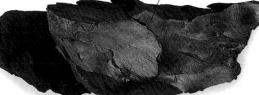

Decayed plant matter

About 60% carbon

PEAT

About 70% carbon

Crumbly texture

LIGNITE (BROWN COAL)

Powdery texture

About 80% carbon

BITUMINOUS COAL

HOW COAL IS FORMED

Increasing layers of overlying sediment

Vegetation

Increasing layers of overlying sediment

Increasing pressure and temperature

Increasing pressure and temperature

Increasing pressure and temperature

Peat (about 60% carbon)

PEAT

Lignite (about 70% carbon)

LIGNITE (BROWN COAL)

Bituminous coal (about 80% carbon)

BITUMINOUS COAL

Shiny surface

About 95% carbon

ANTHRACITE COAL

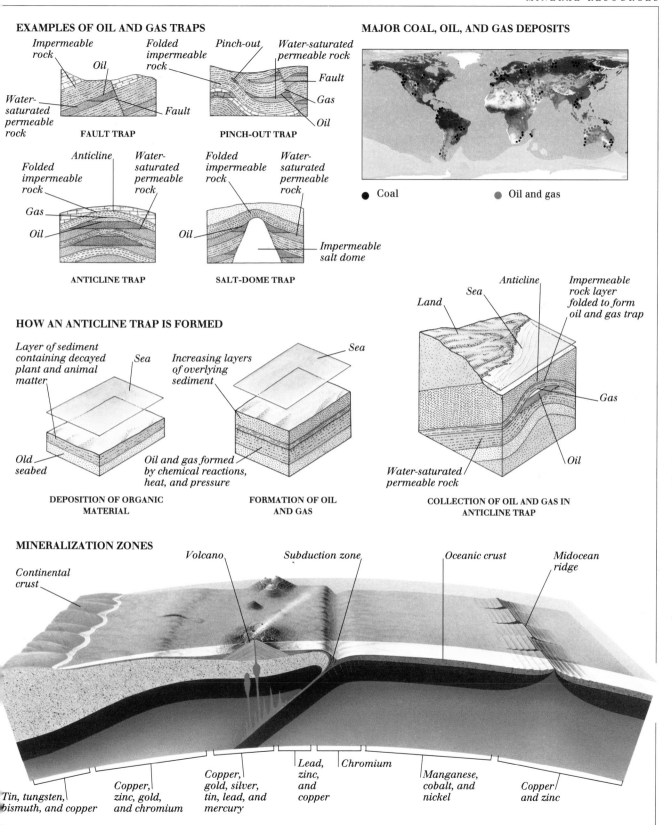

EXAMPLES OF OIL AND GAS TRAPS

Impermeable rock

Oil

Folded impermeable rock

Water-saturated permeable rock

Fault

FAULT TRAP

Pinch-out

Water-saturated permeable rock

Fault

Gas

Oil

PINCH-OUT TRAP

Anticline

Folded impermeable rock

Water-saturated permeable rock

Gas

Oil

ANTICLINE TRAP

Folded impermeable rock

Water-saturated permeable rock

Oil

Impermeable salt dome

SALT-DOME TRAP

MAJOR COAL, OIL, AND GAS DEPOSITS

● Coal   ● Oil and gas

HOW AN ANTICLINE TRAP IS FORMED

Layer of sediment containing decayed plant and animal matter

Sea

Old seabed

DEPOSITION OF ORGANIC MATERIAL

Increasing layers of overlying sediment

Sea

Oil and gas formed by chemical reactions, heat, and pressure

FORMATION OF OIL AND GAS

Land

Sea

Anticline

Impermeable rock layer folded to form oil and gas trap

Gas

Oil

Water-saturated permeable rock

COLLECTION OF OIL AND GAS IN ANTICLINE TRAP

MINERALIZATION ZONES

Continental crust

Volcano

Subduction zone

Oceanic crust

Midocean ridge

Tin, tungsten, bismuth, and copper

Copper, zinc, gold, and chromium

Copper, gold, silver, tin, lead, and mercury

Lead, zinc, and copper

Chromium

Manganese, cobalt, and nickel

Copper and zinc

Weathering and erosion

WEATHERING IS THE BREAKING DOWN of rocks on the Earth's surface. There are two main types: physical (or mechanical), and chemical. Physical weathering may be caused by temperature changes, such as freezing and thawing, or by abrasion from material carried by winds, rivers, or glaciers. Rocks may also be broken down by the actions of animals and plants, such as the burrowing of animals and the growth of roots. Chemical weathering causes rocks to decompose by changing their chemical composition. For example, rainwater may dissolve certain minerals in a rock. Erosion is the wearing away and removal of land surfaces by water, wind, or ice. It is greatest in areas of little or no surface vegetation, such as deserts, where sand dunes may form.

FORMATION OF A ROCK PAVEMENT (HAMADA)

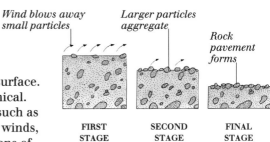

Wind blows away small particles

Larger particles aggregate

Rock pavement forms

FIRST STAGE

SECOND STAGE

FINAL STAGE

FEATURES OF WEATHERING AND EROSION

FEATURES PRODUCED BY WIND ACTION

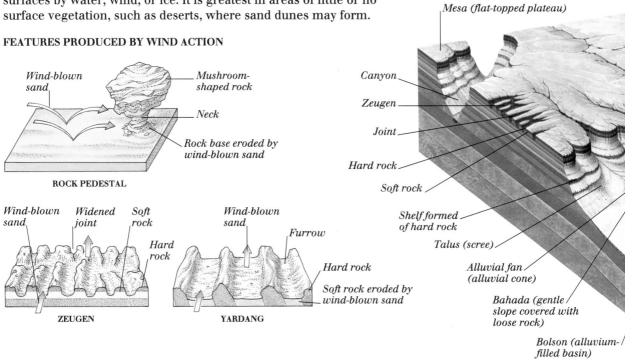

Wind-blown sand

Mushroom-shaped rock

Neck

Rock base eroded by wind-blown sand

ROCK PEDESTAL

Wind-blown sand

Widened joint

Soft rock

Hard rock

ZEUGEN

Wind-blown sand

Furrow

Hard rock

Soft rock eroded by wind-blown sand

YARDANG

Mesa (flat-topped plateau)

Canyon

Zeugen

Joint

Hard rock

Soft rock

Shelf formed of hard rock

Talus (scree)

Alluvial fan (alluvial cone)

Bahada (gentle slope covered with loose rock)

Bolson (alluvium-filled basin)

EXAMPLES OF PHYSICAL WEATHERING PROCESSES

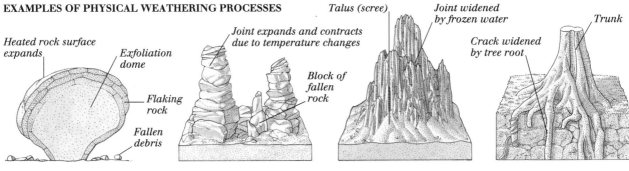

Heated rock surface expands

Exfoliation dome

Flaking rock

Fallen debris

EXFOLIATION (ONION-SKIN WEATHERING)

Joint expands and contracts due to temperature changes

Block of fallen rock

BLOCK DISINTEGRATION

Talus (scree)

Joint widened by frozen water

FROST WEDGING

Trunk

Crack widened by tree root

TREE ROOT ACTION

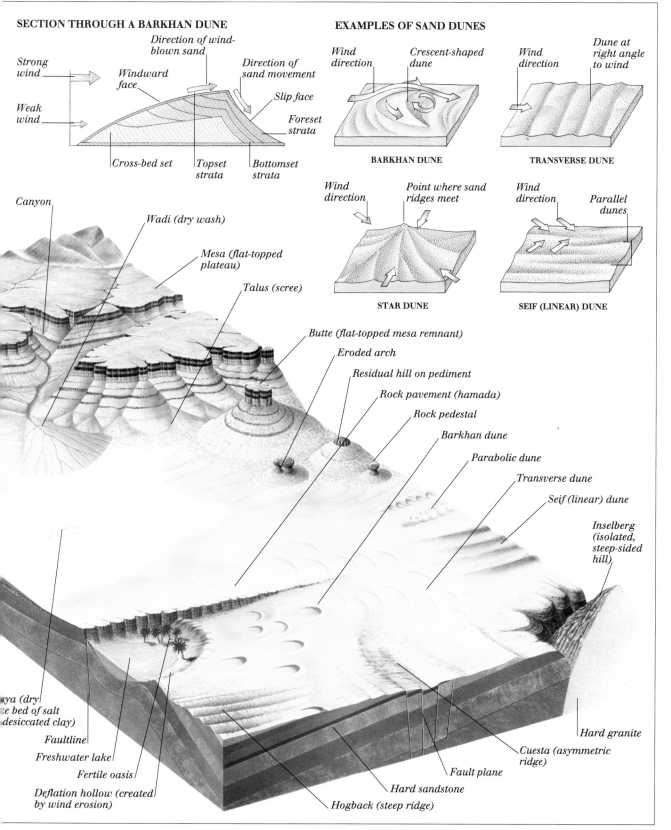

SECTION THROUGH A BARKHAN DUNE

Strong wind

Weak wind

Direction of wind-blown sand

Windward face

Direction of sand movement

Slip face

Foreset strata

Cross-bed set

Topset strata

Bottomset strata

EXAMPLES OF SAND DUNES

Wind direction

Crescent-shaped dune

BARKHAN DUNE

Wind direction

Dune at right angle to wind

TRANSVERSE DUNE

Wind direction

Point where sand ridges meet

STAR DUNE

Wind direction

Parallel dunes

SEIF (LINEAR) DUNE

Canyon

Wadi (dry wash)

Mesa (flat-topped plateau)

Talus (scree)

Butte (flat-topped mesa remnant)

Eroded arch

Residual hill on pediment

Rock pavement (hamada)

Rock pedestal

Barkhan dune

Parabolic dune

Transverse dune

Seif (linear) dune

Inselberg (isolated, steep-sided hill)

Playa (dry lake bed of salt or desiccated clay)

Faultline

Freshwater lake

Fertile oasis

Deflation hollow (created by wind erosion)

Hard sandstone

Hogback (steep ridge)

Fault plane

Cuesta (asymmetric ridge)

Hard granite

283

Caves

CAVES COMMONLY FORM in areas of limestone, although on coastlines they also occur in other rocks. Limestone is made of calcite (calcium carbonate), which dissolves in the carbonic acid naturally present in rainwater, and in humic acids from the decay of vegetation. The acidic water trickles down through cracks and joints in the limestone and between rock layers, breaking up the surface terrain into clints (blocks of rock), separated by grikes (deep cracks), and punctuated by sinkholes (also called swallow holes or potholes) into which surface streams may disappear. Underground, the acidic water dissolves the rock around crevices, opening up a network of passages and caves, which can become large caverns if the roofs collapse. Various features are formed when the dissolved calcite is redeposited. For example, it may be redeposited along an underground stream to form a gour (series of calcite ridges), or in caves and passages to form stalactites and stalagmites. Stalactites develop where calcite is left behind as water drips from the roof; where the drops land, stalagmites build up.

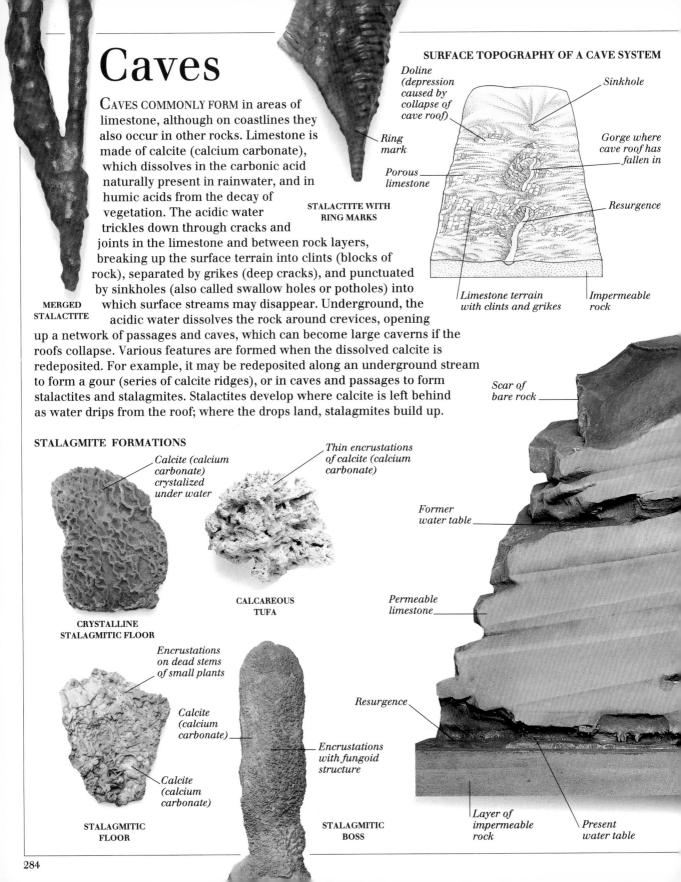

MERGED STALACTITE

STALACTITE WITH RING MARKS

Ring mark

SURFACE TOPOGRAPHY OF A CAVE SYSTEM

Doline (depression caused by collapse of cave roof)

Sinkhole

Porous limestone

Gorge where cave roof has fallen in

Resurgence

Limestone terrain with clints and grikes

Impermeable rock

STALAGMITE FORMATIONS

Calcite (calcium carbonate) crystalized under water

Thin encrustations of calcite (calcium carbonate)

Scar of bare rock

Former water table

Permeable limestone

CRYSTALLINE STALAGMITIC FLOOR

CALCAREOUS TUFA

Encrustations on dead stems of small plants

Calcite (calcium carbonate)

Calcite (calcium carbonate)

Encrustations with fungoid structure

Resurgence

STALAGMITIC FLOOR

STALAGMITIC BOSS

Layer of impermeable rock

Present water table

DEVELOPMENT OF A CAVE SYSTEM

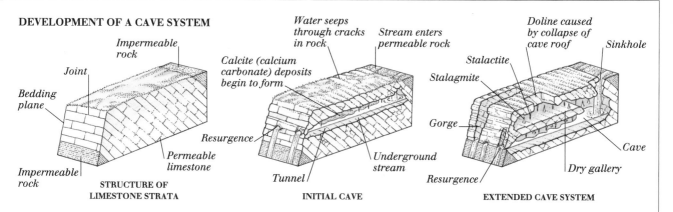

Impermeable rock

Joint

Bedding plane

Impermeable rock

Permeable limestone

STRUCTURE OF LIMESTONE STRATA

Water seeps through cracks in rock

Stream enters permeable rock

Calcite (calcium carbonate) deposits begin to form

Resurgence

Tunnel

Underground stream

INITIAL CAVE

Doline caused by collapse of cave roof

Sinkhole

Stalactite

Stalagmite

Gorge

Resurgence

Cave

Dry gallery

EXTENDED CAVE SYSTEM

INTERCONNECTED CAVE SYSTEM

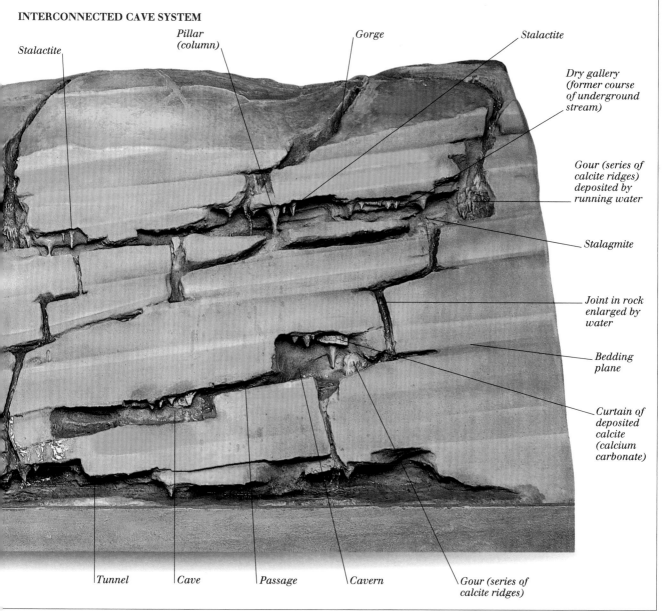

Stalactite

Pillar (column)

Gorge

Stalactite

Dry gallery (former course of underground stream)

Gour (series of calcite ridges) deposited by running water

Stalagmite

Joint in rock enlarged by water

Bedding plane

Curtain of deposited calcite (calcium carbonate)

Tunnel

Cave

Passage

Cavern

Gour (series of calcite ridges)

Glaciers

GLACIER BAY, ALASKA

A VALLEY GLACIER IS A LARGE MASS OF ICE that forms on land and moves slowly downhill under its own weight. It is formed from snow that collects in cirques (mountain hollows also known as corries), compressing into ice as more and more snow accumulates. The cirque is deepened by frost wedging and abrasion (see pp. 282-283), and arêtes (sharp ridges) develop between adjacent cirques. Eventually, so much ice builds up that the glacier begins to flow. As the glacier moves it collects moraine (debris), which may range in size from particles of dust to large boulders. The rocks at the base of the glacier erode the glacial valley, giving it a U-shaped cross section. Under the glacier, *roches moutonnées* (eroded outcrops of hard rock) and drumlins (rounded mounds of rock and clay) are left behind on the valley floor. The glacier ends at a terminus (the snout), where the ice melts as fast as it arrives. If the temperature increases, the ice melts faster than it arrives, and the glacier retreats. The retreating glacier leaves behind its moraine and also erratics (isolated single boulders). Glacial streams from the melting glacier deposit eskers and kames (ridges and mounds of sand and gravel) but carry away the finer sediment to form a stratified outwash plain. Lumps of ice carried on to this plain melt, creating holes called kettles.

VALLEY GLACIER

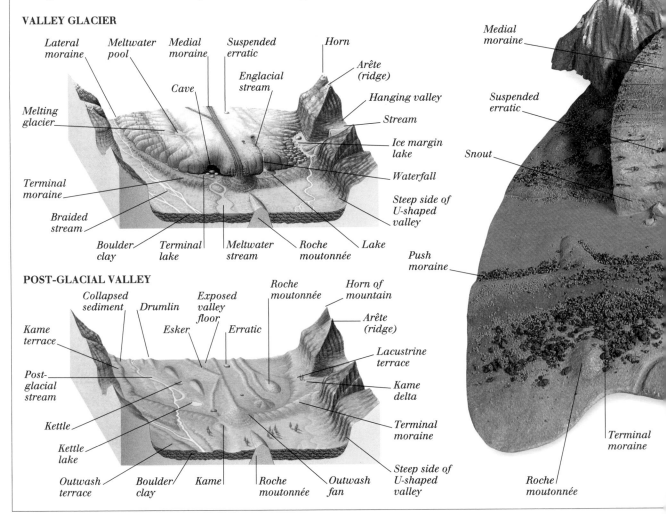

Labels for VALLEY GLACIER diagram:
Lateral moraine, Meltwater pool, Medial moraine, Suspended erratic, Horn, Cave, Englacial stream, Arête (ridge), Hanging valley, Stream, Melting glacier, Ice margin lake, Waterfall, Terminal moraine, Steep side of U-shaped valley, Braided stream, Boulder clay, Terminal lake, Meltwater stream, Roche moutonnée, Lake

POST-GLACIAL VALLEY

Labels for POST-GLACIAL VALLEY diagram:
Collapsed sediment, Drumlin, Exposed valley floor, Roche moutonnée, Horn of mountain, Kame terrace, Esker, Erratic, Arête (ridge), Post-glacial stream, Lacustrine terrace, Kame delta, Kettle, Terminal moraine, Kettle lake, Outwash terrace, Boulder clay, Kame, Roche moutonnée, Outwash fan, Steep side of U-shaped valley

Labels for right-hand illustration:
Medial moraine, Suspended erratic, Snout, Push moraine, Terminal moraine, Roche moutonnée

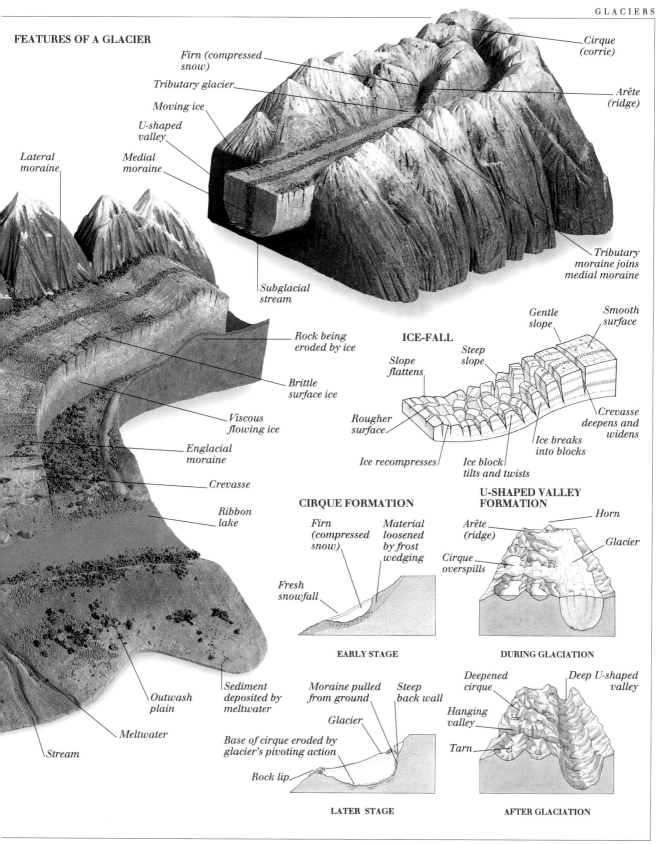

FEATURES OF A GLACIER

Firn (compressed snow)

Tributary glacier

Moving ice

U-shaped valley

Medial moraine

Lateral moraine

Cirque (corrie)

Arête (ridge)

Tributary moraine joins medial moraine

Subglacial stream

Rock being eroded by ice

Brittle surface ice

Viscous flowing ice

Englacial moraine

Crevasse

Ribbon lake

Outwash plain

Meltwater

Stream

Sediment deposited by meltwater

ICE-FALL

Gentle slope

Smooth surface

Steep slope

Slope flattens

Rougher surface

Ice recompresses

Ice block tilts and twists

Ice breaks into blocks

Crevasse deepens and widens

CIRQUE FORMATION

Firn (compressed snow)

Material loosened by frost wedging

Fresh snowfall

EARLY STAGE

Moraine pulled from ground

Steep back wall

Glacier

Base of cirque eroded by glacier's pivoting action

Rock lip

LATER STAGE

U-SHAPED VALLEY FORMATION

Horn

Arête (ridge)

Glacier

Cirque overspills

DURING GLACIATION

Deepened cirque

Deep U-shaped valley

Hanging valley

Tarn

AFTER GLACIATION

Rivers

RIVERS FORM PART of the water cycle—the continuous
circulation of water between the land, sea, and
atmosphere. The source of a river may be a mountain
spring, or lake, or a melting glacier. The course that
the river subsequently takes depends on the slope of
the terrain and on the rock types and formations over
which it flows. In its early, upland stages, a river
tumbles steeply over rocks and boulders and cuts a
steep-sided V-shaped valley. Farther downstream, it
flows smoothly over sediments and forms winding
meanders, eroding sideways to create broad valleys
and plains. On reaching the coast, the river may deposit
sediment, forming an estuary or delta (see pp. 290-291).

RIVER CAPTURE

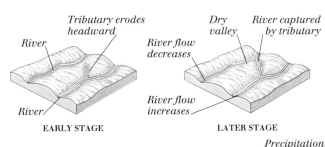

EARLY STAGE LATER STAGE

THE WATER CYCLE

SATELLITE IMAGE OF GANGES RIVER DELTA, BANGLADESH

RIVER DRAINAGE PATTERNS

RADIAL CENTRIPETAL PARALLEL DENDRITIC

DERANGED TRELLISED ANNULAR RECTANGULAR

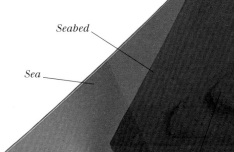

STAGES IN A RIVER'S DEVELOPMENT

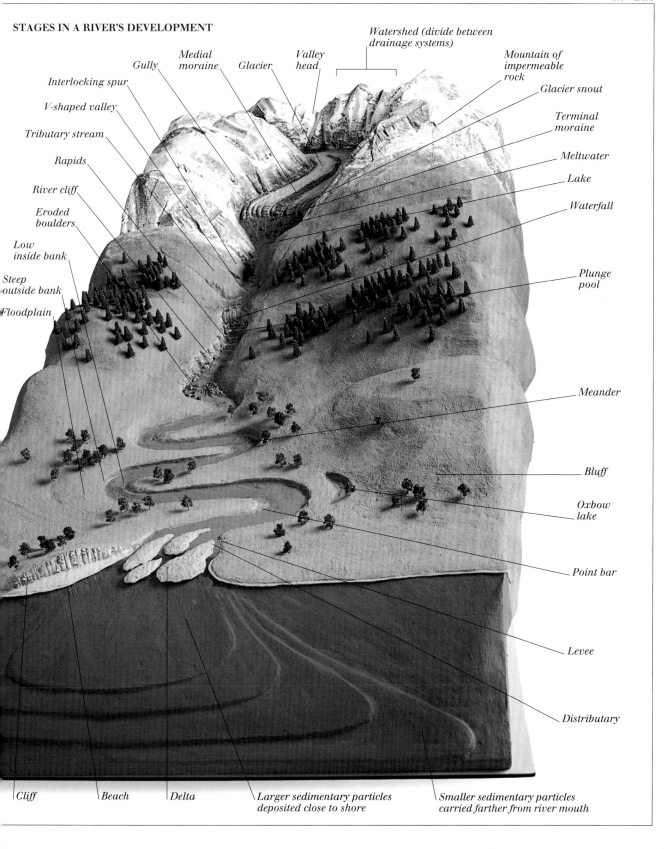

Watershed (divide between drainage systems)

Medial moraine

Gully

Valley head

Mountain of impermeable rock

Glacier

Glacier snout

Interlocking spur

Terminal moraine

V-shaped valley

Meltwater

Tributary stream

Lake

Rapids

Waterfall

River cliff

Eroded boulders

Plunge pool

Low inside bank

Steep outside bank

Floodplain

Meander

Bluff

Oxbow lake

Point bar

Levee

Distributary

Cliff

Beach

Delta

Larger sedimentary particles deposited close to shore

Smaller sedimentary particles carried farther from river mouth

River features

RIVERS ARE ONE OF THE MAJOR FORCES that shape the landscape. Near its source, a river is steep (see pp. 288-289). It erodes downward, carving out V-shaped valleys and deep gorges. Waterfalls and rapids are formed where the river flows from hard rock to softer, more easily eroded rock. Farther downstream, meanders may form and there is greater sideways erosion, resulting in a broad river valley. The river sometimes erodes through the neck of a meander to form an oxbow lake. Sediment deposited on the valley floor by meandering rivers and during floods helps to create a floodplain. Floods may also deposit sediment on the banks of the river to form levees. As a river spills into the sea or a lake, it deposits large amounts of sediment, and may form a delta. A delta is an area of sand bars, swamps and lagoons through which the river flows in several channels called distributaries—the Mississippi delta, for example. Often, a rise in sea level may have flooded the river mouth to form a broad estuary, a tidal section where seawater mixes with fresh water.

HOW WATERFALLS AND RAPIDS ARE FORMED

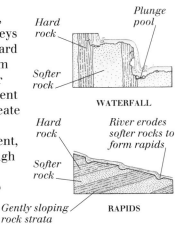

Hard rock

Plunge pool

Softer rock

WATERFALL

Hard rock

River erodes softer rocks to form rapids

Softer rock

Gently sloping rock strata

RAPIDS

A RIVER VALLEY DRAINAGE SYSTEM

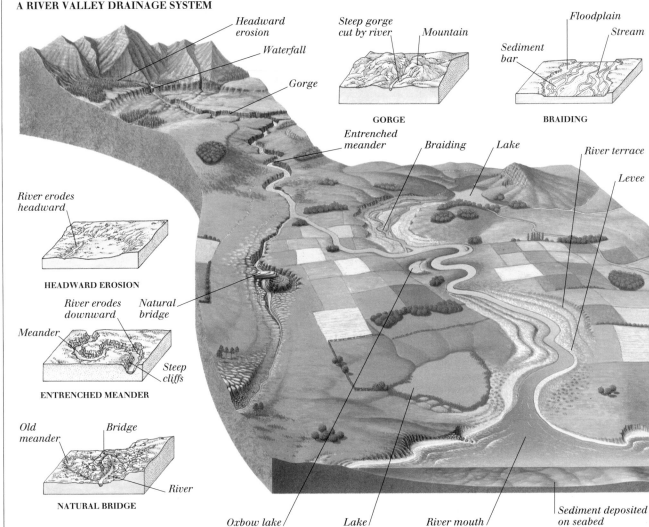

Headward erosion

Waterfall

Gorge

Steep gorge cut by river

Mountain

GORGE

Floodplain

Stream

Sediment bar

BRAIDING

Entrenched meander

Braiding

Lake

River terrace

Levee

River erodes headward

HEADWARD EROSION

River erodes downward

Natural bridge

Meander

Steep cliffs

ENTRENCHED MEANDER

Old meander

Bridge

River

NATURAL BRIDGE

Oxbow lake

Lake

River mouth

Sediment deposited on seabed

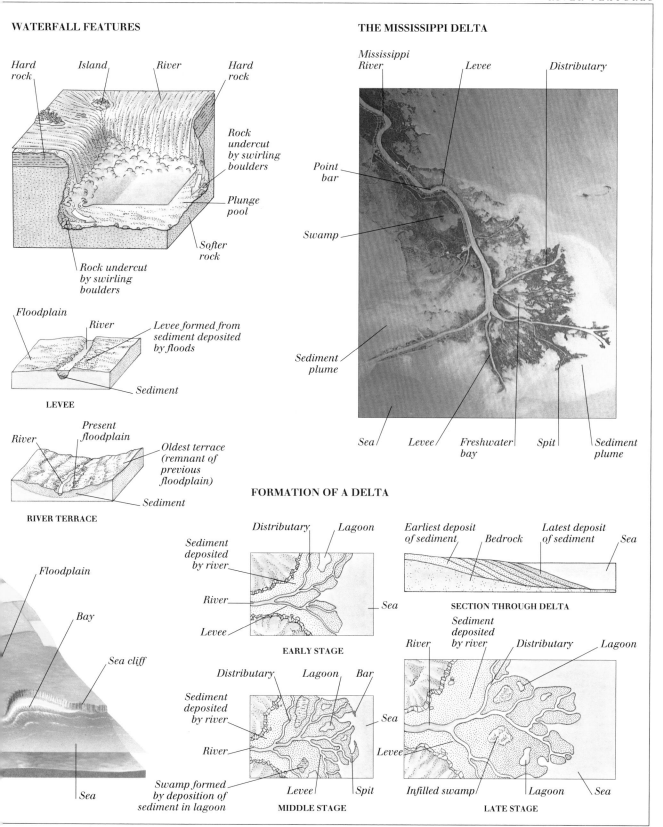

WATERFALL FEATURES

Hard rock

Island

River

Hard rock

Rock undercut by swirling boulders

Plunge pool

Softer rock

Rock undercut by swirling boulders

Floodplain

River

Levee formed from sediment deposited by floods

Sediment

LEVEE

River

Present floodplain

Oldest terrace (remnant of previous floodplain)

Sediment

RIVER TERRACE

Floodplain

Bay

Sea cliff

Sea

THE MISSISSIPPI DELTA

Mississippi River

Levee

Distributary

Point bar

Swamp

Sediment plume

Sea

Levee

Freshwater bay

Spit

Sediment plume

FORMATION OF A DELTA

Distributary

Lagoon

Sediment deposited by river

River

Levee

Sea

EARLY STAGE

Earliest deposit of sediment

Bedrock

Latest deposit of sediment

Sea

SECTION THROUGH DELTA

Distributary

Lagoon

Bar

Sediment deposited by river

River

Sea

Levee

Swamp formed by deposition of sediment in lagoon

Levee

Spit

MIDDLE STAGE

Sediment deposited by river

River

Distributary

Lagoon

Levee

Infilled swamp

Lagoon

Sea

LATE STAGE

Lakes and groundwater

NATURAL LAKES OCCUR WHERE a large quantity of water collects in a hollow in impermeable rock or is prevented from draining away by a barrier, such as moraine (glacial deposits) or solidified lava. Lakes are often relatively short-lived landscape features, because they tend to become silted up by sediment from the streams and rivers that feed them. Some of the more long-lasting lakes are found in deep rift valleys formed by vertical movements of the Earth's crust (see pp. 58-59)—for example, Lake Baikal in Russia, the world's largest freshwater lake, and the Dead Sea in the Middle East, one of the world's saltiest lakes. Where water is able to drain away, it sinks into the ground until it reaches a layer of impermeable rock, then accumulates in the permeable rock above it. This water-saturated permeable rock is called an aquifer. The saturated zone varies in depth according to seasonal and climatic changes. In wet conditions, the water stored underground builds up, while in dry periods it becomes depleted. Where the upper edge of the saturated zone—the water table—meets the ground surface, water emerges as springs. In an artesian basin, where the aquifer is below an aquiclude (layer of impermeable rock), the water table throughout the basin is determined by its height at the rim. At the center of such a basin, the water table is above ground level. The water in the basin is thus trapped below the water table and can rise under its own pressure along fault lines or well shafts.

LAKE BAIKAL, RUSSIA

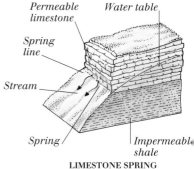

EXAMPLES OF SPRINGS

Permeable limestone
Water table
Spring line
Stream
Spring
Impermeable shale

LIMESTONE SPRING

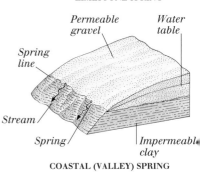

Permeable gravel
Water table
Spring line
Stream
Spring
Impermeable clay

COASTAL (VALLEY) SPRING

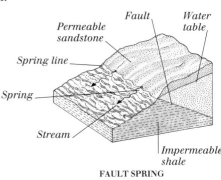

Fault
Water table
Permeable sandstone
Spring line
Spring
Stream
Impermeable shale

FAULT SPRING

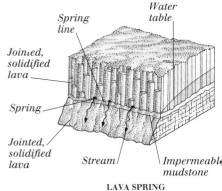

Water table
Spring line
Jointed, solidified lava
Spring
Jointed, solidified lava
Stream
Impermeable mudstone

LAVA SPRING

STRUCTURE OF AN ARTESIAN BASIN

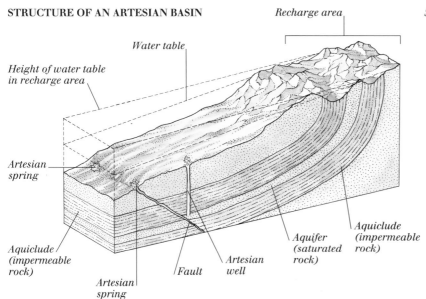

Recharge area
Water table
Height of water table in recharge area
Artesian spring
Aquiclude (impermeable rock)
Artesian spring
Fault
Artesian well
Aquifer (saturated rock)
Aquiclude (impermeable rock)

FEATURES OF A GROUNDWATER SYSTEM

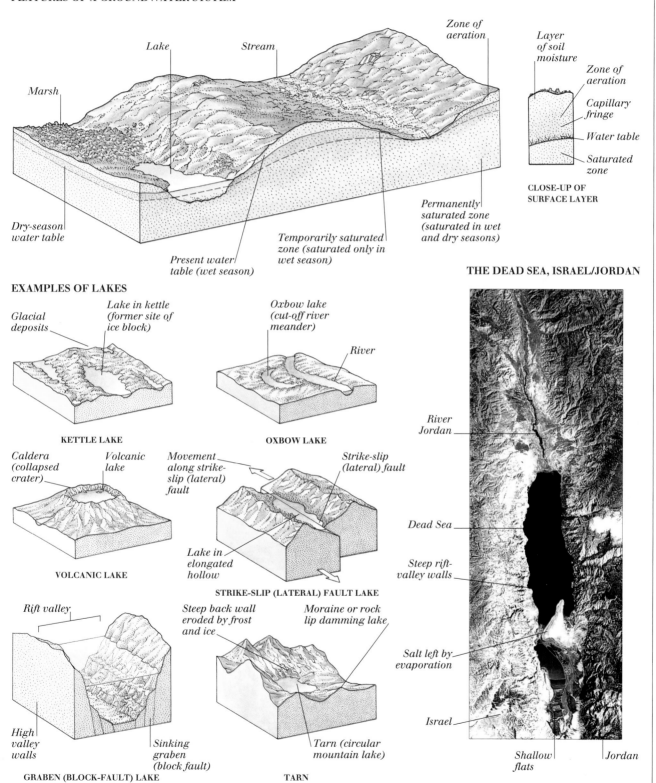

Zone of aeration

Lake

Stream

Layer of soil moisture

Zone of aeration

Capillary fringe

Water table

Saturated zone

Marsh

CLOSE-UP OF SURFACE LAYER

Dry-season water table

Permanently saturated zone (saturated in wet and dry seasons)

Present water table (wet season)

Temporarily saturated zone (saturated only in wet season)

EXAMPLES OF LAKES

Glacial deposits

Lake in kettle (former site of ice block)

Oxbow lake (cut-off river meander)

River

KETTLE LAKE

OXBOW LAKE

Caldera (collapsed crater)

Volcanic lake

Movement along strike-slip (lateral) fault

Strike-slip (lateral) fault

VOLCANIC LAKE

Lake in elongated hollow

STRIKE-SLIP (LATERAL) FAULT LAKE

Rift valley

Steep back wall eroded by frost and ice

Moraine or rock lip damming lake

High valley walls

Sinking graben (block fault)

Tarn (circular mountain lake)

GRABEN (BLOCK-FAULT) LAKE

TARN

THE DEAD SEA, ISRAEL/JORDAN

River Jordan

Dead Sea

Steep rift-valley walls

Salt left by evaporation

Israel

Shallow flats

Jordan

Coastlines

COASTLINES ARE AMONG THE MOST RAPIDLY changing landscape features. Some are eroded by waves, wind, and rain, causing cliffs to be undercut and caves to be hollowed out of solid rock. Others are built up by waves transporting sand and small rocks in a process known as longshore drift and by rivers depositing sediment in deltas. Additional influences include the activities of living organisms such as coral, crustal movements, and sea-level variations due to climatic changes. Rising land or a drop in sea level creates an emergent coastline, with cliffs and beaches standing above the new shoreline. Sinking land or a rise in sea level produces a drowned coastline, typified by fjords (submerged glacial valleys) or submerged river valleys.

FEATURES OF A SEA CLIFF

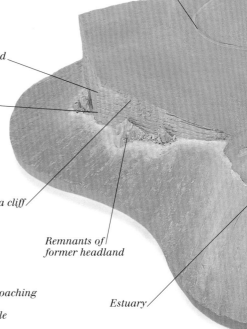

Cliff top

Cliff face

High tide level

Low tide level

Offshore deposits

Wave-cut platform

Undercut area of cliff

Mature river

Headland

Bedding plane

Sea cliff

Remnants of former headland

Estuary

FEATURES OF WAVES

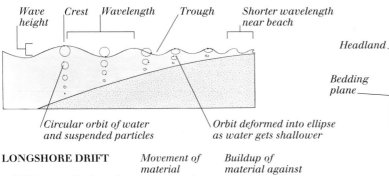

Wave height

Crest

Wavelength

Trough

Shorter wavelength near beach

Circular orbit of water and suspended particles

Orbit deformed into ellipse as water gets shallower

LONGSHORE DRIFT

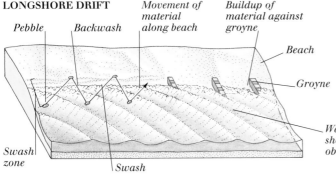

Pebble

Backwash

Movement of material along beach

Buildup of material against groyne

Beach

Groyne

Waves approaching shore at an oblique angle

Swash zone

Swash

DEPOSITIONAL FEATURES OF COASTLINES

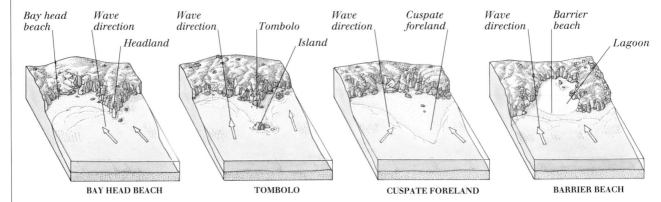

Bay head beach

Wave direction

Headland

Wave direction

Tombolo

Island

Wave direction

Cuspate foreland

Wave direction

Barrier beach

Lagoon

BAY HEAD BEACH

TOMBOLO

CUSPATE FORELAND

BARRIER BEACH

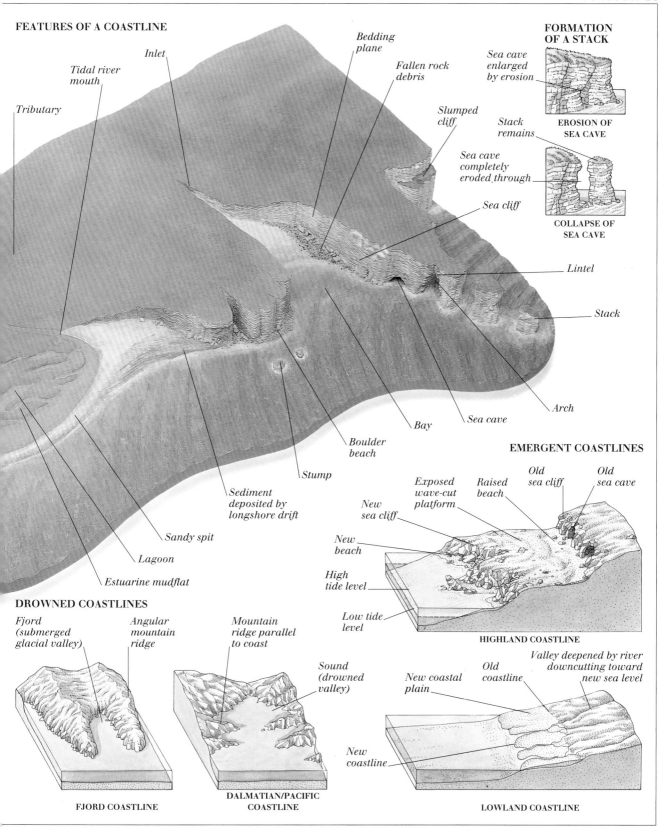

FEATURES OF A COASTLINE

Inlet

Tidal river mouth

Tributary

Bedding plane

Fallen rock debris

Slumped cliff

Sea cliff

Bay

Sea cave

Arch

Boulder beach

Stump

Sediment deposited by longshore drift

Sandy spit

Lagoon

Estuarine mudflat

FORMATION OF A STACK

Sea cave enlarged by erosion

EROSION OF SEA CAVE

Stack remains

Sea cave completely eroded through

COLLAPSE OF SEA CAVE

Lintel

Stack

EMERGENT COASTLINES

Exposed wave-cut platform

Raised beach

Old sea cliff

Old sea cave

New sea cliff

New beach

High tide level

Low tide level

HIGHLAND COASTLINE

Valley deepened by river downcutting toward new sea level

New coastal plain

Old coastline

New coastline

LOWLAND COASTLINE

DROWNED COASTLINES

Fjord (submerged glacial valley)

Angular mountain ridge

Mountain ridge parallel to coast

Sound (drowned valley)

FJORD COASTLINE

DALMATIAN/PACIFIC COASTLINE

Oceans and seas

OCEANS AND SEAS COVER ABOUT 70 PERCENT of the Earth's surface and account for about 97 percent of its total water. These oceans and seas play a crucial role in regulating temperature variations and determining climate. Their waters absorb heat from the Sun, especially in tropical regions, and the surface currents distribute it around the Earth, warming overlying air masses and neighboring land in winter and cooling them in summer. The oceans are never still. Differences in temperature and salinity drive deep current systems, while surface currents are generated by winds blowing over the oceans. All currents are deflected—to the right in the Northern Hemisphere, to the left in the Southern Hemisphere—as a result of the Earth's rotation. This deflective factor is known as the Coriolis force. A current that begins on the surface is immediately deflected. This current in turn generates a current in the layer of water beneath, which is also deflected. As the movement is transmitted downward, the deflections form an Ekman spiral. The waters of the oceans and seas are also moved by the constant ebb and flow of tides. These are caused by the gravitational pull of the Moon and Sun. The highest tides (Spring tides) occur at full and new Moon; the lowest tides (neap tides) occur at first and last quarter.

OFFSHORE CURRENTS

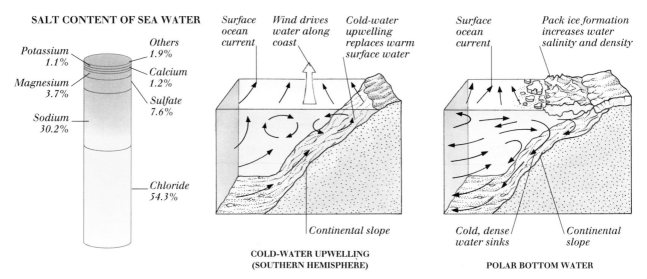

SALT CONTENT OF SEA WATER

Potassium 1.1%
Others 1.9%
Magnesium 3.7%
Calcium 1.2%
Sulfate 7.6%
Sodium 30.2%
Chloride 54.3%

Surface ocean current

Wind drives water along coast

Cold-water upwelling replaces warm surface water

Continental slope

COLD-WATER UPWELLING (SOUTHERN HEMISPHERE)

Surface ocean current

Pack ice formation increases water salinity and density

Cold, dense water sinks

Continental slope

POLAR BOTTOM WATER

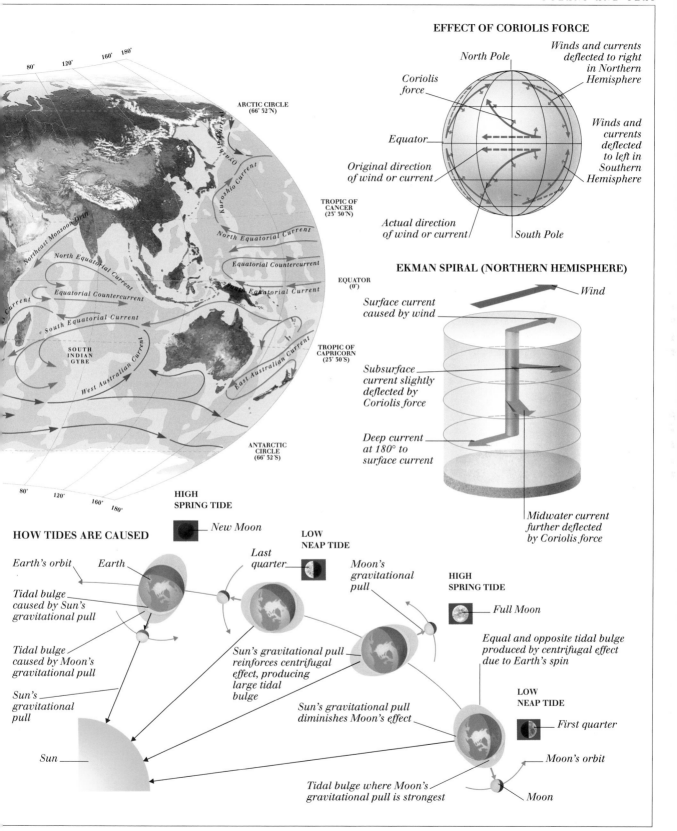

EFFECT OF CORIOLIS FORCE

North Pole

Coriolis force

Winds and currents deflected to right in Northern Hemisphere

Equator

Winds and currents deflected to left in Southern Hemisphere

Original direction of wind or current

Actual direction of wind or current

South Pole

ARCTIC CIRCLE
(66° 32'N)

80° 120° 160° 180°

Oyashio Current

Kuroshio Current

Northeast Monsoon Drift

North Equatorial Current

North Equatorial Current

TROPIC OF CANCER
(23° 30'N)

Equatorial Countercurrent

Equatorial Countercurrent

South Equatorial Current

South Equatorial Current

s. Current

SOUTH INDIAN GYRE

West Australian Current

East Australian Current

TROPIC OF CAPRICORN
(23° 30'S)

ANTARCTIC CIRCLE
(66° 32'S)

80° 120° 160° 180°

EKMAN SPIRAL (NORTHERN HEMISPHERE)

EQUATOR
(0°)

Wind

Surface current caused by wind

Subsurface current slightly deflected by Coriolis force

Deep current at 180° to surface current

Midwater current further deflected by Coriolis force

HIGH SPRING TIDE

New Moon

HOW TIDES ARE CAUSED

LOW NEAP TIDE

Last quarter

Moon's gravitational pull

HIGH SPRING TIDE

Full Moon

Earth's orbit   *Earth*

Tidal bulge caused by Sun's gravitational pull

Tidal bulge caused by Moon's gravitational pull

Sun's gravitational pull

Sun's gravitational pull reinforces centrifugal effect, producing large tidal bulge

Equal and opposite tidal bulge produced by centrifugal effect due to Earth's spin

Sun's gravitational pull diminishes Moon's effect

LOW NEAP TIDE

First quarter

Moon's orbit

Sun

Tidal bulge where Moon's gravitational pull is strongest

Moon

297

The ocean floor

THE OCEAN FLOOR INCLUDES TWO SECTIONS: the continental shelf and slope, and the deep-ocean floor. The continental shelf and slope are part of the continental crust, but may extend far into the ocean. Sloping quite gently to a depth of about 460 feet, the continental shelf is covered in sandy deposits shaped by waves and tidal currents. At the edge of the continental shelf, the seabed slopes down to the abyssal plain, which lies at an average depth of about 12,500 feet. On this deep-ocean floor is a layer of sediment made up of clays, fine oozes formed from the remains of tiny sea creatures, and occasional mineral-rich deposits. Echo-sounding and remote sensing from satellites has revealed that the abyssal plain is divided by a world-circling system of mountain ranges, far bigger than any on land—the midocean ridge. Here, magma (molten rock) wells up from the Earth's interior and solidifies, widening the ocean floor (see pp. 58-59). As the ocean floor spreads, volcanoes that have formed over hot spots in the crust move away from their magma source; they become extinct and are increasingly submerged and eroded. Volcanoes eroded below sea level remain as seamounts (underwater mountains). In warm waters, a volcano that projects above the ocean surface often acquires a fringing coral reef, which may develop into an atoll as the volcano becomes submerged.

CONTINENTAL-SHELF FLOOR

Bedrock exposed by tidal scour

Shoreline

Parallel strips of coarse material left by strong tidal currents

Sand deposited in wavy pattern by weaker currents

Irregular patches of fine sand deposited by weakest currents

FEATURES OF THE OCEAN FLOOR

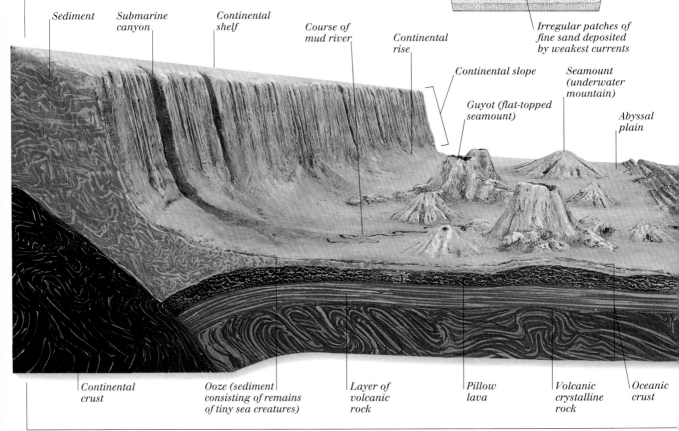

Sediment

Submarine canyon

Continental shelf

Course of mud river

Continental rise

Continental slope

Guyot (flat-topped seamount)

Seamount (underwater mountain)

Abyssal plain

Continental crust

Ooze (sediment consisting of remains of tiny sea creatures)

Layer of volcanic rock

Pillow lava

Volcanic crystalline rock

Oceanic crust

KEY

☐ Calcareous ooze

☐ Pelagic clay

☐ Glacial sediments

☐ Siliceous ooze

☐ Terrigenous sediments

☐ Continental margin sediments

▨ Metalliferous muds

⬚ Major nodule fields

DEEP-OCEAN FLOOR SEDIMENTS

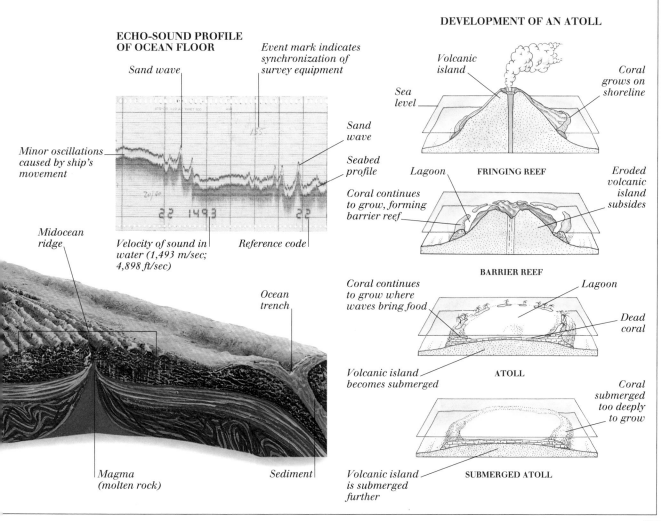

ECHO-SOUND PROFILE OF OCEAN FLOOR

Sand wave

Event mark indicates synchronization of survey equipment

Sand wave

Seabed profile

Minor oscillations caused by ship's movement

Velocity of sound in water (1,493 m/sec; 4,898 ft/sec)

Reference code

Midocean ridge

Ocean trench

Magma (molten rock)

Sediment

DEVELOPMENT OF AN ATOLL

Volcanic island

Sea level

Coral grows on shoreline

FRINGING REEF

Lagoon

Coral continues to grow, forming barrier reef

Eroded volcanic island subsides

BARRIER REEF

Coral continues to grow where waves bring food

Lagoon

Dead coral

Volcanic island becomes submerged

ATOLL

Coral submerged too deeply to grow

Volcanic island is submerged further

SUBMERGED ATOLL

The atmosphere

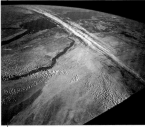

JET STREAM

THE EARTH IS SURROUNDED BY ITS ATMOSPHERE, a blanket of gases that enables life to exist on the planet. This layer has no definite outer edge, gradually becoming thinner until it merges into space, but over 80 percent of atmospheric gases are held by gravity within about 10 miles of the Earth's surface. The atmosphere blocks out much harmful ultraviolet solar radiation, and insulates the Earth against extremes of temperature by limiting both incoming solar radiation and the escape of re-radiated heat into space. This natural balance may be distorted by the greenhouse effect, as gases such as carbon dioxide have built up in the atmosphere, trapping more heat. Close to the Earth's surface, differences in air temperature and pressure cause air to circulate between the equator and poles. This circulation, together with the Coriolis force, gives rise to the prevailing surface winds and the high-level jet streams.

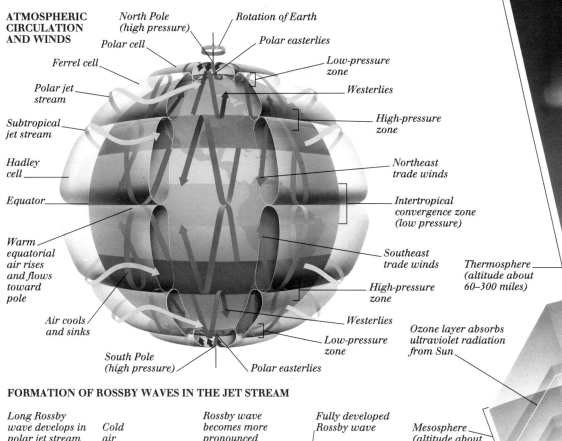

ATMOSPHERIC CIRCULATION AND WINDS

North Pole (high pressure)

Rotation of Earth

Polar cell

Polar easterlies

Ferrel cell

Low-pressure zone

Polar jet stream

Westerlies

Subtropical jet stream

High-pressure zone

Hadley cell

Northeast trade winds

Equator

Intertropical convergence zone (low pressure)

Warm equatorial air rises and flows toward pole

Southeast trade winds

High-pressure zone

Air cools and sinks

Westerlies

South Pole (high pressure)

Low-pressure zone

Polar easterlies

Exosphere (altitude above about 300 miles)

Corona

Thermosphere (altitude about 60–300 miles)

Ozone layer absorbs ultraviolet radiation from Sun

Mesosphere (altitude about 30–60 miles)

Stratosphere (altitude about 6–30 miles)

Troposphere (altitude up to about 6 miles)

FORMATION OF ROSSBY WAVES IN THE JET STREAM

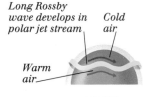

Long Rossby wave develops in polar jet stream

Cold air

Rossby wave becomes more pronounced

Fully developed Rossby wave

Warm air

INITIAL UNDULATION

DEEPENING WAVE

DEVELOPED WAVE

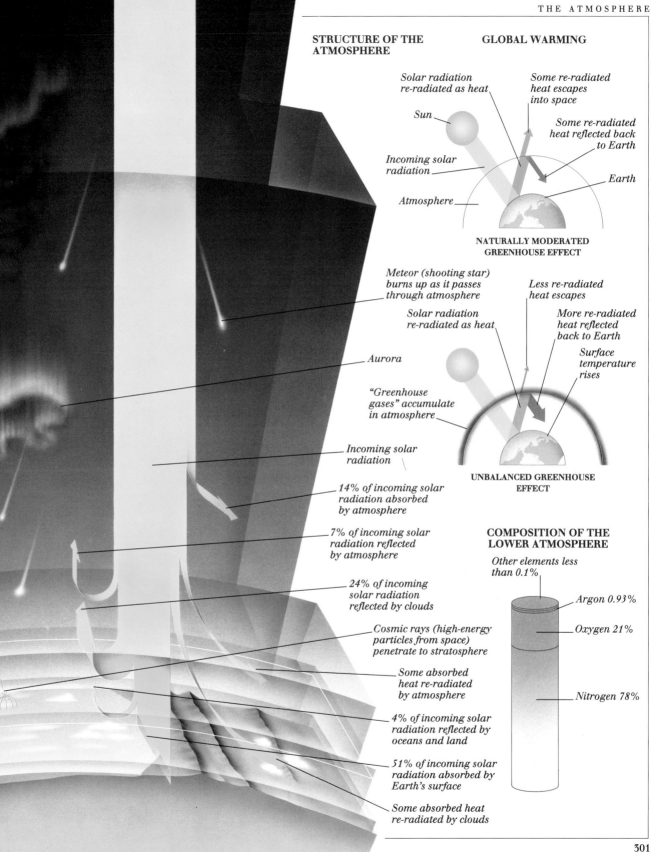

STRUCTURE OF THE ATMOSPHERE

GLOBAL WARMING

Solar radiation re-radiated as heat

Some re-radiated heat escapes into space

Sun

Some re-radiated heat reflected back to Earth

Incoming solar radiation

Earth

Atmosphere

NATURALLY MODERATED GREENHOUSE EFFECT

Meteor (shooting star) burns up as it passes through atmosphere

Less re-radiated heat escapes

Solar radiation re-radiated as heat

More re-radiated heat reflected back to Earth

Surface temperature rises

Aurora

"Greenhouse gases" accumulate in atmosphere

Incoming solar radiation

UNBALANCED GREENHOUSE EFFECT

14% of incoming solar radiation absorbed by atmosphere

7% of incoming solar radiation reflected by atmosphere

COMPOSITION OF THE LOWER ATMOSPHERE

Other elements less than 0.1%

24% of incoming solar radiation reflected by clouds

Argon 0.93%

Cosmic rays (high-energy particles from space) penetrate to stratosphere

Oxygen 21%

Some absorbed heat re-radiated by atmosphere

4% of incoming solar radiation reflected by oceans and land

Nitrogen 78%

51% of incoming solar radiation absorbed by Earth's surface

Some absorbed heat re-radiated by clouds

Weather

WEATHER IS DEFINED AS THE ATMOSPHERIC CONDITIONS at a particular time and place; climate is the average weather conditions for a given region over time. Weather conditions include temperature, wind, cloud cover, and precipitation, such as rain or snow. Good weather is associated with high-pressure areas, where air is sinking. Cloudy, wet, changeable weather is common in low-pressure zones with rising, unstable air. Such conditions occur at temperate latitudes, where warm air meets cool air along the polar fronts. Here, spiraling low-pressure cells known as depressions (mid-latitude cyclones) often form. A depression usually contains a sector of warmer air, beginning at a warm front and ending at a cold front. If the two fronts merge, forming an occluded front, the warm air is pushed upward. An extreme form of low-pressure cell is a hurricane (also called a typhoon or tropical cyclone), which brings torrential rain, and exceptionally strong winds.

TYPES OF OCCLUDED FRONT

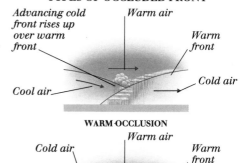

WARM OCCLUSION

COLD OCCLUSION

TYPES OF CLOUD

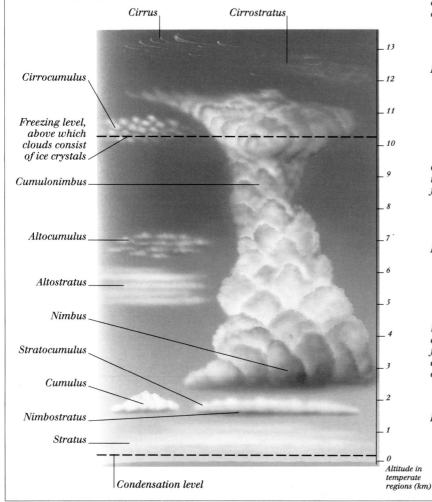

Cirrus

Cirrostratus

Cirrocumulus

Freezing level, above which clouds consist of ice crystals

Cumulonimbus

Altocumulus

Altostratus

Nimbus

Stratocumulus

Cumulus

Nimbostratus

Stratus

13
12
11
10
9
8
7
6
5
4
3
2
1
0

Altitude in temperate regions (km)

Condensation level

FORMS OF PRECIPITATION

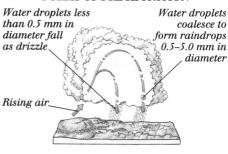

Water droplets less than 0.5 mm in diameter fall as drizzle

Water droplets coalesce to form raindrops 0.5–5.0 mm in diameter

Rising air

RAIN FROM CLOUDS NOT REACHING FREEZING LEVEL

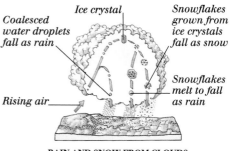

Coalesced water droplets fall as rain

Ice crystal

Snowflakes grown from ice crystals fall as snow

Rising air

Snowflakes melt to fall as rain

RAIN AND SNOW FROM CLOUDS REACHING FREEZING LEVEL

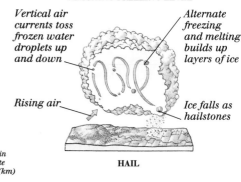

Vertical air currents toss frozen water droplets up and down

Alternate freezing and melting builds up layers of ice

Rising air

Ice falls as hailstones

HAIL

STRUCTURE OF A HURRICANE

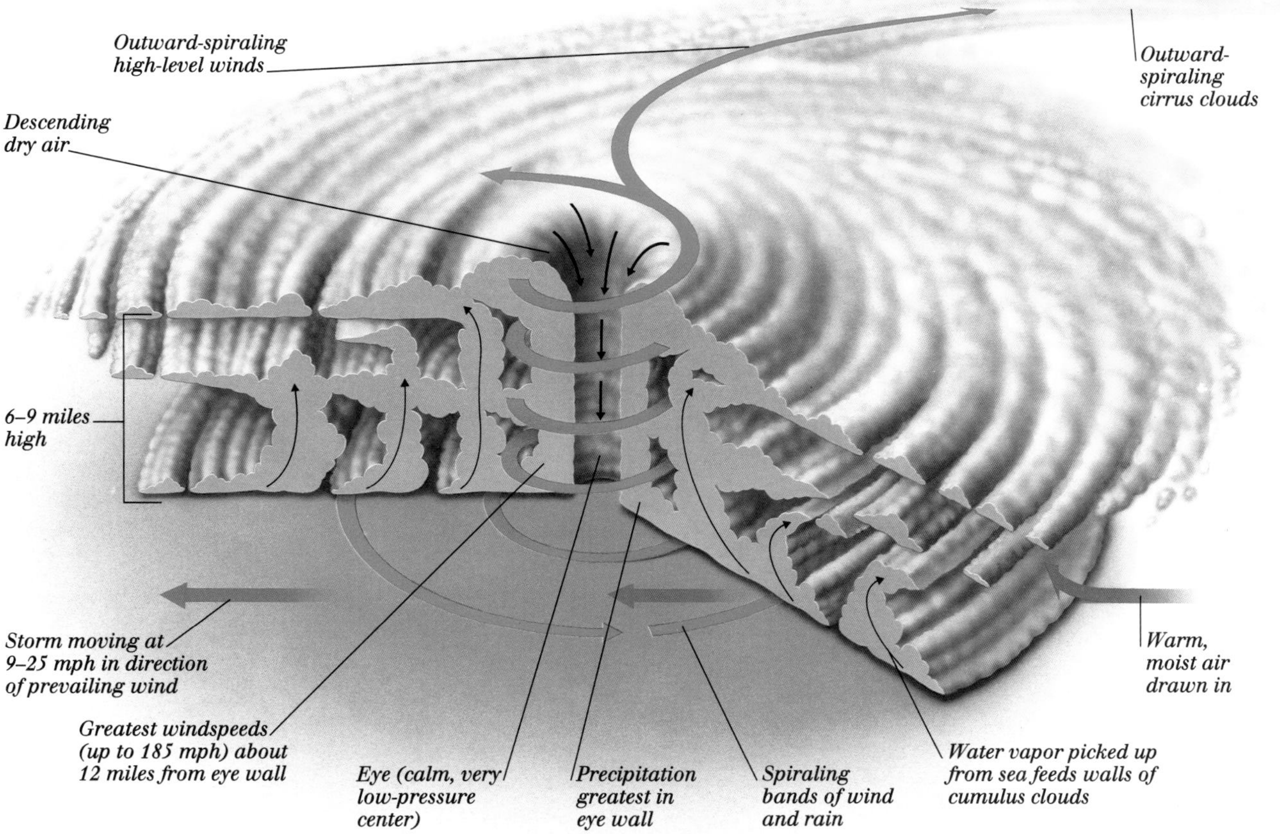

Outward-spiraling
high-level winds

Outward-
spiraling
cirrus clouds

Descending
dry air

6–9 miles
high

Storm moving at
9–25 mph in direction
of prevailing wind

Warm,
moist air
drawn in

Greatest windspeeds
(up to 185 mph) about
12 miles from eye wall

Eye (calm, very
low-pressure
center)

Precipitation
greatest in
eye wall

Spiraling
bands of wind
and rain

Water vapor picked up
from sea feeds walls of
cumulus clouds

WEATHER MAP

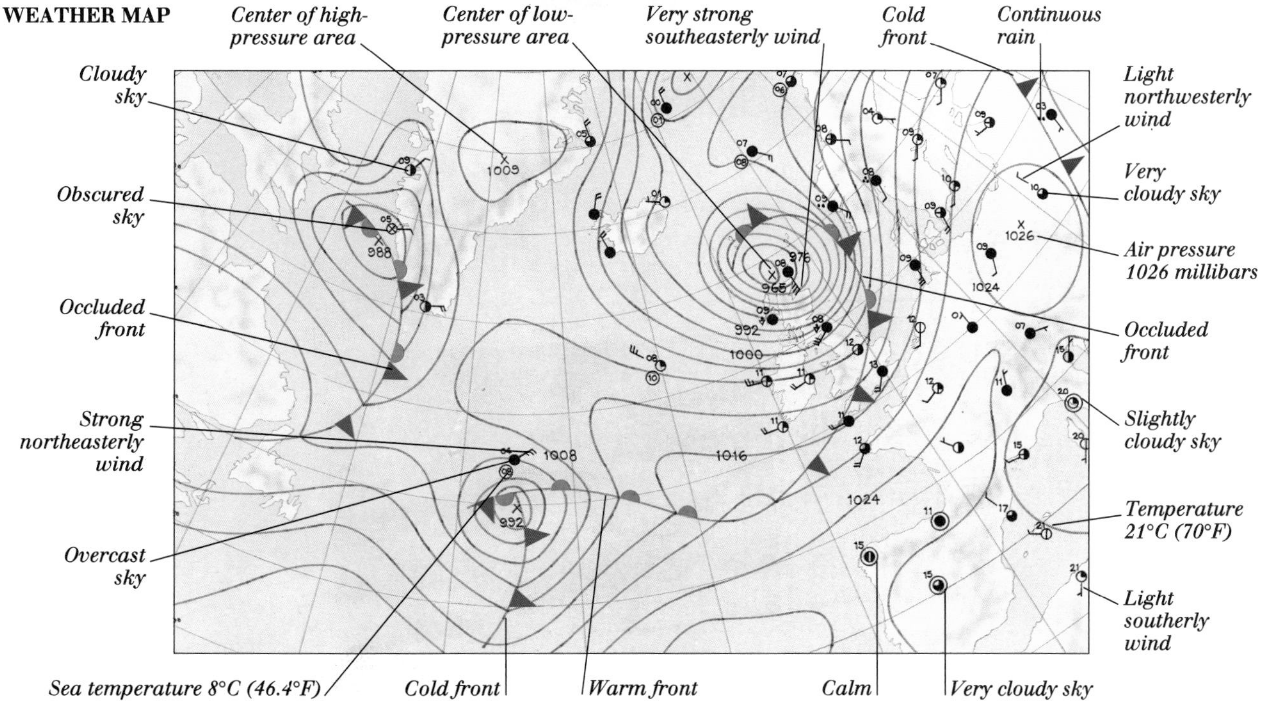

Center of high-
pressure area

Center of low-
pressure area

Very strong
southeasterly wind

Cold
front

Continuous
rain

Cloudy
sky

Light
northwesterly
wind

Obscured
sky

Very
cloudy sky

Air pressure
1026 millibars

Occluded
front

Occluded
front

Slightly
cloudy sky

Strong
northeasterly
wind

Temperature
21°C (70°F)

Overcast
sky

Light
southerly
wind

Sea temperature 8°C (46.4°F)

Cold front

Warm front

Calm

Very cloudy sky

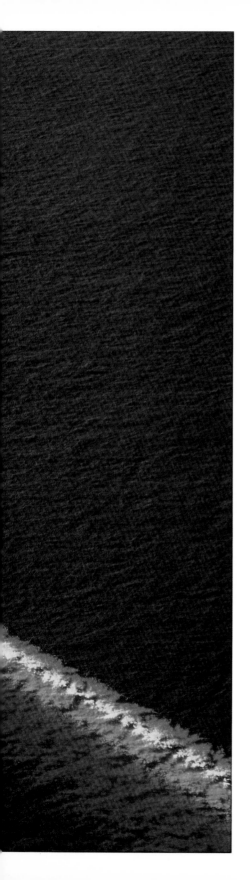

PHYSICS AND CHEMISTRY

THE VARIETY OF MATTER 306

ATOMS AND MOLECULES 308

THE PERIODIC TABLE 310

CHEMICAL REACTIONS 312

ENERGY 314

ELECTRICITY AND MAGNETISM 316

LIGHT 318

FORCE AND MOTION 320

The variety of matter

**PLANT AND INSECT
(LIVING MATTER)**

MATTER IS ANYTHING THAT OCCUPIES SPACE. It includes everything from natural substances, such as minerals or living organisms, to synthetic materials. Matter can exist in three distinct states—solid, liquid, and gas. A solid is rigid and retains its shape. A liquid is fluid, has a definite volume, and will take the shape of its container. A gas (also fluid) fills a space, so its volume will be the same as the volume of its container. Most substances can exist as a solid, a liquid, or a gas: the state is determined by temperature. At very high temperatures, matter becomes plasma, often considered to be a fourth state of matter. All matter is composed of microscopic particles, such as atoms and molecules (see pp. 308-309). The arrangement and interactions of these particles give a substance its physical and chemical properties, by which matter can be identified. There is a huge variety of matter because particles can arrange themselves in countless ways, in one substance or by mixing with others. Natural glass, for example, seems to be a solid but is, in fact, a supercool liquid: the atoms are not locked into a pattern and can flow. Pure substances known as elements (see p. 310) combine to form compounds or mixtures. Mixtures called colloids are made up of larger particles of matter suspended in a solid, liquid, or gas, while a solution is one substance dissolved in another.

TYPES OF COLLOID

HAIR GEL (SOLID IN LIQUID)

**SHAVING CREAM
(AIR IN LIQUID)**

**MIST
(LIQUID IN GAS)**

EXAMPLES OF MATTER

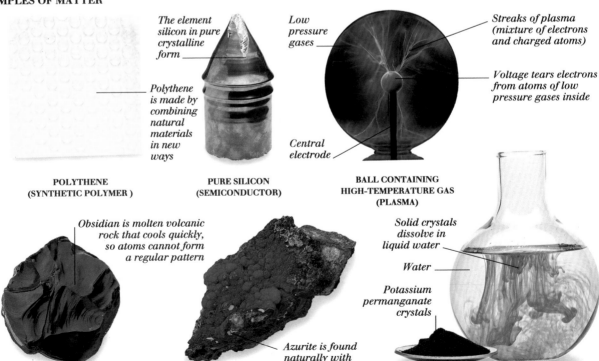

The element silicon in pure crystalline form

Polythene is made by combining natural materials in new ways

**POLYTHENE
(SYNTHETIC POLYMER)**

**PURE SILICON
(SEMICONDUCTOR)**

Low pressure gases

Streaks of plasma (mixture of electrons and charged atoms)

Voltage tears electrons from atoms of low pressure gases inside

Central electrode

**BALL CONTAINING
HIGH-TEMPERATURE GAS
(PLASMA)**

Obsidian is molten volcanic rock that cools quickly, so atoms cannot form a regular pattern

**OBSIDIAN
(NATURAL GLASS)**

Azurite is found naturally with deposits of copper ore

**AZURITE
(CRYSTALLINE MINERAL)**

Solid crystals dissolve in liquid water

Water

Potassium permanganate crystals

**POTASSIUM PERMANGANATE AND WATER
(SOLUTION)**

STATES OF MATTER

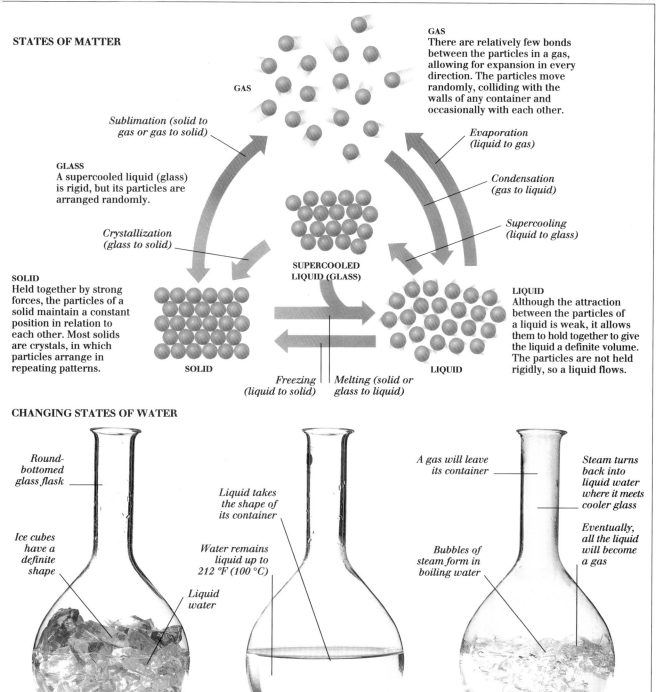

GAS
There are relatively few bonds between the particles in a gas, allowing for expansion in every direction. The particles move randomly, colliding with the walls of any container and occasionally with each other.

GAS

Sublimation (solid to gas or gas to solid)

Evaporation (liquid to gas)

Condensation (gas to liquid)

GLASS
A supercooled liquid (glass) is rigid, but its particles are arranged randomly.

Supercooling (liquid to glass)

Crystallization (glass to solid)

SUPERCOOLED LIQUID (GLASS)

SOLID
Held together by strong forces, the particles of a solid maintain a constant position in relation to each other. Most solids are crystals, in which particles arrange in repeating patterns.

SOLID

LIQUID

LIQUID
Although the attraction between the particles of a liquid is weak, it allows them to hold together to give the liquid a definite volume. The particles are not held rigidly, so a liquid flows.

Freezing (liquid to solid)

Melting (solid or glass to liquid)

CHANGING STATES OF WATER

Round-bottomed glass flask

Ice cubes have a definite shape

Liquid water

Liquid takes the shape of its container

Water remains liquid up to 212 °F (100 °C)

A gas will leave its container

Bubbles of steam form in boiling water

Steam turns back into liquid water where it meets cooler glass

Eventually, all the liquid will become a gas

SOLID STATE: ICE
The solid state of water, ice, forms when liquid water is cooled sufficiently. Ice cubes are rigid, with a definite shape and volume.

LIQUID STATE: WATER
When the temperature of a substance rises above its freezing point, it melts to become a liquid. Ice changes to water.

GASEOUS STATE: STEAM
Above its boiling point, a substance will become a gas. When heated sufficiently, liquid water turns to steam, a colorless gas.

Atoms and molecules

FALSE-COLOR IMAGE
OF ACTUAL GOLD
ATOMS

ATOMS ARE THE smallest individual parts of an element (see pp. 310-311). They are tiny, with diameters in the order of one ten-thousand-millionth of a meter (10^{-10} m). Two or more atoms join together (bond) to form a molecule of a substance known as a compound. For example, when atoms of the elements hydrogen and fluorine join together, they form a molecule of the compound hydrogen fluoride. So molecules are the smallest individual parts of a compound. Atoms themselves are not indivisible —they possess an internal structure. At their center is a dense nucleus consisting of protons, which have a positive electric charge (see p. 316), and neutrons, which are uncharged. Around the nucleus are negatively charged electrons. It is the electrons that give a substance most of its physical and chemical properties. They do not follow definite paths around the nucleus. Instead, electrons are said to be found within certain regions, called orbitals. These are arranged around the nucleus in "shells," each containing electrons of a particular energy. For example, the first shell (1) can hold up to two electrons, in a so-called s-orbital (1s). The second shell (2) can hold up to eight electrons in s-orbitals (2s) and p-orbitals (2p). If an atom loses an electron, it becomes a positive ion (cation). If an electron is gained, an atom becomes a negative ion (anion). Ions of opposite charges will attract and join together in a type of bonding known as ionic bonding. In covalent bonding, the atoms bond by sharing their electrons in what become molecular orbitals.

ATOMIC ORBITALS

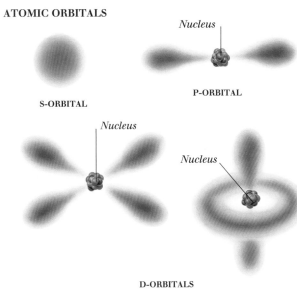

S-ORBITAL

P-ORBITAL

Nucleus

Nucleus

Nucleus

D-ORBITALS

MOLECULAR ORBITALS

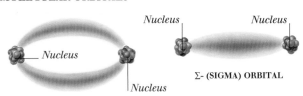

Nucleus

Nucleus

Nucleus

Nucleus

Σ- (SIGMA) ORBITAL

π- (PI) ORBITAL

Nucleus

SP³-HYBRID ORBITAL

EXAMPLE OF IONIC BONDING

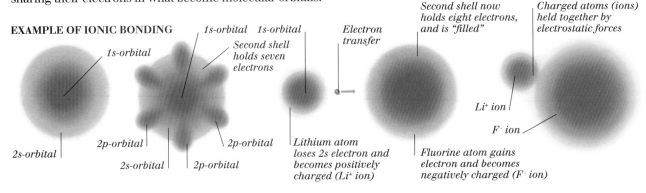

1s-orbital

1s-orbital   1s-orbital

Second shell
holds seven
electrons

2s-orbital

2p-orbital   2p-orbital

2s-orbital   2p-orbital

Electron
transfer

Lithium atom
loses 2s electron and
becomes positively
charged (Li^+ ion)

Second shell now
holds eight electrons,
and is "filled"

Fluorine atom gains
electron and becomes
negatively charged (F^- ion)

Charged atoms (ions)
held together by
electrostatic forces

Li^+ ion

F^- ion

1. NEUTRAL LITHIUM
ATOM (Li)

NEUTRAL FLUORINE
ATOM (F)

2. ELECTRON TRANSFER

3. IONIC BONDING:
LITHIUM FLUORIDE MOLECULE (LiF)

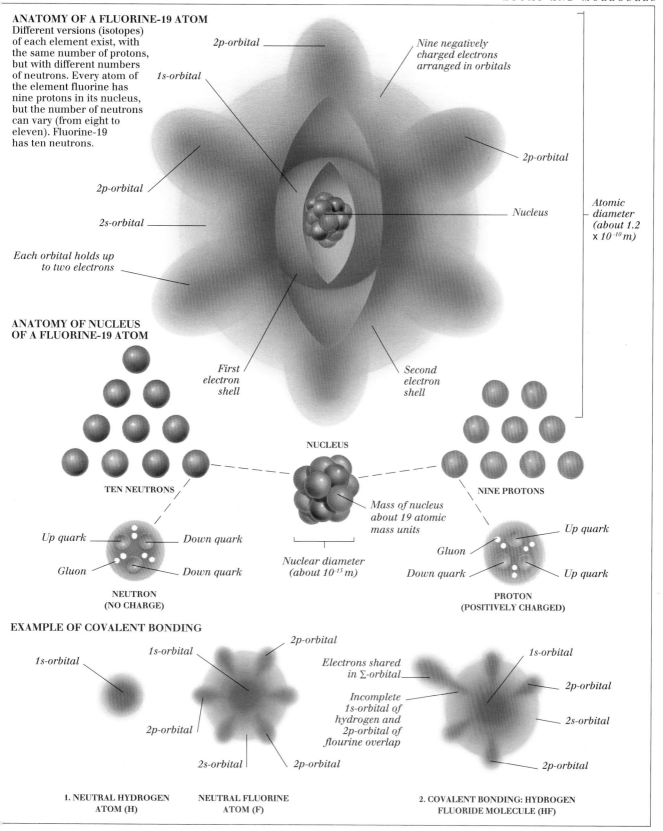

ANATOMY OF A FLUORINE-19 ATOM
Different versions (isotopes) of each element exist, with the same number of protons, but with different numbers of neutrons. Every atom of the element fluorine has nine protons in its nucleus, but the number of neutrons can vary (from eight to eleven). Fluorine-19 has ten neutrons.

2p-orbital

Nine negatively charged electrons arranged in orbitals

1s-orbital

2p-orbital

2p-orbital

2s-orbital

Nucleus

Atomic diameter (about 1.2 × 10⁻¹⁰ m)

Each orbital holds up to two electrons

ANATOMY OF NUCLEUS OF A FLUORINE-19 ATOM

First electron shell

Second electron shell

NUCLEUS

TEN NEUTRONS

NINE PROTONS

Mass of nucleus about 19 atomic mass units

Up quark

Down quark

Gluon

Down quark

Nuclear diameter (about 10⁻¹⁵ m)

Up quark

Gluon

Down quark

Up quark

NEUTRON (NO CHARGE)

PROTON (POSITIVELY CHARGED)

EXAMPLE OF COVALENT BONDING

1s-orbital

1s-orbital

2p-orbital

1s-orbital

Electrons shared in Σ-orbital

2p-orbital

Incomplete 1s-orbital of hydrogen and 2p-orbital of flourine overlap

2s-orbital

2p-orbital

2s-orbital

2p-orbital

2p-orbital

1. NEUTRAL HYDROGEN ATOM (H)

NEUTRAL FLUORINE ATOM (F)

2. COVALENT BONDING: HYDROGEN FLUORIDE MOLECULE (HF)

The periodic table

AN ELEMENT is a substance that consists of atoms of one type only. The 92 elements that occur naturally, and the 17 elements created artificially, are often arranged into a chart called the periodic table. Each element is defined by its atomic number—the number of protons in the nucleus of each of its atoms (it is also the number of electrons present). Atomic numbers increase along each row (period) and down each column (group). The shape of the table is determined by the way in which electrons arrange themselves around the nucleus: the positioning of elements in order of increasing atomic number brings together atoms with a similar pattern of orbiting electrons (orbitals). These appear in blocks. Electrons occupy shells of a certain energy (see pp. 308-309). Periods are ordered according to the filling of successive shells with electrons, while groups reflect the number of electrons in the outer shell (valency electrons). These outer electrons are important—they decide the chemical properties of the atom. Elements that appear in the same group have similar properties because they have the same number of electrons in their outer shell. Elements in Group 0 have filled shells, where the outer shell holds its maximum number of electrons, and are stable. Atoms of Group I elements have just one electron in their outer shell. This makes them unstable—and ready to react with other substances.

METALS AND NON-METALS
Elements at the left-hand side of each period are metals. Metals easily lose electrons and form positive ions. Non-metals, on the right of a period, tend to become negative ions. Semi-metals, which have properties of both metals and non-metals, are between the two.

Atomic number
Chemical symbol
Chemical name
Relative atomic mass

	1
	H
	Hydrogen
	1.0

RELATIVE ATOMIC MASS
Atomic mass (formerly atomic weight) is the mass of each atom of an element. It is equal to the number of protons plus the number of neutrons (electrons have negligible mass). The figures given are the averages for all the different versions (isotopes) of each element, measured relative to the mass of carbon-12.

Group I

Atomic number is number of protons in each nucleus

1
H
Hydrogen
1.0

Group II

Atomic number goes up by one along each period

3	4
Li	**Be**
Lithium	Beryllium
6.9	9.0

11	12
Na	**Mg**
Sodium	Magnesium
23.0	24.3

1st transition metals

19	20	21	22	23	24	25
K	**Ca**	**Sc**	**Ti**	**V**	**Cr**	**Mn**
Potassium	Calcium	Scandium	Titanium	Vanadium	Chromium	Manganese
39.1	40.1	45.0	47.9	50.9	52.0	54.9

37	38	39	40	41	42	43
Rb	**Sr**	**Y**	**Zr**	**Nb**	**Mo**	**Tc**
Rubidium	Strontium	Yttrium	Zirconium	Niobium	Molybdenum	Technetium
85.5	87.6	88.9	91.2	92.9	95.9	99.0

55	56	57-71	72	73	74	75
Cs	**Ba**		**Hf**	**Ta**	**W**	**Re**
Caesium	Barium		Hafnium	Tantalum	Tungsten	Rhenium
132.9	137.4		178.5	181.0	183.9	186.2

87	88	89-103	104	105	106	107
Fr	**Ra**		**Unq**	**Unp**	**Unh**	**Uns**
Francium	Radium		Unnilquadium	Unnilpentium	Unnilhexium	Unnilseptium
223.0	226.0		(261)	(262)	(263)	(262)

s-block

Two series always separated out from the table to give it a coherent shape

d-block

Soft, silvery, and highly reactive metal

Silvery, reactive metal

Hard, silvery metal

SODIUM: GROUP 1 METAL

MAGNESIUM: GROUP 2 METAL

CHROMIUM: 1ST TRANSITION METAL

TYPES OF ELEMENT KEY:

- Alkali metals
- Alkaline earth metals
- Transition metals
- Lanthanides (rare earths)
- Actinides
- Poor metals
- Semi-metals
- Non-metals
- Noble gases

Radioactive metal

PLUTONIUM: ACTINIDE SERIES METAL

57	58	59	60
La	**Ce**	**Pr**	**Nd**
Lanthanum	Cerium	Praseodymium	Neodymium
138.9	140.1	140.9	144.2

89	90	91	92
Ac	**Th**	**Pa**	**U**
Actinium	Thorium	Protactinium	Uranium
227.0	252.0	231.0	238.0

Bright yellow crystal

Purple-black solid turns to gas easily

ALLOTROPES OF CARBON
Some elements exist in more than one form—these are known as allotropes. Carbon powder, graphite, and diamond are allotropes of carbon. They all consist of carbon atoms, but have very different physical properties.

DIAMOND

GRAPHITE

CARBON POWDER

SULFUR:
GROUP 6 SOLID NON-METAL

IODINE:
GROUP 7
SOLID NON-METAL

	Boron and carbon groups		*Nitrogen and oxygen groups*		*Halogens*	*Group 0*	
	Group III	*Group IV*	*Group V*	*Group VI*	*Group VII*	2 **He** Helium 4.0	*Period*
	5 **B** Boron 10.8	6 **C** Carbon 12.0	7 **N** Nitrogen 14.0	8 **O** Oxygen 16.0	9 **F** Fluorine 19.0	10 **Ne** Neon 20.2	*Short period*
	13 **Al** Aluminum 27.0	14 **Si** Silicon 28.1	15 **P** Phosphorus 31.0	16 **S** Sulfur 32.1	17 **Cl** Chlorine 35.5	18 **Ar** Argon 40.0	

2nd transition metals			*3rd transition metals*							
26 **Fe** Iron 55.9	27 **Co** Cobalt 58.9	28 **Ni** Nickel 58.7	29 **Cu** Copper 63.5	30 **Zn** Zinc 65.4	31 **Ga** Gallium 69.7	32 **Ge** Germanium 72.6	33 **As** Arsenic 74.9	34 **Se** Selenium 79.0	35 **Br** Bromine 79.9	36 **Kr** Krypton 83.8
44 **Ru** Ruthenium 101.0	45 **Rh** Rhodium 102.9	46 **Pd** Palladium 106.4	47 **Ag** Silver 107.9	48 **Cd** Cadmium 112.4	49 **In** Indium 114.8	50 **Sn** Tin 118.7	51 **Sb** Antimony 121.8	52 **Te** Tellurium 127.6	53 **I** Iodine 126.9	54 **Xe** Xenon 131.3
76 **Os** Osmium 190.2	77 **Ir** Iridium 192.2	78 **Pt** Platinum 195.1	79 **Au** Gold 197.0	80 **Hg** Mercury 200.6	81 **Tl** Thallium 204.4	82 **Pb** Lead 207.2	83 **Bi** Bismuth 209.0	84 **Po** Polonium 210.0	85 **At** Astatine 210.0	86 **Rn** Radon 222.0
108 **Uno** Unniloctium (265)	109 **Une** Unnilennium (266)									

Long period

d-block

p-block

Atomic mass is estimated, as element exists fleetingly

Unreactive, colorless gas glows red in discharge tube

Shiny semi-metal

NOBLE GASES
Group 0 contains elements that have a filled (complete) outer shell of electrons, which means the atoms do not need to lose or gain electrons by bonding with other atoms. This makes them stable and they do not easily form ions or react with other elements. Noble gases are also called rare or inert gases.

Yellow, unreactive precious metal

GOLD:
3RD TRANSITION METAL

Soft, shiny, reactive metal

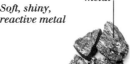

TIN:
GROUP 4 POOR METAL

ANTIMONY:
GROUP 5 SEMI-METAL

NEON:
GROUP 0
COLORLESS GAS

61 **Pm** Promethium 147.0	62 **Sm** Samarium 150.4	63 **Eu** Europium 152.0	64 **Gd** Gadolinium 157.3	65 **Tb** Terbium 158.9	66 **Dy** Dysprosium 162.5	67 **Ho** Holmium 164.9	68 **Er** Erbium 167.3	69 **Tm** Thulium 168.9	70 **Yb** Ytterbium 173.0	71 **Lu** Lutetium 175.0
93 **Np** Neptunium 237.0	94 **Pu** Plutonium 242.0	95 **Am** Americium 243.0	96 **Cm** Curium 247.0	97 **Bk** Berkelium 247.0	98 **Cf** Californium 251.0	99 **Es** Einsteinium 254.0	100 **Fm** Fermium 253.0	101 **Md** Mendelevium 256.0	102 **No** Nobelium 254.0	103 **Lr** Lawrencium 257.0

f-block

Chemical reactions

A CHEMICAL REACTION TAKES PLACE whenever bonds between atoms are broken or made. In each case, atoms or groups of atoms rearrange, making new substances (products) from the original ones (reactants). Reactions happen naturally, or can be made to happen; they may take years, or only an instant. Some of the main types are shown here. A reaction usually involves a change in energy (see pp. 314-315). In a burning reaction, for example, the making of new bonds between atoms releases energy as heat and light. This type of reaction, in which heat is given off, is an exothermic reaction. Many reactions, like burning, are irreversible, but some can take place in either direction, and are said to be reversible. Reactions can be used to form solids from solutions: in a double decomposition reaction, two compounds in solution break down and re-form into two new substances, often creating a precipitate (insoluble solid); in displacement, an element (eg. copper) displaces another element (eg. silver) from a solution. The rate (speed) of a reaction is determined by many different factors, such as temperature, and the size and shape of the reactants. To describe and keep track of reactions, internationally recognized chemical symbols and equations are used. Reactions are also used in the laboratory to identify matter. An experiment with candle wax, for example, demonstrates that it contains carbon and hydrogen.

SALT FORMATION (ACID ON METAL)

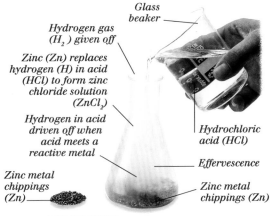

Glass beaker

Hydrogen gas (H_2) given off

Zinc (Zn) replaces hydrogen (H) in acid (HCl) to form zinc chloride solution ($ZnCl_2$)

Hydrogen in acid driven off when acid meets a reactive metal

Zinc metal chippings (Zn)

Hydrochloric acid (HCl)

Effervescence

Zinc metal chippings (Zn)

THE REACTION
Hydrochloric acid added to zinc produces zinc chloride and hydrogen.
$Zn + 2HCl \rightarrow ZnCl_2 + H_2$

DISPLACEMENT

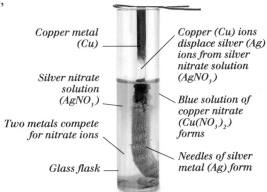

Copper metal (Cu)

Silver nitrate solution ($AgNO_3$)

Two metals compete for nitrate ions

Glass flask

Copper (Cu) ions displace silver (Ag) ions from silver nitrate solution ($AgNO_3$)

Blue solution of copper nitrate ($Cu(NO_3)_2$) forms

Needles of silver metal (Ag) form

THE REACTION
Copper metal added to silver nitrate solution produces copper nitrate and silver metal.
$Cu + 2AgNO_3 \rightarrow Cu(NO_3)_2 + 2Ag$

BURNING MATTER

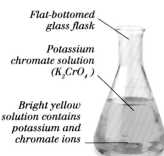

Ammonium dichromate ((NH_4)$_2Cr_2O_7$)

Flame

In this burning reaction, atoms form simpler substances and give off heat and light

Ammonium dichromate ((NH_4)$_2Cr_2O_7$) converts to chromium oxide (Cr_2O_3)

Nitrogen monoxide (NO) and water vapor (H_2O) given off as colorless gases

THE REACTION
When lit, ammonium dichromate combines with oxygen from air.
$(NH_4)_2Cr_2O_7 + O_2 \rightarrow Cr_2O_3 + 4H_2O + 2NO$

A REVERSIBLE REACTION

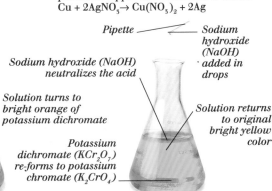

Flat-bottomed glass flask

Potassium chromate solution (K_2CrO_4)

Bright yellow solution contains potassium and chromate ions

Pipette

Hydrochloric acid (HCl) added in drops

Acid causes reaction to take place

Chromate ions converted to orange dichromate ions

Potassium dichromate (KCr_2O_7) forms

Sodium hydroxide (NaOH) neutralizes the acid

Solution turns to bright orange of potassium dichromate

Potassium dichromate (KCr_2O_7) re-forms to potassium chromate (K_2CrO_4)

Pipette

Sodium hydroxide (NaOH) added in drops

Solution returns to original bright yellow color

1. THE REACTANT
Potassium chromate dissolves in water to form potassium ions and chromate ions.
$K_2CrO_4 \rightarrow 2K^+ + CrO_4^{2-}$

2. THE REACTION
Addition of hydrochloric acid changes chromate ions into dichromate ions.
$2CrO_4^{2-} \rightarrow Cr_2O_7^{2-}$

3. REVERSING
Addition of sodium hydroxide changes dichromate ions back into chromate ions.
$Cr_2O_7^{2-} \rightarrow 2CrO_4^{2-}$

FERMENTATION

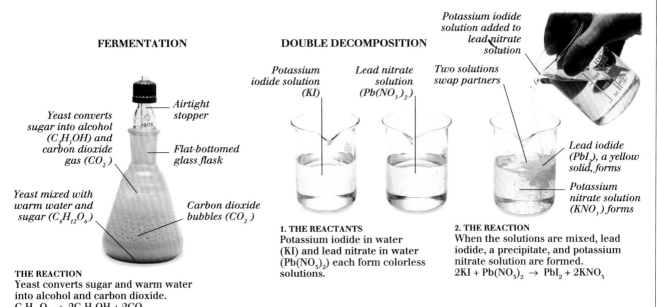

Yeast converts sugar into alcohol (C_2H_5OH) and carbon dioxide gas (CO_2)

Airtight stopper

Flat-bottomed glass flask

Yeast mixed with warm water and sugar ($C_6H_{12}O_6$)

Carbon dioxide bubbles (CO_2)

THE REACTION
Yeast converts sugar and warm water into alcohol and carbon dioxide.
$$C_6H_{12}O_6 \rightarrow 2C_2H_5OH + 2CO_2$$

DOUBLE DECOMPOSITION

Potassium iodide solution (KI)

Lead nitrate solution ($Pb(NO_3)_2$)

Two solutions swap partners

Potassium iodide solution added to lead nitrate solution

Lead iodide (PbI_2), a yellow solid, forms

Potassium nitrate solution (KNO_3) forms

1. THE REACTANTS
Potassium iodide in water (KI) and lead nitrate in water ($Pb(NO_3)_2$) each form colorless solutions.

2. THE REACTION
When the solutions are mixed, lead iodide, a precipitate, and potassium nitrate solution are formed.
$$2KI + Pb(NO_3)_2 \rightarrow PbI_2 + 2KNO_3$$

TESTING CANDLE WAX, AN ORGANIC COMPOUND

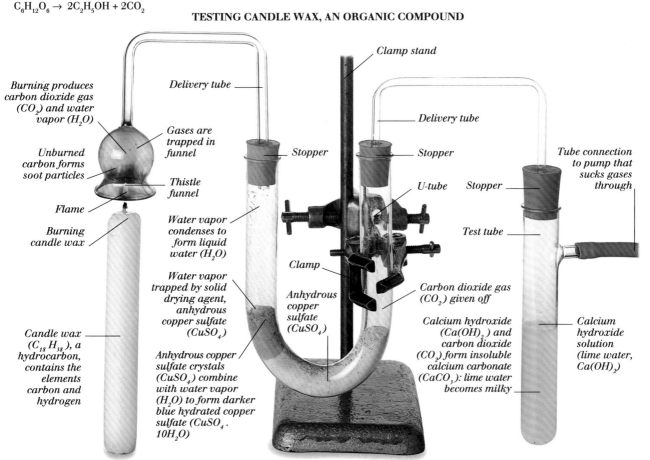

Burning produces carbon dioxide gas (CO_2) and water vapor (H_2O)

Unburned carbon forms soot particles

Flame

Burning candle wax

Candle wax ($C_{18}H_{38}$), a hydrocarbon, contains the elements carbon and hydrogen

Gases are trapped in funnel

Thistle funnel

Water vapor condenses to form liquid water (H_2O)

Water vapor trapped by solid drying agent, anhydrous copper sulfate ($CuSO_4$)

Anhydrous copper sulfate crystals ($CuSO_4$) combine with water vapor (H_2O) to form darker blue hydrated copper sulfate ($CuSO_4 . 10H_2O$)

Delivery tube

Stopper

Clamp stand

Delivery tube

Stopper

U-tube

Clamp

Anhydrous copper sulfate ($CuSO_4$)

Carbon dioxide gas (CO_2) given off

Calcium hydroxide ($Ca(OH)_2$) and carbon dioxide (CO_2) form insoluble calcium carbonate ($CaCO_3$): lime water becomes milky

Stopper

Test tube

Tube connection to pump that sucks gases through

Calcium hydroxide solution (lime water, $Ca(OH)_2$)

1. THE BURNING REACTION
Burning wax produces carbon dioxide gas and water vapor.
$$2C_{18}H_{38} + 55O_2 \rightarrow 36CO_2 + 38H_2O$$

2. TESTING FOR WATER VAPOUR
A solid drying agent traps water vapor, proving the presence of hydrogen in the candle wax.
$$CuSO_4 + 10H_2O \rightarrow CuSO_4 . 10H_2O$$

3. TESTING FOR CARBON DIOXIDE
Calcium hydroxide in solution reacts with carbon dioxide, forming a carbonate and turning milky.
$$Ca(OH)_2 + CO_2 \rightarrow CaCO_3 + H_2O$$

Energy

ANYTHING THAT HAPPENS—from a pin drop to an explosion
—requires energy. Energy is the capacity for doing work
(making something happen). Various forms of energy exist,
including light, heat, sound, electrical, chemical, nuclear,
kinetic, and potential energies. The Law of Conservation
of Energy states that the total amount of energy in the
Universe is fixed—energy cannot be created or destroyed,
it can only change from one form to another (energy
transfer). For example, potential energy is energy that
is stored, and can be used in the future. An object gains
potential energy when it is lifted; as the object is released,
potential energy changes into the energy of motion (kinetic
energy). During transference, some of the energy converts
into heat. A combined heat and power station can put some
of the "waste" heat to useful effect in local schools and
housing. Most of the Earth's energy is provided by the Sun,
in the form of electromagnetic radiation (see pp. 316-317).
Some of this energy transfers to plant and animal life, and
ultimately to fossil fuels, where it is stored in chemical
form. Our bodies obtain energy from the food we eat,
while energy needed for other tasks, such as heating and
transportation, can be obtained by burning fossil fuels
—or by harnessing natural forces like wind or moving
water—to generate electricity. Another source is nuclear
power, where energy is released by reactions in the nucleus
of an atom. All energy is measured by the international
unit, the joule (J). As a guide, one joule is about equal to
the amount of energy needed to lift an apple one yard.

SANKEY DIAGRAM SHOWING ENERGY FLOW IN A COAL-FIRED COMBINED HEAT AND POWER STATION

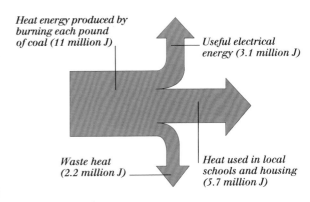

Heat energy produced by
burning each pound
of coal (11 million J)

Useful electrical
energy (3.1 million J)

Waste heat
(2.2 million J)

Heat used in local
schools and housing
(5.7 million J)

CROSS-SECTION OF HYDROELECTRIC POWER STATION WITH FRANCIS TURBINE

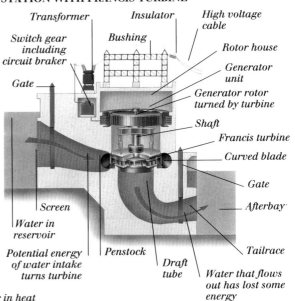

Transformer

Switch gear
including
circuit braker

Gate

Screen

Water in
reservoir

Potential energy
of water intake
turns turbine

Insulator

Bushing

Penstock

Draft
tube

High voltage
cable

Rotor house

Generator
unit

Generator rotor
turned by turbine

Shaft

Francis turbine

Curved blade

Gate

Afterbay

Tailrace

Water that flows
out has lost some
energy

CROSS-SECTION OF NUCLEAR POWER STATION WITH PRESSURIZED WATER REACTOR

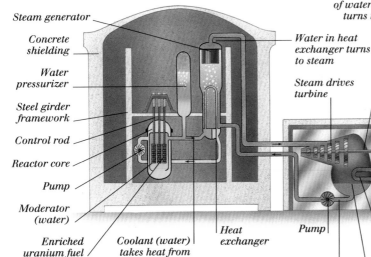

Steam generator

Concrete
shielding

Water
pressurizer

Steel girder
framework

Control rod

Reactor core

Pump

Moderator
(water)

Enriched
uranium fuel

Coolant (water)
takes heat from
reactor core to
heat exchanger

Heat
exchanger

Water pumped back into
steam generator

Water in heat
exchanger turns
to steam

Steam drives
turbine

Pump

Water cools used steam

Steam loses energy to turbine
and condenses back to water

Turbine shaft
turns generator

Generator produces
electric current at
25,000 volts

Transformer
increases voltage
to 300,000 volts

High voltage
cable

Pylon carries
high voltage
electricity

Hot water to
cooling tower

Cold water
from cooling
tower

ENERGY SYSTEMS

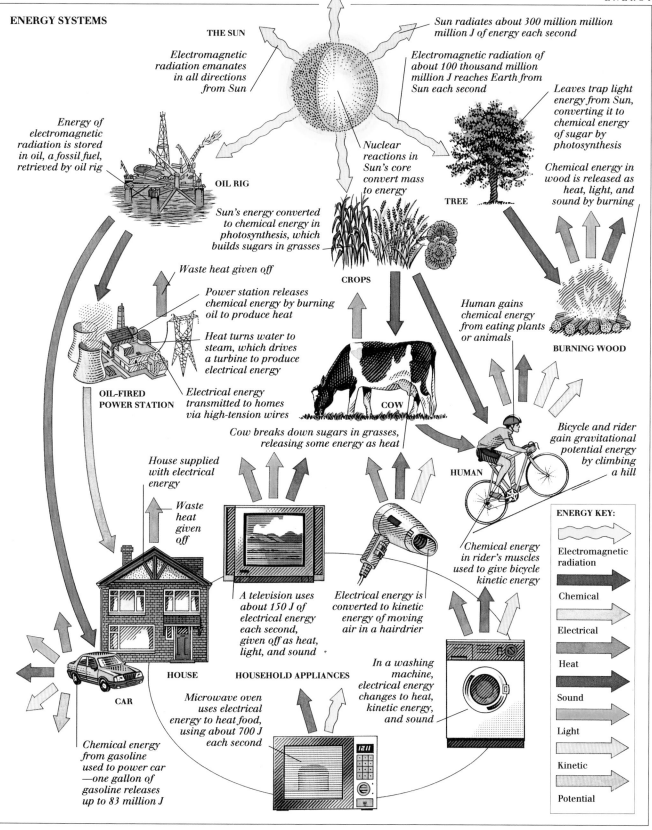

THE SUN

Electromagnetic radiation emanates in all directions from Sun

Sun radiates about 300 million million million J of energy each second

Electromagnetic radiation of about 100 thousand million million J reaches Earth from Sun each second

Energy of electromagnetic radiation is stored in oil, a fossil fuel, retrieved by oil rig

Nuclear reactions in Sun's core convert mass to energy

OIL RIG

Leaves trap light energy from Sun, converting it to chemical energy of sugar by photosynthesis

Chemical energy in wood is released as heat, light, and sound by burning

TREE

Sun's energy converted to chemical energy in photosynthesis, which builds sugars in grasses

Waste heat given off

Power station releases chemical energy by burning oil to produce heat

Heat turns water to steam, which drives a turbine to produce electrical energy

OIL-FIRED POWER STATION

Electrical energy transmitted to homes via high-tension wires

CROPS

Human gains chemical energy from eating plants or animals

BURNING WOOD

Cow breaks down sugars in grasses, releasing some energy as heat

COW

House supplied with electrical energy

Waste heat given off

Bicycle and rider gain gravitational potential energy by climbing a hill

HUMAN

Chemical energy in rider's muscles used to give bicycle kinetic energy

A television uses about 150 J of electrical energy each second, given off as heat, light, and sound

Electrical energy is converted to kinetic energy of moving air in a hairdrier

HOUSE

HOUSEHOLD APPLIANCES

In a washing machine, electrical energy changes to heat, kinetic energy, and sound

CAR

Chemical energy from gasoline used to power car —one gallon of gasoline releases up to 83 million J

Microwave oven uses electrical energy to heat food, using about 700 J each second

ENERGY KEY:

Electromagnetic radiation

Chemical

Electrical

Heat

Sound

Light

Kinetic

Potential

Electricity and magnetism

ELECTRICAL EFFECTS result from an imbalance of electric charge. There are two types of electric charge: positive (carried by protons) and negative (carried by electrons). If charges are opposite (unlike), they attract one another, while like charges repel. These forces of attraction and repulsion (electrostatic forces) exist between any two charged particles. Matter is normally uncharged, but if

LIGHTNING

electrons are gained, an object will gain an overall negative charge; if they are removed, it becomes positive. Objects with an overall negative or positive charge are said to have an imbalance of charge, and exert the same forces as individual negative and positive charges. On this larger scale, the forces will always act to regain the balance of charge. This causes static electricity. Lightning, for example, is produced by clouds discharging a huge excess of negative electrons. If charges are free—in a wire or material that allows electrons to pass through it—the forces cause a flow of charge called an electric current. Some substances exhibit the strange phenomenon of magnetism—which also produces attractive and repulsive forces. Magnetic substances consist of small regions called domains. Normally unmagnetized, they can be magnetized by being placed in a magnetic field. Magnetism and electricity are inextricably linked, a fact put to use in motors and generators.

VAN DE GRAAFF (ELECTROSTATIC) GENERATOR

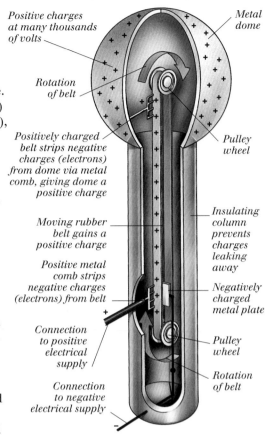

Positive charges at many thousands of volts

Metal dome

Rotation of belt

Positively charged belt strips negative charges (electrons) from dome via metal comb, giving dome a positive charge

Pulley wheel

Moving rubber belt gains a positive charge

Insulating column prevents charges leaking away

Positive metal comb strips negative charges (electrons) from belt

Negatively charged metal plate

Connection to positive electrical supply

Pulley wheel

Rotation of belt

Connection to negative electrical supply

CURRENT ELECTRICITY

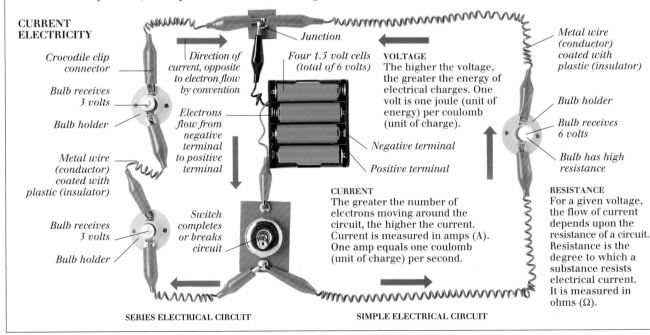

Crocodile clip connector

Bulb receives 3 volts

Bulb holder

Metal wire (conductor) coated with plastic (insulator)

Bulb receives 3 volts

Bulb holder

Direction of current, opposite to electron flow by convention

Junction

Electrons flow from negative terminal to positive terminal

Switch completes or breaks circuit

Four 1.5 volt cells (total of 6 volts)

Negative terminal

Positive terminal

VOLTAGE
The higher the voltage, the greater the energy of electrical charges. One volt is one joule (unit of energy) per coulomb (unit of charge).

CURRENT
The greater the number of electrons moving around the circuit, the higher the current. Current is measured in amps (A). One amp equals one coulomb (unit of charge) per second.

Metal wire (conductor) coated with plastic (insulator)

Bulb holder

Bulb receives 6 volts

Bulb has high resistance

RESISTANCE
For a given voltage, the flow of current depends upon the resistance of a circuit. Resistance is the degree to which a substance resists electrical current. It is measured in ohms (Ω).

SERIES ELECTRICAL CIRCUIT   **SIMPLE ELECTRICAL CIRCUIT**

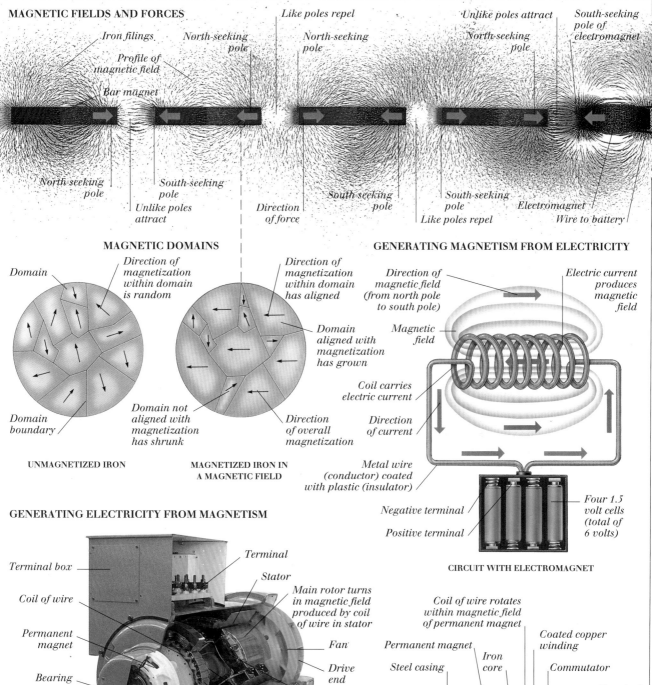

MAGNETIC FIELDS AND FORCES

Iron filings

Profile of magnetic field

Bar magnet

North-seeking pole

North-seeking pole

Like poles repel

North-seeking pole

Unlike poles attract

North-seeking pole

South-seeking pole of electromagnet

North-seeking pole

South-seeking pole

Unlike poles attract

Direction of force

South-seeking pole

South-seeking pole

Like poles repel

Electromagnet

Wire to battery

MAGNETIC DOMAINS

Domain

Direction of magnetization within domain is random

Direction of magnetization within domain has aligned

Domain aligned with magnetization has grown

Domain boundary

Domain not aligned with magnetization has shrunk

Direction of overall magnetization

UNMAGNETIZED IRON

MAGNETIZED IRON IN A MAGNETIC FIELD

GENERATING MAGNETISM FROM ELECTRICITY

Direction of magnetic field (from north pole to south pole)

Electric current produces magnetic field

Magnetic field

Coil carries electric current

Direction of current

Metal wire (conductor) coated with plastic (insulator)

Negative terminal

Positive terminal

Four 1.5 volt cells (total of 6 volts)

CIRCUIT WITH ELECTROMAGNET

GENERATING ELECTRICITY FROM MAGNETISM

Terminal box

Coil of wire

Permanent magnet

Bearing

Non-drive end

Coil of wire

Terminal

Stator

Main rotor turns in magnetic field produced by coil of wire in stator

Fan

Drive end

Coil of wire

Shaft

Secondary (exciter) rotor

ELECTRIC GENERATOR
In a generator, the rotor rotates within the magnetic field of the stator to produce an electric current.

Coil of wire rotates within magnetic field of permanent magnet

Permanent magnet

Steel casing

Iron core

Coated copper winding

Commutator

Terminal

Spindle

End of shaft

Terminal

ELECTRIC MOTOR
In a motor, magnetic forces between the winding and permanent magnet produce a rotary motion.

Light

INFRARED IMAGE
OF A HOUSE

LIGHT IS A FORM OF ENERGY. It is a
type of electromagnetic radiation, like X
rays or radio waves. All electromagnetic
radiation is produced by electric charges
(see pp. 316-317): it is caused by the effects
of oscillating electric and magnetic fields as they travel
through space. Electromagnetic radiation is considered to
have both wave and particle properties. It can be thought
of as a wave of electricity and magnetism. In that case,
the difference between the various forms of
radiation is their wavelength. Radiation can
also be said to consist of particles, or packets
of energy, called photons. The difference
between light and X rays, for instance, is
the amount of energy that each photon
carries. The complete range of radiation is
referred to as the electromagnetic spectrum,
extending from low energy, long wavelength
radio waves to high energy, short wavelength
gamma rays. Light is the only part of the
electromagnetic spectrum that is visible.
White light from the Sun is made up of all
the visible wavelengths of radiation, which
can be seen when it is separated by using a
prism. Light, like all forms of electromagnetic
radiation, can be reflected (bounced back)
and refracted (bent). Different parts of the
electromagnetic spectrum are produced in
different ways. Sometimes visible light—
and infrared radiation—is generated by the
vibrating particles of warm or hot objects.
The emission of light in this way is called
incandescence. Light can also be produced
by fluorescence, a phenomenon in which
electrons gain and lose energy within atoms.

MAXWELLIAN DIAGRAM OF ELECTROMAGNETIC RADIATION AS WAVES

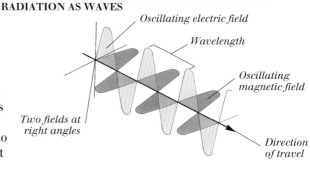

Oscillating electric field

Wavelength

Oscillating
magnetic field

Two fields at
right angles

Direction
of travel

ELECTROMAGNETIC RADIATION AS PARTICLES

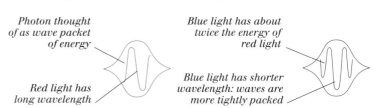

Photon thought
of as wave packet
of energy

Blue light has about
twice the energy of
red light

Red light has
long wavelength

Blue light has shorter
wavelength: waves are
more tightly packed

PHOTON OF RED LIGHT

PHOTON OF BLUE LIGHT

SPLITTING WHITE LIGHT INTO THE SPECTRUM

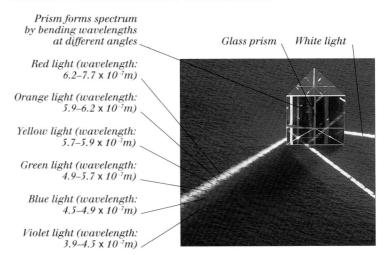

Prism forms spectrum
by bending wavelengths
at different angles

Glass prism

White light

Red light (wavelength:
6.2–7.7×10^{-7}m)

Orange light (wavelength:
5.9–6.2×10^{-7}m)

Yellow light (wavelength:
5.7–5.9×10^{-7}m)

Green light (wavelength:
4.9–5.7×10^{-7}m)

Blue light (wavelength:
4.5–4.9×10^{-7}m)

Violet light (wavelength:
3.9–4.5×10^{-7}m)

THE ELECTROMAGNETIC SPECTRUM

ENERGY (JOULES)	10^{-28}	10^{-27}	10^{-26}	10^{-25}	10^{-24}	10^{-23}	10^{-22}	10^{-21}	10^{-20}

WAVELENGTH (METERS)	10^{4}	10^{3}	10^{2}	10	1	10^{-1}	10^{-2}	10^{-3}	10^{-4}	10^{-5}

Long-wave
radio

Medium-
wave radio

Shortwave
radio

Very high-
frequency
(VHF) radio

Microwaves

Infrared
radiation

Radio waves

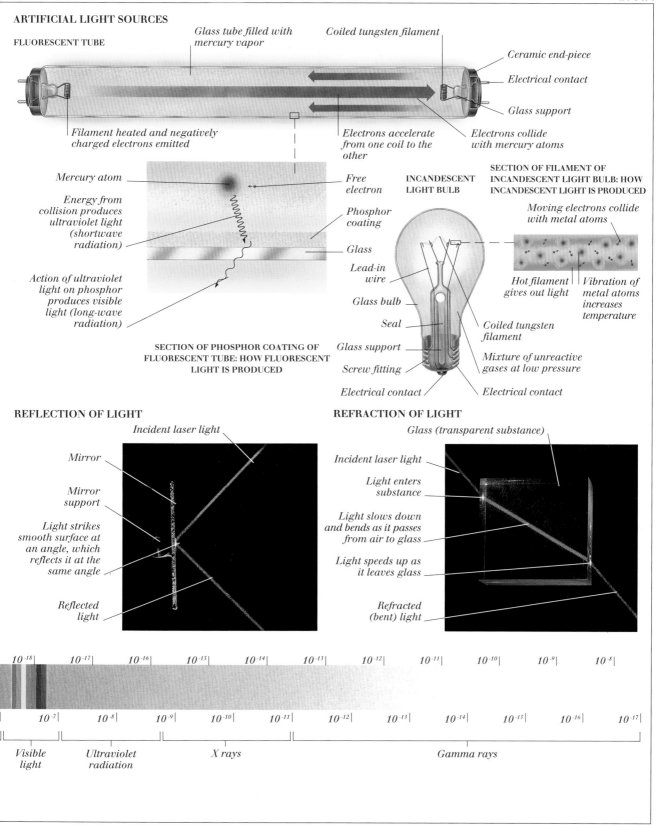

ARTIFICIAL LIGHT SOURCES

FLUORESCENT TUBE

Glass tube filled with mercury vapor

Coiled tungsten filament

Ceramic end-piece

Electrical contact

Glass support

Filament heated and negatively charged electrons emitted

Electrons accelerate from one coil to the other

Electrons collide with mercury atoms

Mercury atom

Free electron

Energy from collision produces ultraviolet light (shortwave radiation)

Action of ultraviolet light on phosphor produces visible light (long-wave radiation)

SECTION OF PHOSPHOR COATING OF FLUORESCENT TUBE: HOW FLUORESCENT LIGHT IS PRODUCED

INCANDESCENT LIGHT BULB

SECTION OF FILAMENT OF INCANDESCENT LIGHT BULB: HOW INCANDESCENT LIGHT IS PRODUCED

Moving electrons collide with metal atoms

Phosphor coating

Glass

Lead-in wire

Glass bulb

Seal

Glass support

Screw fitting

Electrical contact

Coiled tungsten filament

Mixture of unreactive gases at low pressure

Electrical contact

Hot filament gives out light

Vibration of metal atoms increases temperature

REFLECTION OF LIGHT

Incident laser light

Mirror

Mirror support

Light strikes smooth surface at an angle, which reflects it at the same angle

Reflected light

REFRACTION OF LIGHT

Glass (transparent substance)

Incident laser light

Light enters substance

Light slows down and bends as it passes from air to glass

Light speeds up as it leaves glass

Refracted (bent) light

10^{-18} | 10^{-17} | 10^{-16} | 10^{-15} | 10^{-14} | 10^{-13} | 10^{-12} | 10^{-11} | 10^{-10} | 10^{-9} | 10^{-8} |

10^{-7} | 10^{-8} | 10^{-9} | 10^{-10} | 10^{-11} | 10^{-12} | 10^{-13} | 10^{-14} | 10^{-15} | 10^{-16} | 10^{-17} |

Visible light

Ultraviolet radiation

X rays

Gamma rays

Force and motion

FORCES ARE PUSHES OR PULLS that change the motion of objects. To make a stationary object move, or a moving object stop, a force is needed. A force is also required to change the speed or direction of an object. This change in speed or direction is known as acceleration. Acceleration depends on the size (magnitude) of the force, and on the mass of the object. The effects of forces were first summarized by Isaac Newton in his three laws of motion. The international unit of force, named after him, is the newton (N), which is approximately equal to the weight of one apple. Gravity—the force of attraction between any two masses—can be measured using a newton meter (spring balance). Forces are put to useful effect in machines. A simple machine, such as a wheel and axle, is a device that changes the size or direction of an applied force. It allows an applied force (the effort) to produce another force (the load). A lever uses a bar that turns on a fulcrum to exert force. In all simple machines, there is a relationship between force and distance. A small force (in a compound pulley, for instance) moves through a large distance to lift a heavy object a small distance. This is called the Law of Simple Machines.

SIMPLE MACHINES

Single-pulley system (simple pulley)
Pulley wheel
Simple pulley only changes direction of a force
Effort is the same size as the load (10 N) and is pulled the same distance
One rope attached to load
Load of 10 N

Two-pulley system (simple pulley)
Pulley wheel
Effort is half the load (5 N), but the rope must be pulled twice the distance
Two ropes share the force and distance
Pulley wheel
Load of 10 N

Four-pulley system (compound pulley)
Two pulley wheels
Effort is one quarter of the load (2.5 N), but the rope must be pulled four times the distance
Four ropes share the force and distance

SIMPLE AND COMPOUND PULLEYS

Two pulley wheels
Load of 10 N

NEWTON METERS (SPRING BALANCES)

Weight is measured using a spring
When weight pulls downward, pointer moves along scale and measures force
Weight is 10 N
Weight is 20 N
Mass of 1 kg
Mass of 2 kg

Wheel and axle multiplies the effort
Force is transmitted to the wheels by the chain
Pedal
Crank
Effort, provided by cyclist's muscles, is smaller than the load, but moves through a greater distance
A larger force, the load, is produced at the axle
Load of 10 N

WHEEL AND AXLE

A screw, acting like a wedge wrapped around a shaft, multiplies the effort
Effort, a turning force supplied through a screwdriver
Pitch (the angle of the screw thread)
The smaller the angle of pitch, the less force is required, but more turns are needed to move it through a greater distance
A larger force, the load, pulls the screw into wood

SCREW

Effort pushes axe into wood
Axe blade has wedge shape
Wedge multiplies effort
A larger force, the load, moves through a smaller distance to push wood apart

WEDGE

WEIGHT AND MASS
The mass of an object is a measure of the quantity of matter that it possesses. Mass is usually measured in grams (g) or kilograms (kg). The weight of an object is the force exerted on the object's mass by gravity. Since weight is a force, its unit is the newton (N).

NEWTON'S THREE LAWS OF MOTION

NEWTON'S FIRST LAW
When no force acts on a body, it will
continue in a state of rest or uniform motion.

Mass of 1 kg

*Newton meter shows
no applied force*

*Mass of trolley
is negligible*

*Trolley is not in motion, and will
remain at rest until a force acts*

NO FORCE, NO ACCELERATION: STATE OF REST

*Constant
speed*

Mass of 1 kg

*Newton meter
shows no
applied force*

*Trolley is in motion, and will continue at a
constant speed in a straight line until a force acts*

NO FORCE, NO ACCELERATION: UNIFORM MOTION

NEWTON'S SECOND LAW
When a force acts on a body, the motion of the body will change. The size of the change
will depend upon the mass of the object and the magnitude of the applied force.

*Acceleration
is 2 ms⁻²*

*Trolley and mass (1 kg) gain
2 meters per second of speed
each second (2 ms⁻²)*

*Newton meter registers
force of 2 N*

Mass of 1 kg

*Acceleration is
1 ms⁻²*

*Trolley and mass (2 kg)
gain 1 meter per second of
speed each second (1 ms⁻²)*

*Newton meter
registers force of 2 N*

Mass of 2 kg

*With the same applied force, an object with 2 kg mass
accelerates at half the rate of object with 1 kg mass*

FORCE AND ACCELERATION: SMALL MASS, LARGE ACCELERATION

FORCE AND ACCELERATION: LARGE MASS, SMALL ACCELERATION

NEWTON'S THIRD LAW
If one object exerts a force on another, an equal and opposite force,
called the reaction force, is applied by the second object on the first.

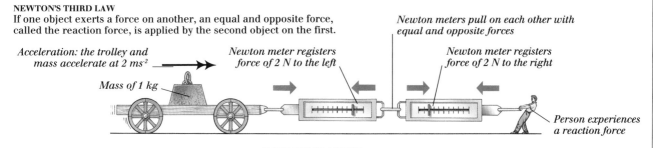

*Acceleration: the trolley and
mass accelerate at 2 ms⁻²*

*Newton meter registers
force of 2 N to the left*

*Newton meters pull on each other with
equal and opposite forces*

*Newton meter registers
force of 2 N to the right*

Mass of 1 kg

*Person experiences
a reaction force*

ACTION AND REACTION

THREE CLASSES OF LEVER

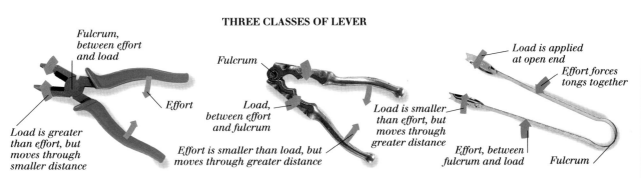

*Fulcrum,
between effort
and load*

Effort

*Load is greater
than effort, but
moves through
smaller distance*

Fulcrum

*Load,
between effort
and fulcrum*

*Effort is smaller than load, but
moves through greater distance*

*Load is applied
at open end*

*Effort forces
tongs together*

*Load is smaller
than effort, but
moves through
greater distance*

*Effort, between
fulcrum and load*

Fulcrum

CLASS 1 LEVER
Pliers consist of two class 1 levers.

CLASS 2 LEVER
Nutcrackers consist of two class 2 levers.

CLASS 3 LEVER
Tongs consist of two class 3 levers.

RAIL AND ROAD

STEAM LOCOMOTIVES 324

DIESEL TRAINS 326

ELECTRIC AND HIGH-SPEED TRAINS 328

TRAIN EQUIPMENT 330

TROLLEYS AND BUSES 332

THE FIRST CARS 334

ELEGANCE AND UTILITY 336

MASS-PRODUCTION 338

THE "PEOPLE'S CAR" 340

EARLY ENGINES 342

MODERN ENGINES 344

ALTERNATIVE ENGINES 346

MODERN BODYWORK 348

MODERN MECHANICS 350

MODERN TRIM 352

ALL-TERRAIN VEHICLES 354

RACING CARS 356

BICYCLE ANATOMY 358

BICYCLES 360

THE MOTORCYCLE 362

THE MOTORCYCLE CHASSIS 364

MOTORCYCLE ENGINES 366

COMPETITION MOTORCYCLES 368

Steam locomotives

W<small>AGONS THAT ARE PULLED</small> along tracks have been used to transport material since the 16th century, but these trains were drawn by men or horses until the invention of the steam locomotive. Steam locomotives enabled the basic railroad system to realize its true potential. In 1804, Richard Trevithick built the world's first working steam locomotive in South Wales. It was not entirely successful, but it encouraged others to develop new designs. By 1829, the British engineer Robert Stephenson had built the Rocket, considered to be the forerunner of the modern locomotive. The Rocket was a self-sufficient unit, carrying coal to heat the boiler and a water supply for generating steam. Steam passed from the boiler to force the pistons back and forth, and this movement turned the driving wheels, propelling the train forward. Used steam was then expelled in characteristic puffs. Later steam locomotives, like Ellerman Lines and the Mallard, worked in a similar way, but on a much larger scale. The simple design and reliability of steam locomotives ensured that they changed very little in 120 years of use, before being replaced in the 1950s by more efficient diesel and electric power (see pp. 326-329).

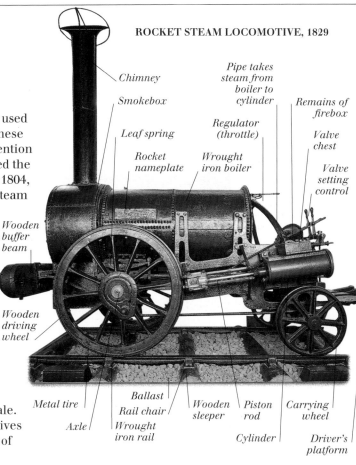

ROCKET STEAM LOCOMOTIVE, 1829

Chimney

Smokebox

Leaf spring

Rocket nameplate

Pipe takes steam from boiler to cylinder

Regulator (throttle)

Wrought iron boiler

Remains of firebox

Valve chest

Valve setting control

Wooden buffer beam

Wooden driving wheel

Metal tire

Axle

Ballast

Rail chair

Wrought iron rail

Wooden sleeper

Piston rod

Cylinder

Carrying wheel

Driver's platform

Stay

ELLERMAN LINES, 1949 (CUTAWAY VIEW)

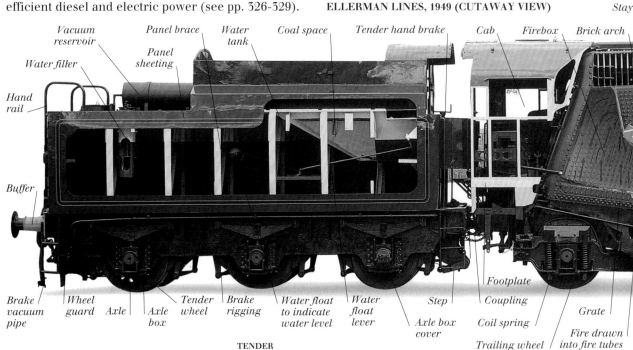

Vacuum reservoir

Panel brace

Water tank

Coal space

Tender hand brake

Cab

Firebox

Brick arch

Water filler

Panel sheeting

Hand rail

Buffer

Brake vacuum pipe

Wheel guard

Axle

Axle box

Tender wheel

Brake rigging

Water float to indicate water level

Water float lever

Step

Axle box cover

Coupling

Coil spring

Footplate

Trailing wheel

Grate

Fire drawn into fire tubes

TENDER

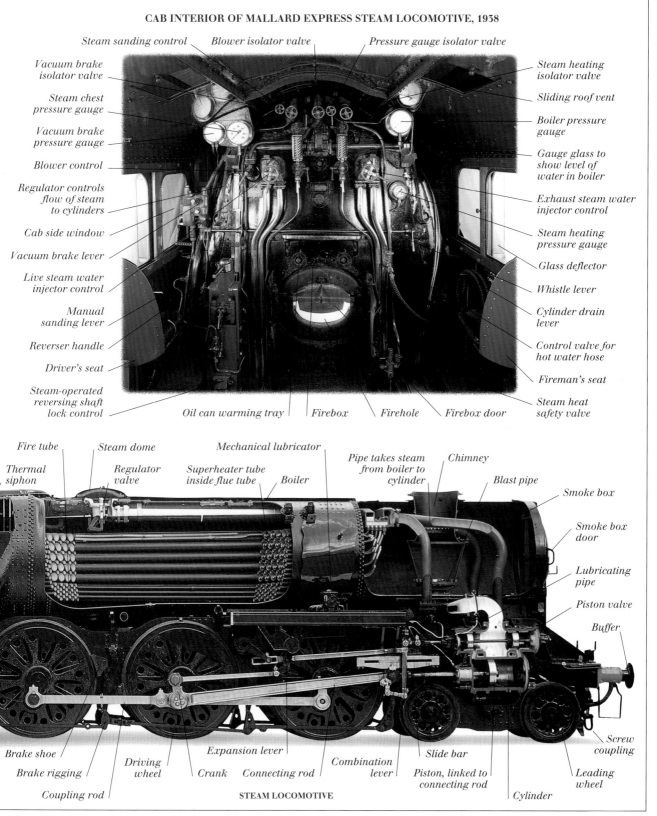

CAB INTERIOR OF MALLARD EXPRESS STEAM LOCOMOTIVE, 1938

Steam sanding control

Blower isolator valve

Pressure gauge isolator valve

Vacuum brake isolator valve

Steam heating isolator valve

Steam chest pressure gauge

Sliding roof vent

Vacuum brake pressure gauge

Boiler pressure gauge

Blower control

Gauge glass to show level of water in boiler

Regulator controls flow of steam to cylinders

Exhaust steam water injector control

Cab side window

Steam heating pressure gauge

Vacuum brake lever

Glass deflector

Live steam water injector control

Whistle lever

Manual sanding lever

Cylinder drain lever

Reverser handle

Control valve for hot water hose

Driver's seat

Fireman's seat

Steam-operated reversing shaft lock control

Steam heat safety valve

Oil can warming tray

Firebox

Firehole

Firebox door

Fire tube

Steam dome

Mechanical lubricator

Pipe takes steam from boiler to cylinder

Chimney

Thermal siphon

Regulator valve

Superheater tube inside flue tube

Boiler

Blast pipe

Smoke box

Smoke box door

Lubricating pipe

Piston valve

Buffer

Brake shoe

Expansion lever

Slide bar

Screw coupling

Brake rigging

Driving wheel

Crank

Connecting rod

Combination lever

Piston, linked to connecting rod

Leading wheel

Coupling rod

Cylinder

STEAM LOCOMOTIVE

Diesel trains

RUDOLF DIESEL FIRST DEMONSTRATED the diesel engine in
Germany in 1898, but it was not until the 1940s that diesel
locomotives were successfully established on both passenger
and freight services in the U.S. Early diesel locomotives like
the Union Pacific were more expensive to build than steam
locomotives, but were more efficient and cheaper to operate,
especially where oil was plentiful. One feature of diesel engines
is that the power output cannot be coupled directly to the wheels.
To convert the mechanical energy produced by diesel engines,
a transmission system is needed. Almost all diesel locomotives
have electric transmissions, and are known as diesel-electric
locomotives. The diesel engine works by drawing air into the
cylinders and compressing it to increase its temperature; a small
quantity of diesel fuel is then injected into it. The resulting
combustion drives the generator (more recently an alternator)
to produce electricity, which is fed to electric motors connected
to the wheels. Diesel-electric locomotives are essentially
electric locomotives that carry their own power plants, and
are used worldwide today. The Deltic diesel-electric
locomotive, similar to the one shown here, replaced
classic express steam locomotives, and ran
at speeds up to 100 mph.

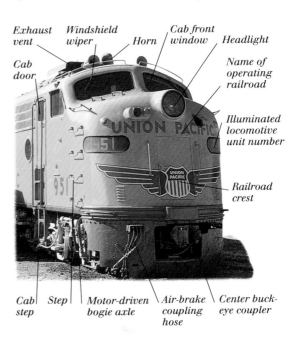

**FRONT VIEW OF UNION PACIFIC
DIESEL-ELECTRIC LOCOMOTIVE, 1950s**

Exhaust vent
Windshield wiper
Horn
Cab front window
Headlight
Cab door
Name of operating railroad
Illuminated locomotive unit number
Railroad crest
Cab step
Step
Motor-driven bogie axle
Air-brake coupling hose
Center buckeye coupler

PROTOTYPE DELTIC DIESEL-ELECTRIC LOCOMOTIVE, 1956

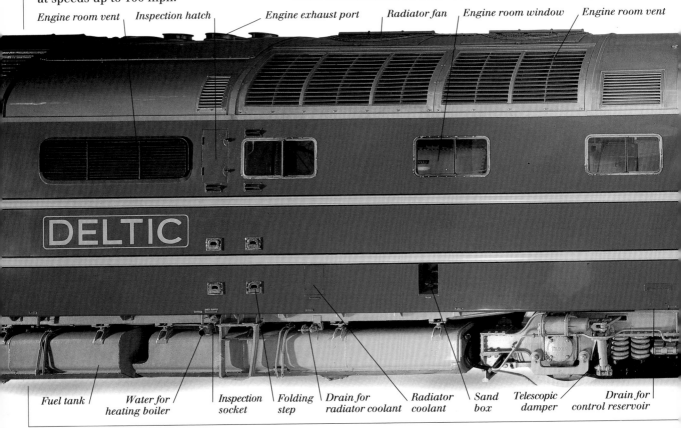

Engine room vent
Inspection hatch
Engine exhaust port
Radiator fan
Engine room window
Engine room vent

DELTIC

Fuel tank
Water for heating boiler
Inspection socket
Folding step
Drain for radiator coolant
Radiator coolant
Sand box
Telescopic damper
Drain for control reservoir

DIESEL ENGINE OF BRITISH RAIL CLASS 20 DIESEL-ELECTRIC LOCOMOTIVE

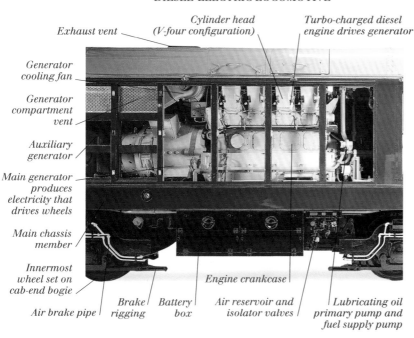

Exhaust vent

Cylinder head
(V-four configuration)

Turbo-charged diesel
engine drives generator

Generator
cooling fan

Generator
compartment
vent

Auxiliary
generator

Main generator
produces
electricity that
drives wheels

Main chassis
member

Innermost
wheel set on
cab-end bogie

Air brake pipe

Brake
rigging

Battery
box

Engine crankcase

Air reservoir and
isolator valves

Lubricating oil
primary pump and
fuel supply pump

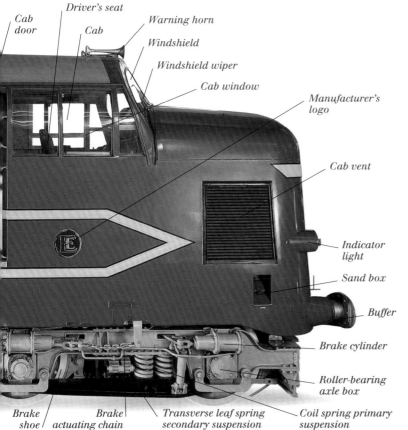

Cab
door

Driver's seat

Cab

Warning horn

Windshield

Windshield wiper

Cab window

Manufacturer's
logo

Cab vent

Indicator
light

Sand box

Buffer

Brake cylinder

Roller-bearing
axle box

Brake
shoe

Brake
actuating chain

Transverse leaf spring
secondary suspension

Coil spring primary
suspension

EXAMPLES OF FREIGHT CARS

BOX CAR

HOPPER CAR

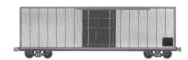

REFRIGERATOR CAR

LIVESTOCK CAR

FLAT CAR WITH BULKHEADS

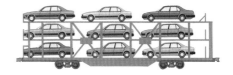

AUTOMOBILE CAR

Electric and high-speed trains

THE FIRST ELECTRIC LOCOMOTIVE ran in 1879 in Berlin, Germany. In Europe, electric trains developed as a more efficient alternative to the steam locomotive and diesel-electric power. Like diesels, electric trains employ electric motors to drive the wheels but, unlike diesels, the electricity is generated externally at a power station. Electric current is picked up either from a catenary (overhead cable) via a pantograph, or from a third rail. Since it does not carry its own power-generating equipment, an electric locomotive has a better power-to-weight ratio and greater acceleration than its diesel-electric equivalent. This makes electric trains highly suitable for urban routes with many stops. They are also faster, quieter, and cause less pollution. The latest electric French TGV (Train à Grande Vitesse) reaches 186 mph; other trains, like the London to Paris and Brussels Eurostar, can run at several voltages and operate between different countries. Simpler electric trains perform special duties—the "People Mover" at Gatwick Airport, London, runs between terminals.

HOW ALTERNATING CURRENT (AC) ELECTRIC TRAINS WORK

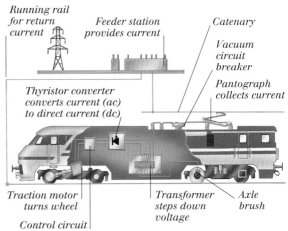

Running rail for return current

Feeder station provides current

Catenary

Vacuum circuit breaker

Pantograph collects current

Thyristor converter converts current (ac) to direct current (dc)

Traction motor turns wheel

Control circuit

Transformer steps down voltage

Axle brush

FRONT VIEW OF PARIS METRO

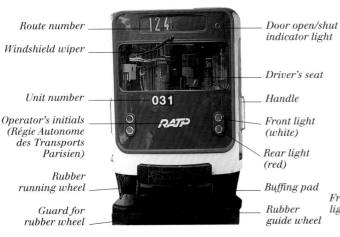

Route number

Windshield wiper

Unit number

Operator's initials (Régie Autonome des Transports Parisien)

Rubber running wheel

Guard for rubber wheel

Door open/shut indicator light

Driver's seat

Handle

Front light (white)

Rear light (red)

Buffing pad

Rubber guide wheel

FRONT VIEW OF ITALIAN STATE RAILWAYS CLASS 402 ELECTRIC LOCOMOTIVE

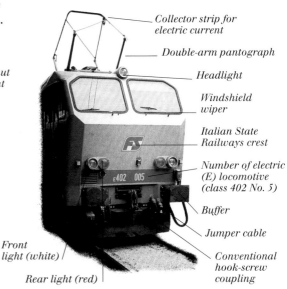

Collector strip for electric current

Double-arm pantograph

Headlight

Windshield wiper

Italian State Railways crest

Number of electric (E) locomotive (class 402 No. 5)

Buffer

Jumper cable

Conventional hook-screw coupling

Front light (white)

Rear light (red)

SIDE VIEW OF GATWICK EXPRESS "PEOPLE MOVER"

Pneumatic rubber wheel

Concrete track

Automatic door

No driver (train controlled by central computer)

EUROSTAR MULTI-VOLTAGE ELECTRIC TRAIN

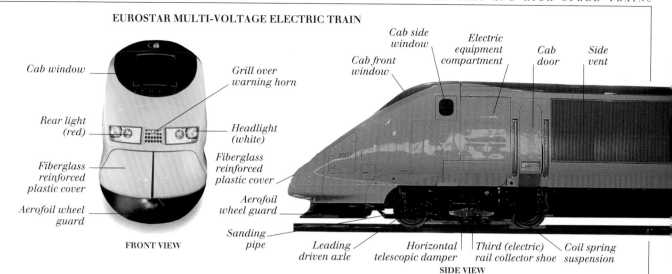

Cab window

Grill over warning horn

Rear light (red)

Headlight (white)

Fiberglass reinforced plastic cover

Fiberglass reinforced plastic cover

Aerofoil wheel guard

FRONT VIEW

Cab side window

Electric equipment compartment

Cab door

Side vent

Cab front window

Aerofoil wheel guard

Sanding pipe

Leading driven axle

Horizontal telescopic damper

Third (electric) rail collector shoe

Coil spring suspension

SIDE VIEW

3002

TGV ELECTRIC HIGH-SPEED TRAIN

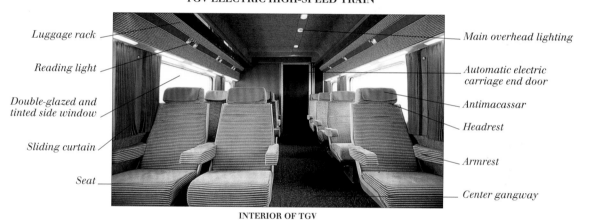

Luggage rack

Reading light

Double-glazed and tinted side window

Sliding curtain

Seat

Main overhead lighting

Automatic electric carriage end door

Antimacassar

Headrest

Armrest

Center gangway

INTERIOR OF TGV

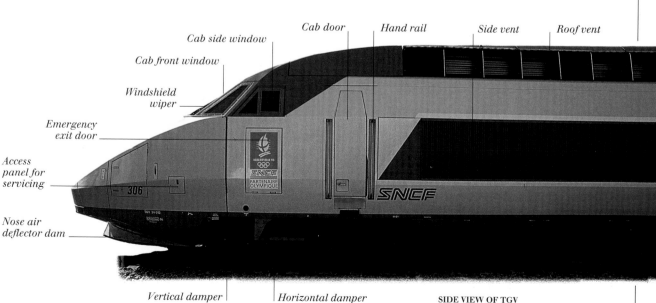

Cab side window

Cab door

Hand rail

Side vent

Roof vent

Cab front window

Windshield wiper

Emergency exit door

Access panel for servicing

Nose air deflector dam

306

SNCF

ALBERTVILLE 92 SNCF PARTENAIRE OLYMPIQUE

Vertical damper

Horizontal damper

SIDE VIEW OF TGV

Train equipment

MODERN RAILROAD TRACK consists of two parallel steel rails clipped onto a support called a sleeper. Sleepers are usually made of reinforced concrete, although wood and steel are still used. The distance between the inside edges of the rails is the track gauge. It evolved in Britain, which uses a gauge of 4 ft 8½ in (1,435 mm), known as the standard gauge. As engineering grew more sophisticated, narrower gauges were adopted because they cost less to build. The loading gauge, which is equally important, determines the size of the largest loaded vehicle that may pass through tunnels and under bridges with adequate clearance. Safe train operation relies on following a signaling system. At first, signaling was based on a simple time interval between trains, but it now depends on maintaining a safe distance between successive trains traveling in the same direction. Most modern signals are colored lights, but older mechanical semaphore signals are still used. On the latest high-speed lines, train drivers receive control instructions by electronic means. Signaling depends on reliable control of the train by effective braking. For fast, modern trains, which have considerable momentum, it is essential that each vehicle in the train can be braked by the driver or by a train control system, such as Automatic Train Protection (ATP). Braking is achieved by the brake shoe acting on the wheel rim (rim brakes), by disc brakes, or, increasingly, by electrical braking.

MECHANICAL SEMAPHORE SIGNAL

Red, square-ended arm in raised position means "all clear"

Red glass

Green glass

Actuating lever system

Motor operating "home" stop signal

Green glass

Yellow glass

Yellow, "distant" warning arm in horizontal position means "caution"

Tubular steel post

Ladder

Electrical relay box

FOUR-ASPECT COLORED LIGHT SIGNAL

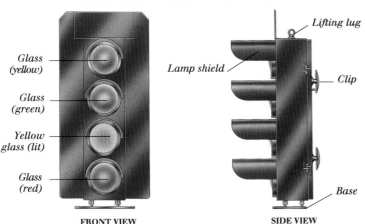

Glass (yellow)

Glass (green)

Yellow glass (lit)

Glass (red)

Lifting lug

Lamp shield

Clip

Base

FRONT VIEW

SIDE VIEW

HOW A MODERN MAIN-LINE SIGNALING SYSTEM WORKS

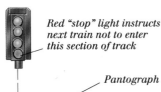
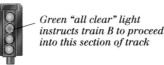
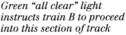
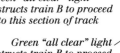

Red "stop" light instructs next train not to enter this section of track

Green "all clear" light instructs train B to proceed into this section of track

Green "all clear" light instructs train B to proceed into this section of track

Green "all clear" light instructs train B to proceed into this section of track

Pantograph

Catenary

Train B

Track

EXAMPLES OF INTERNATIONAL TRACK GAUGES

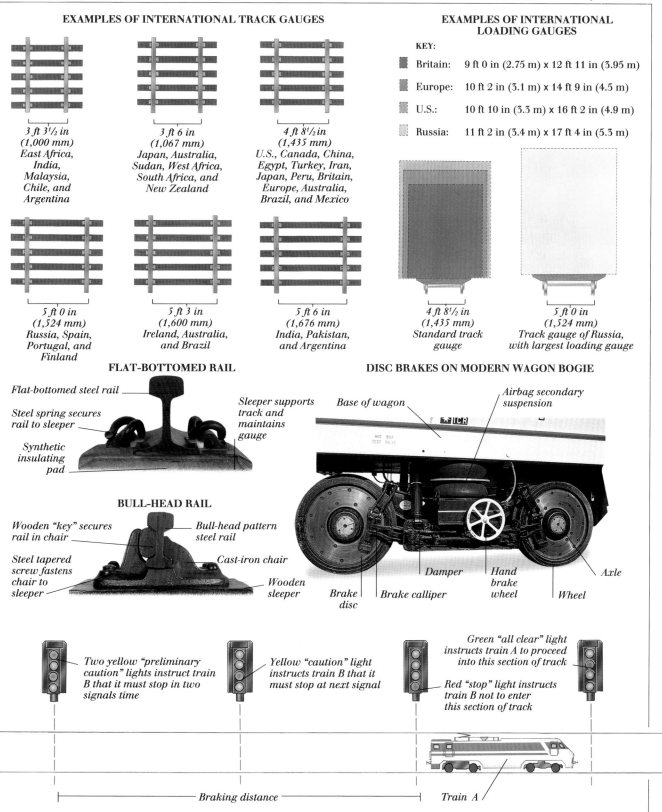

3 ft 3¹/₂ in
(1,000 mm)
*East Africa,
India,
Malaysia,
Chile, and
Argentina*

3 ft 6 in
(1,067 mm)
*Japan, Australia,
Sudan, West Africa,
South Africa, and
New Zealand*

4 ft 8¹/₂ in
(1,435 mm)
*U.S., Canada, China,
Egypt, Turkey, Iran,
Japan, Peru, Britain,
Europe, Australia,
Brazil, and Mexico*

5 ft 0 in
(1,524 mm)
*Russia, Spain,
Portugal, and
Finland*

5 ft 3 in
(1,600 mm)
*Ireland, Australia,
and Brazil*

5 ft 6 in
(1,676 mm)
*India, Pakistan,
and Argentina*

EXAMPLES OF INTERNATIONAL LOADING GAUGES

KEY:

Britain: 9 ft 0 in (2.75 m) x 12 ft 11 in (3.95 m)

Europe: 10 ft 2 in (3.1 m) x 14 ft 9 in (4.5 m)

U.S.: 10 ft 10 in (3.3 m) x 16 ft 2 in (4.9 m)

Russia: 11 ft 2 in (3.4 m) x 17 ft 4 in (5.3 m)

4 ft 8¹/₂ in
(1,435 mm)
*Standard track
gauge*

5 ft 0 in
(1,524 mm)
*Track gauge of Russia,
with largest loading gauge*

FLAT-BOTTOMED RAIL

Flat-bottomed steel rail

Steel spring secures
rail to sleeper

Synthetic
insulating
pad

Sleeper supports
track and
maintains
gauge

BULL-HEAD RAIL

Wooden "key" secures
rail in chair

Steel tapered
screw fastens
chair to
sleeper

Bull-head pattern
steel rail

Cast-iron chair

Wooden
sleeper

DISC BRAKES ON MODERN WAGON BOGIE

Base of wagon

Airbag secondary
suspension

HOT BOX
TEST VALVE

Brake
disc

Brake calliper

Damper

Hand
brake
wheel

Wheel

Axle

Two yellow "preliminary
caution" lights instruct train
B that it must stop in two
signals time

Yellow "caution" light
instructs train B that it
must stop at next signal

Green "all clear" light
instructs train A to proceed
into this section of track

Red "stop" light instructs
train B not to enter
this section of track

Braking distance

Train A

Trolleys and buses

WHEN CITY POPULATIONS exploded in the 1800s, there was an urgent need for mass transportation. Trolleys were an early solution. The first trolleys, like buses, were horse-drawn, but in 1881, electric streetcars appeared in Berlin, Germany. Electric trolleys soon became widespread throughout Europe and North America. Trolleys run on rails along a fixed route, using electric motors that receive power from overhead cables. As road networks developed, motorized buses offered a flexible alternative to trolleys. By the 1930s, they had replaced trolley systems in many cities. City buses typically have doors at both the front and rear to make loading and unloading easier. Double-decker designs are popular, occupying the same amount of street space as single-decker buses but able to transport twice the number of people. Buses are also commonly used for inter-city travel and touring. Tour buses have reclining seats, large windows, luggage space, and toilets. Recently, as city traffic has become increasingly congested, many city planners have designed new electric streetcar routes to run alongside bus routes as part of an integrated transport system.

METROLINK TROLLEY, MANCHESTER, BRITAIN

EARLY TROLLEY, c.1900

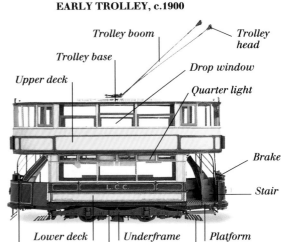

Trolley boom
Trolley head
Trolley base
Drop window
Upper deck
Quarter light
Brake
Stair
Lower deck
Underframe
Platform
Controller
Truck
Lifeguard

MCW METROBUS, LONDON, ENGLAND

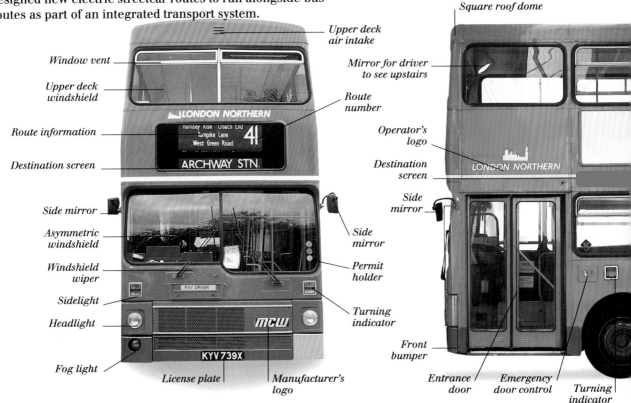

Upper deck air intake
Window vent
Mirror for driver to see upstairs
Upper deck windshield
Route number
Route information
Operator's logo
Destination screen
Destination screen
Side mirror
Side mirror
Asymmetric windshield
Windshield wiper
Side mirror
Sidelight
Permit holder
Headlight
Turning indicator
Fog light
Front bumper
License plate
Manufacturer's logo
Entrance door
Emergency door control
Turning indicator
Square roof dome

LONDON NORTHERN
Hornsey Rise   Crouch End
Turnpike Lane
West Green Road
41
ARCHWAY STN.
PAY DRIVER
mcw
KYV 739X
LONDON NORTHERN

FRONT VIEW

SINGLE-DECKER BUS, NEW YORK CITY, NEW YORK

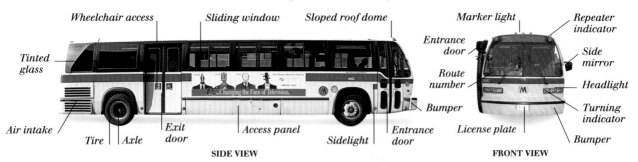

Wheelchair access

Sliding window

Sloped roof dome

Tinted glass

Marker light

Repeater indicator

Entrance door

Side mirror

Route number

Headlight

Bumper

Turning indicator

License plate

Air intake

Tire

Axle

Exit door

Access panel

Sidelight

Entrance door

Bumper

SIDE VIEW

FRONT VIEW

DOUBLE-DECKER TOUR BUS, PARIS, FRANCE

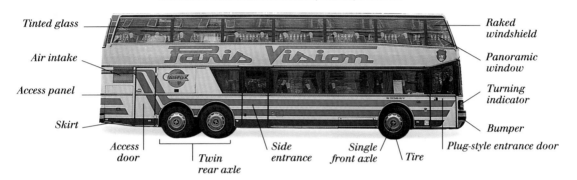

Tinted glass

Air intake

Access panel

Skirt

Access door

Twin rear axle

Side entrance

Single front axle

Tire

Raked windshield

Panoramic window

Turning indicator

Bumper

Plug-style entrance door

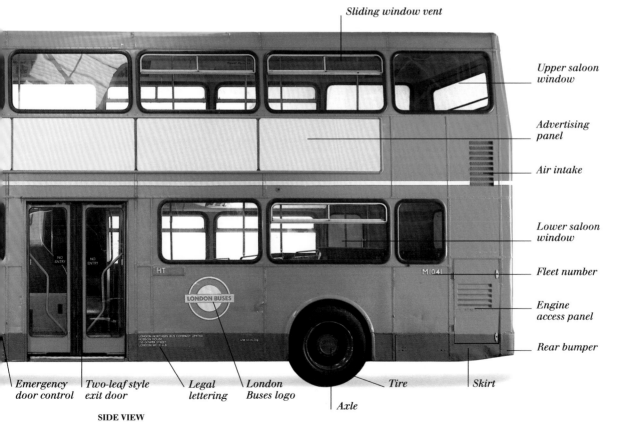

Sliding window vent

Upper saloon window

Advertising panel

Air intake

Lower saloon window

Fleet number

Engine access panel

Rear bumper

Emergency door control

Two-leaf style exit door

Legal lettering

London Buses logo

Tire

Skirt

Axle

SIDE VIEW

The first cars

THE EARLIEST ROAD VEHICLE powered by an engine, the Cugnot steam traction engine, was built in 1770. More practical steam carriages, such as the Bordino, were available in the early 19th century, but they were heavy and cumbersome. Restrictive laws and the introduction of railways, faster and able to carry more passengers, saw the decline of "cars" powered by steam. It was not until 1860 that the first practical power unit for road vehicles was developed with the invention of the internal combustion engine by the Belgian Étienne Lenoir. By around 1890, Karl Benz and Gottlieb Daimler in Germany and Albert de Dion and Armand Peugeot in France were building cars for sale to the public. These early cars, despite being primitive, expensive, and produced in limited numbers, heralded the age of the automobile.

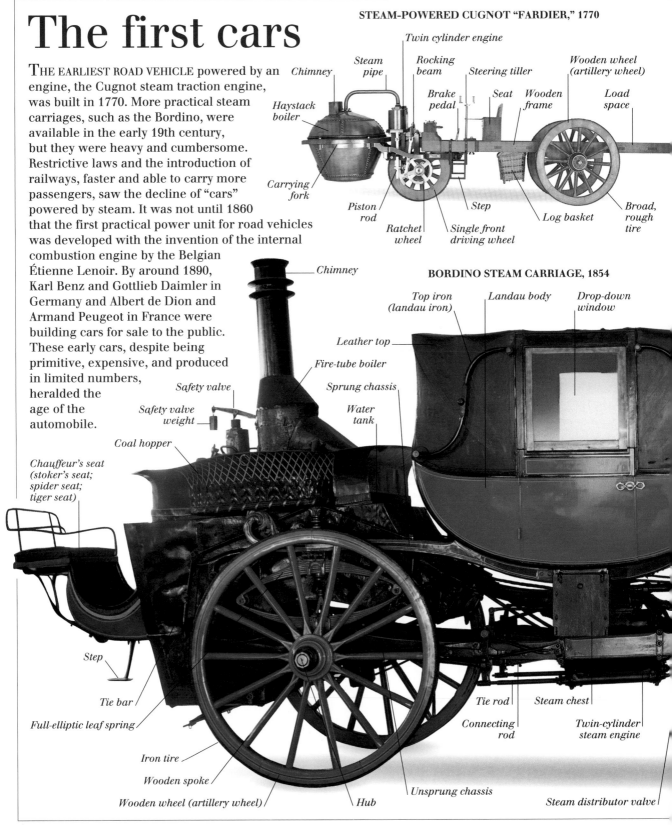

STEAM-POWERED CUGNOT "FARDIER," 1770

Twin cylinder engine

Steam pipe

Rocking beam

Chimney

Steering tiller

Wooden wheel (artillery wheel)

Brake pedal

Seat

Wooden frame

Load space

Haystack boiler

Carrying fork

Piston rod

Ratchet wheel

Single front driving wheel

Step

Log basket

Broad, rough tire

BORDINO STEAM CARRIAGE, 1854

Chimney

Top iron (landau iron)

Landau body

Drop-down window

Leather top

Fire-tube boiler

Sprung chassis

Safety valve

Water tank

Safety valve weight

Coal hopper

Chauffeur's seat (stoker's seat; spider seat; tiger seat)

Step

Tie bar

Full-elliptic leaf spring

Iron tire

Wooden spoke

Wooden wheel (artillery wheel)

Hub

Tie rod

Connecting rod

Steam chest

Twin-cylinder steam engine

Unsprung chassis

Steam distributor valve

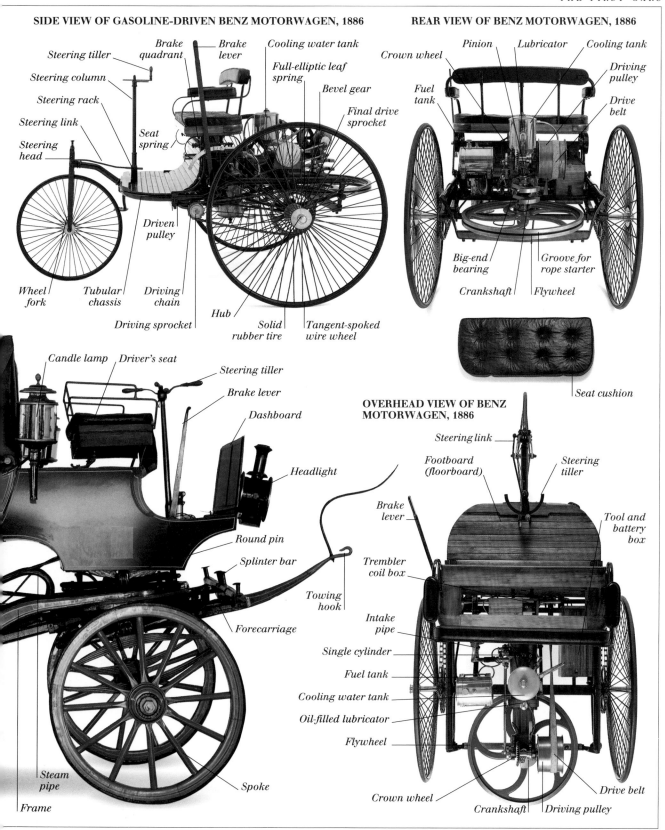

SIDE VIEW OF GASOLINE-DRIVEN BENZ MOTORWAGEN, 1886

Steering tiller
Brake quadrant
Brake lever
Cooling water tank
Full-elliptic leaf spring
Steering column
Steering rack
Bevel gear
Steering link
Final drive sprocket
Steering head
Seat spring
Wheel fork
Tubular chassis
Driving chain
Driven pulley
Driving sprocket
Hub
Solid rubber tire
Tangent-spoked wire wheel

REAR VIEW OF BENZ MOTORWAGEN, 1886

Pinion
Lubricator
Cooling tank
Crown wheel
Driving pulley
Fuel tank
Drive belt
Big-end bearing
Groove for rope starter
Crankshaft
Flywheel
Seat cushion

OVERHEAD VIEW OF BENZ MOTORWAGEN, 1886

Candle lamp
Driver's seat
Steering tiller
Brake lever
Dashboard
Headlight
Round pin
Splinter bar
Towing hook
Forecarriage
Steam pipe
Spoke
Frame

Steering link
Footboard (floorboard)
Steering tiller
Brake lever
Tool and battery box
Trembler coil box
Intake pipe
Single cylinder
Fuel tank
Cooling water tank
Oil-filled lubricator
Flywheel
Crown wheel
Crankshaft
Driving pulley
Drive belt

Elegance and utility

DURING THE FIRST DECADE OF THIS CENTURY, the motorist who could afford it had a choice of some of the finest cars ever made. These handbuilt cars were powerful and luxurious, using the finest wood, leather, and cloth, and bodywork made to the customer's individual requirements. Some had six-cylinder engines as big as 15 liters. The price of such cars was several times that of an average house, and their yearly running costs were also very high. As a result, basic, utilitarian cars became popular. Costing perhaps one-tenth of the price of a luxury car, these cars had very little trim and often had only single-cylinder engines.

1904 OLDSMOBILE SINGLE-CYLINDER ENGINE

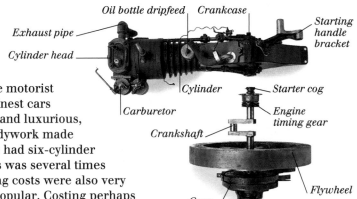

Oil bottle dripfeed
Crankcase
Exhaust pipe
Starting handle bracket
Cylinder head
Cylinder
Starter cog
Carburetor
Engine timing gear
Crankshaft
Gear band
Flywheel

FRONT VIEW OF 1906 RENAULT

SIDE VIEW OF 1906 RENAULT

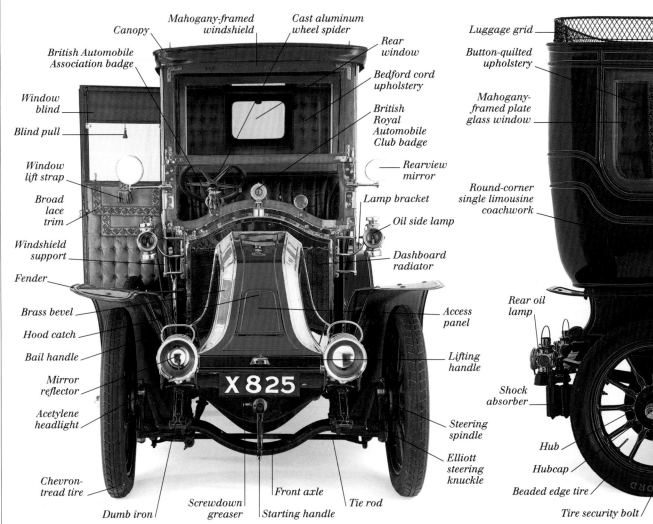

Canopy
Mahogany-framed windshield
Cast aluminum wheel spider
Rear window
British Automobile Association badge
Bedford cord upholstery
Window blind
British Royal Automobile Club badge
Blind pull
Window lift strap
Rearview mirror
Broad lace trim
Lamp bracket
Oil side lamp
Windshield support
Dashboard radiator
Fender
Brass bevel
Access panel
Hood catch
Bail handle
Lifting handle
Mirror reflector
Acetylene headlight
Steering spindle
Chevron-tread tire
Elliott steering knuckle
Dumb iron
Screwdown greaser
Front axle
Starting handle
Tie rod

Luggage grid
Button-quilted upholstery
Mahogany-framed plate glass window
Round-corner single limousine coachwork
Rear oil lamp
Shock absorber
Hub
Hubcap
Beaded edge tire
Tire security bolt

X 825

1904 OLDSMOBILE TRIM AND BODYWORK

1904 OLDSMOBILE CHASSIS

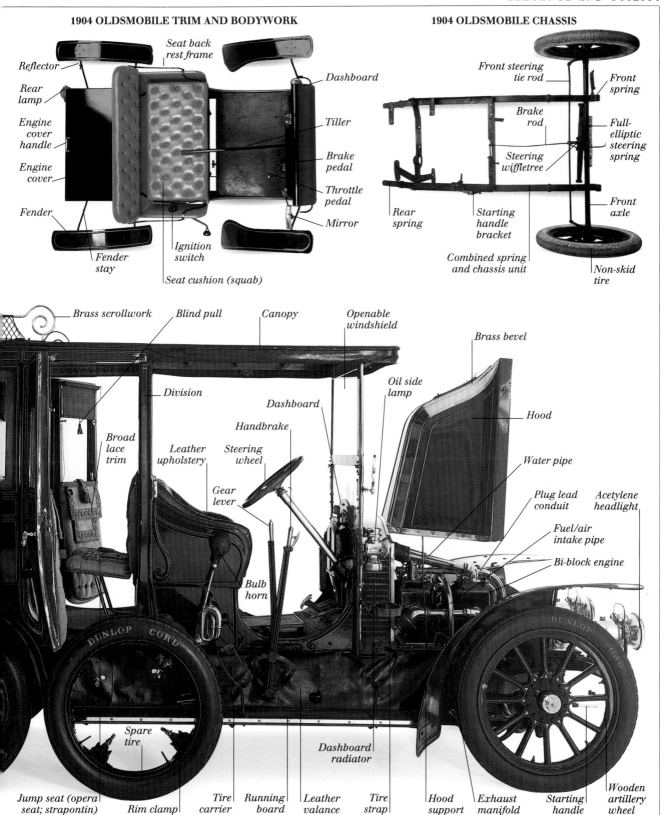

Reflector

Rear lamp

Engine cover handle

Engine cover

Fender

Fender stay

Seat back rest frame

Dashboard

Tiller

Brake pedal

Throttle pedal

Mirror

Ignition switch

Seat cushion (squab)

Front steering tie rod

Front spring

Brake rod

Full-elliptic steering spring

Steering wiffletree

Rear spring

Starting handle bracket

Front axle

Combined spring and chassis unit

Non-skid tire

Brass scrollwork

Blind pull

Canopy

Openable windshield

Brass bevel

Division

Oil side lamp

Dashboard

Hood

Handbrake

Broad lace trim

Leather upholstery

Steering wheel

Water pipe

Gear lever

Plug lead conduit

Acetylene headlight

Fuel/air intake pipe

Bi-block engine

Bulb horn

Spare tire

Jump seat (opera seat; strapontin)

Rim clamp

Tire carrier

Running board

Leather valance

Dashboard radiator

Tire strap

Hood support

Exhaust manifold

Starting handle

Wooden artillery wheel

Mass production

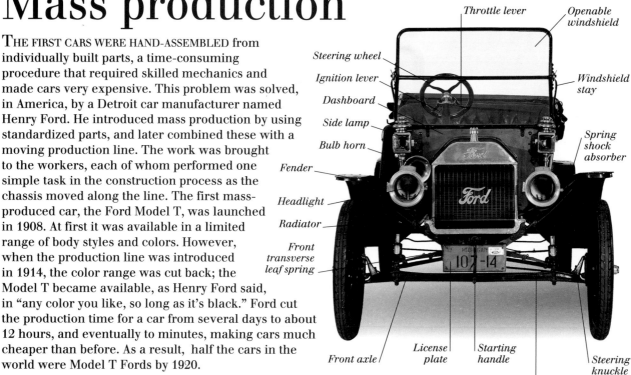

FRONT VIEW OF 1913 FORD MODEL T

Throttle lever

Openable windshield

Steering wheel

Ignition lever

Windshield stay

Dashboard

Side lamp

Bulb horn

Spring shock absorber

Fender

Headlight

Radiator

Front transverse leaf spring

License plate

Starting handle

Steering knuckle

Front axle

Steering spindle connecting-rod

THE FIRST CARS WERE HAND-ASSEMBLED from individually built parts, a time-consuming procedure that required skilled mechanics and made cars very expensive. This problem was solved, in America, by a Detroit car manufacturer named Henry Ford. He introduced mass production by using standardized parts, and later combined these with a moving production line. The work was brought to the workers, each of whom performed one simple task in the construction process as the chassis moved along the line. The first mass-produced car, the Ford Model T, was launched in 1908. At first it was available in a limited range of body styles and colors. However, when the production line was introduced in 1914, the color range was cut back; the Model T became available, as Henry Ford said, in "any color you like, so long as it's black." Ford cut the production time for a car from several days to about 12 hours, and eventually to minutes, making cars much cheaper than before. As a result, half the cars in the world were Model T Fords by 1920.

STAGES OF FORD MODEL T PRODUCTION

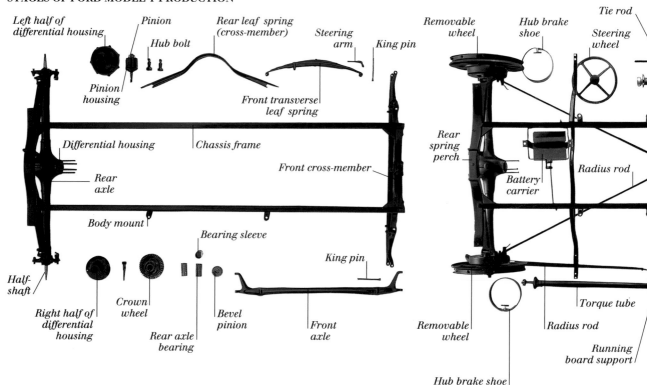

Left half of differential housing

Pinion

Hub bolt

Rear leaf spring (cross-member)

Steering arm

King pin

Removable wheel

Hub brake shoe

Tie rod

Steering wheel

Pinion housing

Front transverse leaf spring

Differential housing

Chassis frame

Rear spring perch

Radius rod

Front cross-member

Rear axle

Battery carrier

Body mount

Bearing sleeve

King pin

Half-shaft

Right half of differential housing

Crown wheel

Rear axle bearing

Bevel pinion

Front axle

Removable wheel

Torque tube

Radius rod

Running board support

Hub brake shoe

SIDE VIEW OF 1913 FORD MODEL T

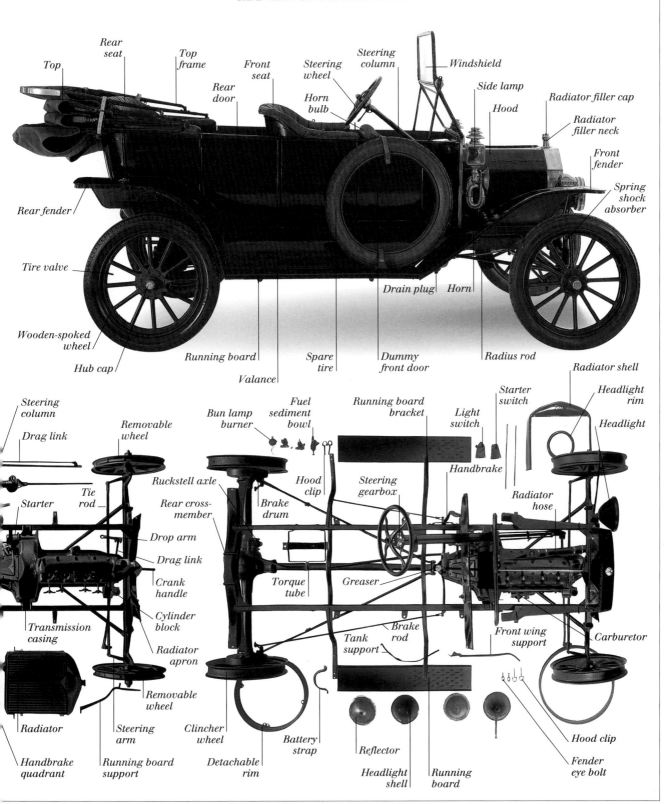

Top

Rear seat

Top frame

Front seat

Steering wheel

Steering column

Windshield

Horn bulb

Side lamp

Hood

Radiator filler cap

Radiator filler neck

Rear door

Front fender

Spring shock absorber

Rear fender

Tire valve

Drain plug

Horn

Wooden-spoked wheel

Running board

Spare tire

Dummy front door

Radius rod

Radiator shell

Hub cap

Valance

Steering column

Drag link

Removable wheel

Bun lamp burner

Fuel sediment bowl

Running board bracket

Light switch

Starter switch

Headlight rim

Headlight

Handbrake

Ruckstell axle

Hood clip

Steering gearbox

Radiator hose

Tie rod

Starter

Rear cross-member

Brake drum

Drop arm

Drag link

Crank handle

Torque tube

Greaser

Cylinder block

Brake rod

Transmission casing

Radiator apron

Tank support

Front wing support

Carburetor

Removable wheel

Radiator

Steering arm

Clincher wheel

Battery strap

Hood clip

Handbrake quadrant

Running board support

Detachable rim

Reflector

Headlight shell

Running board

Fender eye bolt

The "people's car"

THE MOST POPULAR CAR in the history of car manufacture is
the Volkswagen Beetle, originally called the KdF Wagen.
The car was developed in Germany in the 1930s by
Dr. Ferdinand Porsche. At that time, Germany had
only half the number of cars of Britain or France,
and Adolf Hitler took a personal interest in the
development of the Volkswagen ("people's car").
The intention was to provide a new industry,
new jobs, and a car so inexpensive that
anyone with a job could afford it.
Dr. Porsche designed a car that
was cheap to build and run; its
rear-mounted, air-cooled engine
cut down the number of parts
needed and also reduced weight.
However, few civilians managed to
obtain the Beetle before the outbreak
of the Second World War in 1939. After
the war, the Beetle proved so popular
that eventually more than 20 million
were sold.

**CUSTOMIZED
VOLKSWAGEN
BEETLE**

**FLAT-FOUR
CYLINDER
ARRANGEMENT**

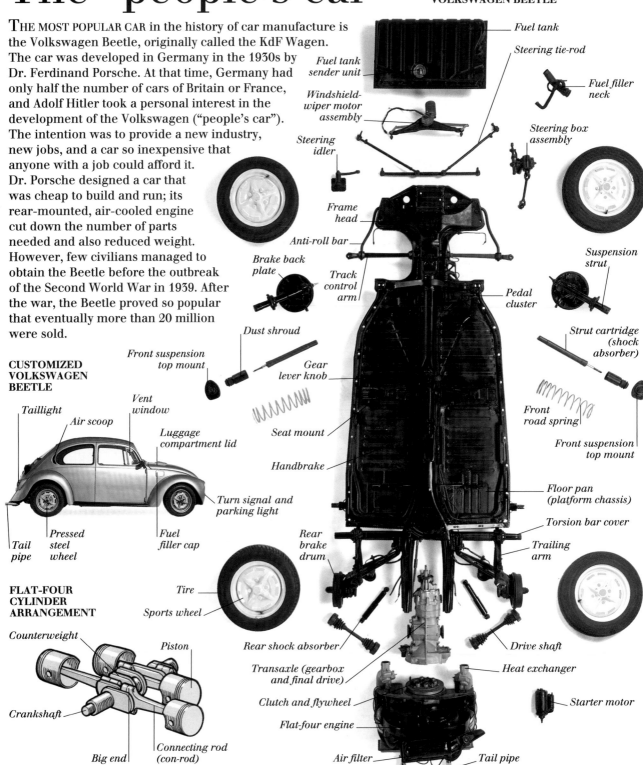

Fuel tank

Fuel tank
sender unit

Steering tie-rod

Fuel filler
neck

Windshield-
wiper motor
assembly

Steering
idler

Steering box
assembly

Frame
head

Anti-roll bar

Suspension
strut

Brake back
plate

Track
control
arm

Pedal
cluster

Dust shroud

Strut cartridge
(shock
absorber)

Front suspension
top mount

Gear
lever knob

Seat mount

Front
road spring

Front suspension
top mount

Handbrake

Taillight

Air scoop

Vent
window

Luggage
compartment lid

Floor pan
(platform chassis)

Torsion bar cover

Turn signal and
parking light

Rear
brake
drum

Trailing
arm

Tail
pipe

Pressed
steel
wheel

Fuel
filler cap

Tire

Sports wheel

Counterweight

Piston

Rear shock absorber

Drive shaft

Transaxle (gearbox
and final drive)

Heat exchanger

Crankshaft

Clutch and flywheel

Starter motor

Flat-four engine

Big end

Connecting rod
(con-rod)

Air filter

Tail pipe

BODY SHELL OF VOLKSWAGEN BEETLE

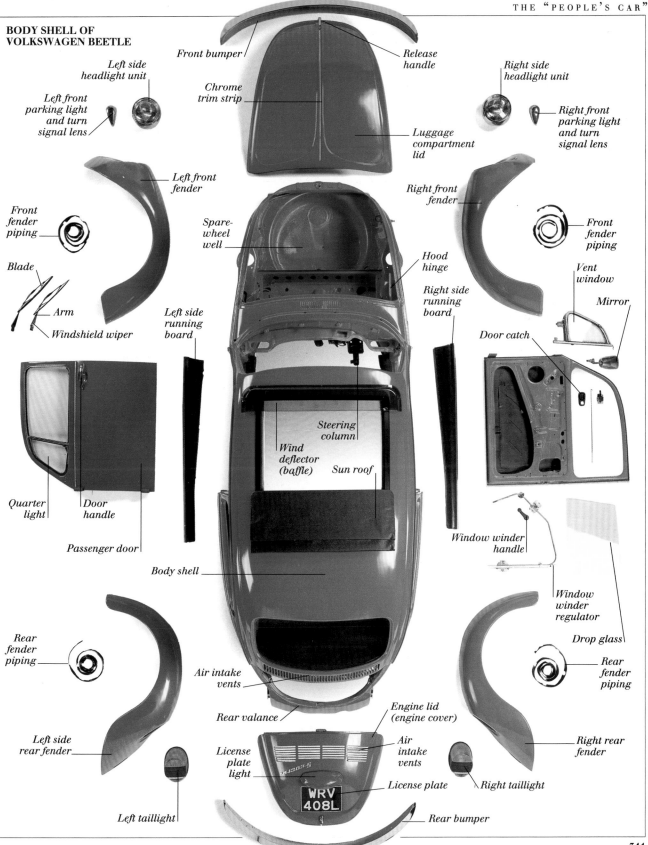

Front bumper

Release handle

Left side headlight unit

Right side headlight unit

Left front parking light and turn signal lens

Chrome trim strip

Right front parking light and turn signal lens

Left front fender

Luggage compartment lid

Right front fender

Front fender piping

Spare-wheel well

Hood hinge

Front fender piping

Blade

Vent window

Mirror

Arm

Windshield wiper

Left side running board

Right side running board

Door catch

Steering column

Wind deflector (baffle)

Sun roof

Quarter light

Door handle

Passenger door

Body shell

Window winder handle

Window winder regulator

Drop glass

Rear fender piping

Air intake vents

Rear fender piping

Rear valance

Engine lid (engine cover)

Air intake vents

Left side rear fender

Right rear fender

License plate light

License plate

Right taillight

Left taillight

Rear bumper

WRV 408L

Early engines

STEAM AND ELECTRICITY were used to power cars until early this century, but neither power source was ideal. Electric cars had to stop frequently to recharge their heavy batteries, and steam cars gave smooth power delivery but were too complicated for the average motorist to use. A rival power source, the internal combustion engine, was invented in 1860 by Étienne Lenoir (see pp. 334-335). This engine converted the force of an explosion into rotary motion to turn the wheels of a vehicle. Early variations on this basic model included sleeve valves, separately cast cylinders, and the two-stroke combustion cycle. Today, all combustion engines, including the Wankel rotary and diesels (see pp. 346-347), use the four-stroke cycle, first demonstrated by Nikolaus Otto in 1876. The Otto cycle has proved the best method of ensuring that the engine turns over smoothly and that exhaust emissions are controllable.

BERSEY ELECTRIC CAB, 1896

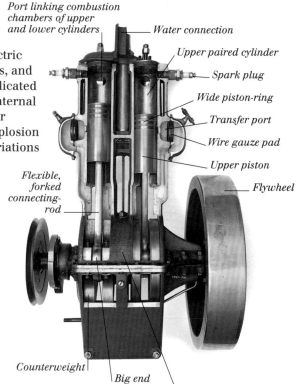

Port linking combustion chambers of upper and lower cylinders

Water connection

Upper paired cylinder

Spark plug

Wide piston-ring

Transfer port

Wire gauze pad

Upper piston

Flywheel

Flexible, forked connecting-rod

Counterweight

Big end

Crankcase

Mounting for tray of 40 batteries

Housing for electric motors

SECTIONED WHITE STEAM CAR, 1903

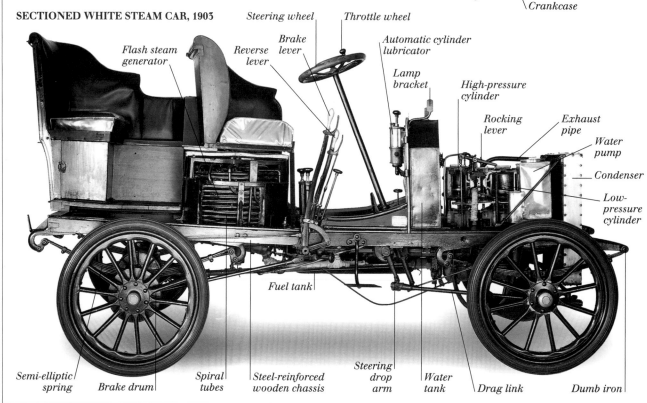

Steering wheel · Throttle wheel · Brake lever · Reverse lever · Flash steam generator · Automatic cylinder lubricator · Lamp bracket · High-pressure cylinder · Rocking lever · Exhaust pipe · Water pump · Condenser · Low-pressure cylinder · Fuel tank · Semi-elliptic spring · Brake drum · Spiral tubes · Steel-reinforced wooden chassis · Steering drop arm · Water tank · Drag link · Dumb iron

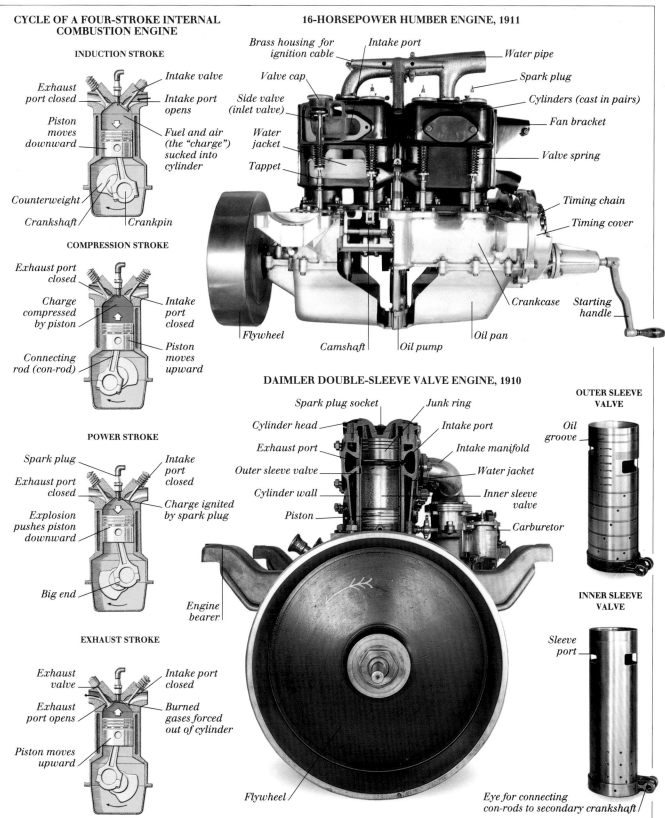

CYCLE OF A FOUR-STROKE INTERNAL COMBUSTION ENGINE

INDUCTION STROKE

Exhaust port closed

Intake valve

Intake port opens

Piston moves downward

Fuel and air (the "charge") sucked into cylinder

Counterweight

Crankshaft

Crankpin

COMPRESSION STROKE

Exhaust port closed

Charge compressed by piston

Intake port closed

Connecting rod (con-rod)

Piston moves upward

POWER STROKE

Spark plug

Intake port closed

Exhaust port closed

Charge ignited by spark plug

Explosion pushes piston downward

Big end

EXHAUST STROKE

Exhaust valve

Intake port closed

Exhaust port opens

Burned gases forced out of cylinder

Piston moves upward

16-HORSEPOWER HUMBER ENGINE, 1911

Brass housing for ignition cable

Intake port

Water pipe

Valve cap

Spark plug

Side valve (inlet valve)

Cylinders (cast in pairs)

Water jacket

Fan bracket

Tappet

Valve spring

Timing chain

Timing cover

Crankcase

Starting handle

Flywheel

Camshaft

Oil pump

Oil pan

DAIMLER DOUBLE-SLEEVE VALVE ENGINE, 1910

Spark plug socket

Junk ring

Cylinder head

Intake port

Exhaust port

Intake manifold

Outer sleeve valve

Water jacket

Cylinder wall

Inner sleeve valve

Piston

Carburetor

Engine bearer

Flywheel

OUTER SLEEVE VALVE

Oil groove

INNER SLEEVE VALVE

Sleeve port

Eye for connecting con-rods to secondary crankshaft

Modern engines

TODAY'S GASOLINE ENGINE WORKS on the same basic principles as the first car engines of a century ago, although it has been greatly refined. Modern engines, often made from special metal alloys, are much lighter than earlier engines. Computerized ignition systems, fuel injectors, and multi-valve cylinder heads achieve a more efficient combustion of the fuel/air mixture (the charge) so that less fuel is wasted. As a result of this greater efficiency, the power and performance of a modern engine are increased, and the level of pollution in the exhaust gases is reduced. Exhaust pollution levels today are also lowered by the increasing use of special filters called catalytic converters, which absorb many exhaust pollutants. The need to produce ever more efficient engines means that it can take up to seven years to develop a new engine for a family car, at a cost of many millions of dollars.

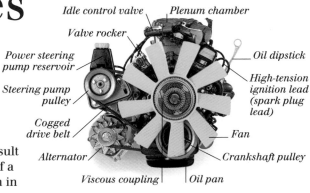

FRONT VIEW OF A FORD COSWORTH V6 12-VALVE

Idle control valve
Plenum chamber
Valve rocker
Power steering pump reservoir
Oil dipstick
Steering pump pulley
High-tension ignition lead (spark plug lead)
Cogged drive belt
Fan
Alternator
Crankshaft pulley
Viscous coupling
Oil pan

FRONT VIEW OF A FORD COSWORTH V6 24-VALVE

Idle control valve
Plenum chamber
Exhaust gas recirculation valve
Camshaft timing gear
Camshaft chain
Steering pump drive pulley
Belt tensioner
Air-conditioning compressor
Alternator cooling fan
Oil pan
Drive belt
Crankshaft pulley

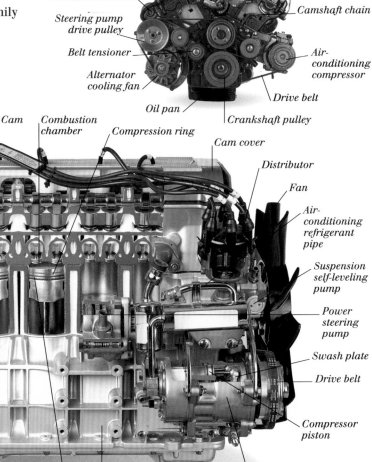

SECTIONED VIEW OF A JAGUAR STRAIGHT 6

Valve spring
Cam lobe
Cam
Combustion chamber
Compression ring
Cam cover
Cam follower (bucket tappet)
Distributor
Camshaft
Fan
Cylinder head
Air-conditioning refrigerant pipe
Valve stem
Exhaust valve
Suspension self-leveling pump
Cylinder liner
Power steering pump
Water jacket
Piston
Swash plate
Connecting rod (con-rod)
Drive belt
Main bearing housing
Big end
Compressor piston
Transmission adaptor plate
Air-conditioning compressor
Crankshaft counterweight
Oil pan
Oil pick-up pipe
Anti-surge baffle
Crankcase
Oil-control ring (scraper ring)

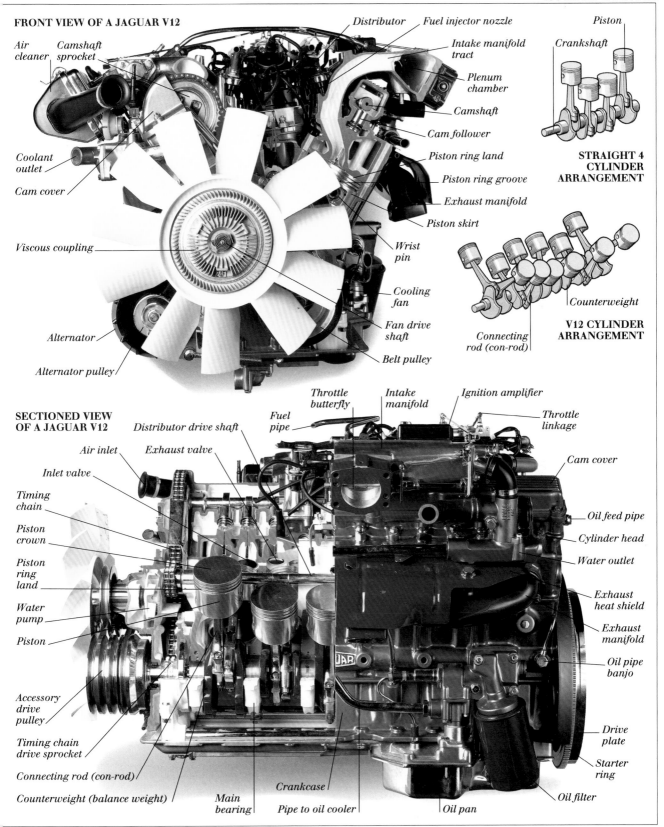

FRONT VIEW OF A JAGUAR V12

Distributor

Fuel injector nozzle

Piston

Air cleaner

Camshaft sprocket

Intake manifold tract

Crankshaft

Plenum chamber

Camshaft

Cam follower

Coolant outlet

Piston ring land

STRAIGHT 4 CYLINDER ARRANGEMENT

Cam cover

Piston ring groove

Exhaust manifold

Piston skirt

Viscous coupling

Wrist pin

Cooling fan

Counterweight

Alternator

Fan drive shaft

V12 CYLINDER ARRANGEMENT

Alternator pulley

Belt pulley

Connecting rod (con-rod)

SECTIONED VIEW OF A JAGUAR V12

Throttle butterfly

Intake manifold

Ignition amplifier

Distributor drive shaft

Fuel pipe

Throttle linkage

Air inlet

Exhaust valve

Cam cover

Inlet valve

Oil feed pipe

Timing chain

Cylinder head

Piston crown

Water outlet

Piston ring land

Exhaust heat shield

Water pump

Exhaust manifold

Piston

Oil pipe banjo

Accessory drive pulley

Drive plate

Timing chain drive sprocket

Starter ring

Connecting rod (con-rod)

Counterweight (balance weight)

Main bearing

Crankcase

Pipe to oil cooler

Oil pan

Oil filter

345

Alternative engines

THE MOST COMMON TYPE OF ALTERNATIVE ENGINE is the diesel engine. Instead of igniting the compressed fuel/air mixture with a spark, the diesel engine uses compression alone, which heats the mixture to the point where it explodes. A diesel engine's fuel consumption is low in comparison with similarly sized piston engines, despite its heavier, reinforced moving parts and cylinder block. Another type of engine is the rotary-combustion, first successfully developed by Felix Wankel in the 1950s. Its two trilobate (three-sided) rotors revolve in housings shaped in a fat figure eight. The four sequences of the four-stroke cycle, which occur consecutively in a piston engine, occur simultaneously in a rotary engine, producing power in a continuous stream.

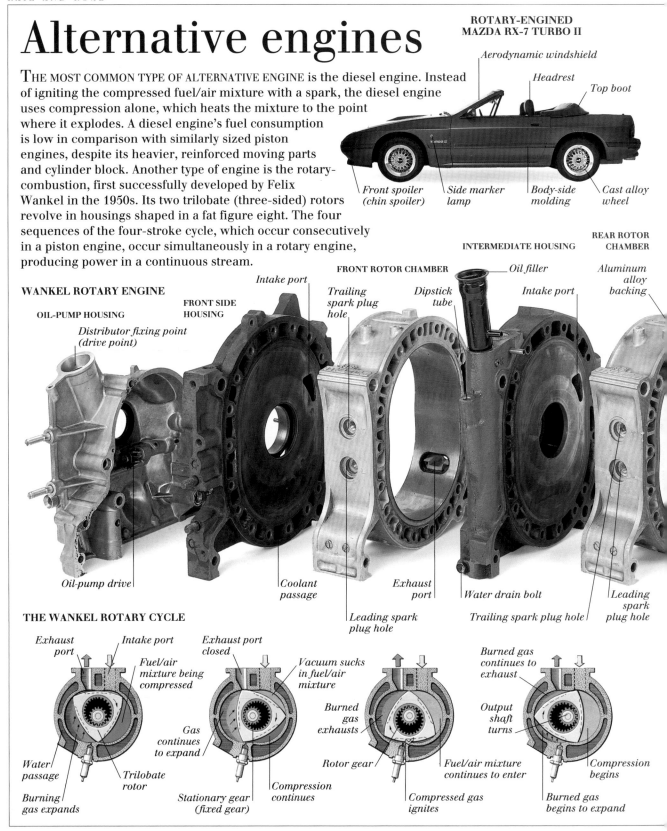

ROTARY-ENGINED MAZDA RX-7 TURBO II

Aerodynamic windshield

Headrest

Top boot

Front spoiler (chin spoiler)

Side marker lamp

Body-side molding

Cast alloy wheel

WANKEL ROTARY ENGINE

OIL-PUMP HOUSING

Distributor fixing point (drive point)

FRONT SIDE HOUSING

Intake port

FRONT ROTOR CHAMBER

Trailing spark plug hole

Dipstick tube

INTERMEDIATE HOUSING

Oil filler

Intake port

REAR ROTOR CHAMBER

Aluminum alloy backing

Oil-pump drive

Coolant passage

Exhaust port

Water drain bolt

Leading spark plug hole

Leading spark plug hole

Trailing spark plug hole

Trailing spark plug hole

THE WANKEL ROTARY CYCLE

Exhaust port

Intake port

Fuel/air mixture being compressed

Water passage

Burning gas expands

Trilobate rotor

Gas continues to expand

Stationary gear (fixed gear)

Compression continues

Exhaust port closed

Vacuum sucks in fuel/air mixture

Burned gas exhausts

Rotor gear

Compressed gas ignites

Burned gas continues to exhaust

Output shaft turns

Fuel/air mixture continues to enter

Burned gas begins to expand

Compression begins

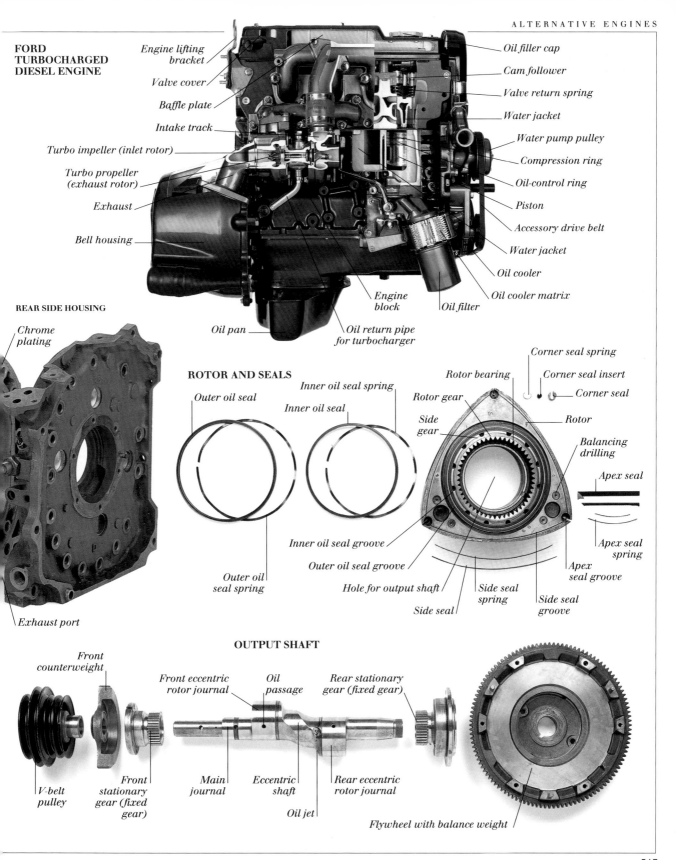

FORD TURBOCHARGED DIESEL ENGINE

Engine lifting bracket

Valve cover

Baffle plate

Intake track

Turbo impeller (inlet rotor)

Turbo propeller (exhaust rotor)

Exhaust

Bell housing

Oil filler cap

Cam follower

Valve return spring

Water jacket

Water pump pulley

Compression ring

Oil-control ring

Piston

Accessory drive belt

Water jacket

Oil cooler

Oil cooler matrix

Engine block

Oil filter

Oil pan

Oil return pipe for turbocharger

REAR SIDE HOUSING

Chrome plating

Exhaust port

ROTOR AND SEALS

Outer oil seal

Inner oil seal spring

Inner oil seal

Outer oil seal spring

Inner oil seal groove

Outer oil seal groove

Hole for output shaft

Side seal

Side seal spring

Rotor bearing

Rotor gear

Side gear

Corner seal spring

Corner seal insert

Corner seal

Rotor

Balancing drilling

Apex seal

Apex seal spring

Apex seal groove

Side seal groove

OUTPUT SHAFT

Front counterweight

Front eccentric rotor journal

Oil passage

Rear stationary gear (fixed gear)

V-belt pulley

Front stationary gear (fixed gear)

Main journal

Eccentric shaft

Oil jet

Rear eccentric rotor journal

Flywheel with balance weight

Modern bodywork

RENAULT LOGO

THE BODY OF A MODERN MASS-PRODUCED CAR is built on the monocoque (single-shell) principle, in which the roof, side panels, and floor are welded into a single integral unit. This bodyshell protects and supports the car's internal parts. Steel and glass are used to construct the bodyshell, creating a unit that is both light and strong. Its lightness helps to conserve energy, while its strength protects the occupants. Modern bodywork is designed with the aid of computers, which are used to predict factors such as aerodynamic efficiency and impact resistance. High technology is also employed on the production line, where robots are used to assemble, weld, and paint the body.

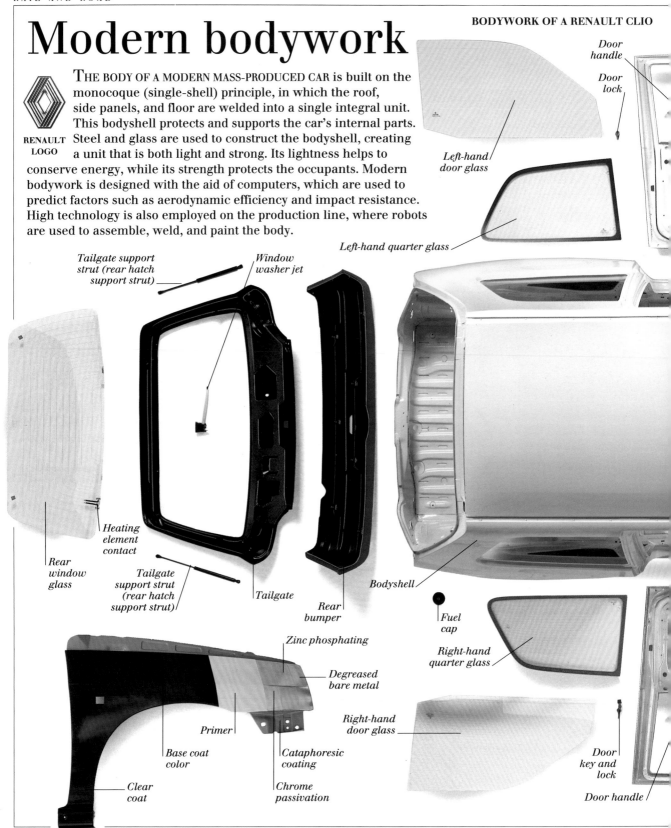

Door handle

Door lock

Left-hand door glass

Left-hand quarter glass

Tailgate support strut (rear hatch support strut)

Window washer jet

Heating element contact

Rear window glass

Tailgate support strut (rear hatch support strut)

Tailgate

Rear bumper

Bodyshell

Fuel cap

Right-hand quarter glass

Zinc phosphating

Degreased bare metal

Primer

Base coat color

Cataphoresic coating

Right-hand door glass

Clear coat

Chrome passivation

Door key and lock

Door handle

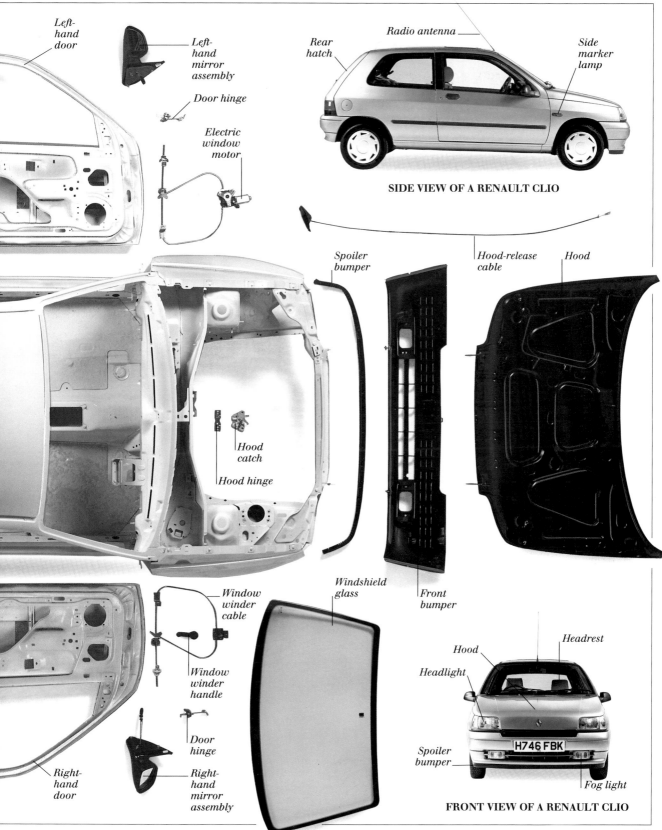

Left-hand door

Left-hand mirror assembly

Door hinge

Electric window motor

Rear hatch

Radio antenna

Side marker lamp

SIDE VIEW OF A RENAULT CLIO

Spoiler bumper

Hood-release cable

Hood

Hood catch

Hood hinge

Windshield glass

Front bumper

Window winder cable

Window winder handle

Door hinge

Right-hand door

Right-hand mirror assembly

Hood

Headrest

Headlight

Spoiler bumper

Fog light

H746 FBK

FRONT VIEW OF A RENAULT CLIO

Modern components

A TYPICAL MODERN CAR has several thousand individual mechanical components. These are assembled to form the car's various mechanical systems: engine and exhaust, transmission, steering, suspension, and brakes. To ensure that each system functions properly, components are manufactured to extremely fine tolerances—to within about one ten-thousandth of an inch in some cases.

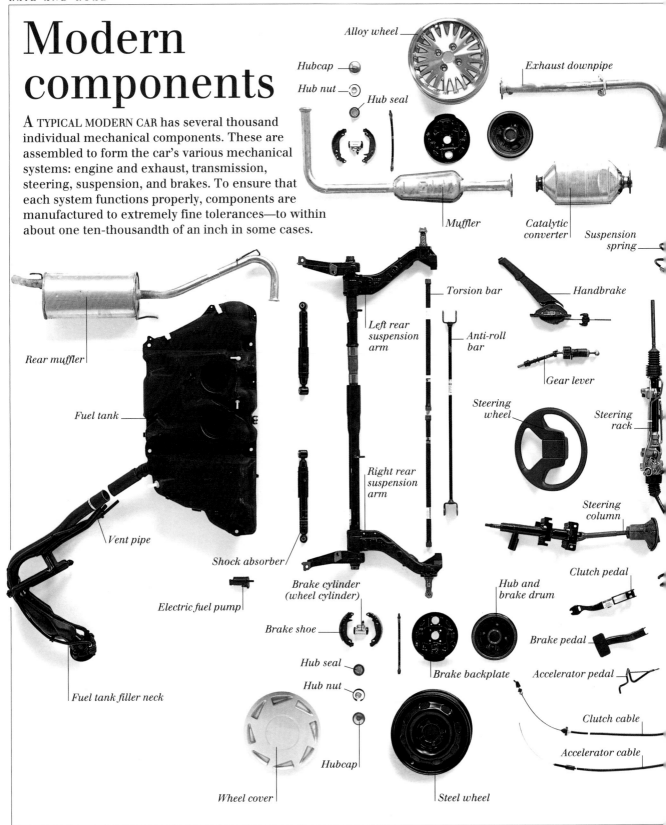

Alloy wheel

Hubcap

Hub nut

Hub seal

Exhaust downpipe

Muffler

Catalytic converter

Suspension spring

Rear muffler

Fuel tank

Vent pipe

Shock absorber

Electric fuel pump

Brake cylinder (wheel cylinder)

Brake shoe

Hub seal

Hub nut

Fuel tank filler neck

Wheel cover

Hubcap

Steel wheel

Brake backplate

Hub and brake drum

Torsion bar

Handbrake

Left rear suspension arm

Anti-roll bar

Right rear suspension arm

Gear lever

Steering wheel

Steering rack

Steering column

Clutch pedal

Brake pedal

Accelerator pedal

Clutch cable

Accelerator cable

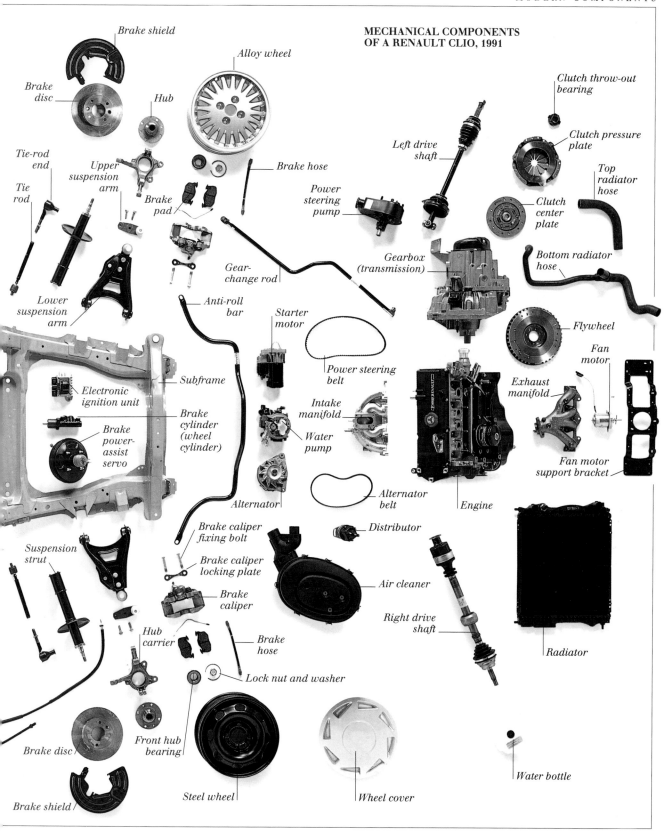

MECHANICAL COMPONENTS OF A RENAULT CLIO, 1991

Brake shield

Alloy wheel

Clutch throw-out bearing

Brake disc

Hub

Left drive shaft

Clutch pressure plate

Brake hose

Tie-rod end

Upper suspension arm

Top radiator hose

Tie rod

Brake pad

Power steering pump

Clutch center plate

Gear-change rod

Gearbox (transmission)

Bottom radiator hose

Lower suspension arm

Anti-roll bar

Starter motor

Flywheel

Fan motor

Electronic ignition unit

Subframe

Power steering belt

Exhaust manifold

Brake cylinder (wheel cylinder)

Intake manifold

Brake power-assist servo

Water pump

Fan motor support bracket

Alternator

Alternator belt

Engine

Suspension strut

Brake caliper fixing bolt

Distributor

Brake caliper locking plate

Air cleaner

Brake caliper

Right drive shaft

Hub carrier

Brake hose

Radiator

Brake disc

Lock nut and washer

Front hub bearing

Brake shield

Steel wheel

Wheel cover

Water bottle

Modern trim

A MODERN CAR HAS TWO TYPES OF TRIM, according to the materials used: hard (chrome and plastics) and soft (upholstered materials). Safety and comfort are priorities in the trim's design: seats help the occupants maintain a comfortable posture, rubber seals keep out dirt and moisture, and headlights light the way. Older cars had interior or leather paneling cut and fitted by craftsmen; modern cars use precisely molded plastics and seat fabrics cut by robot-controlled lasers to reduce costs and production time. Doors are now assembled off the production line so that complex wiring can be built in.

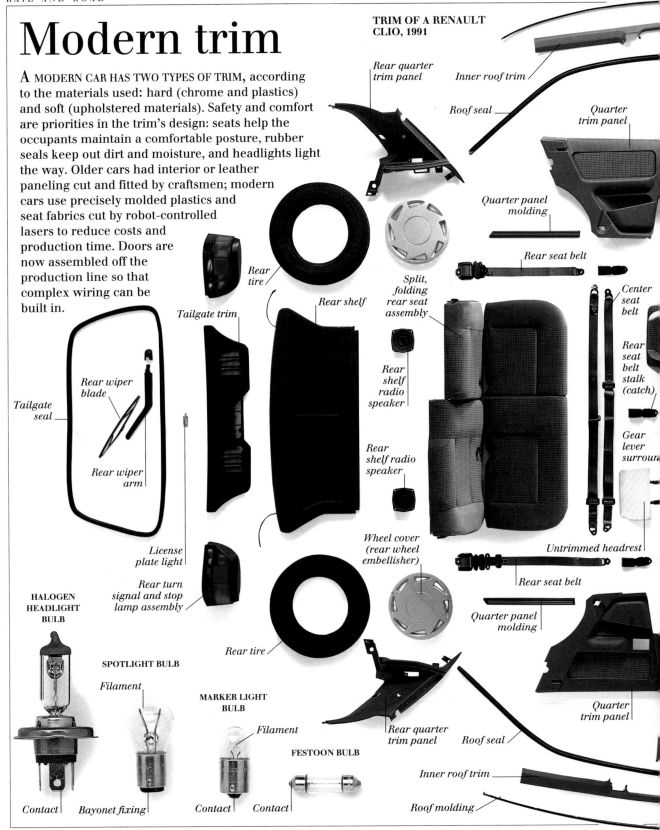

TRIM OF A RENAULT CLIO, 1991

Rear quarter trim panel

Inner roof trim

Roof seal

Quarter trim panel

Quarter panel molding

Rear seat belt

Center seat belt

Rear tire

Split, folding rear seat assembly

Rear seat belt stalk (catch)

Rear shelf

Rear shelf radio speaker

Tailgate trim

Rear shelf radio speaker

Gear lever surround

Tailgate seal

Rear wiper blade

Rear wiper arm

Wheel cover (rear wheel embellisher)

Untrimmed headrest

Rear seat belt

License plate light

Quarter panel molding

HALOGEN HEADLIGHT BULB

Rear turn signal and stop lamp assembly

Rear tire

Quarter trim panel

SPOTLIGHT BULB

Filament

MARKER LIGHT BULB

Filament

FESTOON BULB

Rear quarter trim panel

Roof seal

Inner roof trim

Contact

Bayonet fixing

Contact

Contact

Roof molding

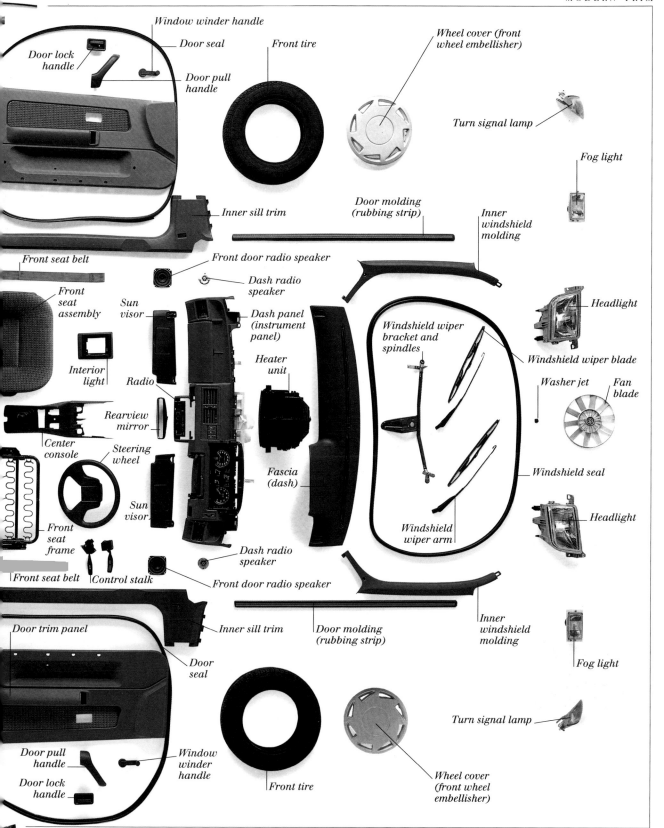

Window winder handle

Door lock handle

Door seal

Door pull handle

Front tire

Wheel cover (front wheel embellisher)

Turn signal lamp

Fog light

Inner sill trim

Door molding (rubbing strip)

Inner windshield molding

Front seat belt

Front door radio speaker

Dash radio speaker

Front seat assembly

Sun visor

Dash panel (instrument panel)

Interior light

Radio

Rearview mirror

Center console

Steering wheel

Sun visor

Heater unit

Windshield wiper bracket and spindles

Headlight

Windshield wiper blade

Washer jet

Fan blade

Fascia (dash)

Windshield seal

Headlight

Front seat frame

Front seat belt

Control stalk

Dash radio speaker

Front door radio speaker

Windshield wiper arm

Inner sill trim

Door molding (rubbing strip)

Inner windshield molding

Fog light

Door trim panel

Door seal

Door pull handle

Door lock handle

Window winder handle

Front tire

Wheel cover (front wheel embellisher)

Turn signal lamp

All-terrain vehicles

THE MODERN ALL-TERRAIN VEHICLE has its origins in the American military Jeep of the 1940s and the British Land Rover. Such vehicles have been used for a wide range of purposes, from safari travel to fire fighting. The principal special features of such cars—including four- or six-wheel drive, high ground clearance, and toughened braking, suspension, and transmission systems—are designed to enable driving under the most difficult off-road conditions. The vehicle shown here is equipped for safari travel and carries a comprehensive range of survival gear.

COOKING EQUIPMENT

TWO-BURNER ALCOHOL STOVE

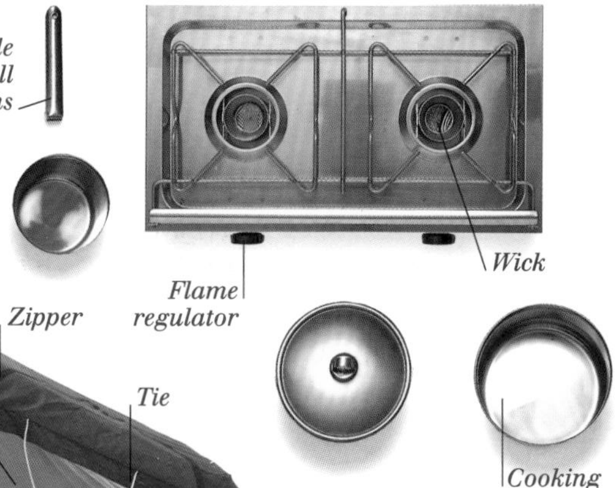
Handle for all pans
Wick
Flame regulator
Cooking pot

HAND WINCH

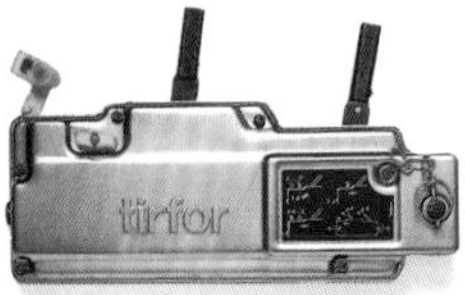
tirfor

SIDE VIEW OF PINZGAUER TURBO D

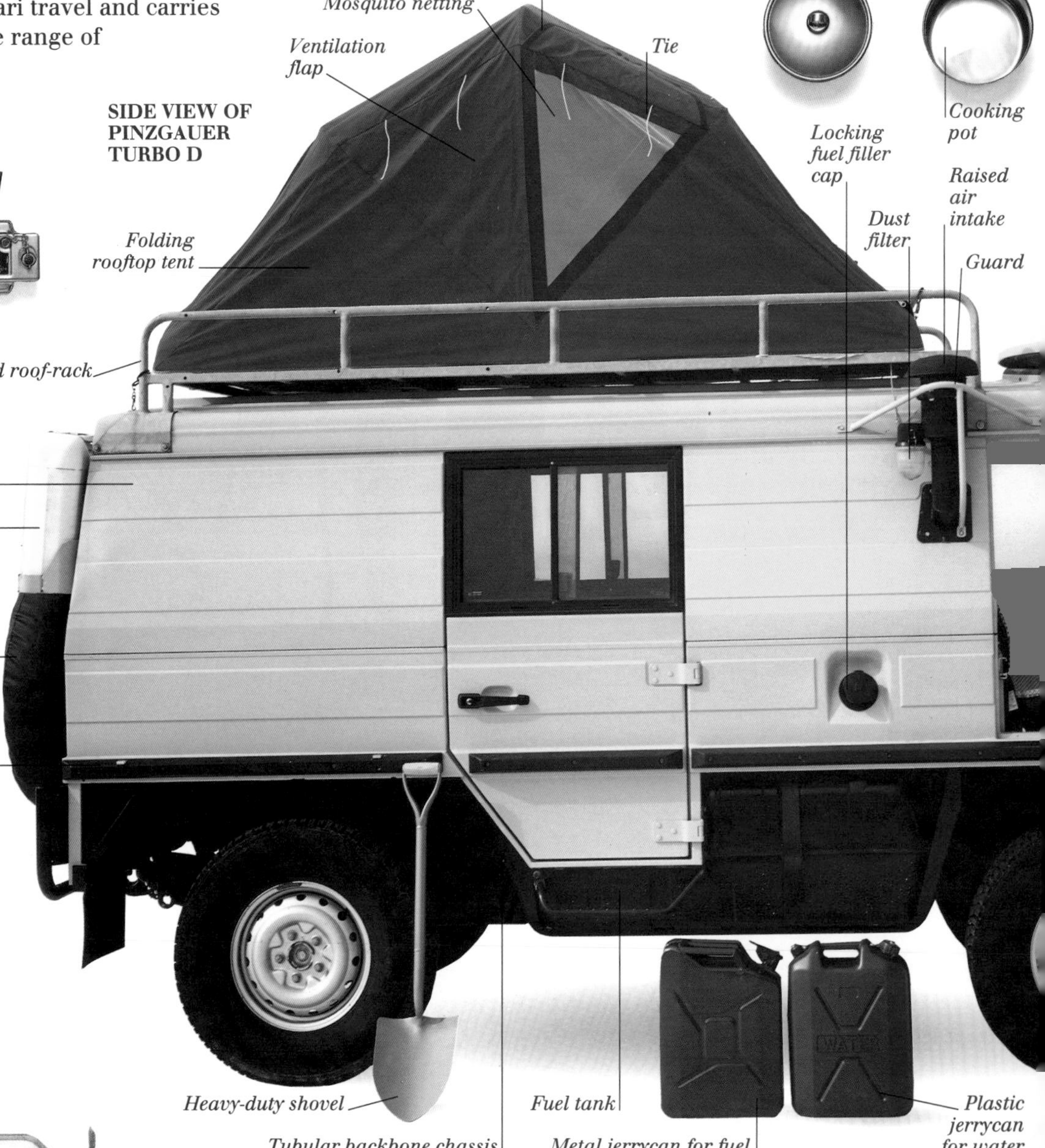
Mosquito netting
Zipper
Ventilation flap
Tie
Locking fuel filler cap
Raised air intake
Dust filter
Guard
Folding rooftop tent
Galvanized roof-rack
Steel body
Jerrycan
Spare wheel and tire
Bodyside molding (rub strip)
Heavy-duty shovel
Tubular backbone chassis
Fuel tank
Metal jerrycan for fuel
Plastic jerrycan for water
WATER

TIRE PUMP

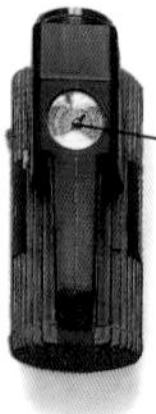
Pressure gauge

TIRE IRON

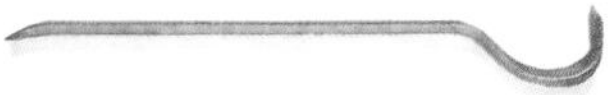

LEFT-HAND
TREAD PLATE

RIGHT-HAND
TREAD PLATE

TOW STRAP

HEAVY-DUTY
SHACKLE

SAFETY WINDSHIELD CLAMPS

WASHING BUCKET

Radio aerial

Observation
roof hatch

Grab
handle

Rearview
mirror

Windshield
washer
bottle

Wrap-
around
bumper

Access step

SECURITY
CHAIN

FRONT VIEW OF PINZGAUER TURBO D

Observation
roof hatch

Radio aerial

Galvanized
roof-rack

Laminated
windshield

Rearview
mirror

Air vent

Indicator

Radiator
grille

Headlight
guard

Headlight

External
step

Independent
swing axle

Locking
differential

Towing
loop

All-terrain
tire

REAR VIEW OF PINZGAUER TURBO D

Roof-rack

Observation
platform

External
step for roof

Jerrycan

Jerrycan
carrier

Spare
wheel

Offset door
hinge

Bodyside
molding (rub
strip)

Rear
bumper

Rear light
cluster

Door and
wheel
support
frame

Mudflap

Off-road
tire

Locking
differential

Independent swing axle

Racing cars

SINCE MOTORING BEGAN, racing cars have been a major focus of innovation in car design. Features that are now commonplace, such as disc brakes, turbochargers, and even safety belts, were used first on competition cars. Research into racing cars has contributed to a new understanding of engine performance, aerodynamics, and tire adhesion, and has led to the development of ultra-light materials such as carbon-fiber for car bodies. Like the 1937 Bugatti Type 57S below, a modern Williams Formula One car has a low, streamlined body and an open cockpit. Unlike its forerunner, it also has a front wing that pushes the front wheels firmly onto the track, huge slick tires for extra grip, and electrical sensors that continually relay information to the pits about the car's performance.

Diffuser

Bodywork bracket

Heat shield

Forward radius arm

Rear wing upper mainplane

Slot

Upper flap

Half shaft

Rear radius arm

Temperature-sensitive sticker

Aeroquip pipe union

Oil tank

Constant velocity joint cover

Rear wing end-plate

Diffuser

Rear brake duct

Oil feed to engine

1937 BUGATTI TYPE 57S

Fuel injection trumpet guard (debris guard)

Mounting point

Fuel injector

Cam cover

Cylinder head

Gearbox fixing stud

Electronic control-unit connector

Water outlet

ENGINE COWLING

Dzus fastener

Tail pipe

Stressed cylinder block

Harmonically tuned exhaust pipe

RENAULT V10 RS1 ENGINE

SIDE FAIRING

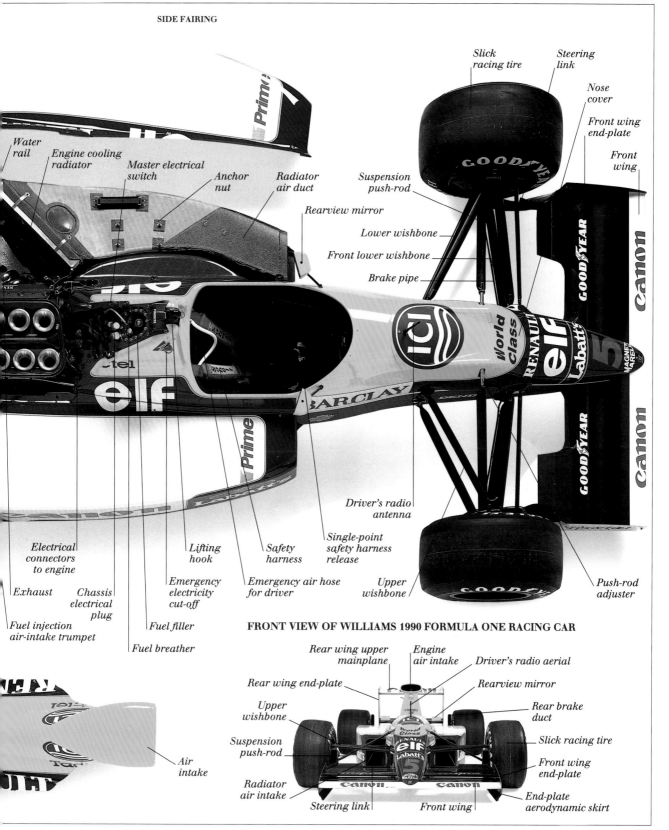

Slick racing tire

Steering link

Nose cover

Front wing end-plate

Front wing

Water rail

Engine cooling radiator

Master electrical switch

Anchor nut

Radiator air duct

Suspension push-rod

Rearview mirror

Lower wishbone

Front lower wishbone

Brake pipe

Driver's radio antenna

Single-point safety harness release

Upper wishbone

Push-rod adjuster

Electrical connectors to engine

Lifting hook

Safety harness

Exhaust

Chassis electrical plug

Emergency electricity cut-off

Emergency air hose for driver

Fuel injection air-intake trumpet

Fuel filler

Fuel breather

Air intake

FRONT VIEW OF WILLIAMS 1990 FORMULA ONE RACING CAR

Rear wing upper mainplane

Engine air intake

Driver's radio aerial

Rear wing end-plate

Rearview mirror

Upper wishbone

Rear brake duct

Suspension push-rod

Slick racing tire

Radiator air intake

Front wing end-plate

Steering link

Front wing

End-plate aerodynamic skirt

Bicycle anatomy

THE BICYCLE IS A TWO-WHEELED, lightweight machine, which is propelled by human power. It is efficient, cheap, easily manufactured, and one of the world's most popular forms of transportation. The first pedal-driven bicycle was built in Scotland in 1839. Since then the basic design—of a frame, wheels, brakes, handlebars, and a saddle—has been gradually improved, with the addition of a chain, gear system, and pneumatic tires (tires inflated with air). The recent invention of the mountain bike (all-terrain bike) has been an important development. With its strong, rugged frame, wide tires, and 21 gears, a mountain bike enables riders to reach rough and hilly areas that were previously inaccessible to cyclists.

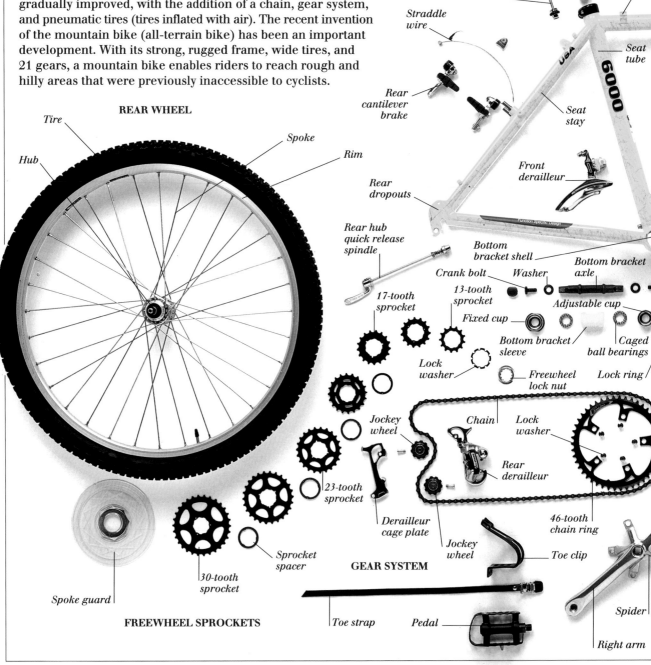

REAR WHEEL

Tire

Spoke

Hub

Rim

Saddle (seat)

Seat post

Cable guide

Seat post quick release bolt

Straddle wire

Seat tube

6000

Rear cantilever brake

Seat stay

Front derailleur

Rear dropouts

Rear hub quick release spindle

Bottom bracket shell

Bottom bracket axle

Crank bolt

Washer

17-tooth sprocket

13-tooth sprocket

Adjustable cup

Fixed cup

Bottom bracket sleeve

Caged ball bearings

Lock washer

Freewheel lock nut

Lock ring

Jockey wheel

Chain

Lock washer

Rear derailleur

23-tooth sprocket

Derailleur cage plate

Jockey wheel

46-tooth chain ring

Sprocket spacer

30-tooth sprocket

Toe clip

Spoke guard

GEAR SYSTEM

FREEWHEEL SPROCKETS

Toe strap

Pedal

Spider

Right arm

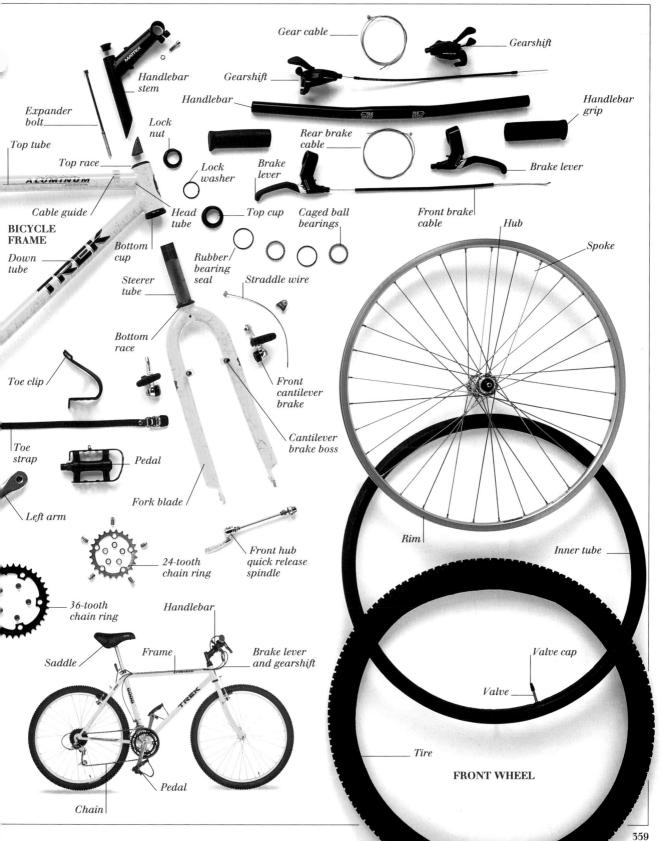

Gear cable

Gearshift

Gearshift

Handlebar
stem

Handlebar

Handlebar
grip

Expander
bolt

Lock
nut

Top tube

Top race

Lock
washer

Brake
lever

Rear brake
cable

Brake lever

Cable guide

Head
tube

Top cup

Caged ball
bearings

Front brake
cable

Hub

Spoke

BICYCLE
FRAME

Down
tube

Bottom
cup

Rubber
bearing
seal

Straddle wire

Steerer
tube

Bottom
race

Front
cantilever
brake

Toe clip

Cantilever
brake boss

Toe
strap

Pedal

Rim

Left arm

Fork blade

Front hub
quick release
spindle

Inner tube

24-tooth
chain ring

36-tooth
chain ring

Handlebar

Valve cap

Saddle

Frame

Brake lever
and gearshift

Valve

Pedal

Tire

Chain

FRONT WHEEL

Bicycles

ALTHOUGH ALL BICYCLES are made up of the same basic components, they can vary greatly in design. A racing bike, such as the Eddy Merckx model, with its light frame and steep head- and seat-angles, is built for speed. Its design forces the rider to adopt the aero tuck, a crouched, aerodynamic position. While a touring bike resembles a racing bike in many respects, it is designed for comfort and stability on long-distance journeys. Touring bikes are characterized by more relaxed frame angles, heavy chain stays that support the rear panniers, and a long wheelbase (the distance between the wheel axles) for reliable handling. All-purpose bicycles, known as hybrids, combine the light weight and speed of sports bikes with the rugged durability of mountain bikes (see pp. 358-359). Bicycles that are not designed for conventional road use include time-trial bikes, which have a short head tube, sloping top tube, aero handlebars, and aerodynamic tubing. Most Human Powered Vehicles (HPVs) are recumbents—the rider has a recumbent position—which maximize power output and minimize drag (resistance). Essential to the safety of all riders are helmets, and both front and rear lights; locks protect against theft.

FRONT AND REAR LIGHTS

HELMET

Hard outer shell

Red rear light

White front light

Air vent

Polystyrene padding

Quick-release strap

EDDY MERCKX RACING BICYCLE

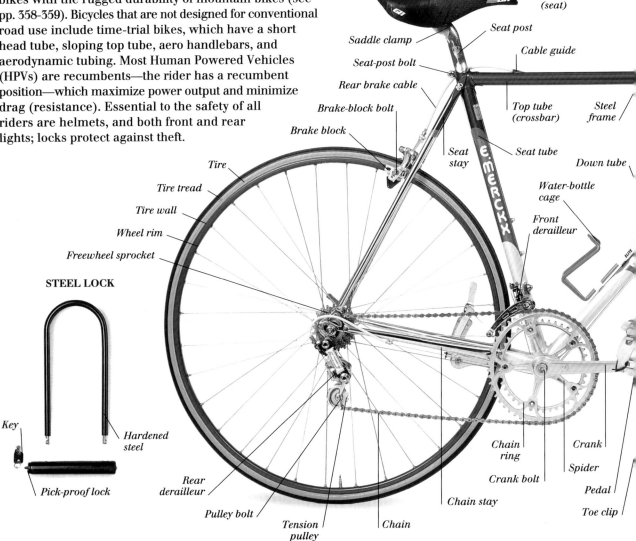

Saddle (seat)

Seat post

Cable guide

Saddle clamp

Seat-post bolt

Rear brake cable

Brake-block bolt

Brake block

Top tube (crossbar)

Steel frame

Seat stay

Seat tube

Down tube

Tire

Water-bottle cage

Tire tread

Front derailleur

Tire wall

Wheel rim

Freewheel sprocket

STEEL LOCK

Key

Hardened steel

Pick-proof lock

Rear derailleur

Pulley bolt

Tension pulley

Chain

Chain stay

Chain ring

Crank bolt

Crank

Spider

Pedal

Toe clip

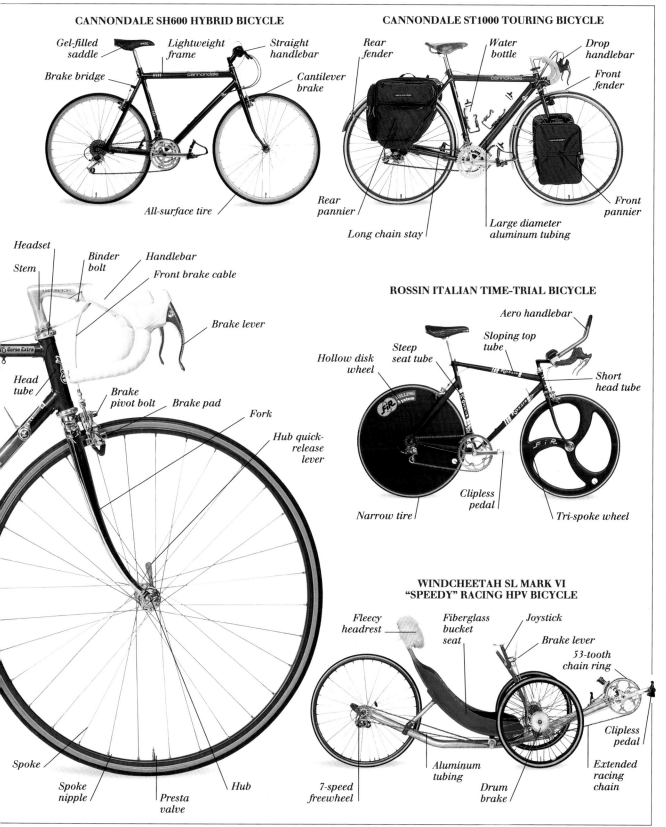

CANNONDALE SH600 HYBRID BICYCLE

Gel-filled saddle

Lightweight frame

Straight handlebar

Brake bridge

Cantilever brake

All-surface tire

CANNONDALE ST1000 TOURING BICYCLE

Rear fender

Water bottle

Drop handlebar

Front fender

Rear pannier

Long chain stay

Large diameter aluminum tubing

Front pannier

Headset

Stem

Binder bolt

Handlebar

Front brake cable

Brake lever

Head tube

Brake pivot bolt

Brake pad

Fork

Hub quick-release lever

ROSSIN ITALIAN TIME-TRIAL BICYCLE

Aero handlebar

Sloping top tube

Steep seat tube

Hollow disk wheel

Short head tube

Narrow tire

Clipless pedal

Tri-spoke wheel

Spoke

Spoke nipple

Presta valve

Hub

WINDCHEETAH SL MARK VI "SPEEDY" RACING HPV BICYCLE

Fleecy headrest

Fiberglass bucket seat

Joystick

Brake lever

53-tooth chain ring

Aluminum tubing

7-speed freewheel

Drum brake

Clipless pedal

Extended racing chain

The motorcycle

THE MOTORCYCLE HAS EVOLVED from a motorized cycle—a basic bicycle with an engine—into a sophisticated, high-performance machine. In 1901, the Werner brothers established the most viable location for the engine, positioning it low in the center of the chassis (see pp. 364-365): the new Werner became the basis for the modern motorcycle. Motorcycles are used for many purposes —for commuting, delivering messages, touring, and racing—and different machines have been developed to suit the demands of different types of riders. The Vespa scooter, for instance, which is small-wheeled, economical, and easy-to-ride, was designed to meet the needs of the commuter. Sidecars provided transportation for the family until the arrival of cheap cars caused their popularity to decline. Serious riders generally favor larger capacity machines that are capable of greater performance and offer more comfort. Four-cylinder machines have been common since the Honda CB750 appeared in 1969. Despite advances in motorcycle technology, many riders are attracted to the traditional look of motorcycles like the twin-cylinder Harley-Davidson. Harley-Davidson Glides exploit the style of the classic American V-twin engine, where the cylinders are placed in a V-formation.

1901 WERNER MOTORCYCLE

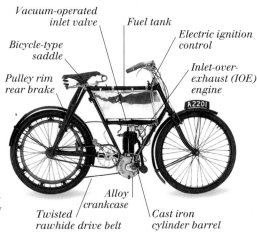

Vacuum-operated inlet valve

Fuel tank

Bicycle-type saddle

Electric ignition control

Pulley rim rear brake

Inlet-over-exhaust (IOE) engine

Alloy crankcase

Twisted rawhide drive belt

Cast iron cylinder barrel

1988 HARLEY-DAVIDSON FLHS ELECTRA GLIDE

1965 BMW R/60 WITH 1952 STEIB CHAIR

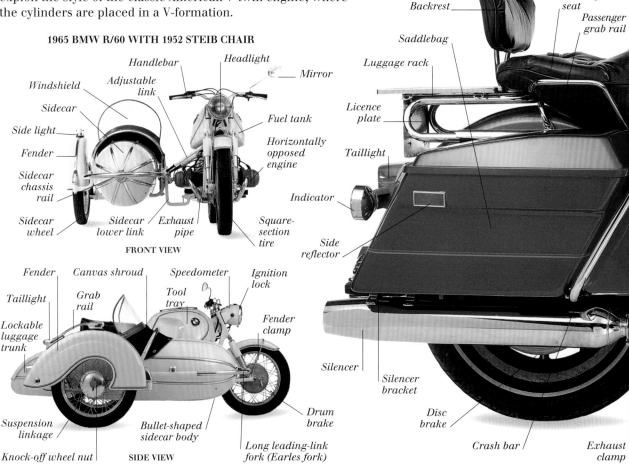

Handlebar

Headlight

Adjustable link

Mirror

Windshield

Sidecar

Side light

Fuel tank

Fender

Horizontally opposed engine

Sidecar chassis rail

Sidecar wheel

Sidecar lower link

Exhaust pipe

Square-section tire

FRONT VIEW

Fender

Canvas shroud

Speedometer

Ignition lock

Taillight

Grab rail

Tool tray

Lockable luggage trunk

Fender clamp

Silencer

Suspension linkage

Bullet-shaped sidecar body

Drum brake

Knock-off wheel nut

SIDE VIEW

Long leading-link fork (Earles fork)

Backrest

Passenger seat

Passenger grab rail

Saddlebag

Luggage rack

Licence plate

Taillight

Indicator

Side reflector

Silencer bracket

Disc brake

Crash bar

Exhaust clamp

1969 HONDA CB750

1963 VESPA GRAND SPORT 160 MARK 1

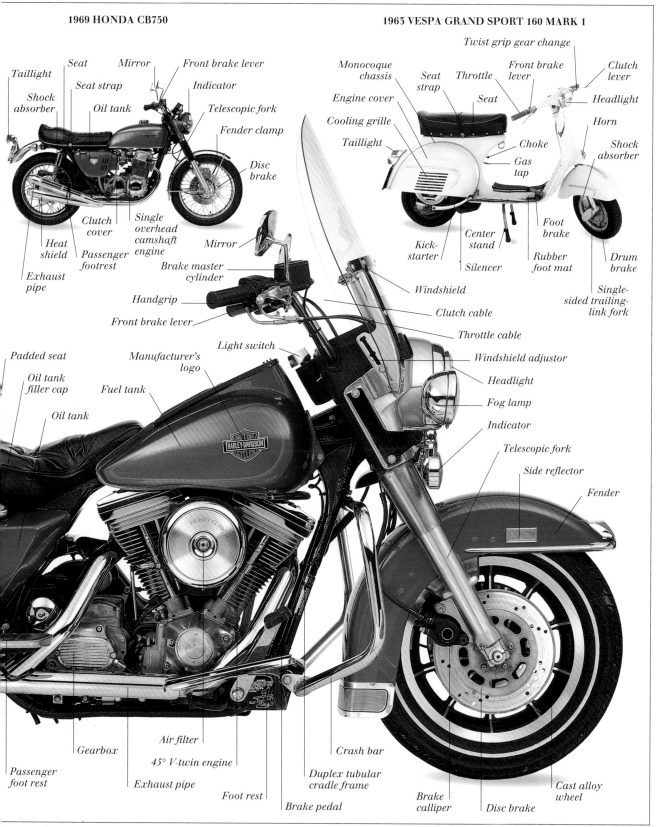

Taillight

Seat

Mirror

Front brake lever

Shock absorber

Seat strap

Indicator

Oil tank

Telescopic fork

Fender clamp

Disc brake

Clutch cover

Single overhead camshaft engine

Mirror

Heat shield

Passenger footrest

Exhaust pipe

Twist grip gear change

Monocoque chassis

Seat strap

Throttle

Front brake lever

Clutch lever

Engine cover

Seat

Headlight

Cooling grille

Horn

Taillight

Choke

Shock absorber

Gas tap

Kick-starter

Center stand

Foot brake

Rubber foot mat

Drum brake

Silencer

Single-sided trailing-link fork

Brake master cylinder

Handgrip

Front brake lever

Windshield

Clutch cable

Throttle cable

Padded seat

Manufacturer's logo

Light switch

Windshield adjustor

Oil tank filler cap

Fuel tank

Headlight

Oil tank

Fog lamp

Indicator

Telescopic fork

Side reflector

Fender

Gearbox

Air filter

Crash bar

45° V-twin engine

Passenger foot rest

Exhaust pipe

Foot rest

Duplex tubular cradle frame

Brake pedal

Brake calliper

Disc brake

Cast alloy wheel

The motorcycle chassis

THE MOTORCYCLE CHASSIS is the main "body" of the motorcycle, to which the engine is attached. Consisting of the frame, wheels, suspension, and brakes, the chassis performs various functions. The frame, which is built from steel or alloy, keeps the wheels in line to maintain the handling of the motorcycle, and serves as a structure for mounting other components. The engine and gearbox unit is bolted into place, while items such as the seat, the fenders, and the fairing are more easily removable. Suspension cushions the rider from irregularities in the road surface. In most suspension systems, coil springs controlled by an oil damper separate the main mass of the motorcycle from the wheels. At the front, the spring and damper are usually incorporated in a telescopic fork; the rear employs a pivoted swing arm. The suspension also helps to retain maximum contact between the tires and the road, necessary to effective braking and steering. Drum brakes were common until the 1970s, but modern motorcycles use disc brakes, which are more powerful.

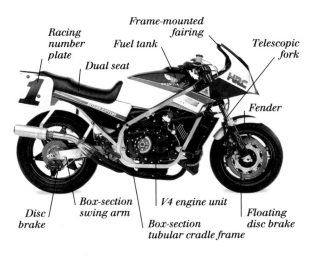

1985 HONDA VF750 WITH BODYWORK

Racing number plate
Frame-mounted fairing
Fuel tank
Telescopic fork
Dual seat
Fender
Disc brake
Box-section swing arm
V4 engine unit
Floating disc brake
Box-section tubular cradle frame

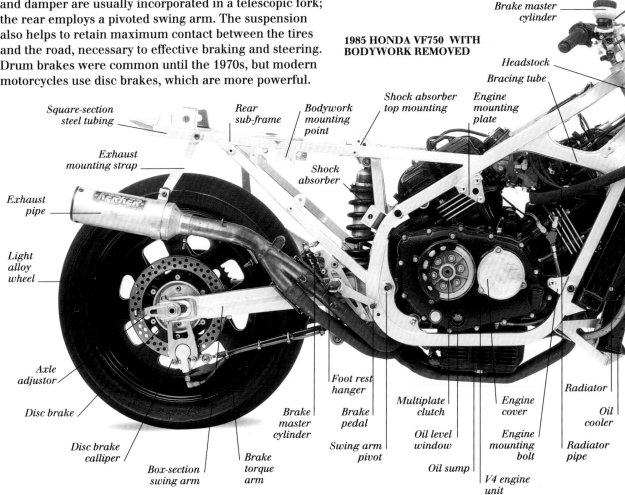

1985 HONDA VF750 WITH BODYWORK REMOVED

Brake master cylinder
Headstock
Bracing tube
Shock absorber top mounting
Engine mounting plate
Square-section steel tubing
Rear sub-frame
Bodywork mounting point
Shock absorber
Exhaust mounting strap
Exhaust pipe
Light alloy wheel
Axle adjustor
Disc brake
Disc brake calliper
Box-section swing arm
Brake torque arm
Brake master cylinder
Foot rest hanger
Brake pedal
Swing arm pivot
Multiplate clutch
Oil level window
Oil sump
Engine cover
Engine mounting bolt
V4 engine unit
Radiator
Oil cooler
Radiator pipe

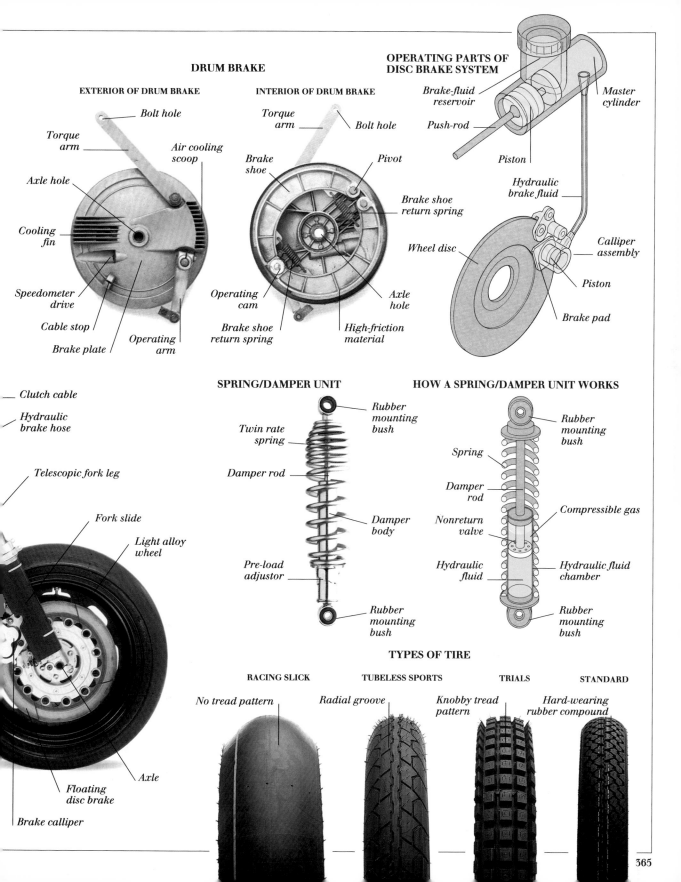

DRUM BRAKE

OPERATING PARTS OF DISC BRAKE SYSTEM

Brake-fluid reservoir

Master cylinder

Push-rod

Piston

Hydraulic brake fluid

Wheel disc

Calliper assembly

Piston

Brake pad

EXTERIOR OF DRUM BRAKE

Bolt hole

Torque arm

Air cooling scoop

Axle hole

Cooling fin

Speedometer drive

Cable stop

Brake plate

Operating arm

INTERIOR OF DRUM BRAKE

Torque arm

Bolt hole

Brake shoe

Pivot

Brake shoe return spring

Operating cam

Axle hole

Brake shoe return spring

High-friction material

Clutch cable

Hydraulic brake hose

Telescopic fork leg

Fork slide

Light alloy wheel

Floating disc brake

Axle

Brake calliper

SPRING/DAMPER UNIT

Rubber mounting bush

Twin rate spring

Damper rod

Damper body

Pre-load adjustor

Rubber mounting bush

HOW A SPRING/DAMPER UNIT WORKS

Rubber mounting bush

Spring

Damper rod

Nonreturn valve

Compressible gas

Hydraulic fluid

Hydraulic fluid chamber

Rubber mounting bush

TYPES OF TIRE

RACING SLICK

No tread pattern

TUBELESS SPORTS

Radial groove

TRIALS

Knobby tread pattern

STANDARD

Hard-wearing rubber compound

Motorcycle engines

MOTORCYCLE ENGINES must be lightweight and compact, and have a good power output. They have between one and six cylinders, can be cooled by air or water, and the capacity of the combustion chamber varies from 49cc (cubic centimeters) to 1500cc. Two types of internal combustion engine are common: the four-stroke, which is used in cars (see pp. 342-343), and the two-stroke. A basic two-stroke engine has only three moving parts—the crankshaft, the connecting rod, and the piston—but the power output is high. The engine fires every two strokes (rather than every four), giving a "power stroke" every revolution (see p. 343). Power is conveyed from the engine to the rear wheel by the transmission system. This usually consists of a clutch, a gearbox, and a final drive system. Clutches are multiplate devices, which run in oil. Gearboxes have five or six speeds and are operated by foot pedal. Shaft and belt drive systems are used in some cases, but chain drive to the rear wheel is most common.

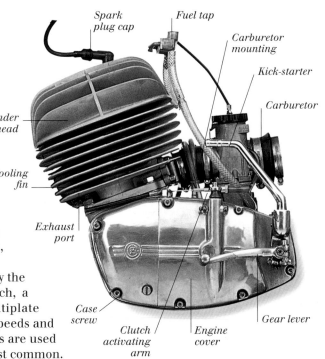

EXTERIOR OF STANDARD TWO-STROKE ENGINE

- Spark plug cap
- Fuel tap
- Carburetor mounting
- Kick-starter
- Carburetor
- Cylinder head
- Cooling fin
- Exhaust port
- Case screw
- Clutch activating arm
- Engine cover
- Gear lever

TRANSMISSION SYSTEM

GEARBOX

- Gear lever selector shaft
- 5th gear
- 2nd gear
- 3rd gear
- 4th gear
- 6th gear
- 1st gear
- Input shaft
- Splines for mounting gear lever
- Bearing
- Output shaft
- Splines for mounting final drive sprocket
- Gear tooth
- Selector fork
- Copper oil feed pipe
- Aluminum outer casing

MULTIPLATE CLUTCH

- Fiber plate
- Outer clutch drum, connected to engine
- Pressure plate, connected to inner clutch drum
- Springs force plates together
- Metal plate
- Key locks fiber plate to outer drum
- Straight-cut primary-drive gear

MODERN O-RING DRIVE CHAIN

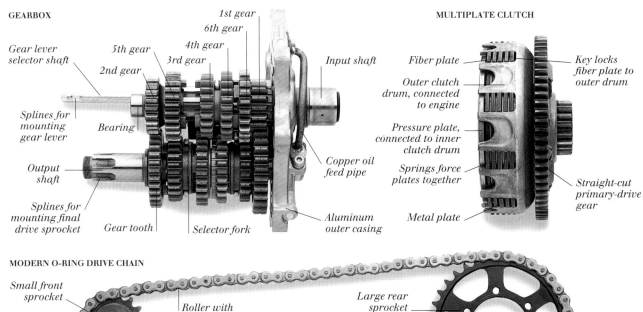

- Small front sprocket
- Roller with sealed-in lubricant
- Large rear sprocket
- Mounting hole
- Plate
- Sprocket tooth
- Hole for retaining bolt

**VELOCETTE OVERHEAD
VALVE (OHV) ENGINE**

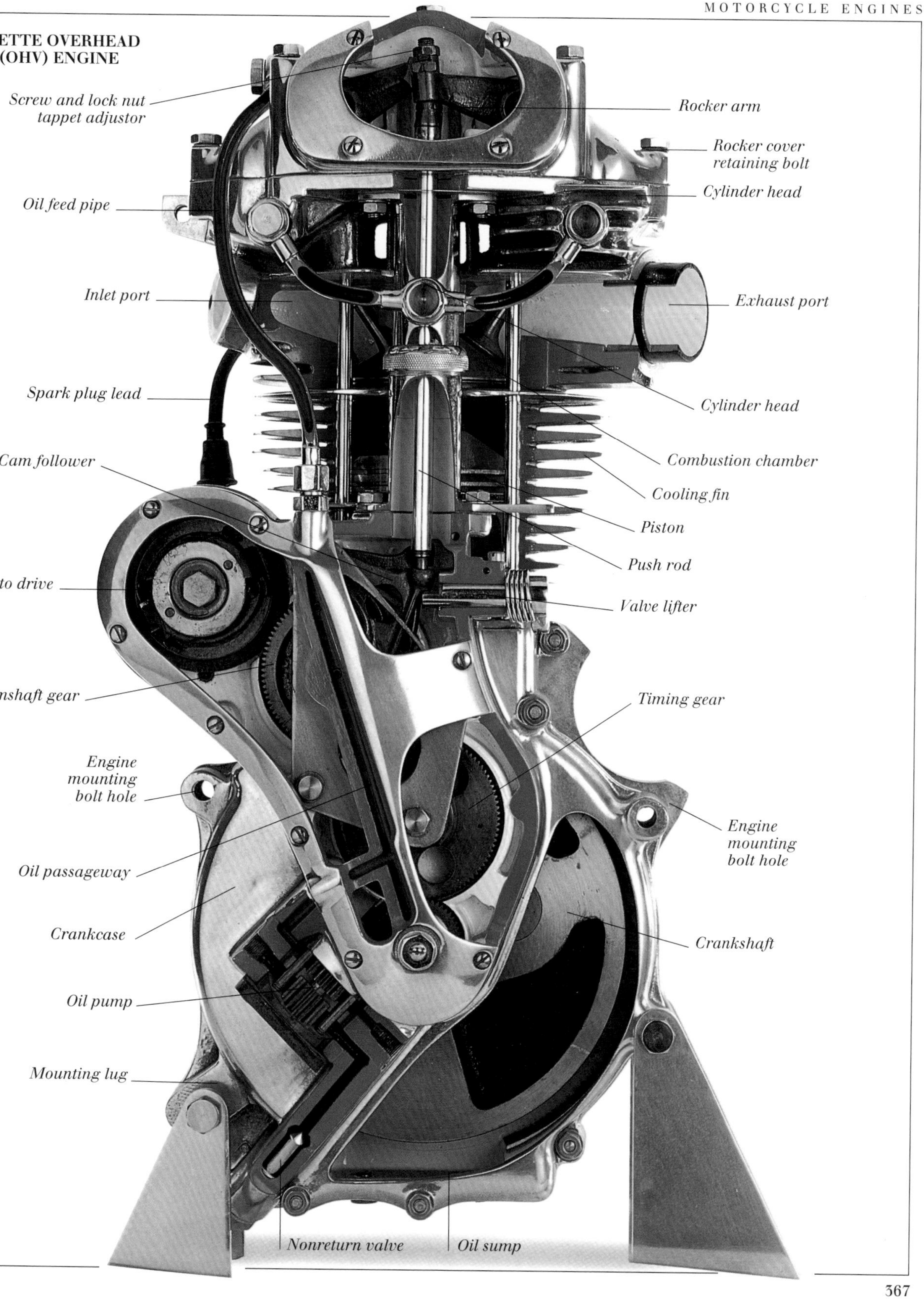

Screw and lock nut
tappet adjustor

Rocker arm

Rocker cover
retaining bolt

Oil feed pipe

Cylinder head

Inlet port

Exhaust port

Spark plug lead

Cylinder head

Combustion chamber

Cam follower

Cooling fin

Piston

Magneto drive

Push rod

Valve lifter

Camshaft gear

Timing gear

Engine
mounting
bolt hole

Engine
mounting
bolt hole

Oil passageway

Crankcase

Crankshaft

Oil pump

Mounting lug

Nonreturn valve

Oil sump

367

Competition motorcycles

THERE ARE MANY TYPES of motorcycle sports and in each, a special machine has evolved to perform to specific requirements. Races take place on roads or tracks or "off-road," in fields, dirt tracks, and even the desert. "Grand Prix" world championships in roadracing exist for 125cc, 250cc, and 500cc classes, as well as for sidecars. The latest racing sidecars have more in common with racing cars than motorcycles. The rider and passenger operate within an all-enclosing, aerodynamic fairing. The Suzuki RGV500 shown here, like other Grand Prix machines, carries advertising, which promotes the manufacturer and helps to cover the cost of developing motorcycle technology. In Speedway, which originated in the U.S. in 1902, motorcycles operate without brakes or a gearbox. Off-road competition motorcycles have less emphasis on high power output. In Motocross, for example, which is held on rough terrain, they must have high ground clearance, flexible long-travel suspension, and tires with a chunky tread pattern, to allow them to grip in sand or mud.

1992 HUSQVARNA MOTOCROSS TC610

Throttle cable
Handlebar brace
Long seat
Racing number
Hand protector
Radiator air vent
Flexible plastic fender
Light-weight exhaust system
Telescopic fork
Plastic guard
Axle
Overhead camshaft engine
Gear lever
Shock absorber
Disc brake
Knobby tire
Disc brake
Brake calliper
Alloy swing arm
Shock absorber linkage

1992 SUZUKI RGV500
SIDE VIEW

Exhaust pipe
Racing number
Air vent
One-piece seat and tail unit
Shock absorber
Minimal seat padding
Arched alloy swing arm
Exhaust pipe
Vent
Silencer
Shock absorber mounting
Three-spoke alloy wheel
Exhaust pipe
Exhaust pipe
Handlebar
Foot rest
Rear brake pedal
Drive chain
Wide, slick tire
Axle adjustor
Disc brake
Rear brake calliper
Slick racing tire
Drive chain
Foot rest
Brake pedal
Disc brake master cylinder
Lightweight alloy frame

REAR VIEW

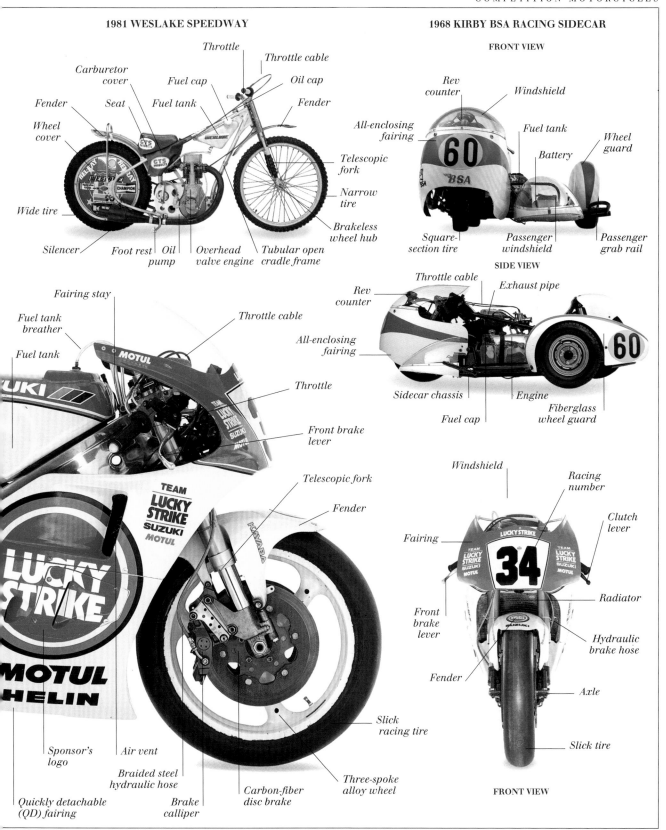

1981 WESLAKE SPEEDWAY

Throttle

Carburetor cover

Throttle cable

Fuel cap

Oil cap

Fender

Seat

Fuel tank

Fender

Wheel cover

Telescopic fork

Narrow tire

Wide tire

Brakeless wheel hub

Silencer

Foot rest

Oil pump

Overhead valve engine

Tubular open cradle frame

Fairing stay

Throttle cable

Fuel tank breather

Throttle

Fuel tank

Front brake lever

Telescopic fork

Fender

Slick racing tire

Sponsor's logo

Air vent

Braided steel hydraulic hose

Brake calliper

Three-spoke alloy wheel

Quickly detachable (QD) fairing

Carbon-fiber disc brake

1968 KIRBY BSA RACING SIDECAR

FRONT VIEW

Rev counter

Windshield

All-enclosing fairing

Fuel tank

Battery

Wheel guard

60

BSA

Square-section tire

Passenger windshield

Passenger grab rail

SIDE VIEW

Throttle cable

Exhaust pipe

Rev counter

All-enclosing fairing

60

Sidecar chassis

Engine

Fuel cap

Fiberglass wheel guard

Windshield

Racing number

Clutch lever

Fairing

34

Radiator

Front brake lever

Hydraulic brake hose

Fender

Axle

Slick tire

FRONT VIEW

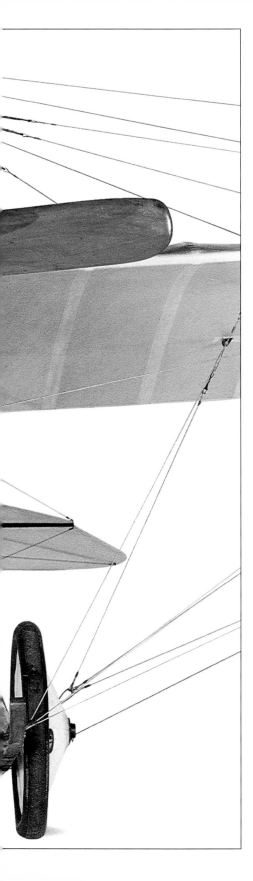

Sea and Air

Ships of Greece and Rome · · · · · 372
Viking Ships · · · · · 374
Medieval Warships and Traders · · · · · 376
The Expansion of Sail · · · · · 378
A Ship of the Line · · · · · 380
Rigging · · · · · 382
Sails · · · · · 384
Mooring and Anchoring · · · · · 386
Ropes and Knots · · · · · 388
Paddlewheels and Propellers · · · · · 390
Anatomy of an Iron Ship · · · · · 392
The Battleship · · · · · 394
Frigates and Submarines · · · · · 396
Pioneers of Flight · · · · · 398
Early Monoplanes · · · · · 400
Biplanes and Triplanes · · · · · 402
World War I Aircraft · · · · · 404
Early Passenger aircraft · · · · · 406
World War II Aircraft · · · · · 408
Modern Piston Aero-engines · · · · · 410
Modern Jetliners 1 · · · · · 412
Modern Jetliners 2 · · · · · 414
Supersonic Jetliners · · · · · 416
Jet Engines · · · · · 418
Modern Military Aircraft · · · · · 420
Helicopters · · · · · 422
Light Aircraft · · · · · 424
Gliders, Hang-gliders, and Microlights 426

Ships of Greece and Rome

ROMAN ANCHOR

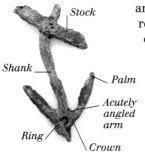

Stock

Shank

Palm

Acutely
angled
arm

Ring

Crown

IN THE EXPANSIVE EMPIRES OF GREECE AND ROME, powerful fleets were needed for battle, trade, and communication. Greek galleys were powered by a sail and many oars. A new armament, the embolos (ram), was fitted on to the galley bow. As ramming duels required fast and maneuverable boats, extra rows of oarsmen were added, culminating in the trireme. During the fifth and fourth centuries B.C., the trireme dominated the Mediterranean. It was powered by 170 oarsmen, each pulling one oar, and ranged on three levels, as the model opposite shows. The trireme also carried archers and soldiers for boarding enemy craft. Galleys were pulled out of the water when not in use, and were kept in dockyard ship-sheds. The merchant ships of the Greeks and Romans were mighty vessels, too. The full-bodied Roman corbita, for example, could hold up to 400 tons of cargo, such as spices, gems, silk, and animals. The construction of these boats was based on a stout hull with planking secured by mortice and tenon. Some of these ships made long trading voyages, sailing even as far as India. To make them easier to steer, corbitas set a foresail called an "artemon." It flew from a forward-leaning mast that was the forerunner of the long bowsprits carried by the great clipper ships of the 19th century.

**ATTIC VASE SHOWING
A GREEK GALLEY**

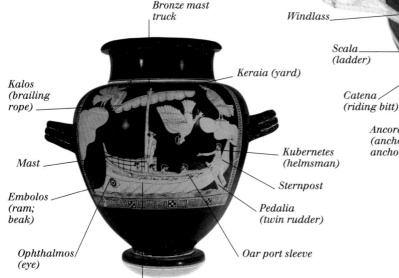

Double halyard   **ROMAN CORBITA**

Bullseye

Antenna
(yard)

Fore mast

Buntline

Brace

Artemon
(fore sail)

Oculus
(eye)

Roband
(rope band)

Ceruchi
(lift)

Heraldic device

Ring

Ruden
(brail line)

Fore stay

Anchor

Sheet

Tabling

Bolt rope

Prow

Windlass

Scala
(ladder)

Catena
(riding bitt)

Ancorale
(anchor rope;
anchor rode)

Bronze mast
truck

Keraia (yard)

Kalos
(brailing
rope)

Mast

Kubernetes
(helmsman)

Sternpost

Embolos
(ram;
beak)

Pedalia
(twin rudder)

Ophthalmos
(eye)

Oar port sleeve

Hatch board

Deck beam

Zosteres (rubbing strake)

Kope (oar)

Cargo hold

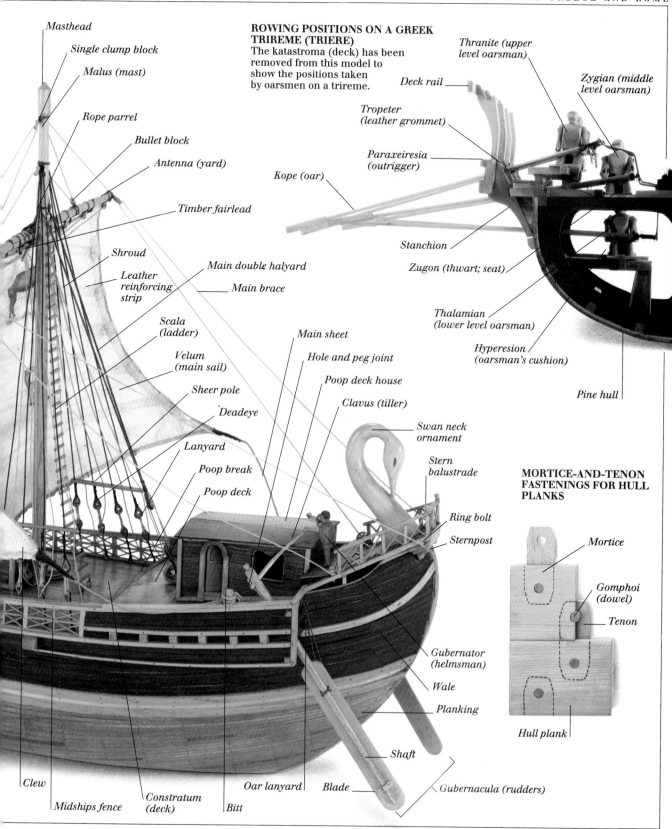

Masthead

Single clump block

Malus (mast)

Rope parrel

Bullet block

Antenna (yard)

Timber fairlead

Shroud

Leather
reinforcing
strip

Main double halyard

Main brace

Scala
(ladder)

Velum
(main sail)

Sheer pole

Deadeye

Lanyard

Poop break

Poop deck

Clew

Midships fence

Constratum
(deck)

Bitt

Main sheet

Hole and peg joint

Poop deck house

Clavus (tiller)

Swan neck
ornament

Stern
balustrade

Ring bolt

Sternpost

Gubernator
(helmsman)

Wale

Planking

Oar lanyard

Blade

Shaft

Gubernacula (rudders)

**ROWING POSITIONS ON A GREEK
TRIREME (TRIERE)**
The katastroma (deck) has been
removed from this model to
show the positions taken
by oarsmen on a trireme.

Thranite (upper
level oarsman)

Zygian (middle
level oarsman)

Deck rail

Tropeter
(leather grommet)

Paraxeiresia
(outrigger)

Kope (oar)

Stanchion

Zugon (thwart; seat)

Thalamian
(lower level oarsman)

Hyperesion
(oarsman's cushion)

Pine hull

**MORTICE-AND-TENON
FASTENINGS FOR HULL
PLANKS**

Mortice

Gomphoi
(dowel)

Tenon

Hull plank

373

Viking ships

IN THE DARK AGES (roughly 500 A.D. to 1000 A.D.) the longships of Scandinavia were among the most feared sights for people of northern Europe. The Vikings launched raids from Scandinavia every summer in longships equipped with a single steering oar on the right, or "steerboard" side (hence, "starboard"). A longboat had one row of oars on each side and a single sail. The hull was clinker-built, with overlapping planks. Prowheads adorned fighting ships during war campaigns. The longship was also used for coastal travel. The karv below was probably built as transport for an important family, while the smaller faering was a rowing boat only. The fleet of William of Normandy that invaded England in 1066 owed much to the Viking boat building tradition, and has been depicted in the Bayeux Tapestry (right). Seals of port towns and royal courts through the ages provide a record of contemporary ship design. The seal opposite shows a European craft from somewhat later than the Viking period. Fighting platforms, or castles, and the addition of more masts and sails changed the character of the medieval ship. Note also that the steering oar has been replaced by a centered rudder.

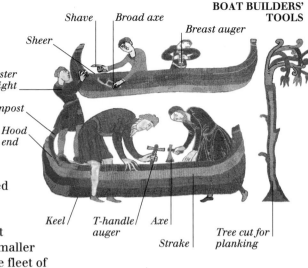

Shave

Broad axe

Breast auger

Sheer

Master shipwright

Stempost

Hood end

Keel

T-handle auger

Axe

Strake

Tree cut for planking

Zoomorphic head

Eye

Tooth

Roband

Leather diagonal reinforcement

Square sail of homespun yarn

Leech (leach)

Braiding

Serpentine neck

Snake-tail ornament

VIKING KARV (COASTER)

Clew

Lozenge-shaped recess

Rectangular cross-band

Tiller

Tye halyard

Sternpost

Foot

DRAGON PROWHEAD

Boss (rudder pivot)

Steering oar (side rudder)

Oar

Starboard (steerboard) side

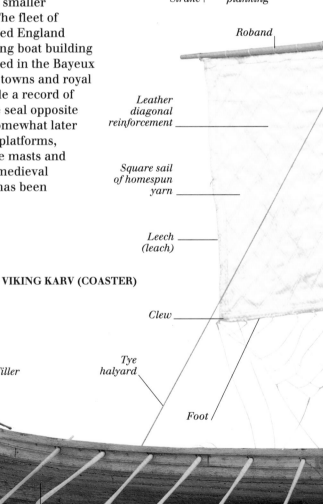

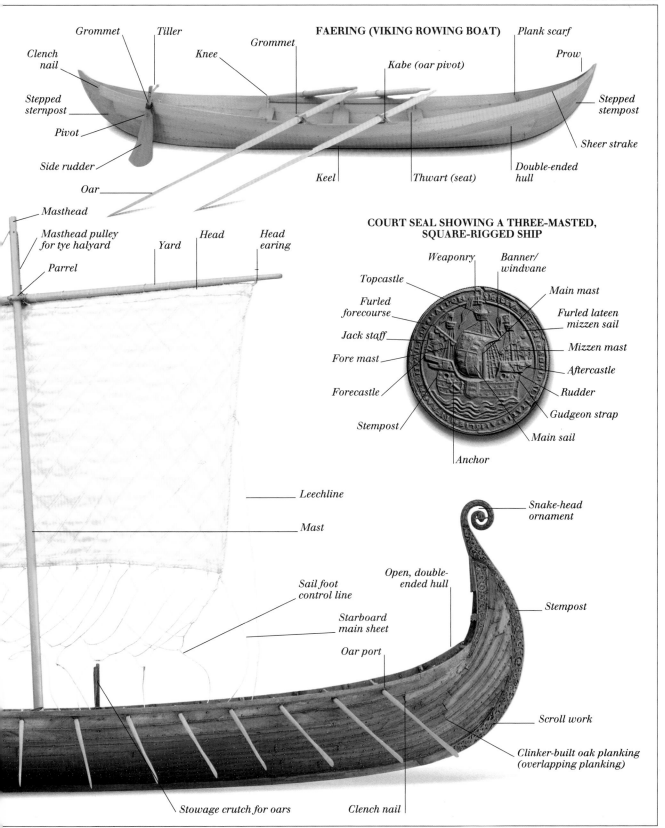

FAERING (VIKING ROWING BOAT)

Grommet

Tiller

Knee

Grommet

Kabe (oar pivot)

Plank scarf

Prow

Clench nail

Stepped sternpost

Pivot

Side rudder

Oar

Keel

Thwart (seat)

Stepped stempost

Sheer strake

Double-ended hull

Masthead

Masthead pulley for tye halyard

Yard

Head

Head earing

Parrel

COURT SEAL SHOWING A THREE-MASTED, SQUARE-RIGGED SHIP

Weaponry

Banner/ windvane

Topcastle

Main mast

Furled forecourse

Furled lateen mizzen sail

Jack staff

Mizzen mast

Fore mast

Aftercastle

Forecastle

Rudder

Stempost

Gudgeon strap

Anchor

Main sail

Leechline

Mast

Snake-head ornament

Sail foot control line

Open, double-ended hull

Starboard main sheet

Stempost

Oar port

Scroll work

Clinker-built oak planking (overlapping planking)

Stowage crutch for oars

Clench nail

375

Medieval warships and traders

FROM THE 16TH CENTURY, SHIPS WERE BUILT WITH A NEW FORM OF HULL, constructed with carvel (edge-to-edge) planking. Warships of the time, like King Henry VIII of England's Mary Rose, boasted awesome fire power. This ship carried both long-range bronze cannon, and short-range, anti personnel guns in iron. Elsewhere, ships took on a multiformity of shapes. Dhows transported slaves from East Africa to Arabia, their fore-and-aft rigged lateen sails allowing them to sail close to the wind around the lands of the Indian Ocean. The Chinese sailed to East Africa and Arabia in junks, trading goods that were carried in watertight compartments. New astronomical tools helped medieval sailors to find their way. Cross-staves and astrolabes were used to measure the altitude of the sun or stars. One of the cross-pieces was slid along the staff of the cross-stave—which was graduated in degrees of altitude—until its top aligned with the celestial body and its base with the horizon. The sighting rule of the astrolabe was simply lined up with a known body, and its altitude read from marks on the metal disk. Sundials used the shadow of the sun to show sailors the time of day.

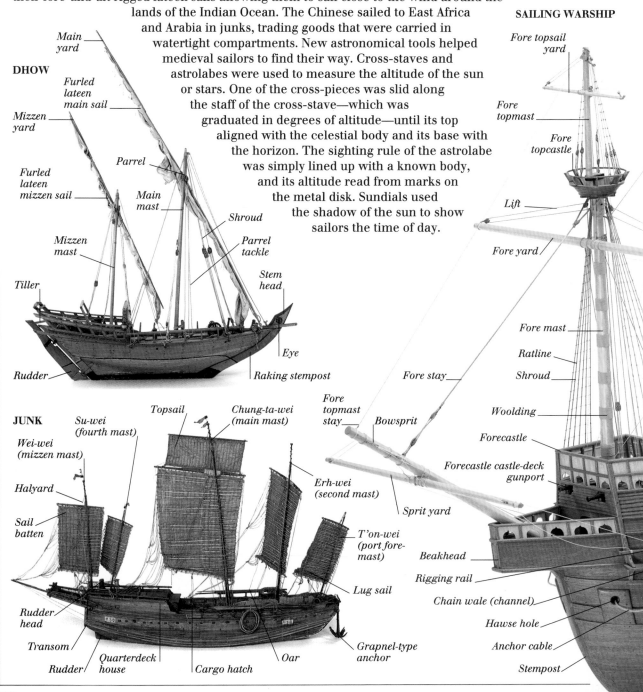

DHOW

Main yard
Furled lateen main sail
Mizzen yard
Parrel
Furled lateen mizzen sail
Main mast
Mizzen mast
Shroud
Parrel tackle
Tiller
Stem head
Rudder
Eye
Raking stempost

JUNK

Su-wei (fourth mast)
Topsail
Chung-ta-wei (main mast)
Wei-wei (mizzen mast)
Halyard
Erh-wei (second mast)
Sail batten
T'on-wei (port fore-mast)
Rudder head
Lug sail
Transom
Grapnel-type anchor
Rudder
Quarterdeck house
Cargo hatch
Oar

SAILING WARSHIP

Fore topsail yard
Fore topmast
Fore topcastle
Fore topmast stay
Bowsprit
Lift
Fore yard
Fore mast
Ratline
Fore stay
Shroud
Woolding
Sprit yard
Forecastle
Forecastle castle-deck gunport
Beakhead
Rigging rail
Chain wale (channel)
Hawse hole
Anchor cable
Stempost

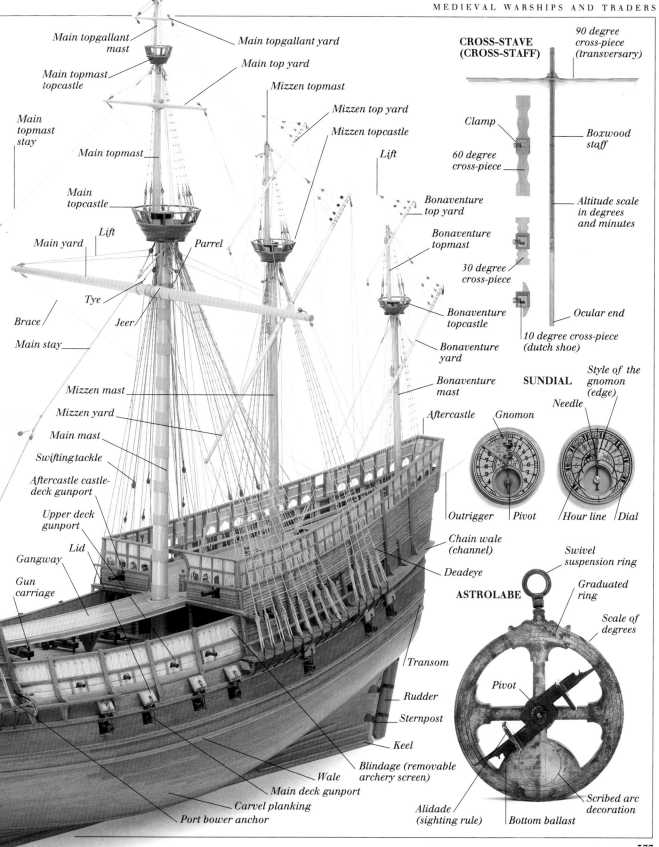

Main topgallant mast

Main topgallant yard

Main topmast topcastle

Mizzen topmast

Mizzen top yard

Main topmast stay

Mizzen topcastle

Main topmast

Lift

Main topcastle

Bonaventure top yard

Lift

Main yard

Bonaventure topmast

Parrel

Tye

30 degree cross-piece

Brace

Jeer

Bonaventure topcastle

Main stay

Bonaventure yard

Mizzen mast

Bonaventure mast

Mizzen yard

Aftercastle

Main mast

Swifting tackle

Aftercastle castle-deck gunport

Upper deck gunport

Chain wale (channel)

Lid

Deadeye

Gangway

Gun carriage

Transom

Rudder

Sternpost

Keel

Blindage (removable archery screen)

Wale

Main deck gunport

Carvel planking

Port bower anchor

CROSS-STAVE (CROSS-STAFF)

90 degree cross-piece (transversary)

Clamp

Boxwood staff

60 degree cross-piece

Altitude scale in degrees and minutes

Ocular end

10 degree cross-piece (dutch shoe)

SUNDIAL

Style of the gnomon (edge)

Needle

Gnomon

Pivot

Hour line

Dial

Outrigger

Swivel suspension ring

Graduated ring

ASTROLABE

Scale of degrees

Pivot

Alidade (sighting rule)

Bottom ballast

Scribed arc decoration

The expansion of sail

BY THE 18TH CENTURY, SAILING SHIPS had become fast and effective floating fortresses. The navies of the north European powers competed with each other by building heavily-armed fighting ships called "men-of-war." The distinctive round stern of the ship below, with its open gallery, balcony, and elaborate wood carving is typical of the period. Hulls around this time were semicircular in cross section, although many boat designers were soon to return to the V-shaped hulls used by the Vikings. Ships of the period carried more sail than ever before. A labyrinth of rigging supported the masts and yards from which the profusion of square sails were set. Ships grew higher as extra masts were fitted above the lower masts, and the bowsprit became longer, to allow the ship to carry staysails, spritsails, and jibs. Ships went into battle in single file, so that broadsides from the multiple decks of guns would have maximum effect. Ships were classified by rates, the rating of a vessel depending on how many guns it had. A first rate ship had more than 100 guns. The guns fired solid round shot, usually made of iron.

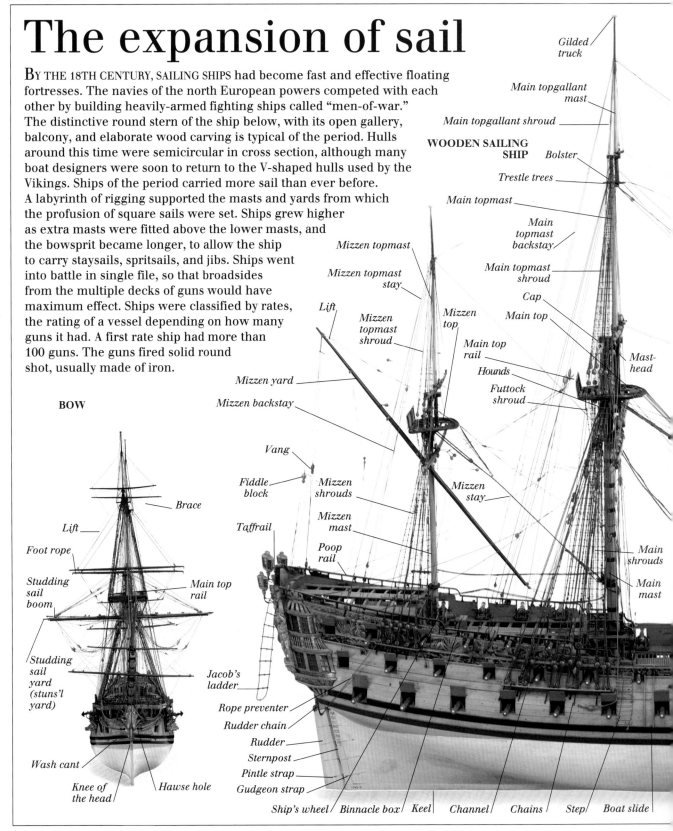

BOW

WOODEN SAILING SHIP

Gilded truck
Main topgallant mast
Main topgallant shroud
Bolster
Trestle trees
Main topmast
Main topmast backstay
Main topmast shroud
Cap
Main top
Masthead
Main top rail
Hounds
Futtock shroud
Main shrouds
Main mast

Mizzen topmast
Mizzen topmast stay
Lift
Mizzen topmast shroud
Mizzen top
Mizzen yard
Mizzen backstay
Vang
Fiddle block
Mizzen shrouds
Mizzen mast
Mizzen stay
Taffrail
Poop rail

Brace
Lift
Foot rope
Studding sail boom
Main top rail
Studding sail yard (stuns'l yard)
Jacob's ladder
Rope preventer
Rudder chain
Rudder
Sternpost
Pintle strap
Gudgeon strap
Wash cant
Knee of the head
Hawse hole
Ship's wheel
Binnacle box
Keel
Channel
Chains
Step
Boat slide

SAIL PATTERN OF A 74-GUN SHIP

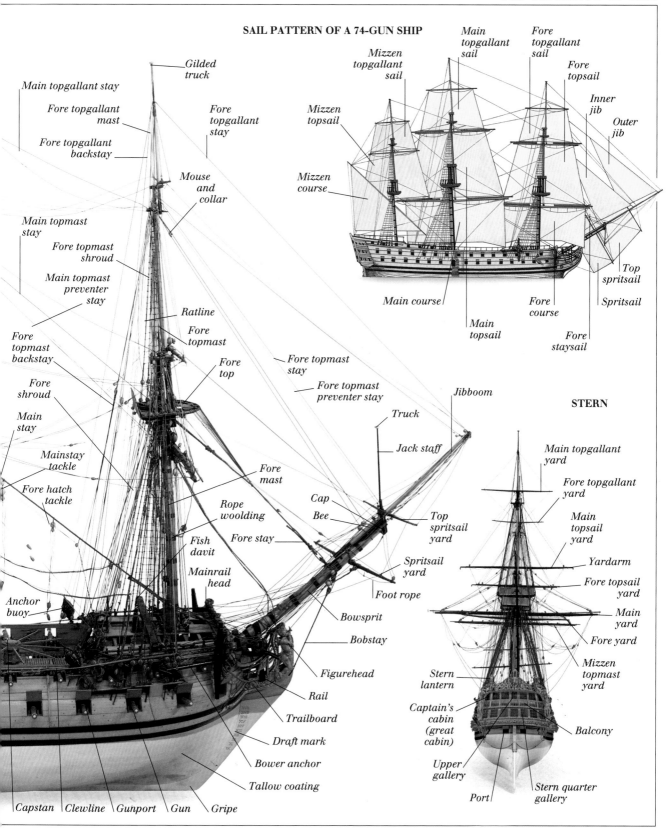

Main topgallant stay

Gilded truck

Fore topgallant mast

Fore topgallant stay

Fore topgallant backstay

Mouse and collar

Mizzen topgallant sail

Main topgallant sail

Fore topgallant sail

Fore topgallant stay

Fore topsail

Mizzen topsail

Inner jib

Outer jib

Mizzen course

Main topmast stay

Fore topmast shroud

Main topmast preventer stay

Ratline

Fore topmast

Top spritsail

Spritsail

Fore topmast backstay

Fore shroud

Fore top

Fore topmast stay

Fore topmast preventer stay

Main course

Main topsail

Fore course

Fore staysail

Jibboom

STERN

Main stay

Mainstay tackle

Fore hatch tackle

Truck

Jack staff

Main topgallant yard

Fore topgallant yard

Fore mast

Rope woolding

Cap

Bee

Fore stay

Top spritsail yard

Main topsail yard

Yardarm

Fish davit

Spritsail yard

Fore topsail yard

Mainrail head

Foot rope

Main yard

Anchor buoy

Bowsprit

Fore yard

Bobstay

Stern lantern

Mizzen topmast yard

Figurehead

Captain's cabin (great cabin)

Rail

Trailboard

Balcony

Draft mark

Bower anchor

Upper gallery

Tallow coating

Port

Stern quarter gallery

Capstan Clewline Gunport Gun Gripe

A ship of the line

THE 74-GUN THIRD-RATER WAS A MAINSTAY of British and French battlefleets in the late 18th and early 19th centuries. (The biggest ships in the fledgling American navy of the time were 44-gun frigates.) The length of such a man-of-war was determined by the number of guns needed for each deck, allowing room for crews to man them. The gun deck of this vessel was about 170 ft (52 m) long. Her decks had to be strong to carry the weight of the guns. The deck planks have been removed in the model below to illustrate the number of beams needed to make the hull strong enough. Only timber with perfect grain was used. The upper deck was open at the waist, but forward and aft were officers' cabins. The forecastle (foc's'l) and quarterdeck carried light guns and provided platforms for handling the rigging and for reconnaissance. The ship's longboats, or launches, were carried on skids between the gangways.

LONGBOAT

Truck · Flag halyard · Mast · Backstay · Jib halyard · Topping lift · Fore stay halyard · Peak halyard · Shrouds · Main sheet · Fore staysail halyard · Gaff · Boom · Parrel · Bowsprit · Traveler · Stem · Waterline · Deadeyes · Oar · Side bench

Thole pins · Windlass bar · Transom · Tiller · Planking · Rabbit line · Sheerplank · Frame · Keel · Rudder · Floor · Thwart (seat)

UPPER DECK OF A 74-GUN SHIP

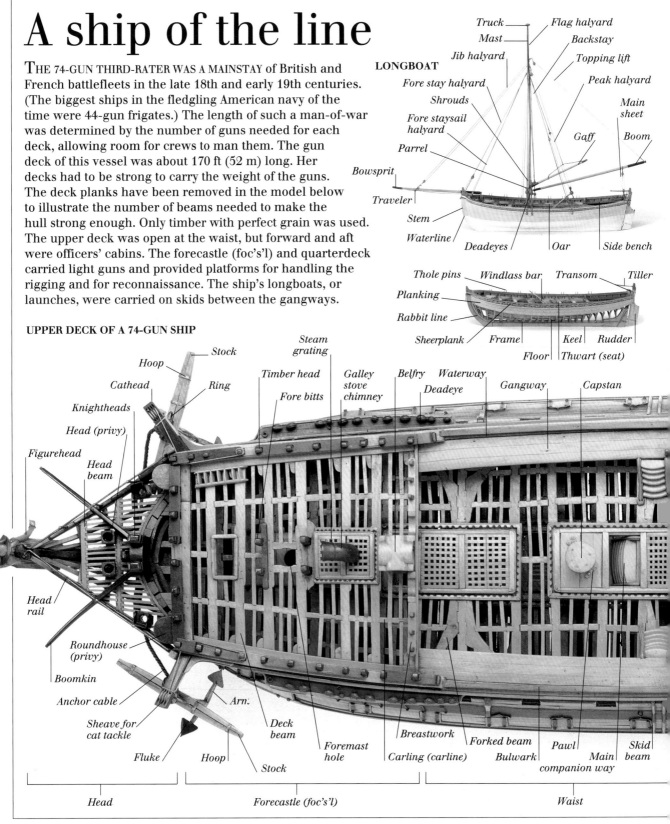

Stock · Hoop · Cathead · Ring · Steam grating · Timber head · Galley stove chimney · Belfry · Waterway · Gangway · Capstan · Knightheads · Fore bitts · Deadeye · Head (privy) · Figurehead · Head beam · Head rail · Roundhouse (privy) · Boomkin · Anchor cable · Arn. · Sheave for cat tackle · Deck beam · Breastwork · Forked beam · Pawl · Skid beam · Fluke · Hoop · Stock · Foremast hole · Carling (carline) · Bulwark · Main companion way · Head · Forecastle (foc's'l) · Waist

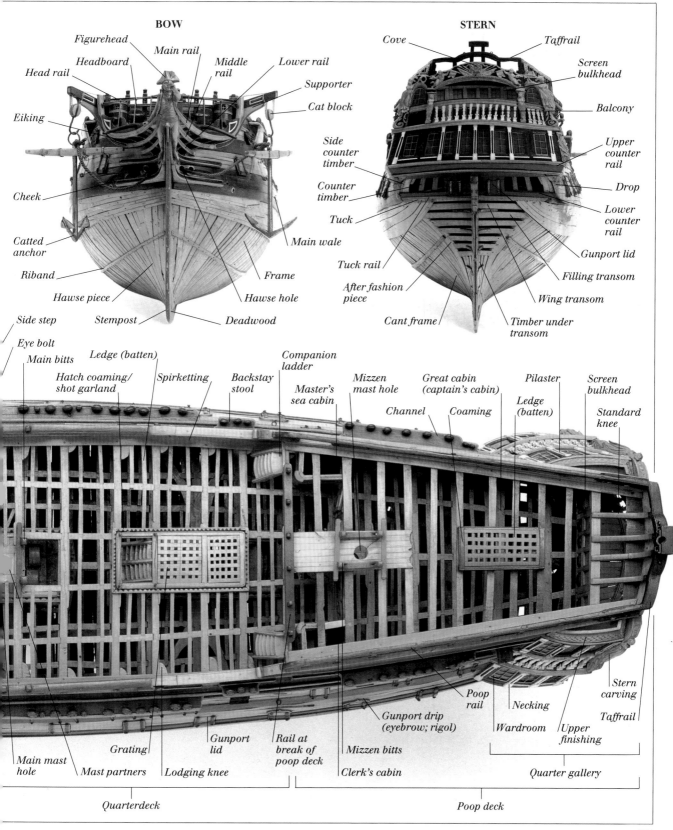

BOW

Figurehead

Main rail

Headboard

Middle rail

Lower rail

Head rail

Supporter

Eiking

Cat block

Cheek

Catted anchor

Riband

Hawse piece

Side step

Eye bolt

Main bitts

Stempost

Deadwood

Main wale

Frame

Hawse hole

STERN

Cove

Taffrail

Screen bulkhead

Balcony

Side counter timber

Upper counter rail

Counter timber

Drop

Tuck

Lower counter rail

Tuck rail

Gunport lid

After fashion piece

Filling transom

Cant frame

Wing transom

Timber under transom

Ledge (batten)

Hatch coaming/ shot garland

Spirketting

Backstay stool

Companion ladder

Master's sea cabin

Mizzen mast hole

Great cabin (captain's cabin)

Pilaster

Screen bulkhead

Channel

Coaming

Ledge (batten)

Standard knee

Main mast hole

Grating

Mast partners

Lodging knee

Gunport lid

Rail at break of poop deck

Gunport drip (eyebrow; rigol)

Mizzen bitts

Clerk's cabin

Poop rail

Necking

Wardroom

Stern carving

Taffrail

Upper finishing

Quarter gallery

Quarterdeck

Poop deck

Rigging

MOST SAILING SHIPS HAVE TWO TYPES OF RIGGING. Standing rigging—kept taut by turnbuckles or old-fashioned lanyards and deadeyes—refers to the ropes, wires, and chains that support the masts and yards (horizontal spars). Running rigging, which includes types of block and tackle, halyards, and sheets, is used to hoist, lower, or trim sails.

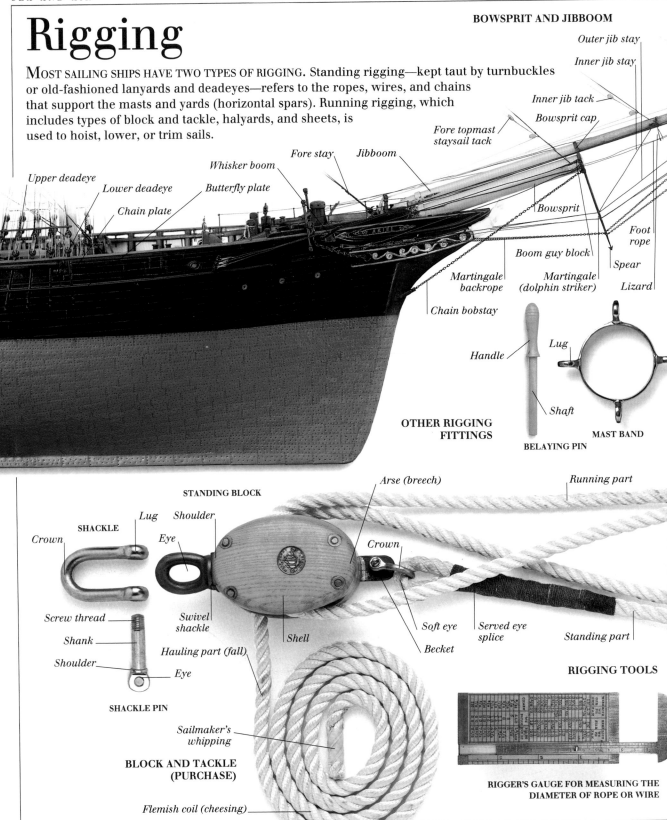

BOWSPRIT AND JIBBOOM

Outer jib stay

Inner jib stay

Inner jib tack

Bowsprit cap

Fore topmast staysail tack

Fore stay

Jibboom

Whisker boom

Butterfly plate

Upper deadeye

Lower deadeye

Chain plate

Bowsprit

Boom guy block

Foot rope

Spear

Lizard

Martingale backrope

Martingale (dolphin striker)

Chain bobstay

Handle

Lug

Shaft

OTHER RIGGING FITTINGS

BELAYING PIN

MAST BAND

Arse (breech)

Running part

STANDING BLOCK

Lug

Shoulder

Eye

Crown

SHACKLE

Crown

Soft eye

Served eye splice

Standing part

Swivel shackle

Screw thread

Shank

Shoulder

Eye

Hauling part (fall)

Shell

Becket

RIGGING TOOLS

SHACKLE PIN

Sailmaker's whipping

BLOCK AND TACKLE (PURCHASE)

RIGGER'S GAUGE FOR MEASURING THE DIAMETER OF ROPE OR WIRE

Flemish coil (cheesing)

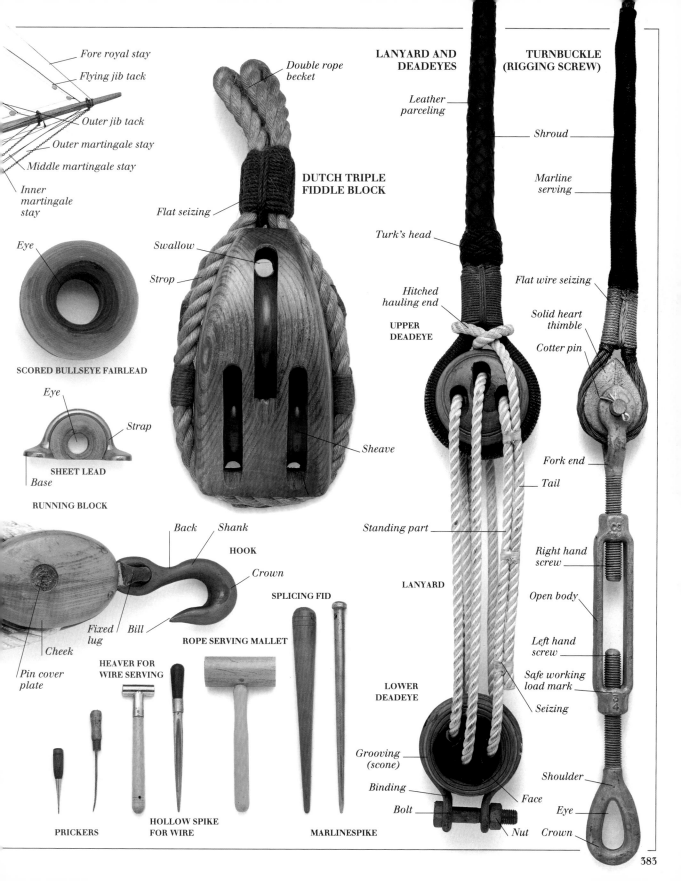

Fore royal stay

Flying jib tack

Outer jib tack

Outer martingale stay

Middle martingale stay

Inner martingale stay

Eye

SCORED BULLSEYE FAIRLEAD

Eye

Strap

SHEET LEAD

Base

RUNNING BLOCK

Double rope becket

DUTCH TRIPLE FIDDLE BLOCK

Flat seizing

Swallow

Strop

Sheave

Back

Shank

HOOK

Crown

Bill

Fixed lug

ROPE SERVING MALLET

SPLICING FID

Cheek

Pin cover plate

HEAVER FOR WIRE SERVING

PRICKERS

HOLLOW SPIKE FOR WIRE

MARLINESPIKE

LANYARD AND DEADEYES

TURNBUCKLE (RIGGING SCREW)

Leather parceling

Shroud

Marline serving

Turk's head

Hitched hauling end

UPPER DEADEYE

Flat wire seizing

Solid heart thimble

Cotter pin

Standing part

Tail

Fork end

LANYARD

Right hand screw

Open body

Left hand screw

LOWER DEADEYE

Safe working load mark

Seizing

Grooving (scone)

Binding

Bolt

Face

Shoulder

Eye

Nut

Crown

Sails

THERE ARE TWO MAIN TYPES OF SAILS: Old-fashioned square sails hang from yards at right angles to the mast, and are powerful drivers with following winds; fore-and-aft sails are set parallel to the length of the boat, with the luff (leading edge) of the sail attached to a mast or a stay. They are more efficient for all-round sailing, and almost all modern sailboats are rigged this way. Some fore-and-aft sails have a gaff at the head; Marconi-rig sails are pointed at the top (below). The bottom (foot) of the sail is on a boom. Sails are made of strips of cloth sewn together. Cotton and flax are traditional sail materials but synthetic fabrics are now more often used.

PARREL BEADS

TOP OF A MARCONI SAIL

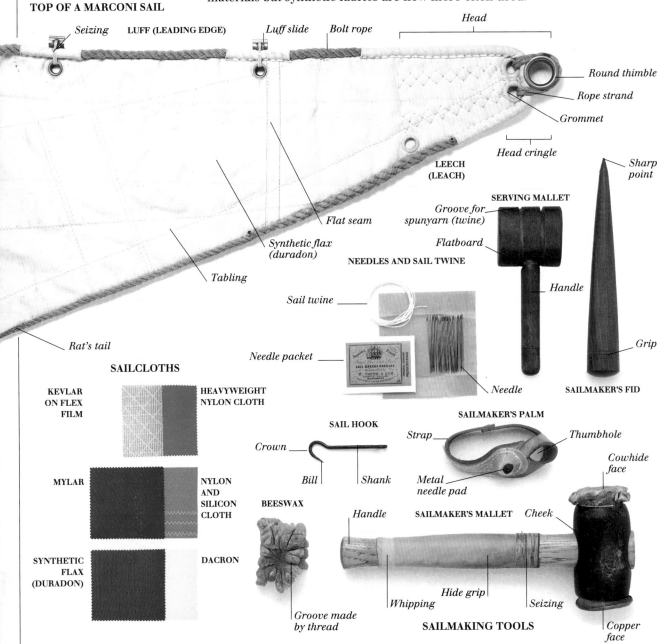

Seizing   LUFF (LEADING EDGE)   Luff slide   Bolt rope   Head

Round thimble
Rope strand
Grommet
Head cringle
Sharp point

LEECH (LEACH)

SERVING MALLET
Groove for spunyarn (twine)
Flatboard
Handle
Grip
SAILMAKER'S FID

Flat seam
Synthetic flax (duradon)
Tabling

NEEDLES AND SAIL TWINE
Sail twine
Needle packet
Needle

Rat's tail

SAILCLOTHS

KEVLAR ON FLEX FILM
HEAVYWEIGHT NYLON CLOTH

MYLAR
NYLON AND SILICON CLOTH

SYNTHETIC FLAX (DURADON)
DACRON

SAIL HOOK
Crown
Bill   Shank

BEESWAX

Strap
Metal needle pad

SAILMAKER'S PALM
Thumbhole
Cowhide face

Handle   SAILMAKER'S MALLET   Cheek

Hide grip
Whipping   Seizing

Groove made by thread

SAILMAKING TOOLS

Copper face

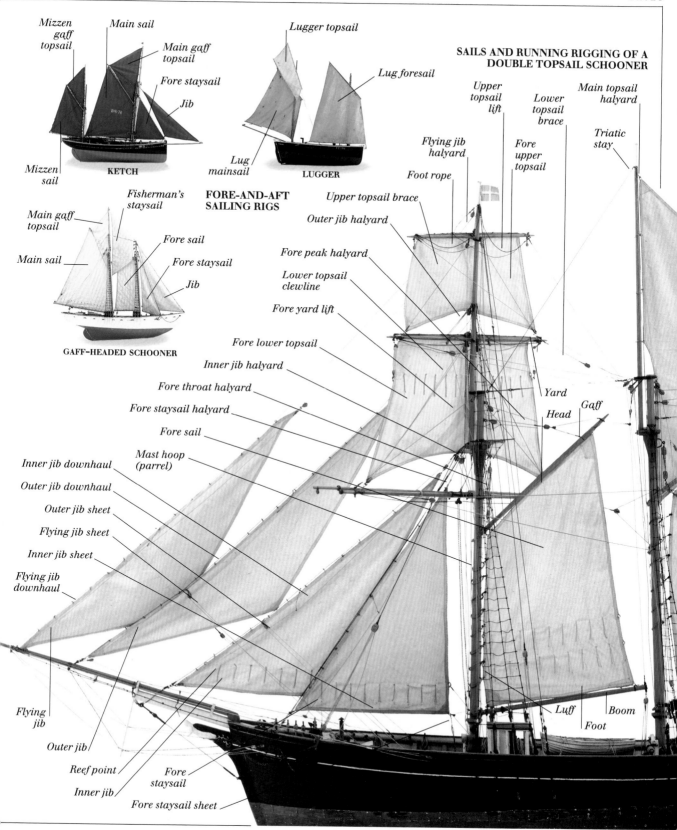

Mizzen gaff topsail

Main sail

Main gaff topsail

Fore staysail

Jib

Mizzen sail

KETCH

Lugger topsail

Lug foresail

Lug mainsail

LUGGER

SAILS AND RUNNING RIGGING OF A DOUBLE TOPSAIL SCHOONER

Upper topsail lift

Lower topsail brace

Main topsail halyard

Flying jib halyard

Fore upper topsail

Triatic stay

Foot rope

FORE-AND-AFT SAILING RIGS

Fisherman's staysail

Main gaff topsail

Fore sail

Main sail

Fore staysail

Jib

GAFF–HEADED SCHOONER

Upper topsail brace

Outer jib halyard

Fore peak halyard

Lower topsail clewline

Fore yard lift

Fore lower topsail

Inner jib halyard

Fore throat halyard

Fore staysail halyard

Fore sail

Mast hoop (parrel)

Inner jib downhaul

Outer jib downhaul

Outer jib sheet

Flying jib sheet

Inner jib sheet

Flying jib downhaul

Yard

Head

Gaff

Luff

Boom

Foot

Flying jib

Outer jib

Reef point

Fore staysail

Inner jib

Fore staysail sheet

Mooring and anchoring

IN MOST HARBORS AND PORTS, a ship can moor (tie up or "make fast") directly to a pier, wharf, or quay (pronounced "key"), using heavy hawsers and docking lines attached to bitts or bollards. Hawsers are tied to each other with knots called bends. In open water, however, ships that are not under way must drop an anchor, which attaches the ship securely to the seabed. The earliest anchors were simply heavy stones. Later, various anchor designs were developed for different uses. Most small vessels today use Danforth or plow anchors, which dig deeply into the sea bottom. A permanent mooring is an anchor set in the bottom to which a ship can tie up without using its own anchor. On old sailing ships, anchors were pulled up, or "weighed," by sailors pushing against bars that turned a capstan, which wound up the anchor cable. Now, most capstans are powered by electricity.

STONE ANCHOR
(KILLICK)

Rope hole

TYPES
OF ANCHOR

CLOSE-
STOWING
ANCHOR

CQR ANCHOR
(PLOW ANCHOR)

BRITISH ADMIRALTY
ANCHOR TYPE ACII

YACHTSMAN'S
ANCHOR (KEDGE)

STOCKLESS
ANCHOR

MUSHROOM ANCHOR
(PERMANENT MOORING ANCHOR)

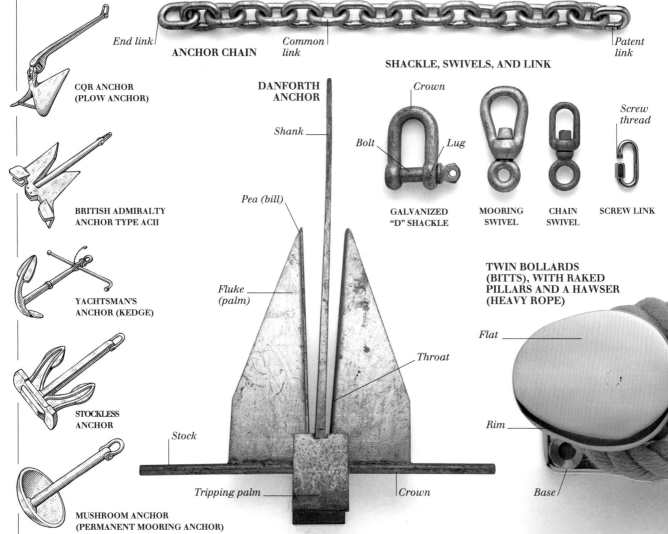

End link

ANCHOR CHAIN

Common link

Patent link

SHACKLE, SWIVELS, AND LINK

DANFORTH
ANCHOR

Shank

Pea (bill)

Fluke
(palm)

Stock

Tripping palm

Crown

Throat

Crown

Bolt

Lug

GALVANIZED
"D" SHACKLE

MOORING
SWIVEL

CHAIN
SWIVEL

Screw
thread

SCREW LINK

TWIN BOLLARDS
(BITTS), WITH RAKED
PILLARS AND A HAWSER
(HEAVY ROPE)

Flat

Rim

Base

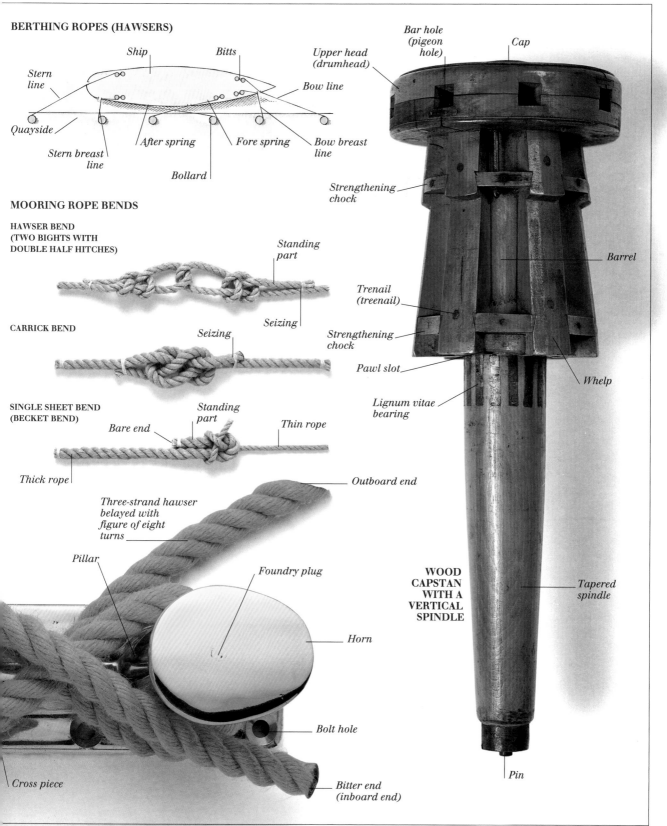

BERTHING ROPES (HAWSERS)

Stern line

Ship

Bitts

Upper head (drumhead)

Bow line

Stern breast line

Quayside

After spring

Fore spring

Bollard

Bow breast line

MOORING ROPE BENDS

HAWSER BEND (TWO BIGHTS WITH DOUBLE HALF HITCHES)

Standing part

Seizing

CARRICK BEND

Seizing

SINGLE SHEET BEND (BECKET BEND)

Bare end

Standing part

Thin rope

Thick rope

Three-strand hawser belayed with figure of eight turns

Outboard end

Pillar

Foundry plug

Horn

Bolt hole

Cross piece

Bitter end (inboard end)

Bar hole (pigeon hole)

Cap

Strengthening chock

Barrel

Trenail (treenail)

Strengthening chock

Pawl slot

Lignum vitae bearing

Whelp

WOOD CAPSTAN WITH A VERTICAL SPINDLE

Tapered spindle

Pin

Ropes and knots

ALL KINDS OF ROPES ARE USED AT SEA, from thin twines and yarn to
thick hawsers. Synthetic fibers are much in use today. Nylon ropes
stretch, and so are ideal for anchoring;
polyester (frequently called by the
trade name Dacron) has little stretch
and is used for halyards and sheets.
Different knots have different
uses. Knots that join two ropes
are often called bends; hitches
join a rope to another object.
Ropes, usually called "lines" on
board ship, can also be joined by
seizing (lashing them together side
by side) or splicing (unraveling the
ends and weaving them together).

**FRENCH BOWLINE
(PORTUGUESE BOWLINE)**

Armpit
bight

Goose
neck

Seizing

HALF HITCH WITH SEIZING

SYNTHETIC ROPES

Multiplait
nylon

Three-strand
polypropylene

Kevlar

Three-strand
polypropylene

Three-strand
prestretched
polyester

Sixteen-plait
polyester

Sixteen-plait
polyester

Braided
polyester

Three-strand
polypropylene

Polyester

ROPEWORK

Whipping

Bight

Eye

Twist

**SQUARE KNOT
(REEF KNOT)**

Bare end

OVERHAND KNOT (HALF HITCH)

HUNTER'S BEND

End

Standing part

Serving mallet

Marline

Flemish coil
(cheesing)

ROLLING HITCH

Handle

Diagonal
turn

**MARLINESPIKE
HITCH**

End

Standing part

CLOVE HITCH

Head

Bight

Score

BOWLINE

Serving

Parceling

Worming

WORMING, PARCELING, AND SERVING

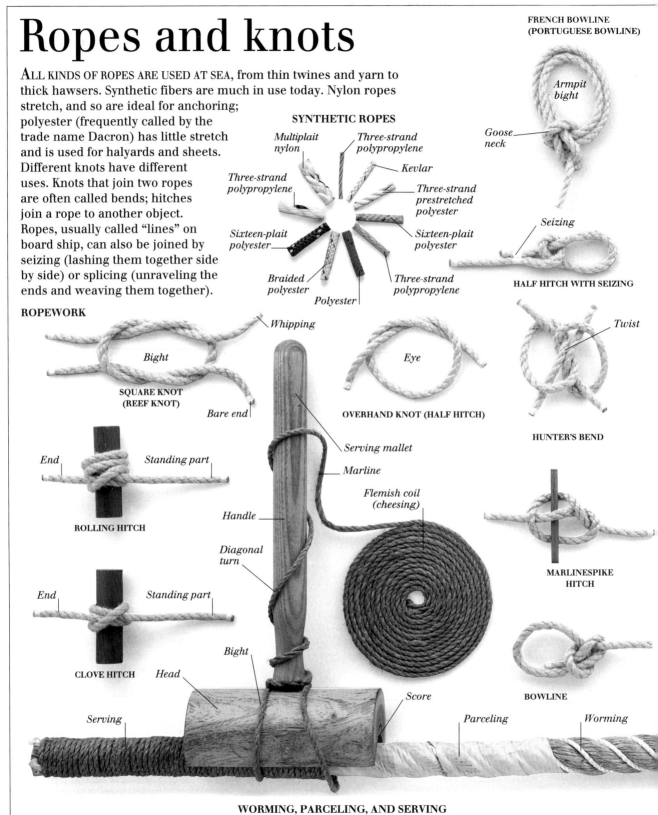

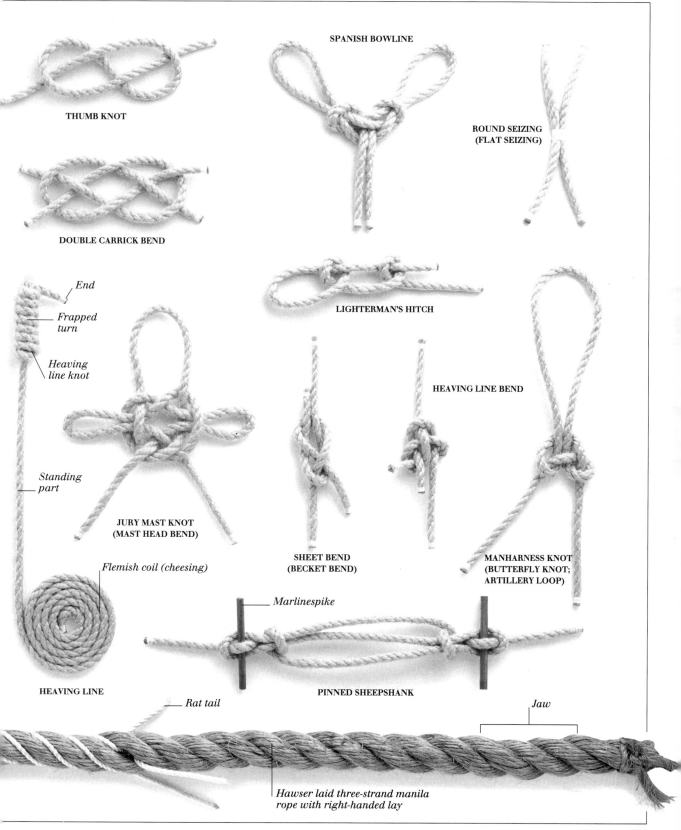

THUMB KNOT

SPANISH BOWLINE

**ROUND SEIZING
(FLAT SEIZING)**

DOUBLE CARRICK BEND

End

*Frapped
turn*

*Heaving
line knot*

LIGHTERMAN'S HITCH

HEAVING LINE BEND

*Standing
part*

**JURY MAST KNOT
(MAST HEAD BEND)**

**SHEET BEND
(BECKET BEND)**

**MANHARNESS KNOT
(BUTTERFLY KNOT;
ARTILLERY LOOP)**

Flemish coil (cheesing)

Marlinespike

HEAVING LINE

PINNED SHEEPSHANK

Rat tail

Jaw

*Hawser laid three-strand manila
rope with right-handed lay*

389

Paddle wheels and propellers

THE INVENTION OF THE STEAM ENGINE IN THE 18TH CENTURY made mechanically driven ships fitted with paddle wheels or propellers a viable alternative to sails. Paddle wheels have fixed or feathered floats, and the model shown below features both types. Feathered floats give more propulsive power than fixed floats because they are almost upright at all times in the water. Paddle wheels were superseded by the propeller on oceangoing vessels in the mid-19th century. Propellers are more efficient, work better in rough water, and are less vulnerable in collisions. The first propellers were two-bladed, but later three- and four-bladed versions are more powerful; the shape and pitch of the blades have also been refined over the years. At the beginning of the 18th century, tillers were replaced on many larger ships by the ship's wheel as a means of steering.

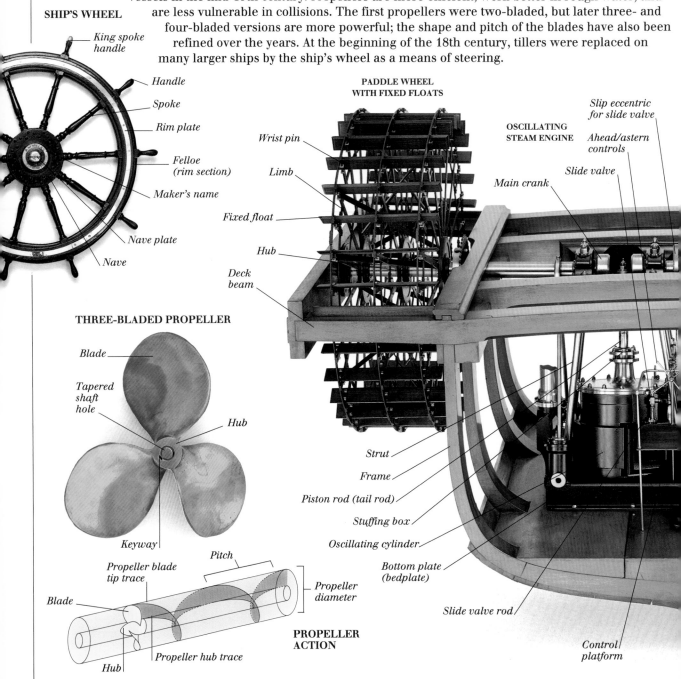

SHIP'S WHEEL

King spoke handle

Handle

Spoke

Rim plate

Felloe (rim section)

Maker's name

Nave plate

Nave

PADDLE WHEEL WITH FIXED FLOATS

Wrist pin

Limb

Fixed float

Hub

Deck beam

OSCILLATING STEAM ENGINE

Slip eccentric for slide valve

Ahead/astern controls

Slide valve

Main crank

THREE-BLADED PROPELLER

Blade

Tapered shaft hole

Hub

Keyway

Strut

Frame

Piston rod (tail rod)

Stuffing box

Oscillating cylinder

Bottom plate (bedplate)

Slide valve rod

Control platform

Pitch

Propeller blade tip trace

Blade

Propeller diameter

Propeller hub trace

Hub

PROPELLER ACTION

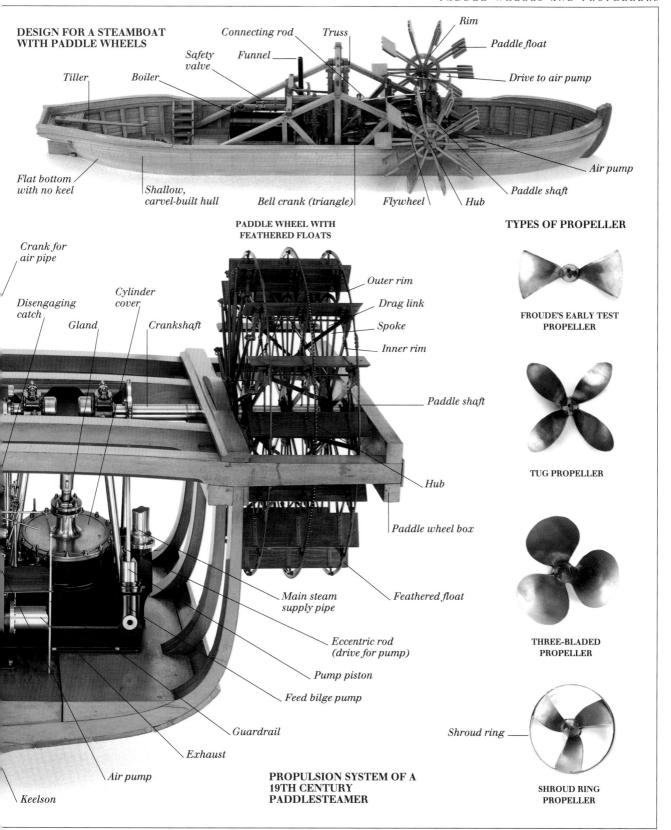

DESIGN FOR A STEAMBOAT WITH PADDLE WHEELS

Rim

Connecting rod

Truss

Paddle float

Safety valve

Funnel

Drive to air pump

Tiller

Boiler

Air pump

Flat bottom with no keel

Paddle shaft

Shallow, carvel-built hull

Bell crank (triangle)

Flywheel

Hub

PADDLE WHEEL WITH FEATHERED FLOATS

TYPES OF PROPELLER

Crank for air pipe

Outer rim

Disengaging catch

Drag link

Cylinder cover

Gland

Spoke

Crankshaft

Inner rim

FROUDE'S EARLY TEST PROPELLER

Paddle shaft

Hub

TUG PROPELLER

Paddle wheel box

Main steam supply pipe

Feathered float

THREE-BLADED PROPELLER

Eccentric rod (drive for pump)

Pump piston

Feed bilge pump

Guardrail

Shroud ring

Exhaust

Air pump

PROPULSION SYSTEM OF A 19TH CENTURY PADDLESTEAMER

Keelson

SHROUD RING PROPELLER

Anatomy of an iron ship

IRON PARTS WERE USED IN WOODEN SHIPS AS EARLY AS 1675, often in the same form as the wooden parts that they replaced. Eventually, as on the tea clipper Cutty Sark (below), iron standing rigging was found to be stronger than the traditional rope. The first "ironclads" were warships whose wooden hulls were protected by iron armor plates. Later ironclads actually had iron hulls. The model opposite is based on the British warship HMS Warrior, launched in 1860, the first battleship built entirely of iron. The plan of an iron paddlesteamer (bottom), built somewhat later, shows that the craft had the masts and bowsprit of a sailing ship; but it also boasted a steam propulsion plant amid ships that turned two side paddlewheels. Early iron plates were painstakingly riveted together (below), but by the 1940s, steel vessels were welded together, whole sections at a time. The Liberty ships built in America during World War II are prime examples of such "production-line" vessels.

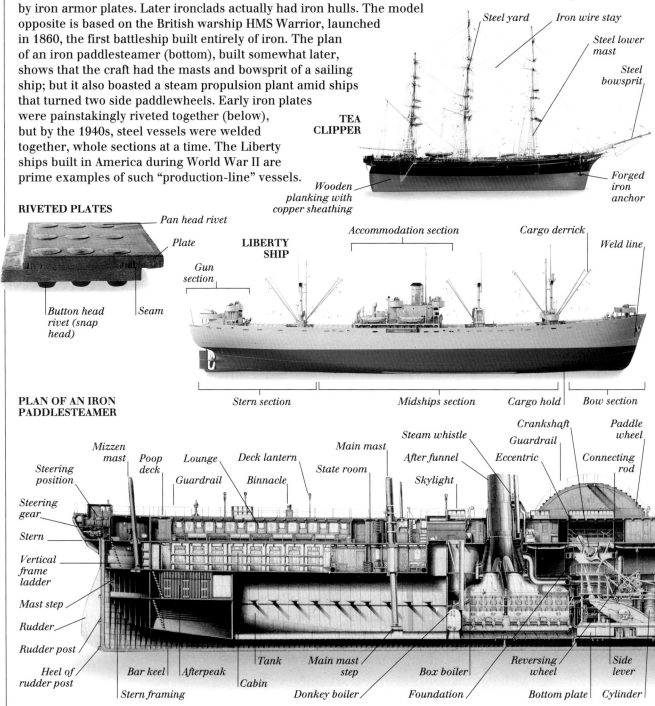

TEA CLIPPER

Steel yard

Iron wire stay

Steel lower mast

Steel bowsprit

Forged iron anchor

Wooden planking with copper sheathing

RIVETED PLATES

Pan head rivet

Plate

Button head rivet (snap head)

Seam

LIBERTY SHIP

Accommodation section

Cargo derrick

Weld line

Gun section

Stern section

Midships section

Cargo hold

Bow section

PLAN OF AN IRON PADDLESTEAMER

Steering position

Mizzen mast

Poop deck

Lounge

Deck lantern

Guardrail

Binnacle

State room

Main mast

Steam whistle

After funnel

Skylight

Crankshaft

Guardrail

Eccentric

Paddle wheel

Connecting rod

Steering gear

Stern

Vertical frame ladder

Mast step

Rudder

Rudder post

Heel of rudder post

Bar keel

Afterpeak

Stern framing

Cabin

Tank

Main mast step

Donkey boiler

Box boiler

Foundation

Reversing wheel

Bottom plate

Side lever

Cylinder

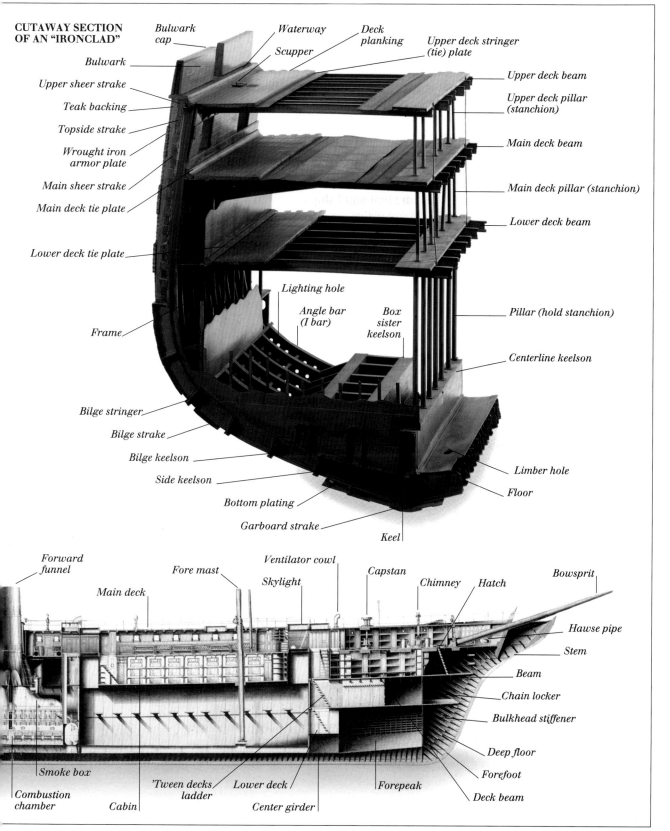

CUTAWAY SECTION OF AN "IRONCLAD"

Bulwark cap

Waterway

Scupper

Deck planking

Upper deck stringer (tie) plate

Bulwark

Upper sheer strake

Teak backing

Topside strake

Wrought iron armor plate

Main sheer strake

Main deck tie plate

Lower deck tie plate

Frame

Lighting hole

Angle bar (I bar)

Box sister keelson

Bilge stringer

Bilge strake

Bilge keelson

Side keelson

Bottom plating

Garboard strake

Keel

Upper deck beam

Upper deck pillar (stanchion)

Main deck beam

Main deck pillar (stanchion)

Lower deck beam

Pillar (hold stanchion)

Centerline keelson

Limber hole

Floor

Forward funnel

Main deck

Fore mast

Ventilator cowl

Skylight

Capstan

Chimney

Hatch

Bowsprit

Hawse pipe

Stem

Beam

Chain locker

Bulkhead stiffener

Deep floor

Forefoot

Deck beam

Forepeak

Smoke box

Combustion chamber

Cabin

'Tween decks ladder

Lower deck

Center girder

The battleship

IN THE EARLY YEARS OF THE 20TH CENTURY, sea warfare—attacking enemy vessels or defending a ship—was revolutionized by the introduction of Dreadnought-type battleships like the Brazilian vessel below. These new ships combined the latest advances in steam propulsion, gunnery, and armor plating. Their gun turrets, protected by armor up to 12 in (30 cm) thick, were designed to fire shells over great distances. The ship shown here, the Minas Geraes, was 500 ft (152 m) long. It was built at Elswick, England, and launched in 1908. Its chief armament was of 12 in (30 cm) guns (firing shells with a 12 in diameter). Other naval weapons developed in the 20th century include the torpedo—as portrayed on the upper cigarette card (right). This was a self-propelled underwater missile, often steered by gyro-control. Depth charges were designed in the First World War for use against submerged U-boats. They are canisters filled with explosives that are detonated by depth-sensitive pistols. The lower cigarette card shows depth charges being fired by a "thrower," fired from a torpedo tube, and rolled from the stern. Ship's shields were fitted to warships from the late 19th century onwards. The shield shown opposite depicts a traditional ship's cannon.

20TH CENTURY WEAPONRY

Torpedo tube

Sight

Warhead

TORPEDOES

DEPTH CHARGES

Side-thrown canister

Stern-rolled canister

Torpedo-fired canister

BRAZILIAN BATTLESHIP

Rangefinder

Light screen

Compass

Compass and rangefinder platform

Ship's wheel

Navigating bridge

Conning tower

Captain's shelter/chart house

Weather shutter for gun

Arms of Brazil

Jack staff

12 in (30 cm) gun

Skylight

Forward funnel

Lifeboat

"F" turret

Boat handling derrick

Gunnery spotting top

Purchase wire

Searchlight

Searchlight platform

Leading block

Tripod mast

Boat winch

Stem (false ram bow)

Porthole

Belt armor

Forward accommodation ladder

Sighting hood

"A" turret

Turret barbette

Open gun mounting

4.7 in (12 cm) gun

Steam launch

Guest boat boom

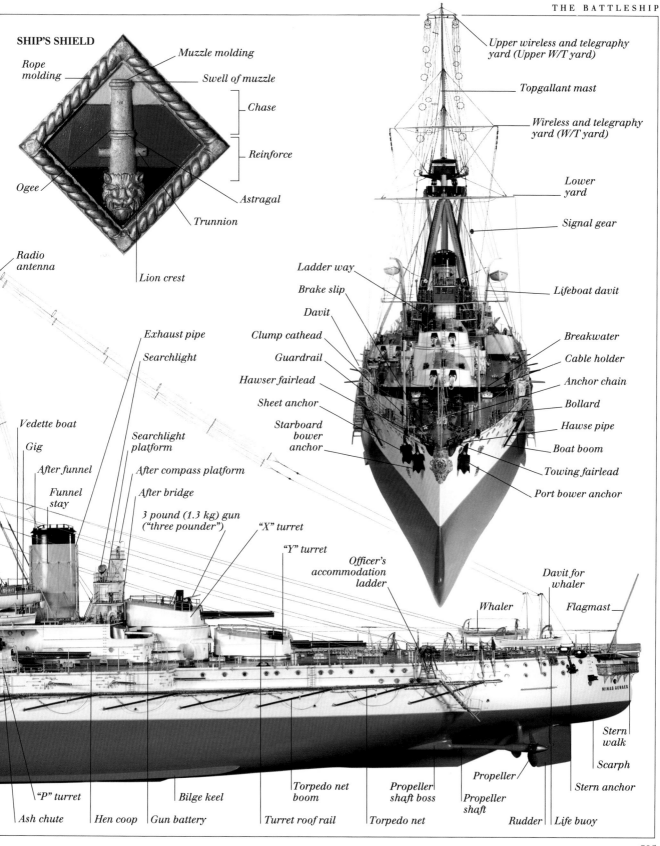

SHIP'S SHIELD

Rope molding

Muzzle molding

Swell of muzzle

Chase

Reinforce

Astragal

Trunnion

Ogee

Lion crest

Radio antenna

Upper wireless and telegraphy yard (Upper W/T yard)

Topgallant mast

Wireless and telegraphy yard (W/T yard)

Lower yard

Signal gear

Ladder way

Brake slip

Davit

Clump cathead

Guardrail

Hawser fairlead

Sheet anchor

Starboard bower anchor

Lifeboat davit

Breakwater

Cable holder

Anchor chain

Bollard

Hawse pipe

Boat boom

Towing fairlead

Port bower anchor

Exhaust pipe

Searchlight

Searchlight platform

After compass platform

After bridge

3 pound (1.3 kg) gun ("three pounder")

"X" turret

"Y" turret

Officer's accommodation ladder

Vedette boat

Gig

After funnel

Funnel stay

Whaler

Davit for whaler

Flagmast

"P" turret

Ash chute

Hen coop

Bilge keel

Gun battery

Torpedo net boom

Turret roof rail

Propeller shaft boss

Torpedo net

Propeller shaft

Propeller

Rudder

Stern anchor

Life buoy

Stern walk

Scarph

Frigates and submarines

FROM THE MID-19TH CENTURY, ARMORED SHIPS provided a new challenge to enemy craft. In response, huge revolving gun turrets were developed. These could shoot in any direction, were loaded quickly from the breech, and fired exploding shells. Today's fighting ships, like the Royal Navy frigate opposite, also carry missile launchers and helicopters. Submarines operate underwater, have great speed, and some can fire missiles while submerged. A nuclear sub can operate for several years without refueling.

Stabilizer fin

Aft hydroplane

Propeller

Lower rudder

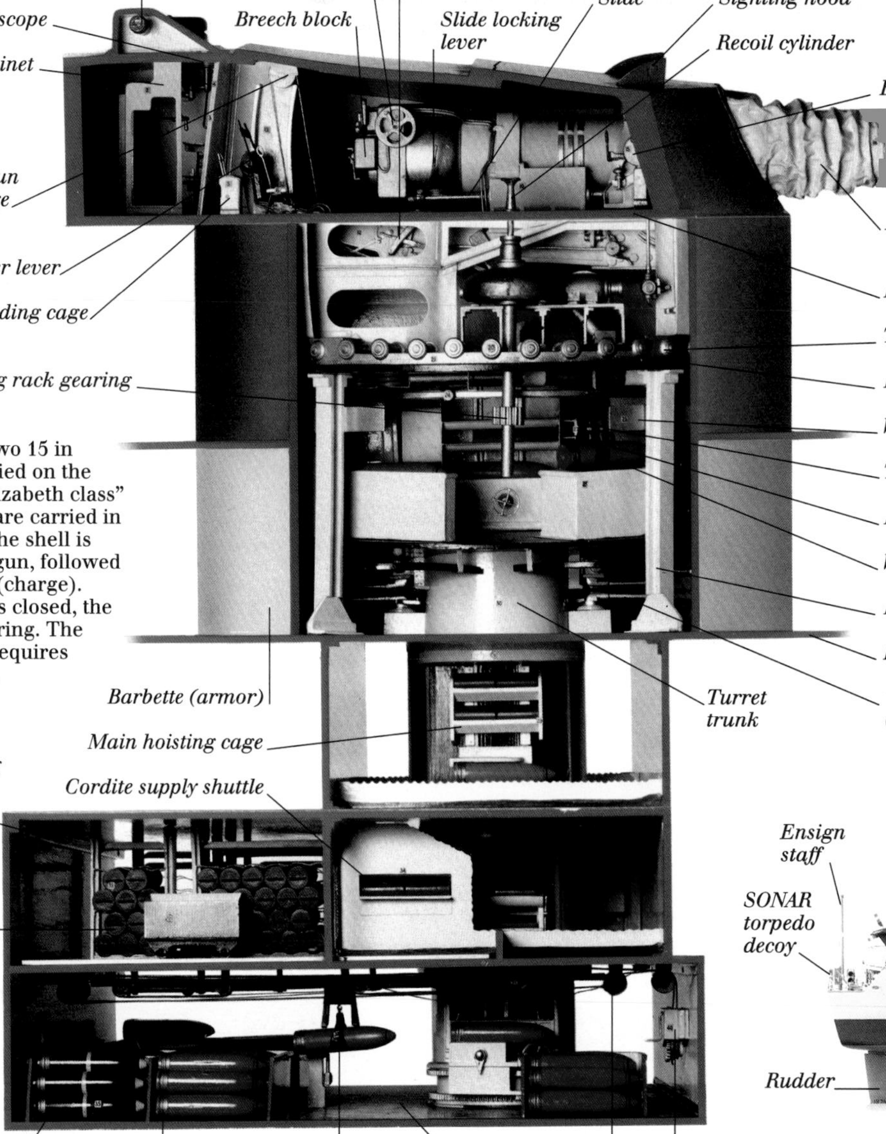

Rangefinder

Look out periscope

Local control cabinet

Breech wheel

Breech block

Loading arm

Slide locking lever

Slide

Sighting hood

Recoil cylinder

Elevating wheel

Guide for gun loading cage

Blast bag (breeches)

Floor of gun house

Rammer lever

Gun loading cage

Turret roller

Roller path

Training rack gearing

Working chamber

Training gear

GUN TURRET
In this turret for two 15 in (37 cm) guns carried on the British "Queen Elizabeth class" battleship, shells are carried in a hoisting cage. The shell is rammed into the gun, followed by the propellant (charge). Once the breech is closed, the gun is ready for firing. The whole operation requires around 70 sailors.

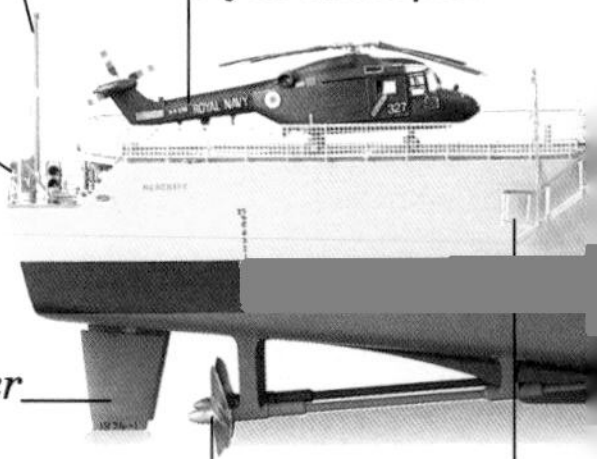

Rammer

Waiting position

Roller path support

Floor

Barbette (armor)

Main hoisting cage

Turret trunk

"Walking pipe" (hydraulic supply)

Cordite handling room

Cordite supply shuttle

Ensign staff

Lynx helicopter

SONAR torpedo decoy

Cordite case

Rudder

Practice projectile

High-explosive projectile

Shell bogie

Shell room

Hydraulic grab

Shell-handling gear

Variable pitch propeller

Accommodation ladder

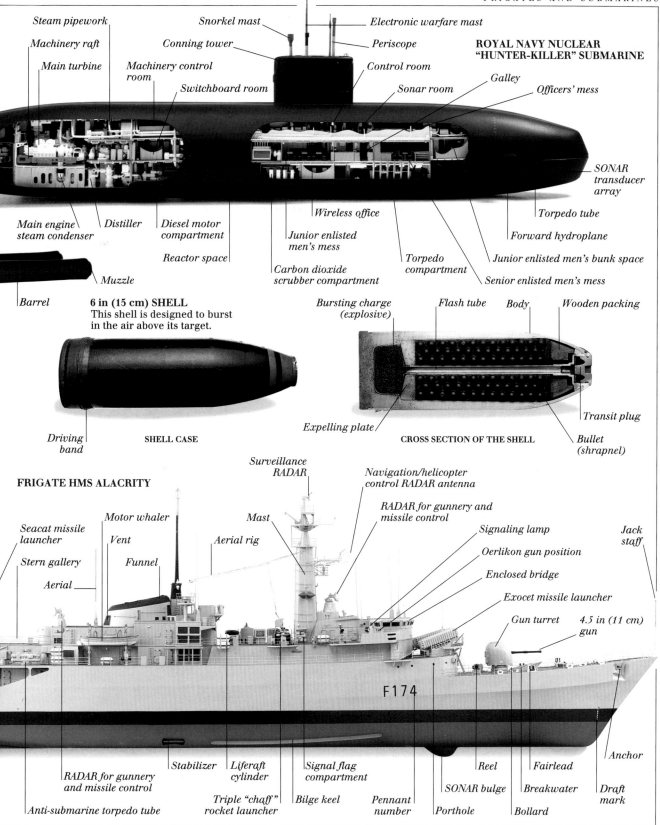

ROYAL NAVY NUCLEAR
"HUNTER-KILLER" SUBMARINE

Steam pipework

Machinery raft

Main turbine

Conning tower

Snorkel mast

Machinery control room

Switchboard room

Electronic warfare mast

Periscope

Control room

Sonar room

Galley

Officers' mess

SONAR transducer array

Main engine steam condenser

Distiller

Diesel motor compartment

Reactor space

Wireless office

Junior enlisted men's mess

Carbon dioxide scrubber compartment

Torpedo compartment

Torpedo tube

Forward hydroplane

Junior enlisted men's bunk space

Senior enlisted men's mess

Barrel

Muzzle

6 in (15 cm) SHELL
This shell is designed to burst in the air above its target.

Bursting charge (explosive)

Flash tube

Body

Wooden packing

Driving band

SHELL CASE

Expelling plate

CROSS SECTION OF THE SHELL

Transit plug

Bullet (shrapnel)

FRIGATE HMS ALACRITY

Surveillance RADAR

Navigation/helicopter control RADAR antenna

RADAR for gunnery and missile control

Mast

Seacat missile launcher

Motor whaler

Vent

Aerial rig

Signaling lamp

Jack staff

Stern gallery

Funnel

Oerlikon gun position

Aerial

Enclosed bridge

Exocet missile launcher

Gun turret

4.5 in (11 cm) gun

F174

RADAR for gunnery and missile control

Stabilizer

Liferaft cylinder

Signal flag compartment

Reel

Fairlead

Anchor

Anti-submarine torpedo tube

Triple "chaff" rocket launcher

Bilge keel

Pennant number

SONAR bulge

Porthole

Breakwater

Bollard

Draft mark

Pioneers of flight

FLIGHT HAS FASCINATED MANKIND for centuries, and countless unsuccessful flying machines have been designed. The first successful flight was made by the French Montgolfier brothers in 1783, when they flew a balloon over Paris. The next major advance was the development of gliders, notably by the Englishman Sir George Cayley, who in 1845 designed the first glider to make a sustained flight, and by the German Otto Lilienthal, who became known as the world's first pilot because he managed to achieve controlled flights. However, powered flight did not become a practical possibility until the invention of lightweight, gas-driven internal-combustion engines at the end of the 19th century. Then, in 1903, the American brothers Orville and Wilbur Wright made the first powered flight in their Wright Flyer biplane, which used a four-cylinder, gas-driven engine. Aircraft design advanced rapidly, and in 1909 the Frenchman Louis Blériot made his pioneering flight across the English Channel (see pp. 400-401). The American Glenn Curtiss also achieved several "firsts" in his Model-D Pusher and its variants, most notably winning the world's first competition for airspeed at Reims in 1909.

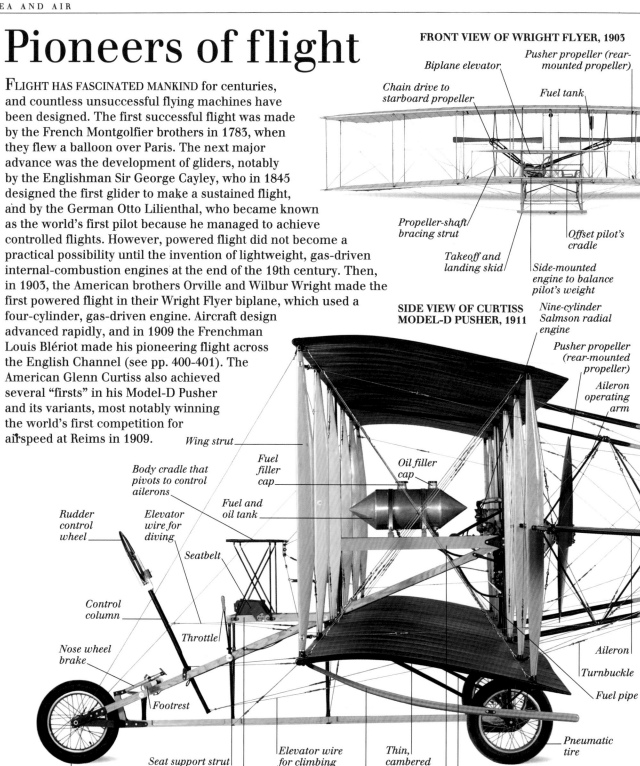

FRONT VIEW OF WRIGHT FLYER, 1903

Biplane elevator

Chain drive to starboard propeller

Pusher propeller (rear-mounted propeller)

Fuel tank

Propeller-shaft bracing strut

Takeoff and landing skid

Offset pilot's cradle

Side-mounted engine to balance pilot's weight

SIDE VIEW OF CURTISS MODEL-D PUSHER, 1911

Nine-cylinder Salmson radial engine

Pusher propeller (rear-mounted propeller)

Aileron operating arm

Wing strut

Body cradle that pivots to control ailerons

Fuel filler cap

Oil filler cap

Elevator wire for diving

Fuel and oil tank

Rudder control wheel

Seatbelt

Control column

Throttle

Nose wheel brake

Aileron

Turnbuckle

Fuel pipe

Footrest

Pneumatic tire

Seat support strut

Elevator wire for climbing

Thin, cambered lower wing

Starboard main landing gear

Rubber-tired nose wheel

Pilot's seat

Wing-protecting skid

Engine and propeller thrust frame

SIDE VIEW OF WRIGHT FLYER, 1903

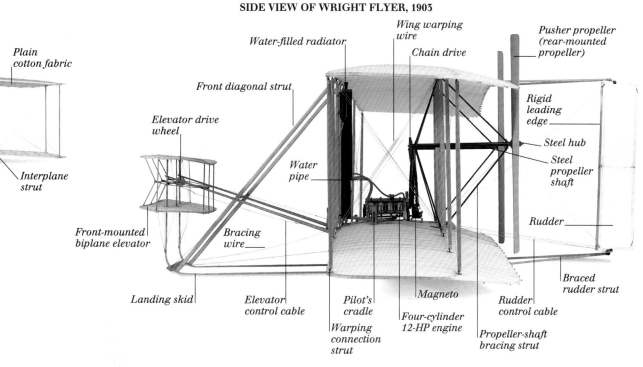

Plain cotton fabric

Interplane strut

Wing warping wire

Water-filled radiator

Chain drive

Pusher propeller (rear-mounted propeller)

Front diagonal strut

Rigid leading edge

Elevator drive wheel

Steel hub

Steel propeller shaft

Water pipe

Front-mounted biplane elevator

Rudder

Bracing wire

Landing skid

Elevator control cable

Pilot's cradle

Magneto

Rudder control cable

Braced rudder strut

Warping connection strut

Four-cylinder 12-HP engine

Propeller-shaft bracing strut

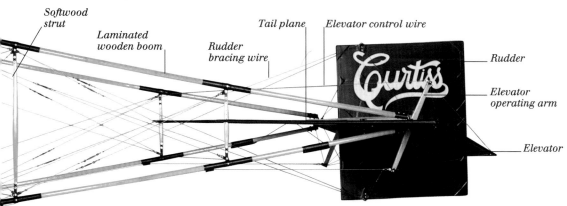

Softwood strut

Tail plane

Elevator control wire

Laminated wooden boom

Rudder

Rudder bracing wire

Elevator operating arm

Elevator

FRONT VIEW OF CURTISS MODEL-D PUSHER, 1911

Rudder control wheel

Fuel and oil tank

Nine-cylinder Salmson radial engine

Elevator operating arm

Anti-lift wire

Aileron operating arm

Starboard aileron

Port aileron

Carved interplane strut

Wing-protecting skid

Wing-protecting skid

Lift wire

Control column

Seat beam

Tubular steel leg

Interplane strut pin-jointed to front spar

Footrest

Axle

Main landing gear lateral brace

Early monoplanes

RUMPLER MONOPLANE, 1908

MONOPLANES HAVE ONE WING on each side of the fuselage. The principal disadvantage of this arrangement in early wooden-framed aircraft was that single wings were weak. They required strong wires to brace them to king posts above and below the fuselage. However, single wings also had advantages: they experienced less drag than multiple wings, allowing greater speed; they also made aircraft more maneuverable because single wings were easier to warp (twist) than double wings, and warping the wings was how pilots controlled the roll of early aircraft. By 1912, the French pilot Louis Blériot had used a monoplane to make the first flight across the English Channel, and the Briton Robert Blackburn and the Frenchman Armand Deperdussin had proved the greater speed of monoplanes. However, a spate of crashes caused by broken wings discouraged monoplane production, except in Germany, where all-metal monoplanes were developed in 1917. The wings of all-metal monoplanes did not need strengthening by struts or bracing wires, but despite this, such planes were not widely adopted until the 1930s.

FRONT VIEW OF BLACKBURN MONOPLANE, 1912

Taut fabric

Carved wooden propeller

King post

Nose ring

Hub bolted to propeller

Pilot's viewing aperture

Exhaust valve push-rod

Gnome seven-cylinder rotary engine

Elevator hinge

Elevator

Landing gear rear cross-member

Wheel fairing

Tailskid

Rubber-sprung wheel

Landing gear front strut

Axle

Landing skid

Landing gear rear strut

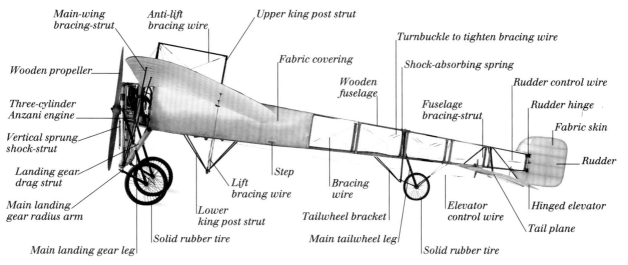

Main-wing bracing-strut
Anti-lift bracing wire
Upper king post strut
Turnbuckle to tighten bracing wire
Shock-absorbing spring
Rudder control wire
Wooden propeller
Fabric covering
Wooden fuselage
Rudder hinge
Three-cylinder Anzani engine
Fuselage bracing-strut
Fabric skin
Vertical sprung shock-strut
Rudder
Landing gear drag strut
Lift bracing wire
Step
Main landing gear radius arm
Bracing wire
Hinged elevator
Lower king post strut
Elevator control wire
Solid rubber tire
Tailwheel bracket
Tail plane
Main landing gear leg
Main tailwheel leg
Solid rubber tire

SIDE VIEW OF BLÉRIOT XI, 1909

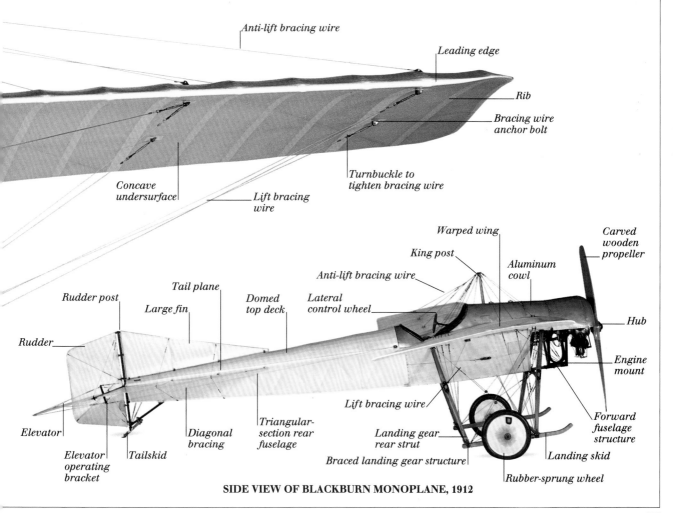

Anti-lift bracing wire
Leading edge
Rib
Bracing wire anchor bolt
Concave undersurface
Turnbuckle to tighten bracing wire
Lift bracing wire

Warped wing
Carved wooden propeller
King post
Aluminum cowl
Anti-lift bracing wire
Lateral control wheel
Rudder post
Tail plane
Domed top deck
Hub
Large fin
Engine mount
Rudder
Lift bracing wire
Forward fuselage structure
Elevator
Diagonal bracing
Triangular-section rear fuselage
Landing gear rear strut
Landing skid
Elevator operating bracket
Tailskid
Braced landing gear structure
Rubber-sprung wheel

SIDE VIEW OF BLACKBURN MONOPLANE, 1912

Biplanes and triplanes

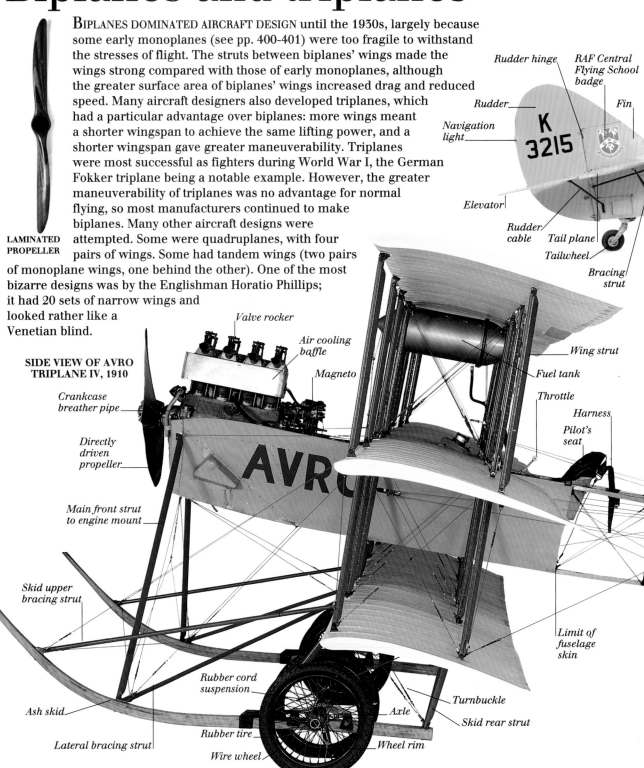

BIPLANES DOMINATED AIRCRAFT DESIGN until the 1930s, largely because some early monoplanes (see pp. 400-401) were too fragile to withstand the stresses of flight. The struts between biplanes' wings made the wings strong compared with those of early monoplanes, although the greater surface area of biplanes' wings increased drag and reduced speed. Many aircraft designers also developed triplanes, which had a particular advantage over biplanes: more wings meant a shorter wingspan to achieve the same lifting power, and a shorter wingspan gave greater maneuverability. Triplanes were most successful as fighters during World War I, the German Fokker triplane being a notable example. However, the greater maneuverability of triplanes was no advantage for normal flying, so most manufacturers continued to make biplanes. Many other aircraft designs were attempted. Some were quadruplanes, with four pairs of wings. Some had tandem wings (two pairs of monoplane wings, one behind the other). One of the most bizarre designs was by the Englishman Horatio Phillips; it had 20 sets of narrow wings and looked rather like a Venetian blind.

LAMINATED PROPELLER

Rudder hinge

RAF Central Flying School badge

Rudder

K 3215

Fin

Navigation light

Elevator

Rudder cable

Tail plane

Tailwheel

Bracing strut

SIDE VIEW OF AVRO TRIPLANE IV, 1910

Valve rocker

Air cooling baffle

Magneto

Wing strut

Fuel tank

Throttle

Harness

Pilot's seat

Crankcase breather pipe

Directly driven propeller

Main front strut to engine mount

AVRO

Skid upper bracing strut

Limit of fuselage skin

Ash skid

Rubber cord suspension

Axle

Turnbuckle

Skid rear strut

Lateral bracing strut

Rubber tire

Wire wheel

Wheel rim

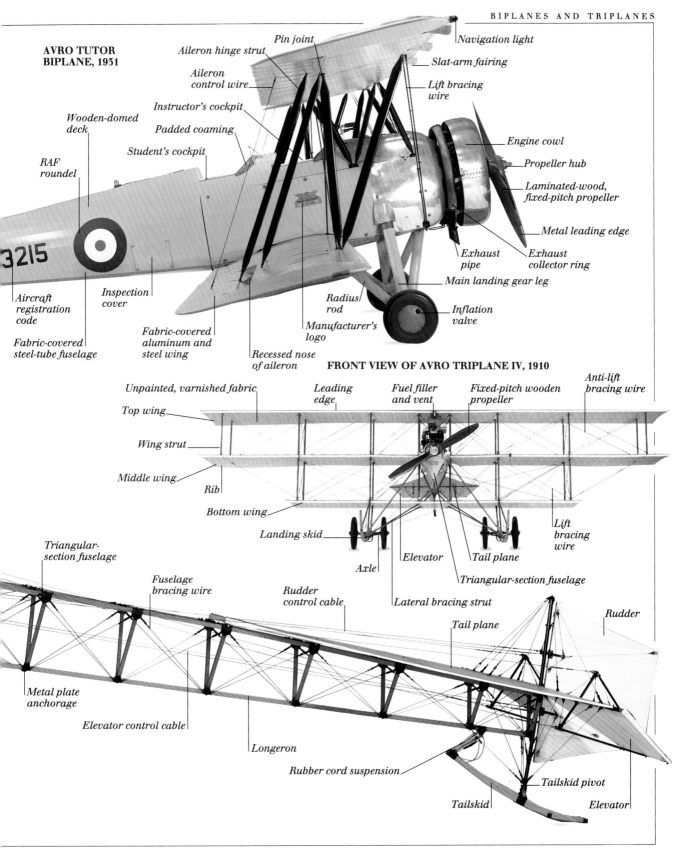

AVRO TUTOR BIPLANE, 1931

Pin joint

Aileron hinge strut

Navigation light

Slat-arm fairing

Aileron control wire

Lift bracing wire

Instructor's cockpit

Wooden-domed deck

Padded coaming

Engine cowl

Student's cockpit

Propeller hub

RAF roundel

Laminated-wood, fixed-pitch propeller

Metal leading edge

3215

Exhaust collector ring

Exhaust pipe

Aircraft registration code

Inspection cover

Main landing gear leg

Fabric-covered aluminum and steel wing

Radius rod

Inflation valve

Fabric-covered steel-tube fuselage

Manufacturer's logo

Recessed nose of aileron

FRONT VIEW OF AVRO TRIPLANE IV, 1910

Unpainted, varnished fabric

Leading edge

Fuel filler and vent

Fixed-pitch wooden propeller

Anti-lift bracing wire

Top wing

Wing strut

Middle wing

Rib

Bottom wing

Landing skid

Axle

Elevator

Tail plane

Lift bracing wire

Triangular-section fuselage

Triangular-section fuselage

Fuselage bracing wire

Rudder control cable

Lateral bracing strut

Tail plane

Rudder

Metal plate anchorage

Elevator control cable

Longeron

Rubber cord suspension

Tailskid

Tailskid pivot

Elevator

World War I aircraft

WHEN WORLD WAR I STARTED in 1914, the main purpose of military aircraft was reconnaissance. The British-built BE 2, of which the BE 2B was a variant, was well suited to this duty; it was very stable in flight, allowing the occupants to study the terrain, take photographs, and make notes. The BE 2 was also one of the first aircraft to drop bombs. One of the biggest problems for aircraft designers during the war was mounting machine guns. On aircraft that had front-mounted propellers, the field of fire was restricted by the propeller and other parts of the aircraft. The problem was solved in 1915 by the Dutchman Anthony Fokker, who designed an interrupter gear that prevented a machine gun from firing when a propeller blade passed in front of the barrel. The German LVG CVI had a forward-firing gun to the right of the engine, as well as a rear-cockpit gun, and bombing capability. It was one of the most versatile aircraft of the war.

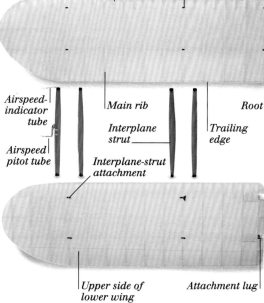

PORT WINGS FROM A BE 2B

Interplane-strut attachment
Intermediate leading-edge rib
Airspeed-indicator tube
Leading edge
Wingtip
Airspeed-indicator tube
Main rib
Root
Interplane strut
Trailing edge
Airspeed pitot tube
Interplane-strut attachment
Upper side of lower wing
Attachment lug

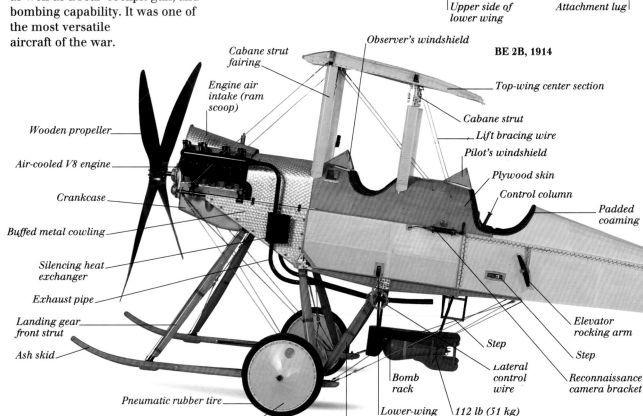

BE 2B, 1914

Cabane strut fairing
Observer's windshield
Engine air intake (ram scoop)
Top-wing center section
Cabane strut
Lift bracing wire
Wooden propeller
Pilot's windshield
Air-cooled V8 engine
Plywood skin
Crankcase
Control column
Padded coaming
Buffed metal cowling
Silencing heat exchanger
Exhaust pipe
Landing gear front strut
Elevator rocking arm
Ash skid
Step
Step
Lateral control wire
Reconnaissance camera bracket
Bomb rack
Pneumatic rubber tire
Lower-wing attachment
112 lb (51 kg) bomb
Wheel cover
V-strut

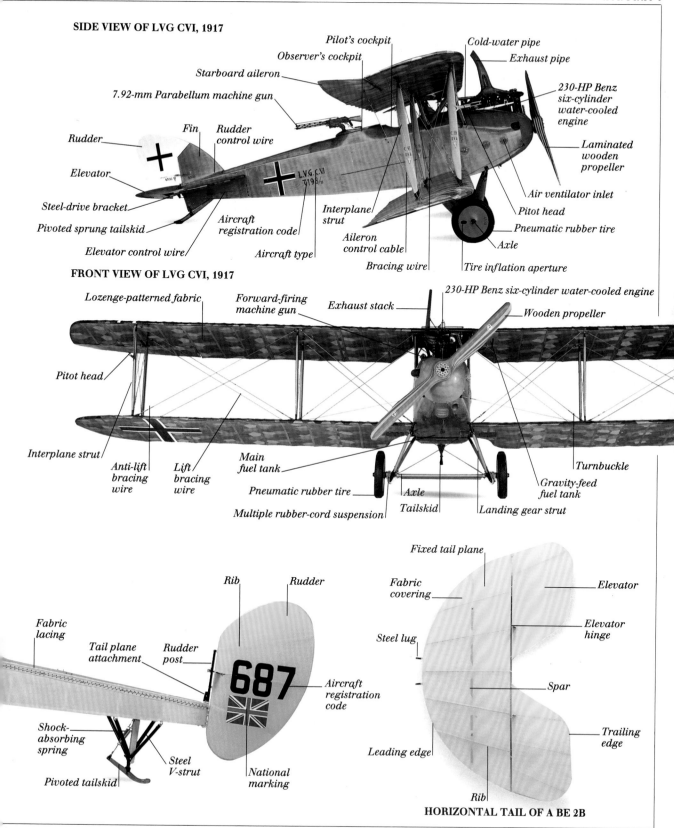

SIDE VIEW OF LVG CVI, 1917

Pilot's cockpit

Observer's cockpit

Cold-water pipe

Exhaust pipe

Starboard aileron

7.92-mm Parabellum machine gun

230-HP Benz
six-cylinder
water-cooled
engine

Rudder

Fin

Rudder
control wire

Elevator

Laminated
wooden
propeller

Steel-drive bracket

Pivoted sprung tailskid

Aircraft
registration code

Interplane
strut

Air ventilator inlet

Pitot head

Pneumatic rubber tire

Elevator control wire

Aircraft type

Aileron
control cable

Axle

Bracing wire

Tire inflation aperture

FRONT VIEW OF LVG CVI, 1917

Lozenge-patterned fabric

Forward-firing
machine gun

Exhaust stack

230-HP Benz six-cylinder water-cooled engine

Wooden propeller

Pitot head

Interplane strut

Anti-lift
bracing
wire

Lift
bracing
wire

Main
fuel tank

Pneumatic rubber tire

Axle

Tailskid

Landing gear strut

Gravity-feed
fuel tank

Turnbuckle

Multiple rubber-cord suspension

Fabric
lacing

Tail plane
attachment

Rudder
post

Rib

Rudder

Fixed tail plane

Fabric
covering

Elevator

Steel lug

Elevator
hinge

687

Aircraft
registration
code

Spar

Shock-
absorbing
spring

Steel
V-strut

Pivoted tailskid

National
marking

Leading edge

Rib

Trailing
edge

HORIZONTAL TAIL OF A BE 2B

405

Early passenger aircraft

FRONT VIEW OF LOCKHEED ELECTRA, 1934

UNTIL THE 1930s, most passenger aircraft were biplanes, with two pairs of wings and a wooden or metal framework covered with fabric or, sometimes, plywood. Such aircraft were restricted to low speeds and low altitudes because of the drag on their wings. Many had an open cockpit, situated behind or in front of an enclosed—but unpressurized—cabin that carried a maximum of 10 people. The passengers usually sat in wicker chairs that were not bolted to the floor, and the journey could be bumpy when flying through turbulence. Warm clothing, and earplugs to reduce the effects of prolonged noise, were often required. During the 1930s, powerful, streamlined, all-metal monoplanes, such as the Lockheed Electra shown here, became widespread. By 1939, the advent of pressurized cabins allowed fast flights at high altitudes, where there is less turbulence. Flying boats were still necessary on many routes until 1945 because of inadequate runways and the frequency of emergency sea landings. World War II, however, resulted in enough good runways being built for land planes to become standard on all major airline routes.

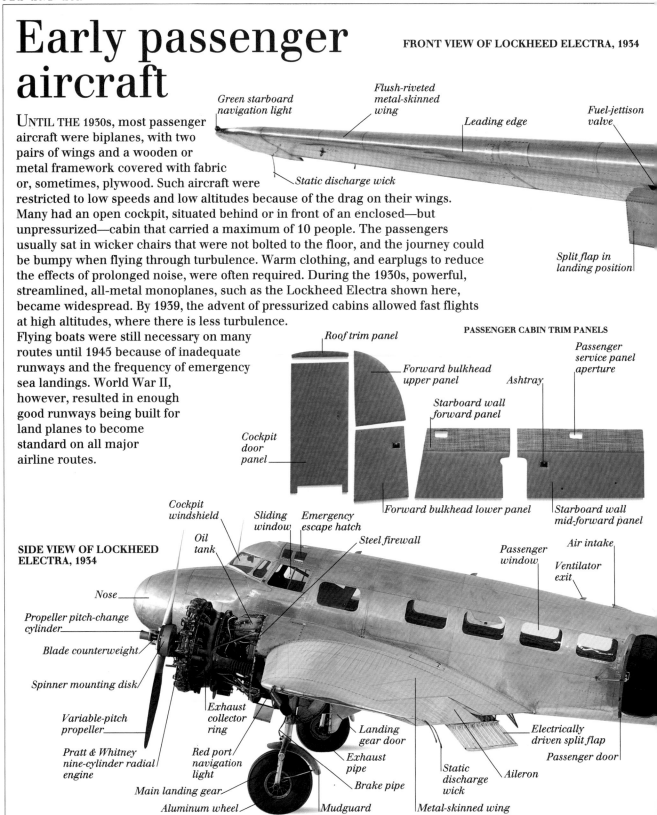

Green starboard navigation light

Flush-riveted metal-skinned wing

Leading edge

Fuel-jettison valve

Static discharge wick

Split flap in landing position

Roof trim panel

PASSENGER CABIN TRIM PANELS

Forward bulkhead upper panel

Passenger service panel aperture

Ashtray

Starboard wall forward panel

Cockpit door panel

Forward bulkhead lower panel

Starboard wall mid-forward panel

SIDE VIEW OF LOCKHEED ELECTRA, 1934

Cockpit windshield

Sliding window

Emergency escape hatch

Steel firewall

Oil tank

Passenger window

Air intake

Ventilator exit

Nose

Propeller pitch-change cylinder

Blade counterweight

Spinner mounting disk

Variable-pitch propeller

Pratt & Whitney nine-cylinder radial engine

Exhaust collector ring

Red port navigation light

Landing gear door

Exhaust pipe

Electrically driven split flap

Passenger door

Main landing gear

Brake pipe

Static discharge wick

Aileron

Aluminum wheel

Mudguard

Metal-skinned wing

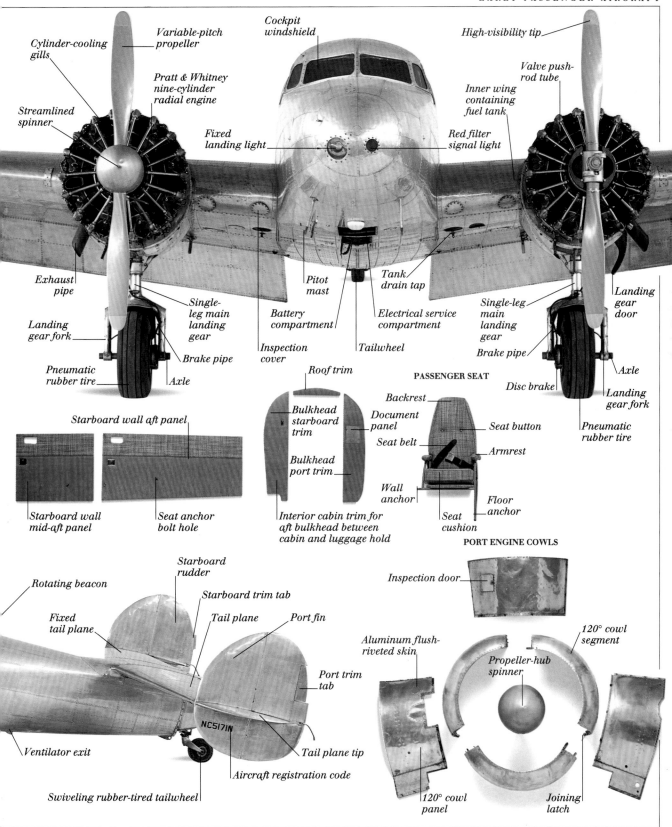

Cylinder-cooling gills

Variable-pitch propeller

Cockpit windshield

High-visibility tip

Pratt & Whitney nine-cylinder radial engine

Streamlined spinner

Valve push-rod tube

Inner wing containing fuel tank

Fixed landing light

Red filter signal light

Exhaust pipe

Single-leg main landing gear

Pitot mast

Tank drain tap

Single-leg main landing gear

Landing gear door

Landing gear fork

Brake pipe

Battery compartment

Electrical service compartment

Brake pipe

Axle

Pneumatic rubber tire

Axle

Inspection cover

Tailwheel

Disc brake

Landing gear fork

Pneumatic rubber tire

Starboard wall aft panel

Roof trim

PASSENGER SEAT

Bulkhead starboard trim

Backrest

Document panel

Seat button

Seat belt

Armrest

Bulkhead port trim

Wall anchor

Floor anchor

Starboard wall mid-aft panel

Seat anchor bolt hole

Interior cabin trim for aft bulkhead between cabin and luggage hold

Seat cushion

PORT ENGINE COWLS

Starboard rudder

Inspection door

Rotating beacon

Starboard trim tab

Fixed tail plane

Tail plane

Port fin

120° cowl segment

Aluminum flush-riveted skin

Propeller-hub spinner

Port trim tab

NC517IN

Ventilator exit

Tail plane tip

Aircraft registration code

Swiveling rubber-tired tailwheel

120° cowl panel

Joining latch

World War II aircraft

WHEN WORLD WAR II began in 1939, air forces had already replaced most of their fabric-skinned biplanes with all-metal stressed-skin monoplanes. Aircraft played a far greater role in military operations during World War II than ever before. The wide range of aircraft duties and the introduction of radar tracking and guidance systems put pressure on designers to improve aircraft performance. The main areas of improvement were speed, range, and engine power. Bombers became larger and more powerful—converting from two to four engines—in order to carry a heavier bomb load; the U.S. B-17 Flying Fortress could carry up to 6 tons of bombs over a distance of about 2,000 miles (3,200 km). Some aircraft increased their range by using drop tanks (fuel tanks that were jettisoned when empty to reduce drag). Fighters needed speed and maneuverability: the Hawker Tempest shown here had a maximum speed of 435 mph (700 kph) and was one of the few Allied aircraft capable of catching the German jet-powered V1 "flying bomb." By 1944, Britain had introduced its first turbojet-powered aircraft, the Gloster Meteor fighter, and Germany had introduced the fastest fighter in the world, the turbojet-powered Me 262, which had a maximum speed of 540 mph (868 kph).

PROPELLER

High-visibility yellow tip

Light-alloy propeller spinner

Variable-pitch aluminum-alloy blade

COMPONENTS OF A HAWKER TEMPEST MARK V, c.1943

Radiator-access cowling

Lower side cowling

Upper side cowling

STARBOARD ENGINE COWLINGS

Cowling fastener

Propeller governor

Radiator header tank

Propeller drive shaft

Distributor

Ejector exhaust

2,400-HP Napier Sabre 24-cylinder engine

Cartridge starter

Magneto

Starter motor

Engine top cowling

Upper side cowling

Lower side cowling

Radiator-access cowling

Cowling fastener

PORT ENGINE COWLINGS

SECTIONED B-17G FLYING FORTRESS BOMBER, c.1943

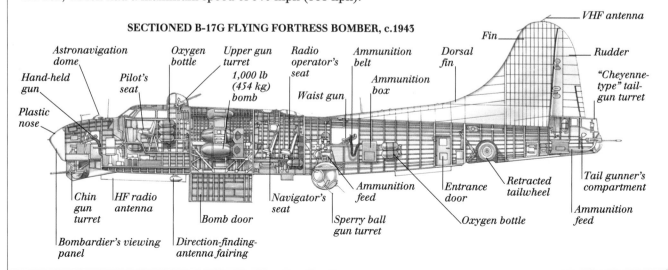

Astronavigation dome

Hand-held gun

Plastic nose

Pilot's seat

Oxygen bottle

Upper gun turret

1,000 lb (454 kg) bomb

Radio operator's seat

Waist gun

Ammunition belt

Ammunition box

Dorsal fin

Fin

VHF antenna

Rudder

"Cheyenne-type" tail-gun turret

Tail gunner's compartment

Ammunition feed

Retracted tailwheel

Oxygen bottle

Entrance door

Ammunition feed

Sperry ball gun turret

Ammunition feed

Navigator's seat

Bomb door

Direction-finding-antenna fairing

Chin gun turret

HF radio antenna

Bombardier's viewing panel

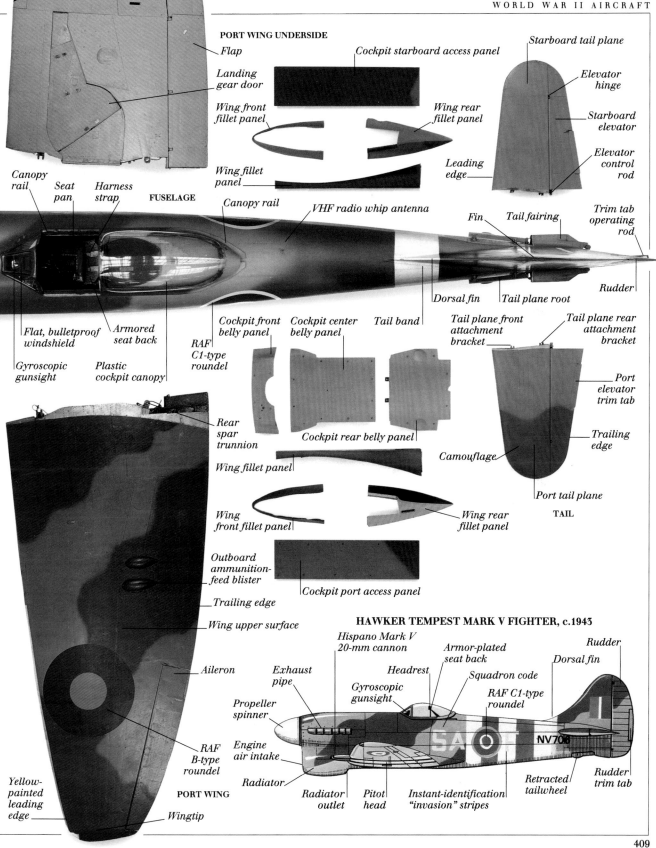

PORT WING UNDERSIDE

Flap

Landing gear door

Cockpit starboard access panel

Wing front fillet panel

Wing rear fillet panel

Starboard tail plane

Elevator hinge

Starboard elevator

Elevator control rod

Wing fillet panel

Leading edge

Canopy rail

Seat pan

Harness strap

FUSELAGE

Canopy rail

VHF radio whip antenna

Fin

Tail fairing

Trim tab operating rod

Rudder

Dorsal fin

Tail plane root

Flat, bulletproof windshield

Armored seat back

Gyroscopic gunsight

Plastic cockpit canopy

RAF C1-type roundel

Cockpit front belly panel

Cockpit center belly panel

Tail band

Tail plane front attachment bracket

Tail plane rear attachment bracket

Port elevator trim tab

Trailing edge

Rear spar trunnion

Cockpit rear belly panel

Camouflage

Port tail plane

TAIL

Wing fillet panel

Wing front fillet panel

Wing rear fillet panel

Outboard ammunition-feed blister

Cockpit port access panel

Trailing edge

Wing upper surface

HAWKER TEMPEST MARK V FIGHTER, c.1943

Aileron

Hispano Mark V 20-mm cannon

Exhaust pipe

Headrest

Armor-plated seat back

Squadron code

Rudder

Dorsal fin

Gyroscopic gunsight

RAF C1-type roundel

Propeller spinner

Engine air intake

RAF B-type roundel

Radiator

Radiator outlet

Pitot head

Instant-identification "invasion" stripes

Retracted tailwheel

Rudder trim tab

Yellow-painted leading edge

PORT WING

Wingtip

SA

NV70

409

Modern piston aircraft engines

MID WEST TWO-STROKE, THREE-CYLINDER ENGINE

PISTON ENGINES today are used mainly to power the vast numbers of light aircraft and ultralights, as well as crop sprayers and crop dusters, small helicopters, and fire-bombers (which dump water on large fires). Virtually all heavier aircraft are now powered by jet engines. Modern piston aircraft engines work on the same basic principles as the engine used by the Wright brothers in the first powered flight in 1903. However, today's engines are more sophisticated than earlier engines. For example, modern aircraft engines may use a two-stroke or a four-stroke combustion cycle; they may have from one to nine air- or liquid-cooled cylinders, which may be arranged horizontally, in-line, in V formation, or radially; and they may drive the aircraft's propeller either directly or through a reduction gearbox. One of the more unconventional types of modern aircraft engine is the rotary engine shown here, which has a trilobate (three-sided) rotor spinning in a chamber shaped like a fat figure-eight.

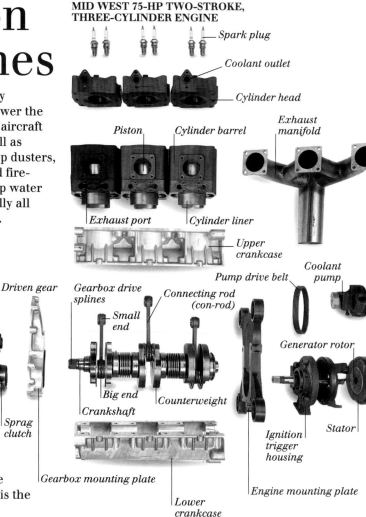

MID WEST 75-HP TWO-STROKE, THREE-CYLINDER ENGINE

Spark plug

Coolant outlet

Cylinder head

Piston

Cylinder barrel

Exhaust manifold

Exhaust port

Cylinder liner

Upper crankcase

Reduction gearbox

Driven gear

Gearbox drive splines

Connecting rod (con-rod)

Small end

Pump drive belt

Coolant pump

Propeller drive flange

Big end

Counterweight

Generator rotor

Crankshaft

Stator

Torsional vibration damper

Sprag clutch

Lower crankcase

Ignition trigger housing

Engine mounting plate

Gearbox mounting plate

ROTOR AND HOUSINGS OF A MID WEST SINGLE-ROTOR ENGINE

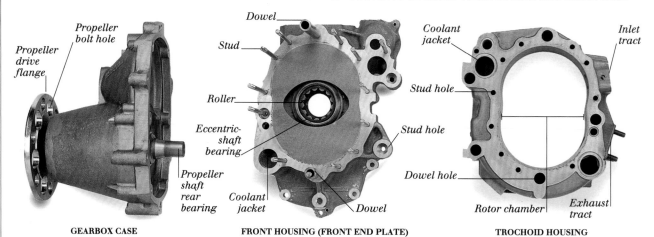

Propeller bolt hole

Propeller drive flange

Dowel

Stud

Coolant jacket

Inlet tract

Roller

Stud hole

Eccentric-shaft bearing

Stud hole

Propeller shaft rear bearing

Coolant jacket

Dowel

Dowel hole

Rotor chamber

Exhaust tract

GEARBOX CASE

FRONT HOUSING (FRONT END PLATE)

TROCHOID HOUSING

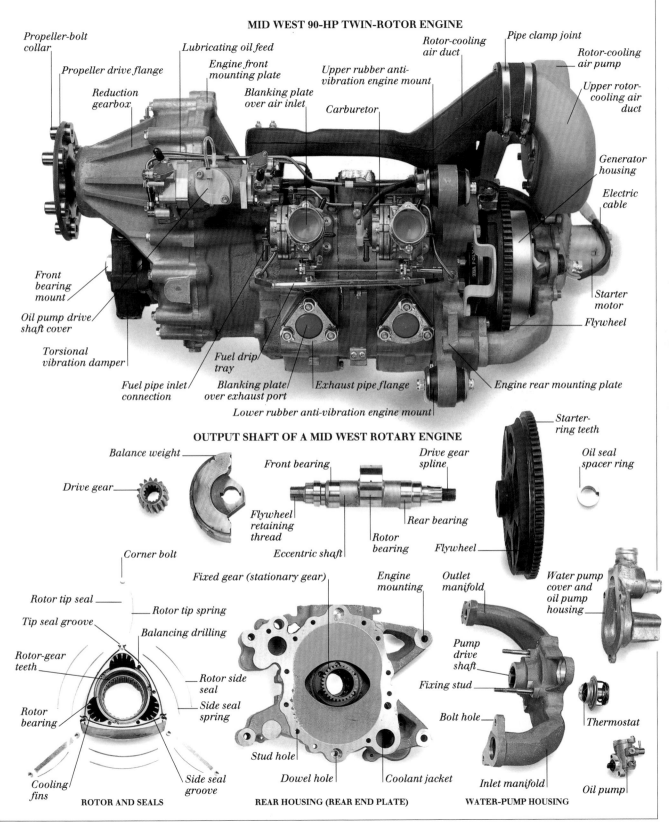

MID WEST 90-HP TWIN-ROTOR ENGINE

Propeller-bolt collar

Propeller drive flange

Reduction gearbox

Lubricating oil feed

Engine front mounting plate

Blanking plate over air inlet

Upper rubber anti-vibration engine mount

Carburetor

Rotor-cooling air duct

Pipe clamp joint

Rotor-cooling air pump

Upper rotor-cooling air duct

Generator housing

Electric cable

Starter motor

Flywheel

Front bearing mount

Oil pump drive shaft cover

Torsional vibration damper

Fuel pipe inlet connection

Fuel drip tray

Blanking plate over exhaust port

Exhaust pipe flange

Engine rear mounting plate

Lower rubber anti-vibration engine mount

OUTPUT SHAFT OF A MID WEST ROTARY ENGINE

Balance weight

Drive gear

Front bearing

Drive gear spline

Starter-ring teeth

Oil seal spacer ring

Flywheel retaining thread

Rear bearing

Eccentric shaft

Rotor bearing

Flywheel

Corner bolt

Rotor tip seal

Tip seal groove

Rotor-gear teeth

Rotor bearing

Cooling fins

Rotor tip spring

Balancing drilling

Rotor side seal

Side seal spring

Side seal groove

ROTOR AND SEALS

Fixed gear (stationary gear)

Engine mounting

Stud hole

Dowel hole

Coolant jacket

REAR HOUSING (REAR END PLATE)

Outlet manifold

Pump drive shaft

Fixing stud

Bolt hole

Inlet manifold

Water pump cover and oil pump housing

Thermostat

Oil pump

WATER-PUMP HOUSING

Modern jetliners 1

MODERN JETLINERS HAVE ENABLED ordinary people to travel to places where once only the wealthy could afford to go. Compared with the first jetliners (which were introduced in the 1940s), modern jetliners are much quieter, burn fuel more efficiently, and produce less air pollution. These advances are largely due to the replacement of turbojet engines with turbofan engines (see pp. 418-419). The greater power of turbofan engines at low speeds enables modern jetliners to carry more fuel and passengers than turbojet aircraft; a modern Boeing 747-400 (popularly known as a "jumbo jet") can fly 400 people for 8,500 miles (13,700 km) without needing to refuel. Jetliners fly at high altitudes, typically cruising at 26,000-36,000 ft (8,000-11,000 m), where they can use fuel efficiently and usually avoid bad weather. The pilot always controls the aircraft during takeoff and landing, but at other times the aircraft is usually controlled by an autopilot. Autopilots are complex onboard mechanisms that detect deviations from an aircraft's route and make appropriate adjustments to the flight controls. Flight decks are also equipped with radar that warns pilots of approaching hazards, such as mountain ranges, bad weather, and other aircraft.

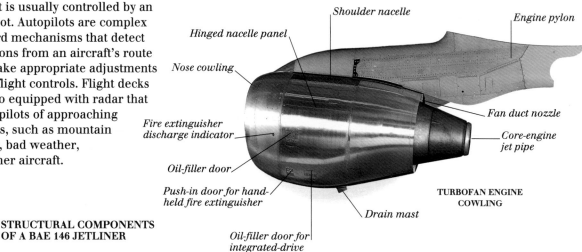

Shoulder nacelle

Engine pylon

Hinged nacelle panel

Nose cowling

Fan duct nozzle

Fire extinguisher discharge indicator

Core-engine jet pipe

Oil-filler door

Push-in door for hand-held fire extinguisher

Drain mast

TURBOFAN ENGINE COWLING

STRUCTURAL COMPONENTS OF A BAE 146 JETLINER

Oil-filler door for integrated-drive generator

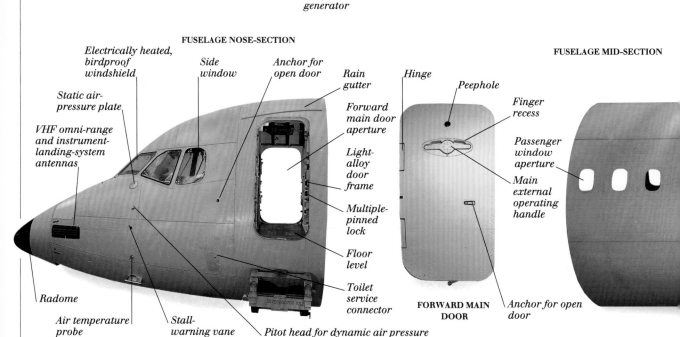

FUSELAGE NOSE-SECTION

FUSELAGE MID-SECTION

Electrically heated, birdproof windshield

Side window

Anchor for open door

Rain gutter

Hinge

Peephole

Finger recess

Static air-pressure plate

Forward main door aperture

VHF omni-range and instrument-landing-system antennas

Light-alloy door frame

Passenger window aperture

Main external operating handle

Multiple-pinned lock

Floor level

Toilet service connector

Radome

Air temperature probe

Stall-warning vane

Pitot head for dynamic air pressure

507E6000760 ISS2

FORWARD MAIN DOOR

Anchor for open door

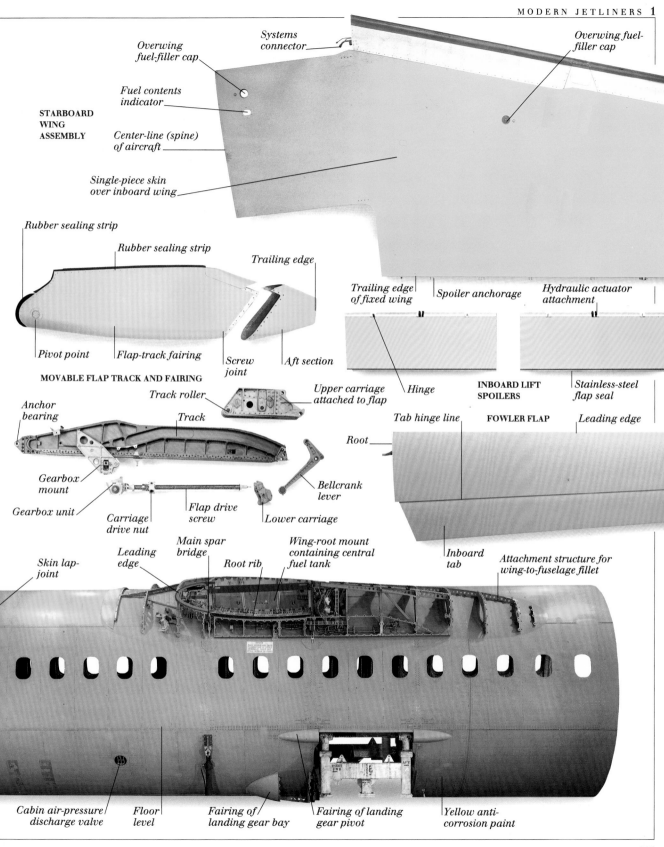

Systems
connector

Overwing
fuel-filler cap

Overwing fuel-
filler cap

**STARBOARD
WING
ASSEMBLY**

Fuel contents
indicator

Center-line (spine)
of aircraft

Single-piece skin
over inboard wing

Rubber sealing strip

Rubber sealing strip

Trailing edge

Trailing edge
of fixed wing

Spoiler anchorage

Hydraulic actuator
attachment

Pivot point

Flap-track fairing

Screw
joint

Aft section

Hinge

**INBOARD LIFT
SPOILERS**

Stainless-steel
flap seal

MOVABLE FLAP TRACK AND FAIRING

Track roller

Upper carriage
attached to flap

Tab hinge line

FOWLER FLAP

Leading edge

Anchor
bearing

Track

Root

Gearbox
mount

Bellcrank
lever

Gearbox unit

Carriage
drive nut

Flap drive
screw

Lower carriage

Inboard
tab

Attachment structure for
wing-to-fuselage fillet

Skin lap-
joint

Leading
edge

Main spar
bridge

Root rib

Wing-root mount
containing central
fuel tank

Cabin air-pressure
discharge valve

Floor
level

Fairing of
landing gear bay

Fairing of landing
gear pivot

Yellow anti-
corrosion paint

Modern jetliners 2

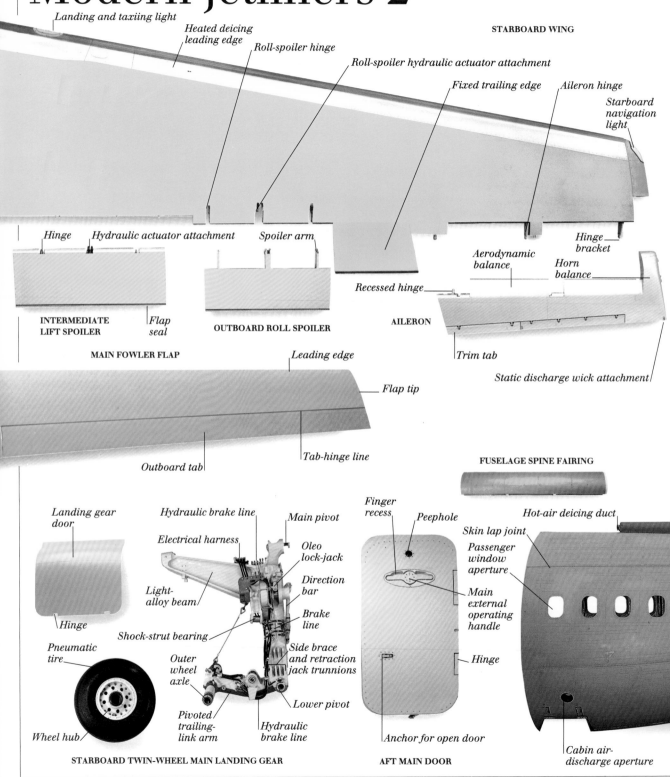

Landing and taxiing light

Heated deicing
leading edge

Roll-spoiler hinge

STARBOARD WING

Roll-spoiler hydraulic actuator attachment

Fixed trailing edge

Aileron hinge

Starboard
navigation
light

Hinge   Hydraulic actuator attachment

Spoiler arm

Hinge
bracket

Aerodynamic
balance

Horn
balance

Recessed hinge

INTERMEDIATE
LIFT SPOILER

Flap
seal

OUTBOARD ROLL SPOILER

AILERON

Trim tab

MAIN FOWLER FLAP

Static discharge wick attachment

Leading edge

Flap tip

FUSELAGE SPINE FAIRING

Outboard tab

Tab-hinge line

Finger
recess

Peephole

Hot-air deicing duct

Landing gear
door

Hydraulic brake line

Main pivot

Skin lap joint

Electrical harness

Oleo
lock-jack

Passenger
window
aperture

Light-
alloy beam

Direction
bar

Main
external
operating
handle

Shock-strut bearing

Brake
line

Hinge

Pneumatic
tire

Side brace
and retraction
jack trunnions

Hinge

Outer
wheel
axle

Pivoted
trailing-
link arm

Lower pivot

Hydraulic
brake line

Anchor for open door

Wheel hub

STARBOARD TWIN-WHEEL MAIN LANDING GEAR

AFT MAIN DOOR

Cabin air-
discharge aperture

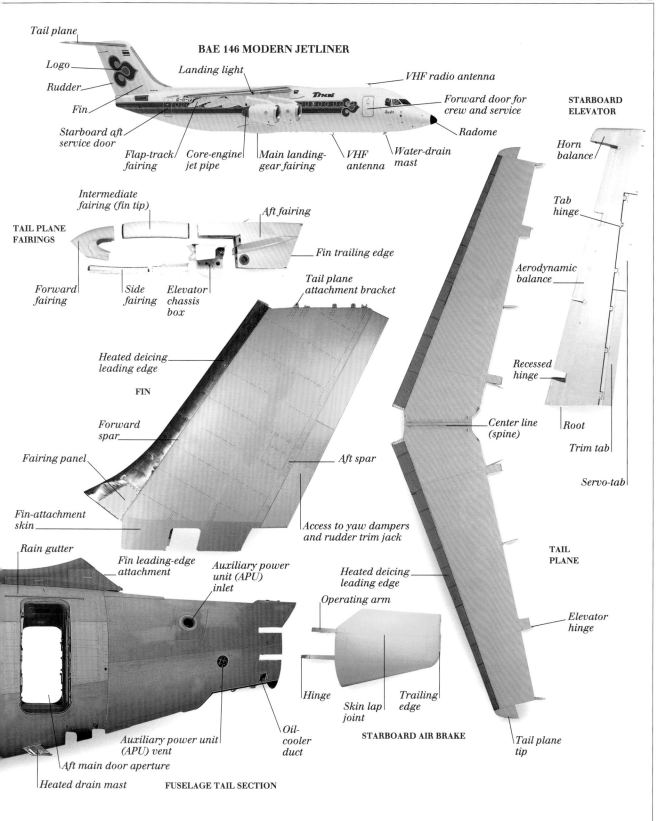

BAE 146 MODERN JETLINER

Tail plane

Logo

Rudder

Fin

Starboard aft
service door

Flap-track
fairing

Core-engine
jet pipe

Main landing-
gear fairing

VHF
antenna

Water-drain
mast

Landing light

VHF radio antenna

Forward door for
crew and service

Radome

STARBOARD
ELEVATOR

Horn
balance

Tab
hinge

Aerodynamic
balance

Recessed
hinge

Root

Trim tab

Servo-tab

TAIL PLANE
FAIRINGS

Intermediate
fairing (fin tip)

Aft fairing

Fin trailing edge

Forward
fairing

Side
fairing

Elevator
chassis
box

Tail plane
attachment bracket

Heated deicing
leading edge

FIN

Forward
spar

Fairing panel

Aft spar

Fin-attachment
skin

Access to yaw dampers
and rudder trim jack

Rain gutter

Fin leading-edge
attachment

Auxiliary power
unit (APU)
inlet

Heated deicing
leading edge

Operating arm

Elevator
hinge

TAIL
PLANE

Auxiliary power unit
(APU) vent

Oil-
cooler
duct

Hinge

Skin lap
joint

Trailing
edge

Tail plane
tip

Aft main door aperture

STARBOARD AIR BRAKE

Heated drain mast

FUSELAGE TAIL SECTION

Center line
(spine)

Supersonic jetliners

**COMPUTER-
DESIGNED SST**

SUPERSONIC AIRCRAFT FLY FASTER than the speed of sound
(Mach 1). There are many supersonic military aircraft, but only
two supersonic passenger-carrying aircraft (also called SSTs, or
supersonic transports) have been produced: the Russian Tu-144,
and the Concorde, produced jointly by Britain and France.
The Tu-144 had a greater maximum speed than
the Concorde but was withdrawn in
1978, after only seven months in service. The Concorde has
remained in service since 1976. It features many innovations,
including a droop nose, which is lowered during takeoff and
landing to aid visibility from the cockpit, and the pumping of fuel
between forward and aft trim tanks to help stabilize the aircraft.
The Concorde has a narrow fuselage and short-span wings to reduce drag during
supersonic flight. Its noisy turbojet engines with afterburners enable it to carry
100 passengers at a cruising speed of Mach 2 at 50,000-60,000 ft (15,000-18,000 m).
Once an aircraft is flying faster than Mach 1, it produces a continuous air-pressure
wave, which is heard as a "sonic boom."

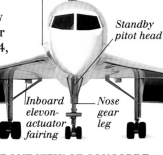

FRONT VIEW OF CONCORDE

Strake

Fin

Standby
pitot head

Starboard
outboard
engine air intake

Inboard
elevon-
actuator
fairing

Nose
gear
leg

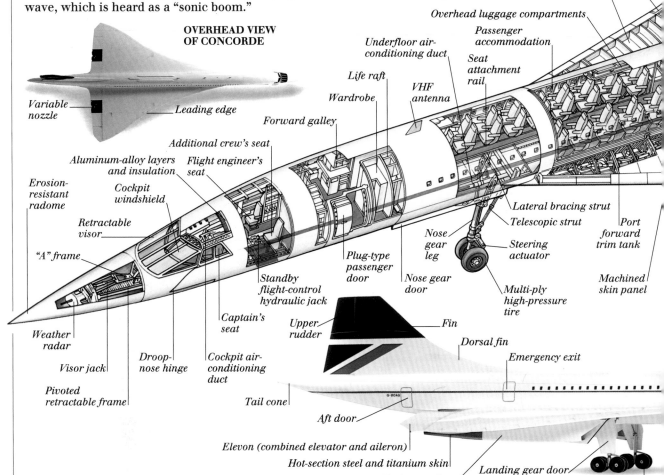

**OVERHEAD VIEW
OF CONCORDE**

Variable
nozzle

Leading edge

Erosion-
resistant
radome

Aluminum-alloy layers
and insulation

Cockpit
windshield

Flight engineer's
seat

Additional crew's seat

Forward galley

Wardrobe

Life raft

VHF
antenna

Underfloor air-
conditioning duct

Seat
attachment
rail

Passenger
accommodation

Overhead luggage compartments

Starboard
forward trim tank

Electrothermal
deicing panel

Toilets

Retractable
visor

"A" frame

Weather
radar

Visor jack

Pivoted
retractable frame

Droop-
nose hinge

Cockpit air-
conditioning
duct

Captain's
seat

Standby
flight-control
hydraulic jack

Plug-type
passenger
door

Upper
rudder

Nose gear
door

Nose
gear
leg

Steering
actuator

Telescopic strut

Lateral bracing strut

Multi-ply
high-pressure
tire

Port
forward
trim tank

Machined
skin panel

Fin

Dorsal fin

Emergency exit

Tail cone

Aft door

Elevon (combined elevator and aileron)

Hot-section steel and titanium skin

Engine cowling

Landing gear door

Bogie main landing gear

SECTIONED VIEW OF CONCORDE

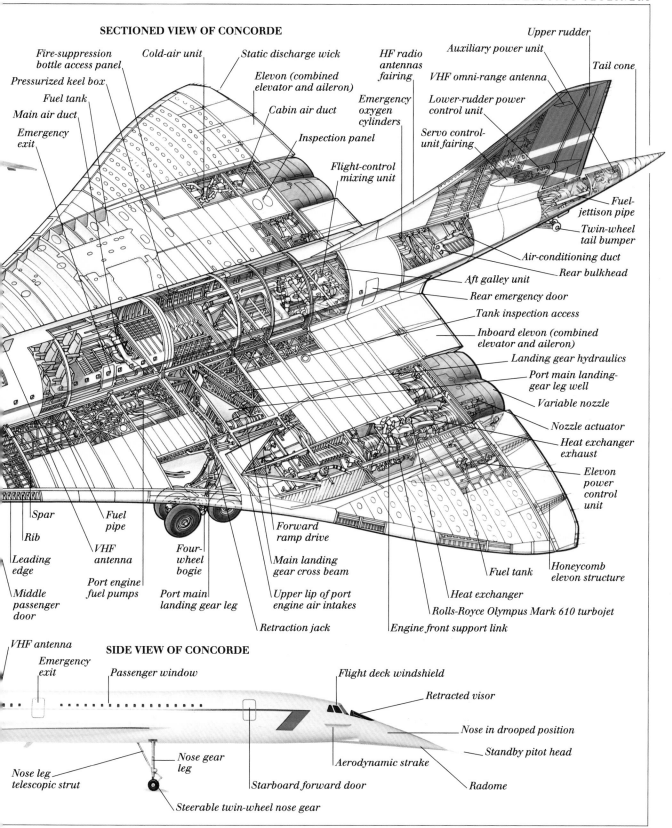

Fire-suppression bottle access panel

Pressurized keel box

Fuel tank

Main air duct

Emergency exit

Cold-air unit

Static discharge wick

Elevon (combined elevator and aileron)

Cabin air duct

Inspection panel

Flight-control mixing unit

HF radio antennas fairing

Emergency oxygen cylinders

Auxiliary power unit

VHF omni-range antenna

Lower-rudder power control unit

Servo control-unit fairing

Upper rudder

Tail cone

Fuel-jettison pipe

Twin-wheel tail bumper

Air-conditioning duct

Rear bulkhead

Rear emergency door

Tank inspection access

Inboard elevon (combined elevator and aileron)

Landing gear hydraulics

Port main landing-gear leg well

Variable nozzle

Nozzle actuator

Heat exchanger exhaust

Elevon power control unit

Aft galley unit

Spar

Rib

Leading edge

Middle passenger door

Fuel pipe

VHF antenna

Port engine fuel pumps

Four-wheel bogie

Port main landing gear leg

Forward ramp drive

Main landing gear cross beam

Upper lip of port engine air intakes

Retraction jack

Heat exchanger

Fuel tank

Honeycomb elevon structure

Rolls-Royce Olympus Mark 610 turbojet

Engine front support link

SIDE VIEW OF CONCORDE

VHF antenna

Emergency exit

Passenger window

Flight deck windshield

Retracted visor

Nose in drooped position

Standby pitot head

Nose gear leg

Nose leg

Nose leg telescopic strut

Starboard forward door

Aerodynamic strake

Radome

Steerable twin-wheel nose gear

Jet engines

JET ENGINES ARE USED BY MOST MILITARY and heavy aircraft and by many helicopters. The simplest type of jet engine, or gas turbine, is the turbojet. It works by continuously burning a mixture of fuel and air in a combustion chamber to produce a jet of hot exhaust gas that is expelled through a nozzle to produce thrust. The hot gas also spins turbine blades which, in turn, spin the blades of an air compressor; the compressor forces air into the combustion chamber. Many of the fastest aircraft use turbojets, with additional booster units called afterburners, but their use is restricted by their high noise emission. Most jetliners use quieter turbofan jet engines. An enormous fan, driven by a low-pressure turbine, feeds some air into the compressor but feeds most of it through bypass ducts to join the exhaust jetstream in the tail cone. The bypass stream produces most of the thrust. Many smaller, propeller-driven aircraft use turboprop jet engines, in which the engine powers a propeller.

NPT 301 MODERN TURBOJET

Fuel sprayer
Turbine rotor
Reverse-flow combustion chamber
Radial diffuser
Centrifugal compressor
Inducer
Exhaust diffuser
Tail cone
Air intake
Jet pipe
Exhaust nozzle
Igniter
Nose cone
Alternator
Nozzle guide vane
Air impingement starter
Combustion chamber casing

Transmission bevel drive
Plenum ring for hot anti-icing air
Integral oil tank
High-pressure compressor
Combustion chamber
High-pressure turbine
Flow splitter
Fuel manifold
Fuel nozzle
Centrifugal compressor
Temperature and pressure sensor
Low-pressure fan
Inlet cone (rotating spinner)
Pressure line
Fan case with special structure to contain broken fan
Electronic engine control and airframe interface connector
Fan duct
Electronic engine control (EEC) unit
Compressor front bearing
Engine front mount
Electrical wiring harness
Fuel and oil heat exchanger
Oil filter
Compressor air-bleed connection

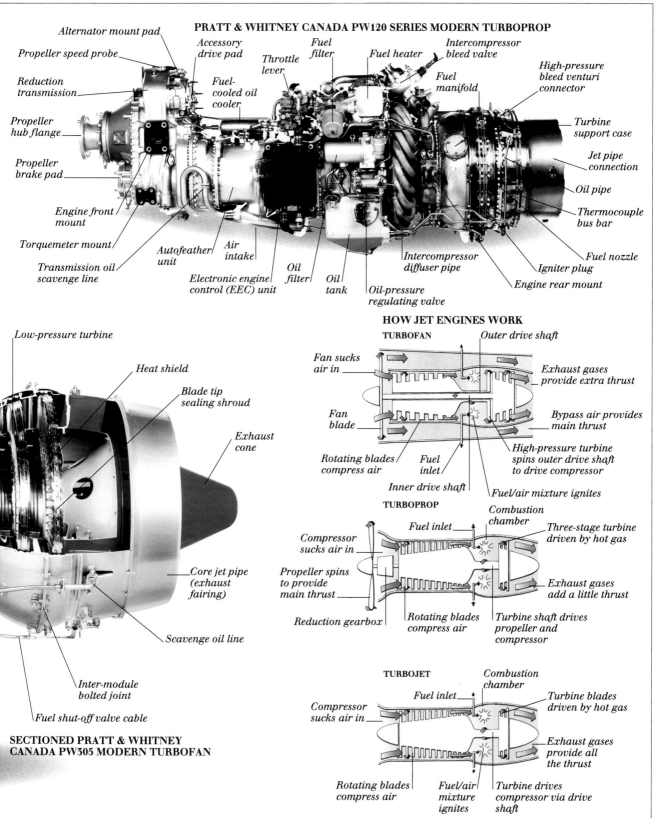

PRATT & WHITNEY CANADA PW120 SERIES MODERN TURBOPROP

Alternator mount pad

Propeller speed probe

Reduction transmission

Propeller hub flange

Propeller brake pad

Engine front mount

Torquemeter mount

Transmission oil scavenge line

Autofeather unit

Air intake

Electronic engine control (EEC) unit

Oil filter

Oil tank

Oil-pressure regulating valve

Accessory drive pad

Throttle lever

Fuel filter

Fuel-cooled oil cooler

Fuel heater

Intercompressor bleed valve

Fuel manifold

High-pressure bleed venturi connector

Turbine support case

Jet pipe connection

Oil pipe

Thermocouple bus bar

Fuel nozzle

Igniter plug

Engine rear mount

Intercompressor diffuser pipe

HOW JET ENGINES WORK

TURBOFAN

Fan sucks air in

Fan blade

Rotating blades compress air

Inner drive shaft

Outer drive shaft

Exhaust gases provide extra thrust

Bypass air provides main thrust

High-pressure turbine spins outer drive shaft to drive compressor

Fuel/air mixture ignites

Fuel inlet

Low-pressure turbine

Heat shield

Blade tip sealing shroud

Exhaust cone

Core jet pipe (exhaust fairing)

Scavenge oil line

Inter-module bolted joint

Fuel shut-off valve cable

SECTIONED PRATT & WHITNEY CANADA PW305 MODERN TURBOFAN

TURBOPROP

Compressor sucks air in

Propeller spins to provide main thrust

Reduction gearbox

Rotating blades compress air

Fuel inlet

Combustion chamber

Three-stage turbine driven by hot gas

Exhaust gases add a little thrust

Turbine shaft drives propeller and compressor

TURBOJET

Compressor sucks air in

Rotating blades compress air

Fuel inlet

Fuel/air mixture ignites

Combustion chamber

Turbine blades driven by hot gas

Exhaust gases provide all the thrust

Turbine drives compressor via drive shaft

Modern military aircraft

MODERN MILITARY AIRCRAFT ARE AMONG THE MOST SOPHISTICATED and expensive products of the 20th century. Fighters need computer-operated controls for maneuverability, powerful engines, and effective air-to-air weapons. Most modern fighters also have guided missiles, radar, and passive, infrared sensors. These developments enable today's fighters to engage in combat with adversaries who are outside visual range. Bombers carry a large weapon load and enough fuel for long-range flights. A few military aircraft, such as the Tornado and the F-14 Tomcat, have variable-sweep ("swing") wings. During takeoff and landing their wings are fully extended, but for high-speed flight and low-level attacks the wings are pivoted fully back. A recent development is the "stealth" bomber, which is designed to absorb or deflect enemy radar in order to remain undetected. Earlier bombers, such as the Tornado, use terrain-following radars to fly so close to the ground that they avoid enemy radar detection.

FRONT VIEW OF A PANAVIA TORNADO

Instrument landing system antenna

Birdproof windshield

Air data probe

Wing-root glove fairing

Port variable-incidence air intake

Starboard inboard stores pylon

Taileron

Starboard main landing-gear door

Main landing-gear leg

Laser ranger and marked-target seeker

Starboard nose gear door

Steerable twin-wheel nose gear

Radome containing ground-mapping, attack, and terrain-following radars

Taxiing light

Wing extended for takeoff and landing

Wing pivoted back for high-speed flight

SWING-WING F-14 TOMCAT FIGHTER

SIDE VIEW OF A PANAVIA TORNADO GR1A (RECONNAISSANCE VERSION), 1986

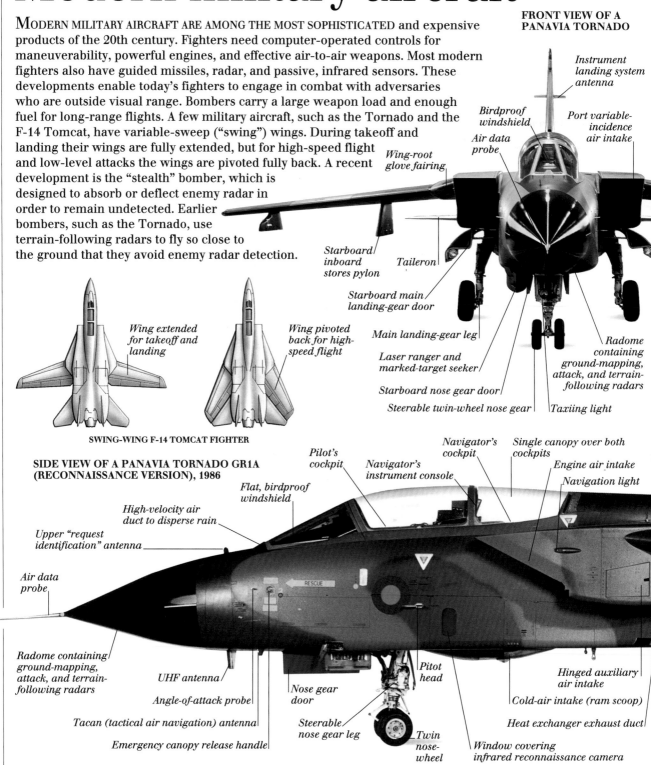

Pilot's cockpit

Navigator's instrument console

Navigator's cockpit

Single canopy over both cockpits

Engine air intake

Navigation light

Flat, birdproof windshield

High-velocity air duct to disperse rain

Upper "request identification" antenna

Air data probe

Radome containing ground-mapping, attack, and terrain-following radars

UHF antenna

Angle-of-attack probe

Tacan (tactical air navigation) antenna

Emergency canopy release handle

Nose gear door

Steerable nose gear leg

Twin nose-wheel

Pitot head

Window covering infrared reconnaissance camera

Hinged auxiliary air intake

Cold-air intake (ram scoop)

Heat exchanger exhaust duct

NORTHROP B-2 ("STEALTH" BOMBER), 1989

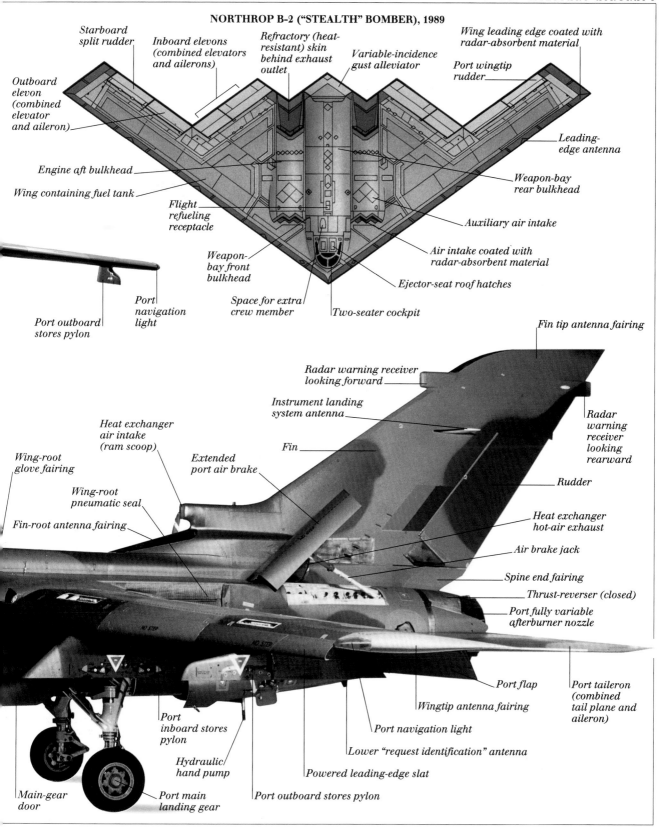

Starboard split rudder

Inboard elevons (combined elevators and ailerons)

Refractory (heat-resistant) skin behind exhaust outlet

Variable-incidence gust alleviator

Wing leading edge coated with radar-absorbent material

Port wingtip rudder

Outboard elevon (combined elevator and aileron)

Leading-edge antenna

Engine aft bulkhead

Wing containing fuel tank

Weapon-bay rear bulkhead

Flight refueling receptacle

Auxiliary air intake

Weapon-bay front bulkhead

Air intake coated with radar-absorbent material

Space for extra crew member

Ejector-seat roof hatches

Two-seater cockpit

Port outboard stores pylon

Port navigation light

Fin tip antenna fairing

Radar warning receiver looking forward

Instrument landing system antenna

Fin

Radar warning receiver looking rearward

Heat exchanger air intake (ram scoop)

Extended port air brake

Rudder

Wing-root glove fairing

Heat exchanger hot-air exhaust

Wing-root pneumatic seal

Air brake jack

Fin-root antenna fairing

Spine end fairing

Thrust-reverser (closed)

Port fully variable afterburner nozzle

Port flap

Port taileron (combined tail plane and aileron)

Port inboard stores pylon

Wingtip antenna fairing

Hydraulic hand pump

Port navigation light

Lower "request identification" antenna

Powered leading-edge slat

Main-gear door

Port main landing gear

Port outboard stores pylon

Helicopters

HELICOPTERS USE ROTATING BLADES for lift, propulsion, and steering. The first machine to achieve sustained, controlled flight using rotating blades was the autogiro built in the 1920s by Juan de la Cierva of Spain. His machine had unpowered blades above the fuselage that relied on the flow of air to rotate them and provide lift while the autogiro was driven forward by a conventional propeller. Then, in 1939, the Russian-born American Igor Sikorsky produced his VS-300, the forerunner of the modern helicopter. Its engine-driven blades provided lift, propulsion, and steering. It could take off vertically, hover, and fly in any direction, and had a tail rotor to prevent the helicopter body from spinning. The introduction of gas turbine jet engines to helicopters in 1955 produced quieter, safer, and more powerful machines. Because of their versatility in flight, helicopters are used today for many purposes, including crop spraying, traffic surveillance, and transporting crews to deep-sea oil rigs, as well as acting as gunships, air ambulances, and air taxis.

BELL 47G-3B1

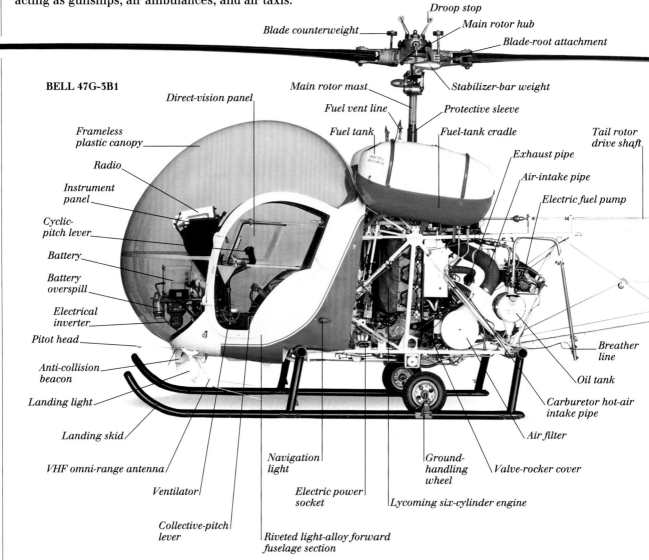

BELL 47G-3B1

Droop stop
Blade counterweight
Main rotor hub
Blade-root attachment
Main rotor mast
Stabilizer-bar weight
Direct-vision panel
Fuel vent line
Protective sleeve
Frameless plastic canopy
Fuel tank
Fuel-tank cradle
Tail rotor drive shaft
Radio
Exhaust pipe
Instrument panel
Air-intake pipe
Cyclic-pitch lever
Electric fuel pump
Battery
Battery overspill
Electrical inverter
Pitot head
Breather line
Anti-collision beacon
Oil tank
Landing light
Carburetor hot-air intake pipe
Landing skid
Air filter
VHF omni-range antenna
Navigation light
Ground-handling wheel
Valve-rocker cover
Ventilator
Electric power socket
Lycoming six-cylinder engine
Collective-pitch lever
Riveted light-alloy forward fuselage section

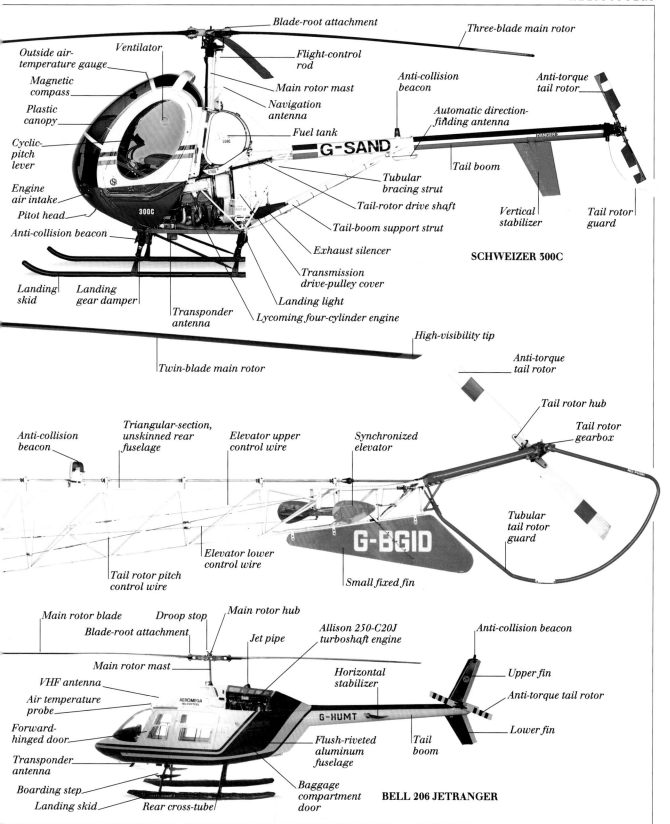

Blade-root attachment

Three-blade main rotor

Outside air-temperature gauge

Ventilator

Flight-control rod

Anti-collision beacon

Anti-torque tail rotor

Magnetic compass

Main rotor mast

Automatic direction-finding antenna

Plastic canopy

Navigation antenna

Cyclic-pitch lever

Fuel tank

G-SAND

DANGER

Engine air intake

Tubular bracing strut

Tail boom

Pitot head

Tail-rotor drive shaft

Anti-collision beacon

Tail-boom support strut

Vertical stabilizer

Tail rotor guard

Exhaust silencer

SCHWEIZER 300C

Transmission drive-pulley cover

Landing skid

Landing gear damper

Landing light

Transponder antenna

Lycoming four-cylinder engine

High-visibility tip

Anti-torque tail rotor

Twin-blade main rotor

Tail rotor hub

Anti-collision beacon

Triangular-section, unskinned rear fuselage

Elevator upper control wire

Synchronized elevator

Tail rotor gearbox

Elevator lower control wire

G-BGID

Tubular tail rotor guard

Tail rotor pitch control wire

Small fixed fin

Main rotor blade

Droop stop

Main rotor hub

Allison 250-C20J turboshaft engine

Anti-collision beacon

Blade-root attachment

Jet pipe

Main rotor mast

Horizontal stabilizer

Upper fin

VHF antenna

AEROMEGA HELICOPTERS

Anti-torque tail rotor

Air temperature probe

G-HUMT

Lower fin

Forward-hinged door

Transponder antenna

Flush-riveted aluminum fuselage

Tail boom

Boarding step

Baggage compartment door

BELL 206 JETRANGER

Landing skid

Rear cross-tube

Light aircraft

LIGHT AIRCRAFT, SUCH AS THE ARV SUPER 2 shown here, are small, lightweight, and of simple construction. More than a million have been built since World War I, mainly for recreational use by private owners. Virtually all light aircraft have piston engines, most of which are air-cooled, although some are liquid-cooled. Open cockpits, almost universal in the 1920s, have now been replaced by enclosed cabins. The cabins of high-wing aircraft have one or two doors, while those of low-wing aircraft usually have a sliding or hinged canopy. Most modern light aircraft are made of aluminum alloy, although some are made of wood or of fiber-reinforced materials. Light aircraft today also usually have navigational instruments, an electrical system, cabin heating, wheel brakes, and a two-way radio.

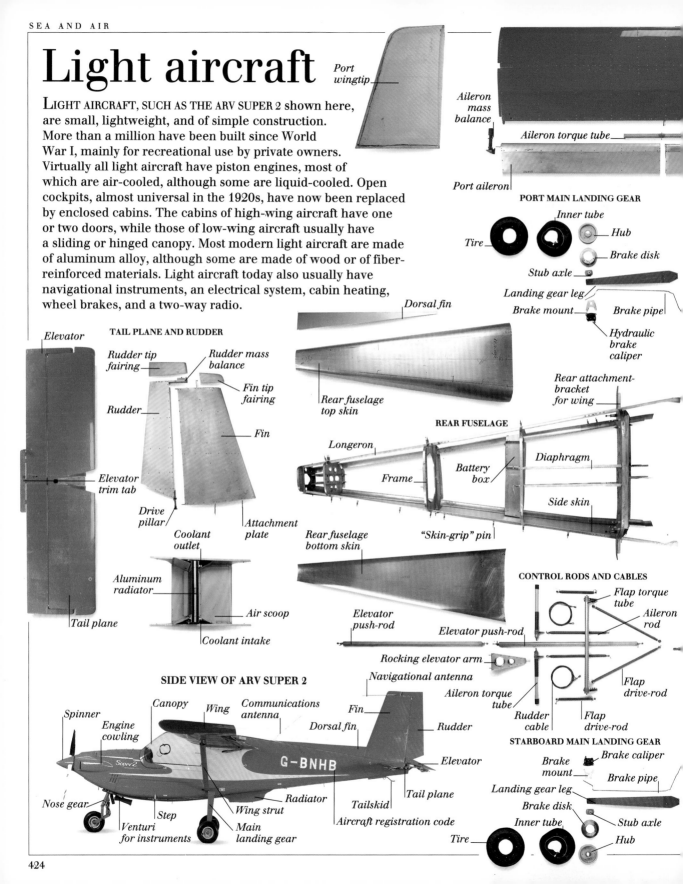

Port wingtip

Aileron mass balance

Aileron torque tube

Port aileron

PORT MAIN LANDING GEAR

Inner tube

Tire

Hub

Brake disk

Stub axle

Landing gear leg

Brake mount

Brake pipe

Hydraulic brake caliper

Dorsal fin

Rear attachment-bracket for wing

Elevator

TAIL PLANE AND RUDDER

Rudder tip fairing

Rudder mass balance

Fin tip fairing

Rudder

Fin

Rear fuselage top skin

REAR FUSELAGE

Longeron

Frame

Battery box

Diaphragm

Side skin

Elevator trim tab

Drive pillar

Attachment plate

Rear fuselage bottom skin

"Skin-grip" pin

Tail plane

Coolant outlet

Aluminum radiator

Air scoop

Coolant intake

Elevator push-rod

Elevator push-rod

Rocking elevator arm

Navigational antenna

Aileron torque tube

CONTROL RODS AND CABLES

Flap torque tube

Aileron rod

Flap drive-rod

Rudder cable

Flap drive-rod

SIDE VIEW OF ARV SUPER 2

Spinner

Canopy

Wing

Communications antenna

Fin

Dorsal fin

Rudder

Engine cowling

Elevator

Nose gear

Step

Venturi for instruments

Wing strut

Main landing gear

Radiator

Tailskid

Aircraft registration code

Tail plane

G-BNHB

STARBOARD MAIN LANDING GEAR

Brake mount

Brake caliper

Brake pipe

Landing gear leg

Brake disk

Inner tube

Stub axle

Tire

Hub

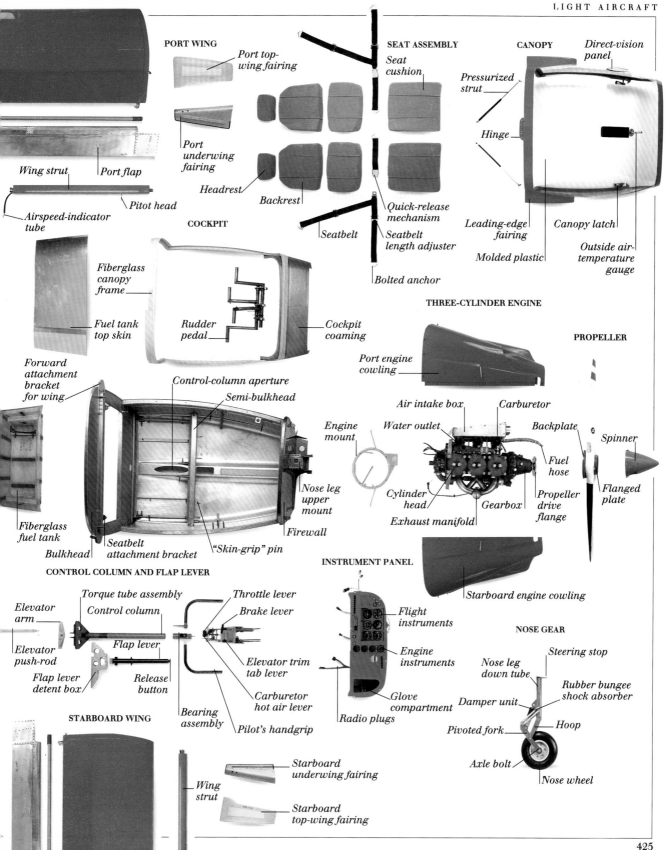

PORT WING

Port top-wing fairing

Port underwing fairing

Wing strut

Port flap

Pitot head

Airspeed-indicator tube

Headrest

Backrest

Seatbelt

SEAT ASSEMBLY

Seat cushion

Quick-release mechanism

Seatbelt length adjuster

Bolted anchor

CANOPY

Direct-vision panel

Pressurized strut

Hinge

Leading-edge fairing

Canopy latch

Outside air-temperature gauge

Molded plastic

COCKPIT

Fiberglass canopy frame

Fuel tank top skin

Rudder pedal

Cockpit coaming

THREE-CYLINDER ENGINE

Port engine cowling

Air intake box

Carburetor

Water outlet

Backplate

PROPELLER

Spinner

Fuel hose

Engine mount

Cylinder head

Gearbox

Propeller drive flange

Flanged plate

Exhaust manifold

Forward attachment bracket for wing

Control-column aperture

Semi-bulkhead

Nose leg upper mount

Firewall

Fiberglass fuel tank

Bulkhead

Seatbelt attachment bracket

"Skin-grip" pin

CONTROL COLUMN AND FLAP LEVER

Torque tube assembly

Throttle lever

Brake lever

Control column

Elevator arm

Elevator push-rod

Flap lever

Flap lever detent box

Release button

Elevator trim tab lever

Carburetor hot air lever

Bearing assembly

Pilot's handgrip

INSTRUMENT PANEL

Flight instruments

Engine instruments

Glove compartment

Radio plugs

Starboard engine cowling

NOSE GEAR

Steering stop

Nose leg down tube

Rubber bungee shock absorber

Damper unit

Pivoted fork

Hoop

Axle bolt

Nose wheel

STARBOARD WING

Wing strut

Starboard underwing fairing

Starboard top-wing fairing

Gliders, hang gliders, and ultralights

NOSE SHELL

Grommet for front pylon strut

Instrument panel

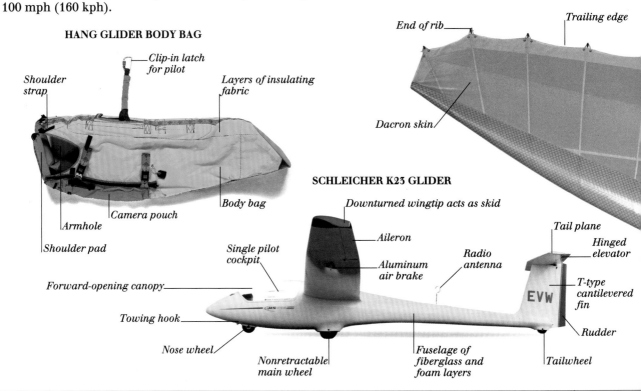

HANG GLIDER

MODERN GLIDERS ARE AMONG the most graceful and aerodynamically efficient of all aircraft. Unpowered but with a large wingspan (up to about 82 ft, or 25 m), gliders use currents of hot, rising air (thermals) to stay aloft, and a rudder, elevators, and ailerons for control. Modern gliders have achieved flights of more than 900 miles (1,450 km) and altitudes above 49,000 ft (15,000 m). Hang gliders consist of a simple frame across which rigid or flexible material is stretched to form the wings. The pilot is suspended below the wings in a harness or body bag and, gripping a triangular A-frame, steers by shifting weight from side to side. Like gliders, hang gliders rely on thermals for lift. Ultralights are basically powered hang gliders. A small engine and an open fiberglass car (trike), which can hold a crew of two, are suspended beneath a stronger version of a hang glider frame; the frame may have rigid or flexible wings. Ultralight pilots, like hang glider pilots, steer by shifting their weight against an A-frame. Ultralights can reach speeds of up to 100 mph (160 kph).

King post

Apex

PEGASUS XL SE ULTRALIGHT

Apex wire

Stiffening rib

Center-line beam

Main suspension

Rear-mounted propeller (pusher propeller)

Fuel tank

Nose shell

Nose gear mount

Main wheel

Fixed nose wheel

Wheel part

Trike nacelle

HANG GLIDER BODY BAG

Clip-in latch for pilot

Shoulder strap

Layers of insulating fabric

Armhole

Camera pouch

Body bag

Shoulder pad

End of rib

Trailing edge

Dacron skin

SCHLEICHER K23 GLIDER

Downturned wingtip acts as skid

Tail plane

Aileron

Hinged elevator

Single pilot cockpit

Radio antenna

Aluminum air brake

T-type cantilevered fin

Forward-opening canopy

EVW

Towing hook

Rudder

Nose wheel

Nonretractable main wheel

Fuselage of fiberglass and foam layers

Tailwheel

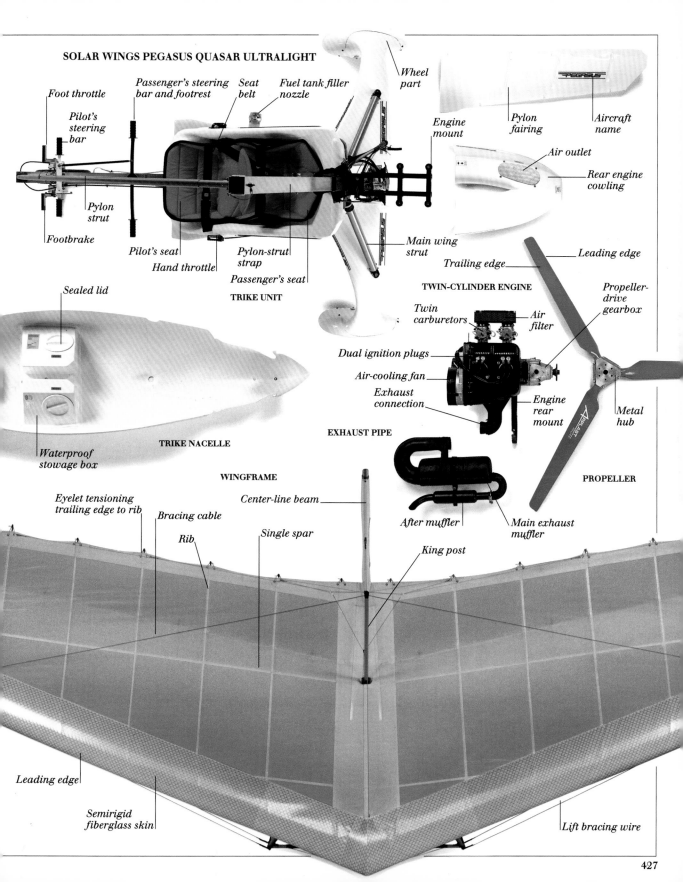

SOLAR WINGS PEGASUS QUASAR ULTRALIGHT

Wheel part

Foot throttle

Passenger's steering bar and footrest

Seat belt

Fuel tank filler nozzle

Pilot's steering bar

Engine mount

Pegasus

Pylon fairing

Aircraft name

Air outlet

Rear engine cowling

Pylon strut

Footbrake

Pilot's seat

Hand throttle

Pylon-strut strap

Passenger's seat

Main wing strut

TRIKE UNIT

Leading edge

Trailing edge

TWIN-CYLINDER ENGINE

Propeller-drive gearbox

Sealed lid

Twin carburetors

Air filter

Dual ignition plugs

Air-cooling fan

Exhaust connection

Engine rear mount

Metal hub

Waterproof stowage box

TRIKE NACELLE

EXHAUST PIPE

PROPELLER

WINGFRAME

Center-line beam

Eyelet tensioning trailing edge to rib

Bracing cable

Rib

Single spar

King post

After muffler

Main exhaust muffler

Leading edge

Semirigid fiberglass skin

Lift bracing wire

427

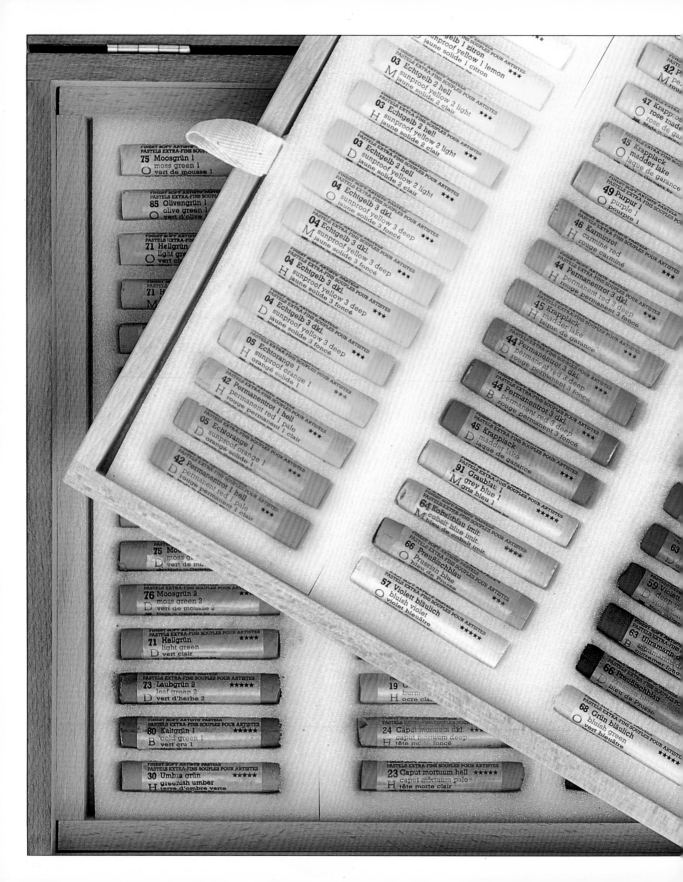

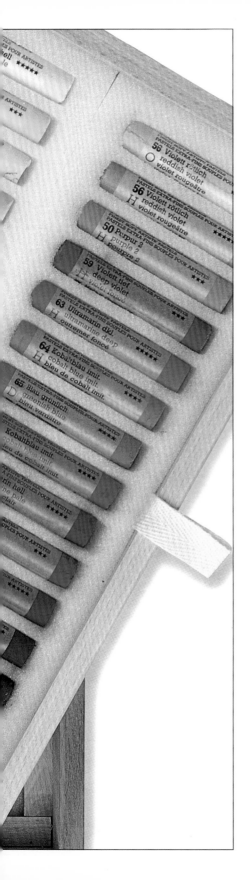

THE VISUAL ARTS

DRAWING 430

TEMPERA 432

FRESCO 434

OILS 436

WATERCOLOR 438

PASTELS 440

ACRYLICS 442

CALLIGRAPHY 444

PRINTMAKING 1 446

PRINTMAKING 2 448

MOSAIC 450

SCULPTURE 1 452

SCULPTURE 2 454

Drawing

DRAWINGS CAN BE FINISHED WORKS OF ART, or preparatory studies for paintings and other visual arts. They can be made using a wide variety of drawing instruments such as pencils, graphite sticks, chalks, charcoal, pens and inks, and silver wires. The most common drawing instrument is the graphite pencil. A graphite pencil consists of a thin rod of graphite mixed with clay, encased in wood. Charcoal is one of the oldest drawing instruments. It is produced by firing twigs of willow, vine, or other woods at high temperatures in airtight containers. Erasers can be used to rub out marks made by drawing materials such as graphite pencils or charcoal, or to achieve a particular effect—such as smudging. Fixative is often applied—using a mouth diffuser or aerosol spray fixative—to prevent smudging once a drawing is finished. Silver lines can be produced by drawing silver wire across specially prepared paper—a technique known as silverpoint. The lines are permanent and cannot be erased. In time the silver lines oxidize and turn brown.

FIXATIVE AND MOUTH DIFFUSER

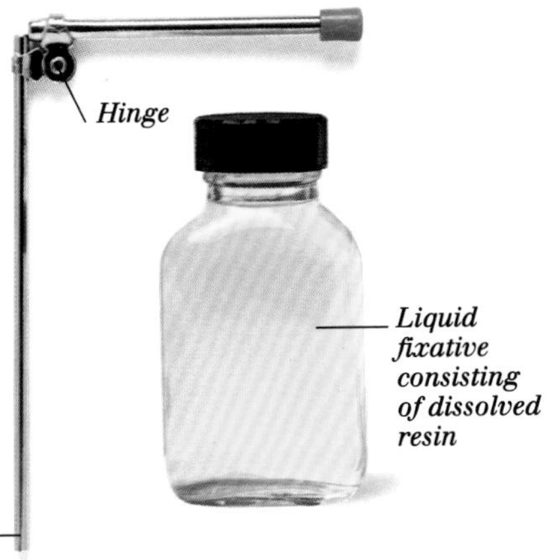

Hinge

Liquid fixative consisting of dissolved resin

Fixative is sucked into tube and sprayed onto drawing

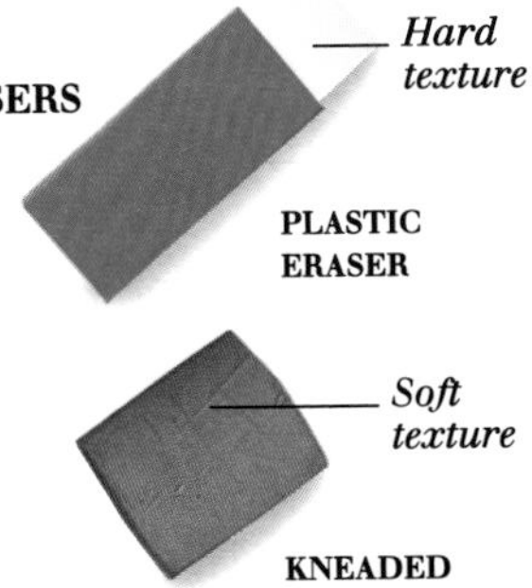

CHALK, CRAYON, AND CHARCOAL

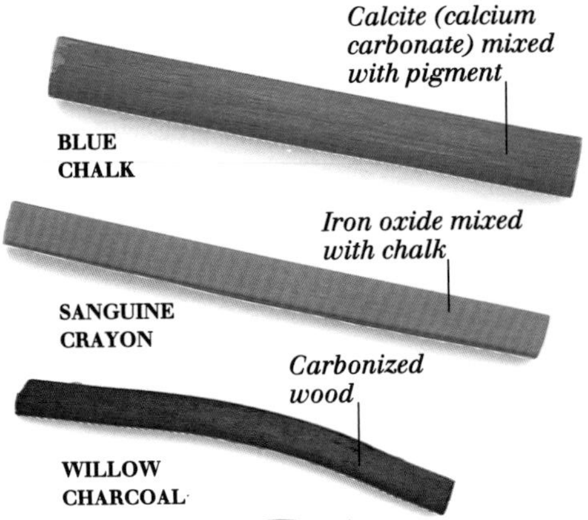

Calcite (calcium carbonate) mixed with pigment

BLUE CHALK

Iron oxide mixed with chalk

SANGUINE CRAYON

Carbonized wood

WILLOW CHARCOAL

ERASERS

Hard texture

Medium-soft, light line

PLASTIC ERASER

Soft texture

Very soft, dark line

KNEADED ERASER

DRAWING INSTRUMENTS

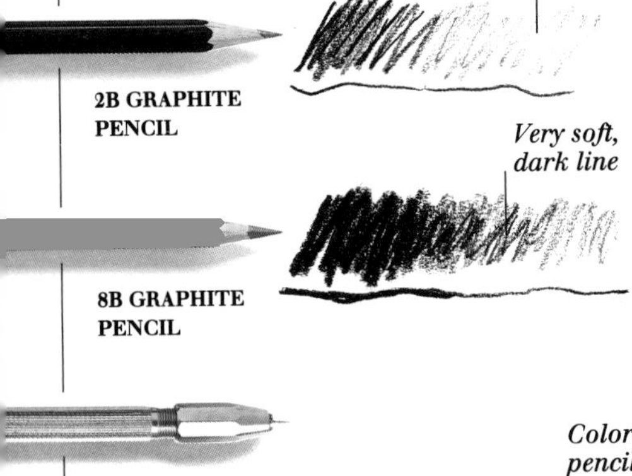

2B GRAPHITE PENCIL

8B GRAPHITE PENCIL

SILVER WIRE IN A METAL HOLDER

DRAWING BOARD

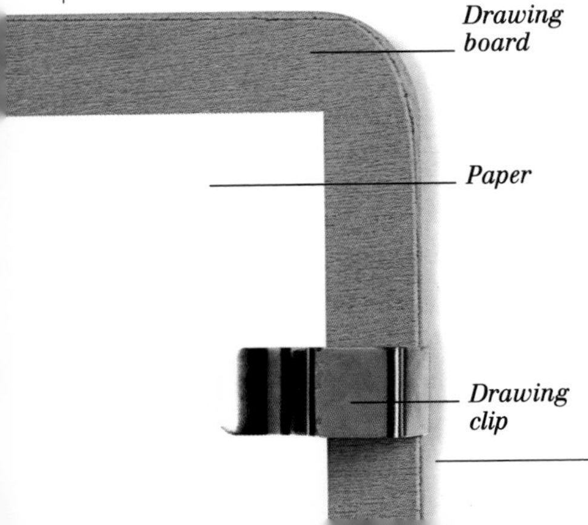

Drawing board

Paper

Drawing clip

DRAWING MATERIALS

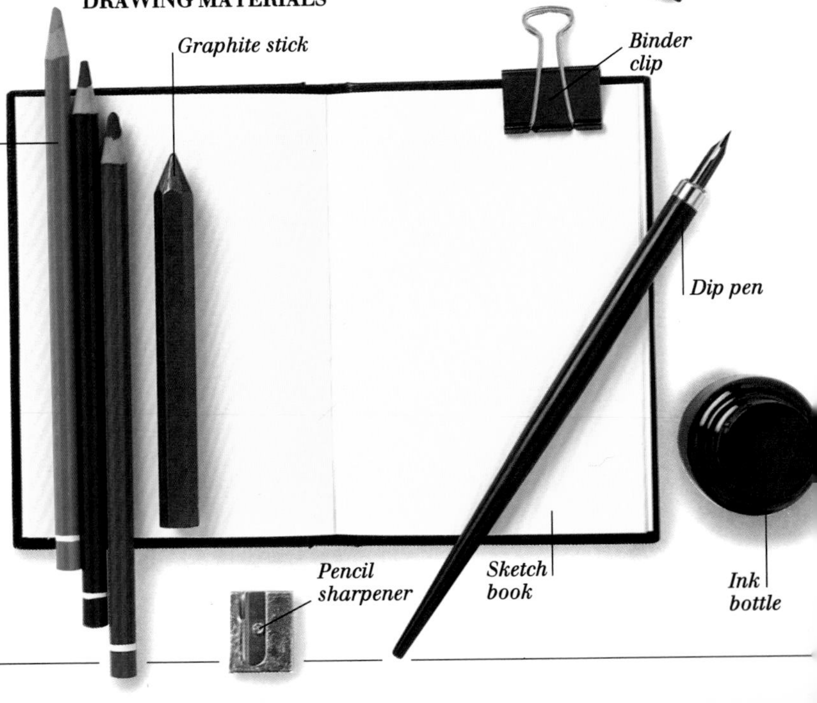

Graphite stick

Binder clip

Colored pencil

Dip pen

Pencil sharpener

Sketch book

Ink bottle

Silver lines
oxidize to a
light brown
color

Vanishing
point located
on head of
man riding
rearing horse

Figures drawn
in ink on top
of lines

Lines of
squared
pavement slabs
recede toward
a single
vanishing
point

Line drawn
in silverpoint
using a ruler

Complex perspective
drawing done as a
preparatory study
for a painting

Paper prepared
with size (glue)
and pigment

EXAMPLE OF A SILVERPOINT DRAWING
The Adoration of the Magi, Leonardo da Vinci, 1481
Pen and ink over silverpoint on paper
6½ x 11½ in (16.5 x 29.2 cm)

Handmade, tinted
paper

One of a series
of drawings
recording
London during
1944–1945

Charcoal lines
softened by
rubbing and
smudging

Broad charcoal
mark

Charcoal
gives strong,
expressive lines

Lines rapidly
drawn on site

EXAMPLE OF A CHARCOAL DRAWING
St. Paul's and the River, David Bomberg, 1945
Charcoal on paper
20 x 25⅛ in (50.8 x 65.8 cm)

Tempera

ILLUMINATED
MANUSCRIPT

THE TERM TEMPERA is applied to any paint in which pigment is tempered (mixed) with a water-based binding medium—usually egg yolk. Egg tempera is applied to a smooth surface such as vellum (for illuminated manuscripts) or more commonly to hardwood panels prepared with gesso—a mixture of chalk and size (glue). Bristle brushes are used to apply the gesso. A layer of gesso grosso (coarse gesso) is followed by successive layers of gesso sotile (fine gesso) that are sanded between coats to provide a smooth, yet absorbent ground. The paint is applied with fine sable brushes in thin layers, using light brushstrokes. Tempera dries quickly to form a tough skin with a satin sheen. The luminous white surface of the gesso combined with the overlaid paint produces the brilliant crispness and rich colors particular to this medium. Egg tempera paintings are frequently gilded with gold. Leaves of finely beaten gold are applied to a bole (reddish-brown clay) base and polished by burnishing.

MATERIALS FOR GILDING

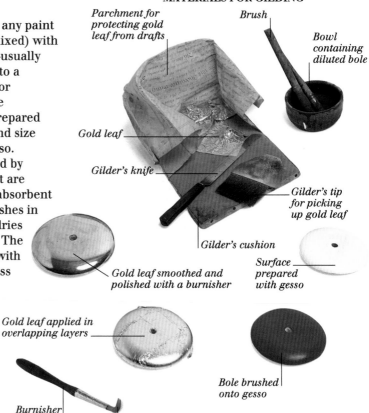

Parchment for protecting gold leaf from drafts

Brush

Bowl containing diluted bole

Gold leaf

Gilder's knife

Gilder's tip for picking up gold leaf

Gilder's cushion

Gold leaf smoothed and polished with a burnisher

Surface prepared with gesso

Gold leaf applied in overlapping layers

Bole brushed onto gesso

Burnisher

Agate tip

MATERIALS FOR TEMPERA PANEL PAINTING

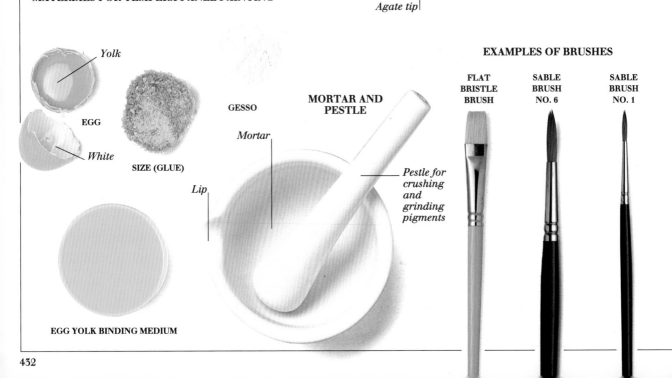

Yolk

EGG

White

SIZE (GLUE)

GESSO

MORTAR AND PESTLE

Mortar

Lip

Pestle for crushing and grinding pigments

EGG YOLK BINDING MEDIUM

EXAMPLES OF BRUSHES

FLAT BRISTLE BRUSH

SABLE BRUSH NO. 6

SABLE BRUSH NO. 1

EXAMPLE OF A TEMPERA PAINTING
Presentation in the Temple, Ambrogio Lorenzetti, 1342
Tempera on wood, 8 ft 5⅛ in x 5 ft 6⅛ in (257 x 168 cm)

Altarpiece commissioned for Siena Cathedral, Italy

The red tinge of the bole is just visible beneath the gold

Vine black used to create the dim cathedral interior

Red drapery painted in vermilion

Receding floor tiles create the impression of depth

Textured gold ornament made by punching motifs into the gilded surface

Edge of a sheet of gold leaf

Crisp edge characteristic of tempera painting

Highlights on the beard made by applying thin layers of white over dried paint

Raised right hand and pointing finger is the gesture of prophecy

Patch of discolored varnish, left from last cleaning

VERDACCIO

**VERMILION AND
LEAD WHITE**

VERMILION

**RED EARTH
(IRON OXIDE)**

EXAMPLES OF PIGMENTS

MALACHITE

**ULTRAMARINE
LAPIS LAZULI**

VINE BLACK

LEAD TIN YELLOW

Warm flesh tones achieved by layering vermilion and white over an undercoat of verdaccio

Ultramarine lapis lazuli, as costly as gold, was reserved for significant figures such as the Virgin Mary

Patterned gold halo glitters in candlelight

Craquelure (pattern of cracks in the paint)

**DETAIL FROM "PRESENTATION
IN THE TEMPLE"**

Fresco

FRESCO IS A METHOD OF WALL PAINTING. In buon fresco (true fresco), pigments are mixed with water and applied to an intonaco (layer of fresh, damp lime-plaster). The intonaco absorbs and binds the pigments as it dries making the picture a permanent part of the wall surface. The intonaco is applied in sections called giornate (daily sections). The size of each giornata depends on the artist's estimate of how much can be painted before the plaster sets. The junctions between giornate are sometimes visible on a finished fresco. The range of colors used in buon fresco are limited to lime-resistant pigments such as earth colors (below). Slaked lime (burnt lime mixed with water), bianco di San Giovanni (slaked lime that has been partly exposed to air), and chalk can be used to produce fresco whites. In fresco secco (dry fresco), pigments are mixed with a binding medium and applied to dry plaster. The pigments are not completely absorbed into the plaster and may flake off over time.

CROSS-SECTION SHOWING FRESCO LAYERS

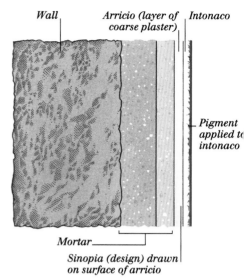

Wall

Arricio (layer of coarse plaster)

Intonaco

Pigment applied to intonaco

Mortar

Sinopia (design) drawn on surface of arricio

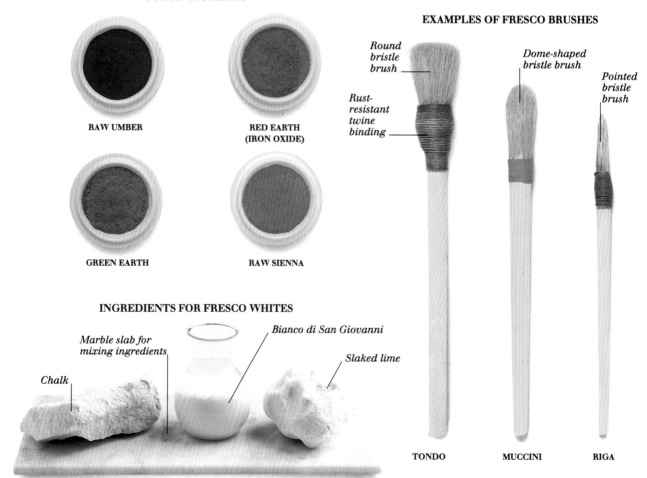

EXAMPLES OF EARTH COLOR PIGMENTS

RAW UMBER

RED EARTH (IRON OXIDE)

GREEN EARTH

RAW SIENNA

EXAMPLES OF FRESCO BRUSHES

Round bristle brush

Rust-resistant twine binding

Dome-shaped bristle brush

Pointed bristle brush

INGREDIENTS FOR FRESCO WHITES

Marble slab for mixing ingredients

Bianco di San Giovanni

Slaked lime

Chalk

TONDO

MUCCINI

RIGA

EXAMPLE OF A FRESCO
The Expulsion of the Merchants from the Temple, Giotto, c.1306
Fresco, 78 x 72 in (200 x 185 cm)

One of a series of frescoes in the Arena Chapel, Padua, Italy

Temple acts as a backdrop for the action

Bianco di San Giovanni often used for fresco whites

Gold leaf applied to apostle's halo

Green earth pigment applied to robe

Child painted on top of apostle's robe

Patches of azurite blue have turned green due to reaction with carbon dioxide

Hairline junction between giornate is visible

Red earth pigment applied in buon fresco has retained rich hue

Azurite blue applied in fresco secco has flaked off to reveal the plaster beneath

Dry, matt surface characteristic of buon fresco

Paint applied in buon fresco to child's face

White dove represents the Holy Ghost

Paint applied in fresco secco to child's body has flaked off

A fresco was generally worked in zones from the top down

Sinopia (design) sketched in red earth

DETAIL FROM "THE EXPULSION"

Artist has to finish giornata before plaster dries

Junction between giornate

Area with little detail can be painted quickly, allowing a larger giornata to be completed

Highly detailed area takes a longer time to paint, restricting the size of the giornata

GIORNATE (DAILY SECTIONS) IN "THE EXPULSION"

Oils

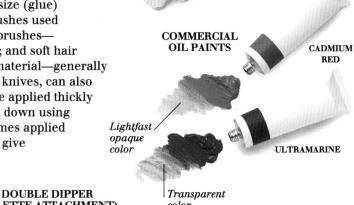

OIL PAINTS ARE MADE BY MIXING and grinding pigment with a drying vegetable oil such as linseed oil. The paint can be applied to many different surfaces and textures—the most common being canvas. Before painting, the canvas is stretched on a wooden frame and its surface is prepared with layers of size (glue) and primer. The two main types of brushes used in oil painting are stiff hog hair bristle brushes—generally used for covering large areas; and soft hair brushes made from sable or synthetic material—generally used for fine detail. Other tools, including painting knives, can also be used to achieve different effects. Oil paint can be applied thickly (a technique known as impasto), or can be thinned down using a solvent such as turpentine. Varnishes are sometimes applied to finished paintings to protect their surface and to give them a matt or gloss finish.

KIDNEY-SHAPED PALETTE

DAMMAR RESIN VARNISH

Crystals are dissolved and applied to painting to protect its surface

COMMERCIAL OIL PAINTS

CADMIUM RED

ULTRAMARINE

Lightfast opaque color

Transparent color

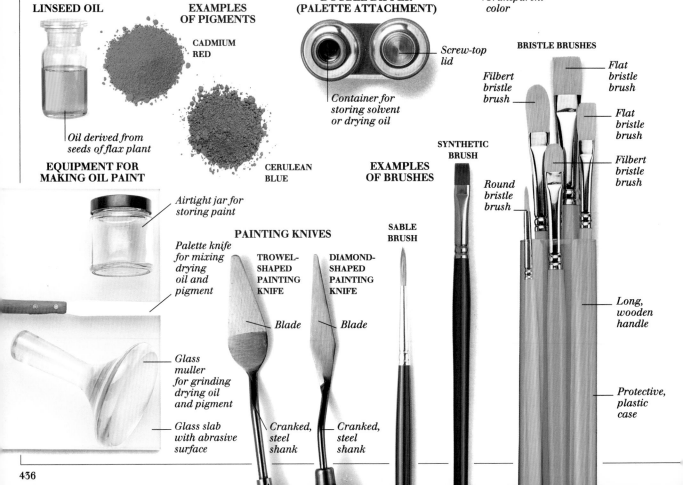

LINSEED OIL

Oil derived from seeds of flax plant

EXAMPLES OF PIGMENTS

CADMIUM RED

CERULEAN BLUE

DOUBLE DIPPER (PALETTE ATTACHMENT)

Screw-top lid

Container for storing solvent or drying oil

BRISTLE BRUSHES

Flat bristle brush

Flat bristle brush

Filbert bristle brush

Filbert bristle brush

Round bristle brush

SYNTHETIC BRUSH

EXAMPLES OF BRUSHES

EQUIPMENT FOR MAKING OIL PAINT

Airtight jar for storing paint

Palette knife for mixing drying oil and pigment

PAINTING KNIVES

TROWEL-SHAPED PAINTING KNIFE

DIAMOND-SHAPED PAINTING KNIFE

SABLE BRUSH

Blade

Blade

Glass muller for grinding drying oil and pigment

Glass slab with abrasive surface

Cranked, steel shank

Cranked, steel shank

Long, wooden handle

Protective, plastic case

EXAMPLE OF AN OIL PAINTING
Fritillarias, Vincent van Gogh, 1886
Oil on canvas, 29 x 24 in (73.5 x 60.5 cm)

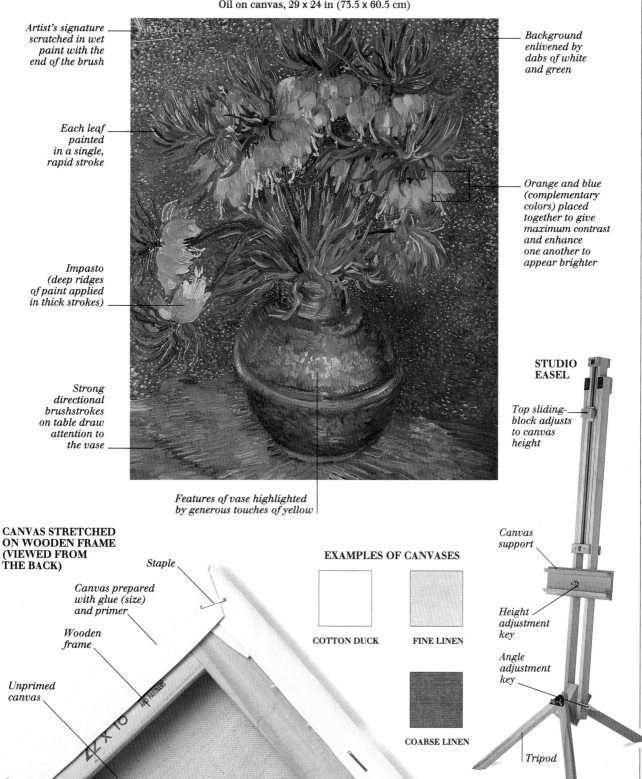

Artist's signature scratched in wet paint with the end of the brush

Background enlivened by dabs of white and green

Each leaf painted in a single, rapid stroke

Orange and blue (complementary colors) placed together to give maximum contrast and enhance one another to appear brighter

Impasto (deep ridges of paint applied in thick strokes)

Strong directional brushstrokes on table draw attention to the vase

Features of vase highlighted by generous touches of yellow

STUDIO EASEL

Top sliding-block adjusts to canvas height

Canvas support

Height adjustment key

Angle adjustment key

Tripod

CANVAS STRETCHED ON WOODEN FRAME (VIEWED FROM THE BACK)

Staple

Canvas prepared with glue (size) and primer

Wooden frame

Unprimed canvas

EXAMPLES OF CANVASES

COTTON DUCK

FINE LINEN

COARSE LINEN

Watercolor

WATERCOLOR PAINT IS MADE OF GROUND PIGMENT mixed with a water-soluble binding medium, usually gum arabic. It is usually applied to paper using soft hair brushes such as sable, goat hair, squirrel, and synthetic brushes. Watercolors are often diluted and applied as overlaying washes (thin, transparent layers) to build up depth of color. Washes can be laid in a variety of ways to create a range of different effects. For example, a wet-in-wet wash can be achieved by laying a wash on top of another wet wash. The two washes blend together to give a fused effect. Sponges are used to modify washes by soaking up paint so that areas of pigment are lightened or removed from the paper. Watercolors can also be applied undiluted—a technique known as dry brush—to create a broken-color effect. Watercolors are generally transparent and allow light to reflect from the surface of the paper through the layers of paint to give a luminous effect. They can be thickened and made opaque by adding body color (Chinese white).

GUM ARABIC

Natural sap from acacia tree

NATURAL SPONGE

ANATOMY OF A SABLE BRUSH

Soft red sable hair

Toe (tip)

Wooden handle

SOFT HAIR BRUSHES

Hair trimmed and cemented into ferrule

ROUND SABLE BRUSH (NO. 6)

Round ferrule

Hair tied with clove hitch knot

ROUND SABLE BRUSH (NO. 1)

TUBES OF WATERCOLOR PAINT

SYNTHETIC WASH BRUSH

WINSOR GREEN

SQUIRREL MOP WASH BRUSH

PORTABLE BOX OF WATERCOLOR PAINTS

Painted color swatch

CADMIUM YELLOW

Chinese white

Pan of watercolor paint

Lid can be used for mixing colors

LARGE GOAT HAKE WASH BRUSH

EXAMPLE OF A WATERCOLOR
Burning of the Houses of Parliament, Turner, 1834
Watercolor on paper, 11½ x 17½ in (29.2 x 44.5 cm)

Transparent washes laid on top of each other to create tonal depth

Transparent washes allow light to reflect off the surface of the paper to give a luminous effect

Highlight scratched out with a scalpel

Paper shows through thin wash to give flames added highlight

Crowd painted with thin strokes laid over a pale wash

Undiluted paint applied, then partly washed out, to create the impression of water

EXAMPLES OF WASHES

WASH OVER DRY BRUSH
Wash laid over paint applied with dry brush gives two-tone effect

GRADED WASH
Strong wash applied to tilted paper gives graded effect

DRY BRUSH
Undiluted paint dragged across surface of paper gives broken effect

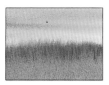

WET-IN-WET
Two diluted washes left to run together to give fused effect

EXAMPLES OF WATERCOLOR PAPERS

SMOOTH-TEXTURED PAPER

MEDIUM-TEXTURED PAPER

ROUGH-TEXTURED PAPER

COLOR WHEEL OF WATERCOLOR PAINTS

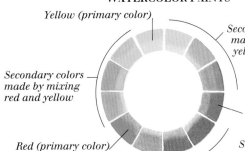

Yellow (primary color)

Secondary colors made by mixing yellow and blue

Secondary colors made by mixing red and yellow

Blue (primary color)

Red (primary color)

Secondary colors made by mixing blue and red

Pastels

PASTELS ARE STICKS OF PIGMENT made by mixing ground pigment with chalk and a binding medium, such as gum arabic. They vary in hardness depending on the proportion of the binding medium to the chalk. Soft pastel—the most common form of pastel—contains just enough binding medium to hold the pigment in stick form. Pastels can be applied directly to any support (surface) with sufficient tooth (texture). When a pastel is drawn over a textured surface, the pigment crumbles and lodges in the fibers of the support. Pastel marks have a particular soft, matt quality and are suitable for techniques such as blending, scumbling, and feathering. Blending is a technique of rubbing and fusing two or more colors on the support using fingers or various tools such as tortillons (paper stumps), soft hair brushes, kneaded erasers, and soft bread. Scumbling is a technique of building up layers of pastel colors. The side or blunted tip of a soft pastel is lightly drawn over an underpainted area so that patches of the color beneath show through. Feathering is a technique of applying parallel strokes of color with the point of a pastel, usually over an existing layer of pastel color. A thin spray of fixative can be applied—using a mouth diffuser (see pp. 430-431) or aerosol spray fixative—to a finished pastel painting, or in between layers of color, to prevent smudging.

EQUIPMENT FOR MAKING PASTELS

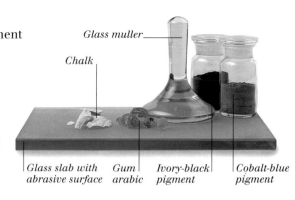

Glass muller

Chalk

Glass slab with abrasive surface

Gum arabic

Ivory-black pigment

Cobalt-blue pigment

EXAMPLES OF SOFT PASTELS

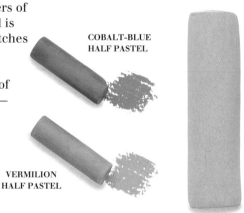

COBALT-BLUE HALF PASTEL

VERMILION HALF PASTEL

OLIVE-GREEN FULL PASTEL

MAUVE FULL PASTEL

BOXED PASTEL SET

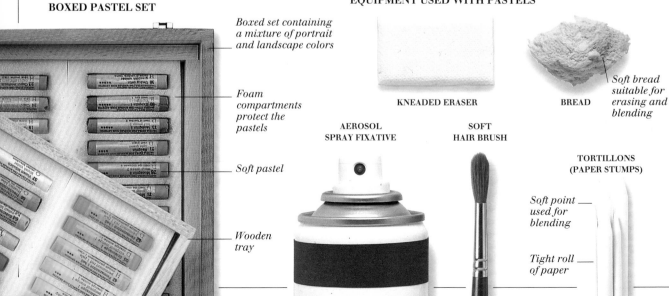

Boxed set containing a mixture of portrait and landscape colors

Foam compartments protect the pastels

Soft pastel

Wooden tray

EQUIPMENT USED WITH PASTELS

KNEADED ERASER

BREAD

Soft bread suitable for erasing and blending

AEROSOL SPRAY FIXATIVE

SOFT HAIR BRUSH

TORTILLONS (PAPER STUMPS)

Soft point used for blending

Tight roll of paper

EXAMPLE OF A PASTEL PAINTING
Woman Drying her Neck, Edgar Degas, c.1898
Pastel on cardboard, 24½ x 25½ in (62.5 x 65.5 cm)

Pastels applied directly to support

Colors are blended together using fingers or tools such as tortillons

Built up layers of pastel

Rich color of fabric created by overlaying yellows and oranges

Broken colors, characteristic of scumbling technique

Toned color of paper visible beneath thinly applied pastels

Pure bright colors laid side by side produce strong contrasts

DETAIL FROM "WOMAN DRYING HER NECK"

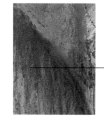

Feathering technique used to produce skin tones

EXAMPLES OF TEXTURED PAPERS AND PASTEL BOARDS

WATERCOLOR PAPER (ROUGH TEXTURE)

GLASS PAPER

WATERCOLOR PAPER (MEDIUM TEXTURE)

INGRES PAPER

FLOCKED PASTEL BOARD

CANSON PAPER

EXAMPLES OF COLORED AND TINTED PAPERS

Acrylics

ACRYLIC PAINT IS MADE BY MIXING PIGMENT with a synthetic resin. It can be thinned with water but dries to become water insoluble. Acrylics are applied to many surfaces, such as paper and acrylic-primed board and canvas. A variety of brushes, painting knives, rollers, air-brushes, plastic scrapers, and other tools are used in acrylic painting. The versatility of acrylics makes them suitable for a wide range of techniques. They can be used opaquely or—by adding water—in a transparent, watercolor style. Acrylic mediums can be added to the paint to adjust its consistency for special effects such as glazing and impasto (ridges of paint applied in thick strokes) or to make it more matt or glossy. Acrylics are quick-drying, which allows layers of paint to be applied on top of each other almost immediately.

EXAMPLES OF BRUSHES

Sable brush

Bristle sash brush

Synthetic bristle brush

Synthetic sable brush

Bristle brush

Goat hair brush

Synthetic wash brush

Ox hair brush

EXAMPLES OF PAINTS USED IN ACRYLICS

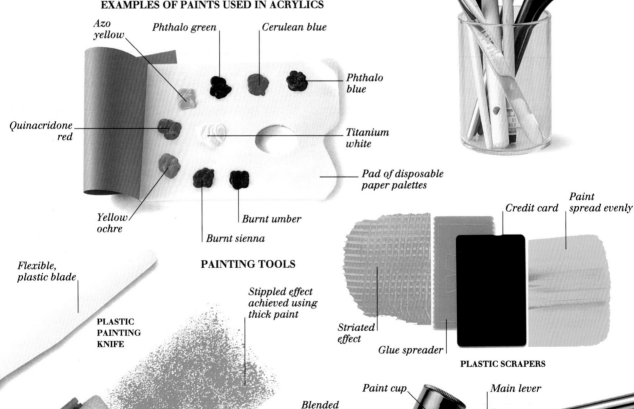

Azo yellow

Phthalo green

Cerulean blue

Phthalo blue

Quinacridone red

Titanium white

Pad of disposable paper palettes

Yellow ochre

Burnt umber

Burnt sienna

PAINTING TOOLS

Flexible, plastic blade

Stippled effect achieved using thick paint

Credit card

Paint spread evenly

Striated effect

Glue spreader

PLASTIC PAINTING KNIFE

PLASTIC SCRAPERS

Blended tones

Paint cup

Main lever

Nozzle

AIR-BRUSH

Plastic handle

SPONGE ROLLER

Uniform tone

Air hose

EXAMPLE OF AN ACRYLIC PAINTING
A Bigger Splash, David Hockney, 1967
Acrylic on canvas, 95½ x 96 in (242.5 x 243.8 cm)

Paint applied evenly using a roller

Cotton duck canvas support (surface)

Flatness of rollered areas enhanced by adding gel medium to the paint

Masking tape stuck onto canvas to define main shapes, and paint applied within these areas using a roller

Thin strip of pool edge left unpainted

Splash painted using thicker paint and small brush

Imprecise edge on end of spring board where paint has seeped under masking tape

EXAMPLES OF ACRYLIC PAINTS AND TECHNIQUES

Paint applied using painting knife

Opaque effect

Extruded (squeezed) effect

PURPLE ACRYLIC PAINT

YELLOW ACRYLIC PAINT

ORANGE ACRYLIC PAINT

Transparent, watercolor effect

Translucent, impasto glaze

Thick impasto with coarse texture

BLUE ACRYLIC PAINT DILUTED WITH WATER

GREEN ACRYLIC PAINT MIXED WITH GEL MEDIUM

RED ACRYLIC PAINT MIXED WITH TEXTURE PASTE

443

Calligraphy

CALLIGRAPHY IS BEAUTIFULLY FORMED LETTERING. The term applies to written text and illumination (the decoration of manuscripts using gold leaf and color). The essential materials needed to practice calligraphy are a writing tool, ink, and a writing surface. Quills are among the oldest writing tools. They are usually made from goose or turkey feathers, and are noted for their flexibility and ability to produce fine lines. A quill point, however, is not very durable and constant recutting and trimming is required. The most commonly used writing instrument in western calligraphy is a detachable, metal nib held in a penholder. The metal nib is very durable, and there are a wide range of different types. Particular types of nibs—such as copperplate, speedball, and round-hand nibs—are used for specific styles of lettering. Some nibs have integral ink reservoirs and others have reservoirs that are detachable. Brushes are also used for writing, and for filling in outlined letters and painting decoration. Other writing tools used in calligraphy are fountain pens, felt-tipped pens, rotring pens, and reed pens. Calligraphy inks may come in liquid form, or as a solid ink stick. Ink sticks are ground down in distilled water to form a liquid ink. The most common writing surfaces for calligraphy are good quality, smooth -surfaced papers. To achieve the best writing position, the calligrapher places the paper on a drawing board set at an angle.

EQUIPMENT USED IN BRUSH LETTERING

Brush rest

Wolf hair brush

Goat hair brush

BRUSHES AND BRUSH REST

Liquid ink made by grinding down ink stick in distilled water

Solid carbon ink stick

Ink stone

INK STICK AND STONE

PENS, NIBS, AND BRUSHES USED IN CALLIGRAPHY

PENHOLDER

COPPERPLATE NIB

SPEEDBALL NIB

FELT-TIPPED PEN

ROUND-HAND NIB AND DETACHABLE INK RESERVOIR

ROTRING PEN

Feather

Feather stripped for better handling

Barrel

REED PEN

SQUARE SABLE BRUSH

POINTED SABLE BRUSH

Hand-cut point

GOOSE-FEATHER QUILL

GOAT HAIR BRUSH

WOLF HAIR BRUSH

FOUNTAIN PEN AND INK

Bottle of permanent black ink

Barrel

Clip

Nib

Outer cap

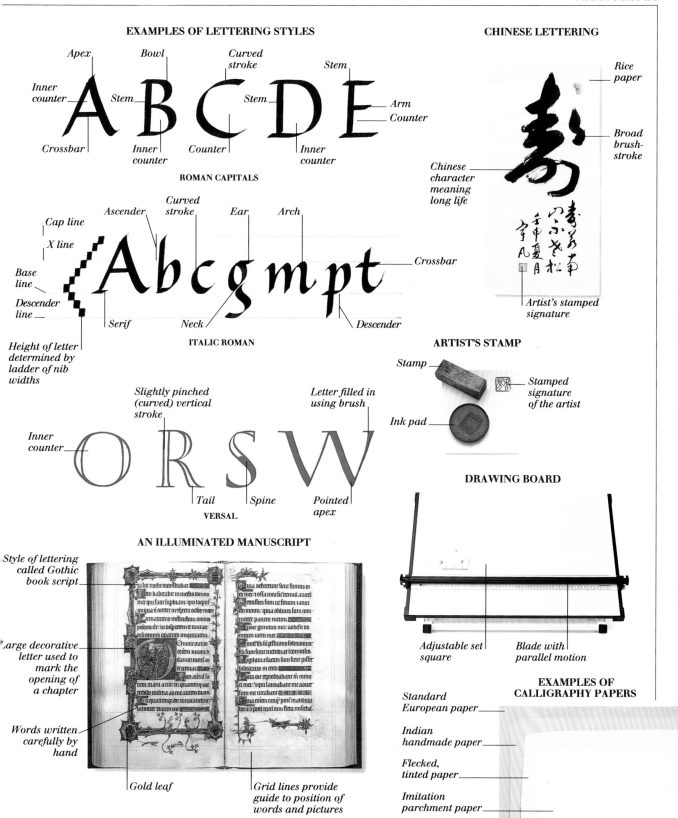

EXAMPLES OF LETTERING STYLES

ROMAN CAPITALS

Apex
Inner counter
Stem
Crossbar

Bowl
Stem
Inner counter

Curved stroke
Counter

Stem
Counter

Stem
Arm
Counter
Inner counter

ITALIC ROMAN

Cap line
X line
Base line
Descender line
Height of letter determined by ladder of nib widths

Ascender
Serif

Curved stroke
Neck

Ear

Arch
Crossbar
Descender

VERSAL

Inner counter

Slightly pinched (curved) vertical stroke

Letter filled in using brush

Tail
Spine

Pointed apex

CHINESE LETTERING

Rice paper
Broad brush-stroke
Chinese character meaning long life
Artist's stamped signature

ARTIST'S STAMP

Stamp
Stamped signature of the artist
Ink pad

DRAWING BOARD

Adjustable set square
Blade with parallel motion

AN ILLUMINATED MANUSCRIPT

Style of lettering called Gothic book script
Large decorative letter used to mark the opening of a chapter
Words written carefully by hand
Gold leaf
Grid lines provide guide to position of words and pictures

EXAMPLES OF CALLIGRAPHY PAPERS

Standard European paper
Indian handmade paper
Flecked, tinted paper
Imitation parchment paper

Printmaking 1

PRINTS ARE MADE BY FOUR BASIC printing processes – intaglio, lithographic, relief, and screen. In intaglio printing, lines are engraved or etched onto the surface of a metal plate. Lines are engraved using sharp metal tools. They are etched by corroding the metal plate with acid, using acid-resistant ground to protect the areas not to be etched. The plate is then inked and wiped, leaving the grooves filled with ink and the surface clean. Dampened paper is laid over the plate, and both paper and plate are passed through the rollers of an etching press. The pressure of the rollers forces the paper into the grooves, so that it takes up the ink, leaving an impression on the paper. Lithographic printing is based on the antipathy between grease and water. An image is drawn on a surface—usually a stone or metal plate—with a greasy medium, such as tusche (lihographic ink). The greasy drawing is fixed onto the plate by applying an acidic solution, such as gum arabic. The surface is then dampened and rolled with ink. The ink adheres only to the greasy areas and is repelled by the water. Paper is laid on the plate and pressure is applied by means of a press. In relief printing, the non-printing areas of a wood or linoleum block are cut away using gouges, knives, and other tools. The printing areas are left raised in relief and are rolled with ink. Paper is laid on the inked block and pressure is applied by means of a press or by burnishing (rubbing) the back of the paper. The most common forms of relief printing are woodcut, wood engraving, and linocut. In screen printing, the printing surface is a mesh stretched across a wooden frame. A stencil is applied to the mesh to seal the non-printing areas and ink is scraped through the mesh to produce an image.

THE FOUR MAIN PRINTING PROCESSES

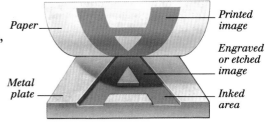

Paper — Printed image

— Engraved or etched image

Metal plate — Inked area

INTAGLIO

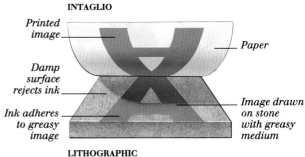

Printed image

Damp surface rejects ink

Ink adheres to greasy image

Paper

Image drawn on stone with greasy medium

LITHOGRAPHIC

Paper — Printed image

Raised figure

Wood block — Inked surface

RELIEF

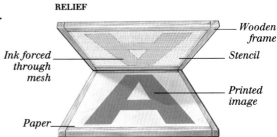

Ink forced through mesh

Paper

Wooden frame

Stencil

Printed image

SCREEN

LEATHER INK DABBER

EQUIPMENT USED IN INTAGLIO PRINTING

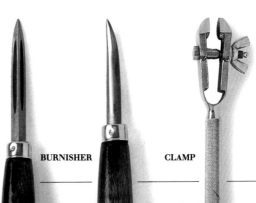

ROCKER   SCRIBER   ROULETTE   SCRAPER   BURNISHER   CLAMP

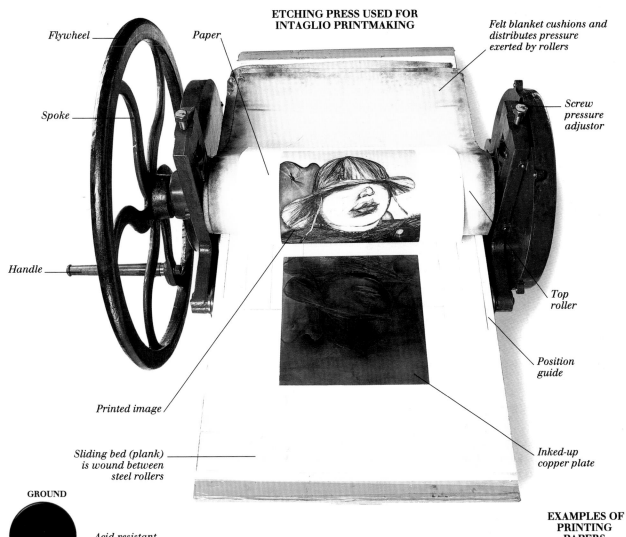

ETCHING PRESS USED FOR INTAGLIO PRINTMAKING

Flywheel

Paper

Felt blanket cushions and distributes pressure exerted by rollers

Spoke

Screw pressure adjustor

Handle

Top roller

Position guide

Printed image

Sliding bed (plank) is wound between steel rollers

Inked-up copper plate

GROUND

Acid-resistant ground rolled onto metal plate before etching

EXAMPLES OF PRINTING PAPERS

GROUND ROLLER

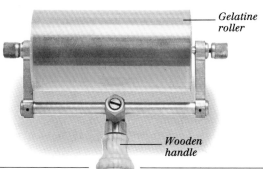

Gelatine roller

Wooden handle

EXAMPLE OF AN INTAGLIO PRINT
Annie with a Sun Hat, Jock McFadyen, 1993
Etched copper plate, 16 x 15¾ in (41 x 40 cm)

Printmaking 2

EXAMPLE OF A LITHOGRAPHIC STONE AND PRINT
Crown Gateway 2, Mandy Bonnell, 1987
Lithograph, 19½ x 15¾ in (50 x 40 cm)

IMAGE DRAWN ON STONE   LITHOGRAPIC PRINT

EXAMPLE OF A SCREEN PRINT
Sea Change, Patrick Hughes, 1992
Screen print, 30 x 37 in (77 x 94.5 cm)

SCREEN AND SQUEEGEE

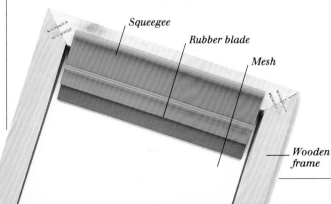

Squeegee

Rubber blade

Mesh

Wooden frame

EQUIPMENT USED IN LITHOGRAPHIC PRINTING

CRAYON AND HOLDER

LITHOGRAPHIC PENCIL

TUSCHE (LITHOGRAPHIC INK) PEN

ERASING STICK

EXPANDABLE SPONGE

TUSCHE (LITHOGRAPHIC INK) STICK

RUBBING INK

INK ROLLER

MILD ACIDIC SOLUTION   GUM ARABIC SOLUTION

WATER-BASED SCREEN PRINTING INKS

BLUE ACRYLIC INK   RED ACRYLIC INK   BROWN TEXTILE INK

EQUIPMENT USED IN RELIEF PRINTING

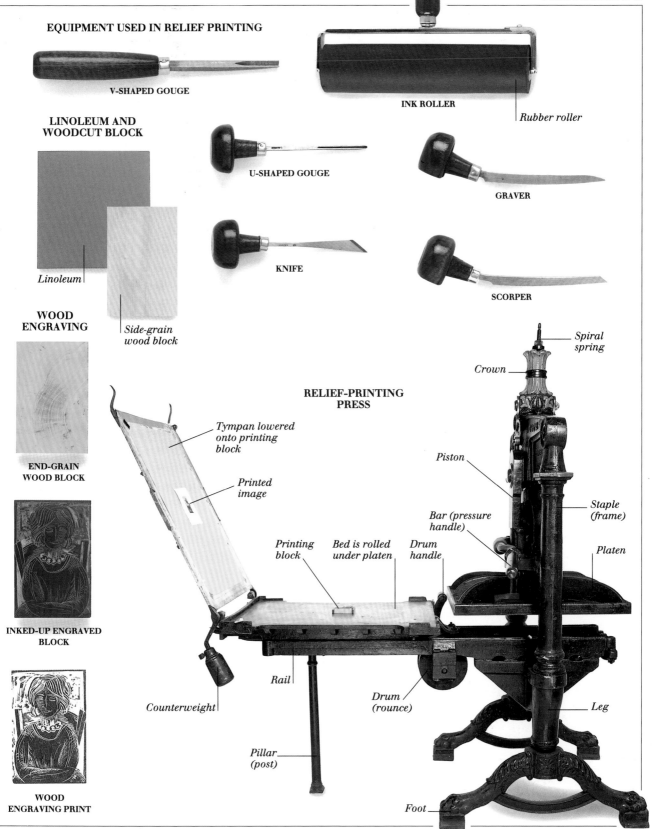

V-SHAPED GOUGE

INK ROLLER

Rubber roller

LINOLEUM AND WOODCUT BLOCK

Linoleum

U-SHAPED GOUGE

GRAVER

KNIFE

SCORPER

WOOD ENGRAVING

Side-grain wood block

END-GRAIN WOOD BLOCK

INKED-UP ENGRAVED BLOCK

WOOD ENGRAVING PRINT

RELIEF-PRINTING PRESS

Spiral spring

Crown

Piston

Tympan lowered onto printing block

Printed image

Bar (pressure handle)

Staple (frame)

Printing block

Bed is rolled under platen

Drum handle

Platen

Rail

Counterweight

Drum (rounce)

Leg

Pillar (post)

Foot

Mosaic

MOSAIC IS THE ART OF MAKING patterns and pictures from tesserae (small, colored pieces of glass, marble, and other materials). Different materials are cut into tesserae using different tools. Smalti (glass enamel) and marble are cut into pieces using a hammer and a hardy (a pointed blade) embedded in a log. Vitreous glass is cut into pieces using a pair of pliers. Mosaics can be made using a direct or indirect method. In the direct method, the tesserae are laid directly into a bed of cement–based adhesive. In the indirect method, the design is drawn in reverse on paper or cloth. The tesserae are then stuck face down on the paper or cloth using water-soluble glue. Adhesive is spread with a trowel onto a solid surface—such as a wall—and the back of the mosaic is laid into the adhesive. Finally, the paper or cloth is soaked off to reveal the mosaic. Gaps between tesserae can be filled with grout. Grout is forced into gaps by dragging a grouting squeegee across the face of the mosaic. Mosaics are usually used to decorate walls and floors, but they can also be applied to smaller objects.

EQUIPMENT FOR BREAKING MARBLE

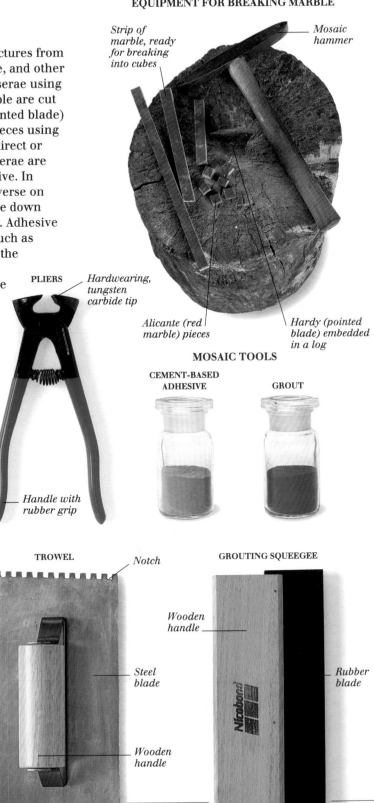

Strip of marble, ready for breaking into cubes

Mosaic hammer

Alicante (red marble) pieces

Hardy (pointed blade) embedded in a log

PLIERS

Hardwearing, tungsten carbide tip

Handle with rubber grip

MOSAIC TOOLS

CEMENT-BASED ADHESIVE

GROUT

SMALTI (GLASS ENAMEL)

EXAMPLE OF A MOSAIC (DIRECT METHOD)
Seascape, Tessa Hunkin, 1993
Smalti mosaic on board
31½ in (80 cm) diameter

RED SMALTI

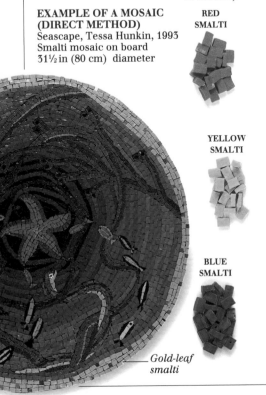

YELLOW SMALTI

BLUE SMALTI

Gold-leaf smalti

TROWEL

Notch

Steel blade

Wooden handle

GROUTING SQUEEGEE

Wooden handle

Rubber blade

Nicobond

STAGES IN THE CREATION OF A MOSAIC (INDIRECT METHOD)

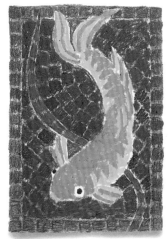

COLOR SKETCH
A color sketch is drawn
in oil pastel to give a clear
impression of how the finished
mosaic will look.

REVERSE IMAGE
Tesserae are glued face down
on reverse image on paper.
Mosaic is then attached to solid
surface and paper is removed.

MOSAIC POT

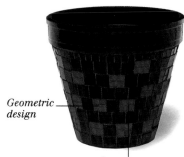

Geometric design

Grout

MOSAIC MOSQUE DESIGN

Floral design

Geometric border

---

*Andamenti
(line along
which tesserae
are laid)*

*Gold tessera
with ripple
finish*

*Gold tessera
placed upside-
down*

*Grout fills
the gaps
between the
tesserae*

*Mosaic
mounted
on board*

*Vitreous
glass cut into
triangular
shape with
pliers*

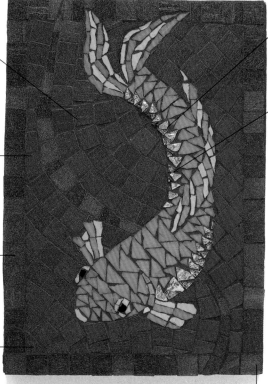

FINISHED MOSAIC
Goldfish, Tessa Hunkin, 1993
Vitreous glass mosaic on board
14 x 10 in (35.5 x 25.5 cm)

*Border of square
vitreous glass*

VITREOUS GLASS

**GREEN VITREOUS
GLASS WITH GOLD LEAF**

*Plain
finish*

*Ripple
finish*

**RED VITREOUS
GLASS**

**BLUE VITREOUS
GLASS**

SHEETS OF VITREOUS GLASS

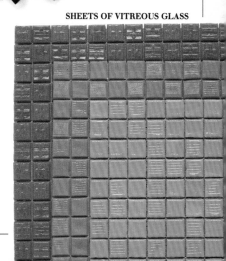

Sculpture 1

THE TWO TRADITIONAL SCULPTURE METHODS are carving and modeling. A carved sculpture is made by cutting away the surplus from a block of hard material such as stone, marble, or wood. The tools used for carving vary according to the material being carved. Heavy steel points, claws, and chisels that are struck with a lump hammer are generally used for stone and marble. Sharp gouges and chisels that are struck with a wooden mallet are used for wood. Sculptures formed from hard materials are generally finished by filing with rasps, rifflers, and other abrasive implements. Modeling is a process by which shapes are built up, using malleable materials such as clay, plaster, and wax. The material is cut with wire-ended tools and modeled with the fingers or a variety of hardwood and metal implements. For large or intricate modeled sculptures an armature (frame), made from metal or wood, is used to provide internal support. Sculptures formed in soft materials may harden naturally or can be made more durable by firing in a kiln. Modeled sculptures are often first designed in wax or another material to be cast later in a metal (see pp. 454-455) such as bronze. The development of many new materials in the 20th century has enabled sculptors to experiment with new techniques such as construction (joining preformed pieces of material such as machine components, mirrors, and furniture) and kinetic (mobile) sculpture.

EXAMPLES OF MARBLE-CARVING TOOLS

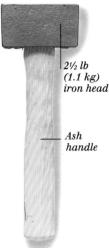

2½ lb (1.1 kg) iron head

Ash handle

LUMP HAMMER

EXAMPLES OF WOOD-CARVING TOOLS

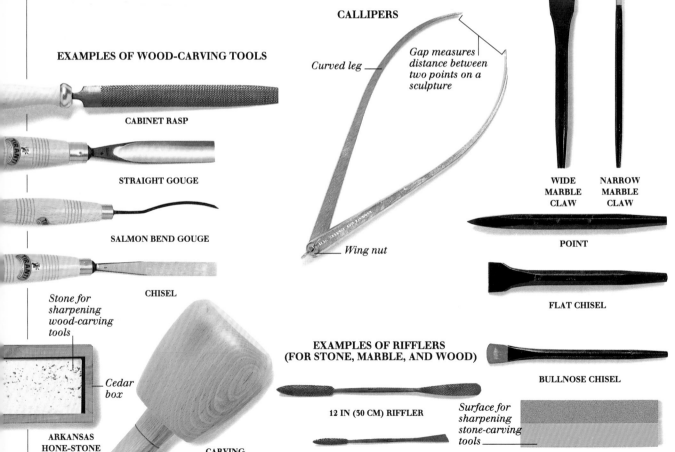

CABINET RASP

STRAIGHT GOUGE

SALMON BEND GOUGE

CHISEL

Stone for sharpening wood-carving tools

Cedar box

ARKANSAS HONE-STONE

CARVING MALLET

CALLIPERS

Curved leg

Gap measures distance between two points on a sculpture

Wing nut

WIDE MARBLE CLAW

NARROW MARBLE CLAW

POINT

FLAT CHISEL

BULLNOSE CHISEL

EXAMPLES OF RIFFLERS (FOR STONE, MARBLE, AND WOOD)

12 IN (30 CM) RIFFLER

6 IN (15 CM) RIFFLER

Surface for sharpening stone-carving tools

DIAMOND WHETSTONE

Tiny holes along
the hairline made
with a point

Soft skin texture tooled
with a fine-toothed
marble claw

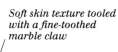

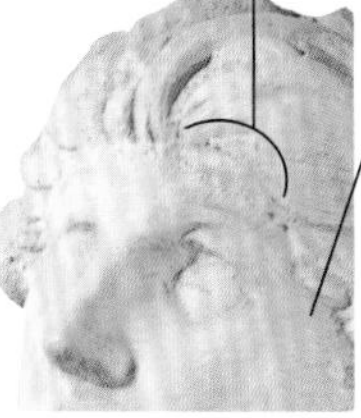

**DETAIL OF
SLAVE'S HEAD**

EXAMPLE OF A CARVED MARBLE SCULPTURE
The Rebel Slave, Michelangelo, 1513-1516
Marble, height 7ft (213 cm)

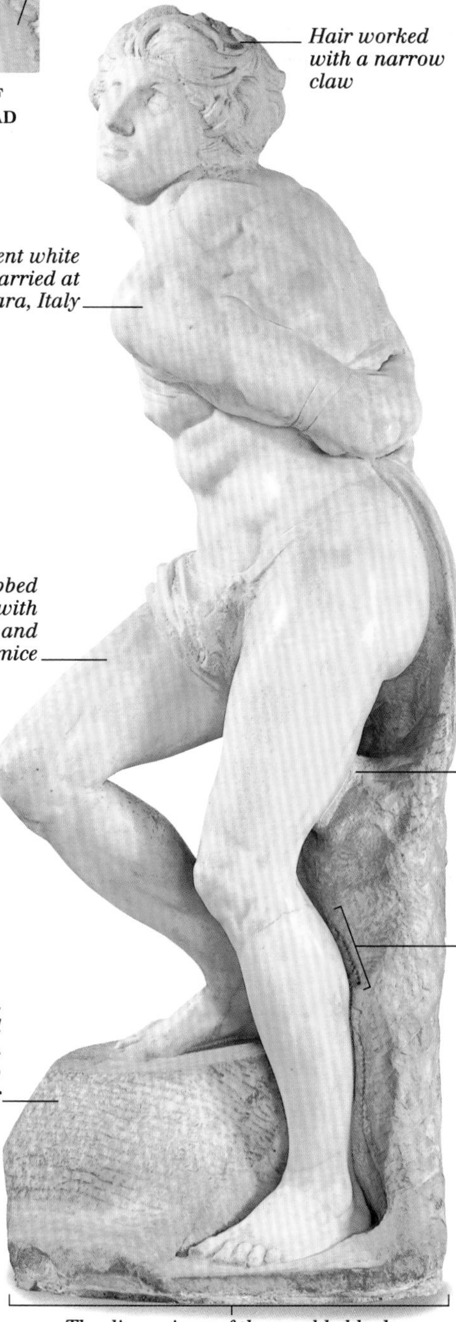

EXAMPLE OF A CARVED WOOD SCULPTURE
Mary Magdalene, Donatello, 1454-1455
Poplar wood, height 6 ft 2 in (188 cm)

Hair worked
with a narrow
claw

Translucent white
marble, quarried at
Carrara, Italy

Surface rubbed
smooth with
rifflers and
pumice

Strut gives added
support to long
slender limb

Series of tiny
punch holes,
made with a
fine point,
outline the
form

Base scored with
jagged parallel
cuts made with
point and lump
hammer

Delicately
modeled
hand carved
with a chisel

Hair
highlighted
with gold
leaf

Figure cut
from single
length of
poplar

Deep
ridges of
hair cut
with a
gouge

Wood prepared
with gesso
(chalk and glue)
and painted

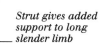

Foot carved in
deep relief

Rough surface
made by driving
a point into the
marble at an
oblique angle

The dimensions of the marble block
determine the size of the sculpture

DETAIL OF SLAVE'S FOOT

Sculpture 2

EXAMPLES OF MODELING TOOLS

WIRE-ENDED CUTTING TOOL

CURVED MOLDING TOOL

SPATULA-ENDED WAX MODELING TOOL

ROUNDED WAX MODELING TOOL

EXAMPLES OF BRONZE FINISHING TOOLS

HOOKED RIFFLER   **POINTED RIFFLER**

ALCOHOL BURNER (FOR HEATING WAX MODELING TOOLS)

Wick

Brass holder

Glass bowl

Denatured alcohol

STAGES IN THE LOST-WAX METHOD OF CASTING
Based on Mars, Giambologna, c.1546

Wax-covered wire armature

ORIGINAL MODEL
An original, solid wax model is made and preserved so that numerous replicas can be cast.

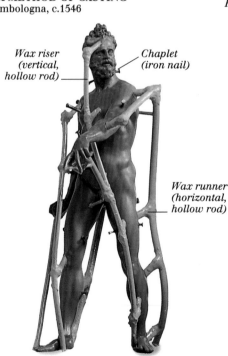

Wax riser (vertical, hollow rod)

Chaplet (iron nail)

Wax runner (horizontal, hollow rod)

HOLLOW WAX FIGURE IS CAST
A new, hollow wax model is cast from the original model. It is filled with a plaster core that is held in place with nails. Wax runners and risers are attached.

Fire-resistant clay

FIGURE IS BAKED IN CASTING MOLD
The model is encased in clay and baked. The wax melts away (through the channels made by the wax rods) and is replaced by molten bronze.

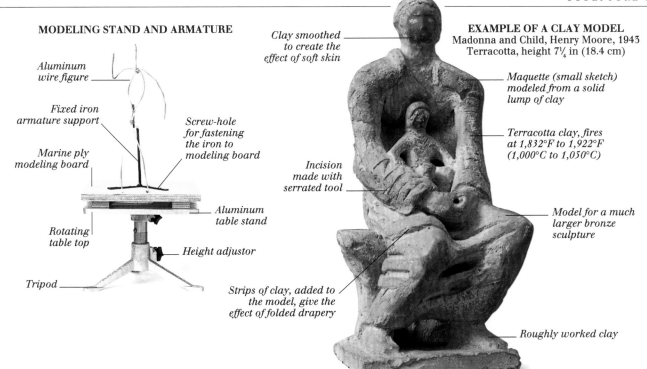

MODELING STAND AND ARMATURE

Aluminum wire figure

Fixed iron armature support

Screw-hole for fastening the iron to modeling board

Marine ply modeling board

Aluminum table stand

Rotating table top

Height adjustor

Tripod

Clay smoothed to create the effect of soft skin

Incision made with serrated tool

Strips of clay, added to the model, give the effect of folded drapery

EXAMPLE OF A CLAY MODEL
Madonna and Child, Henry Moore, 1943
Terracotta, height 7¼ in (18.4 cm)

Maquette (small sketch) modeled from a solid lump of clay

Terracotta clay, fires at 1,832°F to 1,922°F (1,000°C to 1,050°C)

Model for a much larger bronze sculpture

Roughly worked clay

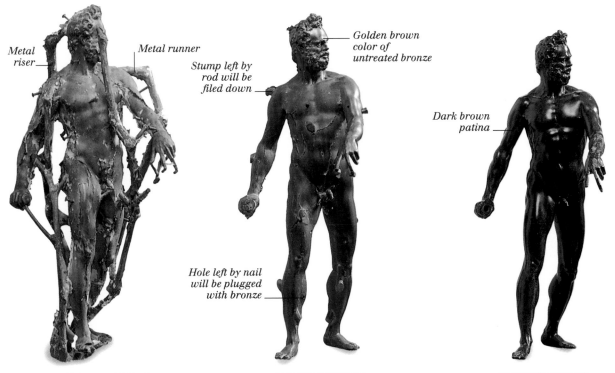

Metal riser

Metal runner

Golden brown color of untreated bronze

Stump left by rod will be filed down

Dark brown patina

Hole left by nail will be plugged with bronze

STATUE IS STRIPPED OF CLAY
When the bronze has cooled, the clay mold is broken open to reveal the bronze statue with solid metal runners and risers.

STATUE IS FINISHED
The nails are pulled out and a large hole is made to remove the plaster core. When the metal rods have been sawn off, the sculpture is filed to refine the surface.

STATUE IS CLEANED
Finally the work is cleaned and polished. An artificial patina (coloring) is achieved by treating the surface with chemicals.

ARCHITECTURE

ANCIENT EGYPT 458

ANCIENT GREECE 460

ANCIENT ROME 1 462

ANCIENT ROME 2 464

MEDIEVAL CASTLES AND HOUSES 466

MEDIEVAL CHURCHES 468

GOTHIC 1 470

GOTHIC 2 472

RENAISSANCE 1 474

RENAISSANCE 2 476

BAROQUE AND NEOCLASSICAL 1 478

BAROQUE AND NEOCLASSICAL 2 480

BAROQUE AND NEOCLASSICAL 3 482

ARCHES AND VAULTS 484

DOMES 486

ISLAMIC BUILDINGS 488

SOUTH AND EAST ASIA 490

THE 19TH CENTURY 492

THE EARLY 20TH CENTURY 494

MODERN BUILDINGS 1 496

MODERN BUILDINGS 2 498

Ancient Egypt

Cornice decorated with cavetto molding

Campaniform (open papyrus) capital

Architrave

Papyrus-bud capital

Socle

Side aisle   *Central nave*   *Side aisle*

THE CIVILIZATION OF THE ANCIENT EGYPTIANS (which lasted from about 3100 BC until it was finally absorbed into the Roman empire in 30 BC) is famous for its temples and tombs. Egyptian temples were often huge and geometric, like the Temple of Amon-Re (below and right). They were usually decorated with hieroglyphs (sacred characters used for picture writing) and painted reliefs depicting gods, Pharaohs (kings), and queens. Tombs were particularly important to the Egyptians, who believed that the dead were resurrected in the afterlife. The tombs were often decorated—for example, the surround of the false door opposite—in order to give comfort to the dead. The best-known ancient Egyptian tombs are the pyramids, which were designed to symbolize the rays of the sun. Many of the architectural forms used by the ancient Egyptians were later adopted by other civilizations. For example, columns and capitals were later used by the ancient Greeks (see pp. 460-461) and ancient Romans (see pp. 462-465).

Horus, the sun-god   *Architrave*   *Stone slab forming flat roof of side aisle*

SIDE VIEW OF HYPOSTYLE HALL, TEMPLE OF AMON-RE, KARNAK, EGYPT, c.1290 BC

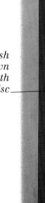

Kepresh crown with disc

Chons, the moon-god / *Amon-Re, king of the gods* / *Hathor, the sky-goddess* / *Papyrus motif*   *Cartouche (oval border) containing the titles of the Pharaoh (king)*   *Socle*   *Aisle running north–south*

LIMESTONE FALSE DOOR WITH HIEROGLYPHS, TOMB OF KING TJETJI, GIZA, EGYPT, c.2400 BC

Lintel

Hieroglyph representing a house

Disc representing sun or light

Eroded image of Tjetji

Limestone stela (slab)

Hoe-shaped hieroglyph representing "mr" sound

Head of false door

Image of Tjetji's wife

Image of Tjetji's daughter

PLANT CAPITAL OF THE PTOLEMAIC-ROMAN PERIOD, EGYPT, 332-30 BC

Palm leaf

Papyrus flower

Papyrus leaf

Papyrus stem

Lotus bud

Lotus stem

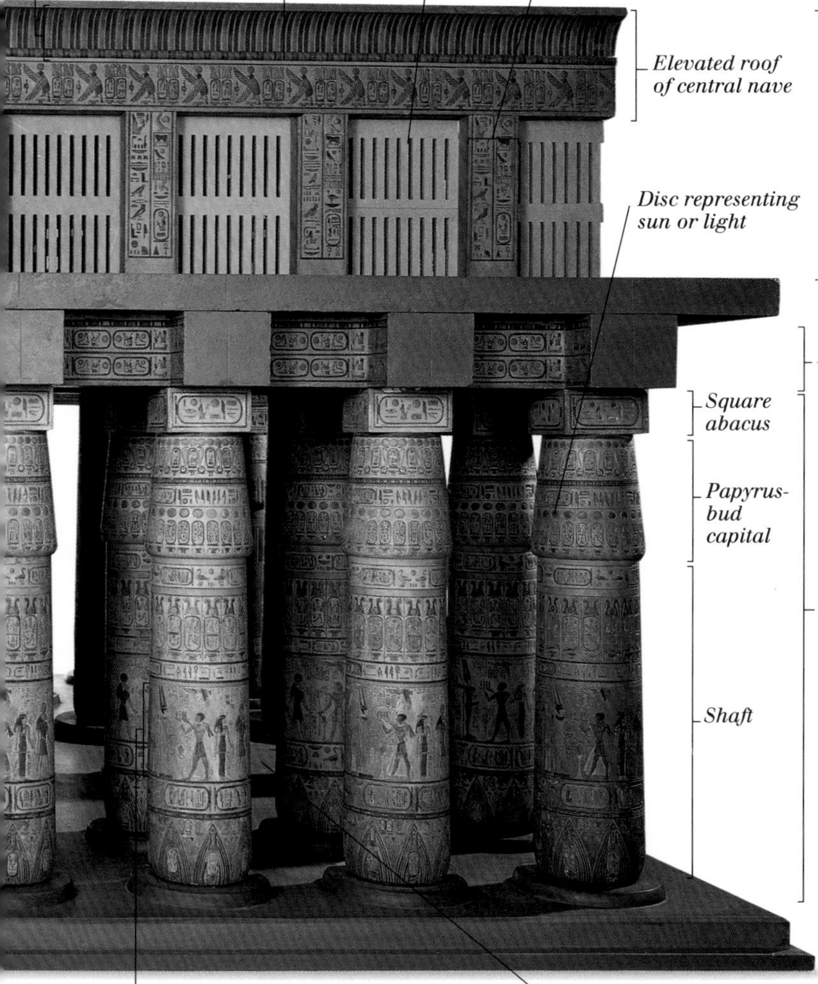

Cornice decorated with cavetto molding

Bead molding

Trellis window

Rectangular pier decorated with hieroglyphs

Elevated roof of central nave

Clerestory

Disc representing sun or light

Architrave

Square abacus

Papyrus-bud capital

Papyriform column

Shaft

Scene depicting a Pharaoh (king) paying homage to the god Amon-Re

Central nave

ANCIENT EGYPTIAN BUILDING DECORATION

DECORATED WINDOW, MEDINET HABU, EGYPT, C.1198 BC

ROPE AND PATERAE DECORATION

CAPITAL WITH THE HEAD OF THE SKY-GODDESS HATHOR, TEMPLE OF ISIS, PHILAE, EGYPT, 283-47 BC

LOTUS AND PAPYRUS FRIEZE DECORATION

Ancient Greece

THE CLASSICAL TEMPLES OF ANCIENT GREECE were built according to the belief that certain forms and proportions were pleasing to the gods. There were three main ancient Greek architectural orders (styles), which can be distinguished by the decoration and proportions of their columns, capitals (column tops), and entablatures (structures resting on the capitals). The oldest is the Doric order, which dates from the seventh century BC and was used mainly on the Greek mainland and in the western colonies, such as Sicily and southern Italy. The Temple of Neptune, shown here, is a classic example of this order. It is hypaethral (roofless) and peripteral (surrounded by a single row of columns). About a century later, the more decorative Ionic order developed on the Aegean Islands. Features of this order include volutes (spiral scrolls) on capitals and acroteria (pediment ornaments). The Corinthian order was invented in Athens in the fifth century BC and is typically identified by an acanthus leaf on the capitals. This order was later widely used in ancient Roman architecture.

CAPITALS OF THE THREE ORDERS OF ANCIENT GREEK ARCHITECTURE

Abacus

Echinus

Annulet

Trachelion (neck)

DORIC CAPITAL, THE PROPYLAEUM (GATEWAY), THE ACROPOLIS, ATHENS, GREECE, 449 BC

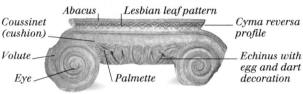

Abacus — Lesbian leaf pattern

Coussinet (cushion)

Cyma reversa profile

Volute

Echinus with egg and dart decoration

Eye — Palmette

IONIC CAPITAL, THE PROPYLAEUM (GATEWAY), TEMPLE OF ATHENA POLIAS, PRIENE, GREECE, c.334 BC

Mask

Abacus

Volute

Cauliculus

Acanthus leaf

Bell-shaped core

CORINTHIAN CAPITAL FROM A STOA (PORTICO), PROBABLY FROM ASIA MINOR

TEMPLE OF NEPTUNE, PAESTUM, ITALY, c.460 BC

Raking cornice

Trachelion (neck)   Taenia   Triglyph   Metope   Glyph (channel)

Pediment

Doric entablature

Pteron (external colonnade)

Euthynteria   Drum   Stylobate   Column of the Doric order

PLAN OF THE TEMPLE OF NEPTUNE, PAESTUM

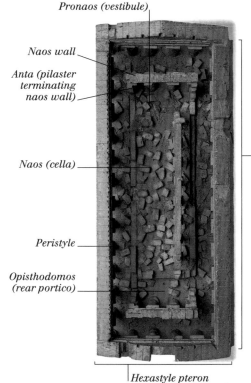

Pronaos (vestibule)

Naos wall

Anta (pilaster
terminating
naos wall)

Naos (cella)

Peristyle

Opisthodomos
(rear portico)

Pteron
(external
colonnade)

Hexastyle pteron
(colonnade of six columns)

ANCIENT GREEK BUILDING DECORATION

Volute

**FAÇADE, TREASURY OF ATREUS, MYCENAE,
GREECE, 1350-1250 BC**

Meander

**FRETWORK, PARTHENON, ATHENS,
GREECE, 447-436 BC**

**ACROTERION,
TEMPLE OF
APHAIA, AEGINA,
GREECE, 490 BC**

Griffon
(gryphon)

Raking
cornice

**ANTEFIXA,
TEMPLE
OF APHAIA,
AEGINA,
GREECE,
490 BC**

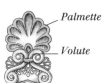

Palmette

Volute

Regula (short fillet beneath taenia)

Eaves

Cornice

Frieze

Architrave

Capital

Shaft

Crepidoma
(stepped
base)

Entasis (slight curve of a column)

Intercolumniation

Fluting

Ancient Rome 1

FESTOON, TEMPLE OF VESTA, TIVOLI, ITALY, C.80 BC

RICHLY DECORATED ROMAN OVUM

IN THE EARLY PERIOD OF THE ROMAN EMPIRE extensive use was made of ancient Greek architectural ideas, particularly those of the Corinthian order (see pp. 460-461). As a result, many early Roman buildings—such as the Temple of Vesta (opposite)—closely resemble ancient Greek buildings. A distinctive Roman style began to evolve in the first century AD. This style developed the interiors of buildings (the Greeks had concentrated on the exterior) by wing arches, vaults, and domes inside the buildings and by ornamenting internal walls; many of these features can be seen in the Pantheon. Exterior columns were often used for decorative rather than structural purposes, as in the Colosseum and the Porta Nigra (see pp. 464-465). Smaller buildings had timber frames with wattle-and-daub walls, as in the mill (see pp. 464-465). Roman architecture remained influential for many centuries, with some of its principles being used in the 11th century in Romanesque buildings (see pp. 468-469) and also in the 15th and 16th centuries in Renaissance buildings (see pp. 474-477).

INTERIOR OF THE PANTHEON, ROME, ITALY, 118-c.128

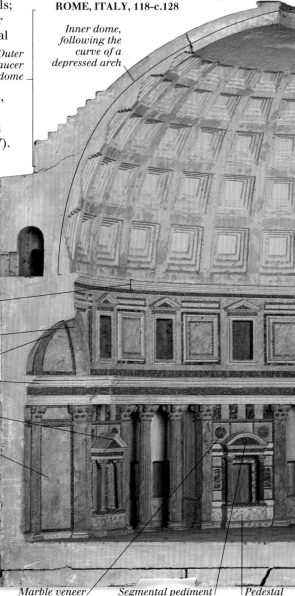

Inner dome, following the curve of a depressed arch

Outer saucer dome

Entablature

Curved cornice

Lesene

Cornice

Triangular pediment

Concave niche

Marble veneer — *Segmental pediment* — *Pedestal*

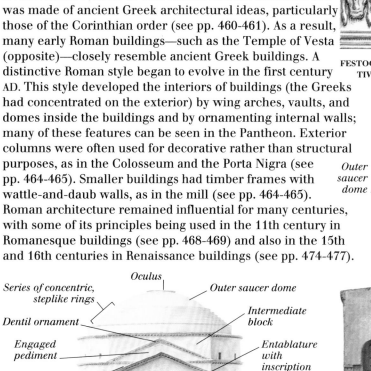

Series of concentric, steplike rings

Oculus

Outer saucer dome

Dentil ornament

Intermediate block

Engaged pediment

Entablature with inscription

Raking cornice

Pediment

Rotunda

Octastyle portico (eight-column portico)

FRONT VIEW OF THE PANTHEON

SIDE VIEW OF THE PANTHEON

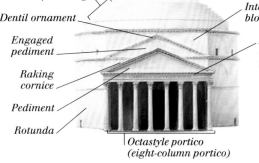

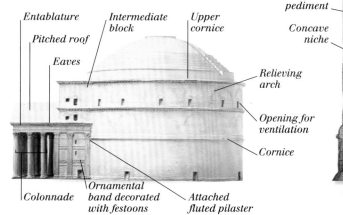

Entablature

Intermediate block

Upper cornice

Pitched roof

Eaves

Relieving arch

Opening for ventilation

Cornice

Colonnade

Ornamental band decorated with festoons

Attached fluted pilaster

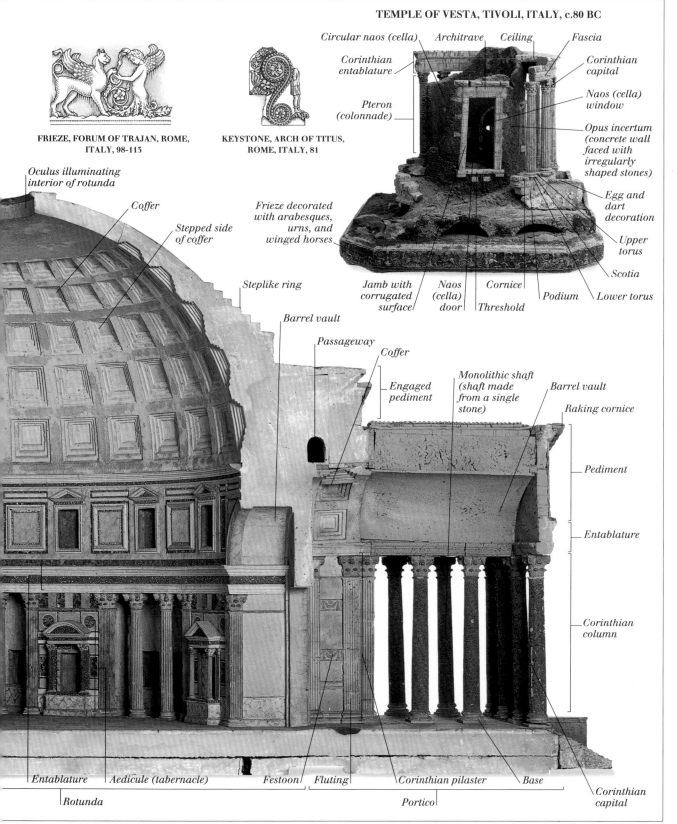

TEMPLE OF VESTA, TIVOLI, ITALY, c.80 BC

FRIEZE, FORUM OF TRAJAN, ROME, ITALY, 98-113

KEYSTONE, ARCH OF TITUS, ROME, ITALY, 81

Circular naos (cella)

Corinthian entablature

Pteron (colonnade)

Architrave

Ceiling

Fascia

Corinthian capital

Naos (cella) window

Opus incertum (concrete wall faced with irregularly shaped stones)

Egg and dart decoration

Upper torus

Scotia

Lower torus

Oculus illuminating interior of rotunda

Coffer

Stepped side of coffer

Steplike ring

Barrel vault

Passageway

Coffer

Engaged pediment

Monolithic shaft (shaft made from a single stone)

Barrel vault

Raking cornice

Pediment

Entablature

Corinthian column

Frieze decorated with arabesques, urns, and winged horses

Jamb with corrugated surface

Naos (cella) door

Cornice

Threshold

Podium

Entablature

Rotunda

Aedicule (tabernacle)

Festoon

Fluting

Corinthian pilaster

Portico

Base

Corinthian capital

Ancient Rome 2

SIDE VIEW OF A ROMAN MILL

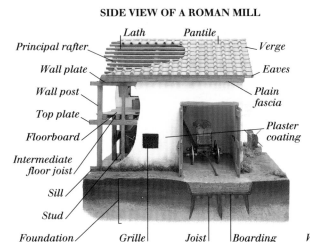

Lath
Pantile
Principal rafter
Verge
Wall plate
Eaves
Wall post
Plain fascia
Top plate
Plaster coating
Floorboard
Intermediate floor joist
Sill
Stud
Foundation
Grille
Joist
Boarding

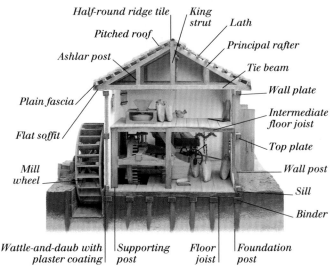

Half-round ridge tile
King strut
Lath
Pitched roof
Principal rafter
Ashlar post
Tie beam
Plain fascia
Wall plate
Flat soffit
Intermediate floor joist
Top plate
Wall post
Mill wheel
Sill
Binder
Wattle-and-daub with plaster coating
Supporting post
Floor joist
Foundation post

THE COLOSSEUM (FLAVIAN AMPHITHEATER), ROME, ITALY, 70-82

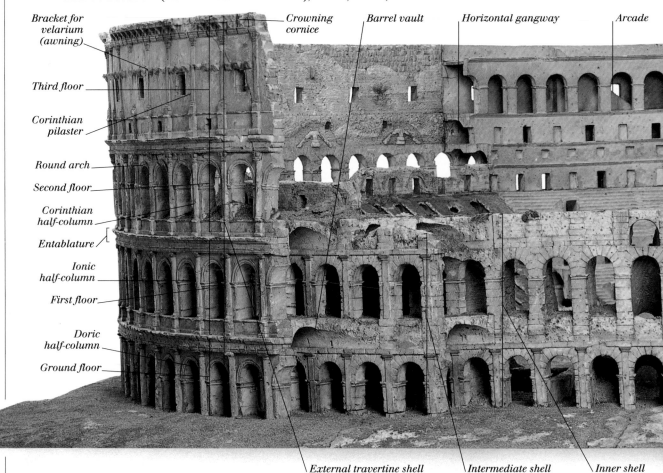

Bracket for velarium (awning)
Crowning cornice
Barrel vault
Horizontal gangway
Arcade
Third floor
Corinthian pilaster
Round arch
Second floor
Corinthian half-column
Entablature
Ionic half-column
First floor
Doric half-column
Ground floor
External travertine shell
Intermediate shell
Inner shell

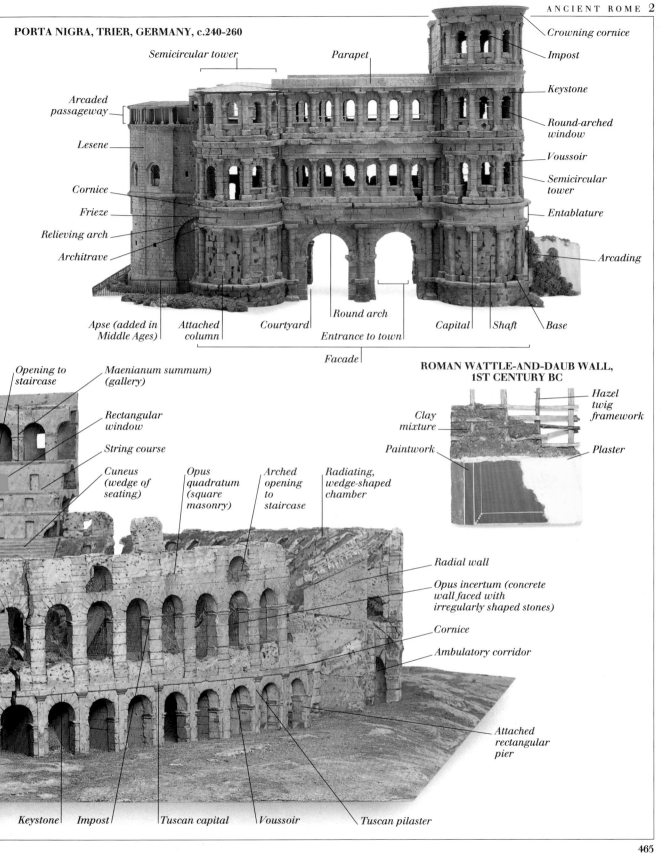

PORTA NIGRA, TRIER, GERMANY, c.240-260

Semicircular tower

Parapet

Crowning cornice

Impost

Arcaded passageway

Keystone

Round-arched window

Lesene

Voussoir

Semicircular tower

Cornice

Frieze

Relieving arch

Architrave

Entablature

Arcading

Apse (added in Middle Ages)

Attached column

Courtyard

Round arch

Entrance to town

Capital

Shaft

Base

Facade

Opening to staircase

Maenianum summum) (gallery)

ROMAN WATTLE-AND-DAUB WALL, 1ST CENTURY BC

Rectangular window

Hazel twig framework

Clay mixture

String course

Paintwork

Plaster

Cuneus (wedge of seating)

Opus quadratum (square masonry)

Arched opening to staircase

Radiating, wedge-shaped chamber

Radial wall

Opus incertum (concrete wall faced with irregularly shaped stones)

Cornice

Ambulatory corridor

Attached rectangular pier

Keystone

Impost

Tuscan capital

Voussoir

Tuscan pilaster

Medieval castles and houses

WARFARE WAS COMMON IN EUROPE in the Middle Ages, and many monarchs and nobles built castles as a form of defense. Typical medieval castles have outer walls surrounding a moat. Inside the moat is a bailey (courtyard), protected by a chemise (jacket wall). The innermost and strongest part of a medieval castle is the keep. There are two main types of keep: towers called donjons, such as the Tour de César and Coucy-le-Château in France, and rectangular keeps ("hall-keeps"), such as the Tower of London. Castles were often guarded by salients (projecting fortifications), like those of the Bastille. Medieval houses typically had timber cruck (tent-like) frames, wattle-and-daub walls, and pitched roofs, like those on medieval London Bridge (opposite).

DONJON, TOUR DE CESAR, PROVINS, FRANCE, 12TH CENTURY

Oculus
Battlements (crenellations)
Loophole
Conical spire
Hemispherical cupola
Flying buttress
Gallery
Hexahedral hall
Squinch
Semicircular turret
Vaulted room
Fireplace
Main entrance
Bailey
Staircase to chemise (jacket wall)
Embrasure
Chemise (jacket wall)
Plain impost
Depressed cupola
Vaulted staircase
Motte

Loophole

SALIENT, CAERNARVON CASTLE, BRITAIN, 1283-1323

Timber cruck frame

CRUCK-FRAMED HOUSE, BRITAIN, c.1200

Blind, rounded relieving arch
Merlon
Battlements (crenellations)
Tetrahedral spire
Crenel
Loophole
Rectangular turret
Wooden staircase leading to entrance above ground level
Quoin
Timber-framed house
Cornice
Buttress
Round-arched window with twin openings
Cruck frame
Paling

TOWER OF LONDON, BRITAIN, FROM 1070

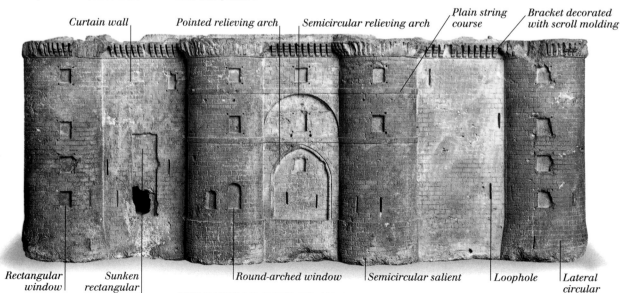

Curtain wall
Pointed relieving arch
Semicircular relieving arch
Plain string course
Bracket decorated with scroll molding
Rectangular window
Sunken rectangular panel
Round-arched window
Semicircular salient
Loophole
Lateral circular salient

THE BASTILLE, PARIS, FRANCE, 14TH CENTURY

MEDIEVAL LONDON BRIDGE, BRITAIN, 1176 (WITH 14TH-CENTURY BATTLEMENTED BUILDING, NONESUCH HOUSE, AND TWO-TOWERED GATE)

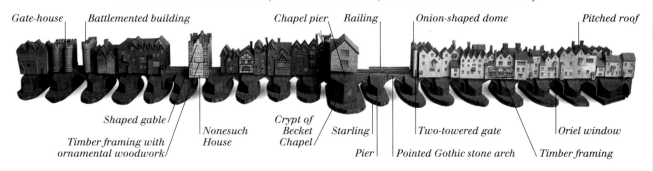

Gate-house

Battlemented building

Chapel pier

Railing

Onion-shaped dome

Pitched roof

Shaped gable

Nonesuch House

Crypt of Becket Chapel

Starling

Two-towered gate

Oriel window

Timber framing with ornamental woodwork

Pier

Pointed Gothic stone arch

Timber framing

DONJON, COUCY-LE-CHATEAU, AISNE, FRANCE, 1225-1245

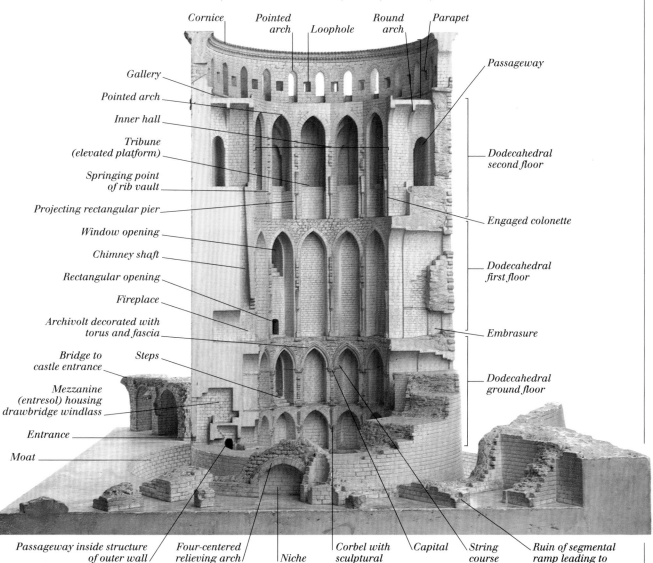

Cornice

Pointed arch

Loophole

Round arch

Parapet

Gallery

Passageway

Pointed arch

Inner hall

Tribune (elevated platform)

Dodecahedral second floor

Springing point of rib vault

Projecting rectangular pier

Engaged colonette

Window opening

Chimney shaft

Dodecahedral first floor

Rectangular opening

Fireplace

Archivolt decorated with torus and fascia

Embrasure

Bridge to castle entrance

Steps

Dodecahedral ground floor

Mezzanine (entresol) housing drawbridge windlass

Entrance

Moat

Passageway inside structure of outer wall

Four-centered relieving arch

Niche

Corbel with sculptural decoration

Capital

String course

Ruin of segmental ramp leading to chemise (jacket wall)

Medieval churches

LARGE NUMBERS OF CHURCHES were built in Europe in the Middle Ages. European churches of this period typically have high vaults supported by massive piers and columns. In the 10th century, the Romanesque style developed. Romanesque architects adopted many Roman or early Christian architectural ideas, such as cross-shaped ground plans—like that of Angoulême Cathedral (opposite)—and the basilican system of a nave with a central vessel and side aisles. In the mid-12th century, flying buttresses and pointed vaults appeared. These features later became widely used in Gothic architecture (see pp. 470-471). Bagneux Church (opposite) has both styles: a Romanesque tower and a Gothic nave and choir.

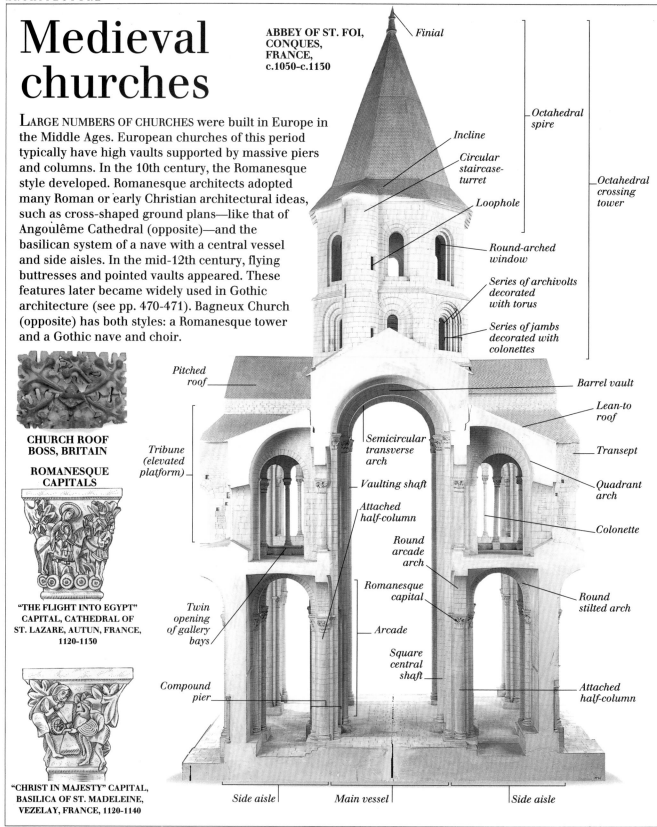

ABBEY OF ST. FOI, CONQUES, FRANCE, c.1050-c.1130

Finial

Incline

Circular staircase-turret

Loophole

Octahedral spire

Octahedral crossing tower

Round-arched window

Series of archivolts decorated with torus

Series of jambs decorated with colonettes

Pitched roof

Barrel vault

Lean-to roof

Semicircular transverse arch

Transept

Tribune (elevated platform)

Vaulting shaft

Quadrant arch

Attached half-column

Colonette

Round arcade arch

Romanesque capital

Round stilted arch

Twin opening of gallery bays

Arcade

Square central shaft

Compound pier

Attached half-column

Side aisle | Main vessel | Side aisle

CHURCH ROOF BOSS, BRITAIN

ROMANESQUE CAPITALS

"THE FLIGHT INTO EGYPT" CAPITAL, CATHEDRAL OF ST. LAZARE, AUTUN, FRANCE, 1120-1130

"CHRIST IN MAJESTY" CAPITAL, BASILICA OF ST. MADELEINE, VEZELAY, FRANCE, 1120-1140

GROUND PLAN OF ANGOULEME CATHEDRAL, FRANCE, FROM c.1105

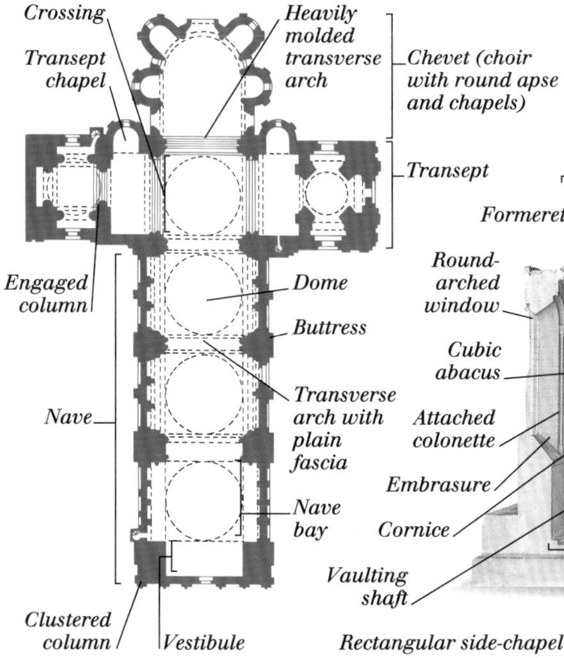

Crossing

Transept chapel

Heavily molded transverse arch

Chevet (choir with round apse and chapels)

Transept

Engaged column

Dome

Buttress

Transverse arch with plain fascia

Nave

Attached colonette

Embrasure

Cornice

Clustered column

Vestibule

Nave bay

Vaulting shaft

Rectangular side-chapel

CHOIR, CHURCH OF ST. SERGE, ANGERS, FRANCE, c.1215-1220

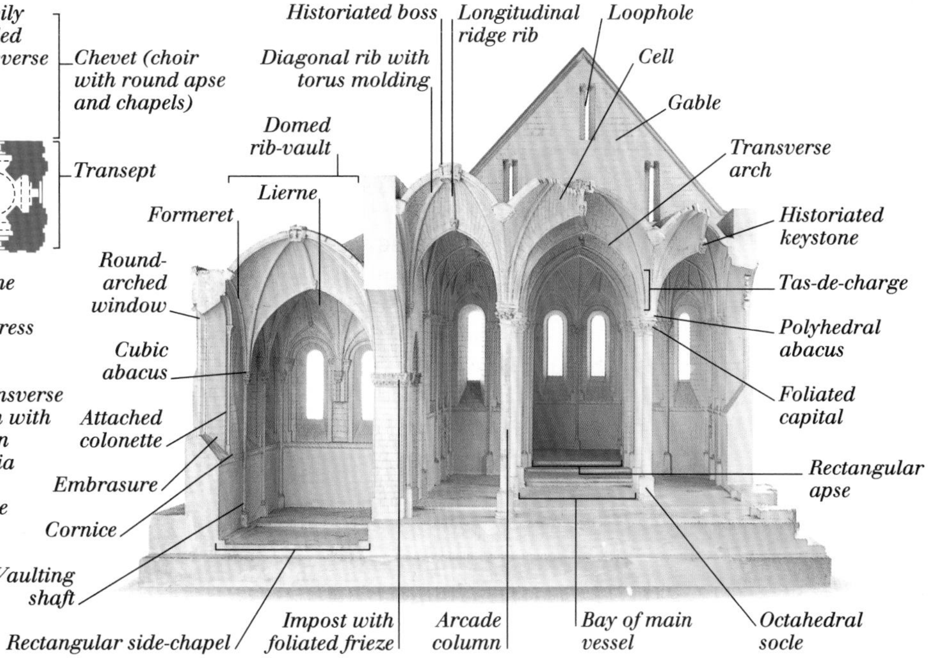

Historiated boss

Longitudinal ridge rib

Loophole

Cell

Gable

Diagonal rib with torus molding

Transverse arch

Historiated keystone

Domed rib-vault

Lierne

Formeret

Tas-de-charge

Polyhedral abacus

Round-arched window

Foliated capital

Cubic abacus

Rectangular apse

Impost with foliated frieze

Arcade column

Bay of main vessel

Octahedral socle

BAGNEUX CHURCH, FRANCE, 1170-1190

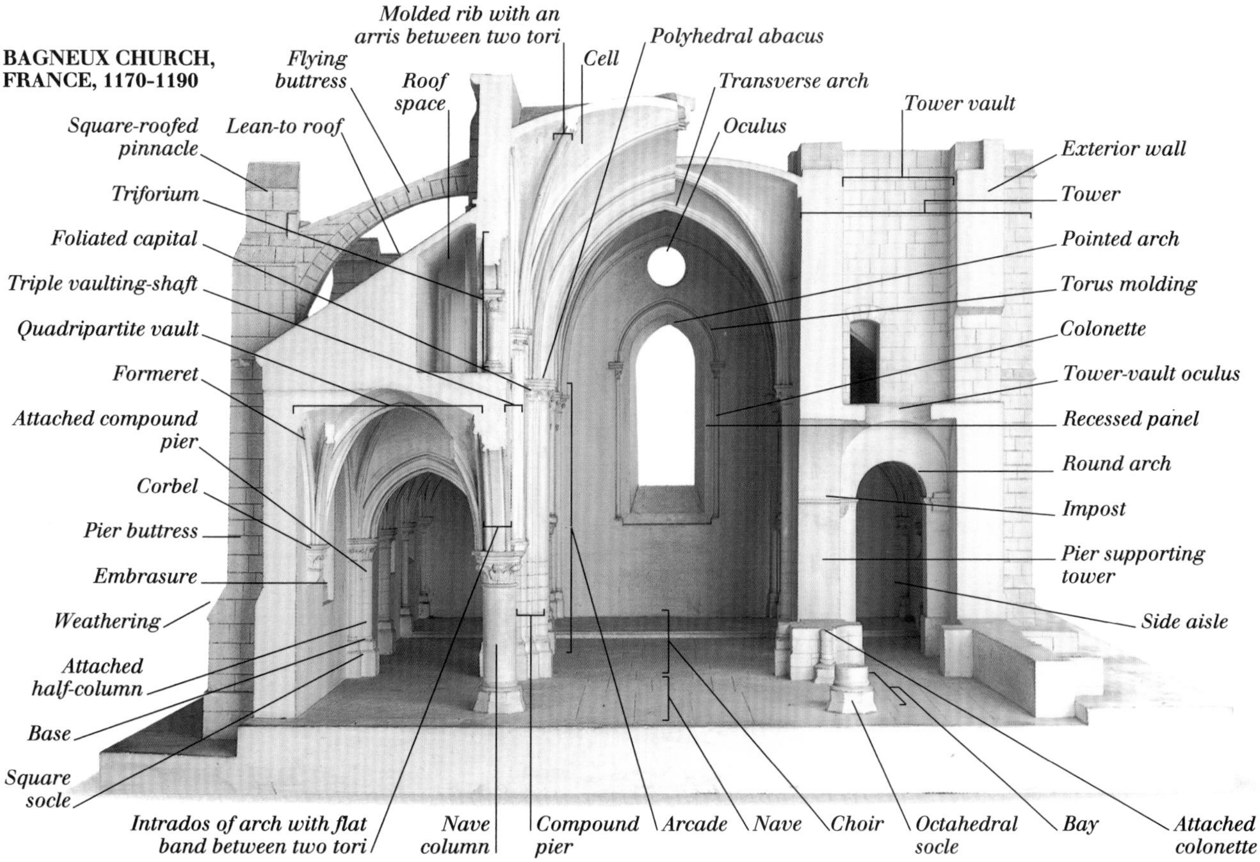

Molded rib with an arris between two tori

Cell

Polyhedral abacus

Transverse arch

Tower vault

Flying buttress

Roof space

Oculus

Square-roofed pinnacle

Lean-to roof

Exterior wall

Tower

Triforium

Pointed arch

Foliated capital

Torus molding

Triple vaulting-shaft

Colonette

Quadripartite vault

Tower-vault oculus

Formeret

Recessed panel

Attached compound pier

Round arch

Corbel

Impost

Pier buttress

Pier supporting tower

Embrasure

Weathering

Side aisle

Attached half-column

Base

Square socle

Intrados of arch with flat band between two tori

Nave column

Compound pier

Arcade

Nave

Choir

Octahedral socle

Bay

Attached colonette

Gothic 1

GOTHIC STAINED GLASS WITH FOLIATED SCROLL MOTIF, ON WOODEN FORM

GOTHIC BUILDINGS are characterized by rib vaults, pointed or lancet arches, flying buttresses, decorative tracery and gables, and stained-glass windows. Typical Gothic buildings include the Cathedrals of Salisbury and old St. Paul's in England, and Notre Dame de Paris in France (see pp. 472-473). The Gothic style developed out of Romanesque architecture in France (see pp. 468-469) in the mid-12th century and then spread throughout Europe. The decorative elements of Gothic architecture became highly developed in buildings of the English Decorated style (late 13th-14th century) and the French Flamboyant style (15th-16th century). These styles are exemplified by the tower of Salisbury Cathedral and by the staircase in the Church of St. Maclou (see pp. 472-473), respectively. In both of these styles, embellishments such as ballflowers and curvilinear (flowing) tracery were used liberally. The English Perpendicular style (late 14th-15th century), which followed the Decorated style, emphasized the vertical and horizontal elements of a building. A notable feature of this style is the hammer-beam roof.

GROUND PLAN OF SALISBURY CATHEDRAL

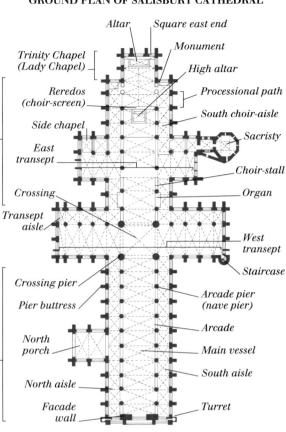

- Altar
- Square east end
- Trinity Chapel (Lady Chapel)
- Monument
- High altar
- Reredos (choir-screen)
- Processional path
- Side chapel
- South choir-aisle
- Choir
- Sacristy
- East transept
- Choir-stall
- Crossing
- Organ
- Transept aisle
- West transept
- Crossing pier
- Staircase
- Pier buttress
- Arcade pier (nave pier)
- Arcade
- North porch
- Main vessel
- Nave
- South aisle
- North aisle
- Facade wall
- Turret

GOTHIC TORUS WITH BALLFLOWERS

- Limestone block
- Block members carved into rolls
- Block members cut polygonally
- Pencil guideline
- Early stage of ballflower carving

BLOCK AFTER INITIAL CUTTING

BLOCK WITH MEMBERS CUT INTO ROLLS

- Torus
- Ballflower
- Fillet
- Mason's mark

FINISHED BLOCK

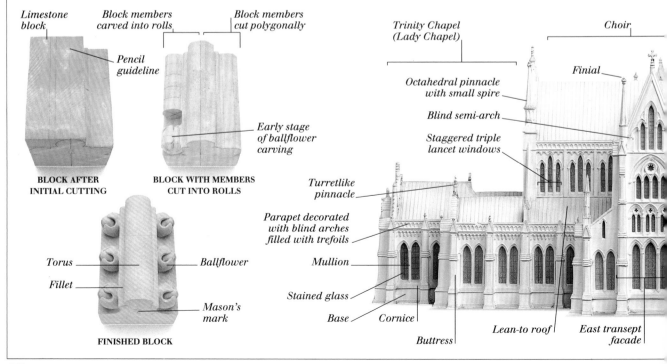

- Trinity Chapel (Lady Chapel)
- Choir
- Octahedral pinnacle with small spire
- Finial
- Blind semi-arch
- Staggered triple lancet windows
- Turretlike pinnacle
- Parapet decorated with blind arches filled with trefoils
- Mullion
- Stained glass
- Base
- Cornice
- Buttress
- Lean-to roof
- East transept facade

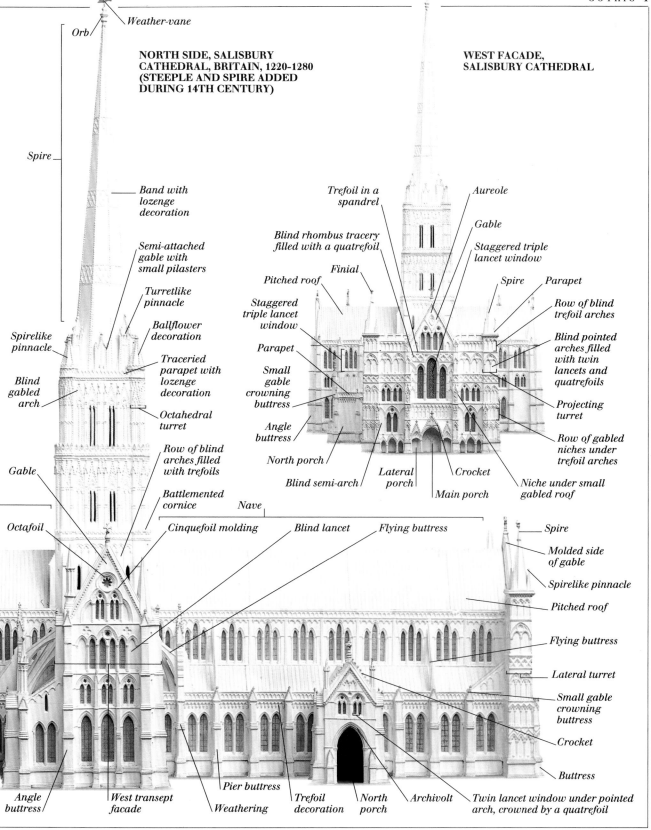

Orb

Weather-vane

NORTH SIDE, SALISBURY CATHEDRAL, BRITAIN, 1220-1280 (STEEPLE AND SPIRE ADDED DURING 14TH CENTURY)

WEST FACADE, SALISBURY CATHEDRAL

Spire

Band with lozenge decoration

Semi-attached gable with small pilasters

Turretlike pinnacle

Ballflower decoration

Spirelike pinnacle

Traceried parapet with lozenge decoration

Blind gabled arch

Octahedral turret

Gable

Row of blind arches filled with trefoils

Octafoil

Battlemented cornice

Cinquefoil molding

Nave

Trefoil in a spandrel

Blind rhombus tracery filled with a quatrefoil

Finial

Pitched roof

Staggered triple lancet window

Parapet

Small gable crowning buttress

Angle buttress

North porch

Blind semi-arch

Aureole

Gable

Staggered triple lancet window

Spire

Parapet

Row of blind trefoil arches

Blind pointed arches filled with twin lancets and quatrefoils

Projecting turret

Row of gabled niches under trefoil arches

Niche under small gabled roof

Lateral porch

Crocket

Main porch

Blind lancet

Flying buttress

Spire

Molded side of gable

Spirelike pinnacle

Pitched roof

Flying buttress

Lateral turret

Small gable crowning buttress

Crocket

Buttress

Angle buttress

West transept facade

Weathering

Pier buttress

Trefoil decoration

North porch

Archivolt

Twin lancet window under pointed arch, crowned by a quatrefoil

Gothic 2

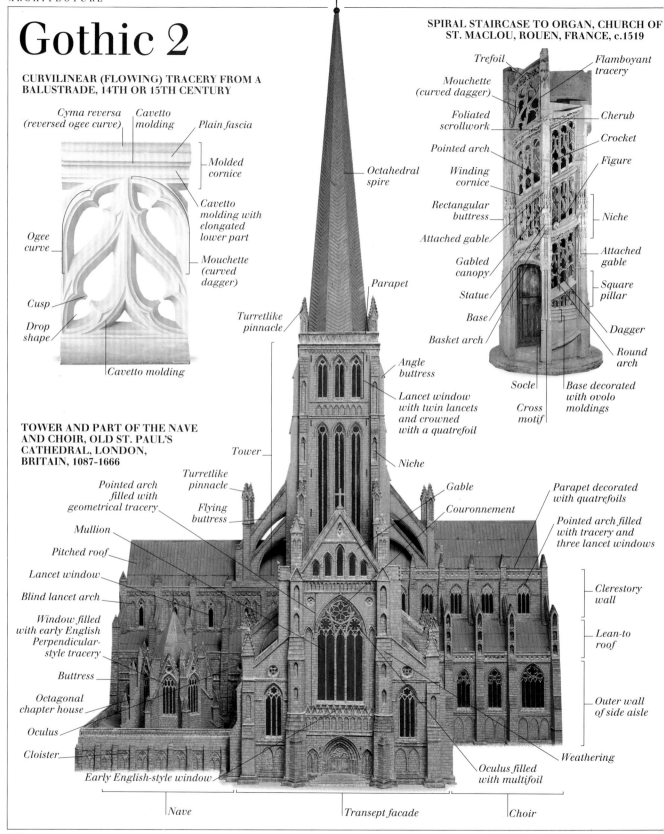

CURVILINEAR (FLOWING) TRACERY FROM A BALUSTRADE, 14TH OR 15TH CENTURY

Cyma reversa (reversed ogee curve)
Cavetto molding
Plain fascia
Molded cornice
Cavetto molding with elongated lower part
Mouchette (curved dagger)
Ogee curve
Cusp
Drop shape
Cavetto molding

Trefoil
Mouchette (curved dagger)
Foliated scrollwork
Pointed arch
Winding cornice
Rectangular buttress
Attached gable
Gabled canopy
Statue
Base
Basket arch
Flamboyant tracery
Cherub
Crocket
Figure
Niche
Attached gable
Square pillar
Dagger
Round arch
Socle
Base decorated with ovolo moldings
Cross motif

Octahedral spire
Parapet
Turretlike pinnacle
Angle buttress
Lancet window with twin lancets and crowned with a quatrefoil
Niche

TOWER AND PART OF THE NAVE AND CHOIR, OLD ST. PAUL'S CATHEDRAL, LONDON, BRITAIN, 1087-1666

Tower
Turretlike pinnacle
Flying buttress
Pointed arch filled with geometrical tracery
Mullion
Pitched roof
Lancet window
Blind lancet arch
Window filled with early English Perpendicular-style tracery
Buttress
Octagonal chapter house
Oculus
Cloister
Early English-style window

Gable
Couronnement
Parapet decorated with quatrefoils
Pointed arch filled with tracery and three lancet windows
Clerestory wall
Lean-to roof
Outer wall of side aisle
Weathering
Oculus filled with multifoil

Nave
Transept facade
Choir

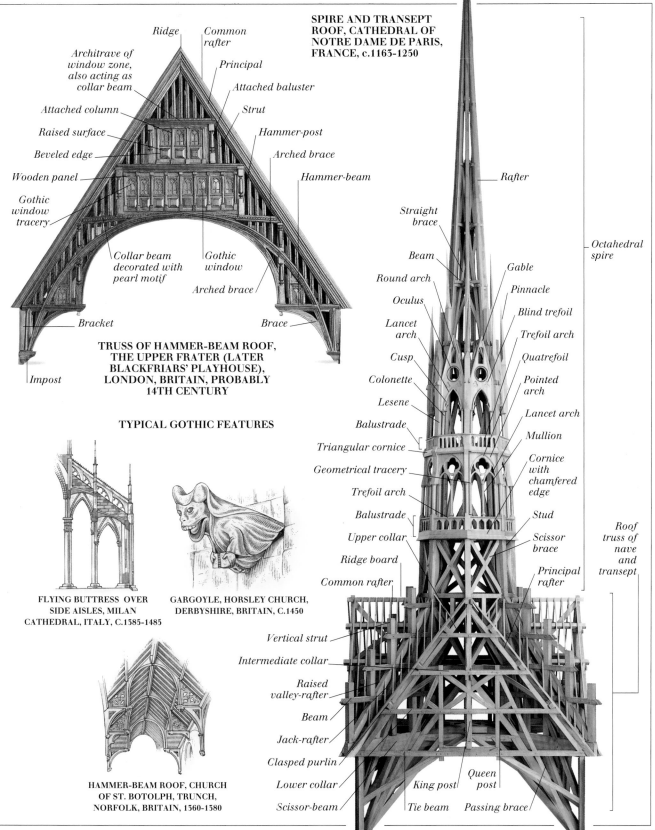

Ridge

Common rafter

SPIRE AND TRANSEPT ROOF, CATHEDRAL OF NOTRE DAME DE PARIS, FRANCE, c.1163-1250

Architrave of window zone, also acting as collar beam

Principal

Attached baluster

Attached column

Strut

Hammer-post

Raised surface

Arched brace

Beveled edge

Hammer-beam

Rafter

Wooden panel

Gothic window tracery

Straight brace

Beam

Gable

Round arch

Pinnacle

Oculus

Blind trefoil

Lancet arch

Trefoil arch

Cusp

Quatrefoil

Colonette

Pointed arch

Lesene

Lancet arch

Balustrade

Mullion

Collar beam decorated with pearl motif

Gothic window

Arched brace

Bracket

Brace

TRUSS OF HAMMER-BEAM ROOF, THE UPPER FRATER (LATER BLACKFRIARS' PLAYHOUSE), LONDON, BRITAIN, PROBABLY 14TH CENTURY

Impost

Triangular cornice

Geometrical tracery

Cornice with chamfered edge

Trefoil arch

Stud

Balustrade

Scissor brace

Upper collar

Principal rafter

Ridge board

Common rafter

Octahedral spire

Roof truss of nave and transept

TYPICAL GOTHIC FEATURES

FLYING BUTTRESS OVER SIDE AISLES, MILAN CATHEDRAL, ITALY, C.1385-1485

GARGOYLE, HORSLEY CHURCH, DERBYSHIRE, BRITAIN, C.1450

Vertical strut

Intermediate collar

Raised valley-rafter

Beam

Jack-rafter

Clasped purlin

HAMMER-BEAM ROOF, CHURCH OF ST. BOTOLPH, TRUNCH, NORFOLK, BRITAIN, 1360-1380

Lower collar

Scissor-beam

King post

Queen post

Tie beam

Passing brace

Renaissance 1

THE RENAISSANCE was a period in European history—lasting roughly from the 14th century to the mid-17th century—during which the arts and sciences underwent great changes. In architecture, these changes were marked by a return to the classical forms and proportions of ancient Roman buildings. The Renaissance originated in Italy, and the buildings most characteristic of its style can be found there, such as the Palazzo Strozzi shown here. Mannerism is a branch of the Renaissance style that distorts the classical forms; an example is the Laurentian Library staircase. As the Renaissance style spread to other European countries, many of its features were incorporated into the local architecture. For example, the Château de Montal in France (see pp. 476-477) incorporates aedicules (tabernacles).

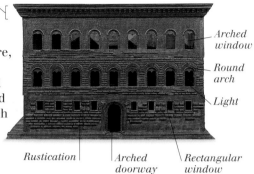

Crowning cornice
Arched window
Round arch
Light
Rustication
Arched doorway
Rectangular window

SIDE VIEW OF PALAZZO STROZZI, FLORENCE, ITALY, 1489 (BY G. DA SANGALLO, B. DA MAIANO, AND CRONACA)

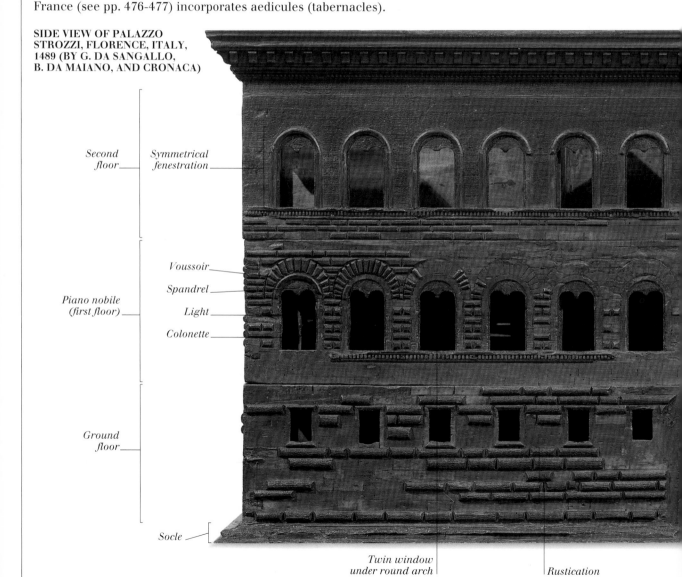

Second floor
Symmetrical fenestration
Voussoir
Spandrel
Piano nobile (first floor)
Light
Colonette
Ground floor
Socle
Twin window under round arch
Rustication

DETAILS FROM ITALIAN RENAISSANCE BUILDINGS

PANEL FROM DRUM OF DOME,
FLORENCE CATHEDRAL, 1420-1436

COFFERING IN DOME,
PAZZI CHAPEL,
FLORENCE, 1429-1461

STAIRCASE,
LAURENTIAN LIBRARY,
FLORENCE, 1559

PORTICO, VILLA ROTUNDA,
VICENZA, 1567-1569

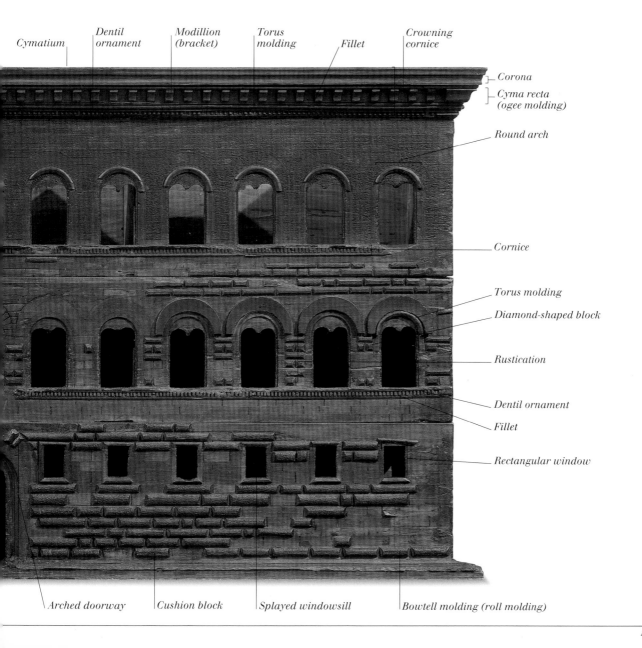

Cymatium

Dentil ornament

Modillion (bracket)

Torus molding

Fillet

Crowning cornice

Corona

Cyma recta (ogee molding)

Round arch

Cornice

Torus molding

Diamond-shaped block

Rustication

Dentil ornament

Fillet

Rectangular window

Arched doorway

Cushion block

Splayed windowsill

Bowtell molding (roll molding)

Renaissance 2

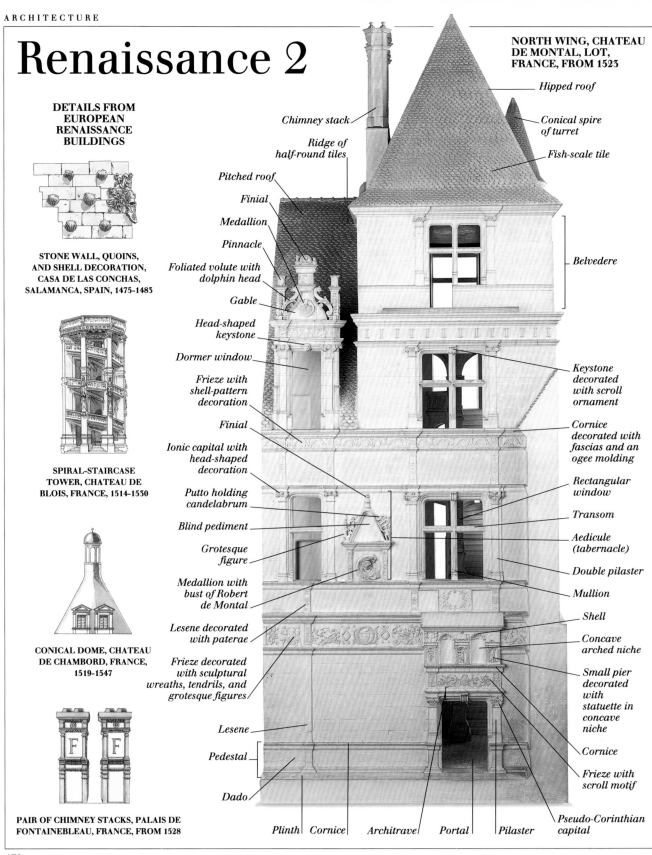

DETAILS FROM EUROPEAN RENAISSANCE BUILDINGS

STONE WALL, QUOINS, AND SHELL DECORATION, CASA DE LAS CONCHAS, SALAMANCA, SPAIN, 1475-1483

SPIRAL-STAIRCASE TOWER, CHATEAU DE BLOIS, FRANCE, 1514-1530

CONICAL DOME, CHATEAU DE CHAMBORD, FRANCE, 1519-1547

PAIR OF CHIMNEY STACKS, PALAIS DE FONTAINEBLEAU, FRANCE, FROM 1528

NORTH WING, CHATEAU DE MONTAL, LOT, FRANCE, FROM 1523

Hipped roof

Conical spire of turret

Fish-scale tile

Belvedere

Chimney stack

Ridge of half-round tiles

Pitched roof

Finial

Medallion

Pinnacle

Foliated volute with dolphin head

Gable

Head-shaped keystone

Dormer window

Frieze with shell-pattern decoration

Finial

Ionic capital with head-shaped decoration

Putto holding candelabrum

Blind pediment

Grotesque figure

Medallion with bust of Robert de Montal

Lesene decorated with paterae

Frieze decorated with sculptural wreaths, tendrils, and grotesque figures

Lesene

Pedestal

Dado

Keystone decorated with scroll ornament

Cornice decorated with fascias and an ogee molding

Rectangular window

Transom

Aedicule (tabernacle)

Double pilaster

Mullion

Shell

Concave arched niche

Small pier decorated with statuette in concave niche

Cornice

Frieze with scroll motif

Pseudo-Corinthian capital

Plinth   Cornice   Architrave   Portal   Pilaster

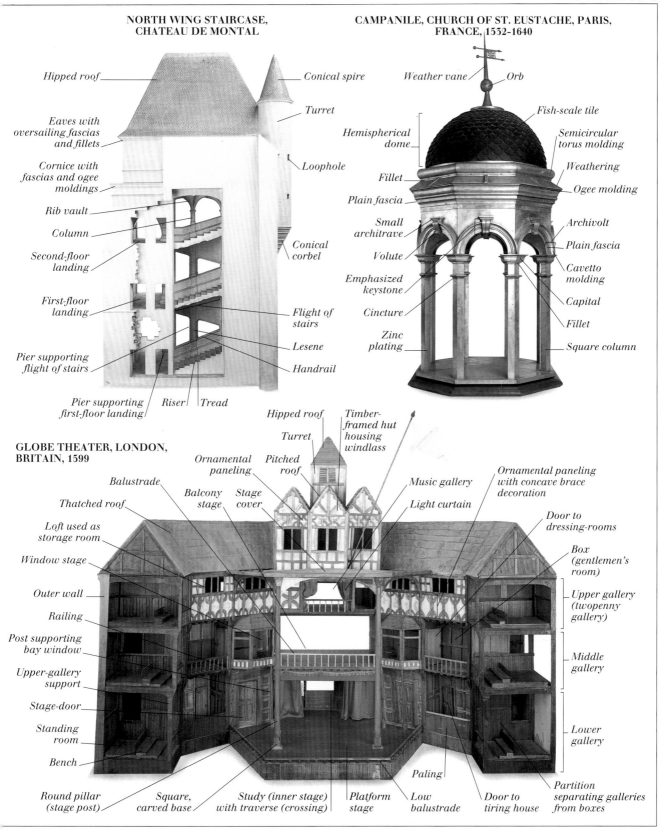

NORTH WING STAIRCASE, CHATEAU DE MONTAL

- Hipped roof
- Eaves with oversailing fascias and fillets
- Cornice with fascias and ogee moldings
- Rib vault
- Column
- Second-floor landing
- First-floor landing
- Pier supporting flight of stairs
- Pier supporting first-floor landing
- Riser
- Tread
- Conical spire
- Turret
- Loophole
- Conical corbel
- Flight of stairs
- Lesene
- Handrail

CAMPANILE, CHURCH OF ST. EUSTACHE, PARIS, FRANCE, 1532-1640

- Weather vane
- Orb
- Hemispherical dome
- Fillet
- Plain fascia
- Small architrave
- Volute
- Emphasized keystone
- Cincture
- Zinc plating
- Fish-scale tile
- Semicircular torus molding
- Weathering
- Ogee molding
- Archivolt
- Plain fascia
- Cavetto molding
- Capital
- Fillet
- Square column

GLOBE THEATER, LONDON, BRITAIN, 1599

- Balustrade
- Thatched roof
- Loft used as storage room
- Window stage
- Outer wall
- Railing
- Post supporting bay window
- Upper-gallery support
- Stage-door
- Standing room
- Bench
- Round pillar (stage post)
- Square, carved base
- Study (inner stage) with traverse (crossing)
- Platform stage
- Low balustrade
- Door to tiring house
- Partition separating galleries from boxes
- Ornamental paneling
- Balcony stage
- Stage cover
- Hipped roof
- Turret
- Pitched roof
- Timber-framed hut housing windlass
- Music gallery
- Light curtain
- Ornamental paneling with concave brace decoration
- Door to dressing-rooms
- Box (gentlemen's room)
- Upper gallery (twopenny gallery)
- Middle gallery
- Lower gallery
- Paling

Baroque and neoclassical 1

THE BAROQUE STYLE EVOLVED IN THE EARLY 17TH CENTURY in Rome. It is characterized by curved outlines and ostentatious decoration, as can be seen in the Italian church details (right). The baroque style was particularly widely favored in Italy, Spain, and Germany. It was also adopted in Britain and France, but with adaptations. The British architects Sir Christopher Wren and Nicholas Hawksmoor, for example, used baroque features—such as the concave walls of St. Paul's Cathedral and the curved buttresses of the Church of St. George in the East (see pp. 480-481)—but they did so with restraint. Similarly, the curved buttresses and volutes of the Parisian Church of St. Paul-St. Louis are relatively plain. In the second half of the 17th century, a distinct classical style (known as neoclassicism) developed in northern Europe as a reaction to the excesses of baroque. Typical of this new style were churches such as the Madeleine (a proposed facade is shown below), as well as secular buildings such as the Cirque Napoleon (opposite) and the buildings of the British architect Sir John Soane (see pp. 482-483). In early 18th century France, an extremely lavish form of baroque developed, known as rococo. The balcony from Nantes (see pp. 482-483) with its twisted ironwork and head-shaped corbels is typical of this style.

SCROLLED BUTTRESS,
CHURCH OF ST. MARIA DELLA
SALUTE, VENICE, 1631-1682

STATUE OF THE ECSTASY OF
ST. THERESA, CHURCH OF ST. MARIA
DELLA VITTORIA, ROME, 1645-1652

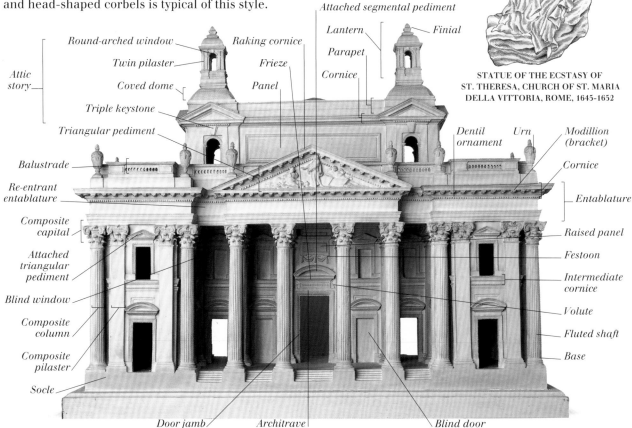

PROPOSED FACADE, THE MADELEINE (NEOCLASSICAL), PARIS, FRANCE, 1764 (BY P. CONTANT D'IVRY)

Attached segmental pediment

Lantern

Finial

Parapet

Cornice

Raking cornice

Frieze

Panel

Round-arched window

Twin pilaster

Coved dome

Triple keystone

Triangular pediment

Balustrade

Re-entrant entablature

Composite capital

Attached triangular pediment

Blind window

Composite column

Composite pilaster

Socle

Attic story

Dentil ornament

Urn

Modillion (bracket)

Cornice

Entablature

Raised panel

Festoon

Intermediate cornice

Volute

Fluted shaft

Base

Door jamb

Architrave

Blind door

CIRQUE NAPOLEON (NEOCLASSICAL), PARIS, FRANCE, 1852 (BY J.I. HITTORFF)

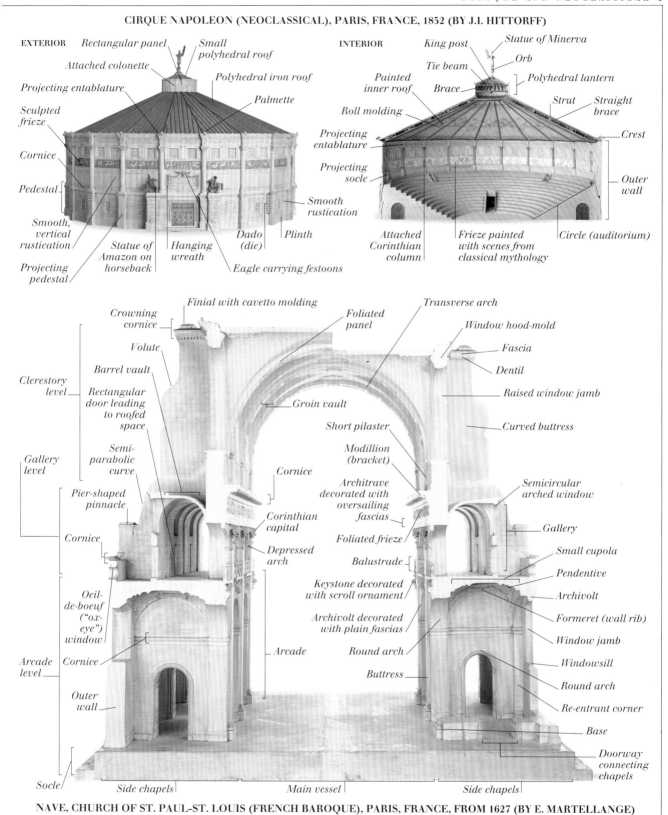

EXTERIOR

Rectangular panel

Small polyhedral roof

Attached colonette

Polyhedral iron roof

Projecting entablature

Palmette

Sculpted frieze

Cornice

Pedestal

Smooth, vertical rustication

Projecting pedestal

Statue of Amazon on horseback

Hanging wreath

Dado (die)

Plinth

Smooth rustication

Eagle carrying festoons

INTERIOR

King post

Statue of Minerva

Tie beam

Orb

Brace

Polyhedral lantern

Painted inner roof

Roll molding

Strut

Straight brace

Projecting entablature

Crest

Projecting socle

Outer wall

Attached Corinthian column

Frieze painted with scenes from classical mythology

Circle (auditorium)

Finial with cavetto molding

Transverse arch

Crowning cornice

Foliated panel

Window hood-mold

Volute

Fascia

Barrel vault

Dentil

Clerestory level

Rectangular door leading to roofed space

Groin vault

Raised window jamb

Gallery level

Semi-parabolic curve

Short pilaster

Curved buttress

Pier-shaped pinnacle

Cornice

Modillion (bracket)

Semicircular arched window

Corinthian capital

Architrave decorated with oversailing fascias

Gallery

Cornice

Foliated frieze

Depressed arch

Small cupola

Balustrade

Pendentive

Oeil-de-boeuf ("ox-eye") window

Keystone decorated with scroll ornament

Archivolt

Archivolt decorated with plain fascias

Formeret (wall rib)

Arcade level

Cornice

Arcade

Round arch

Window jamb

Buttress

Windowsill

Outer wall

Round arch

Re-entrant corner

Base

Doorway connecting chapels

Socle

Side chapels

Main vessel

Side chapels

NAVE, CHURCH OF ST. PAUL-ST. LOUIS (FRENCH BAROQUE), PARIS, FRANCE, FROM 1627 (BY E. MARTELLANGE)

Baroque and neoclassical 2

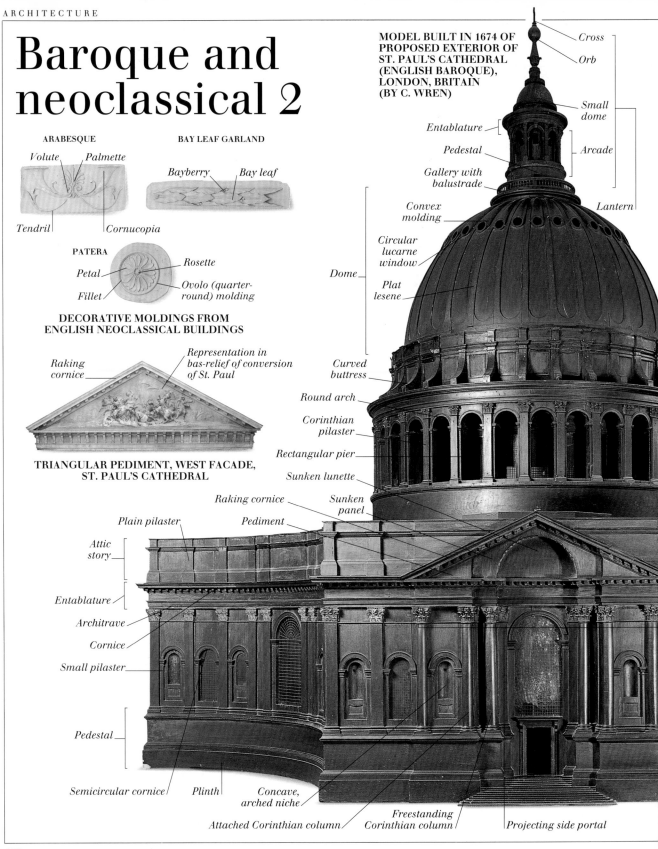

ARABESQUE

Volute Palmette

Tendril Cornucopia

BAY LEAF GARLAND

Bayberry Bay leaf

PATERA

Petal Rosette

Fillet Ovolo (quarter-round) molding

DECORATIVE MOLDINGS FROM ENGLISH NEOCLASSICAL BUILDINGS

Raking cornice

Representation in bas-relief of conversion of St. Paul

TRIANGULAR PEDIMENT, WEST FACADE, ST. PAUL'S CATHEDRAL

MODEL BUILT IN 1674 OF PROPOSED EXTERIOR OF ST. PAUL'S CATHEDRAL (ENGLISH BAROQUE), LONDON, BRITAIN (BY C. WREN)

Cross

Orb

Small dome

Entablature

Pedestal

Arcade

Gallery with balustrade

Convex molding

Lantern

Circular lucarne window

Dome

Plat lesene

Curved buttress

Round arch

Corinthian pilaster

Rectangular pier

Sunken lunette

Raking cornice

Sunken panel

Plain pilaster

Pediment

Attic story

Entablature

Architrave

Cornice

Small pilaster

Pedestal

Semicircular cornice Plinth Concave, arched niche

Attached Corinthian column

Freestanding Corinthian column

Projecting side portal

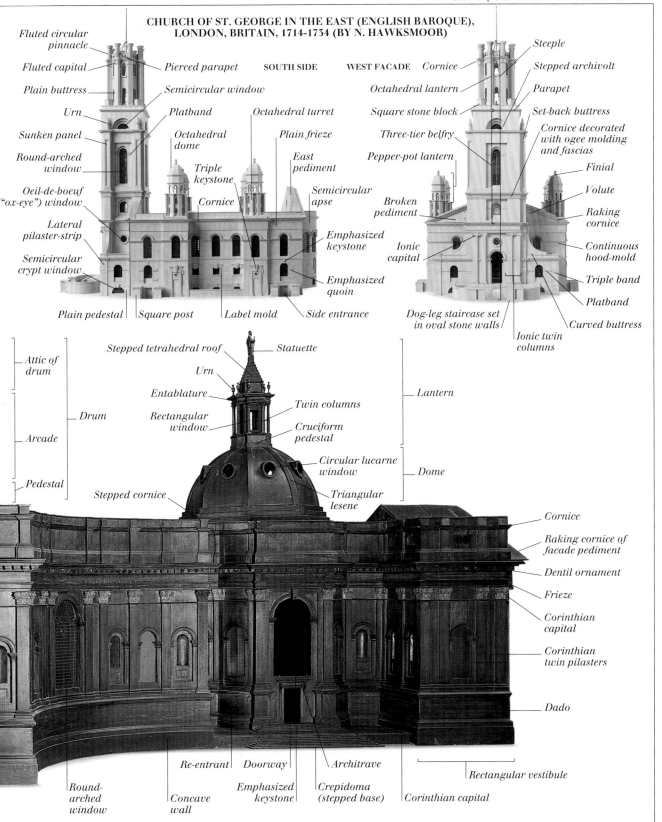

CHURCH OF ST. GEORGE IN THE EAST (ENGLISH BAROQUE), LONDON, BRITAIN, 1714-1734 (BY N. HAWKSMOOR)

SOUTH SIDE

Fluted circular pinnacle

Fluted capital — Pierced parapet

Plain buttress — Semicircular window

Urn

Sunken panel — Platband

Round-arched window — Octahedral dome

Oeil-de-boeuf ("ox-eye") window — Triple keystone

Lateral pilaster-strip — Cornice

Semicircular crypt window

Plain pedestal — Square post — Label mold

Octahedral turret

Plain frieze

East pediment

Semicircular apse

Emphasized keystone

Emphasized quoin

Side entrance

WEST FACADE

Cornice — Steeple

Octahedral lantern — Stepped archivolt

Square stone block — Parapet

Three-tier belfry — Set-back buttress

Pepper-pot lantern — Cornice decorated with ogee molding and fascias

Broken pediment — Finial

Ionic capital — Volute

Raking cornice

Continuous hood-mold

Triple band

Platband

Dog-leg staircase set in oval stone walls — Curved buttress

Ionic twin columns

Attic of drum

Drum

Arcade

Pedestal

Stepped tetrahedral roof — Statuette

Urn

Entablature

Rectangular window — Twin columns

Cruciform pedestal

Circular lucarne window

Triangular lesene

Stepped cornice

Lantern

Dome

Cornice

Raking cornice of facade pediment

Dentil ornament

Frieze

Corinthian capital

Corinthian twin pilasters

Dado

Round-arched window

Re-entrant — Doorway — Architrave

Concave wall

Emphasized keystone — Crepidoma (stepped base)

Corinthian capital

Rectangular vestibule

Baroque and neoclassical 3

DETAILS FROM BAROQUE, NEOCLASSICAL, AND ROCOCO BUILDINGS

PORTICO, THE VYNE, HAMPSHIRE, BRITAIN, 1654 (NEOCLASSICAL)

GILT IRONWORK FROM SCREEN, PALAIS DE VERSAILLES, FRANCE, 1669-1674 (FRENCH BAROQUE)

WINDOW, PALAZZO STANGA, CREMONA, ITALY, EARLY 18TH CENTURY (ROCOCO)

ATLAS (MALE CARYATID), UPPER BELVEDERE, VIENNA, AUSTRIA, 1721 (GERMAN-STYLE BAROQUE)

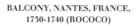

BALCONY, NANTES, FRANCE, 1730-1740 (ROCOCO)

MASONRY OF A NICHE IN THE ROTUNDA (NEOCLASSICAL), BANK OF ENGLAND, LONDON, BRITAIN, 1794 (BY J. SOANE)

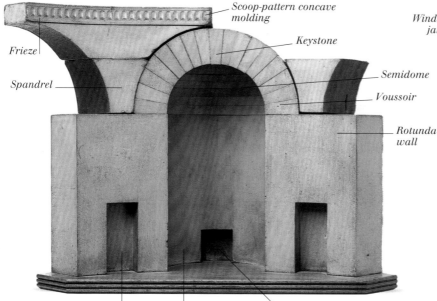

- Scoop-pattern concave molding
- Keystone
- Semidome
- Voussoir
- Rotunda wall
- Frieze
- Spandrel
- Flat, rectangular niche
- Rounded niche
- Flat, square niche

CORNER OF THE NEW STATE PAPER OFFICE (NEOCLASSICAL), LONDON, BRITAIN, 1830-1831 (BY J. SOANE)

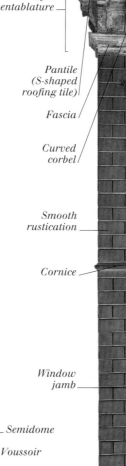

- Classical-style entablature
- Cornice
- Frieze
- Architrave
- Pantile (S-shaped roofing tile)
- Fascia
- Curved corbel
- Eaves
- Scroll-shaped corbel
- Smooth rustication
- Second-floor window
- Cornice
- Drip-cap
- Cornice
- Frieze
- Window architrave
- Window jamb
- First-floor window
- Windowsill in the form of a frieze
- Ground-floor window
- Splayed windowsill
- Vermiculated rustication

TYRINGHAM HOUSE (NEOCLASSICAL), BUCKINGHAMSHIRE, BRITAIN, 1793-1797 (BY J. SOANE)

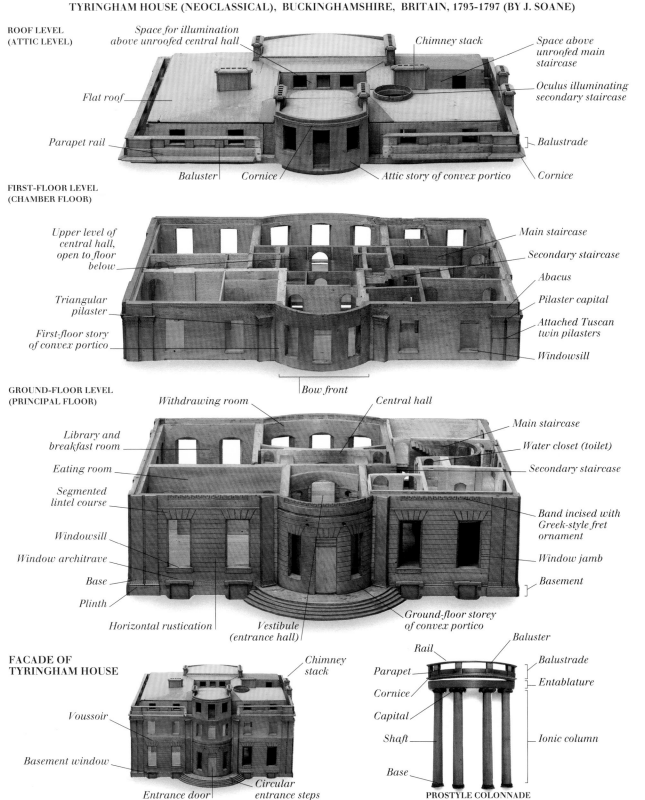

ROOF LEVEL (ATTIC LEVEL)

Space for illumination above unroofed central hall

Chimney stack

Space above unroofed main staircase

Oculus illuminating secondary staircase

Flat roof

Parapet rail

Balustrade

Baluster

Cornice

Attic story of convex portico

Cornice

FIRST-FLOOR LEVEL (CHAMBER FLOOR)

Upper level of central hall, open to floor below

Main staircase

Secondary staircase

Abacus

Pilaster capital

Attached Tuscan twin pilasters

Windowsill

Triangular pilaster

First-floor story of convex portico

Bow front

GROUND-FLOOR LEVEL (PRINCIPAL FLOOR)

Withdrawing room

Central hall

Main staircase

Water closet (toilet)

Secondary staircase

Library and breakfast room

Eating room

Segmented lintel course

Windowsill

Window architrave

Base

Plinth

Band incised with Greek-style fret ornament

Window jamb

Basement

Horizontal rustication

Vestibule (entrance hall)

Ground-floor storey of convex portico

FACADE OF TYRINGHAM HOUSE

Voussoir

Chimney stack

Basement window

Entrance door

Circular entrance steps

Rail

Baluster

Parapet

Balustrade

Cornice

Entablature

Capital

Shaft

Ionic column

Base

PROSTYLE COLONNADE

Arches and vaults

ARCHES ARE CURVED STRUCTURES used to bridge spans and to support the weight of upper parts of buildings, such as domes, as in St. Paul's Cathedral (below) and the historical temple (opposite). The voussoirs (wedge-shaped blocks) that form an arch (right) support each other and convert the downward force of the weight of the building into an outward force. This outward force is in turn transferred to buttresses, piers, or abutments. A vault is an arched roof or ceiling. There are four main types of vault (opposite). A barrel vault is a single vault, semicircular in cross-section; a groin vault consists of two barrel vaults intersecting at right angles; a rib vault is a groin vault reinforced by ribs; and a fan vault is a rib vault in which the ribs radiate from the springing point (where the arch begins) like a fan.

PARTS OF AN ARCH

Voussoir   *Keystone*   *Crown*   *Abutment*

Abutment

Impost

Abutment

Intrados (soffit)

Springing point

Span

Keystone

Extrados

Haunch

Intrados (soffit)

Abutment

FRONT   **SIDE**

ARCHES AND BASE OF DOME, ST. PAUL'S CATHEDRAL, LONDON, BRITAIN, 1675-1710 (BY C. WREN)

Pendentive

Opening to passageway

Base

Pilaster

Inner dome

Colonnade

Passageway

Cornice

Pedestal of outer dome

"Whispering Gallery"

Triangular buttress

Molded bracket

Semidome

Upper barrel-vaulted passage opening onto side aisle

Abutment

Upper arch (concealing difference in heights between main arch and minor arches)

Extrados

Intrados (soffit)

Springing point

Impost

Round arch

Barrel vault

Passage leading to side aisle

Strut built into masonry to strengthen pier (added in the 20th century)

Minor arch leading to side aisle

Main arch leading to nave

Pier

Minor arch

TYPES OF ARCH

HORSESHOE ARCH (MOORISH ARCH), GREAT MOSQUE, CORDOBA, SPAIN, 785

BASKET ARCH (SEMI-ELLIPTICAL ARCH), PALATINE CHAPEL, AIX-LA-CHAPELLE, FRANCE, 790-798

TUDOR ARCH, TOWER OF LONDON, BRITAIN, C.1086-1097

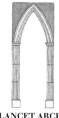

LANCET ARCH, WESTMINSTER ABBEY, LONDON, BRITAIN, 1503-1519

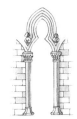

TREFOIL ARCH, BEVERLEY MINSTER, YORKSHIRE, BRITAIN, C.1500

TYPES OF VAULT

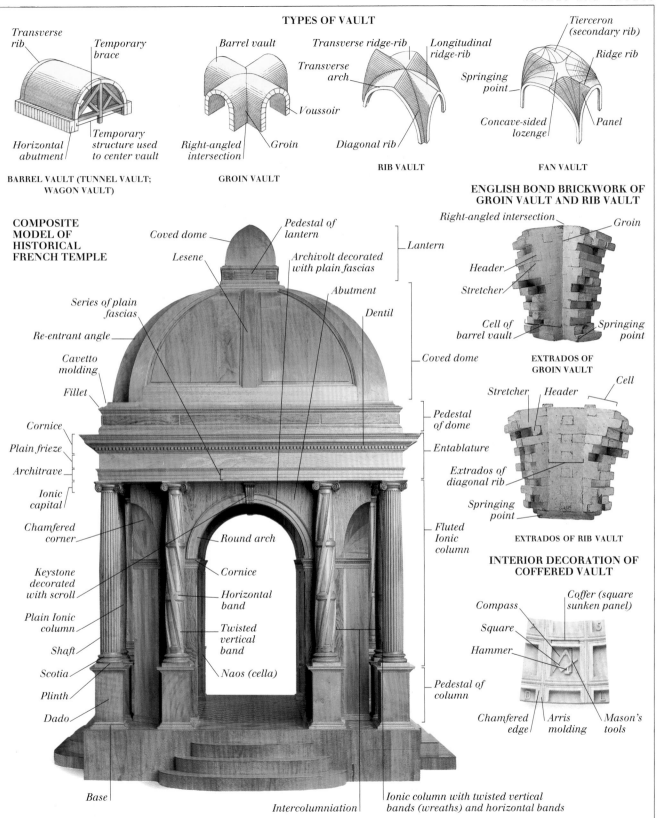

Transverse rib

Temporary brace

Horizontal abutment

Temporary structure used to center vault

BARREL VAULT (TUNNEL VAULT; WAGON VAULT)

Barrel vault

Right-angled intersection

Voussoir

Groin

GROIN VAULT

Transverse ridge-rib

Transverse arch

Longitudinal ridge-rib

Diagonal rib

RIB VAULT

Tierceron (secondary rib)

Ridge rib

Springing point

Concave-sided lozenge

Panel

FAN VAULT

COMPOSITE MODEL OF HISTORICAL FRENCH TEMPLE

Coved dome

Lesene

Series of plain fascias

Re-entrant angle

Cavetto molding

Fillet

Cornice

Plain frieze

Architrave

Ionic capital

Chamfered corner

Keystone decorated with scroll

Plain Ionic column

Shaft

Scotia

Plinth

Dado

Base

Pedestal of lantern

Archivolt decorated with plain fascias

Abutment

Dentil

Round arch

Cornice

Horizontal band

Twisted vertical band

Naos (cella)

Intercolumniation

Lantern

Coved dome

Pedestal of dome

Entablature

Fluted Ionic column

Pedestal of column

Ionic column with twisted vertical bands (wreaths) and horizontal bands

ENGLISH BOND BRICKWORK OF GROIN VAULT AND RIB VAULT

Right-angled intersection

Groin

Header

Stretcher

Cell of barrel vault

Springing point

EXTRADOS OF GROIN VAULT

Stretcher

Header

Cell

Extrados of diagonal rib

Springing point

EXTRADOS OF RIB VAULT

INTERIOR DECORATION OF COFFERED VAULT

Compass

Square

Hammer

Coffer (square sunken panel)

Chamfered edge

Arris molding

Mason's tools

Domes

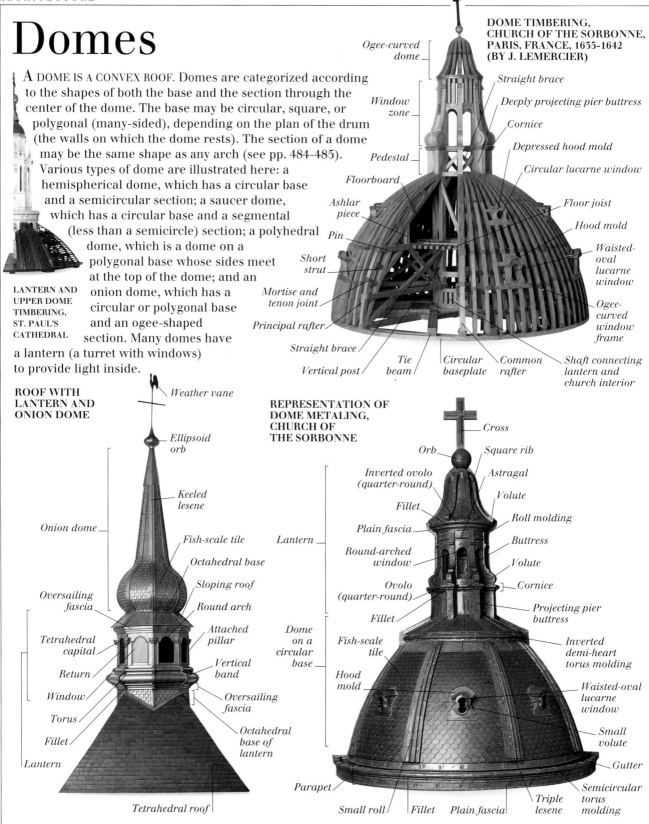

A DOME IS A CONVEX ROOF. Domes are categorized according to the shapes of both the base and the section through the center of the dome. The base may be circular, square, or polygonal (many-sided), depending on the plan of the drum (the walls on which the dome rests). The section of a dome may be the same shape as any arch (see pp. 484-485). Various types of dome are illustrated here: a hemispherical dome, which has a circular base and a semicircular section; a saucer dome, which has a circular base and a segmental (less than a semicircle) section; a polyhedral dome, which is a dome on a polygonal base whose sides meet at the top of the dome; and an onion dome, which has a circular or polygonal base and an ogee-shaped section. Many domes have a lantern (a turret with windows) to provide light inside.

LANTERN AND UPPER DOME TIMBERING, ST. PAUL'S CATHEDRAL

DOME TIMBERING, CHURCH OF THE SORBONNE, PARIS, FRANCE, 1635-1642 (BY J. LEMERCIER)

Ogee-curved dome
Straight brace
Deeply projecting pier buttress
Window zone
Cornice
Depressed hood mold
Circular lucarne window
Pedestal
Floorboard
Floor joist
Ashlar piece
Hood mold
Pin
Waisted-oval lucarne window
Short strut
Mortise and tenon joint
Ogee-curved window frame
Principal rafter
Straight brace
Tie beam
Circular baseplate
Common rafter
Shaft connecting lantern and church interior
Vertical post

ROOF WITH LANTERN AND ONION DOME

Weather vane
Ellipsoid orb
Keeled lesene
Onion dome
Fish-scale tile
Octahedral base
Sloping roof
Round arch
Oversailing fascia
Attached pillar
Tetrahedral capital
Vertical band
Return
Window
Oversailing fascia
Torus
Octahedral base of lantern
Fillet
Lantern
Tetrahedral roof

REPRESENTATION OF DOME METALING, CHURCH OF THE SORBONNE

Cross
Orb
Square rib
Inverted ovolo (quarter-round)
Astragal
Fillet
Volute
Plain fascia
Roll molding
Round-arched window
Buttress
Volute
Ovolo (quarter-round)
Cornice
Fillet
Projecting pier buttress
Lantern
Fish-scale tile
Inverted demi-heart torus molding
Dome on a circular base
Hood mold
Waisted-oval lucarne window
Small volute
Gutter
Parapet
Semicircular torus molding
Small roll
Fillet
Plain fascia
Triple lesene

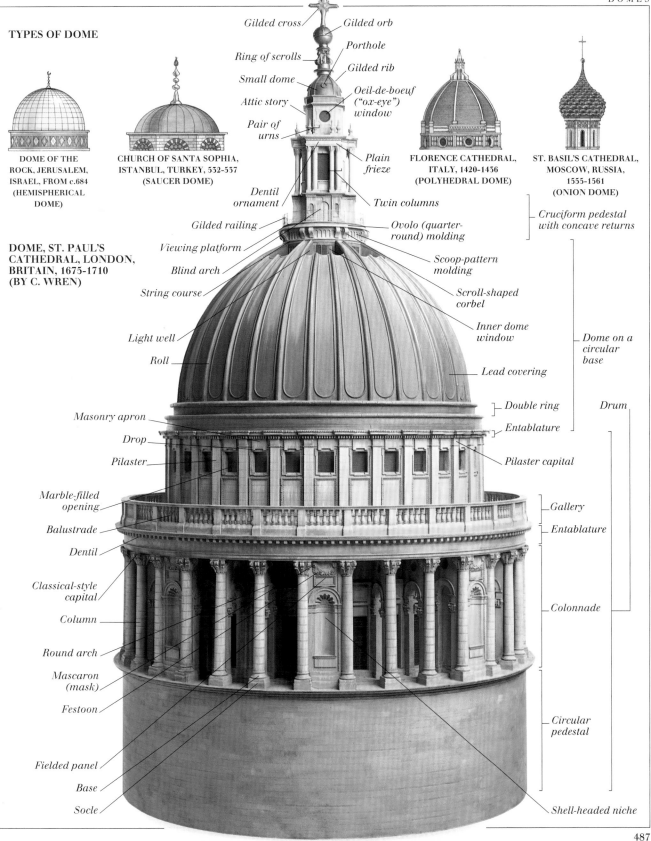

TYPES OF DOME

DOME OF THE
ROCK, JERUSALEM,
ISRAEL, FROM c.684
(HEMISPHERICAL
DOME)

CHURCH OF SANTA SOPHIA,
ISTANBUL, TURKEY, 552-537
(SAUCER DOME)

FLORENCE CATHEDRAL,
ITALY, 1420-1436
(POLYHEDRAL DOME)

ST. BASIL'S CATHEDRAL,
MOSCOW, RUSSIA,
1555-1561
(ONION DOME)

**DOME, ST. PAUL'S
CATHEDRAL, LONDON,
BRITAIN, 1675-1710
(BY C. WREN)**

Gilded cross

Gilded orb

Porthole

Ring of scrolls

Small dome

Gilded rib

Attic story

Oeil-de-boeuf
("ox-eye")
window

Pair of
urns

Plain
frieze

Dentil
ornament

Twin columns

Gilded railing

Ovolo (quarter-
round) molding

Viewing platform

Scoop-pattern
molding

Blind arch

String course

Scroll-shaped
corbel

Light well

Inner dome
window

Roll

Lead covering

Masonry apron

Double ring

Drop

Entablature

Pilaster

Pilaster capital

Marble-filled
opening

Gallery

Balustrade

Entablature

Dentil

Classical-style
capital

Colonnade

Column

Round arch

Mascaron
(mask)

Festoon

Fielded panel

Circular
pedestal

Base

Socle

Shell-headed niche

Cruciform pedestal
with concave returns

Dome on a
circular
base

Drum

487

Islamic buildings

THE ISLAMIC RELIGION was founded by the prophet Mohammed, who was born in Mecca (in present-day Saudi Arabia) about 570 AD. During the next three centuries, Islam spread from Arabia to North Africa and Spain, as well as into India and much of the rest of Asia. The worldwide influence of Islam remains strong today. Common characteristics of Islamic buildings include ogee arches and roofs, onion domes, and walls decorated with carved stone, paintings, inlays, or mosaics. The most important type of Islamic building is the mosque—the place of worship—which generally has a minaret (tower) from which the muezzin (official crier) calls Muslims to prayer. Most mosques have a mihrab (decorative niche) that indicates the direction of Mecca. As figurative art is not allowed in Islam, buildings are ornamented with geometric and arabesque motifs and inscriptions (frequently Koranic verses).

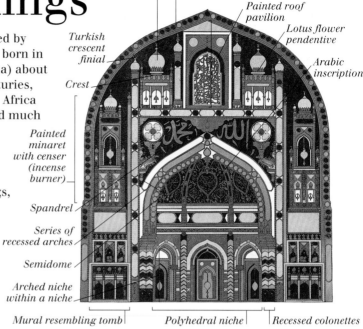

Budlike onion dome
Depressed arch surrounding mihrab
Painted roof pavilion
Turkish crescent finial
Lotus flower pendentive
Crest
Arabic inscription
Painted minaret with censer (incense burner)
Spandrel
Series of recessed arches
Semidome
Arched niche within a niche
Mural resembling tomb
Polyhedral niche
Recessed colonettes

MIHRAB, JAMI MASJID (PRINCIPAL OR CONGREGATIONAL MOSQUE), BIJAPUR, INDIA, c.1636

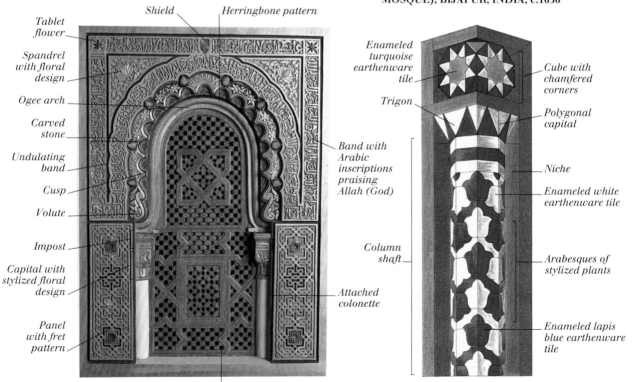

Tablet flower
Shield
Herringbone pattern
Spandrel with floral design
Ogee arch
Carved stone
Undulating band
Cusp
Volute
Impost
Capital with stylized floral design
Panel with fret pattern
Band with Arabic inscriptions praising Allah (God)
Attached colonette
Jali (latticed screen) with geometrical patterns

ARCH, THE ALHAMBRA, GRANADA, SPAIN, 1333-1354

Enameled turquoise earthenware tile
Trigon
Cube with chamfered corners
Polygonal capital
Niche
Enameled white earthenware tile
Column shaft
Arabesques of stylized plants
Enameled lapis blue earthenware tile

MIHRAB WITH COLUMN, EL-AINYI MOSQUE, CAIRO, EGYPT, 15TH CENTURY

EXAMPLES OF ISLAMIC MOSAICS, EGYPT AND SYRIA

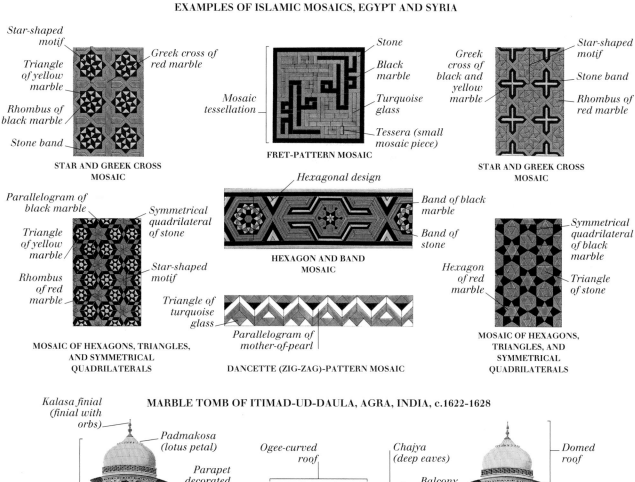

Star-shaped motif
Triangle of yellow marble
Rhombus of black marble
Stone band
Greek cross of red marble

STAR AND GREEK CROSS MOSAIC

Mosaic tessellation
Stone
Black marble
Turquoise glass
Tessera (small mosaic piece)

FRET-PATTERN MOSAIC

Greek cross of black and yellow marble
Star-shaped motif
Stone band
Rhombus of red marble

STAR AND GREEK CROSS MOSAIC

Parallelogram of black marble
Triangle of yellow marble
Rhombus of red marble
Symmetrical quadrilateral of stone
Star-shaped motif

MOSAIC OF HEXAGONS, TRIANGLES, AND SYMMETRICAL QUADRILATERALS

Hexagonal design
Band of black marble
Band of stone

HEXAGON AND BAND MOSAIC

Triangle of turquoise glass
Parallelogram of mother-of-pearl

DANCETTE (ZIG-ZAG)-PATTERN MOSAIC

Symmetrical quadrilateral of black marble
Hexagon of red marble
Triangle of stone

MOSAIC OF HEXAGONS, TRIANGLES, AND SYMMETRICAL QUADRILATERALS

MARBLE TOMB OF ITIMAD-UD-DAULA, AGRA, INDIA, c.1622-1628

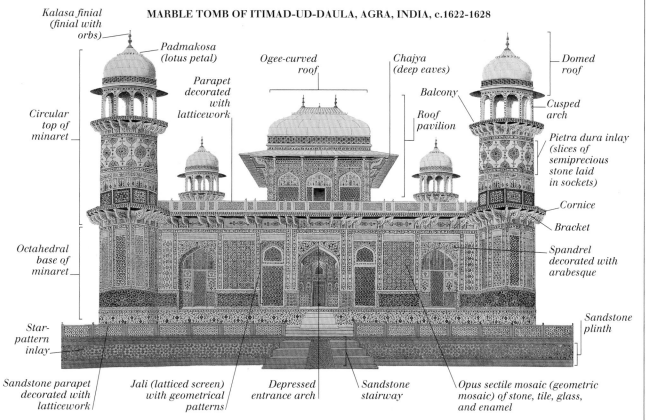

Kalasa finial (finial with orbs)
Padmakosa (lotus petal)
Ogee-curved roof
Chajya (deep eaves)
Domed roof
Circular top of minaret
Parapet decorated with latticework
Balcony
Roof pavilion
Cusped arch
Pietra dura inlay (slices of semiprecious stone laid in sockets)
Cornice
Bracket
Octahedral base of minaret
Spandrel decorated with arabesque
Star-pattern inlay
Sandstone plinth
Sandstone parapet decorated with latticework
Jali (latticed screen) with geometrical patterns
Depressed entrance arch
Sandstone stairway
Opus sectile mosaic (geometric mosaic) of stone, tile, glass, and enamel

South and east Asia

THE TRADITIONAL ARCHITECTURE of south and east Asia has been profoundly influenced by the spread from India of Buddhism and Hinduism. This influence is shown by both the abundance and by the architectural styles of temples and shrines in the region. Many early Hindu temples consist of rooms carved from solid rock faces. However, freestanding structures began to be built in southern India from about the eighth century AD. Many were built in the Dravidian style, like the Temple of Virupaksha (opposite), with its characteristic antarala (terraced tower), perforated windows, and numerous arches, pilasters, and carvings. The earliest Buddhist religious monuments were Indian stupas, which consisted of a single hemispherical dome surmounted by a chattravali (shaft) and surrounded by railings with ornate gates. Later Indian stupas and those built elsewhere were sometimes modified. For example, in Sri Lanka, the dome became bell-shaped, and was called a dagoba. Buddhist pagodas, such as the Burmese example (right), are multistoried temples, each story having a projecting roof. The form of these buildings probably derived from the yasti (pointed spire) of the stupa. Another feature of many traditional Asian buildings is their imaginative roof forms, such as gambrel (mansard) roofs, and roofs with angle rafters (below).

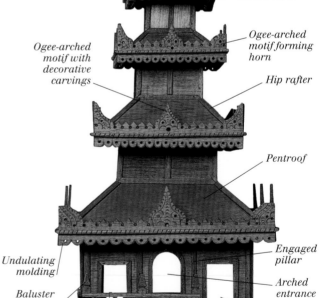

Gilded band

Gilded iron hti (crown)

Dubika (mast)

Arrow motif

Torus molding with spiral carving

Decorative eaves board

Ogee-arched motif with decorative carvings

Ogee-arched motif forming horn

Hip rafter

Pentroof

Undulating molding

Engaged pillar

Baluster finial

Arched entrance

Balustrade

Rectangular window

Pillar

Baluster

Straight brace

DETAILS FROM EAST ASIAN BUILDINGS

KASUGA-STYLE ROOF WITH SUMIGI (ANGLE RAFTERS), KASUGADO SHRINE OF ENJOJI, NARA, JAPAN, 12TH-14TH CENTURY

TERRACES, TEMPLE OF HEAVEN, BEIJING, CHINA, 15TH CENTURY

GAMBREL (MANSARD) ROOF WITH UPSWEPT EAVES AND UNDULATING GABLES, HIMEJI CASTLE, HIMEJI, JAPAN, 1608-1609

CORNER CAPITAL WITH ROOF BEAMS, POPCHU-SA TEMPLE, POPCHU-SA, SOUTH KOREA, 17TH CENTURY

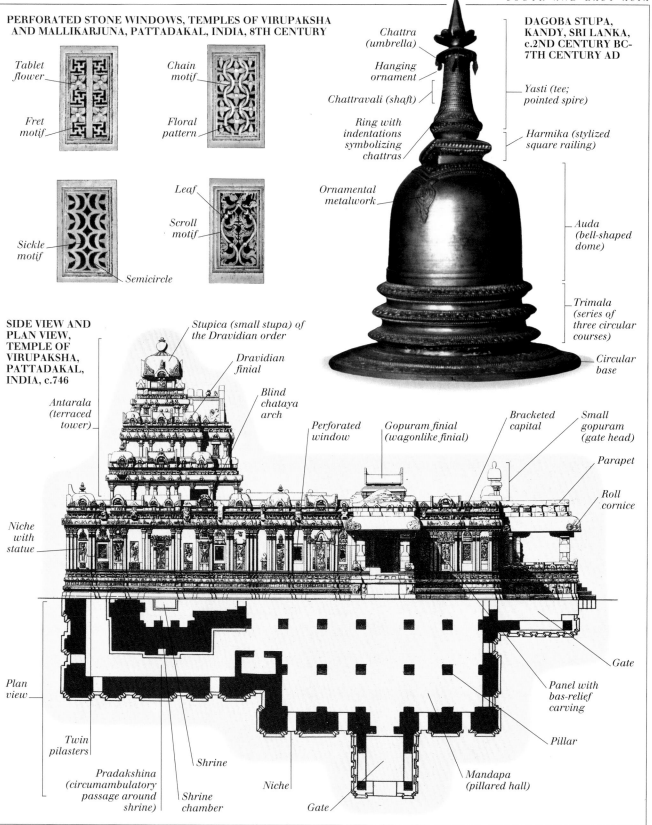

PERFORATED STONE WINDOWS, TEMPLES OF VIRUPAKSHA AND MALLIKARJUNA, PATTADAKAL, INDIA, 8TH CENTURY

Tablet flower
Chain motif
Fret motif
Floral pattern
Sickle motif
Leaf
Scroll motif
Semicircle

DAGOBA STUPA, KANDY, SRI LANKA, c.2ND CENTURY BC-7TH CENTURY AD

Chattra (umbrella)
Hanging ornament
Chattravali (shaft)
Ring with indentations symbolizing chattras
Ornamental metalwork
Yasti (tee; pointed spire)
Harmika (stylized square railing)
Auda (bell-shaped dome)
Trimala (series of three circular courses)
Circular base

SIDE VIEW AND PLAN VIEW, TEMPLE OF VIRUPAKSHA, PATTADAKAL, INDIA, c.746

Stupica (small stupa) of the Dravidian order
Dravidian finial
Blind chataya arch
Perforated window
Gopuram finial (wagonlike finial)
Bracketed capital
Small gopuram (gate head)
Parapet
Roll cornice
Antarala (terraced tower)
Niche with statue
Gate
Panel with bas-relief carving
Pillar
Plan view
Twin pilasters
Pradakshina (circumambulatory passage around shrine)
Shrine
Shrine chamber
Niche
Gate
Mandapa (pillared hall)

491

The 19th century

BUILDINGS OF THE 19TH CENTURY are characterized by the use of new materials and by a great diversity of architectural styles. From the end of the 18th century, iron and steel became widely used as alternatives to wood for the framework of buildings, as in the flax-spinning mill shown here. Built in Britain in 1796, this mill exemplifies an architectural style that became common throughout the industrialized world for more than a century. The Industrial Revolution also brought mass production of building parts—a development that enabled the British architect Sir Joseph Paxton to erect London's Crystal Palace (a building made entirely of iron and glass) in only nine months, ready for the Great Exhibition of 1851. The 19th century saw a widespread revival of older architectural styles. For example, in the United States and Germany, Neo-Greek architecture was fashionable; in Britain and France, Neo-Baroque, Neo-Byzantine, and Neo-Gothic styles (as seen in the Palace of Westminster and Tower Bridge, London) were dominant.

SECTION THROUGH A FLAX-SPINNING MILL

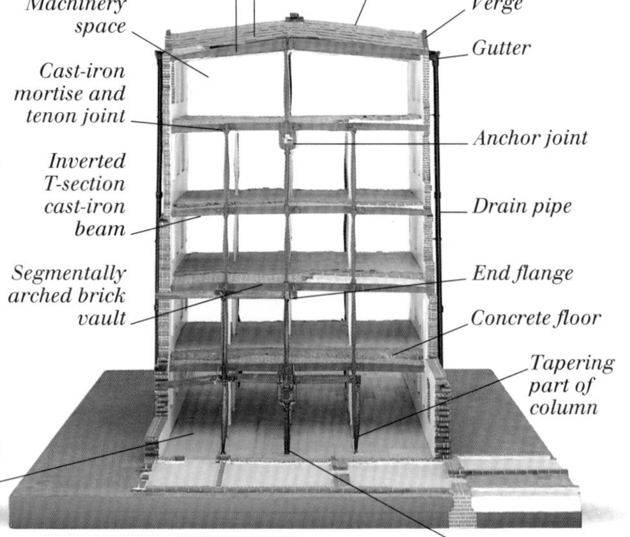

Cast-iron wall plate
Pitched roof
Ridge
Machinery space
Verge
Gutter
Cast-iron mortise and tenon joint
Inverted T-section cast-iron beam
Anchor joint
Drain pipe
Segmentally arched brick vault
End flange
Concrete floor
Tapering part of column
Paved ground floor
Strengthened central column

FLAX-SPINNING MILL, SHREWSBURY, BRITAIN, 1796 (BY C. BAGE)

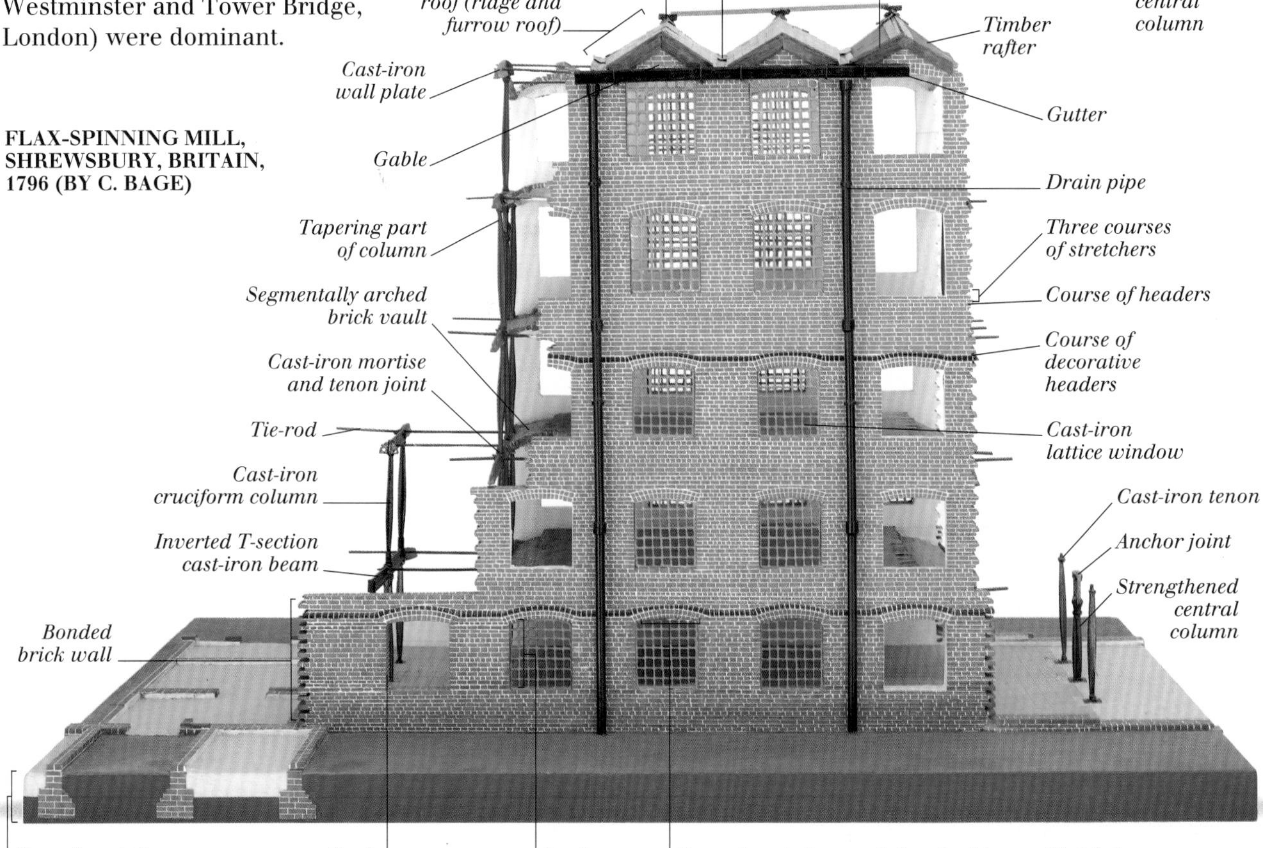

Multi-gabled roof (ridge and furrow roof)
Ridge
Furrow
Verge
Timber rafter
Cast-iron wall plate
Gutter
Gable
Drain pipe
Tapering part of column
Three courses of stretchers
Segmentally arched brick vault
Course of headers
Cast-iron mortise and tenon joint
Course of decorative headers
Tie-rod
Cast-iron lattice window
Cast-iron cruciform column
Cast-iron tenon
Inverted T-section cast-iron beam
Anchor joint
Strengthened central column
Bonded brick wall
Stone foundation
Quoin
Jamb
Gauged arch (segmental arch of tapered bricks)

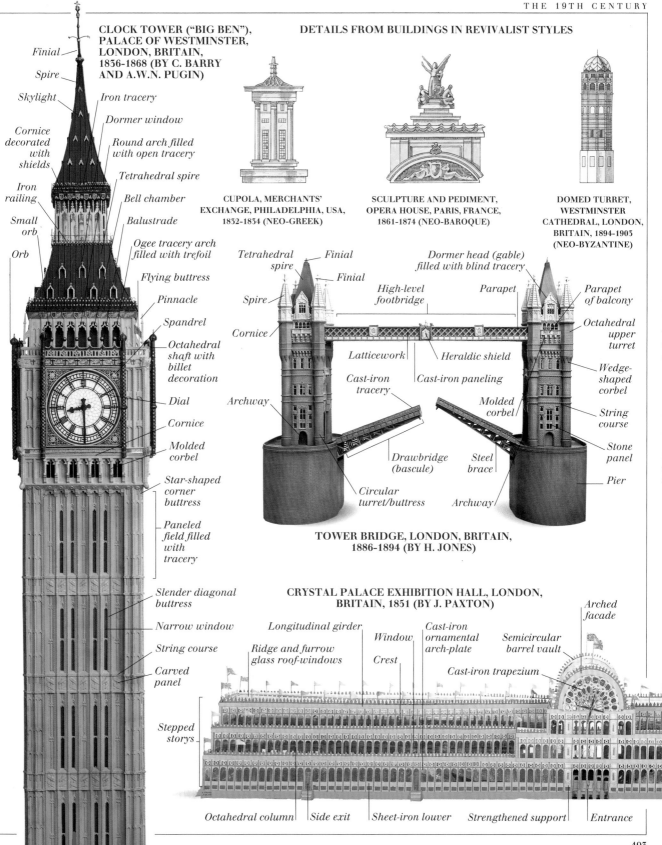

CLOCK TOWER ("BIG BEN"), PALACE OF WESTMINSTER, LONDON, BRITAIN, 1836-1868 (BY C. BARRY AND A.W.N. PUGIN)

Finial
Spire
Skylight
Iron tracery
Dormer window
Cornice decorated with shields
Round arch filled with open tracery
Tetrahedral spire
Iron railing
Bell chamber
Small orb
Balustrade
Orb
Ogee tracery arch filled with trefoil
Flying buttress
Pinnacle
Spandrel
Octahedral shaft with billet decoration
Dial
Cornice
Molded corbel
Star-shaped corner buttress
Paneled field filled with tracery
Slender diagonal buttress
Narrow window
String course
Carved panel

DETAILS FROM BUILDINGS IN REVIVALIST STYLES

CUPOLA, MERCHANTS' EXCHANGE, PHILADELPHIA, USA, 1832-1834 (NEO-GREEK)

SCULPTURE AND PEDIMENT, OPERA HOUSE, PARIS, FRANCE, 1861-1874 (NEO-BAROQUE)

DOMED TURRET, WESTMINSTER CATHEDRAL, LONDON, BRITAIN, 1894-1903 (NEO-BYZANTINE)

Tetrahedral spire
Finial
Finial
Dormer head (gable) filled with blind tracery
Parapet
Parapet of balcony
Spire
High-level footbridge
Octahedral upper turret
Cornice
Latticework
Heraldic shield
Wedge-shaped corbel
Archway
Cast-iron tracery
Cast-iron paneling
Molded corbel
String course
Drawbridge (bascule)
Steel brace
Stone panel
Circular turret/buttress
Archway
Pier

TOWER BRIDGE, LONDON, BRITAIN, 1886-1894 (BY H. JONES)

CRYSTAL PALACE EXHIBITION HALL, LONDON, BRITAIN, 1851 (BY J. PAXTON)

Arched facade
Longitudinal girder
Window
Cast-iron ornamental arch-plate
Semicircular barrel vault
Ridge and furrow glass roof-windows
Crest
Cast-iron trapezium
Stepped storys
Octahedral column
Side exit
Sheet-iron louver
Strengthened support
Entrance

The early 20th century

ARCHITECTURE OF THE EARLY 20TH CENTURY is notable for radical new types of steel and glass buildings—particularly skyscrapers—and the widespread use of steel-reinforced concrete. The steel-framed skyscraper was pioneered in Chicago in the 1880s but did not become widespread until the first decades of the 20th century. As construction techniques were refined, skyscrapers became higher and higher. For example, the Empire State Building (right) of 1929-1931 has 102 storys. Many buildings of this period were constructed from lightweight concrete slabs that could be supported by cantilever beams or by pilotis (stilts), as in the Villa Savoye (below). The early 20th century also produced a great variety of architectural styles, some of which are illustrated opposite. Despite their diversity, the styles of this period generally had one thing in common: they were completely new, with few links to past architectural styles. This originality is in marked contrast to 19th-century architecture (see pp. 492-493), much of which was revivalist.

EMPIRE STATE BUILDING, NEW YORK, USA, 1929-1931 (BY R. H. SHREVE, T. LAMB, AND A. L. HARMON)

Radio mast

Circular lantern

Art Deco splayed seashell form

Chamfered corner

Stepped plinth

Colonnaded storey

Ornamentation

Set-back

Ziggurat-style step-back

Steel mullion

Flush window

Vertical pier

Regular fenestration

Solid-panel infill

Fanlike Art Deco decoration

Decorated stone lintel

Stone structure line

Limestone and granite cladding

Flat roof

Parapet

Stepped cornice

Plinth

Ground-floor entrance

Base

Square bay

VILLA SAVOYE, POISSY, FRANCE, 1929-1931 (BY LE CORBUSIER)

TOP VIEW

Fixed table

Parapet

Slab floor

Screen

Ramp

Handrail

Windowsill

Flat roof

Flat roof

Curved wall

Directional skylight

Terrace

Raised planting bed

SIDE VIEW

Terrace

Cement-rendered wall of lightweight slabs

Solarium

Sliding pane of glass

Mullion

Piano nobile (first floor)

Reinforced-concrete pilotis (stilt)

Rooms for staff

Ribbon window of long living room

Curved glazing

Covered driveway

MIDWAY GARDENS, CHICAGO, USA, 1914 (BY F. L. WRIGHT)

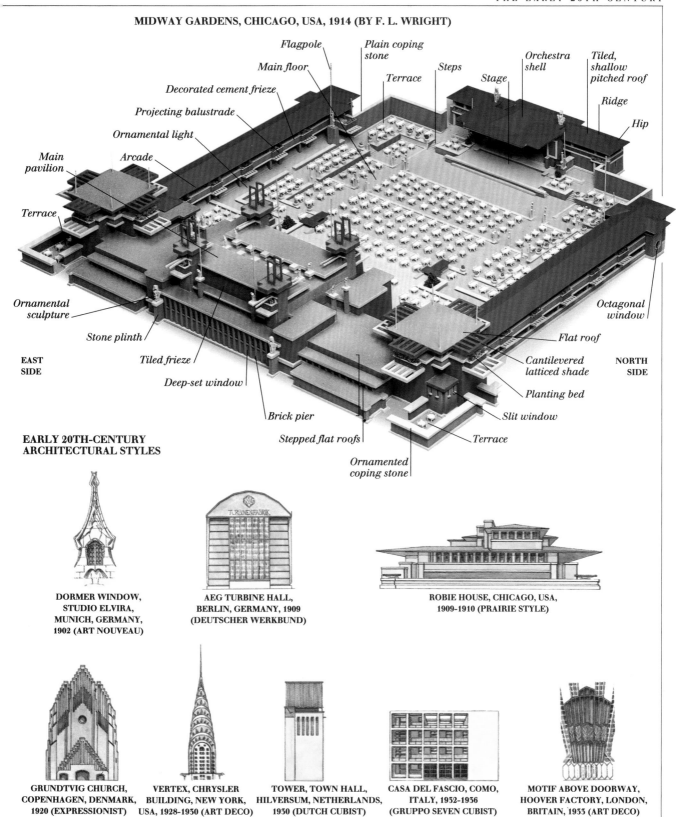

Flagpole

Plain coping stone

Main floor

Decorated cement frieze

Terrace

Steps

Stage

Orchestra shell

Tiled, shallow pitched roof

Projecting balustrade

Ridge

Ornamental light

Hip

Main pavilion

Arcade

Terrace

Ornamental sculpture

Stone plinth

EAST SIDE

Tiled frieze

Deep-set window

Brick pier

Stepped flat roofs

Ornamented coping stone

Octagonal window

Flat roof

Cantilevered latticed shade

NORTH SIDE

Planting bed

Slit window

Terrace

EARLY 20TH-CENTURY ARCHITECTURAL STYLES

DORMER WINDOW, STUDIO ELVIRA, MUNICH, GERMANY, 1902 (ART NOUVEAU)

AEG TURBINE HALL, BERLIN, GERMANY, 1909 (DEUTSCHER WERKBUND)

ROBIE HOUSE, CHICAGO, USA, 1909-1910 (PRAIRIE STYLE)

GRUNDTVIG CHURCH, COPENHAGEN, DENMARK, 1920 (EXPRESSIONIST)

VERTEX, CHRYSLER BUILDING, NEW YORK, USA, 1928-1930 (ART DECO)

TOWER, TOWN HALL, HILVERSUM, NETHERLANDS, 1930 (DUTCH CUBIST)

CASA DEL FASCIO, COMO, ITALY, 1932-1936 (GRUPPO SEVEN CUBIST)

MOTIF ABOVE DOORWAY, HOOVER FACTORY, LONDON, BRITAIN, 1933 (ART DECO)

Modern buildings 1

KAWANA HOUSE, JAPAN, FROM 1987 (BY N. FOSTER)

ARCHITECTURE SINCE ABOUT THE 1950s is generally known as modern architecture. One of its main influences has been functionalism—a belief that a building's function should be apparent in its design. Both the Centre Georges Pompidou (below and opposite) and the Hong Kong and Shanghai Bank (see pp. 498-499) are functionalist buildings. On each, elements of engineering and the building's services are clearly visible on the outside. In the 1980s, some architects rejected functionalism in favor of postmodernism, in which historical styles—particularly neoclassicism—were revived, using modern building materials and techniques. In many modern buildings, walls are made of glass or concrete hung from a frame, as in the Kawana House (right); this type of wall construction is known as curtain walling. Other modern construction techniques include the intricate interlocking of concrete vaults—as in the Sydney Opera House (see pp. 498-499)—and the use of high-tension beams to create complex roof shapes, such as the paraboloid roof of the Church of St. Pierre de Libreville (see pp. 498-499).

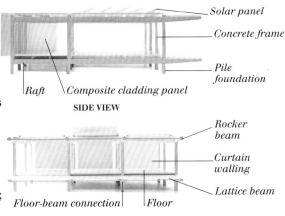

Solar panel
Concrete frame
Pile foundation
Raft
Composite cladding panel
SIDE VIEW

Rocker beam
Curtain walling
Lattice beam
Floor-beam connection
Floor
FRONT VIEW

SERVICES FACADE, CENTRE GEORGES POMPIDOU, PARIS, FRANCE, 1977 (BY R. PIANO AND R. ROGERS)

Metal-faced fire-resistant panel
Air-conditioning duct
Cooling tower
Water pipe

Grand gallery level

Main gallery levels

Library level

Administrative level

Mezzanine gallery level

Reception level

Staircase to grand hall
Electrical plant
Water-cooled fire-resistant column
Continuous glazing
Tinted glass
Services entrance

PRINCIPAL FACADE, CENTRE GEORGES POMPIDOU

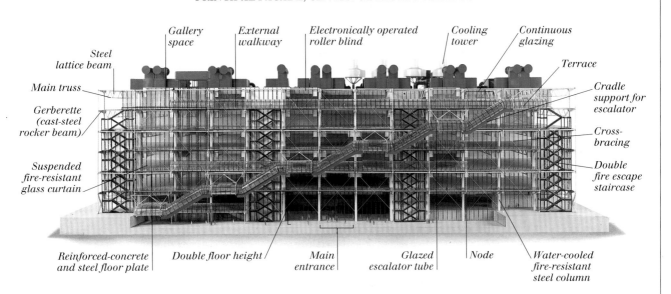

Steel
lattice beam

Gallery
space

External
walkway

Electronically operated
roller blind

Cooling
tower

Continuous
glazing

Main truss

Terrace

Gerberette
(cast-steel
rocker beam)

Cradle
support for
escalator

Cross-
bracing

Suspended
fire-resistant
glass curtain

Double
fire escape
staircase

Reinforced-concrete
and steel floor plate

Double floor height

Main
entrance

Glazed
escalator tube

Node

Water-cooled
fire-resistant
steel column

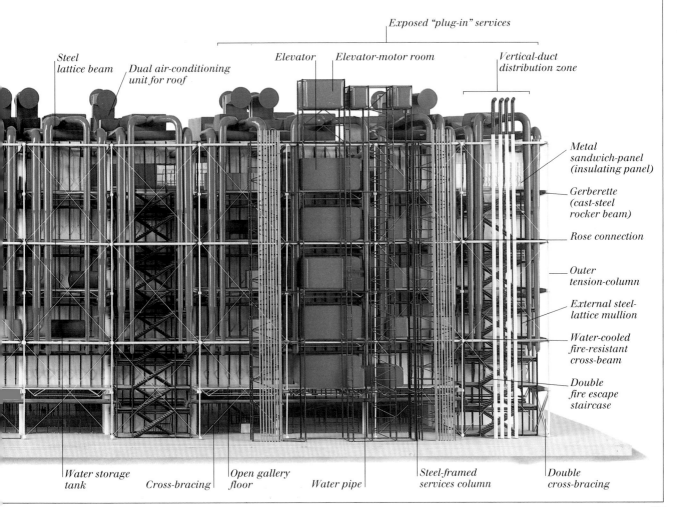

Exposed "plug-in" services

Steel
lattice beam

Dual air-conditioning
unit for roof

Elevator

Elevator-motor room

Vertical-duct
distribution zone

Metal
sandwich-panel
(insulating panel)

Gerberette
(cast-steel
rocker beam)

Rose connection

Outer
tension-column

External steel-
lattice mullion

Water-cooled
fire-resistant
cross-beam

Double
fire escape
staircase

Water storage
tank

Cross-bracing

Open gallery
floor

Water pipe

Steel-framed
services column

Double
cross-bracing

Modern buildings 2

HONG KONG AND SHANGHAI BANK, HONG KONG, 1981-1985 (BY N. FOSTER)

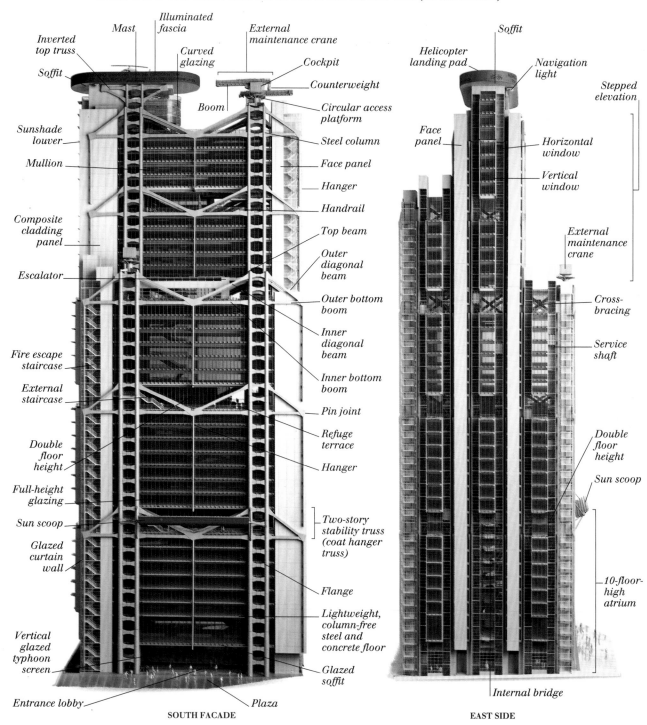

Inverted top truss
Mast
Illuminated fascia
External maintenance crane
Soffit
Curved glazing
Cockpit
Counterweight
Boom
Circular access platform
Sunshade louver
Steel column
Mullion
Face panel
Hanger
Handrail
Composite cladding panel
Top beam
Outer diagonal beam
Escalator
Outer bottom boom
Inner diagonal beam
Fire escape staircase
Inner bottom boom
External staircase
Pin joint
Refuge terrace
Double floor height
Hanger
Full-height glazing
Sun scoop
Two-story stability truss (coat hanger truss)
Glazed curtain wall
Flange
Lightweight, column-free steel and concrete floor
Vertical glazed typhoon screen
Glazed soffit
Entrance lobby
Plaza

SOUTH FACADE

Soffit
Helicopter landing pad
Navigation light
Stepped elevation
Face panel
Horizontal window
Vertical window
External maintenance crane
Cross-bracing
Service shaft
Double floor height
Sun scoop
10-floor-high atrium
Internal bridge

EAST SIDE

**CHURCH OF ST. PIERRE,
LIBREVILLE, GABON, 1990**

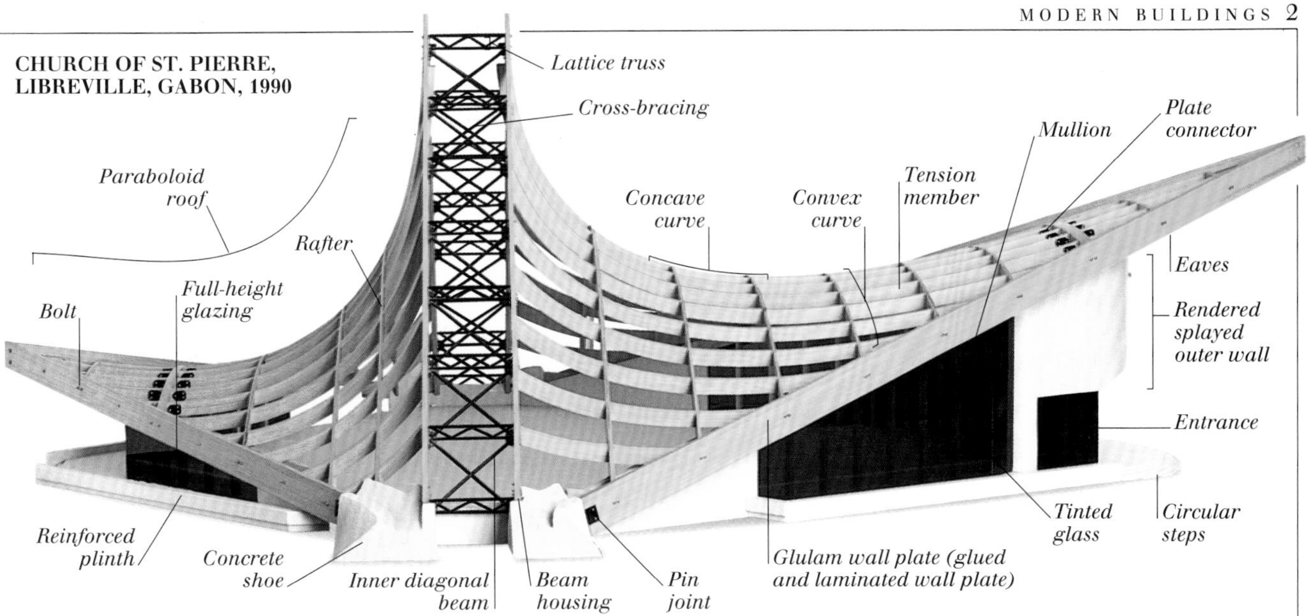

Lattice truss

Cross-bracing

Mullion

Plate
connector

*Paraboloid
roof*

Rafter

Concave
curve

Convex
curve

Tension
member

Eaves

Bolt

*Full-height
glazing*

Rendered
splayed
outer wall

Entrance

*Reinforced
plinth*

*Concrete
shoe*

*Inner diagonal
beam*

*Beam
housing*

*Pin
joint*

Glulam wall plate (glued
and laminated wall plate)

Tinted
glass

Circular
steps

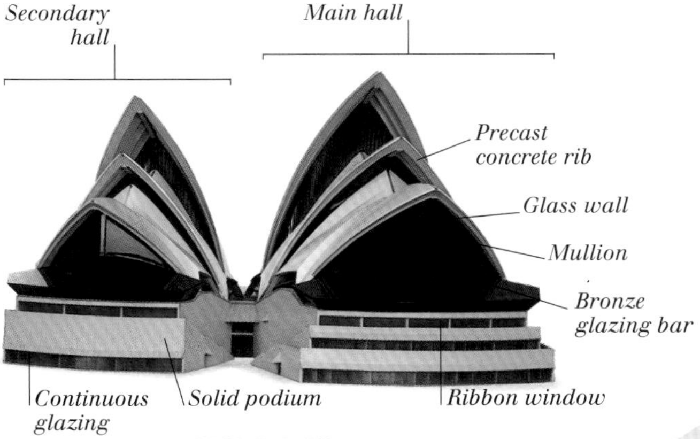

*Secondary
hall*

Main hall

Precast
concrete rib

**OPERA HOUSE, SYDNEY, AUSTRALIA,
1959-1973 (BY J. UTZON)**

Vaults with curved ribs

Glass wall

Mullion

Bronze
glazing bar

Main hall

*Continuous
glazing*

Solid podium

Ribbon window

Precast concrete
rib segment

HARBOR FACADE

Ridge

*Vault roof constructed
of chevron-shaped
precast tiles*

*Vault over
restaurant*

Staircase

Pink cladding

*Pink granite-aggregate
paving slab*

Main line of support

Awning

Staircase

Terrace

Solid podium

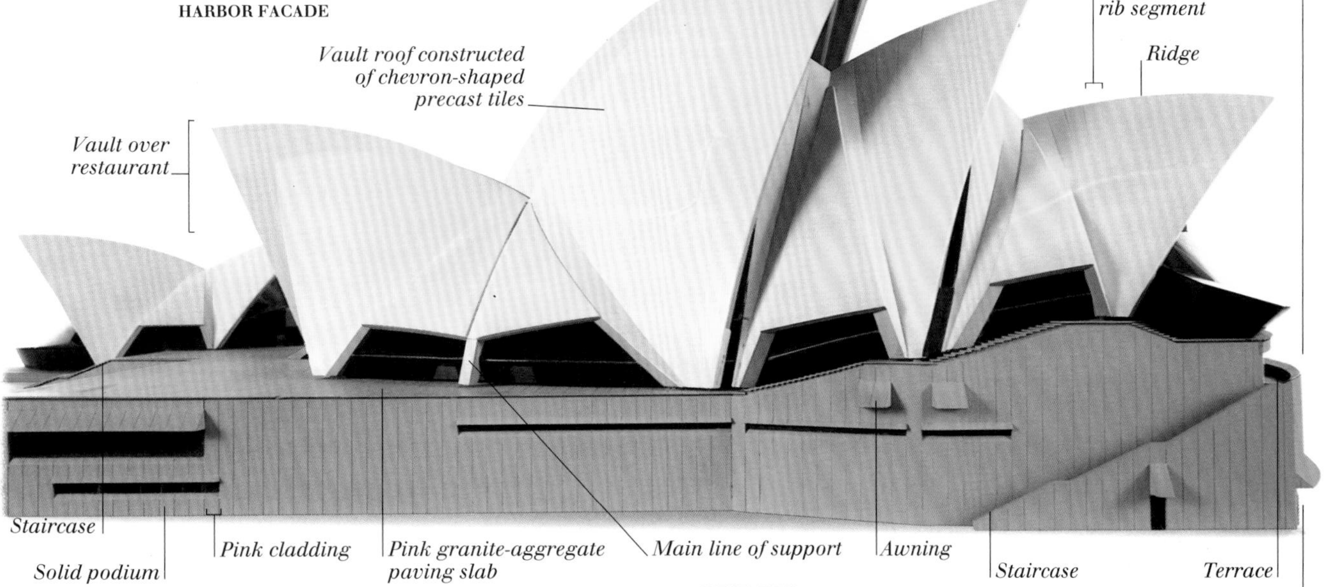

WEST SIDE

499

MUSIC

MUSICAL NOTATION 502

ORCHESTRAS 504

BRASS INSTRUMENTS 506

WOODWIND INSTRUMENTS 508

STRINGED INSTRUMENTS 510

GUITARS 512

KEYBOARD INSTRUMENTS 514

PERCUSSION INSTRUMENTS 516

DRUMS 518

ELECTRONIC INSTRUMENTS 520

Musical notation

MUSICAL NOTATION IS ANY METHOD by which sounds are written down so that they can be read and performed by others. The present-day conventional system of notation uses a five-line stave (staff)—divided by vertical lines into sections known as bars—on which notes, rests, clefs, key signatures, time signatures, accidentals, and other symbols are written. A note indicates the duration of a sound and, according to its position on the stave, its pitch. Notes can be arranged on the stave in order of pitch to form a scale. A silence in the music is indicated by a rest. The clef, which is placed at the begininng of a stave, fixes the pitch. The key signature, which is placed after the clef, indicates the key. The time signature, placed after the key signature, shows the number of beats in a bar. Accidentals are used to indicate the raising or lowering of the pitch of a note.

ELEMENTS OF MUSICAL NOTATION

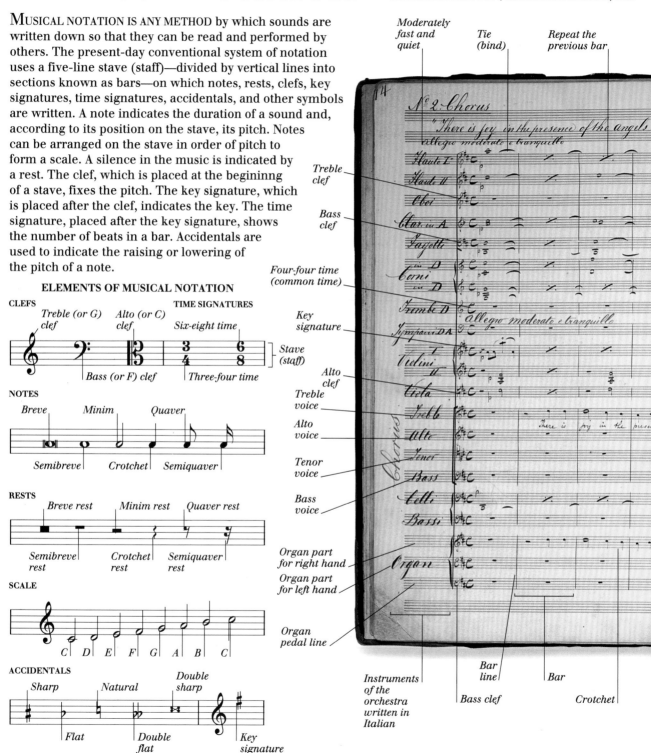

502

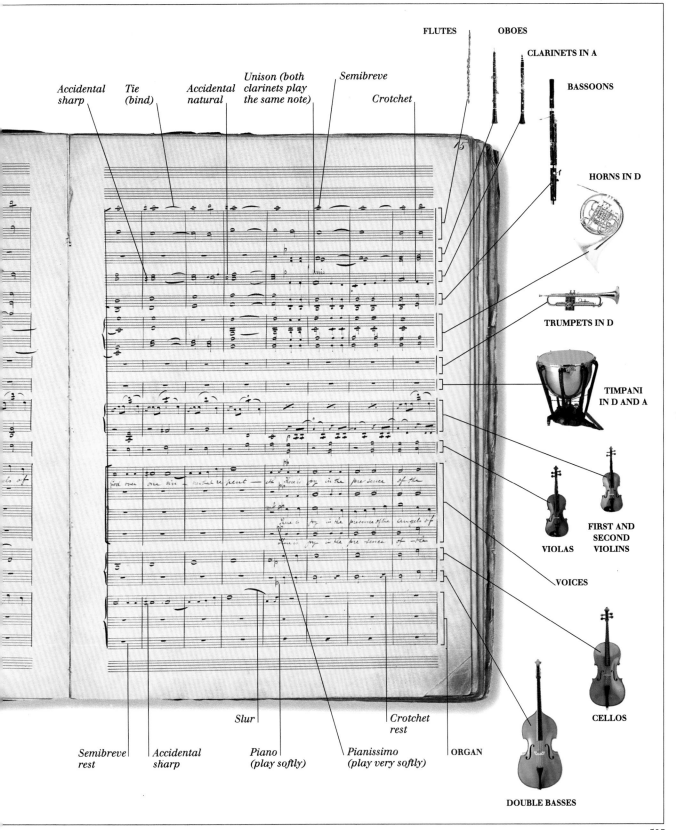

FLUTES

OBOES

CLARINETS IN A

BASSOONS

Accidental sharp

Tie (bind)

Accidental natural

Unison (both clarinets play the same note)

Semibreve

Crotchet

HORNS IN D

TRUMPETS IN D

TIMPANI IN D AND A

FIRST AND SECOND VIOLINS

VIOLAS

VOICES

CELLOS

ORGAN

DOUBLE BASSES

Semibreve rest

Accidental sharp

Slur

Piano (play softly)

Pianissimo (play very softly)

Crotchet rest

Orchestras

AN ORCHESTRA IS A GROUP of musicians that plays music written for a specific combination of instruments. The number and type of instruments included in the orchestra depends on the style of music being played. The modern orchestra (also known as a symphony orchestra) is made up of four sections of instruments—stringed, woodwind, brass, and percussion. The stringed section consists of violins, violas, cellos (violoncellos), double basses, and sometimes a harp (see pp. 510-511). The main instruments of the woodwind section are flutes, oboes, clarinets, and bassoons—the piccolo, cor anglais, bass clarinet, saxophone, and double bassoon (contrabassoon) can also be included if the music requires them (see pp. 508-509). The brass section usually consists of horns, trumpets, trombones, and the tuba (see pp. 506-507). The main instruments of the percussion section are the timpani (see pp. 518-519). The snare drum, bass drum, cymbals, tambourine, triangle, tubular bells, xylophone, vibraphone, gong (tam-tam), castanets, and maracas can also be included in the percussion section (see pp. 516-517). The musicians are usually arranged in a semi-circle—strings spread along the front, woodwind and brass in the center, and percussion at the back. A conductor stands in front of the musicians and controls the tempo (speed) of the music and the overall balance of the sound, ensuring that no instruments are too loud or too soft in relation to the others.

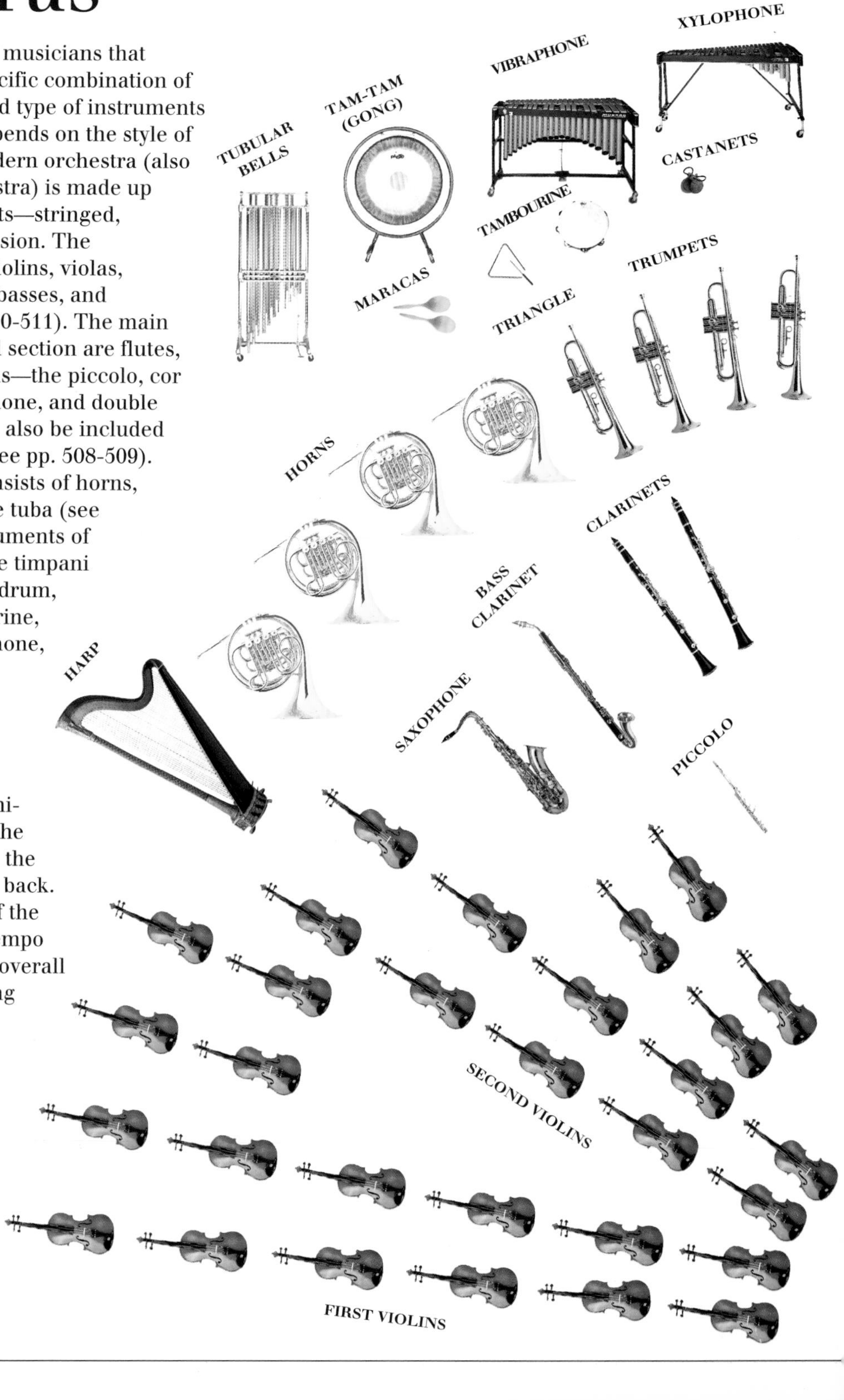

TUBULAR BELLS

TAM-TAM (GONG)

VIBRAPHONE

XYLOPHONE

CASTANETS

TAMBOURINE

MARACAS

TRIANGLE

TRUMPETS

HORNS

CLARINETS

BASS CLARINET

HARP

SAXOPHONE

PICCOLO

SECOND VIOLINS

FIRST VIOLINS

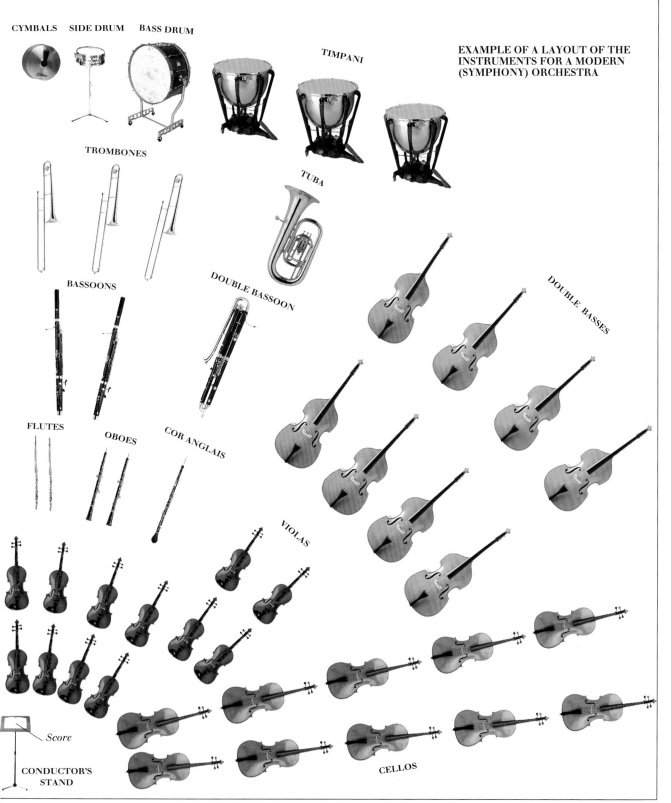

CYMBALS SIDE DRUM BASS DRUM

TIMPANI

**EXAMPLE OF A LAYOUT OF THE
INSTRUMENTS FOR A MODERN
(SYMPHONY) ORCHESTRA**

TROMBONES

TUBA

BASSOONS

DOUBLE BASSOON

DOUBLE BASSES

FLUTES

OBOES

COR ANGLAIS

VIOLAS

Score

CONDUCTOR'S
STAND

CELLOS

Brass instruments

BUGLE

BRASS INSTRUMENTS ARE WIND INSTRUMENTS that are made of metal, usually brass. Although they appear in many different shapes and sizes, all brass instruments have a mouthpiece, a length of hollow tube, and a flared bell. The mouthpiece of a brass instrument may be cup-shaped, as in the cornet, or cone-shaped, as in the horn. The tube may be wide or narrow, mainly conical, as in the horn and tuba, or mainly cylindrical, as in the trumpet and trombone. The sound of a brass instrument is made by the player's lips vibrating against the mouthpiece, so that the air vibrates in the tube. By changing lip tension, the player can vary the vibrations and produce notes of different pitches. The range of notes produced by a brass instrument can be extended by means of a valve system. Most brass instruments, such as the trumpet, have piston valves that divert the air in the instrument along an extra piece of tubing (known as a valve slide) when pressed down. The total length of the tube is increased and the pitch of the note produced is lowered. Instead of valves, the trombone has a movable slide that can be pushed away from or drawn toward the player. The sound of a brass instrument can also be changed by inserting a mute into the bell of the instrument.

Brace

Tuning slide

Counterbalancing weight

SIMPLIFIED DIAGRAM SHOWING HOW A PISTON VALVE SYSTEM WORKS

Piston valves at rest

Air bypasses piston valves

PISTON VALVES AT REST

First piston valve pressed down

Second and third piston valves at rest

Air diverted through first valve slide

PISTON VALVE PRESSED DOWN

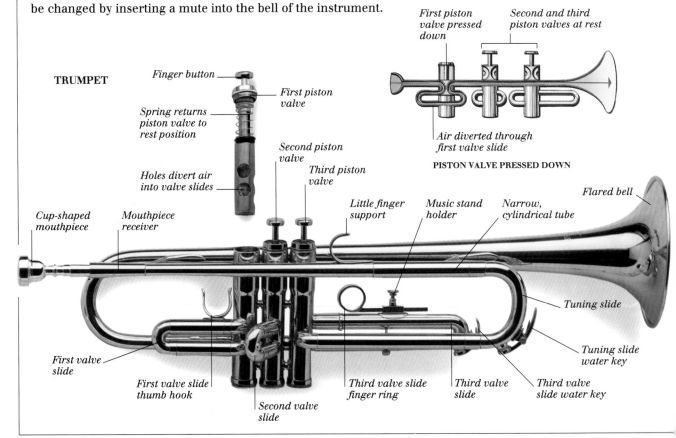

TRUMPET

Finger button

First piston valve

Spring returns piston valve to rest position

Second piston valve

Third piston valve

Holes divert air into valve slides

Little finger support

Music stand holder

Narrow, cylindrical tube

Flared bell

Cup-shaped mouthpiece

Mouthpiece receiver

Tuning slide

First valve slide

Tuning slide water key

First valve slide thumb hook

Third valve slide finger ring

Third valve slide

Third valve slide water key

Second valve slide

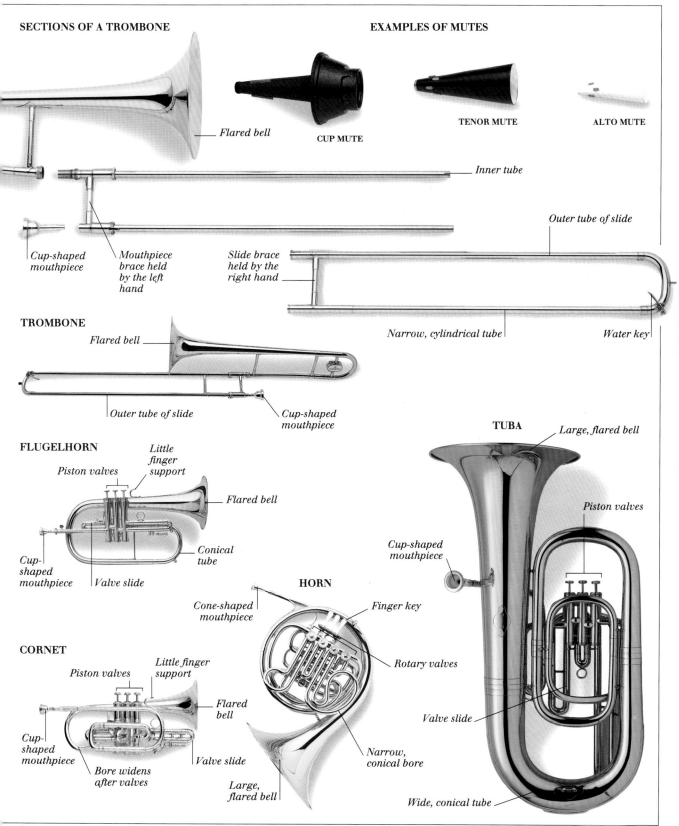

SECTIONS OF A TROMBONE

EXAMPLES OF MUTES

Flared bell

CUP MUTE

TENOR MUTE

ALTO MUTE

Inner tube

Outer tube of slide

Cup-shaped mouthpiece

Mouthpiece brace held by the left hand

Slide brace held by the right hand

Narrow, cylindrical tube

Water key

TROMBONE

Flared bell

Outer tube of slide

Cup-shaped mouthpiece

TUBA

Large, flared bell

FLUGELHORN

Little finger support

Piston valves

Flared bell

Cup-shaped mouthpiece

Valve slide

Conical tube

Piston valves

Cup-shaped mouthpiece

HORN

Cone-shaped mouthpiece

Finger key

Rotary valves

Narrow, conical bore

Large, flared bell

Valve slide

CORNET

Piston valves

Little finger support

Flared bell

Cup-shaped mouthpiece

Bore widens after valves

Valve slide

Wide, conical tube

Woodwind instruments

WOODWIND INSTRUMENTS ARE wind instruments that are generally made of wood, although some are made of metal or plastic. The sound of a woodwind instrument is produced by the vibration of air in a hollow tube. The air is made to vibrate by blowing across a blow hole—as in the flute and piccolo—or by blowing through a single reed—as in the clarinet and saxophone—or a double reed—as in the bassoon, cor anglais, and oboe. The pitch of a woodwind instrument can be changed by opening or closing holes cut into the tube of the instrument.

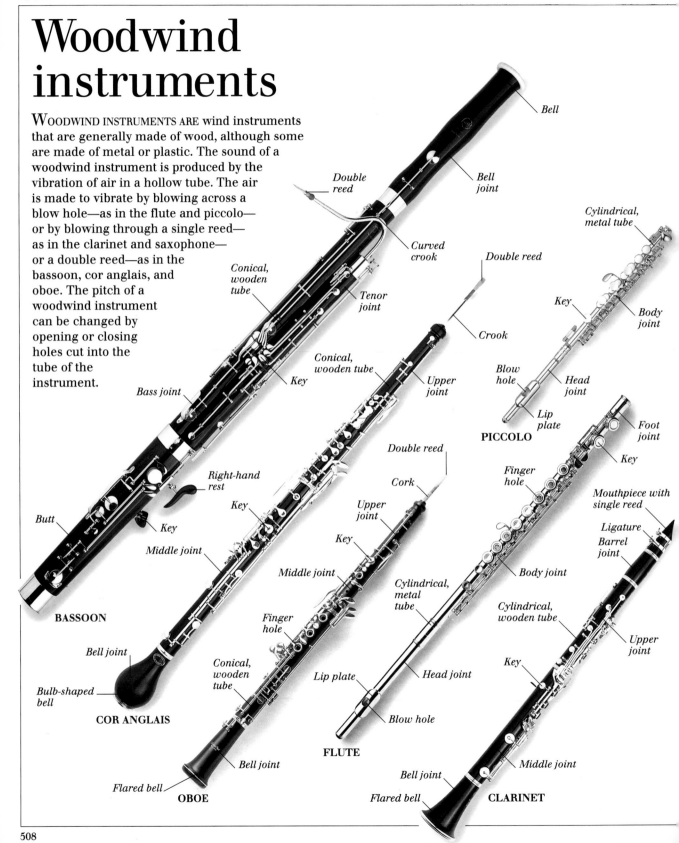

Bell

Double reed

Bell joint

Cylindrical, metal tube

Double reed

Curved crook

Key

Body joint

Conical, wooden tube

Tenor joint

Blow hole

Head joint

Lip plate

PICCOLO

Conical, wooden tube

Upper joint

Crook

Foot joint

Key

Bass joint

Key

Double reed

Finger hole

Key

Right-hand rest

Cork

Mouthpiece with single reed

Key

Upper joint

Ligature

Barrel joint

Butt

Key

Middle joint

Key

Body joint

Middle joint

Cylindrical, metal tube

Cylindrical, wooden tube

BASSOON

Finger hole

Head joint

Key

Upper joint

Bell joint

Conical, wooden tube

Lip plate

Bulb-shaped bell

COR ANGLAIS

Blow hole

Bell joint

Middle joint

Bell joint

FLUTE

Flared bell

Flared bell

CLARINET

OBOE

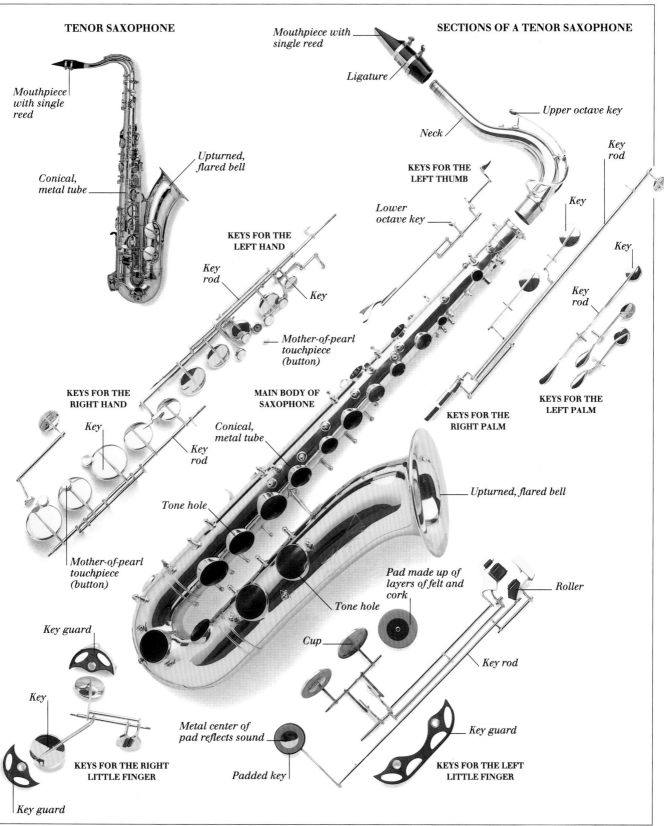

TENOR SAXOPHONE

SECTIONS OF A TENOR SAXOPHONE

Mouthpiece with single reed

Ligature

Mouthpiece with single reed

Upper octave key

Neck

Key rod

KEYS FOR THE LEFT THUMB

Conical, metal tube

Upturned, flared bell

Lower octave key

Key

KEYS FOR THE LEFT HAND

Key rod

Key

Key

Key rod

Mother-of-pearl touchpiece (button)

KEYS FOR THE RIGHT HAND

MAIN BODY OF SAXOPHONE

Conical, metal tube

KEYS FOR THE RIGHT PALM

KEYS FOR THE LEFT PALM

Key

Key rod

Tone hole

Upturned, flared bell

Mother-of-pearl touchpiece (button)

Pad made up of layers of felt and cork

Roller

Tone hole

Key guard

Cup

Key

Key rod

Metal center of pad reflects sound

Key guard

Key guard

KEYS FOR THE RIGHT LITTLE FINGER

Padded key

KEYS FOR THE LEFT LITTLE FINGER

509

Stringed instruments

STRINGED INSTRUMENTS PRODUCE SOUND by the vibration of stretched strings. This may be done by drawing a bow across the strings, as in the violin; or by plucking the strings, as in the harp and guitar (see pp. 512-513). The four modern members of the bowed string family are the violin, viola, cello (violoncello), and double bass. Each consists of a hollow, wooden body, a long neck, and four strings. The bow is a wooden stick with horsehair stretched across its length. The vibrations made by drawing the bow across the strings are transmitted to the hollow body, and this itself vibrates, amplifying and enriching the sound produced. The harp consists of a set of strings of different lengths stretched across a wooden frame. The strings are plucked by the player's thumbs and fingers—except the little finger of each hand—which produces vibrations that are amplified by the harp's sound board. The pitch of the note produced by any stringed instrument depends on the length, weight, and tension of the string. A shorter, lighter, or tighter string gives a higher note.

Scroll eye

Scroll

Peg hole

Ebony tuning pegs

Neck made of maple wood

Fingerboard

Strings

Rounded shoulder

Belly (sound board)

Waist

Sound hole

Rib

Bridge

Purfling

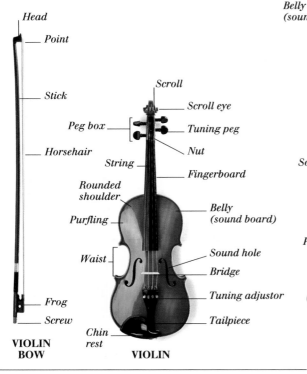

Head

Point

Stick

Scroll

Scroll eye

Peg box

Tuning peg

Horsehair

Nut

String

Fingerboard

Rounded shoulder

Belly (sound board)

Purfling

Waist

Sound hole

Bridge

Tuning adjustor

Frog

Tailpiece

Screw

Chin rest

VIOLIN BOW

VIOLIN

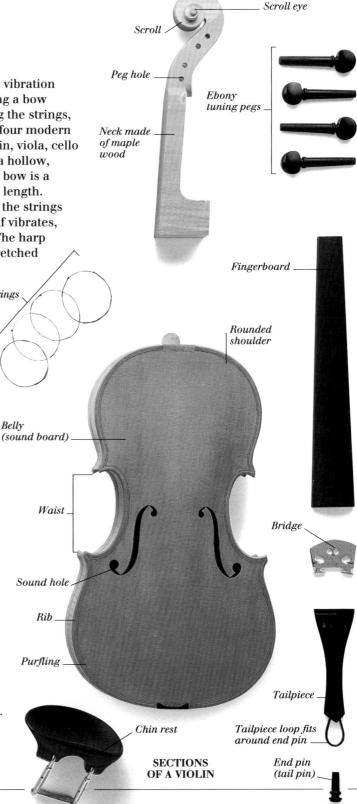

Chin rest

Tailpiece

Tailpiece loop fits around end pin

SECTIONS OF A VIOLIN

End pin (tail pin)

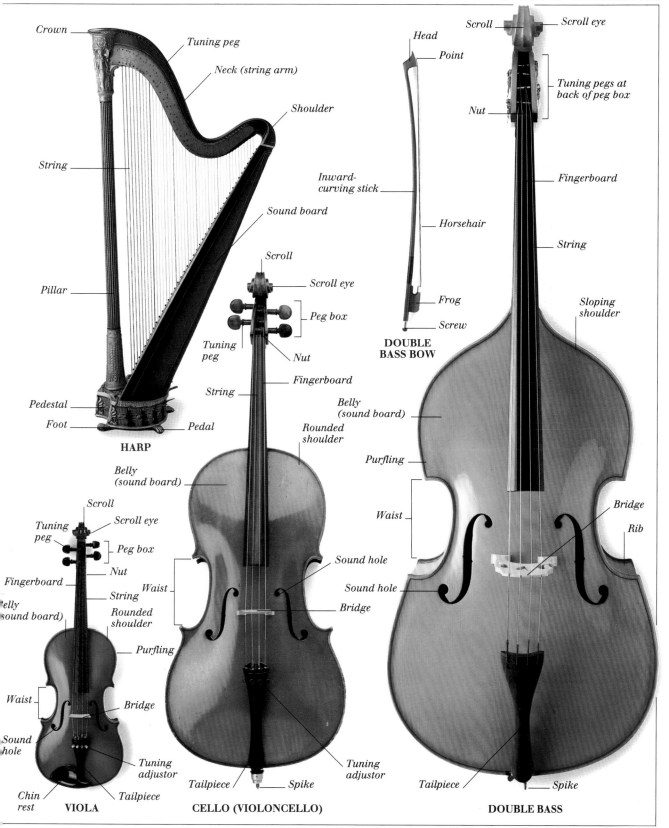

Crown

Tuning peg

Neck (string arm)

Shoulder

String

Sound board

Pillar

Pedestal

Foot

Pedal

HARP

Scroll

Scroll eye

Peg box

Tuning peg

Nut

Fingerboard

String

Rounded shoulder

Belly (sound board)

Waist

Sound hole

Bridge

Tuning adjustor

Tailpiece

Spike

CELLO (VIOLONCELLO)

Scroll

Tuning peg

Scroll eye

Peg box

Nut

Fingerboard

String

Belly (sound board)

Rounded shoulder

Purfling

Waist

Bridge

Sound hole

Chin rest

Tuning adjustor

Tailpiece

VIOLA

Head

Point

Inward-curving stick

Horsehair

Frog

Screw

DOUBLE BASS BOW

Scroll

Scroll eye

Tuning pegs at back of peg box

Nut

Fingerboard

String

Sloping shoulder

Belly (sound board)

Purfling

Waist

Bridge

Rib

Sound hole

Tailpiece

Spike

DOUBLE BASS

511

Guitars

THE GUITAR IS A PLUCKED stringed instrument (see pp. 510-511). There are two types of guitar—acoustic and electric. Acoustic guitars have hollow bodies and six or twelve strings. Plucking or strumming the strings produces vibrations that are amplified by their hollow bodies. Electric guitars usually have solid bodies and six strings. Pick-ups placed under the strings convert vibrations into electronic signals that are magnified by an amplifier, and sent to a loudspeaker where they are converted into sounds (see pp. 520-521). Electric bass guitars are very similar in structure to electric guitars, and produce sound in the same way, but have four heavier-gage strings and play lower pitched notes.

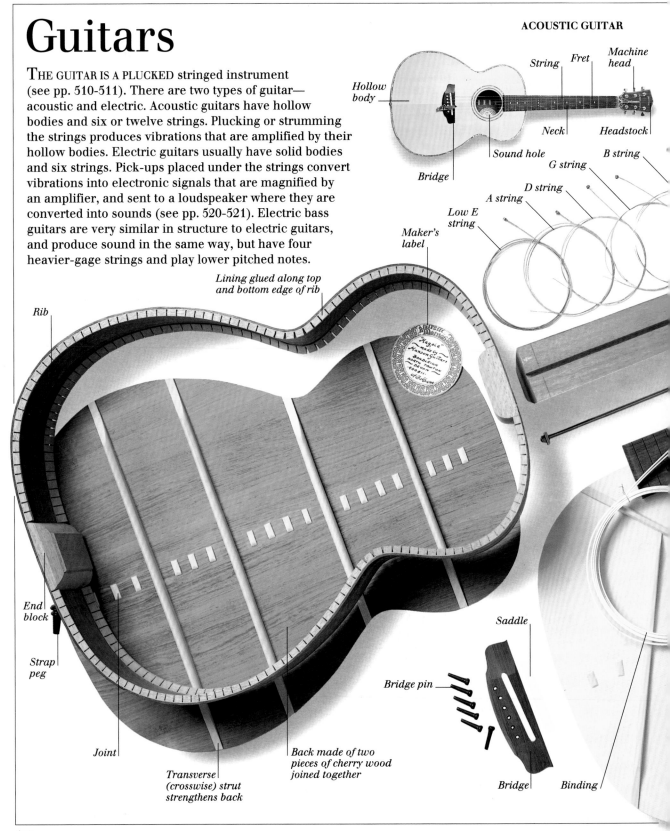

Hollow body

String

Fret

Machine head

Neck

Headstock

Sound hole

B string

Bridge

G string

D string

A string

Low E string

Maker's label

Lining glued along top and bottom edge of rib

Rib

End block

Strap peg

Joint

Transverse (crosswise) strut strengthens back

Back made of two pieces of cherry wood joined together

Bridge pin

Saddle

Bridge

Binding

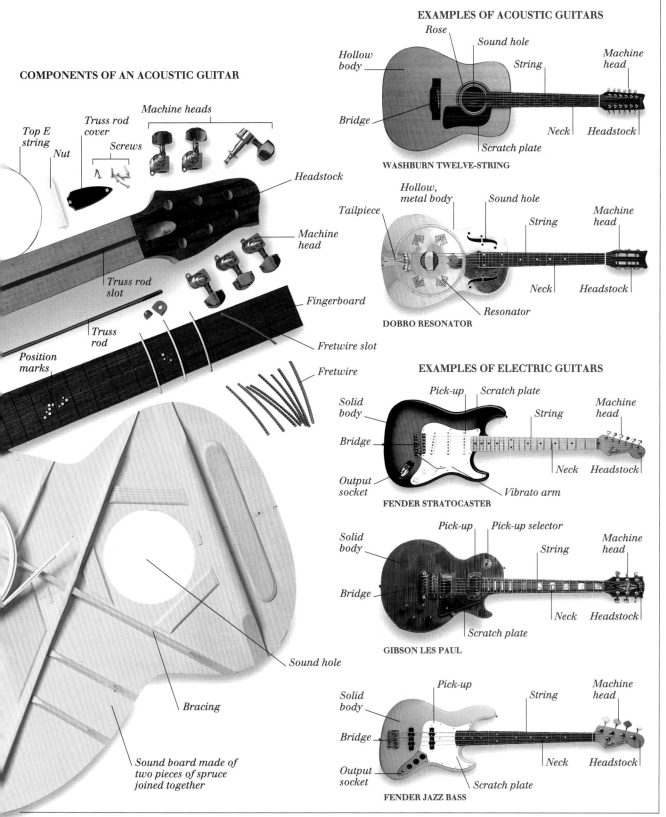

EXAMPLES OF ACOUSTIC GUITARS

Rose

Sound hole

Machine head

String

Hollow body

Bridge

Neck

Headstock

Scratch plate

WASHBURN TWELVE-STRING

COMPONENTS OF AN ACOUSTIC GUITAR

Machine heads

Top E string

Truss rod cover

Nut

Screws

Headstock

Machine head

Truss rod slot

Fingerboard

Truss rod

Fretwire slot

Position marks

Fretwire

Sound hole

Bracing

Sound board made of two pieces of spruce joined together

Hollow, metal body

Sound hole

Machine head

Tailpiece

String

Neck

Headstock

Resonator

DOBRO RESONATOR

EXAMPLES OF ELECTRIC GUITARS

Pick-up

Scratch plate

Machine head

String

Solid body

Bridge

Neck

Headstock

Output socket

Vibrato arm

FENDER STRATOCASTER

Pick-up

Pick-up selector

Machine head

Solid body

String

Bridge

Neck

Headstock

Scratch plate

GIBSON LES PAUL

Pick-up

Machine head

Solid body

String

Bridge

Neck

Headstock

Output socket

Scratch plate

FENDER JAZZ BASS

Keyboard instruments

KEYBOARD INSTRUMENTS are instruments that are sounded by means of a keyboard. The organ and piano are two of the principal members of the keyboard family. The organ consists of pipes which are operated by one or more keyboards and foot pedals. The pipes are lined up in rows (known as ranks or registers) on top of a wind chest. The sound of the organ is made when air is admitted into a pipe by pressing a key or pedal. The piano consists of wire strings stretched over a metal frame, and a keyboard and pedals that operate hammers and dampers. The piano frame is either vertical—as in the upright piano—or horizontal—as in the grand piano. When a key is at rest, a damper lies against the string to keep it from vibrating. When a key is pressed down, the damper moves away from the string as the hammer strikes it, causing the string to vibrate and sound a note.

ORGAN PIPE

UPRIGHT PIANO

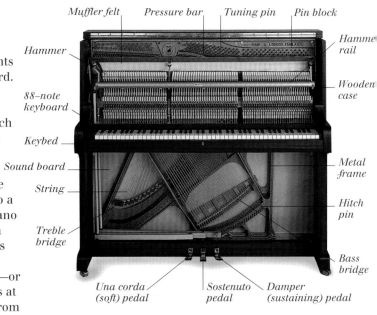

Muffler felt
Pressure bar
Tuning pin
Pin block
Hammer rail
Hammer
Wooden case
88–note keyboard
Keybed
Metal frame
Sound board
String
Hitch pin
Treble bridge
Bass bridge
Una corda (soft) pedal
Sostenuto pedal
Damper (sustaining) pedal

ORGAN CONSOLE

UPRIGHT PIANO ACTION

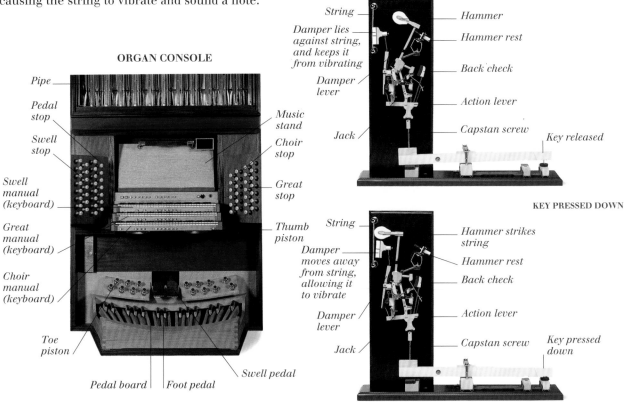

KEY AT REST

Pipe
Pedal stop
Swell stop
Swell manual (keyboard)
Great manual (keyboard)
Choir manual (keyboard)
Toe piston
Pedal board
Foot pedal
Music stand
Choir stop
Great stop
Thumb piston
Swell pedal

String
Hammer
Damper lies against string, and keeps it from vibrating
Hammer rest
Back check
Damper lever
Action lever
Jack
Capstan screw
Key released

KEY PRESSED DOWN

String
Hammer strikes string
Damper moves away from string, allowing it to vibrate
Hammer rest
Back check
Damper lever
Action lever
Jack
Capstan screw
Key pressed down

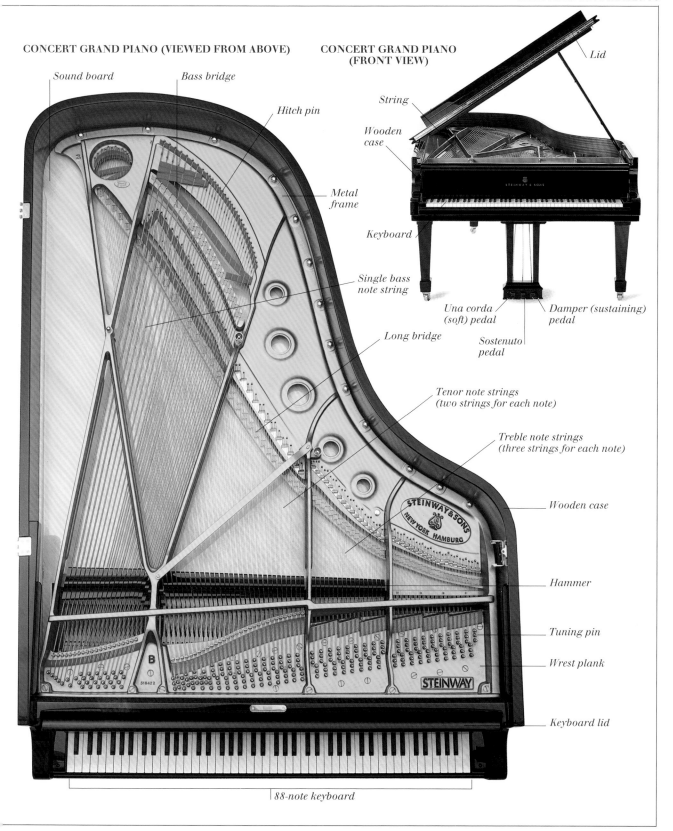

CONCERT GRAND PIANO (VIEWED FROM ABOVE)

CONCERT GRAND PIANO (FRONT VIEW)

Lid

Sound board

Bass bridge

Hitch pin

String

Wooden case

Metal frame

Keyboard

Single bass note string

Long bridge

Una corda (soft) pedal

Damper (sustaining) pedal

Sostenuto pedal

Tenor note strings (two strings for each note)

Treble note strings (three strings for each note)

Wooden case

Hammer

Tuning pin

Wrest plank

Keyboard lid

88-note keyboard

STEINWAY & SONS NEW YORK HAMBURG

STEINWAY

B
518422

Percussion instruments

PERCUSSION INSTRUMENTS are a large group of instruments that produce sound by being struck, shaken, scraped, or clashed together. Some percussion instruments—such as the gong (tam-tam), cymbals, and maracas—do not have a definite pitch and are used for rhythm and impact, and the distinctive timber (color) of their sound. Other percussion instruments—such as the xylophone, vibraphone, and tubular bells—are tuned to a definite pitch and can play melody, harmony, and rhythms. The xylophone and vibraphone each have two rows of bars that are arranged in a similar way to the black and white keys of a piano. Metal tubes are suspended below the bars to amplify the sound. The vibraphone has electrically operated fans that rotate in the tubes and produce a vibrato (wavering pitch) effect.

TEMPLE BLOCKS

TUBULAR BELLS

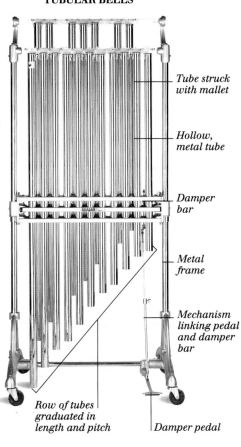

Tube struck with mallet

Hollow, metal tube

Damper bar

Metal frame

Mechanism linking pedal and damper bar

Row of tubes graduated in length and pitch

Damper pedal

EXAMPLES OF MALLETS

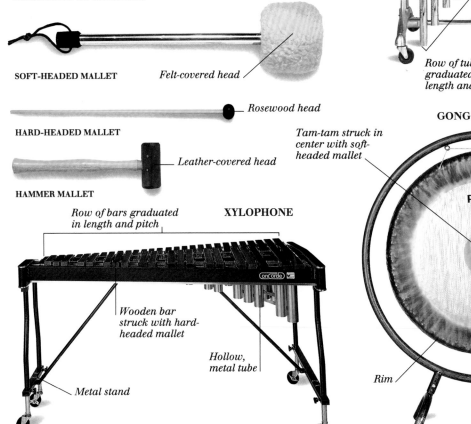

SOFT-HEADED MALLET

Felt-covered head

Rosewood head

HARD-HEADED MALLET

Leather-covered head

HAMMER MALLET

Row of bars graduated in length and pitch

XYLOPHONE

Wooden bar struck with hard-headed mallet

Hollow, metal tube

Metal stand

GONG (TAM-TAM)

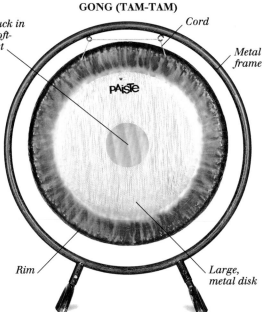

Tam-tam struck in center with soft-headed mallet

Cord

Metal frame

Rim

Large, metal disk

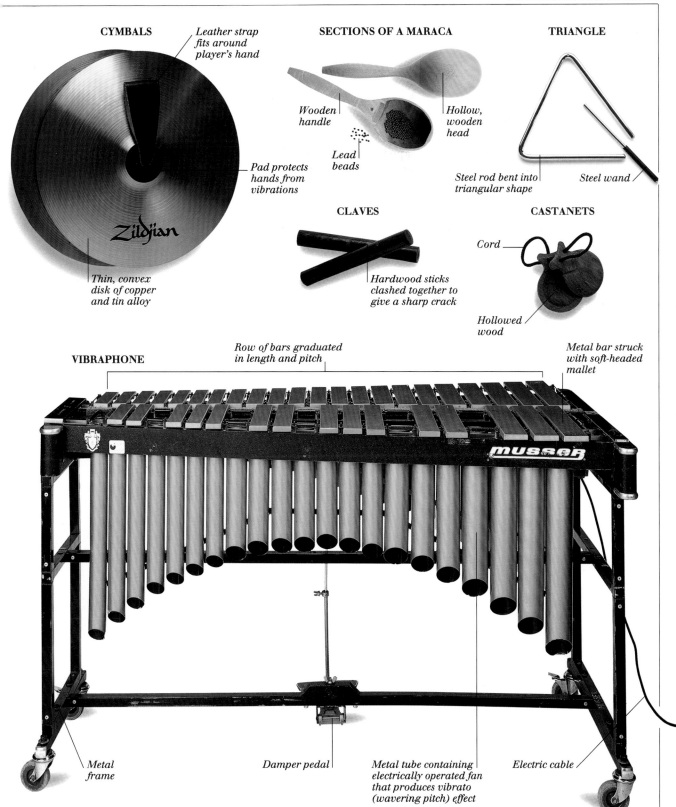

CYMBALS

Leather strap fits around player's hand

Pad protects hands from vibrations

Thin, convex disk of copper and tin alloy

SECTIONS OF A MARACA

Wooden handle

Hollow, wooden head

Lead beads

TRIANGLE

Steel rod bent into triangular shape

Steel wand

CLAVES

Hardwood sticks clashed together to give a sharp crack

CASTANETS

Cord

Hollowed wood

VIBRAPHONE

Row of bars graduated in length and pitch

Metal bar struck with soft-headed mallet

Metal frame

Damper pedal

Metal tube containing electrically operated fan that produces vibrato (wavering pitch) effect

Electric cable

Drums

A DRUM IS A percussion instrument that consists of a drumhead, made of skin or plastic, stretched over one or both ends of a hollow vessel (the body shell). Drums are played in most parts of the world and are made in a number of different shapes and sizes. They can be divided into three groups according to the shape of the body shell: frame drums (e.g., tambourines), bowl-shaped drums (e.g., timpani), and tubular drums (e.g., congas). Drums are usually sounded by striking the drumhead with the hands or with mallets, such as a hard-headed stick. The drumhead vibrates, and its vibrations are amplified by the hollow body shell. The snare drum has wires—known as snares—stretched across the lower drumhead; the snares vibrate against the lower drumhead when the drum is played. Most drums, such as congas, do not have a definite pitch and can play only rhythms (see pp. 516-517). Other drums, such as timpani, have a definite pitch and can play melody, harmony, and rhythms. They can be tuned by adjusting the tension of the drumhead. Different types of drum can be combined together with other percussion instruments to form a drum kit. The basic components of the drum kit are bass drum, tom-toms, floor tom (tenor drum), snare drum, and cymbals.

TAMBOURINE

Crash cymbal

Tension key

DRUM KIT

Tension rod

Tom-tom

Lug

Hi-hat cymbal

Snare drum

SNARE DRUM (VIEWED FROM BELOW)

Snare mounting

Adjustable damper

Lug

Transparent lower drumhead

Tripod stand

Chain

Tension screw

Felt-covered mallet

Pedal

Upper drumhead

Snare

Stick

Snare release lever

Pedal

EXAMPLES OF STICKS

Acorn

HARD-HEADED STICK

Taper

SOFT-HEADED STICK

Felt-covered head

WIRE BRUSH

Wire bristles

Ride cymbal

Tension key

Tom-tom

Tension rod

Lug

Height adjustment key

Floor tom (tenor drum)

Tension rod

Lug

Wooden body shell

Height adjustment key

Leg

Bass drum

Rubber foot

CONGAS

Metal hoop

Drumhead

Tension rod

Wooden body shell

Tripod stand

Leg

TIMPANUM (KETTLE DRUM)

Drumhead

Tension rod

Metal hoop

Tuning gauge

Copper body shell

Strut

Crown

Tension rod

Tuning pedal

Castor

Electronic instruments

ELECTRONIC INSTRUMENTS generate electronic signals that are magnified by an amplifier, and sent to a loudspeaker where they are converted into sounds. Synthesizers, and other electronic instruments, simulate the characteristic sounds of conventional instruments, and also create entirely new sounds. Most electronic instruments are keyboard instruments, but electronic wind and percussion instruments are also popular. A digital sampler records and stores sounds from musical instruments or other sources. When the sound is played back, the pitch of the original sound can be altered. A keyboard can be connected to the sampler so that a tune can be played using the sampled sounds. With a MIDI (Musical Instrument Digital Interface) system, a computer can be linked with other electronic instruments, such as keyboards and electronic drums, to make sounds together or in sequence. It is also possible, using music software, to compose and play music on a home computer.

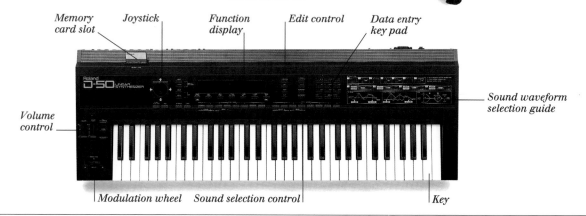

ELECTRONIC DRUMS

Drum pad

Height adjustment key

Tripod

HOME KEYBOARD

Power button

Volume control

Function display

Sequence record button

Tone editor control

Demonstration tune button

Modulation wheel

Multi-accompaniment system control

Tone and rhythm pattern selector

Key

SYNTHESIZER

Memory card slot

Joystick

Function display

Edit control

Data entry key pad

Sound waveform selection guide

Volume control

Modulation wheel

Sound selection control

Key

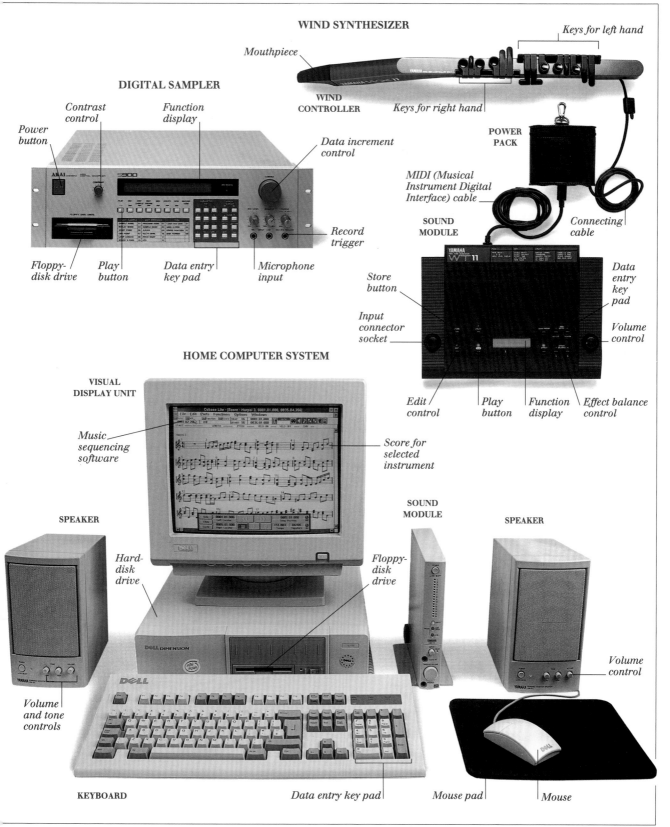

WIND SYNTHESIZER

Keys for left hand

Mouthpiece

WIND CONTROLLER

Keys for right hand

DIGITAL SAMPLER

Contrast control

Function display

Power button

Data increment control

POWER PACK

MIDI (Musical Instrument Digital Interface) cable

Connecting cable

Record trigger

SOUND MODULE

Floppy-disk drive

Play button

Data entry key pad

Microphone input

Data entry key pad

Store button

Volume control

Input connector socket

HOME COMPUTER SYSTEM

VISUAL DISPLAY UNIT

Edit control

Play button

Function display

Effect balance control

Music sequencing software

Score for selected instrument

SPEAKER

SOUND MODULE

SPEAKER

Hard-disk drive

Floppy-disk drive

Volume control

Volume and tone controls

KEYBOARD

Data entry key pad

Mouse pad

Mouse

521

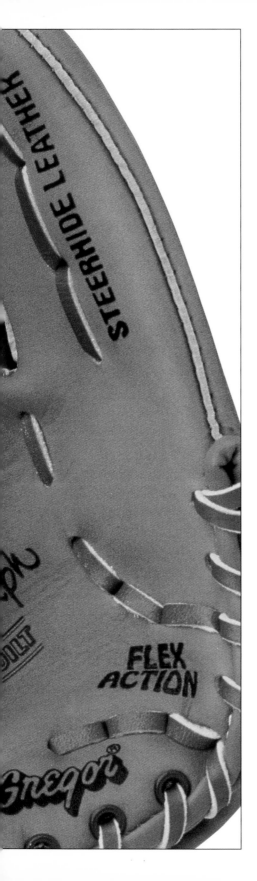

SPORTS

SOCCER · 524

FOOTBALL · 526

AUSTRALIAN RULES AND GAELIC FOOTBALL · · 528

RUGBY · 530

BASKETBALL · 532

VOLLEYBALL, NETBALL, AND HANDBALL · · · 534

BASEBALL · 536

CRICKET · 538

FIELD HOCKEY, LACROSSE, AND HURLING · · 540

TRACK AND FIELD · 542

RACKET SPORTS · 544

GOLF · 546

ARCHERY AND SHOOTING · · · · · · · · · · · · · · 548

ICE HOCKEY · 550

ALPINE SKIING · 552

EQUESTRIAN SPORTS · · · · · · · · · · · · · · · · · · 554

JUDO AND FENCING · · · · · · · · · · · · · · · · · · · 556

SWIMMING AND DIVING · · · · · · · · · · · · · · · 558

KAYAKING, ROWING, AND SAILING · · · · · · · 560

ANGLING · 562

Soccer

GAMES INVOLVING KICKING A BALL have a long history and were recorded in China as early as 300 BC; in medieval Europe, street football was banned as a menace to the public; only in 1863 were the rules established, specifically banning carrying the ball for all players except the goalkeeper, and separating rugby from soccer. Soccer, also known as association football, is a team sport in which players attempt to score goals by passing and dribbling the ball down the field past opposing defenders, and kicking or heading the ball into the goal net, outwitting the defending goalkeeper or "goalie." Each team consists of ten outfield players (defenders, midfielders, and strikers) and a goalkeeper. Players from the opposing team may challenge the player in possession of the ball, but an illegal or foul tackle results in a penalty if a foul occurs inside the penalty area or a free kick if outside the penalty area. The round ball used in soccer is more easily controlled than the oval balls used in American, Canadian, and Australian rules football and in rugby. The result is a more "open" or flowing game which is played and watched by millions of people worldwide.

LINESMAN'S FLAG

Lightweight, brightly colored fabric

Handle with rubber grip

REFEREE'S EQUIPMENT

Red card

Yellow card

Referee's whistle

Stopwatch

FIELD MARKINGS

Halfway line

5 ft (1.5 m)

HALFWAY-LINE FLAG

Corner arc

CORNER FLAG

24 ft (7.3 m)

Goal line

GOAL

SOCCER FIELD

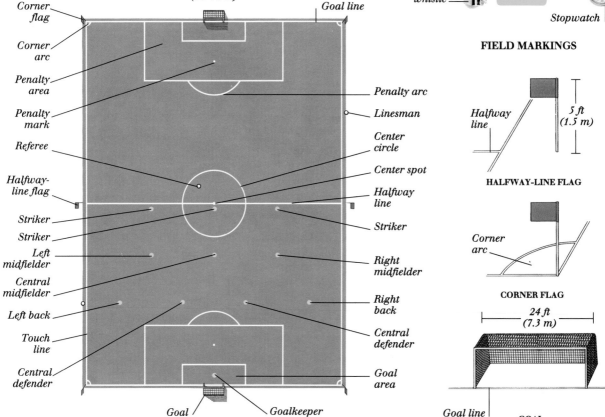

150–300 ft (46–91 m)

Goal line

Corner flag

Corner arc

Penalty area

Penalty mark

Referee

Halfway-line flag

Striker

Striker

Left midfielder

Central midfielder

Left back

Touch line

Central defender

Goal

Goalkeeper

Penalty arc

Linesman

Center circle

Center spot

Halfway line

Striker

Right midfielder

Right back

Central defender

Goal area

GOALKEEPER

Goalkeeper's shirt

Shorts

Glove

Shin guard

Sock

Soccer shoe

SOCCER UNIFORM

Open-neck collar

Lightweight, man-made fabric team shirt

Team logo

Manufacturer's logo

Ribbed welt

Sponsor's logo

MAKING A SOCCER BALL

Hole punched in panel for stitching

Ball size number

Manufacturer's name

Edge cut to fit perfectly

Waxed thread

Needle

Bladder valve

8½–9 in (22–23 cm)

Bladder made from latex rubber

Long cotton sock

Club crest

Team shorts

Laminated panel

Panels sewn together with ball inside out

Synthetic shoelace

Interchangeable nylon stud

SOCCER SHOE

Football

IN AMERICAN AND CANADIAN FOOTBALL, the object of the game is to get the ball across the opponent's goal line, either by passing or carrying it across (a touchdown), or by kicking it between their goalposts (a field goal). An American football team has 11 players on the field at a time, although up to 40 players can appear for each side in a single game. The agile offense tries to score points, and the heavy hitting defense holds back the opposition. When in possession of the ball, a team has four chances (downs), to move it at least ten yards up the field to make a first down. The opposition gains possession if they fail, or by tackling and intercepting the ball. Canadian football is played on a larger field, with 12 men on each side. A team has only three chances, instead of four, to achieve a first down. Otherwise, the game is very similar to American football. Helmets, face masks, and layers of body padding are worn by the players for protection.

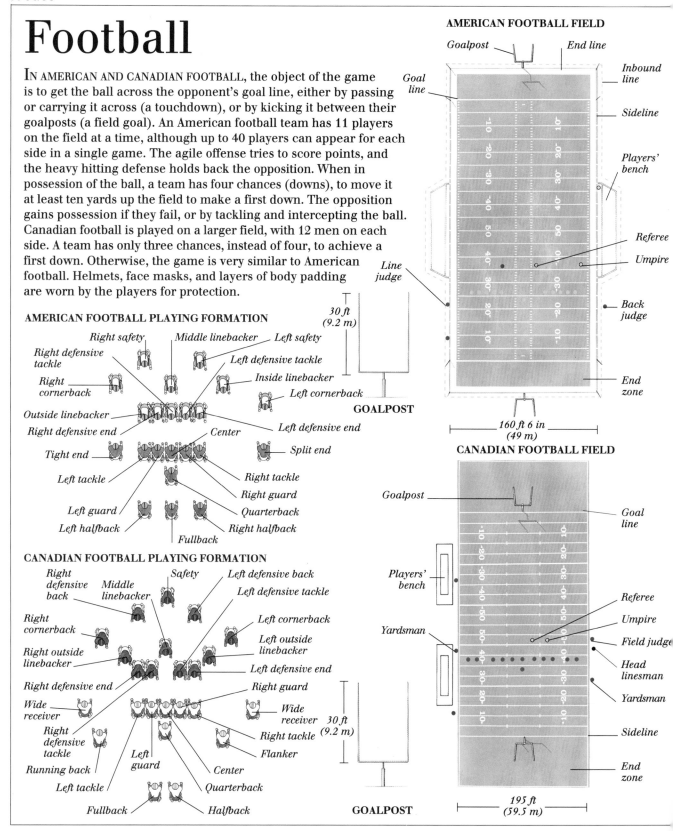

AMERICAN FOOTBALL FIELD

Goalpost

End line

Goal line

Inbound line

Sideline

Players' bench

Referee

Umpire

Back judge

Line judge

30 ft (9.2 m)

GOALPOST

End zone

160 ft 6 in (49 m)

AMERICAN FOOTBALL PLAYING FORMATION

Right safety
Middle linebacker
Left safety
Right defensive tackle
Left defensive tackle
Right cornerback
Inside linebacker
Left cornerback
Outside linebacker
Left defensive end
Right defensive end
Center
Tight end
Split end
Left tackle
Right tackle
Right guard
Left guard
Quarterback
Left halfback
Right halfback
Fullback

CANADIAN FOOTBALL FIELD

Goalpost

Goal line

Players' bench

Referee

Umpire

Field judge

Yardsman

Head linesman

Yardsman

Sideline

End zone

30 ft (9.2 m)

GOALPOST

195 ft (59.5 m)

CANADIAN FOOTBALL PLAYING FORMATION

Right defensive back
Middle linebacker
Safety
Left defensive back
Left defensive tackle
Right cornerback
Left cornerback
Left outside linebacker
Right outside linebacker
Left defensive end
Right defensive end
Right guard
Wide receiver
Wide receiver
Right defensive tackle
Right tackle
Left guard
Flanker
Running back
Center
Left tackle
Quarterback
Fullback
Halfback

PLAYER

Team logo

Helmet

Wrist pad

Player's number

Thigh pad

Pants

Studded shoe

PROTECTIVE EQUIPMENT

11 in (28 cm)

Painted white ring

Lace

Brown pebbled leather

FOOTBALL

195

Tie to shoulder pads

HELMET

Non-breakable plastic

Rubber-coated plastic

Shock absorber

Riddell

SHOULDER PAD

BIKE

BIKE

AIR·LITE

BLUE·LASER 40-42

Chest protector weight up to 5 lb 8 oz (2.5 kg)

REFEREE'S SIGNALS

TIME OUT

TOUCHDOWN OR FIELD GOAL

PERSONAL FOUL

OFFSIDE OR ENCROACHMENT

HOLDING

ILLEGAL MOTION

FIRST DOWN

PASS INTERFERENCE

BIKE

UPPER ARM PAD

BIKE

ELBOW PAD

FINGERLESS GLOVE

Screw-in stud

PONY

FOOTWEAR

Fold-over leather tongue

RIB PADS

Strap ties onto shoulder pad

Tail bone pad

Foam-sponge filling

BIKE AL60

BIKE AL60

HIP PAD

Rigid plastic covering

BIKE AL62

BIKE AL62

THIGH PAD

PANTS

KNEE PAD

Australian rules and Gaelic football

VARIETIES OF FOOTBALL have developed all over the world and Australian rules football is considered to be one of the roughest versions, allowing full body tackles although participants wear no protective padding. Two teams of 18 players play on a large, oval pitch. Players can kick or punch the ball, which is shaped like a rugby ball, but cannot throw it. Running with the ball is permitted, as long as the ball touches the ground at least once every ten meters. The full backs defend two sets of posts. Teams try to score goals (six points) between the inner posts or behinds (one point) inside the outer posts. Each game has four quarters of 25 minutes, and the team with the most points at the end of the allotted time is the winner. In Gaelic football, an Irish version of soccer (see pp. 524–525), a size 5 association football is used. Each team can have 15 players on the field at a time. Players are allowed to catch, fist, and kick the ball, or dribble it using their hands or feet, but cannot throw it. Teams are awarded three points for getting the ball into the net, and one point for getting it through the posts above the crossbar. Gaelic football is rarely played outside of Ireland.

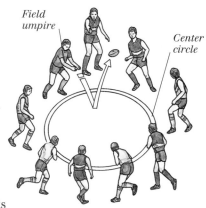

START OF PLAY

Field umpire

Center circle

SCORING

GOAL
(6 POINTS)

BEHIND
(1 POINT)

AUSTRALIAN RULES FOOTBALL FIELD

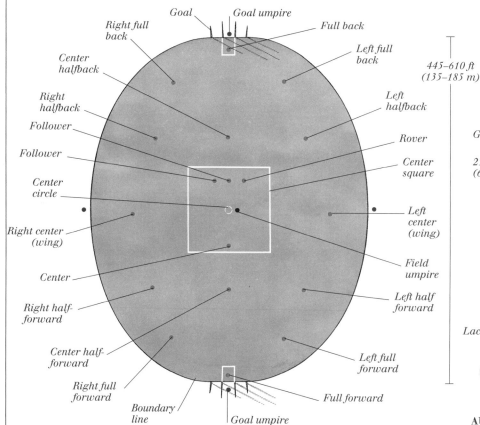

Goal

Goal umpire

Right full back

Full back

Center halfback

Left full back

Right halfback

Left halfback

Follower

Rover

Follower

Center square

Center circle

Left center (wing)

Right center (wing)

Center

Field umpire

Right half-forward

Left half forward

Center half-forward

Left full forward

Right full forward

Full forward

Boundary line

Goal umpire

445–610 ft (135–185 m)

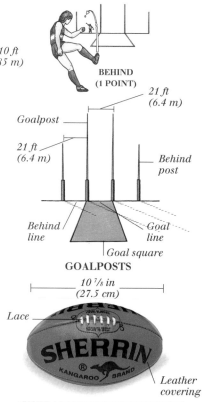

21 ft (6.4 m)

Goalpost

21 ft (6.4 m)

Behind post

Behind line

Goal line

Goal square

GOALPOSTS

10 7/8 in (27.5 cm)

Lace

SHERRIN

KANGAROO BRAND

Leather covering

AUSTRALIAN RULES FOOTBALL

AUSTRALIAN RULES FOOTBALL SKILLS

RUNNING WITH THE BALL

KICKING

TACKLING

TAKING A MARK

PASSING THE BALL

AUSTRALIAN RULES FOOTBALL UNIFORM

Australian Football League logo

Team colors

Sleeveless team guernsey

Sock

Shorts

GAELIC FOOTBALL PITCH

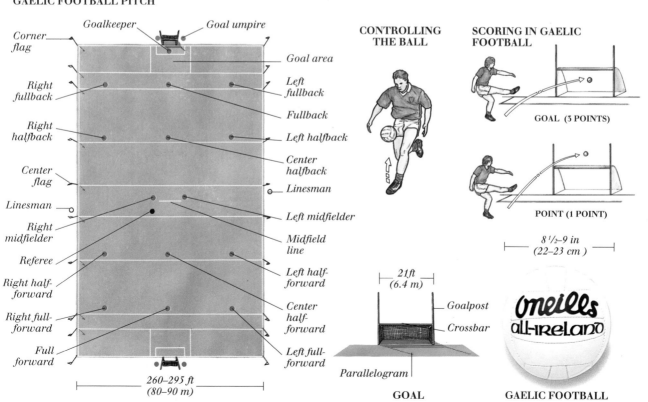

Corner flag

Goalkeeper

Goal umpire

Goal area

Right fullback

Left fullback

Fullback

Right halfback

Left halfback

Center halfback

Center flag

Linesman

Linesman

Left midfielder

Right midfielder

Midfield line

Referee

Left half-forward

Right half-forward

Center half-forward

Right full-forward

Left full-forward

Full forward

260–295 ft
(80–90 m)

CONTROLLING THE BALL

SCORING IN GAELIC FOOTBALL

GOAL (3 POINTS)

POINT (1 POINT)

8 1/2–9 in
(22–23 cm)

21 ft
(6.4 m)

Goalpost

Crossbar

Parallelogram

GOAL

oneills
all-ireland

GAELIC FOOTBALL

Rugby

RUGBY IS PLAYED WITH AN OVAL BALL which may be carried, thrown, or kicked. There are two types of rugby. Rugby Union is an amateur game played by two teams of 15 players. Players can score points in two ways: by placing the ball behind the opponents' goal line (a try, scoring four points) or by kicking it over the crossbar of the opponent's goal (a conversion, scoring two points; a penalty kick, scoring three points; or a drop-kick, scoring three points). Rugby League developed from the Union game but is played by 13 players at amateur and professional levels. In League games, a try scores four points; a conversion scores two points; a drop goal scores three points, and a penalty kick scores two points. In both forms of the game, whenever a rule is broken, play is resumed with a scrum. In a scrum, each team's forwards bind together facing each other and fight for possession of the ball.

RUGBY UNION FIELD

Goal
Dead-ball line
Touch in-goal line
Goal line
5 m line
Scrum-half
10 m line
Loose-head prop
Flanker
Lock forward
Center
Left wing
Center
Full back
Touch-line
Referee
Hooker
Tight-head prop
Linesman
Flanker
Lock forward
Right wing
Number 8
Fly-half
In-goal area
225 ft (68 m) maximum

RUGBY UNION SCRUM

Loose-head prop
Hooker
Tight-head prop
Scrum-half
Flanker
Flanker
Lock forward
Lock forward
Number 8

RUGBY UNION GOALPOST

18 ft (5.5 m)
Upright
Crossbar
Protective padding
9 ft 10 in (3 m)

RUGBY LEAGUE FIELD

Goal
Dead-ball line
Touch in-goal
Goal line
10 m line
Referee
Blind-side prop
Linesman
Second-row forward
Loose forward
Left wing
Full back
Touch in-goal line
Touch-line
Hooker
Open-side prop
Linesman
Second-row forward
Scrum-half
Stand-off half
Center
Center
Right wing
225 ft (68 m) maximum

RUGBY LEAGUE SCRUM

Hooker
Open-side prop
Scrum-half
Blind-side prop
Second-row forward
Second-row forward
Loose forward

RUGBY LEAGUE GOALPOST

18 ft (5.5 m)
Upright
Crossbar
Protective padding

RUGBY SCORING AND SKILLS

GOAL

Goal line

TRY

PASS

PLACE KICK

FLYING TACKLE

RUGBY UNION PLAYER

Shirt in team color

Knee-high sock

Team shorts

Studded boot

RUGBY UNION BALL

Four-panel construction

Laminated leather panel covered with textured plastic

Mitre MULTIPLEX

11–12 in (28–30 cm)

RUGBY LEAGUE BALL

Four-panel construction

Laminated leather panel covered with smooth plastic

Mitre MULTIPLEX E

11 in (28 cm)

Official logo of the British Rugby Football League

RUGBY LEAGUE SHIRT

Team crest

Three-quarter sleeve

UMBRO

WIDNES R.L.F.C.

RUGBY UNION SHIRT

FFR

Team crest

Button-up collar

Ankle support

Mizuno ALL BLACK

Circular stud

RUGBY SHOE

Team color

Long sleeve

RUGBY SHIRTS

Basketball

.BASKETBALL IS A BALL GAME for two teams of five players, originally devised in 1890 by James Naismath for the Y.M.C.A. in Springfield, Massachusetts. The object of the game is to take possession of the ball and score points by throwing the ball into the opposing team's basket. A player moves the ball up and down the court by bouncing it along the ground or "dribbling"; the ball may be passed between players by throwing, bouncing, or rolling. Players may not run with or kick the ball, although pivoting on one foot is allowed. The game begins with the referee throwing the ball into the air and a player from each team jumping up to try and "tip" the ball to a teammate. The length of the game and the number of periods played varies at different levels. There are amateur, professional, and international rules. No game ends in a draw. As many extra periods as necessary are played to break the tie. In addition to the five players on court, each team has up to seven substitutes, but players may only leave the court with the permission of the referee. Basketball is a noncontact sport and fouls on other players are penalized by a throw-in awarded against the offending team; a free throw at the basket is awarded when a player is fouled in the act of shooting. Basketball is a fast-moving game, requiring both physical and mental coordination. Skillful tactical play matters more than simple physical strength and the agility of the players makes the game an excellent spectator sport.

BASKETBALL SKILLS

CHEST PASS

DRIBBLE

OVERHEAD PASS

LAY-UP SHOT

JUMP SHOT

LONG PASS

INTERNATIONAL BASKETBALL COURT

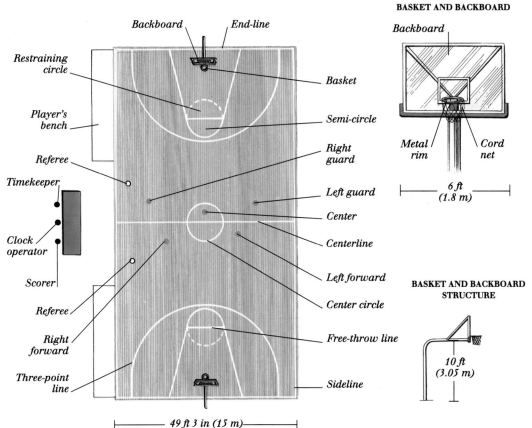

Backboard

End-line

Restraining circle

Player's bench

Referee

Timekeeper

Clock operator

Scorer

Referee

Right forward

Three-point line

Basket

Semi-circle

Right guard

Left guard

Center

Centerline

Left forward

Center circle

Free-throw line

Sideline

49 ft 3 in (15 m)

BASKET AND BACKBOARD

Backboard

Metal rim

Cord net

6 ft (1.8 m)

BASKET AND BACKBOARD STRUCTURE

10 ft (3.05 m)

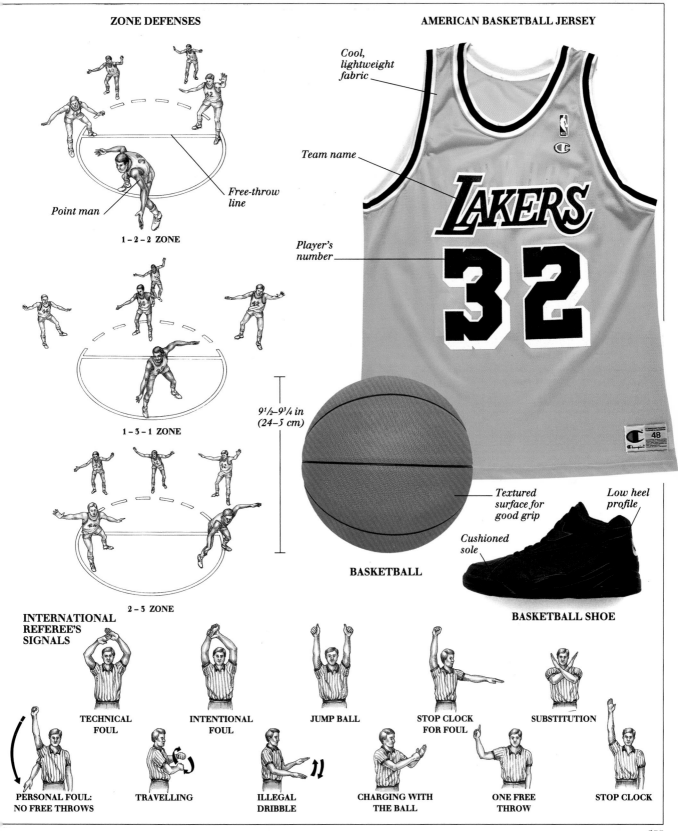

ZONE DEFENSES

Point man

Free-throw line

1 – 2 – 2 ZONE

1 – 3 – 1 ZONE

$9^1/_2$–$9^3/_4$ in (24–5 cm)

2 – 3 ZONE

AMERICAN BASKETBALL JERSEY

Cool, lightweight fabric

Team name

Player's number

LAKERS

32

Textured surface for good grip

BASKETBALL

Low heel profile

Cushioned sole

BASKETBALL SHOE

INTERNATIONAL REFEREE'S SIGNALS

TECHNICAL FOUL

INTENTIONAL FOUL

JUMP BALL

STOP CLOCK FOR FOUL

SUBSTITUTION

PERSONAL FOUL: NO FREE THROWS

TRAVELLING

ILLEGAL DRIBBLE

CHARGING WITH THE BALL

ONE FREE THROW

STOP CLOCK

Volleyball, netball, and handball

VOLLEYBALL, NETBALL, AND HANDBALL are fast-moving team sports played with balls, usually on courts with a hard surface. In volleyball, the object of the game is to hit the ball over a net strung across the center of the court so that it touches the ground on the opponent's side. The team of six players can take three hits to direct the ball over the net, although the same player cannot hit the ball twice in a row. Players can hit the ball with their arms, hands or any other part of their upper body. Teams score points only while serving. The first team to score 15 points, with a two-point margin over their opponent, wins the game. Netball is similar to basketball (see pp. 532–533), but is played on a slightly larger court with seven players instead of five. A team moves the ball toward the goal by throwing, passing, and catching it with the aim of throwing the ball through the opponents' goal net. Players are confined by their playing position to specific areas of the court. Team handball is one of the world's fastest games. Each side has seven players. A team moves the ball by dribbling, passing, or bouncing it as they run. Players may stop, catch, throw, bounce, or strike the ball with any part of the body above the knees. Each team tries to score goals by directing the ball past the opposition's goalkeeper into the net, which is similar to a soccer goal net (see pp. 524–525).

VOLLEYBALL SHOTS

OVERHAND SERVE   SPIKE (SMASH)

UNDERHAND SERVE   FOREARM PASS (DIG)

VOLLEYBALL KIT

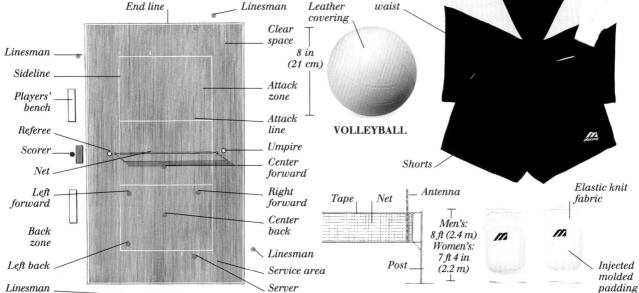

Team colors

Ribbed cuff

Cotton-knit jersey

Leather covering

Elastic waist

8 in (21 cm)

VOLLEYBALL

Shorts

Elastic knit fabric

Antenna

Tape   Net

Men's: 8 ft (2.4 m)
Women's: 7 ft 4 in (2.2 m)

Post

Injected molded padding

VOLLEYBALL NET

KNEE PADS

VOLLEYBALL COURT

End line

Linesman

Clear space

Linesman

Sideline

Attack zone

Players' bench

Attack line

Referee

Umpire

Scorer

Center forward

Net

Left forward

Right forward

Center back

Back zone

Linesman

Left back

Service area

Linesman

Server

29 ft 6 in (9 m)

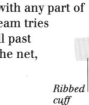

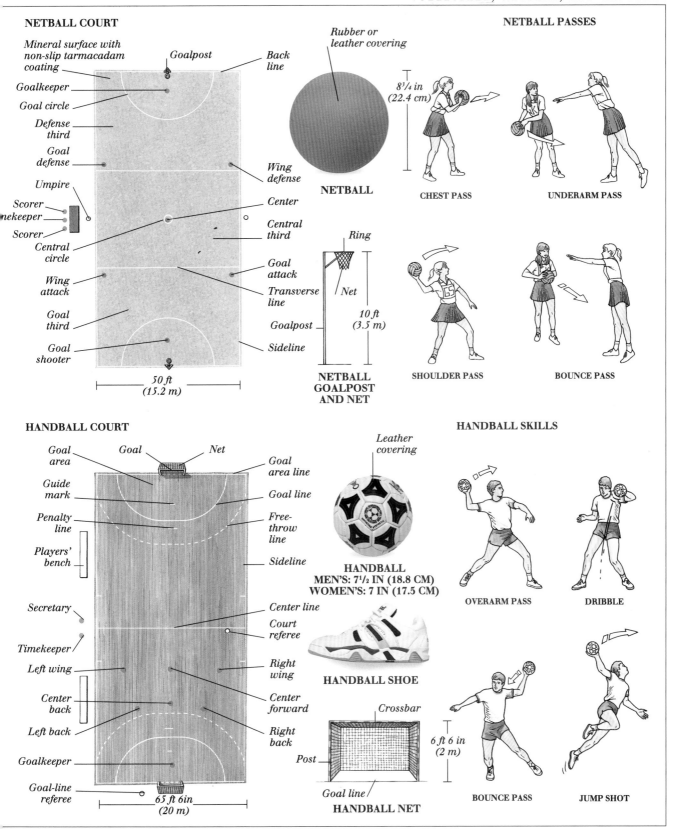

NETBALL COURT

Mineral surface with non-slip tarmacadam coating

Goalpost

Back line

Goalkeeper

Goal circle

Defense third

Goal defense

Wing defense

Umpire

Scorer

Timekeeper

Scorer

Central circle

Center

Central third

Goal attack

Transverse line

Wing attack

Goal third

Goal shooter

Sideline

50 ft (15.2 m)

NETBALL PASSES

Rubber or leather covering

8³/4 in (22.4 cm)

NETBALL

CHEST PASS

UNDERARM PASS

Ring

Net

Goalpost

10 ft (3.5 m)

NETBALL GOALPOST AND NET

SHOULDER PASS

BOUNCE PASS

HANDBALL COURT

Goal area

Goal

Net

Goal area line

Guide mark

Goal line

Penalty line

Free-throw line

Players' bench

Sideline

Secretary

Center line

Court referee

Timekeeper

Right wing

Left wing

Center forward

Center back

Left back

Right back

Goalkeeper

Goal-line referee

65 ft 6in (20 m)

HANDBALL SKILLS

Leather covering

HANDBALL
MEN'S: 7¹/2 IN (18.8 CM)
WOMEN'S: 7 IN (17.5 CM)

OVERARM PASS

DRIBBLE

HANDBALL SHOE

Crossbar

6 ft 6 in (2 m)

Post

Goal line

HANDBALL NET

BOUNCE PASS

JUMP SHOT

535

Baseball

BASEBALL IS A BALL GAME for two teams of nine players. The batter hits the ball thrown by the opposing team's pitcher, into the area between the foul lines. He then runs round all four fixed bases in order to score a run, touching or "tagging" each base in turn. The pitcher must throw the ball at a height between the batter's armpits and knees, a height which is called the strike zone. A ball pitched in this area that crosses over the home plate is called a "strike" and the batter has three strikes in which to try to hit the ball (otherwise he has "struck out"). The fielding team tries to get the batting team out by catching the ball before it bounces, tagging a player of the batting team who is running between bases with the ball, or by tagging a base before the player has reached it. Members of the batting team may stop safely at a base as long as it is not occupied by another member of their team. When the batter runs to first base, his teammate at first base must run onto second – this is called a force play. A game consists of nine innings and each team will bat once during an inning. When three members of the batting team are out, the teams swap roles. The team with the most runs wins the game.

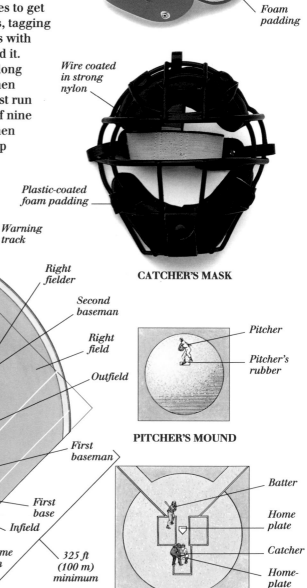

BATTER'S HELMET

Plastic shell

Peak

Foam padding

Wire coated in strong nylon

Plastic-coated foam padding

CATCHER'S MASK

BASEBALL FIELD

Center fielder

Center field

Warning track

Left fielder

Right fielder

Left field

Second baseman

Right field

Foul line

Outfield

Shortstop

First baseman

Umpire

Third baseman

First base

Third base

Infield

Coach's box

Home run

Second base

Dugout

On-deck circle

Pitcher's mound

325 ft (100 m) minimum

Pitcher

Pitcher's rubber

PITCHER'S MOUND

Batter

Home plate

Catcher

Home-plate umpire

HOME PLATE

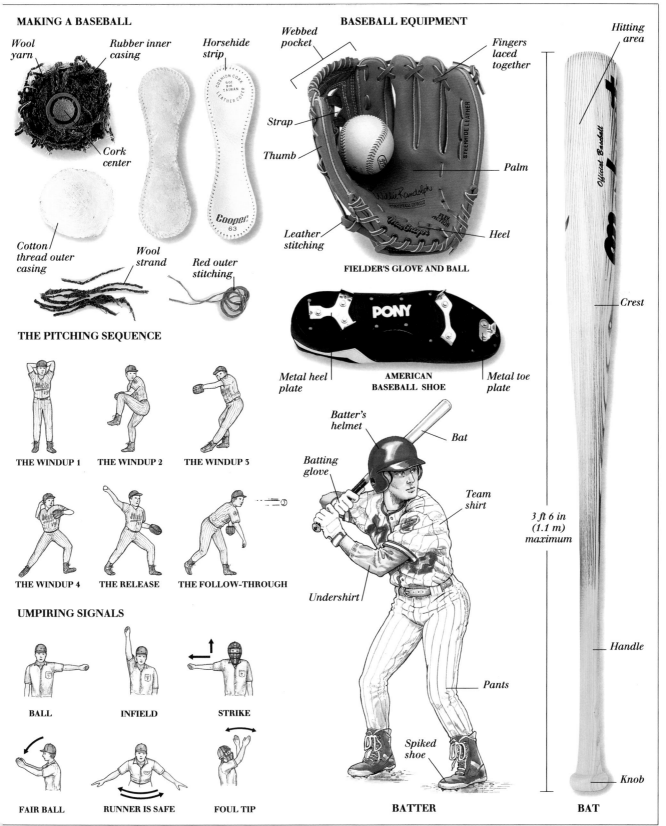

MAKING A BASEBALL

Wool yarn

Rubber inner casing

Horsehide strip

CUSHION CORK 5 OZ. 9 IN. TAIWAN. LEATHER COVER

Cork center

Cooper 63

Cotton thread outer casing

Wool strand

Red outer stitching

THE PITCHING SEQUENCE

THE WINDUP 1

THE WINDUP 2

THE WINDUP 3

THE WINDUP 4

THE RELEASE

THE FOLLOW-THROUGH

UMPIRING SIGNALS

BALL

INFIELD

STRIKE

FAIR BALL

RUNNER IS SAFE

FOUL TIP

BASEBALL EQUIPMENT

Webbed pocket

Fingers laced together

Strap

Thumb

STEERHIDE LEATHER

Palm

Willie Randolph

Leather stitching

Heel

FIELDER'S GLOVE AND BALL

PONY

Metal heel plate

AMERICAN BASEBALL SHOE

Metal toe plate

Batter's helmet

Bat

Batting glove

Team shirt

Undershirt

Pants

Spiked shoe

BATTER

Hitting area

Official Baseball

Crest

3 ft 6 in (1.1 m) maximum

Handle

Knob

BAT

Cricket

CRICKET IS A BALL GAME PLAYED by two teams of eleven players on a pitch with two sets of three stumps (wickets). The bowler bowls the ball down the pitch to the batsman of the opposing team, who must defend the wicket in front of which he stands. The object of the game is to score as many runs as possible. Runs can be scored individually by running the length of the playing strip, or by hitting a ball which lands outside the boundary (six), or which lands inside the boundary but bounces or rolls outside (four); the opposing team will bowl and field, attempting to dismiss the batsmen. A batsman can be dismissed in one of several ways: by the bowler hitting the wicket with the ball ("bowled"); by a fielder catching the ball hit by the batsman before it touches the ground ("caught"); by the wicket-keeper or another fielder breaking the wicket while the batsman is attempting a run and is therefore out of his ground ("stumped" or "run out"); by the batsman breaking the wicket with his own bat or body ("hit wicket"); by a part of the batsman's body being hit by a ball that would otherwise have hit the wicket ("leg before wicket" ["lbw"]). A match consists of one or two innings and each innings ends when the tenth batsman of the batting team is out, when a certain number of overs (a series of six balls bowled) have been played, or when the captain of the batting team "declares" ending the innings voluntarily.

CRICKET STROKES

FORWARD DEFENSIVE STROKE

BACKWARD DEFENSIVE STROKE

ON-DRIVE

OFF-DRIVE

PULL

HOOK

SQUARE CUT

LEG GLANCE

CRICKET BALL AND WICKET

Leather skin

Seam

BALL

Bail

WICKET

Stump

CRICKET PITCH

Wicket-keeper

Batsman

Wicket

Bowling crease

66 ft (20 m)

Bowler

Return crease

Umpire

Non-striking batsman

POSSIBLE FIELD POSITIONS FOR AN AWAY SWING BOWLER TO A RIGHT-HANDED BATSMAN (IN RED) AND OTHER FIELD POSITIONS

Long on

Umpire

Boundary line

Deep mid-wicket

Mid-on

Silly mid-on

Forward short leg

Square leg

Deep square leg

Square-leg umpire

Batsman

Long leg

Leg slip

Wicket-keeper

Fine leg

Sight screen

Long off

Bowler

Non-striking batsman

Extra cover

Mid-off

Silly mid-off

Cover

Point

Gulley

Third man

Second slip

First slip

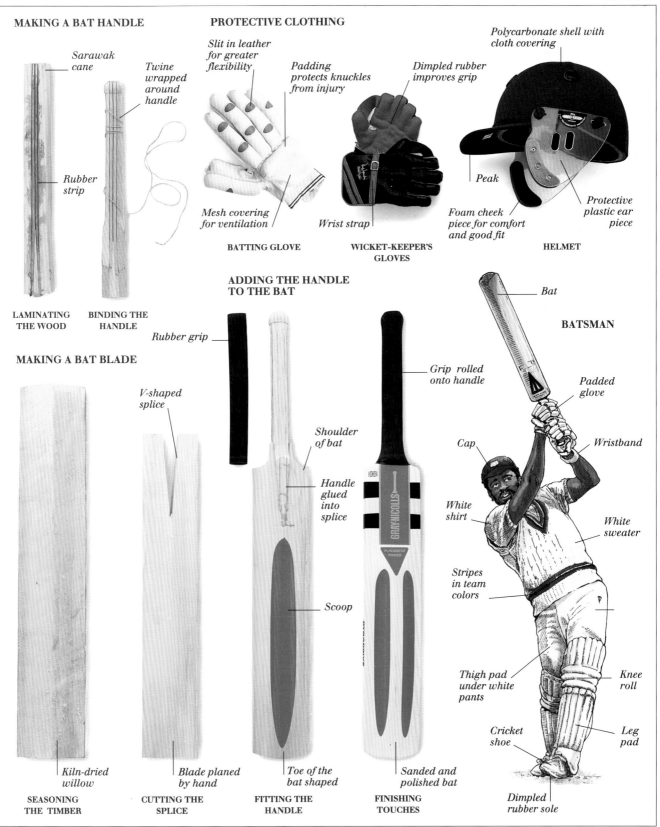

MAKING A BAT HANDLE

Sarawak cane

Twine wrapped around handle

Rubber strip

LAMINATING THE WOOD

BINDING THE HANDLE

MAKING A BAT BLADE

Kiln-dried willow

SEASONING THE TIMBER

V-shaped splice

Blade planed by hand

CUTTING THE SPLICE

PROTECTIVE CLOTHING

Slit in leather for greater flexibility

Padding protects knuckles from injury

Mesh covering for ventilation

BATTING GLOVE

Dimpled rubber improves grip

Wrist strap

WICKET-KEEPER'S GLOVES

Polycarbonate shell with cloth covering

Peak

Foam cheek piece for comfort and good fit

Protective plastic ear piece

HELMET

ADDING THE HANDLE TO THE BAT

Rubber grip

Shoulder of bat

Handle glued into splice

Scoop

Toe of the bat shaped

FITTING THE HANDLE

Grip rolled onto handle

Sanded and polished bat

FINISHING TOUCHES

GRAYNICOLLS

PLACEMENT POWER

Bat

BATSMAN

Padded glove

Wristband

Cap

White shirt

White sweater

Stripes in team colors

Thigh pad under white pants

Knee roll

Cricket shoe

Leg pad

Dimpled rubber sole

Field hockey, lacrosse, and hurling

ALL OVER THE WORLD, TEAM GAMES have evolved which require that a ball be struck or carried, and tossed at the end of a stick. Early forms of these games include hurling, shinty, bandy, and pelota. Field hockey is played by men and women: two teams of eleven players try to gain and keep possession of the ball and score goals by using the hockey stick to propel the ball into their opponents' goal net. Skills such as passing, pushing, or hitting the ball by slapping or lifting it in a flicking movement, and shooting at the goal are crucial. Field hockey is played indoors and outdoors on grass or synthetic fields. Lacrosse is played internationally as a 12-a-side game for women and as 10-a-side game for men. The women's field has no absolute boundaries but the men's has clearly defined sidelines and end lines. The ball is kept in play by being carried, thrown or batted with the crosse, and rolled or kicked in any direction. In men's and women's lacrosse, play can continue behind the marked goal areas. Similar skills are required in hurling – a Gaelic field game played on the same pitch as Gaelic football (see pp. 528–529), using the same goalposts and net. In hurling, the ball may be struck with or carried on the hurley and, when off the ground, may be struck with the hand or kicked. Goals (three points) are scored when the ball passes between the posts and under the crossbar; one point is scored when the ball passes between the posts and over the crossbar.

GOALKEEPER'S EQUIPMENT

Hard shell
Air vent
Face mask
HELMET
Strap

Rigid palm

Padded wrist
GAUNTLET

FIELD HOCKEY STICK AND BALL

STICK
Handle
Tape
Steam-bent ash head
Blade
Slazenger FLEXI

3 ft (91 cm)

Stitched seam
2³⁄₄–3 in (7–7.5 cm)

BALL

FIELD HOCKEY FIELD

Sideline
Center forward
Inside right
Right wing
Right half
Right back
Corner flag
Shooting circle
Goal
Penalty spot
Five yard mark
Goal line
Inside left
Left wing
Umpire
Center half
Left half
Left back
Goalkeeper

180 ft (55 m)

Protective overshoe
Padding protects toes against the hard ball
Strap
GOALKEEPER'S BOOT

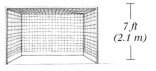

7 ft (2.1 m)

FIELD HOCKEY GOAL

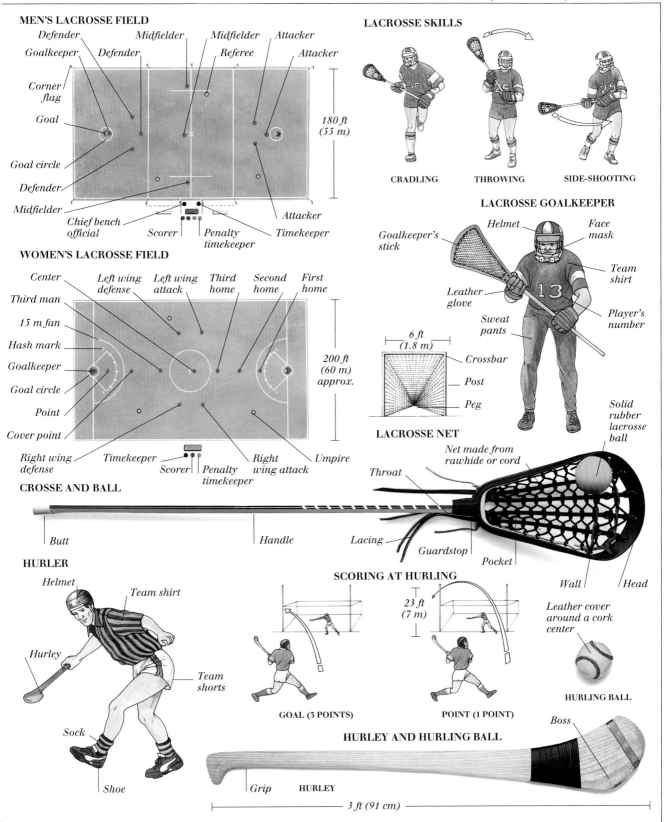

MEN'S LACROSSE FIELD

Defender
Goalkeeper
Defender
Midfielder
Midfielder
Referee
Attacker
Attacker
Corner flag
Goal
Goal circle
Defender
Midfielder
Chief bench official
Scorer
Penalty timekeeper
Attacker
Timekeeper

180 ft (55 m)

WOMEN'S LACROSSE FIELD

Center
Left wing defense
Left wing attack
Third home
Second home
First home
Third man
15 m fan
Hash mark
Goalkeeper
Goal circle
Point
Cover point
Right wing defense
Timekeeper
Scorer
Penalty timekeeper
Right wing attack
Umpire

200 ft (60 m) approx.

CROSSE AND BALL

Butt
Handle
Lacing
Throat
Guardstop
Pocket
Net made from rawhide or cord
Wall
Head

HURLER

Helmet
Team shirt
Hurley
Team shorts
Sock
Shoe

LACROSSE SKILLS

CRADLING
THROWING
SIDE-SHOOTING

LACROSSE GOALKEEPER

Goalkeeper's stick
Leather glove
Sweat pants
Helmet
Face mask
Team shirt
Player's number

6 ft (1.8 m)
Crossbar
Post
Peg

LACROSSE NET

Solid rubber lacrosse ball

SCORING AT HURLING

23 ft (7 m)

GOAL (3 POINTS)
POINT (1 POINT)

Leather cover around a cork center

HURLING BALL

Boss

HURLEY AND HURLING BALL

Grip
HURLEY

3 ft (91 cm)

Track and field

THE SPORTS that make up athletics are divided into two main groups: track events – which include sprinting, middle, and long distance running, relay running, hurdling, and walking – and field events which require jumping and throwing skills. Contests designed to test the speed, strength, agility, and stamina of athletes were held by the ancient Greeks over 4,000 years ago. However, the abolition of the Olympic Games in 393 AD meant that track and field events were neglected until the revival of large-scale competitions in the mid-nineteenth century. Modern stadiums offer areas reserved for the long jump, triple jump, and pole vault usually situated outside the running track. The javelin, shot, hammer, and discus are thrown within the track area. Most athletes specialize in one or two events but, in the heptathlon, women compete in seven events, held over two days: 200 m and 800 m races, 100 m hurdles, javelin, shot put, high jump, and long jump. In the decathlon, men compete in ten events over two days: 100 m, 400 m, and 1,500 m races, 110 m hurdles, javelin, discus, shot put, pole vault, high jump, and long jump.

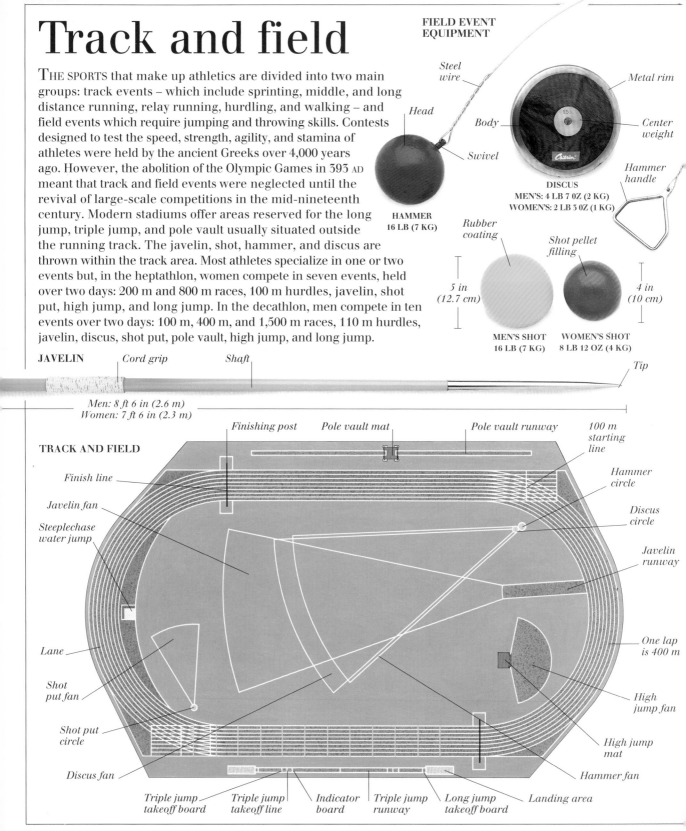

FIELD EVENT EQUIPMENT

Steel wire

Head

Body

Swivel

HAMMER
16 LB (7 KG)

Metal rim

Center weight

DISCUS
MEN'S: 4 LB 7 OZ (2 KG)
WOMEN'S: 2 LB 3 OZ (1 KG)

Hammer handle

Rubber coating

Shot pellet filling

5 in (12.7 cm)

4 in (10 cm)

MEN'S SHOT
16 LB (7 KG)

WOMEN'S SHOT
8 LB 12 OZ (4 KG)

JAVELIN
Cord grip
Shaft
Tip

Men: 8 ft 6 in (2.6 m)
Women: 7 ft 6 in (2.3 m)

TRACK AND FIELD

Finishing post
Pole vault mat
Pole vault runway
100 m starting line

Finish line
Hammer circle

Javelin fan
Discus circle

Steeplechase water jump
Javelin runway

Lane
One lap is 400 m

Shot put fan
High jump fan

Shot put circle
High jump mat

Discus fan
Hammer fan

Triple jump takeoff board
Triple jump takeoff line
Indicator board
Triple jump runway
Long jump takeoff board
Landing area

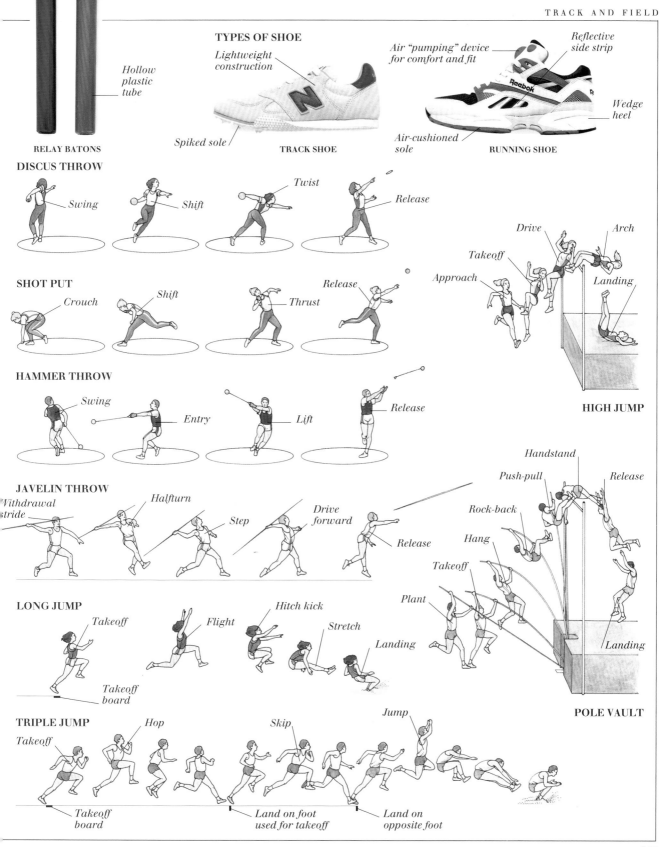

RELAY BATONS

Hollow plastic tube

TYPES OF SHOE

Lightweight construction

Spiked sole

TRACK SHOE

Air "pumping" device for comfort and fit

Reflective side strip

Wedge heel

Air-cushioned sole

RUNNING SHOE

DISCUS THROW

Swing

Shift

Twist

Release

SHOT PUT

Crouch

Shift

Release

Thrust

HAMMER THROW

Swing

Entry

Lift

Release

JAVELIN THROW

Withdrawal stride

Halfturn

Step

Drive forward

Release

HIGH JUMP

Drive

Arch

Takeoff

Approach

Landing

LONG JUMP

Takeoff

Flight

Hitch kick

Stretch

Landing

Takeoff board

POLE VAULT

Handstand

Push-pull

Release

Rock-back

Hang

Takeoff

Plant

Landing

TRIPLE JUMP

Takeoff

Hop

Skip

Jump

Takeoff board

Land on foot used for takeoff

Land on opposite foot

Racket sports

PROTECTIVE EYEWEAR

THE OBJECT OF ALL RACKET SPORTS is to make shots the opponent cannot return. Games are played by two players (singles) or four players (doubles). Racket shape and size is tailored to each sport, but all rackets are constructed of wood, plastic, aluminum, or high-performance materials such as fiberglass and carbon graphite. Racket strings are usually synthetic, although natural gut is still used. Tennis is played on a court divided by a low net. Opposing players serve alternate games. At least six games must be won to gain a set, and two or sometimes three sets are needed to win a match. Tennis courts may be concrete, grass, clay, or synthetic, each surface requiring a different style of play. Badminton is an indoor sport that is played with light, flexible rackets and a birdie on a court with a high net. Players can score points only on their serve. The first to reach 15 points (11 points for women's singles) wins the game. Two games are needed to win a match. Squash and racketball are both played in enclosed courts. One player hits the ball against the front wall, and the other tries to return it before it bounces on the floor more than once. Squash rackets have smaller, rounder heads and stiffer frames than badminton rackets. International courts are wider than those in the U.S., where a much harder ball is used. Squash games are played to nine points (international) or 15 points (U.S.). In racketball, players use a ball that is larger and bouncier than a squash ball. The racketball racket is thick and sturdy, with a large head, short handle, and a strap that loops around the wrist. Points can be won only when serving, and the first player to reach 21 points wins.

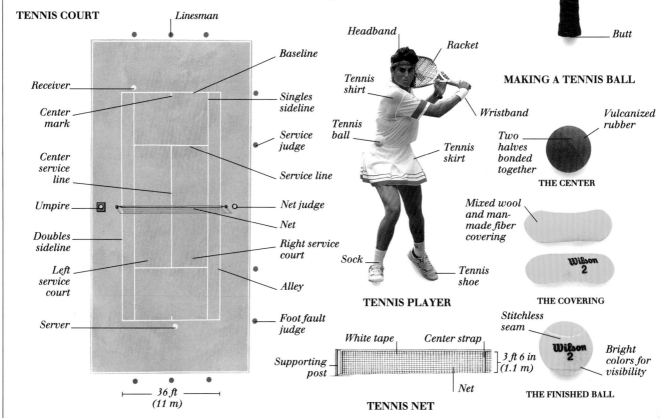

TENNIS RACKET

Synthetic string

Frame

Head

Logo

Throat

Grip

Butt

TENNIS COURT

Linesman

Baseline

Receiver

Center mark

Singles sideline

Service judge

Center service line

Service line

Umpire

Net judge

Net

Doubles sideline

Right service court

Left service court

Alley

Server

Foot fault judge

36 ft (11 m)

TENNIS PLAYER

Headband

Racket

Tennis shirt

Wristband

Tennis ball

Tennis skirt

Sock

Tennis shoe

TENNIS NET

White tape

Center strap

Supporting post

Net

3 ft 6 in (1.1 m)

MAKING A TENNIS BALL

Vulcanized rubber

Two halves bonded together

THE CENTER

Mixed wool and man-made fiber covering

Wilson 2

THE COVERING

Stitchless seam

Wilson 2

Bright colors for visibility

THE FINISHED BALL

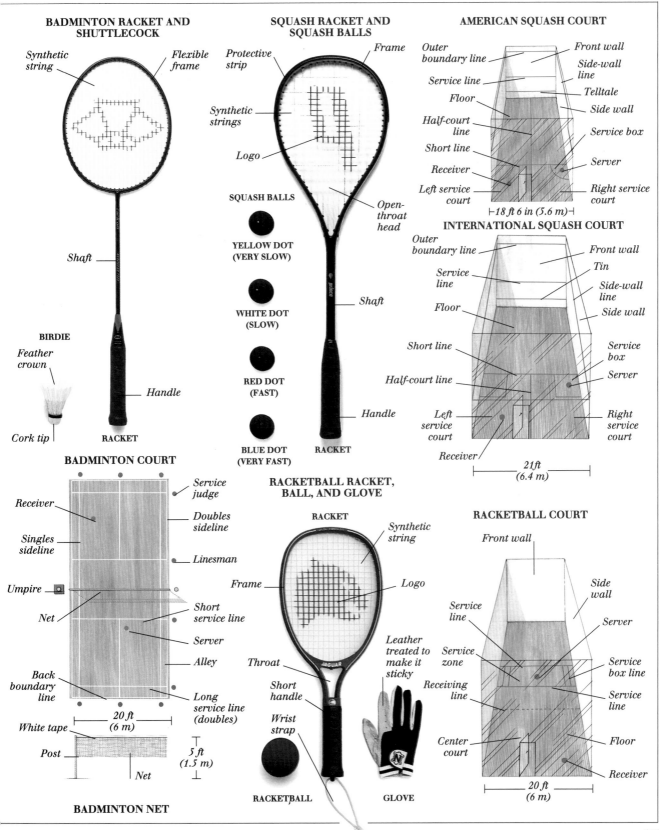

BADMINTON RACKET AND SHUTTLECOCK

Synthetic string

Flexible frame

Shaft

Handle

BIRDIE

Feather crown

Cork tip

RACKET

BADMINTON COURT

Receiver

Singles sideline

Umpire

Net

Back boundary line

Service judge

Doubles sideline

Linesman

Short service line

Server

Alley

Long service line (doubles)

20 ft (6 m)

White tape

Post

Net

5 ft (1.5 m)

Net

BADMINTON NET

SQUASH RACKET AND SQUASH BALLS

Protective strip

Synthetic strings

Logo

Frame

Open-throat head

Shaft

Handle

RACKET

SQUASH BALLS

YELLOW DOT (VERY SLOW)

WHITE DOT (SLOW)

RED DOT (FAST)

BLUE DOT (VERY FAST)

RACKETBALL RACKET, BALL, AND GLOVE

RACKET

Synthetic string

Frame

Logo

Throat

Short handle

Wrist strap

RACKETBALL

Leather treated to make it sticky

GLOVE

AMERICAN SQUASH COURT

Outer boundary line

Service line

Floor

Half-court line

Short line

Receiver

Left service court

Front wall

Side-wall line

Telltale

Side wall

Service box

Server

Right service court

18 ft 6 in (5.6 m)

INTERNATIONAL SQUASH COURT

Outer boundary line

Service line

Floor

Short line

Half-court line

Left service court

Receiver

Front wall

Tin

Side-wall line

Side wall

Service box

Server

Right service court

21 ft (6.4 m)

RACKETBALL COURT

Front wall

Service line

Service zone

Receiving line

Center court

Side wall

Server

Service box line

Service line

Floor

Receiver

20 ft (6 m)

Golf

THE GAME OF GOLF was first played in Scotland some 400 years ago. Players are required to hit a ball, using a wooden or iron club, from a smooth level point or teeing ground, down the fairway, and onto a putting green where the target hole is located. The fairway is a strip of clear land along which there are natural hazards – such as ponds and streams, man-made hazards – such as bunkers (sand pits), and rough (areas of uncut grass). Championship golf courses have 18 holes. The object of the game is to hit the ball into each hole in turn, and to complete the "round" using as few strokes as possible. Players may compete individually or in teams, playing the course together in groups of two, three, or four. The two basic forms of competition are match play and stroke play. In match play, the side winning the majority of holes over a certain number of rounds wins the match. In stroke play, the winner is the player who finishes a certain number of rounds having made the fewest strokes.

GOLF BALL AND TEE

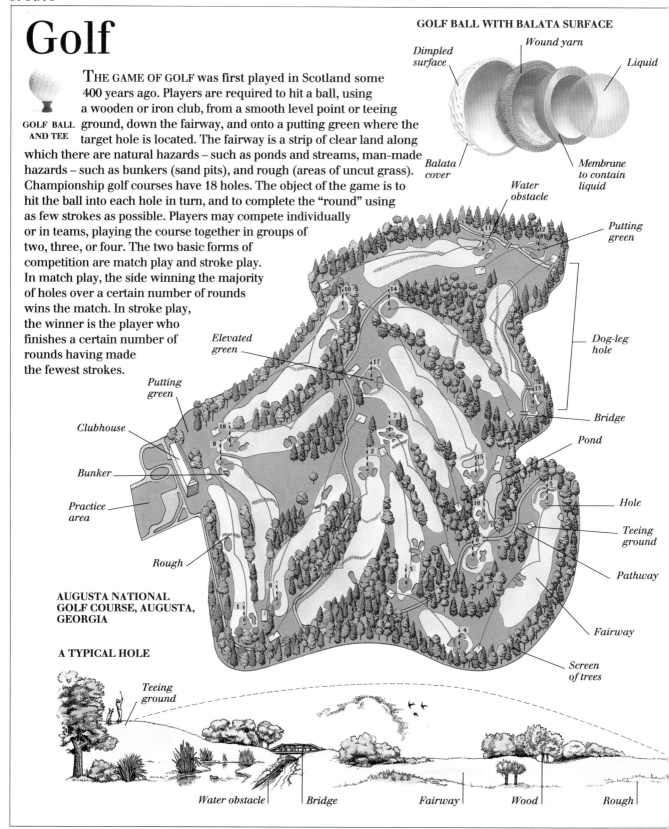

GOLF BALL WITH BALATA SURFACE

Dimpled surface

Wound yarn

Liquid

Balata cover

Membrane to contain liquid

Water obstacle

Putting green

Dog-leg hole

Bridge

Pond

Hole

Teeing ground

Pathway

Fairway

Screen of trees

Elevated green

Putting green

Clubhouse

Bunker

Practice area

Rough

AUGUSTA NATIONAL GOLF COURSE, AUGUSTA, GEORGIA

A TYPICAL HOLE

Teeing ground

Water obstacle

Bridge

Fairway

Wood

Rough

MAKING A WOODEN CLUB

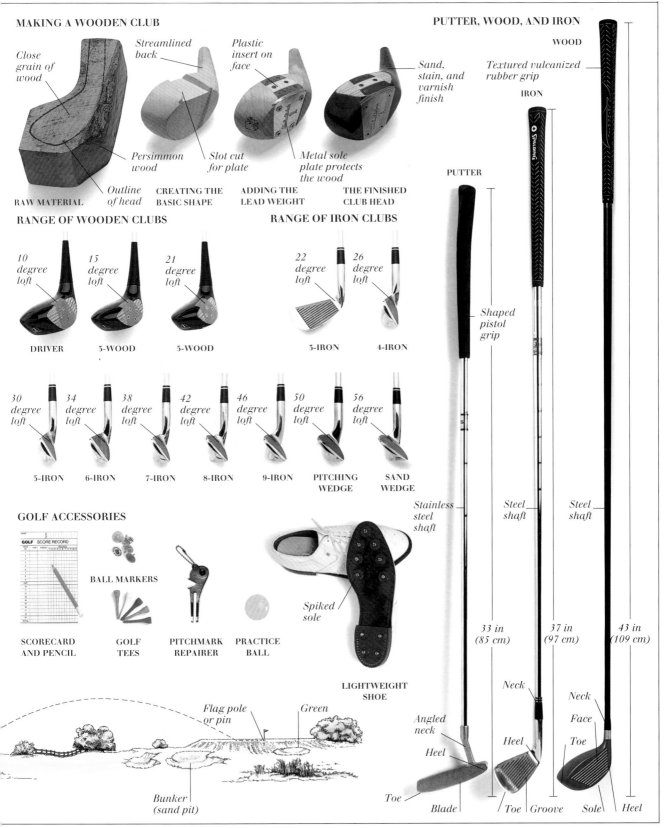

Close grain of wood

Streamlined back

Plastic insert on face

Sand, stain, and varnish finish

Persimmon wood

Slot cut for plate

Metal sole plate protects the wood

Outline of head

RAW MATERIAL

CREATING THE BASIC SHAPE

ADDING THE LEAD WEIGHT

THE FINISHED CLUB HEAD

RANGE OF WOODEN CLUBS

10 degree loft

15 degree loft

21 degree loft

DRIVER

3-WOOD

5-WOOD

30 degree loft

34 degree loft

38 degree loft

42 degree loft

46 degree loft

50 degree loft

56 degree loft

5-IRON

6-IRON

7-IRON

8-IRON

9-IRON

PITCHING WEDGE

SAND WEDGE

RANGE OF IRON CLUBS

22 degree loft

26 degree loft

3-IRON

4-IRON

PUTTER, WOOD, AND IRON

WOOD

Textured vulcanized rubber grip

IRON

PUTTER

Shaped pistol grip

Stainless steel shaft

Steel shaft

Steel shaft

33 in (85 cm)

37 in (97 cm)

43 in (109 cm)

Angled neck

Neck

Neck

Face

Heel

Heel

Toe

Toe

Blade

Toe

Groove

Sole

Heel

GOLF ACCESSORIES

GOLF SCORE RECORD

SCORECARD AND PENCIL

BALL MARKERS

GOLF TEES

PITCHMARK REPAIRER

PRACTICE BALL

Spiked sole

LIGHTWEIGHT SHOE

Flag pole or pin

Green

Bunker (sand pit)

Archery and shooting

Target shooting and archery evolved as practice for hunting and battle skills. Modern bows, although designed according to the principles of early hunting bows, use laminates, fiberglass, dacron, and carbon, and are equipped with sights and stabilizers. Competitors in target archery shoot over distances of 100 ft (30 m), 165 ft (50 m), 230 ft (70 m), and 300 ft (90 m) for men, and 100 ft (30 m), 165 ft (50 m), 200 ft (60 m), and 230 ft (70 m) for women. The closer the shot is to the center of the target, the higher the score. The individual scores are added up, and the archer with the highest total wins the competition. Crossbows are used in match competitions over 33 ft (10 m), and 100 ft (30 m). Rifle shooting is divided into three categories: smallbore, bigbore, and air rifle. Contests take place over a variety of distances and further subdivisions are based on the type of shooting position used; prone, kneeling, or standing. The Olympic biathlon combines cross-country skiing and rifle shooting over a course of approximately $12^1/_2$ miles (20 km). Additional magazines of ammunition are carried in the butt of the rifles. Bigbore rifles fitted with a telescopic sight can be used for hunting and running game target shooting. Pistol shooting events, using rapid-fire pistols, target pistols, and air pistols, take place over 33 ft (10 m), 82 ft (25 m), and 165 ft (50 m) distances. In rapid-fire pistol shooting, a total of 60 shots are fired from a distance of 82 ft (25 m).

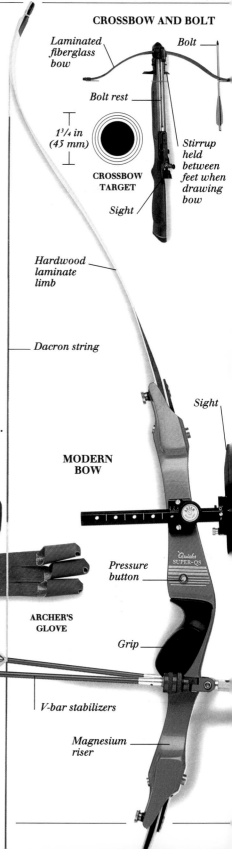

CROSSBOW AND BOLT

Laminated fiberglass bow

Bolt

Bolt rest

$1^3/_4$ in (45 mm)

CROSSBOW TARGET

Stirrup held between feet when drawing bow

Sight

Hardwood laminate limb

Dacron string

Sight

MODERN BOW

Pressure button

Grip

V-bar stabilizers

Magnesium riser

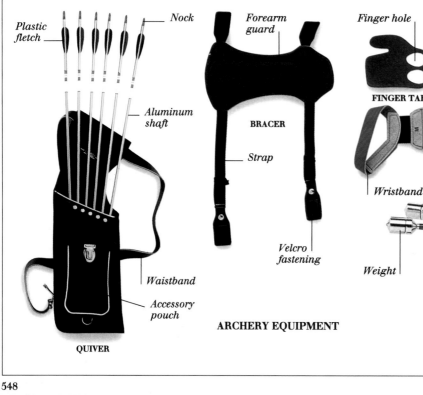

Plastic fletch

Nock

Forearm guard

Finger hole

Aluminum shaft

BRACER

FINGER TAB

Strap

Wristband

Weight

Velcro fastening

Waistband

Accessory pouch

ARCHERY EQUIPMENT

QUIVER

ARCHER'S GLOVE

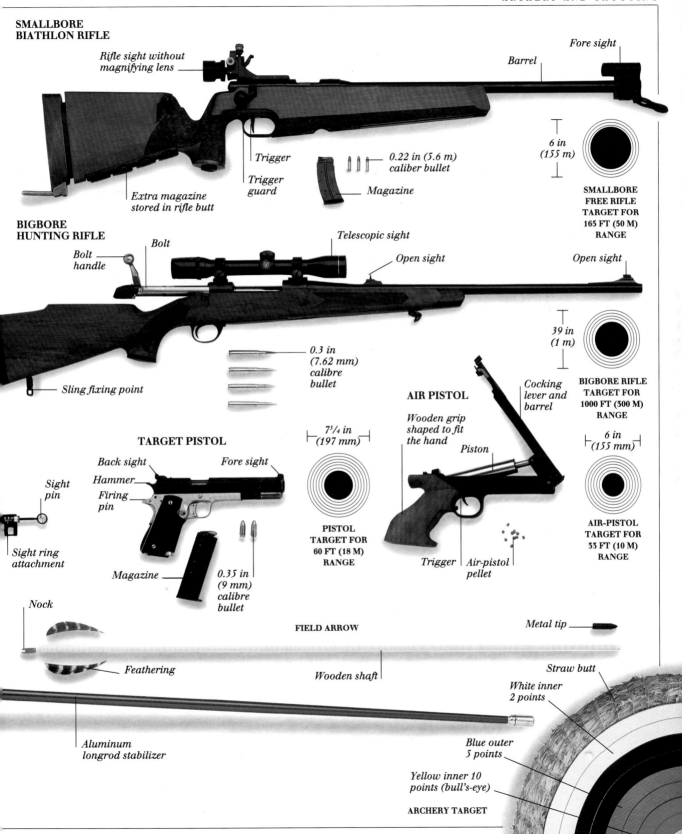

**SMALLBORE
BIATHLON RIFLE**

*Rifle sight without
magnifying lens*

Barrel

Fore sight

Trigger

*Trigger
guard*

*0.22 in (5.6 m)
caliber bullet*

Magazine

*Extra magazine
stored in rifle butt*

*6 in
(155 m)*

**SMALLBORE
FREE RIFLE
TARGET FOR
165 FT (50 M)
RANGE**

**BIGBORE
HUNTING RIFLE**

Bolt

*Bolt
handle*

Telescopic sight

Open sight

Open sight

*0.3 in
(7.62 mm)
calibre
bullet*

Sling fixing point

*39 in
(1 m)*

*Cocking
lever and
barrel*

**BIGBORE RIFLE
TARGET FOR
1000 FT (300 M)
RANGE**

AIR PISTOL

*Wooden grip
shaped to fit
the hand*

Piston

*6 in
(155 mm)*

TARGET PISTOL

Back sight

Fore sight

Hammer

*Firing
pin*

*Sight
pin*

*Sight ring
attachment*

Magazine

*0.35 in
(9 mm)
calibre
bullet*

*7³/₄ in
(197 mm)*

**PISTOL
TARGET FOR
60 FT (18 M)
RANGE**

Trigger

*Air-pistol
pellet*

**AIR-PISTOL
TARGET FOR
33 FT (10 M)
RANGE**

Nock

FIELD ARROW

Metal tip

Feathering

Wooden shaft

Straw butt

*White inner
2 points*

*Aluminum
longrod stabilizer*

*Blue outer
5 points*

*Yellow inner 10
points (bull's-eye)*

ARCHERY TARGET

Ice hockey

ICE HOCKEY IS PLAYED by two teams of six players on an ice rink, with a goal net at each end. The object of this fast, and often dangerous, game is to hit a frozen rubber puck into the opposing team's net with an ice hockey stick. The game begins when the referee drops the puck between the sticks of two players from opposing teams, who face off. The rink is divided into three areas: defending, neutral, and attacking zones. Players may move with the puck and pass it to one another along the ice, but the puck should not travel more than two zones across the rink markings. A goal is scored when the puck entirely crosses the goal-line between the posts and under the crossbar of the goal. A team may field up to 20 players although only six players are allowed on the ice at one time; substitutions occur frequently. Each game consists of three periods of 20 minutes, divided by breaks of 15 minutes.

GOALKEEPER

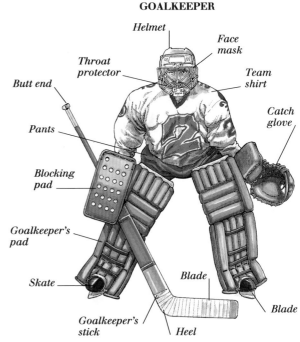

Helmet
Face mask
Throat protector
Team shirt
Butt end
Catch glove
Pants
Blocking pad
Goalkeeper's pad
Skate
Blade
Blade
Goalkeeper's stick
Heel

ICE HOCKEY RINK

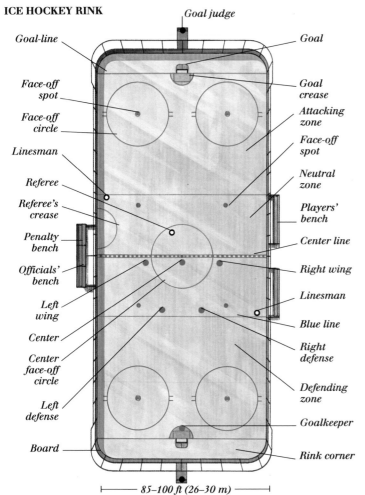

Goal judge
Goal-line
Goal
Face-off spot
Goal crease
Face-off circle
Attacking zone
Linesman
Face-off spot
Referee
Neutral zone
Referee's crease
Players' bench
Penalty bench
Center line
Officials' bench
Right wing
Left wing
Linesman
Center
Blue line
Center face-off circle
Right defense
Left defense
Defending zone
Board
Goalkeeper
Rink corner

├── 85–100 ft (26–30 m) ──┤

THE FACE OFF

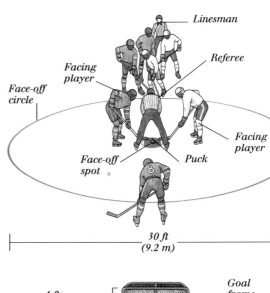

Linesman
Facing player
Referee
Face-off circle
Facing player
Face-off spot
Puck

├── 30 ft (9.2 m) ──┤

4 ft (1.22 m)
Goal frame
Netting
6 ft (1.83 m)
Goal crease

ICE HOCKEY GOAL

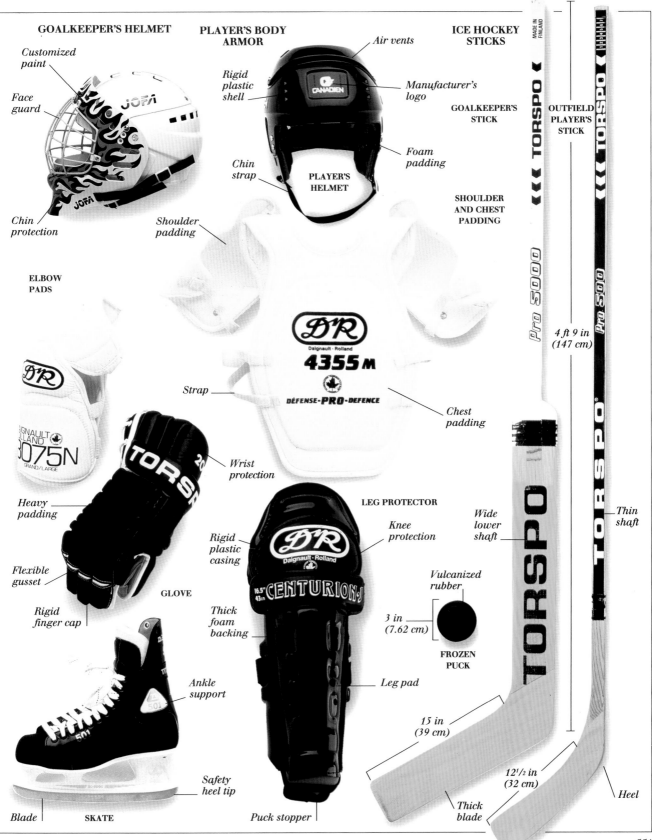

GOALKEEPER'S HELMET

Customized paint

Face guard

Chin protection

PLAYER'S BODY ARMOR

Air vents

Rigid plastic shell

Manufacturer's logo

Chin strap

Foam padding

PLAYER'S HELMET

Shoulder padding

ICE HOCKEY STICKS

GOALKEEPER'S STICK

SHOULDER AND CHEST PADDING

MADE IN FINLAND

TORSPO

Pro 5000

OUTFIELD PLAYER'S STICK

TORSPO

Pro 500

4 ft 9 in (147 cm)

ELBOW PADS

Heavy padding

Flexible gusset

Rigid finger cap

GLOVE

TORSPO

Strap

Wrist protection

DR

Daignault · Rolland

4355 M

DÉFENSE·PRO·DEFENCE

Chest padding

LEG PROTECTOR

Knee protection

Rigid plastic casing

DR

Daignault · Rolland

16.5" 43cm CENTURION-J

Thick foam backing

Leg pad

Vulcanized rubber

3 in (7.62 cm)

FROZEN PUCK

Wide lower shaft

TORSPO

Thin shaft

Ankle support

Safety heel tip

Blade

SKATE

Puck stopper

15 in (39 cm)

12¹/₂ in (32 cm)

Thick blade

Heel

Alpine skiing

DOWNHILL SKIER

COMPETITIVE ALPINE SKIING is divided into four disciplines: downhill, slalom, giant slalom, and super-giant slalom (Super-G). Each one tests different skills. In downhill skiing, competitors race down a slope marked out by control flags, known as "gates," and are timed on a single run only. Competitors wear crash helmets, one-piece Lycra suits, and long skis with flattened tips to minimize air resistance. Slalom and giant slalom skiers negotiate a twisting course requiring balance, agility, and quick reactions. Courses are defined by pairs of gates. Racers must pass through each pair of gates to complete the course successfully. Competitors are timed on two runs over different courses, and the skier who completes the courses in the shortest time wins. The equipment and protective guards used by slalom skiers are shown opposite. In Super-G races, competitors ski a single run that combines the technical challenge of slalom with the speed of downhill. The course requires skiers to complete medium-to-long radius turns at high speed, and contain up to two jumps. Clothing is the same as for downhill, but slightly shorter skis are used.

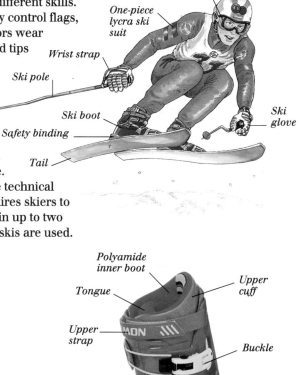

Ski goggles
Helmet
One-piece lycra ski suit
Wrist strap
Ski pole
Basket
Ski boot
Safety binding
Tail
Ski glove

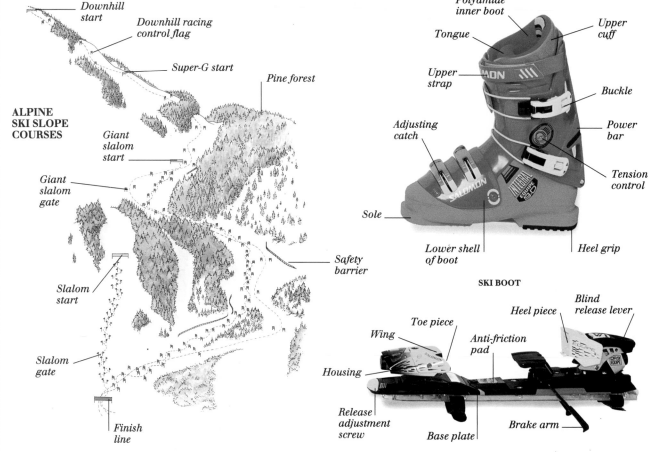

ALPINE SKI SLOPE COURSES

Downhill start
Downhill racing control flag
Super-G start
Pine forest
Giant slalom start
Giant slalom gate
Slalom start
Slalom gate
Safety barrier
Finish line

Polyamide inner boot
Tongue
Upper cuff
Upper strap
Buckle
Adjusting catch
Power bar
Tension control
Sole
Lower shell of boot
Heel grip

SKI BOOT

Toe piece
Heel piece
Blind release lever
Wing
Anti-friction pad
Housing
Release adjustment screw
Base plate
Brake arm

SAFETY BINDING

SLALOM CLOTHING AND EQUIPMENT

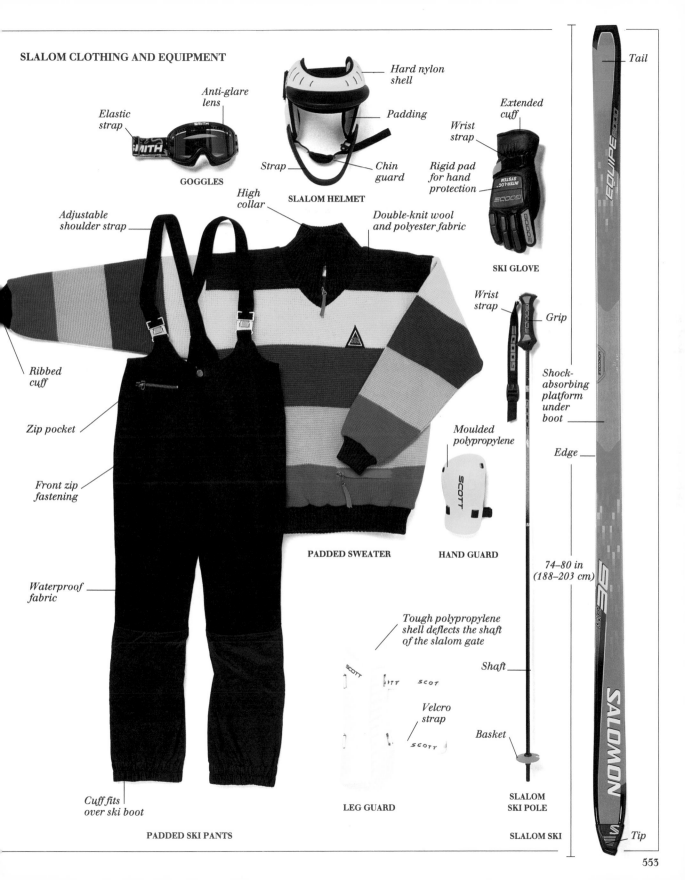

Elastic strap

Anti-glare lens

GOGGLES

Hard nylon shell

Padding

Strap

Chin guard

SLALOM HELMET

Extended cuff

Wrist strap

Rigid pad for hand protection

SKI GLOVE

Tail

Adjustable shoulder strap

High collar

Double-knit wool and polyester fabric

Ribbed cuff

Zip pocket

Front zip fastening

Wrist strap

Grip

Shock-absorbing platform under boot

Edge

Moulded polypropylene

HAND GUARD

PADDED SWEATER

Waterproof fabric

74–80 in (188–203 cm)

Tough polypropylene shell deflects the shaft of the slalom gate

Shaft

Velcro strap

Basket

Cuff fits over ski boot

LEG GUARD

SLALOM SKI POLE

PADDED SKI PANTS

SLALOM SKI

Tip

Equestrian sports

EQUESTRIAN SPORTS HAVE TAKEN place throughout the world for centuries: events involving mounted horses were recorded in the Olympic Games of 642 BC. Show jumping, however, is a much more recent innovation, and the first competitions were held at the beginning of the 1900s. In this sport, horse and rider must negotiate a course of variable, unfixed obstacles, making as few mistakes as possible. Show-jumping fences consist of wooden stands, known as standards or wings, that support planks or poles. Parts of the fence are designed to collapse on impact, preventing injury to the horse and rider. Judges penalize competitors for errors, such as knocking down obstacles, refusing jumps, or deviating from the course. Depending on the type of competition, the rider with the fewest faults, most points, or fastest time wins. There are two basic forms of horse racing – flat races and races with jumps, such as steeplechase or hurdle races. Thoroughbred horses are used in this sport, because they have great strength and stamina and can achieve speeds of up to 40 mph (65 kph). Jockeys wear silks – caps and jackets designed in distinctive colors and patterns which help identify the horses. In harness racing, the horse is driven from a light, two-wheeled carriage called a sulky. Horses are trained to trot and to pace, and different races are held for each of these types of gait. In pacing races, the horses wear hobbles to prevent them from breaking into a trot or gallop. Breeds such as the Standard-bred and the French Trotter have been developed especially for this sport.

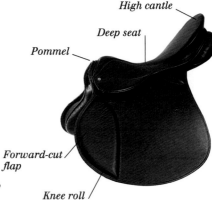

SHOW-JUMPING SADDLE

High cantle
Deep seat
Pommel
Forward-cut flap
Knee roll

SHOW-JUMPING FENCES

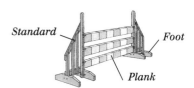

Standard
Foot
Plank

UPRIGHT PLANKS

Standard
Foot
Pole

UPRIGHT POLES

Back pole
Standard
Foot
Pole

TRIPLE BAR (STAIRCASE)

Standard
Pole
Foot

HOG'S-BACK

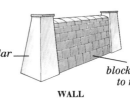

Pillar
Wood block paint to resemb a bri

WALL

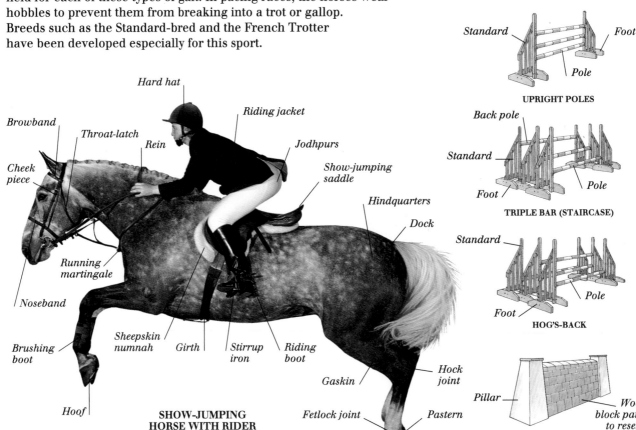

Hard hat
Browband
Throat-latch
Rein
Riding jacket
Jodhpurs
Cheek piece
Show-jumping saddle
Hindquarters
Dock
Running martingale
Noseband
Brushing boot
Sheepskin numnah
Girth
Stirrup iron
Riding boot
Hoof
Gaskin
Hock joint
Fetlock joint
Pastern
Coronet

SHOW-JUMPING HORSE WITH RIDER

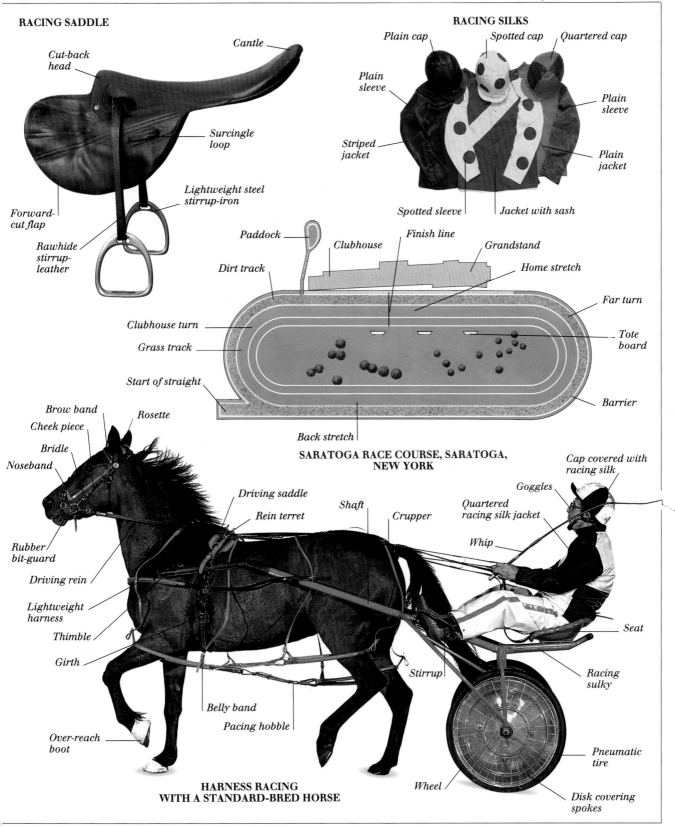

RACING SADDLE

Cut-back head

Cantle

Surcingle loop

Lightweight steel stirrup-iron

Forward-cut flap

Rawhide stirrup-leather

RACING SILKS

Plain cap

Spotted cap

Quartered cap

Plain sleeve

Plain sleeve

Striped jacket

Plain jacket

Spotted sleeve

Jacket with sash

Paddock

Finish line

Clubhouse

Grandstand

Dirt track

Home stretch

Far turn

Clubhouse turn

Grass track

Tote board

Start of straight

Barrier

Back stretch

SARATOGA RACE COURSE, SARATOGA, NEW YORK

Brow band

Rosette

Cheek piece

Driving saddle

Shaft

Crupper

Cap covered with racing silk

Bridle

Rein terret

Goggles

Noseband

Quartered racing silk jacket

Whip

Rubber bit-guard

Driving rein

Lightweight harness

Thimble

Seat

Girth

Racing sulky

Stirrup

Belly band

Pacing hobble

Over-reach boot

Pneumatic tire

Wheel

Disk covering spokes

HARNESS RACING WITH A STANDARD-BRED HORSE

Judo and fencing

COMBAT SPORTS ARE BASED ON THE SKILLS used in fighting. In these sports, the competitors may be unarmed – as in judo and boxing – or armed – as in fencing and kendo. Judo is a system of unarmed combat developed in the East. Translated from the Japanese the name means "the gentle way." Students learn how to turn an opponent's force to their own advantage. The usual uniform is loose white pants and a jacket, fastened with a cloth belt. The color of belt indicates the student's level of expertise, from white-belted novices to the expert black belts. Competitions take place on a mat or "shiaijo," 30 or 33 ft (9 or 10 m) square in size, bounded by "danger" and "safety" areas to prevent injury. Competitors try to throw, pin, or master their opponent by applying pressure to the arm joints or neck. Judo matches are strictly monitored, and competitors receive points for superior technique, not for injuring their opponent. Fencing is a combat sport using swords, which takes place on a narrow piste or strip 46 ft (14 m) long. Competitors try to hit specific target areas on their opponent with their sword or foil while avoiding being touched themselves. The winner is the one who scores the greatest number of hits. Fencers wear uniforms made from strong white material, which affords maximum protection while allowing freedom of movement, steel mesh masks with padded bibs to protect the fencer's neck, and a long white glove on their sword hand. Fencing foils do not have sharpened blades, and their tips end in a blunt button to prevent injuries. Three types of swords are used – foils, épées, and sabres. Official foil and épée competitions always use an electric scoring system. The sword tips are connected to lights by a long wire that passes underneath each fencer's jacket. A bulb flashes when a hit is made.

JUDO HOLDS AND THROWS

SIDE FOUR QUARTER HOLD

SINGLE WING

BODY DROP

ONE ARM SHOULDER THROW

SHOULDER WHEEL

SWEEPING LOW THROW

STOMACH THROW

KNEE WHEEL

JUDO KIT

JUDO MAT

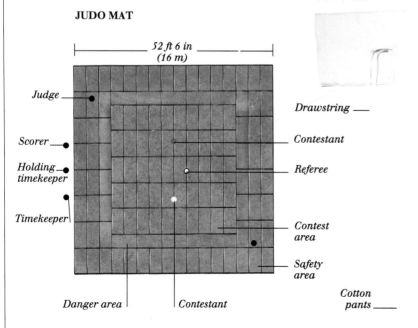

52 ft 6 in (16 m)

Judge

Scorer

Holding timekeeper

Timekeeper

Danger area

Contestant

Drawstring

Contestant

Referee

Contest area

Safety area

Cotton pants

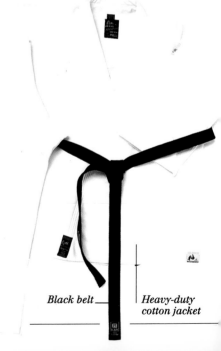

Black belt

Heavy-duty cotton jacket

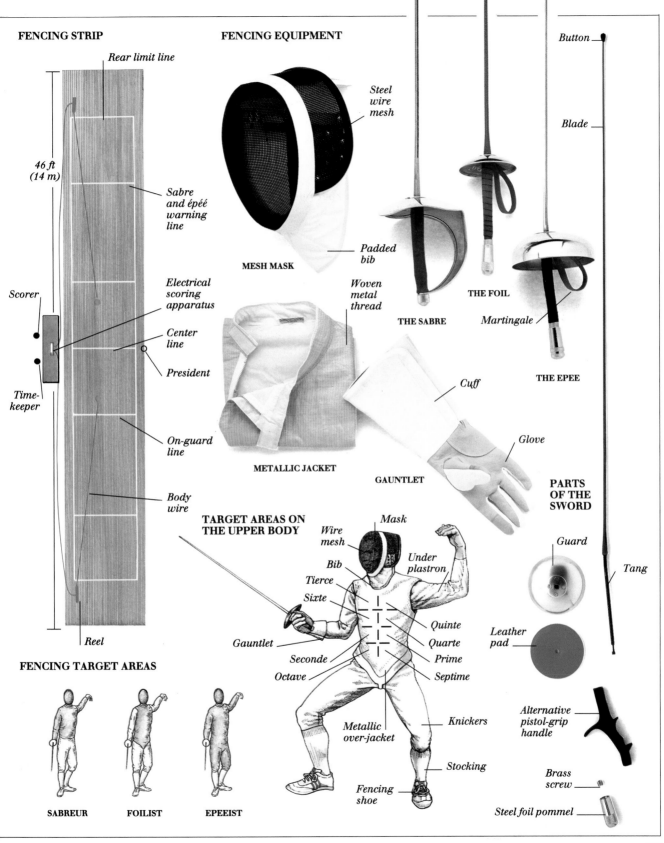

FENCING STRIP

Rear limit line

46 ft (14 m)

Sabre and épéé warning line

Scorer

Electrical scoring apparatus

Center line

President

On-guard line

Body wire

Timekeeper

Reel

FENCING EQUIPMENT

Steel wire mesh

Padded bib

MESH MASK

Woven metal thread

METALLIC JACKET

THE SABRE

THE FOIL

Martingale

THE EPEE

Button

Blade

Cuff

Glove

GAUNTLET

PARTS OF THE SWORD

Guard

Leather pad

Tang

Alternative pistol-grip handle

Brass screw

Steel foil pommel

TARGET AREAS ON THE UPPER BODY

Mask

Wire mesh

Bib

Tierce

Sixte

Under plastron

Quinte

Quarte

Prime

Septime

Gauntlet

Seconde

Octave

Metallic over-jacket

Knickers

Stocking

Fencing shoe

FENCING TARGET AREAS

SABREUR

FOILIST

EPEEIST

Swimming and diving

SWIMMING GOGGLES

SWIMMING WAS INCLUDED in the first modern Olympic Games in 1896 and diving events were added in 1904. Swimming is both an individual and a team sport and races take place over a predetermined distance in one of the four major categories of stroke – freestyle (usually front crawl), butterfly, breaststroke, and backstroke. Competition pools are clearly marked for racing and anti-turbulence lane lines are used to separate the swimmers and help keep the water calm. The first team or individual to finish the race is the winner. Competitive diving is divided into men's and women's springboard and platform (highboard) events. There are six official groups of dives: forward dives, backward dives, armstand dives, twist dives, reverse dives, and inward dives. Competitors perform a set number of dives and after each one a panel of judges awards marks according to the quality of execution and the degree of difficulty.

STYLES OF DIVES

Starting position

Hands above head

Legs fully stretched

Flight

Arched back

Toes pointed

Entry

Feet together

Hands close together

FORWARD DIVE

BACKWARD DIVE

SWIMWEAR

Latex rubber molds to shape of head

CAPS

Rubber-covered wire

NOSE CLIP

Molded rubber

EARPLUG

High neckline

Man-made stretch fabric

Drawstring

High-cut leg

Strong seam

SWIMSUIT

TRUNKS

SWIMMING POOL

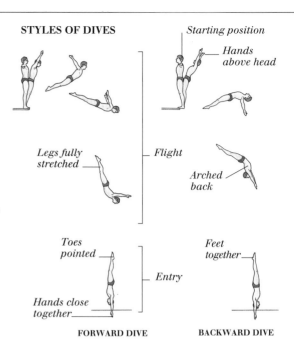

Swimmer

Lane number

Starting block

Lane timekeeper

Chief timekeeper

End wall

Placing judge

Starter

Recorder

Side wall

Backstroke marker 49 ft (15 m) from end of pool

Anti-turbulence lane line

Referee

Stroke judge

Backstroke turn indicator 16 ft (5 m) from end of pool

High-cut leg

Bottom line

Turning judge

Turning wall

Lane

75 ft 6 in (23 m)

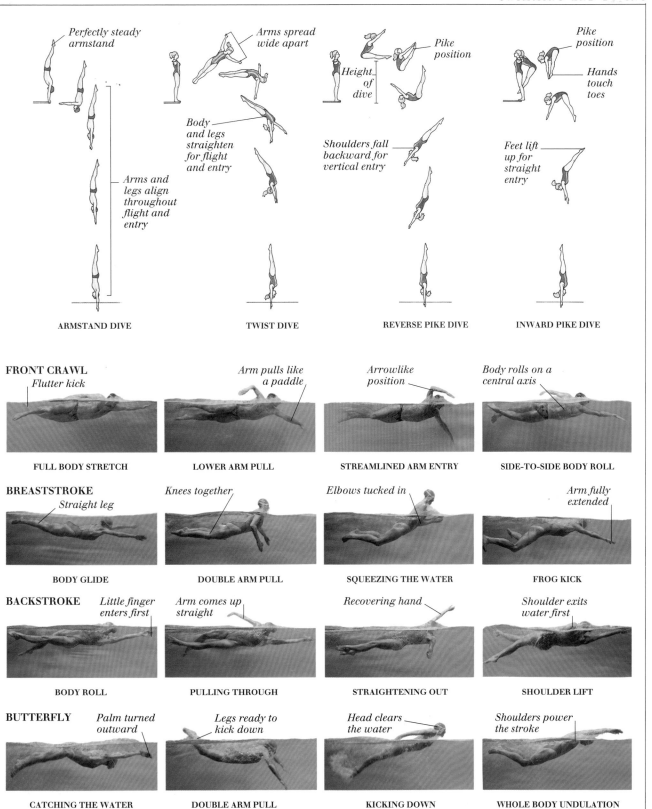

Perfectly steady armstand

Arms and legs align throughout flight and entry

ARMSTAND DIVE

Arms spread wide apart

Body and legs straighten for flight and entry

TWIST DIVE

Pike position

Height of dive

Shoulders fall backward for vertical entry

REVERSE PIKE DIVE

Pike position

Hands touch toes

Feet lift up for straight entry

INWARD PIKE DIVE

FRONT CRAWL
Flutter kick

FULL BODY STRETCH

Arm pulls like a paddle

LOWER ARM PULL

Arrowlike position

STREAMLINED ARM ENTRY

Body rolls on a central axis

SIDE-TO-SIDE BODY ROLL

BREASTSTROKE
Straight leg

BODY GLIDE

Knees together

DOUBLE ARM PULL

Elbows tucked in

SQUEEZING THE WATER

Arm fully extended

FROG KICK

BACKSTROKE
Little finger enters first

BODY ROLL

Arm comes up straight

PULLING THROUGH

Recovering hand

STRAIGHTENING OUT

Shoulder exits water first

SHOULDER LIFT

BUTTERFLY
Palm turned outward

CATCHING THE WATER

Legs ready to kick down

DOUBLE ARM PULL

Head clears the water

KICKING DOWN

Shoulders power the stroke

WHOLE BODY UNDULATION

Kayaking, rowing, and sailing

WATERBORNE SPORTS are as varied as the crafts used. There are two disciplines in rowing; sweep rowing, in which each rower has one oar, and sculling, in which rowers use two oars. There are a number of different Olympic and competitive rowing events for both men and women. The number of rowers and weight classes vary. Some rowing events use a coxswain; a steersman who does not row but directs the crew. Kayaks are used in straight sprint and slalom races. Slalom races take place over a course consisting of 20 to 25 gates, including at least six upstream gates. In yacht racing, competitors must complete prescribed courses, organized by the race committees, in the shortest possible time, using sail power only. Olympic events include classes for keel boats, dinghies, catamarans, and windsurfers.

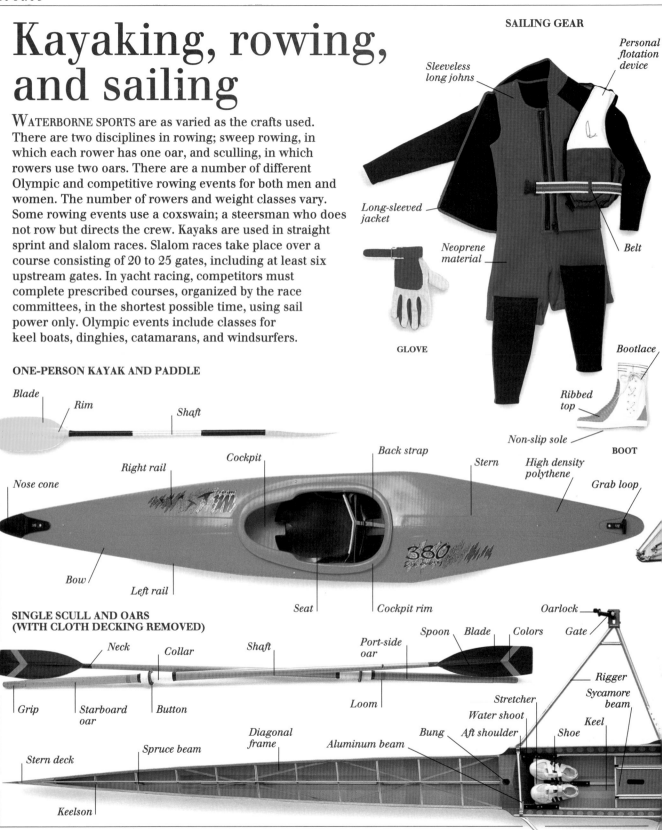

SAILING GEAR

Sleeveless long johns

Personal flotation device

Long-sleeved jacket

Neoprene material

Belt

GLOVE

Bootlace

Ribbed top

Non-slip sole

BOOT

ONE-PERSON KAYAK AND PADDLE

Blade

Rim

Shaft

Nose cone

Right rail

Cockpit

Back strap

Stern

High density polythene

Grab loop

Bow

Left rail

Seat

Cockpit rim

**SINGLE SCULL AND OARS
(WITH CLOTH DECKING REMOVED)**

Neck

Collar

Shaft

Port-side oar

Spoon

Blade

Colors

Oarlock

Gate

Grip

Starboard oar

Button

Loom

Rigger

Sycamore beam

Stretcher

Water shoot

Bung

Aft shoulder

Shoe

Keel

Stern deck

Spruce beam

Diagonal frame

Aluminum beam

Keelson

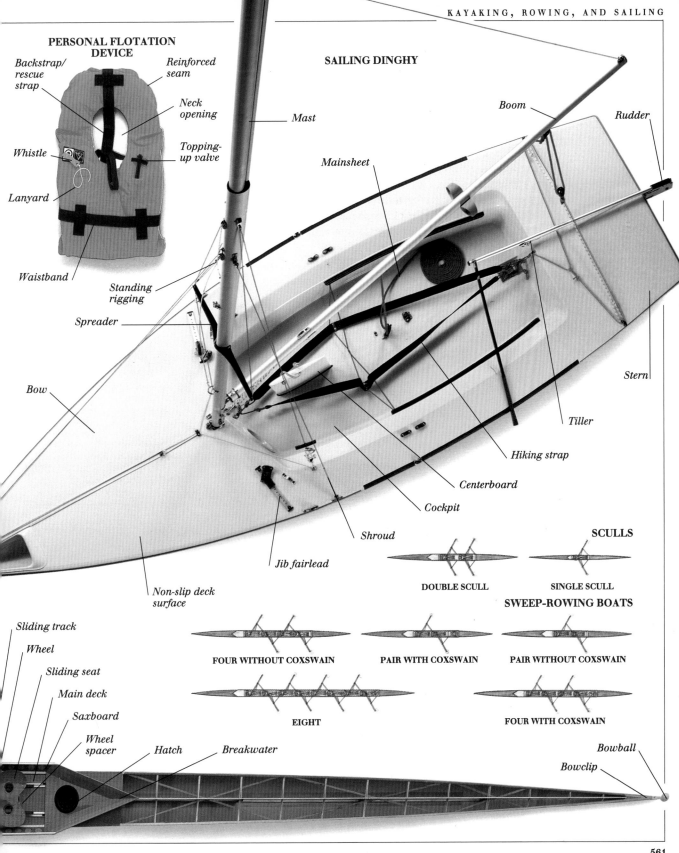

PERSONAL FLOTATION DEVICE

Backstrap/ rescue strap

Reinforced seam

Neck opening

Whistle

Topping-up valve

Lanyard

Waistband

Standing rigging

Spreader

Bow

SAILING DINGHY

Mast

Boom

Rudder

Mainsheet

Stern

Tiller

Hiking strap

Centerboard

Cockpit

Shroud

Jib fairlead

Non-slip deck surface

SCULLS

DOUBLE SCULL

SINGLE SCULL

SWEEP-ROWING BOATS

FOUR WITHOUT COXSWAIN

PAIR WITH COXSWAIN

PAIR WITHOUT COXSWAIN

EIGHT

FOUR WITH COXSWAIN

Sliding track

Wheel

Sliding seat

Main deck

Saxboard

Wheel spacer

Hatch

Breakwater

Bowball

Bowclip

Angling

ANGLING MEANS FISHING WITH A ROD, reel, line, and lure. There are several different types of angling: freshwater coarse angling, for members of the carp family and pike; freshwater game angling, for salmon and trout; and sea angling, for sea fish such as flatfish, bass, and mackerel. Anglers use a variety of methods of catching fish. These include bait fishing, in which bait (food to allure the fish) is placed on a hook and cast into the water; fly fishing, in which a natural or artificial fly is used to lure the fish; and spinning, in which a lure that looks like a small fish revolves as it is pulled through the water. The angler uses the rod, reel, and line to cast the lure over the water. The reel controls the line as it spills off the spool and as it is wound back. Weights may be fixed to the line so that it will sink. Swivels are attached to prevent the line from twisting. When a fish bites, the hook must become embedded in its mouth and remain there while the catch is reeled in.

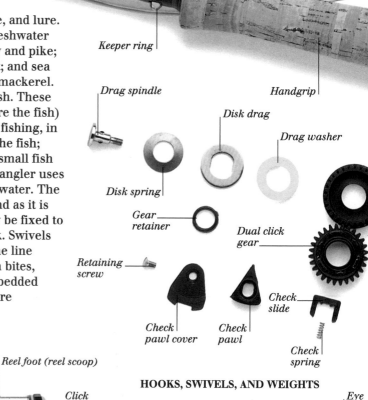

BUTT SECTION

Keeper ring

Drag spindle

Disk drag

Handgrip

Drag washer

Disk spring

Gear retainer

Dual click gear

Retaining screw

Check slide

Check pawl cover

Check pawl

Check spring

REELS

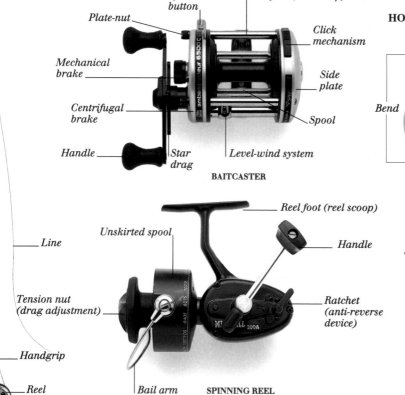

Plate-nut

Spool-release button

Reel foot (reel scoop)

Click mechanism

Mechanical brake

Side plate

Centrifugal brake

Spool

Handle

Star drag

Level-wind system

BAITCASTER

Unskirted spool

Reel foot (reel scoop)

Handle

Line

Ratchet (anti-reverse device)

Tension nut (drag adjustment)

Handgrip

Reel

Bail arm

SPINNING REEL

HOOKS, SWIVELS, AND WEIGHTS

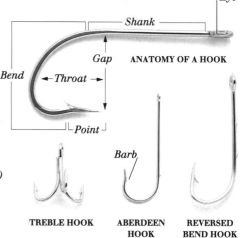

Eye

Shank

Gap

ANATOMY OF A HOOK

Bend

Throat

Point

Barb

TREBLE HOOK

ABERDEEN HOOK

REVERSED BEND HOOK

EXAMPLES OF BARREL SWIVELS

HILLMAN ANTI-KINK WEIGHT

FLY ROD AND REEL

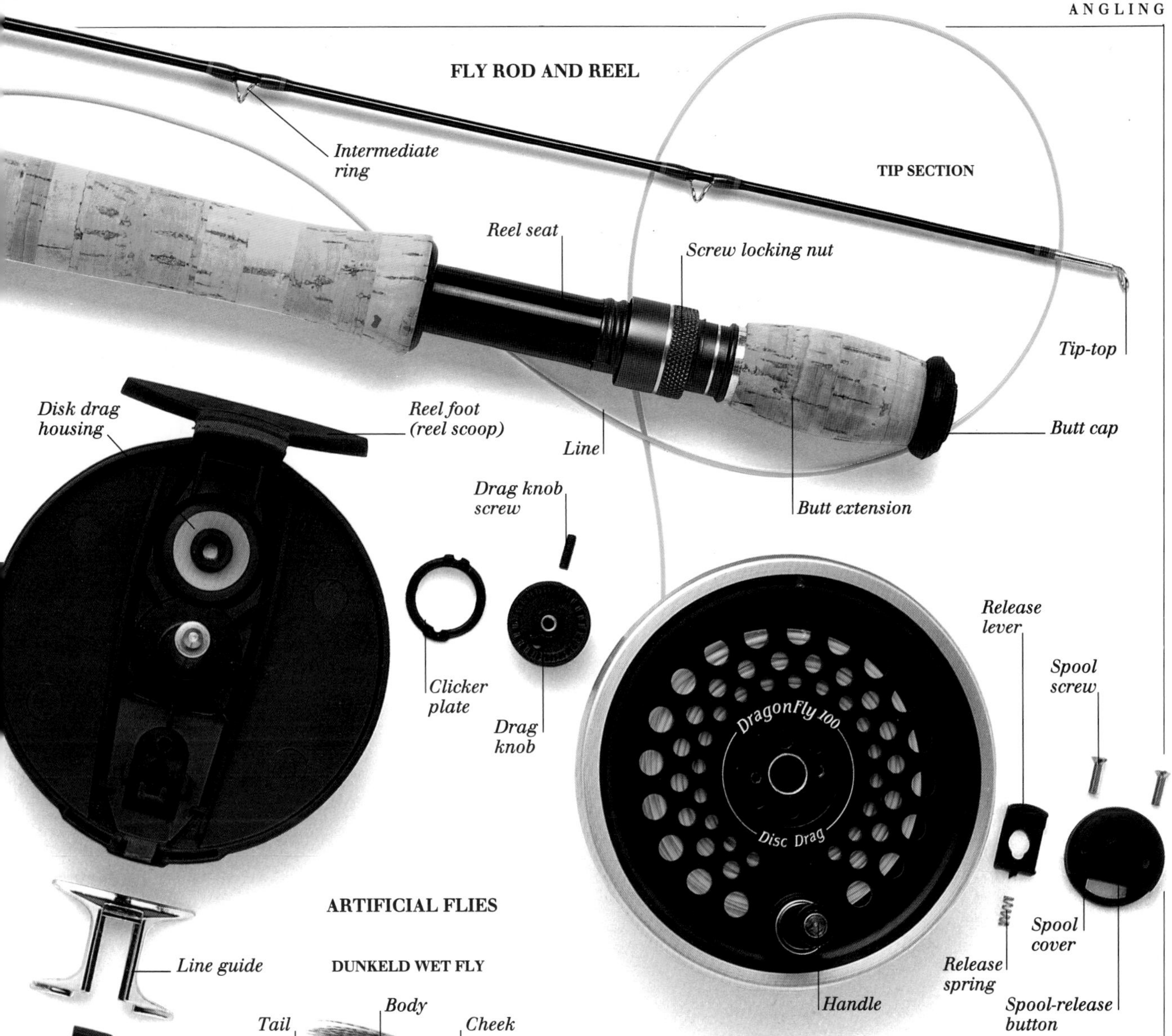

Intermediate ring

TIP SECTION

Reel seat

Screw locking nut

Tip-top

Butt cap

Disk drag housing

Reel foot (reel scoop)

Line

Drag knob screw

Butt extension

Release lever

Spool screw

Clicker plate

DragonFly 100

Disc Drag

Spool cover

Drag knob

ARTIFICIAL FLIES

Line guide

DUNKELD WET FLY

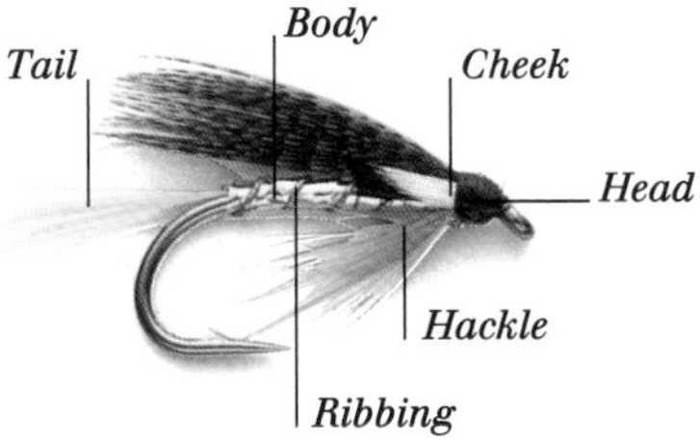

Body

Tail

Cheek

Head

Release spring

Spool-release button

Handle

Line guide cover

Hackle

Retaining screw

Ribbing

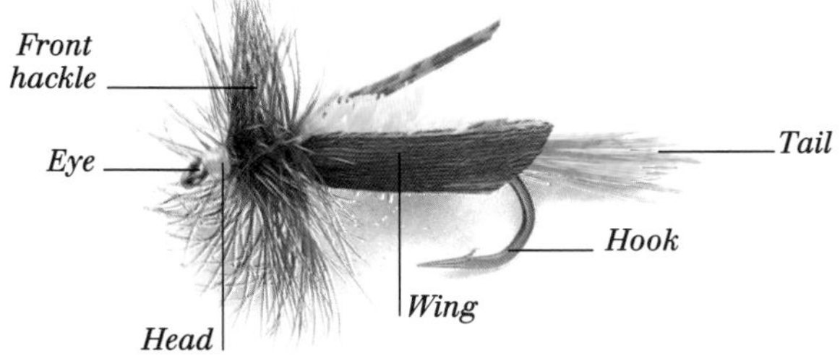

ARTIFICIAL LURES

DEVON MINNOW

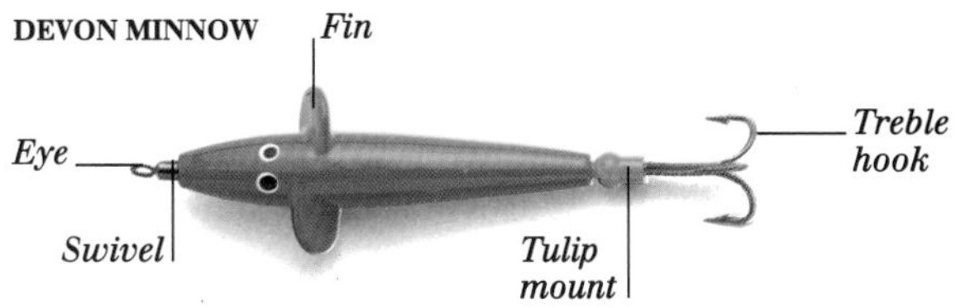

Fin

Eye

Treble hook

Swivel

Tulip mount

DEER HOPPER DRY FLY

Front hackle

Eye

Tail

JOINTED PLUG

Hook

Adjustable vane

Joint

Wing

Head

Treble hook

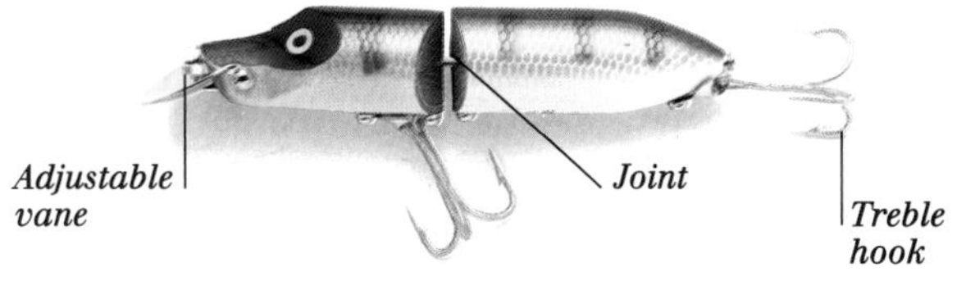

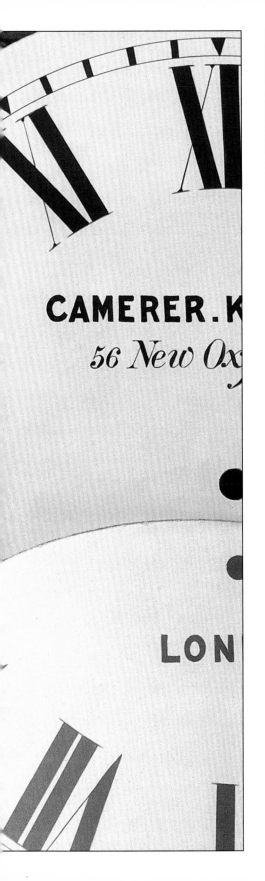

EVERYDAY THINGS

DRILLS 566

SHOES 568

CLOCK 570

LAMP 572

MINI-TELEVISION 574

CHAIR 576

TOASTER 578

LAWNMOWER 580

SADDLE 582

CD-ROM 584

BOOKS 586

CAMERA 588

Drills

THE ELECTRICALLY POWERED MOTOR OF A POWER DRILL, cooled by a fan, turns a shaft at high speed. The shaft connects, in turn, to a system of gears that rotates a chuck even faster. Clamped by the chuck, a sharp drill bit cuts out the hole, and at the same time the bit's screw-shaped grooves channel the waste out of the hole. For drilling hard materials, many power drills have a hammer mechanism; when this is operated a ratchet in the gearcase causes the chuck and bit to pound in and out as they drill. A hand drill, although slower and less forceful than a power drill, is easier to control. For cutting wide holes, carpenters often prefer a brace-and-bit. This acts like a lever: the bowed handle of the brace moves a larger distance than the bit, turning the bit with extra force.

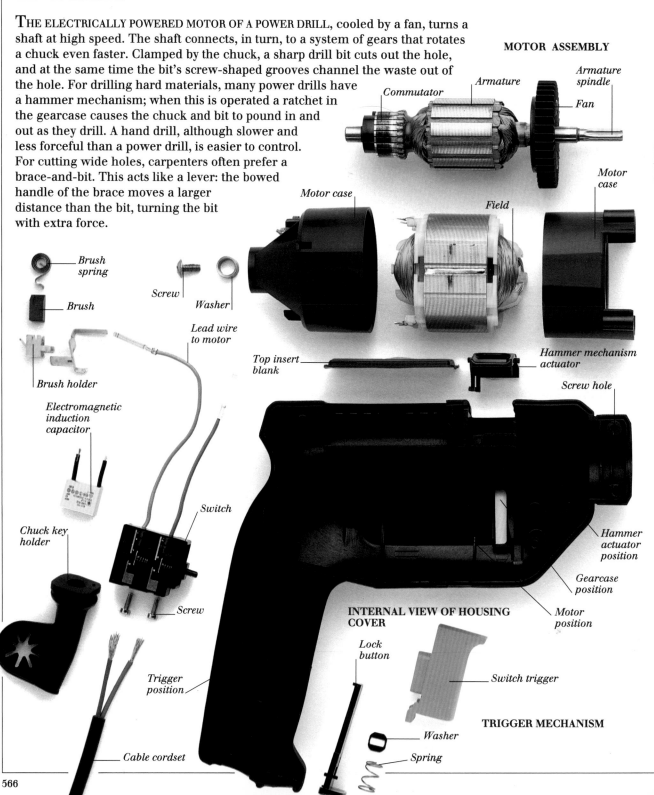

MOTOR ASSEMBLY

Commutator · Armature · Armature spindle · Fan · Motor case · Field

Brush spring · Brush · Screw · Washer · Brush holder · Lead wire to motor · Electromagnetic induction capacitor · Top insert blank · Hammer mechanism actuator · Screw hole · Chuck key holder · Switch · Screw · Hammer actuator position · Gearcase position · Motor position

INTERNAL VIEW OF HOUSING COVER

Lock button · Switch trigger · Trigger position · Cable cordset · Washer · Spring

TRIGGER MECHANISM

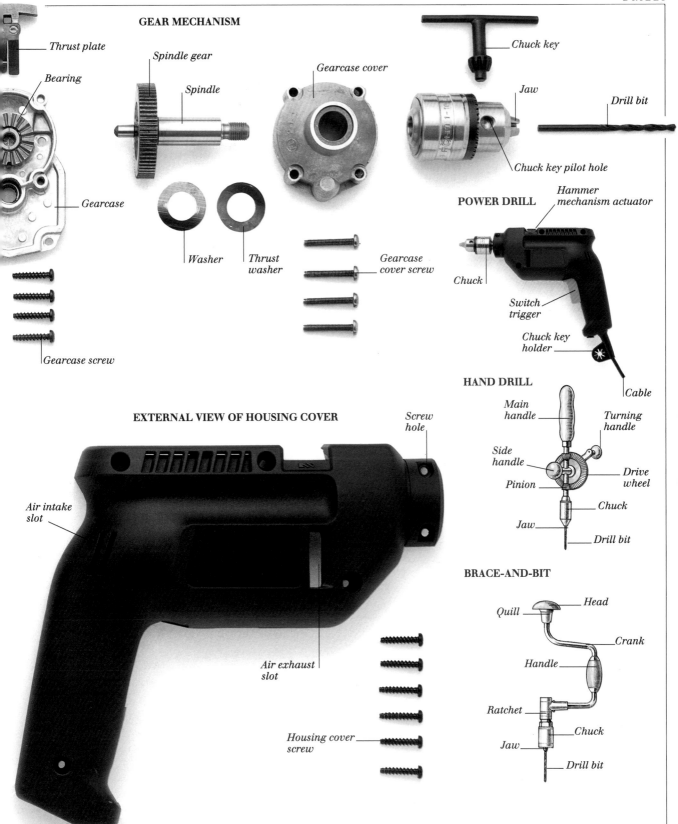

GEAR MECHANISM

Thrust plate

Bearing

Gearcase

Gearcase screw

Spindle gear

Spindle

Washer

Thrust washer

Gearcase cover

Gearcase cover screw

Chuck key

Jaw

Chuck key pilot hole

Drill bit

POWER DRILL

Hammer mechanism actuator

Chuck

Switch trigger

Chuck key holder

Cable

HAND DRILL

Main handle

Turning handle

Side handle

Pinion

Drive wheel

Chuck

Jaw

Drill bit

EXTERNAL VIEW OF HOUSING COVER

Screw hole

Air intake slot

Air exhaust slot

Housing cover screw

BRACE-AND-BIT

Quill

Head

Crank

Handle

Ratchet

Chuck

Jaw

Drill bit

Shoes

WELL MADE SHOES PROTECT THE FEET and are also comfortable and long lasting. The best shoemakers use a wood or plastic mold, called a last, which matches the shape of the customer's foot. The different parts of a shoe are stitched and glued together around the last; rivets and nails are used only in the heel, which is built up from layers of leather and rubber. The steel shank gives support to the arch of the foot and, with the seat lift, helps the wearer maintain posture. The layers of the sole give strength, while the soft insole cushions the foot. The leather welt sewn between the leather uppers and the sole ensures a strong join.

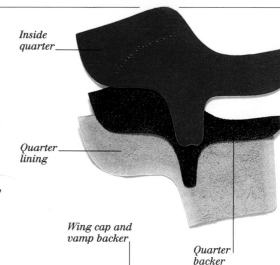

Inside quarter

Quarter lining

Wing cap and vamp backer

Quarter backer

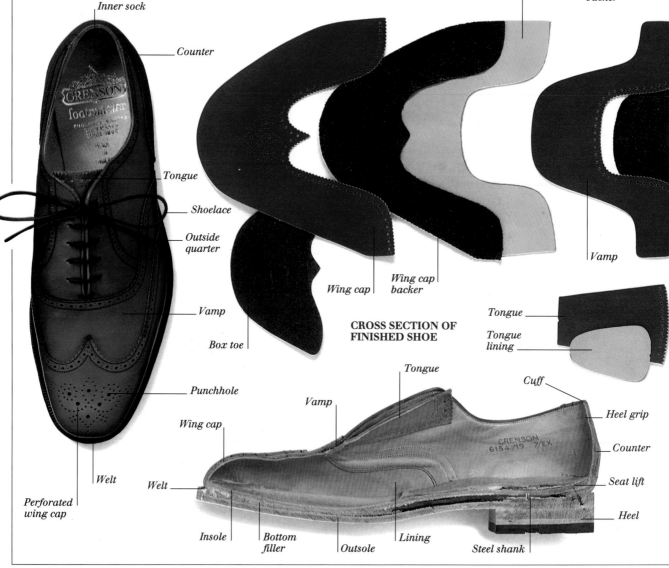

Inner sock

Counter

Tongue

Shoelace

Outside quarter

Vamp

Box toe

Wing cap

Wing cap backer

Vamp

Tongue

Tongue lining

Punchhole

CROSS SECTION OF FINISHED SHOE

Welt

Perforated wing cap

Wing cap

Welt

Vamp

Tongue

Cuff

Heel grip

Counter

Seat lift

Heel

Insole

Bottom filler

Outsole

Lining

Steel shank

CRENSON 6154/19 7/EX

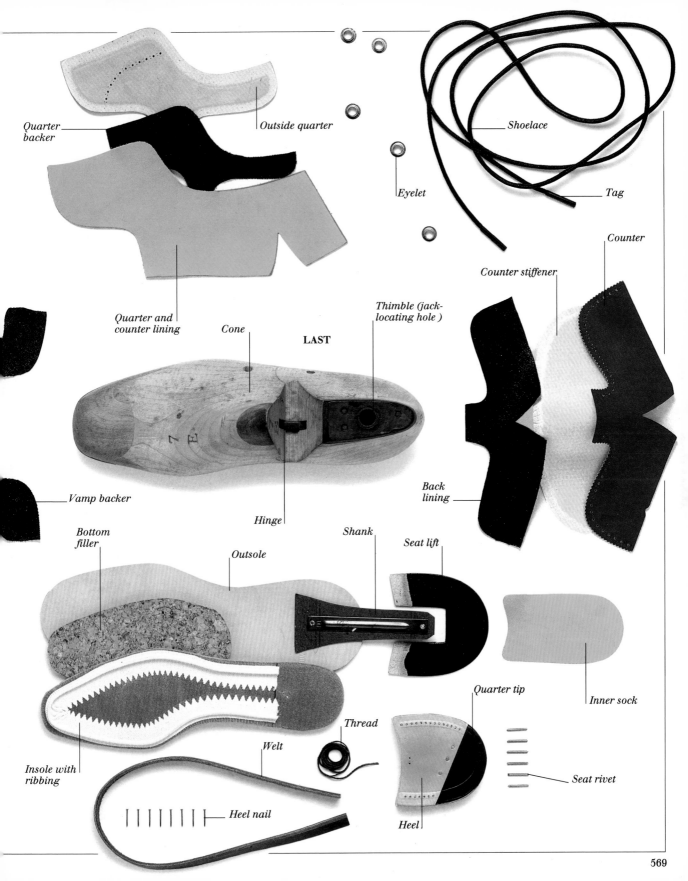

Quarter backer

Outside quarter

Shoelace

Eyelet

Tag

Counter

Counter stiffener

Quarter and counter lining

Cone

LAST

Thimble (jack-locating hole)

Back lining

Vamp backer

Hinge

Shank

Seat lift

Bottom filler

Outsole

Inner sock

Quarter tip

Insole with ribbing

Thread

Welt

Seat rivet

Heel nail

Heel

569

Clock

MECHANICAL CLOCKS HAVE TWO essential elements: a mainspring and a pendulum. When the clock is wound with the key, the mainspring is tightened. As the mainspring unwinds, it turns the gears, which move the minute and hour hands at different speeds around the face of the clock. The pendulum ensures that the hands move at a regular pace. At the top of the pendulum are two hooks called pallets. As the pendulum swings, the pallets allow the escape wheel to turn slowly and evenly.

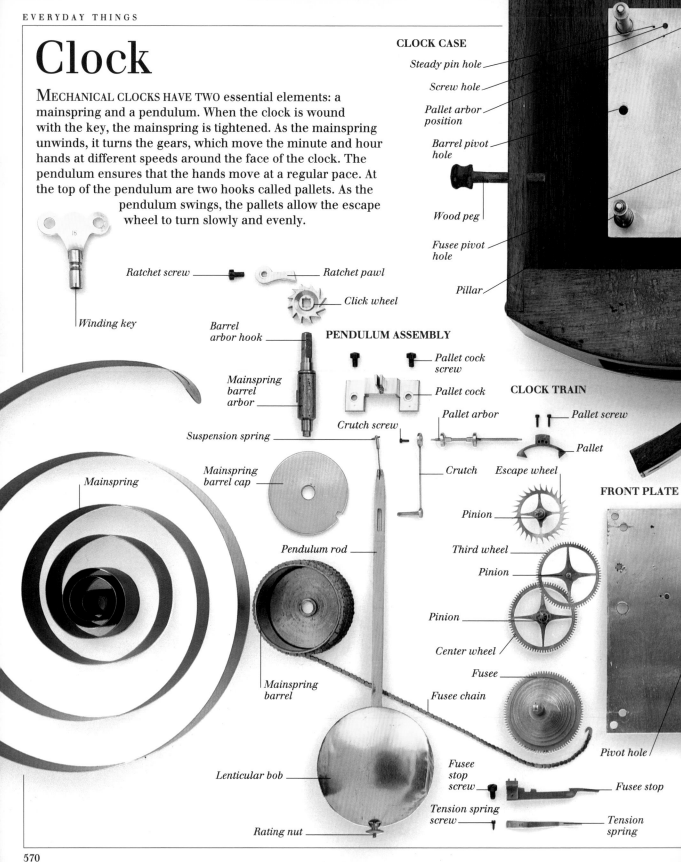

CLOCK CASE

Steady pin hole

Screw hole

Pallet arbor position

Barrel pivot hole

Wood peg

Fusee pivot hole

Pillar

Winding key

Ratchet screw

Ratchet pawl

Click wheel

PENDULUM ASSEMBLY

Barrel arbor hook

Mainspring barrel arbor

Suspension spring

Crutch screw

Pallet cock screw

Pallet cock

Pallet arbor

CLOCK TRAIN

Pallet screw

Pallet

Crutch

Escape wheel

Mainspring

Mainspring barrel cap

Pendulum rod

Pinion

FRONT PLATE

Third wheel

Pinion

Pinion

Center wheel

Mainspring barrel

Fusee

Fusee chain

Pivot hole

Lenticular bob

Fusee stop screw

Fusee stop

Tension spring screw

Tension spring

Rating nut

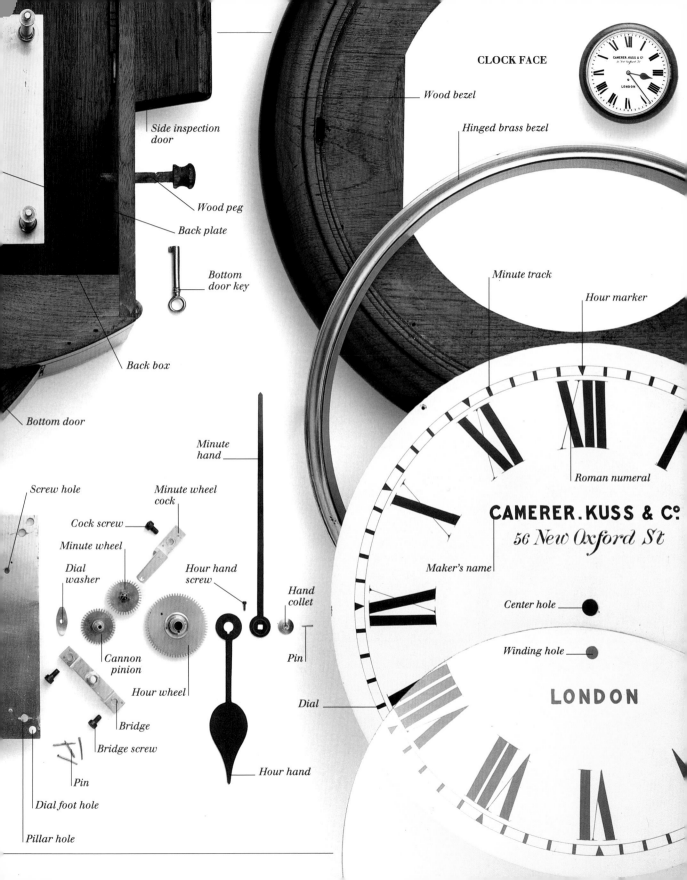

Side inspection door

Wood peg

Back plate

Bottom door key

Back box

Bottom door

Screw hole

Minute wheel cock

Cock screw

Minute wheel

Dial washer

Hour hand screw

Minute hand

Hand collet

Pin

Cannon pinion

Hour wheel

Bridge

Bridge screw

Pin

Dial foot hole

Pillar hole

Hour hand

Dial

CLOCK FACE

Wood bezel

Hinged brass bezel

Minute track

Hour marker

Roman numeral

CAMERER. KUSS & C°.
56 New Oxford St

Maker's name

Center hole

Winding hole

LONDON

Lamp

THE FIRST SPRING-TENSIONED, adjustable work lamp was designed in 1934 by George Carwardine. This type of lamp imitates the human arm in the way that it can be kept in a fixed position or moved easily and precisely. In the arm, such control is achieved by coordinating the opposing action of paired muscles (e.g., when the biceps contracts, the triceps relaxes and the arm bends). In the work lamp, one muscle of a pair is represented by the springs that pull on the rigid bars of the lamp; the other muscle is represented by the nuts, bolts, screws, and washers in the lamp's joints that resist the pull of the springs. By balancing the pull of the springs against the resistance in the joints, the lamp's height and angle can be adjusted with minimal pressure.

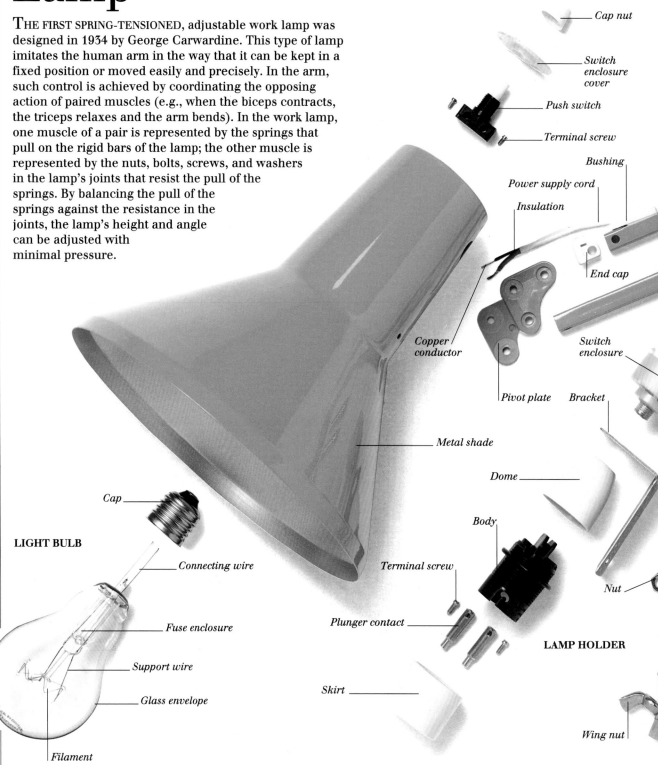

Cap nut

Switch enclosure cover

Push switch

Terminal screw

Bushing

Power supply cord

Insulation

End cap

Copper conductor

Switch enclosure

Pivot plate

Bracket

Metal shade

Dome

Body

Cap

LIGHT BULB

Connecting wire

Terminal screw

Nut

Fuse enclosure

Plunger contact

LAMP HOLDER

Support wire

Glass envelope

Skirt

Filament

Wing nut

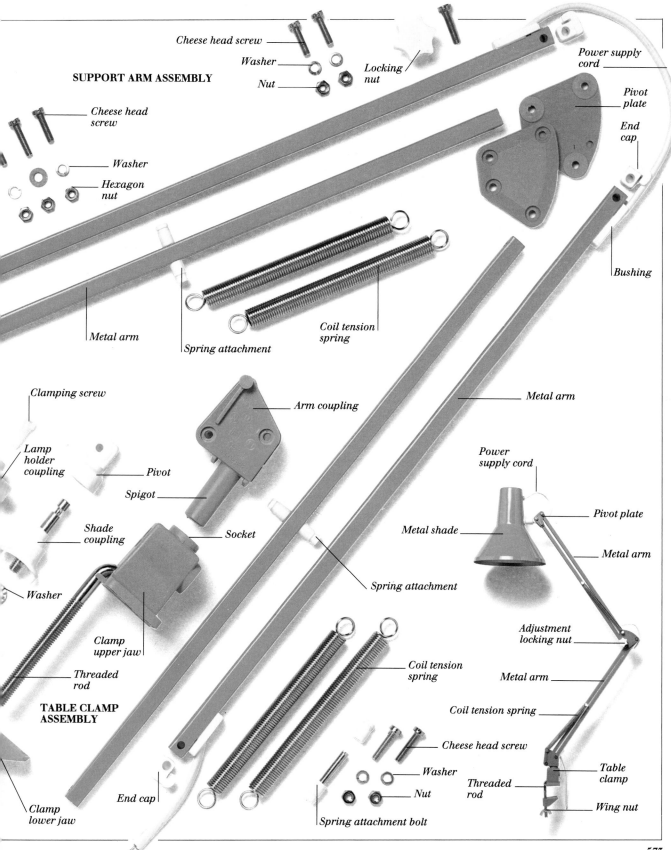

SUPPORT ARM ASSEMBLY

Cheese head screw

Washer

Nut

Locking nut

Power supply cord

Pivot plate

End cap

Cheese head screw

Washer

Hexagon nut

Bushing

Metal arm

Spring attachment

Coil tension spring

Metal arm

Clamping screw

Arm coupling

Lamp holder coupling

Pivot

Power supply cord

Spigot

Metal shade

Pivot plate

Shade coupling

Socket

Metal arm

Washer

Spring attachment

Clamp upper jaw

Adjustment locking nut

Threaded rod

Metal arm

Coil tension spring

TABLE CLAMP ASSEMBLY

Coil tension spring

Cheese head screw

Washer

Table clamp

Clamp lower jaw

End cap

Nut

Threaded rod

Wing nut

Spring attachment bolt

Mini television

MINIATURIZED TELEVISION SETS are small enough to be held in the hand while being watched. A signal sent by a broadcast transmitter is picked up by the television antenna and passed to an electron gun at the back of the television set. In response to the signal this gun produces an electron beam that is passed through a deflection yoke. The yoke contains magnets and coils that cause the beam to scan across the screen in a series of lines. The screen is coated with phosphor, which glows when hit by the beam. As the beam scans the screen, its strength is varied so that the phosphor glows with different intensities in different parts of the screen. A continuous sequence of 25 black-and-white pictures per second appears on the screen so rapidly that the illusion of a moving picture is created.

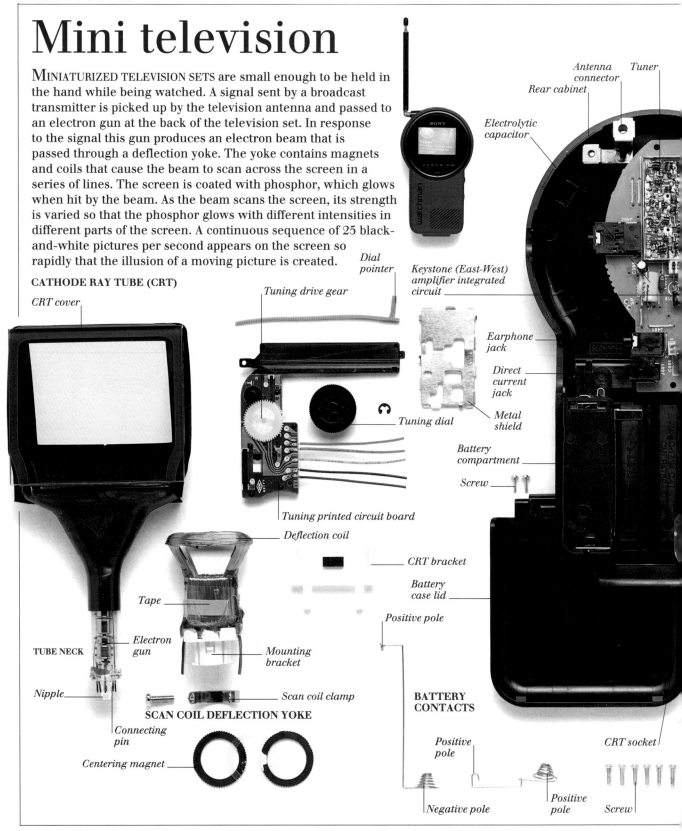

CATHODE RAY TUBE (CRT)

CRT cover

Dial pointer

Tuning drive gear

Keystone (East-West) amplifier integrated circuit

Earphone jack

Direct current jack

Tuning dial

Metal shield

Battery compartment

Screw

Tuning printed circuit board

Deflection coil

CRT bracket

Tape

Battery case lid

Electron gun

Mounting bracket

Positive pole

TUBE NECK

Scan coil clamp

BATTERY CONTACTS

Nipple

SCAN COIL DEFLECTION YOKE

Positive pole

CRT socket

Connecting pin

Centering magnet

Negative pole

Positive pole

Screw

Antenna connector

Tuner

Rear cabinet

Electrolytic capacitor

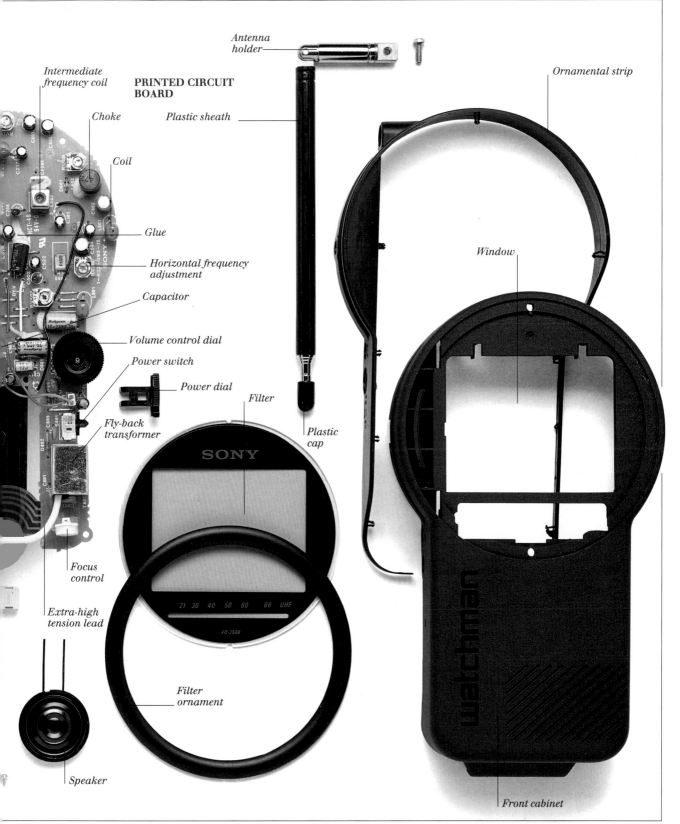

Intermediate frequency coil

PRINTED CIRCUIT BOARD

Antenna holder

Ornamental strip

Choke

Plastic sheath

Coil

Window

Glue

Horizontal frequency adjustment

Capacitor

Volume control dial

Power switch

Power dial

Plastic cap

Fly-back transformer

Filter

SONY

Focus control

Extra-high tension lead

21 30 40 50 60 68 UHF

FD-250B

Filter ornament

Front cabinet

Speaker

Chair

A TRADITIONALLY MADE DINING CHAIR, such as the Regency-style carver shown here, is held together, not by nails or bolts, but by snugly fitting joints, screws, dowels, and glue. Its curved arms and top splats, as well as its tapering legs, are cut from seasoned—that is, dried—mahogany. Mortice slots in the back legs receive the tenon tongues of the top and bottom splats; angled grooves at the top of the back legs, called rebates, take the curved arm rail. Though the various joints are so tight-fitting that they could produce a solid frame on their own, screws and glue are used to give the joints added strength. The comfortable, upholstered seat pad shown here consists of a patterned cover, calico lining, and foam padding that has been treated for fire safety; it is supported by webbing stretched across a wood frame.

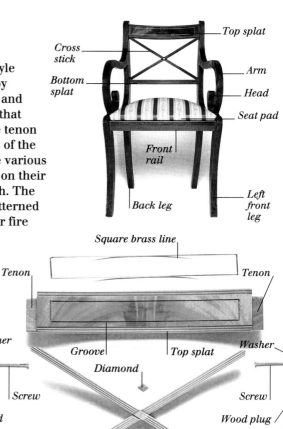

Cross stick
Top splat
Arm
Bottom splat
Head
Seat pad
Front rail
Back leg
Left front leg

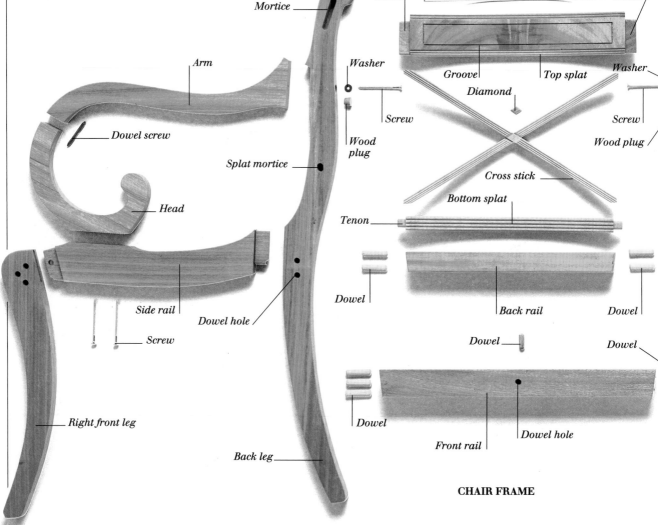

Mortice
Arm
Dowel screw
Head
Splat mortice
Side rail
Screw
Dowel hole
Right front leg
Back leg

Washer
Screw
Wood plug
Tenon
Dowel

Square brass line
Tenon
Tenon
Groove
Top splat
Washer
Diamond
Screw
Wood plug
Cross stick
Bottom splat
Back rail
Dowel
Dowel
Dowel
Dowel
Front rail
Dowel hole
Dowel

CHAIR FRAME

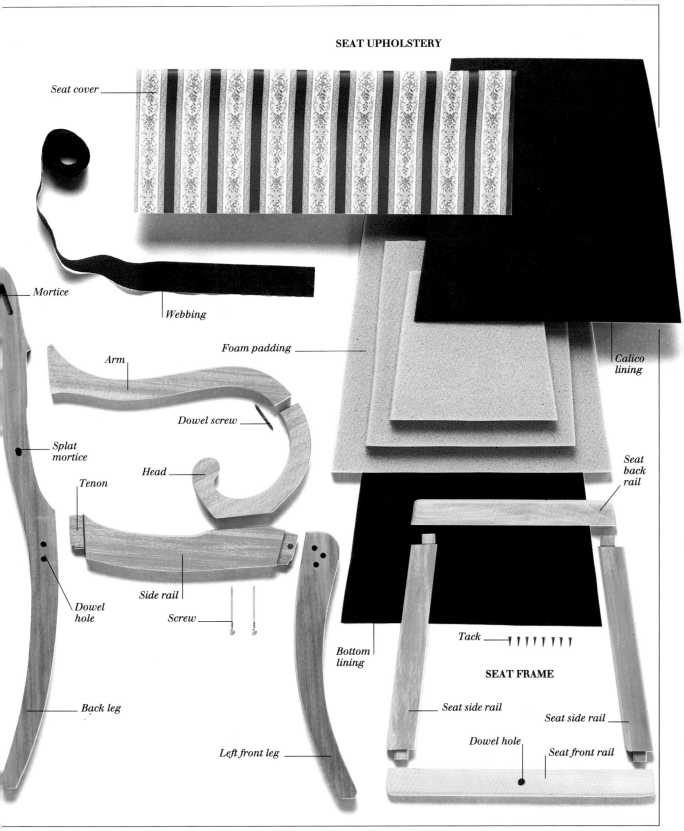

SEAT UPHOLSTERY

Seat cover

Mortice

Webbing

Arm

Dowel screw

Foam padding

Calico lining

Splat mortice

Head

Tenon

Seat back rail

Side rail

Screw

Dowel hole

Back leg

Bottom lining

Tack

SEAT FRAME

Seat side rail

Left front leg

Seat side rail

Dowel hole

Seat front rail

Toaster

MOST ELECTRIC TOASTERS NOT ONLY GRILL slices of bread, they also pop them up when ready. While the slices rest on a spring-loaded rack, electric heating elements toast the bread. At the same time, a bimetallic strip heats and expands. One of the two metals in this strip expands more quickly than the other, causing the strip to curve. As it bends, it completes an electrical circuit and activates an electromagnet. The magnet attracts a catch, releasing the spring that holds the rack down in the toaster. The elements switch off, and the toasted slices pop up.

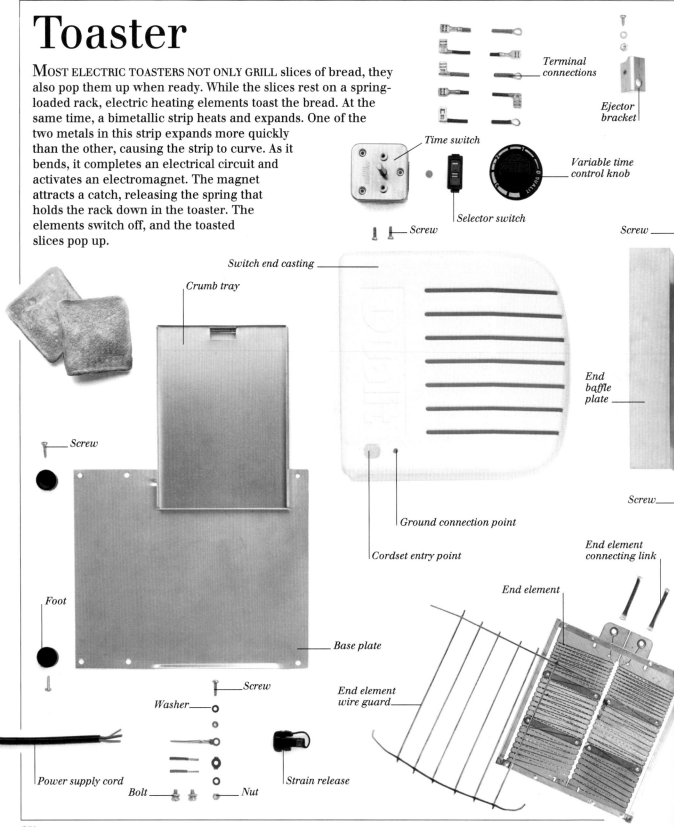

Terminal connections

Ejector bracket

Time switch

Variable time control knob

Selector switch

Screw

Screw

Switch end casting

Crumb tray

End baffle plate

Screw

Screw

Ground connection point

Cordset entry point

End element connecting link

End element

Foot

Base plate

End element wire guard

Screw

Washer

Power supply cord

Bolt

Nut

Strain release

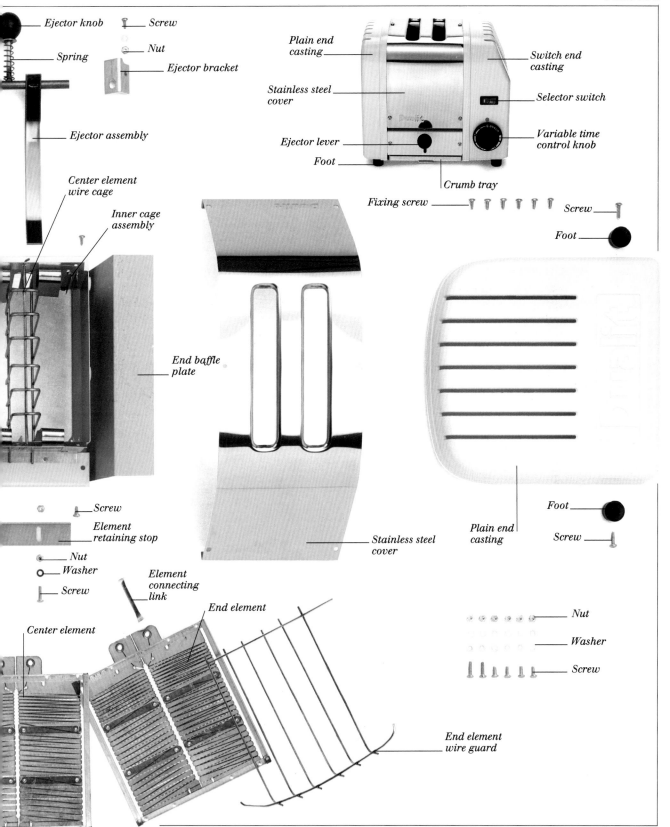

Ejector knob

Screw

Spring

Nut

Ejector bracket

Plain end casting

Switch end casting

Stainless steel cover

Selector switch

Ejector assembly

Ejector lever

Variable time control knob

Foot

Crumb tray

Center element wire cage

Fixing screw

Screw

Inner cage assembly

Foot

End baffle plate

Screw

Element retaining stop

Foot

Nut

Washer

Screw

Stainless steel cover

Plain end casting

Screw

Element connecting link

End element

Nut

Washer

Center element

Screw

End element wire guard

Lawnmower

THE SHARP BLADES OF A LAWNMOWER—whether driven by electrical, gasoline, or human power—shave grass close to the ground. The gasoline-powered type shown here has a small engine that is electrically ignited by a battery and spark plug. This engine rotates a horizontal blade at the base of the lawnmower, which then slices the grass against a fixed blade. A grass bag at the back of the machine collects the cuttings. As the engine rotates the blades, it also turns the rear wheels, moving the lawnmower forward. Gears ensure that the horizontal blade spins faster than the wheels so that all of the grass is cut neatly before the lawnmower moves on.

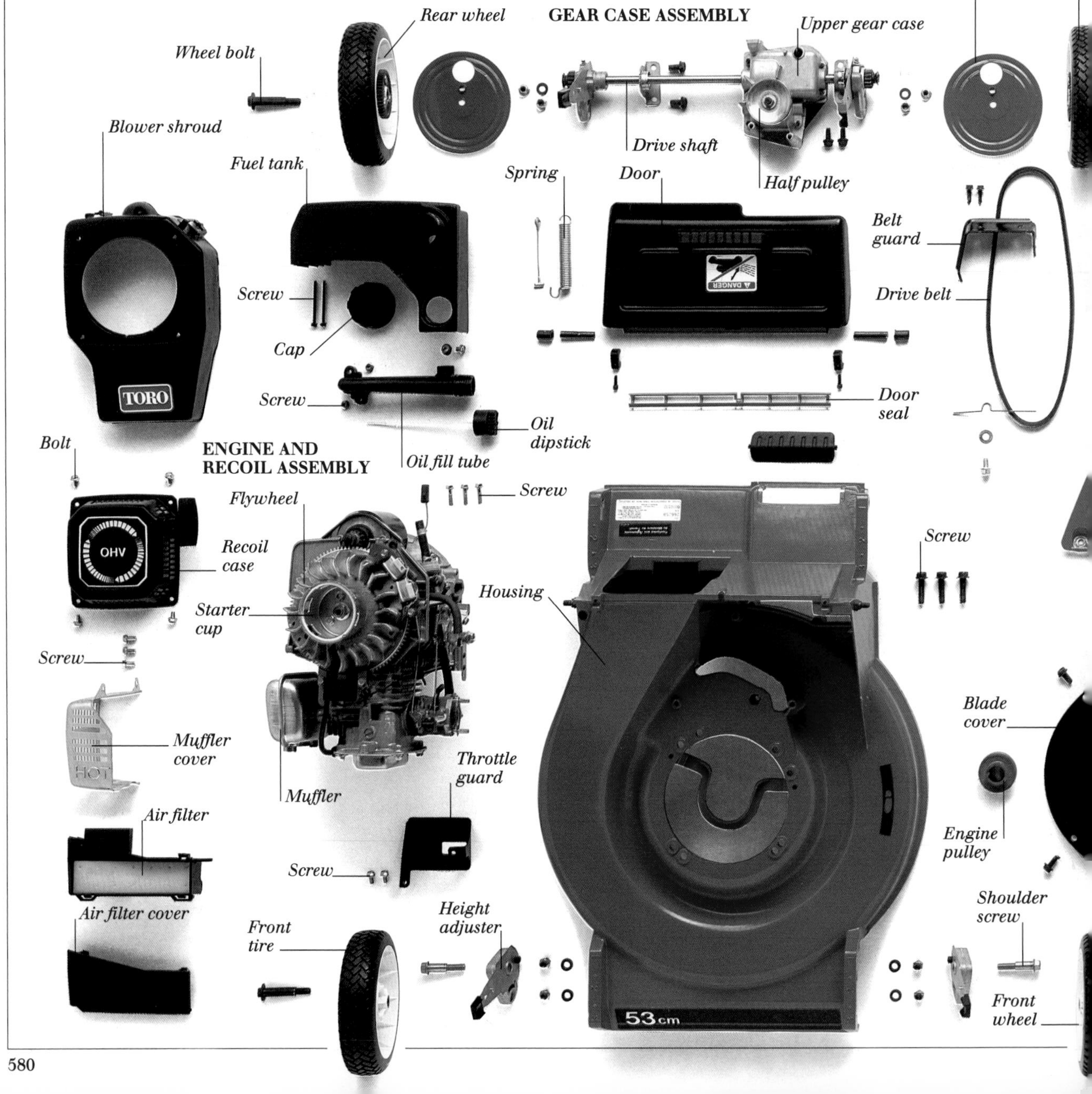

Rear tire

Wheel cover

Rear wheel

GEAR CASE ASSEMBLY

Upper gear case

Wheel bolt

Drive shaft

Blower shroud

Fuel tank

Spring

Door

Half pulley

Belt guard

Screw

Cap

Drive belt

Screw

Oil dipstick

Door seal

Bolt

ENGINE AND RECOIL ASSEMBLY

Oil fill tube

Screw

Flywheel

Recoil case

Housing

Screw

Starter cup

Screw

Blade cover

Muffler cover

Throttle guard

Engine pulley

Air filter

Muffler

Screw

Air filter cover

Front tire

Height adjuster

Shoulder screw

53 cm

Front wheel

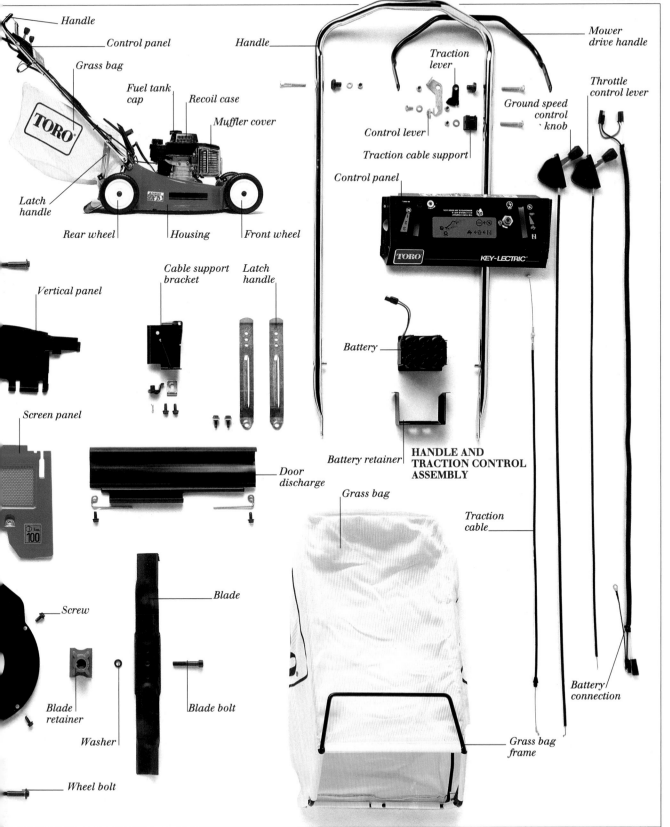

Handle

Control panel

Grass bag

Fuel tank cap

Recoil case

Muffler cover

Latch handle

Rear wheel

Housing

Front wheel

Handle

Traction lever

Control lever

Traction cable support

Control panel

Battery

Battery retainer

Mower drive handle

Throttle control lever

Ground speed control knob

TORO KEY-LECTRIC

HANDLE AND TRACTION CONTROL ASSEMBLY

Vertical panel

Cable support bracket

Latch handle

Screen panel

Door discharge

Grass bag

Traction cable

Screw

Blade

Blade retainer

Washer

Blade bolt

Grass bag frame

Battery connection

Wheel bolt

Saddle

THE FIRST HORSEBACK RIDERS HAD NO SADDLES; they sat bareback, clinging to the animal's mane. Next came a simple cloth saddle. The leather saddle, which was invented about 2,000 years ago by the warriors of the Asian steppes, revolutionized horseback riding. On this saddle, horsemen could gallop toward the enemy, fire arrows in all directions, and stay on their horses. Modern saddles are of two main types. The Western saddle is a heavy, working saddle used mainly by ranch hands in the United States. It has a metal horn at the front for securing a lasso and a high cantle at the back to keep the rider on the horse. The English saddle is much lighter. Designed for sport, it allows the horse to gallop fast. Its drawback is that it provides less stability; to stay on the horse, the rider must grip the animal with the knees.

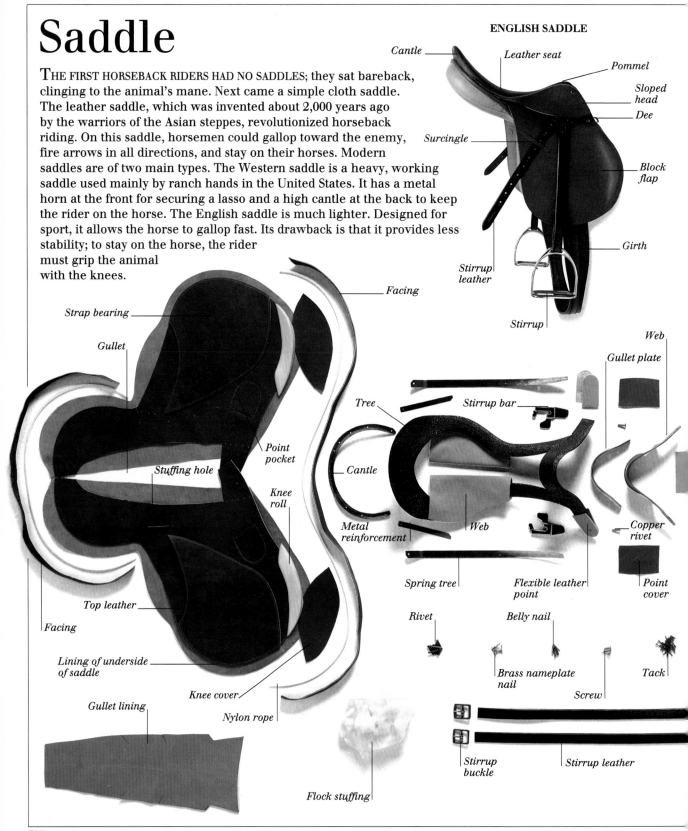

ENGLISH SADDLE

Cantle

Leather seat

Pommel

Sloped head

Dee

Surcingle

Block flap

Girth

Stirrup leather

Stirrup

Facing

Strap bearing

Gullet

Point pocket

Stuffing hole

Knee roll

Top leather

Facing

Lining of underside of saddle

Gullet lining

Knee cover

Nylon rope

Flock stuffing

Tree

Stirrup bar

Cantle

Metal reinforcement

Web

Spring tree

Flexible leather point

Web

Gullet plate

Copper rivet

Point cover

Rivet

Belly nail

Brass nameplate nail

Screw

Tack

Stirrup buckle

Stirrup leather

SHAPED GIRTH

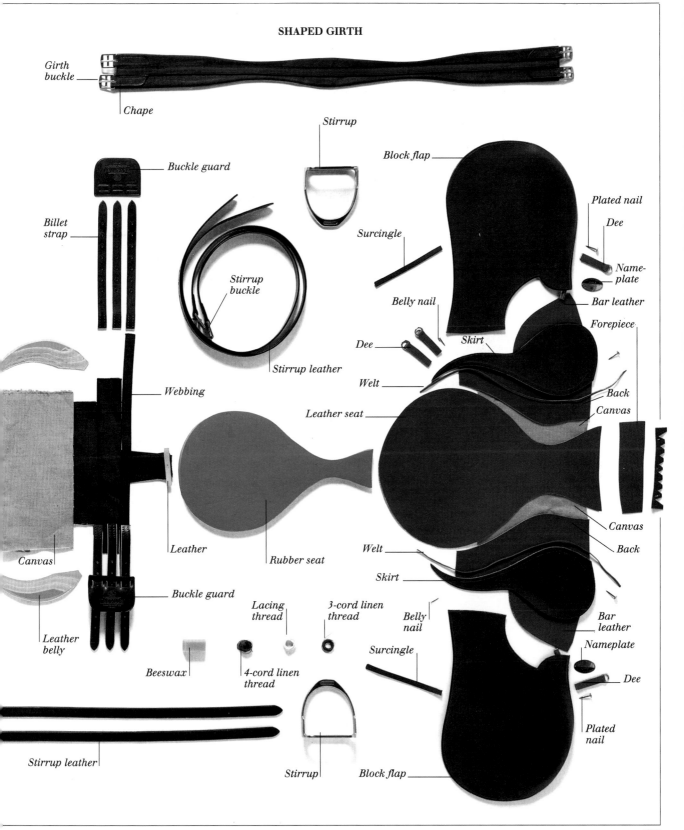

Girth buckle

Chape

Stirrup

Block flap

Plated nail

Dee

Buckle guard

Surcingle

Nameplate

Billet strap

Stirrup buckle

Belly nail

Bar leather

Forepiece

Dee

Skirt

Welt

Back

Stirrup leather

Leather seat

Canvas

Webbing

Canvas

Leather

Back

Canvas

Rubber seat

Welt

Leather belly

Skirt

Buckle guard

Lacing thread

3-cord linen thread

Belly nail

Bar leather

Beeswax

4-cord linen thread

Surcingle

Nameplate

Dee

Stirrup leather

Plated nail

Stirrup

Block flap

CD-ROM

A CD-ROM IS A TYPE OF COMPACT DISC (CD) that can be used to produce images on a computer screen. ROM stands for Read Only Memory, which means that the digitally recorded data registered in pits on the surface of the disc is fixed and cannot be altered or replaced. The CD is loaded into the CD-ROM player, where the data on the spinning disc is read by a laser. CD-ROMs are different from vinyl records in that they are not read along a spiral groove, from outer circumference to inner edge: instead each image or piece of information has a coordinate on the disc, which is located by the laser. Information picked up by the laser is relayed to the computer, where it is translated into the text and images that appear on screen. The information is relayed through a SCSI (Small Computer System Interface), which processes the electronic impulses between the disc drive and the computer system. The user can move around the program by clicking on different parts of the screen with a mouse (a hand-held tool with a clicking button whose movement on its pad is mimicked by an icon on the screen). The image in the viewing area (see opposite) can be changed by clicking on the active scrolling button: this moves a rectangular panel down the scrolling figure in the navigational panel. Clicking on active text will provide a new screen with more information, either in the form of text and diagrams, or as narrated animated sequences.

CD-ROM drive

CD loading tray

Caddy cover flap

Front bezel

Push button

CD-ROM CASING

CD-ROM drive motor

Film strip connector

Laser

Connector

Roller bearing

Washer

Guide post

Gearing mechanism

Spring

Insulating grommet

Power connector to CD-ROM

SCSI connectors

Connector clasp

SCSI selector switch

Ground connection to case

Power switch

Washer

Ground wire

Surface-mounted integrated circuit

Power supply screening cover

Mounting rail

Transistor

Power on/off LED (Light Emitting Diode)

CD-ROM disc

Screws

CD-ROM DISC DRIVE

CD-ROM LOADING MECHANISM

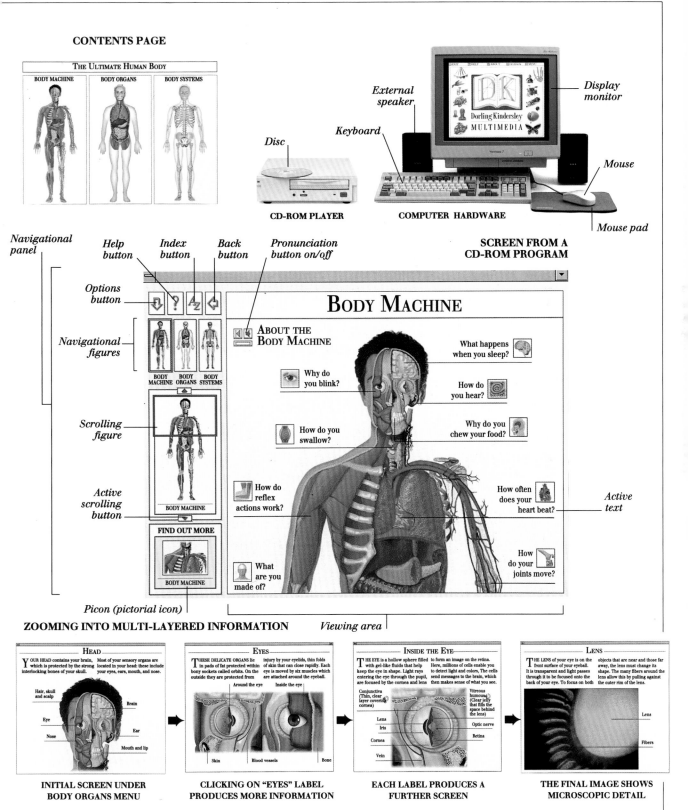

CONTENTS PAGE

THE ULTIMATE HUMAN BODY

| BODY MACHINE | BODY ORGANS | BODY SYSTEMS |

External speaker

Keyboard

Disc

Display monitor

Mouse

Mouse pad

CD-ROM PLAYER

COMPUTER HARDWARE

SCREEN FROM A CD-ROM PROGRAM

Navigational panel

Help button

Index button

Back button

Pronunciation button on/off

Options button

Navigational figures

BODY MACHINE BODY ORGANS BODY SYSTEMS

Scrolling figure

Active scrolling button

BODY MACHINE

FIND OUT MORE

BODY MACHINE

Picon (pictorial icon)

BODY MACHINE

ABOUT THE BODY MACHINE

Why do you blink?

What happens when you sleep?

How do you hear?

How do you swallow?

Why do you chew your food?

How do reflex actions work?

How often does your heart beat?

Active text

What are you made of?

How do your joints move?

ZOOMING INTO MULTI-LAYERED INFORMATION

Viewing area

HEAD

YOUR HEAD contains your brain, which is protected by the strong interlocking bones of your skull. Most of your sensory organs are located in your head: these include your eyes, ears, mouth, and nose.

Hair, skull and scalp

Brain

Eye

Nose

Ear

Mouth and lip

EYES

THESE DELICATE ORGANS lie in pads of fat protected within bony sockets called orbits. On the outside they are protected from injury by your eyelids, thin folds of skin that can close rapidly. Each eye is moved by six muscles which are attached around the eyeball.

Around the eye

Inside the eye

Skin

Blood vessels

Bone

INSIDE THE EYE

THE EYE is a hollow sphere filled with gel-like fluids that help keep the eye in shape. Light rays entering the eye through the pupil, are focused by the cornea and lens to form an image on the retina. Here, millions of cells enable you to detect light and colors, The cells send messages to the brain, which then makes sense of what you see.

Conjunctiva (Thin, clear layer covering cornea)

Vitreous humour (Clear jelly that fills the space behind the lens)

Lens

Optic nerve

Iris

Cornea

Retina

Vein

LENS

THE LENS of your eye is on the front surface of your eyeball. It is transparent and light passes through it to be focused onto the back of your eye. To focus on both objects that are near and those far away, the lens must change its shape. The many fibers around the lens allow this by pulling against the outer rim of the lens.

Lens

Fibers

INITIAL SCREEN UNDER BODY ORGANS MENU

CLICKING ON "EYES" LABEL PRODUCES MORE INFORMATION

EACH LABEL PRODUCES A FURTHER SCREEN

THE FINAL IMAGE SHOWS MICROSCOPIC DETAIL

Books

THOUGH THE PROCESS OF BOOKBINDING today is usually mechanized, some books are still bound by hand. The pages of a book are printed on large sheets of paper called sections, or signatures. When folded, sections usually make 8, 16, or 32 pages. To assemble a hand-bound hardback book, the binder first places the folded sections in the correct order within the endpapers. Next, he or she sews the sections together along the spine edge using strong thread and then pastes them with glue for extra strength. After trimming the pages, the binder puts the book in a press and hammers the spine to shape it. The binder then glues one or more linings on the spine. The cover, or case, comes last. To make this, the bookbinder sticks cover boards to the endpapers, front and back, and then covers them with cloth or leather.

HALF-BOUND BOOK

LEATHER-BOUND BOOK

Corner piece

Spine

Fore edge

Rib

Spine

Tail

Marbleized paper

Joint

Leather cover

Spine

Tail

Ribbon

Gold tooling

HALF-BOUND BOOK

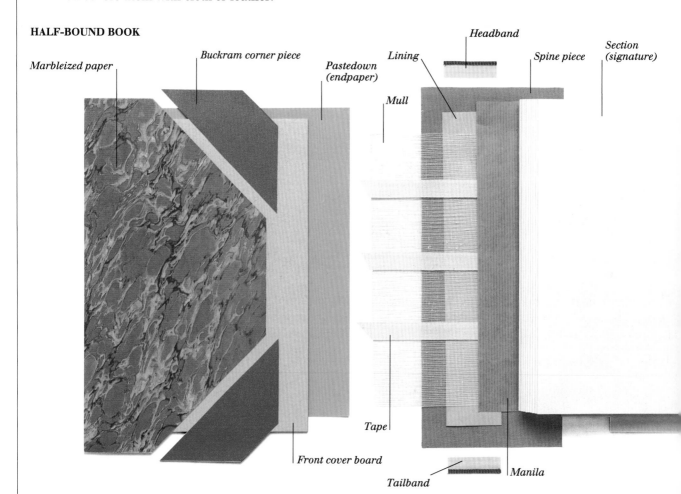

Marbleized paper

Buckram corner piece

Pastedown (endpaper)

Headband

Lining

Mull

Spine piece

Section (signature)

Tape

Front cover board

Tailband

Manila

LEATHER-BOUND BOOK

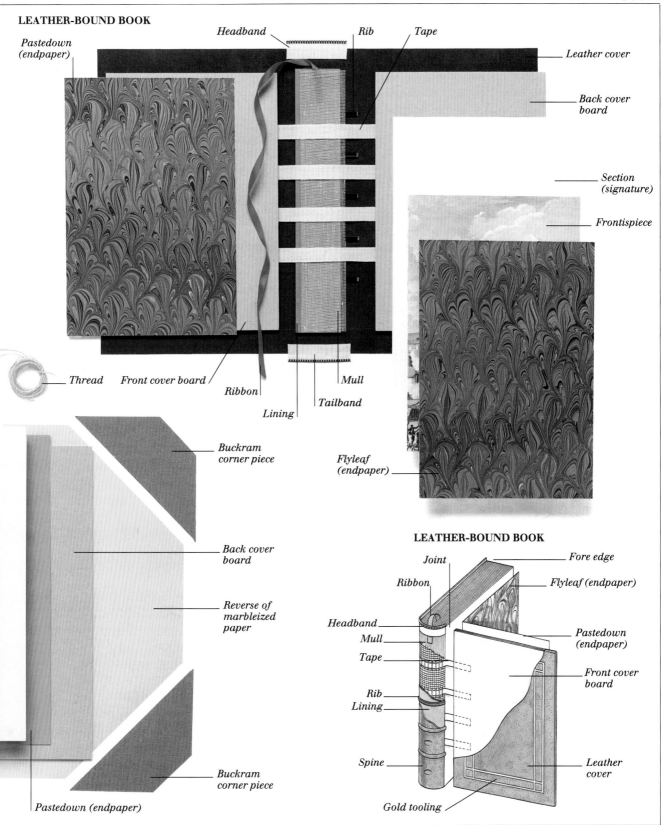

Pastedown (endpaper)

Headband

Rib

Tape

Leather cover

Back cover board

Section (signature)

Frontispiece

Thread

Front cover board

Ribbon

Mull

Lining

Tailband

Flyleaf (endpaper)

Buckram corner piece

Back cover board

Reverse of marbleized paper

Buckram corner piece

Pastedown (endpaper)

LEATHER-BOUND BOOK

Joint

Ribbon

Headband

Mull

Tape

Rib

Lining

Spine

Gold tooling

Fore edge

Flyleaf (endpaper)

Pastedown (endpaper)

Front cover board

Leather cover

Camera

A CAMERA IS AN INSTRUMENT used for recording images on photographic film. It consists of a light-tight box with a shutter, a lens containing a diaphragm, and a viewing system. When the shutter is released, the film is exposed to light from the subject that is being photographed. Adjusting the shutter speed alters the time for which the film is exposed to light. The diaphragm, by altering the aperture of the lens, controls the intensity of light entering the camera. The total amount of light entering the camera is called the exposure. The lens focuses the light onto the film. When there is insufficient light to produce an adequate image, a flashgun may be used to give extra light.

FRONT VIEW OF CAMERA

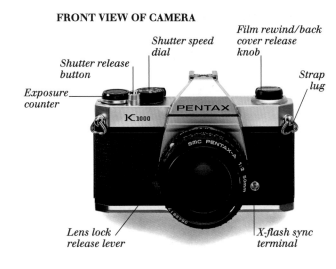

Shutter release button
Shutter speed dial
Film rewind/back cover release knob
Strap lug
Exposure counter
Lens lock release lever
X-flash sync terminal

FRONT BOARD ASSEMBLY

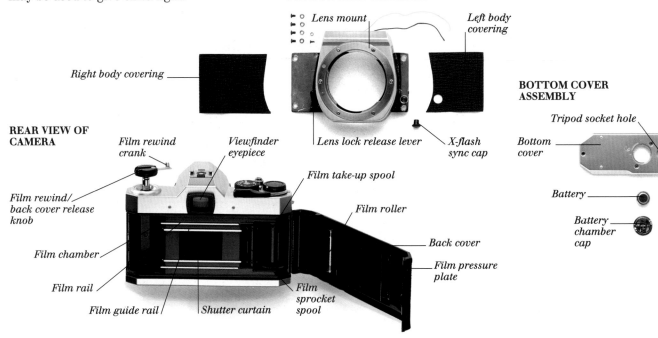

Lens mount
Left body covering
Right body covering
Lens lock release lever
X-flash sync cap

BOTTOM COVER ASSEMBLY

Tripod socket hole
Bottom cover
Battery
Battery chamber cap

REAR VIEW OF CAMERA

Film rewind crank
Viewfinder eyepiece
Film take-up spool
Film rewind/back cover release knob
Film roller
Film chamber
Back cover
Film pressure plate
Film rail
Film guide rail
Shutter curtain
Film sprocket spool

LENS BARREL ASSEMBLY

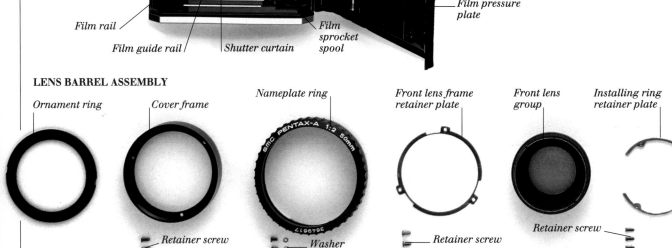

Ornament ring
Cover frame
Nameplate ring
Front lens frame retainer plate
Front lens group
Installing ring retainer plate
Retainer screw
Washer
Retainer screw
Retainer screw

TOP COVER ASSEMBLY

Shutter dial knob spring
Film speed indicator
Shutter speed dial
Speed dial knob
Retainer screw

Counter dial housing
Film wind lever
Wind lever collar
Top cover
X-contact
Hot shoe
Rewind shaft
Film rewind/back cover release knob

Counter dial cover
Exposure counter dial
Wind lever install spring

Retainer screw
Washer
Rewind shaft bushing

Window
Shutter release button
Shutter speed index
Film rewind crank

MAIN BODY

Prism retainer plate
Prism retainer spring
Pentaprism
Cover frame
Retainer screw

Strap lug
Viewfinder eyepiece

TOP VIEW OF CAMERA

Focusing ring
Aperture/distance index
Subject distance scale

Hole for film rewind button
Depth-of-field guide
Lens alignment node
Lens lock release lever
Shutter release button

Aperture auto-lock button
Shutter cocked indicator
Exposure counter

Retainer screw
Film rewind crank
Film rewind/back cover release knob
Hot shoe
X-contact
Shutter speed index
Film speed indicator
Shutter speed dial
Film wind lever

Supporter ring retainer plate
Supporter ring
Diaphragm blade
Installing ring
Main barrel assembly
Rear lens group

Opening and closing plate

Appendix: useful data

UNITS OF MEASUREMENT

U.S. unit	Equivalent
Length	
1 foot (ft)	12 inches (in)
1 yard (yd)	3 feet
1 rod (rd)	5.5 yards
1 mile (mi)	1,760 yards
Mass	
1 dram (dr)	27.344 grains (gr)
1 ounce (oz)	16 drams
1 pound (lb)	16 ounces
1 hundredweight (cwt) (long)	112 pounds
1 hundredweight (cwt) (short)	100 pounds
1 ton (long)	2,240 pounds
1 ton (short)	2,000 pounds
Area	
1 square foot (ft²)	144 square inches (in²)
1 square yard (yd²)	9 square feet
1 acre	4,840 square yards
1 square mile	640 acres
Volume	
1 cubic foot	1,728 cubic inches
1 cubic yard	27 cubic feet
Capacity (liquid and dry measures)	
1 fluidram (fl dr)	60 minims (min)
1 fluid ounce (fl oz)	8 fluidrams
1 gill (gi)	4 fluid ounces
1 pint (pt)	4 gills
1 quart (qt)	2 pints
1 gallon (gal)	4 quarts
1 peck (pk)	2 gallons
1 bushel (bu)	4 pecks

Metric unit	Equivalent
Length	
1 centimeter (cm)	10 millimeters (mm)
1 meter (m)	100 centimeters
1 kilometer (km)	1,000 meters
Mass	
1 kilogram (kg)	1,000 grams (g)
1 tonne (t)	1,000 kilograms
Area	
1 square centimeter (cm²)	100 square millimeters (mm²)
1 square meter (m²)	10,000 square centimeters
1 hectare	10,000 square meters
1 square kilometer (km²)	1,000,000 square meters
Volume	
1 cubic centimeter (cc)	1 milliliter (ml)
1 liter (l)	1,000 milliliters
1 cubic meter (m³)	1,000 liters
Capacity (liquid and dry measures)	
1 centiliter (cl)	10 milliliters (ml)
1 deciliter (dl)	10 centiliters
1 liter (l)	10 deciliters
1 decaliter (dal)	10 liters
1 hectoliter (hi)	10 decaliters
1 kiloliter (kl)	10 hectoliters

TEMPERATURE SCALES

To convert from Celsius (C) to Fahrenheit (F): $F = (C \times 9 \div 5) + 32$
To convert from Fahrenheit to Celsius: $C = (F - 32) \times 5 \div 9$
To convert from Celsius to Kelvin (K): $K = C + 273$
To convert from Kelvin to Celsius: $C = K - 273$

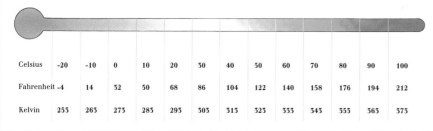

Celsius	-20	-10	0	10	20	30	40	50	60	70	80	90	100
Fahrenheit	-4	14	32	50	68	86	104	122	140	158	176	194	212
Kelvin	253	263	273	283	293	303	313	323	333	343	353	363	373

AREAS AND VOLUMES

Radius r
Diameter
d = 2 x r

CIRCLE
Circumference = $2 \times \pi \times r$
Area = $\pi \times r^2$
$(\pi = 3.1416)$

Height h
Sides a, b, c

TRIANGLE
Perimeter = a + b + c
Area = $\frac{1}{2} \times b \times h$

Sides a, b

RECTANGLE
Perimeter = $2 \times (a + b)$
Area = a x b

Height h
Radius r

CYLINDER
Surface area = $2 \times \pi \times r \times h$
(excluding ends)
Volume = $\pi \times r^2 \times h$

Height h
Radius r
Side l

CONE
Surface area = $\pi \times r \times l$ (excluding base)
Volume = $\frac{1}{3} \times \pi \times r^2 \times l$

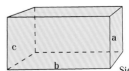

Sides a, b, c

RECTANGULAR BLOCK
Surface area = $2 \times (a \times b + b \times c + a \times c)$
Volume = a x b x c

U.S. – METRIC CONVERSIONS

To convert	Into	Multiply by
Length		
Inches	centimeters	2.5400
Feet	meters	0.3048
Miles	kilometers	1.6090
Yards	meters	0.9144
Mass		
Ounces	grams	28.3500
Pounds	kilograms	0.4536
Long tons	tonnes	1.0160
Short tons	tonnes	0.9070
Area		
Square inches	square centimeters	6.4520
Square feet	square meters	0.0929
Acres	hectares	0.4047
Square miles	square kilometers	2.5900
Square yards	square meters	0.8361
Volume		
Cubic inches	cubic centimeters	16.3900
Cubic feet	cubic meters	0.0283
Capacity		
Pints (liquid)	liters	0.4730
Gallons (liquid)	liters	3.7850

METRIC – U.S. CONVERSIONS

To convert	Into	Multiply by
Length		
Centimeters	inches	0.3937
Meters	feet	3.2810
Kilometers	miles	0.6214
Meters	yards	1.0940
Mass		
Grams	ounces	0.0352
Kilograms	pounds	2.2050
Tonnes	long tons	0.9843
Tonnes	short tons	1.1025
Area		
Square centimeters	square inches	0.1550
Square meters	square feet	10.7600
Hectares	acres	2.4710
Square kilometers	square miles	0.3861
Square meters	square yards	1.1960
Volume		
Cubic centimeters	cubic inches	0.0610
Cubic meters	cubic feet	35.3100
Capacity		
Liters	pints (liquid)	2.1142
Liters	gallons (liquid)	0.2642

NUMBER SYSTEMS

Roman	Arabic
I	1
II	2
III	3
IV	4
V	5
VI	6
VII	7
VIII	8
IX	9
X	10
XI	11
XII	12
XIII	13
XIV	14
XV	15
XX	20
XXI	21
XXX	30
XL	40
L	50
LX	60
LXX	70
LXXX	80
XC	90
C	100
CI	101
CC	200
CCC	300
CD	400
D	500
DC	600
DCC	700
DCCC	800
CM	900
M	1,000
MM	2,000

PHYSICS SYMBOLS

Symbol	Meaning
α	alpha particle
β	beta ray
γ	gamma ray; photon
ϵ	electromotive force
η	efficiency; viscosity
λ	wavelength
μ	micro-; permeability
ν	frequency; neutrino
ρ	density; resistivity
σ	conductivity
c	velocity of light
e	electronic charge

MATHEMATICS SYMBOLS

Symbol	Meaning
$+$	plus
$-$	minus
$\pm$	plus or minus
$\times$	multiplied by
$\div$	divided by
$=$	equals
$>$	is greater than
$<$	is less than
$\geq$	is greater than or equal to
$\leq$	is less than or equal to
$\%$	per cent
$\sqrt{}$	root
π	pi (3.1416)
$°$	degree
∞	infinity
$\approx$	is approximately equal to
$\angle$	angle

CHEMISTRY SYMBOLS

Symbol	Meaning
$+$	plus; together with
$-$	single bond
$\cdot$	single bond; single unpaired electron; two separate parts or compounds regarded as loosely joined
$=$	double bond
$\equiv$	triple bond
R	group
X	halogen atom
Z	atomic number

BIOLOGY SYMBOLS

Symbol	Meaning
○	female individual (used in inheritance charts)
□	male individual (used in inheritance charts)
♀	female
♂	male
$\times$	crossed with; hybrid
$+$	wild type
F_1	offspring of the first generation
F_2	offspring of the second generation

POWERS OF TEN USED WITH SCIENTIFIC UNITS

Factor	Name	Prefix	Symbol
10^{18}	quintillion	exa-	E
10^{15}	quadrillion	peta-	P
10^{12}	trillion	tera-	T
10^{9}	billion	giga-	G
10^{6}	million	mega-	M
10^{3}	thousand	kilo-	k
10^{2}	hundred	hecto-	h
10^{1}	ten	deca-	da
10^{-1}	one tenth	deci-	d
10^{-2}	one hundredth	centi-	c
10^{-3}	one thousandth	milli-	m
10^{-6}	one millionth	micro-	μ
10^{-9}	one billionth	nano-	n
10^{-12}	one trillionth	pico-	p
10^{-15}	one quadrillionth	femto-	f
10^{-18}	one quintillionth	atto-	a

Index

A

Aa lava 273
Abacus
  Ancient Egyptian temple 459
  Ancient Greek building 460
  Medieval church 469
  Neoclassical building 483
Abalone 176
Abaxial epidermis 139
Abaxial surface
  Butterwort leaf 161
  Fern pinnule 121
  Mulberry leaf 130
  Water hyacinth leaf 158
  Water lily leaf 159
  Welwitschia leaf 123
Abbey of St. Foi 468
Abdomen
  Crab 172
  Crayfish 172
  Human 211
  Insect 168-169
  Rattlesnake 185
  Scorpion 170
  Shrimp 172
  Spider 171
Abdominal aorta 215, 255
Abdominal artery 173
Abdominal cavity 215
Abdominal segment
  Butterfly 169
  Crayfish 172
  Eurypterid fossil 79
  Extinct shrimp 79
Abductor digiti minimus muscle 231, 233
Abductor pollicis brevis muscle 231
Aberdeen hook 562
Abies Concolor 66
Abomasum 198
Aboral surface
  Sea urchin 175
  Starfish 174
Abortive ovule 151
Abortive seed 146
Abrasion
  Glacier 286
  Weathering and erosion 282
Absolute magnitude
  Hertzsprung-Russell diagram 23
  Stars 22
Absorption lines 22-23
Absorptive hyphae 114
Abutment 484-485
Abyssal plain 298
Acacia tree sap 438
Acadagnostus 64
Acamar 19
Acanthostachys strobilacea 112-113
Acanthostega 80
Acanthus leaf 460
Accelerated electron 319
Acceleration 320-321
  Electric train 328
  Motorcycle 364
Access door 333
Accessory drive pad 419
Accessory pouch 548
Access panel 329, 333
Access step 355
Accidentals 502-503

Accretion disc 27-29
AC electric train 328
Acer pseudoplatanus 131, 151
Acer sp. 127
Acetabularia sp. 116
Acetabular labrum 225
Acetabulum
  Eryops 81
  Ornithischian 82
  Saurischian 82
Acetylene headlamp 336-337
Achenes 150
Achernar 19
Achilles tendon 232-233
Acid
  Intaglio printing 446
  Reversible reaction 312
  Salt formation 312
Acidalia Planitia 43
Acidic solution 446, 448
Acid-resistant ground 446-447
Acid-secreting stomach cell 217
Acipenser sturio 180
Acorn 131
Acoustic guitar 512-513
Acropolis 460
Acrosomal cap 259
Acroterion 460-461
Acroteuthis 278
Acrux
  Centaurus and Crux 21
  Southern stars 21
Acrylic ink 448
Acrylic paint techniques 443
Acrylic-primed board 442
Acrylics **442-443**
Actinia equina 166
Actinides 310
Actinium 310
Actinothoe sphyrodeta 166
Action 321
Action lever 514
Active galaxy 12
Active scrolling button 584-585
Active text 585
Active volcano 272
  Igneous and metamorphic rocks 275
  Mountain building 62
Actuating lever system 330
Acuminate leaf apex 136-137
Acute leaf apex 137
Adam's apple 212, 244-245
Adam's ring
  Neptune's rings 50
  Structure of Neptune 51
Adaptation 112
  Dryland plants 156-157
  Wetland plants 158-159
Adaxial epidermis 139
Adaxial surface
  Butterwort leaf 161
  Mulberry leaf 130
  Tree mallow leaf 131
  Water hyacinth leaf 158
  Water lily leaf 159
  Welwitschia leaf 123
Adductor longus muscle 225, 226
Adductor magnus muscle 227

Adductor muscle 173
Adductor pollicis muscle 231
Adductor tubercle 225
Adenine 216
Adhara 18, 21
Adipose tissue 215, 235
Adjustable damper 518
Adjustable link 362
Adjustable vane 563
Adjusting catch 552
Adjusting screw 560
Adjustment locking nut 573
Admiralty anchor Type ACII 386
Admiralty pattern anchor 386
Adrenal gland 215, 257
Adventitious buds 154
Adventitious roots
  Aechmea miniata 162
  Canadian pond weed 158
  Couch grass 113
  Fern 121
  Horsetail 120
  Ivy 131
  Monocotyledon 126
  Potato 128
  Rock stonecrop 128
  Tree fern 112
  Vegetative reproduction 154-155
  Water fern 158
  Water hyacinth 158
  Water lily 159
Advertising 368
Advertising panel 333
Aechmea miniata 162
Aedicule
  Ancient Roman building 463
  Renaissance building 474, 476
AEG Turbine Hall 495
Aegyptopithecus 75
Aeration zone 293
Aerial
  Frigate 397
  Mini-television 574
  Renault Clio 349
Aerial mammals 104
Aerial rig 397
Aerial root 162
Aerial shoot 155
Aerial stem 119, 155
Aerodynamic balance 414-415
Aerodynamic tubing 360
Aerodynamic windshield 346
Aerofoil guard 329
A("Aero" handlebars 360-561
Aeroquip pipe union 556
Aerosol spray fixative 430, 440
Aerotuck position 360
Aesculus hippocastanum 130
Aesculus parviflora 137
A-frame
  Concorde 416
  Gliders, hang-gliders, and microlights 426
Africa
  Cretaceous period 72-73
  Earth's physical features 264-265
  Great Rift Valley 60
  Jurassic period 70
  Late Carboniferous period 66

Middle Ordovician period 64
  Quaternary period 76-77
  Tertiary period 74-75
  Triassic period 68
African elephant 200-201
African plate 59
Aft anchor 395
Aft door 416
Afterbay 314
After breast rope 387
After bridge 395
Afterburner
  Jet engine 418
  Supersonic jetliner 416
Afterburner nozzle 421
Aftercastle
  Sailing warship 377
  Square-rigged ship 375
Aftercastle castle-deck gunport 377
After compass platform 395
After funnel
  Battleship 395
  Iron paddlesteamer 392
Afterpeak 392
After silencer 427
After spring rope 387
Aft fairing 415
Aft galley unit 417
Aft hydroplane 396
Aft main door 414-415
Aft shoulder 560
Aft spar 415
Agate burnisher tip 432
Aggregate fruits 148-149
  Bramble 130
  Development 146-147
Aghulas current 297
Agnatha 178
Agropyron repens 113
Ahead/astern controls 390
Aileron
  ARV light aircraft 424
  BAe-146 components 414
  Curtiss biplane 398-399
  Hawker Tempest components 409
  Lockheed Electra airliner 406
  LVG CVI fighter 405
  Schleicher glider 426
Aileron control wire 403
Aileron hinge strut 403
Aileron mass balance 424
Aileron operating arm 398-399
Aino Planitia 36-37
Air
  Atmosphere 300
  Oceans and seas 296
  Weather 302-303
Air ambulance 422
Airbag suspension 331
Air bladder 117
Air brake
  BAe-146 components 415
  Schleicher glider 426
  Tornado 421
Air-brake coupling hose 526
Air-brake jack 421
Air brushes 442
Air chamber 118
Air cleaner
  Jaguar V12 engine 345
  Renault Clio 351
Air compression 326
Air conditioning 496-497
Air-conditioning compressor 344
Air-conditioning duct 417
Air-conditioning pump 344

Air-conditioning refrigerant pipe 344
Air-cooled engine
  Motorcycle engine 366
  V8 engine 404
Air-cooling baffle 402
Air-cooling fan 427
Air-cooling scoop 565
Air-cushioned sole 543
Air data probe 420
Air filter
  Bell-47 helicopter 422
  Harley Davidson FLHS Electra Glide 363
  Pegasus Quasar microlight 427
  Volkswagen Beetle 340
Air filter cover 580
Air hose 442
Air impingement starter 418
Air inlet
  Jaguar V12 engine 345
  Power drill 567
Air intake
  Concorde 416
  Double-decker tour bus 333
  Lockheed Electra airliner 406
  MCW Metrobus 332-333
  Modern military aircraft 420-421
  Pinzgauer Turbo D 354
  Single-decker bus 333
  Turbojet engine 418
  Turboprop engine 419
  Formula One racing car 357
Air intake box 425
Air intake vent 341
Air mass 296
Air outlet 427
Air passage
  Lambeosaurus 99
  Parasaurolophus 99
Air pistol 548-549
Air plants 162
Air pressure 303
Air pump
  Oscillating steam engine 391
  Steamboat with paddle wheels 391
Air reservoir valve 327
Air resistance 552
Air rifle shooting 548
Air sac
  Chicken's egg 192
  Scots pine 122
Air scoop
  ARV Super 2 424
  Volkswagen Beetle 340
Air spaces
  Clubmoss stem 120
  Mare's tail stem 135
  Moss 119
  Root 132
  Stem 135
  Wetland plants 158-159
Airspeed-indicator tube
  ARV light aircraft 425
  BE 2B wings 404
Airspeed pitot tube 404
Air taxi 422
Air temperature 300
Air temperature probe
  BAe-146 components 412
  Bell Jetranger helicopter 423
Air vent
  Bicycle helmet 360
  Hockey helmet 540
  Pinzgauer Turbo D 355
  Suzuki RGV500 368-369

Air ventilator inlet 405
Aisle
  Ancient Egyptian temple 458
  Cathedral dome 484
  Gothic church 470, 472-473
  Medieval church 468-469
Akna Montes 37
Ala 213, 223
Alar groove 213
Alba Fossae 43
Alba Patera 43
Albategnius 40
Albertosaurus 84
Albireo 20
Albumen 192
Albumen gland 177
Alcohol burner 454
Alcohol fermentation 313
Alcor 19
Alcyone 20
Aldebaran 18, 21
Alderamin 19
Aldpuk cell 114
Algae 56, **112, 116-117**
  Desmid 112
  Earth's evolution 56
  Fossil record 279
  Lichen symbiote 114
Algal cell 114
Algal layer 114
Algedi 20
Algenib 19, 20
Algieba 18
Algol 19, 20
Alhambra 488
Alhena 18, 21
Alicante 450
Alidade 377
Alimentary canal 248-249
Alioth 18
  The Plow 19
Alkaid 18
  The Plow 19
Alkali metals 310
Allantoic fluid 192
Allantois 192-193
"All clear" position 330
All-enclosing fairing 369
Alley
  Badminton court 545
  Tennis court 544
Alligator 186
Allison 250-C20J turboshaft engine 423
Allium sp. 143
Allosaurus 71, 85
Allotropes 311
Alloy disc 517
Alloy frame 368
Alloy wheel
  Honda VF750 364-565
  Renault Clio 350-351
  Suzuki RGV500 368-369
All-purpose bicycle 360
All-terrain bicycle 358
All-terrain vehicles 554-555
Alluvial cone 282
Alluvial fan 282
Alluvium-filled basin 282
Almach 19, 20
  Pegasus and Andromeda 19
Al Nair 19, 20
Alnilam 18
Alnitak
  Horsehead Nebula 16
  Orion 18
Alouatta seniculus 203
Alpha Centauri 21
Alpha Hydri 20
Alpha Mensae 20
Alphard 18, 21

Alpha Regio 36-37
Alpha ring 48
Alphecca 18, 21
Alpheratz 19, 20
  Pegasus and Andromeda 19
Alphonsus 40
Alpine skiing 552-553
Alps 60, 265
Alrami 21
Alsatian dog 195
Alstroemeria aurea 129
Altair 19, 20
Altar 470
Alternating current 328
Alternative engines 346-347
Alternator
  Diesel train 326
  Ford V6 12-valve engine 344
  Jaguar V12 engine 345
  NPT 301 turbojet 418
  Renault Clio 351
Alternator belt 351
Altitude scale 377
Alto clef 502
Altocumulus cloud 302
Alto mute 507
Altostratus cloud 302
Alto voice 502
Aludra 21
Alula 191
Aluminum 311
  Earth's composition 39
  Earth's crust 58
Aluminum alloy backing 346
Aluminum arrow shaft 548
Aluminum beam 560
Aluminum cowl 401
Aluminum flush-riveted skin 407
Aluminum gearbox casing 366
Aluminum racket 544
Aluminum wheel 406
Aluminum wire figure 455
Alveolar artery and vein 247
Alveolar bone 247
Alveoli 254-255
Amaryllis 155
Amateur rules 532
Amazon Basin 39
Amazonis Planitia 43
Amazon River 264
Ambiens muscle
  Albertosaurus 84
  Iguanodon 97
Ambulacral groove 79, 175
Ambulatory corridor 465
Amelodentinal junction 247
American alligator 186
American beaver 197
American black bear 195
American squash court 545
American squash game 544
Americium 311
Ammonia
  Jupiter's atmosphere 45
  Saturn's atmosphere 47
  Structure of Neptune 51
  Structure of Uranus 49
Ammonite 278-279
Ammonite shell 267
Ammonium dichromate 312
Ammonium hydrosulfide
  Jupiter's atmosphere 45
  Saturn's atmosphere 47
Ammophila arenaria 113

Ammunition 548-549
Ammunition box 408
Amnion 192-193, 260
Amniotic egg 80
Amniotic fluid 192, 260
Amniotic sac 260
Amoebocyte 166
Amphibia 182
Amphibian 80-81, 182-183
  Earth's evolution 56
  Fossil 278
  Fossil record 279
  Primitive 68-69, 78
Amphibole 275
Amphitheatre 464-465
Amplification
  Drums 518
  Electronic instruments 520
  Guitar 512
  Stringed instruments 510
  Vibraphone 516
  Xylophone 516
Amplifier 520
Amps 316
Ampulla
  Ear 242-243
  Fallopian tube 258-259
  Sea urchin 175
  Starfish 174
Ampullar nerve 242
Anal canal 249
Anal clasper 169
Anal fin
  Bony fish 180-181
  Lamprey 178
Anal fin ray 180
Anal flap 200
Anal sphincter muscle 249
Anchisaurus 88-89
Anchor
  74-gun ship 380
  BAe-146 components 412, 414
  Battleship 394-395
  Frigate 397
  Junk 376
  Roman corbita 372
  Square-rigged ship 375
  Tea clipper 392
  Types 386
  Wooden sailing ship 379
Anchor bearing 413
Anchor buoy 379
Anchor cable
  74-gun ship 380
  Sailing warship 376
Anchor chain 386, 395
Anchoring 386-387
Anchor-joint 492
Anchor rode 372
Anchor rope 372-373
Ancient Egyptian building 458-459
Ancient Greek building 460-461, 462
Ancient Greeks 542
Ancient Roman building 462-465, 474
Ancillary drive belt 347
Ancillary drive pulley 345
Ancorale 372
Andamenti 451
Andes
  Cretaceous period 73
  Earth's external features 39
  Jurassic period 71
  Quaternary period 77
  Satellite map 264
  Tertiary period 75
  Triassic period 69
Androecium 140-141, 143
Andromeda 19, 20
Andromeda Galaxy 14, 19

Anemonia viridis 166
Anemophilous pollination 144
Angiogram 214
Angiospermophyta 112, 126
Angiosperms 279
Angle 572
Angle bar 393
Angle buttress 471, 472
Angle-of-attack probe 420
Anglerfish 180
Angling 562-563
Angoulême Cathedral 468-469
Angular mountain ridge 295
Angular notch 249
Angular process 194
Angular unconformity 276
Anhydrous copper sulfate 313
Animal life
  Electromagnetic radiation 314
  Primitive 78
Animal remains
  Fossils 278
  Sedimentary rocks 276
Animal stances 82
Animals 65, 67, 78
Animated sequences 584
Anions 308
Ankle
  Anchisaurus 89
  Corythosaurus 98
  Edmontonia 95
  Herrerasaurus 86
  Human 211
  Iguanodon 96
  Pachycephalosaurus 100
  Psittacosaurus 103
  Stegoceras 101
  Stegosaurus 92
  Triceratops 102
  Tyrannosaurus 84
Ankle joint
  Brachiosaurus 90
  Diplodocus 90
  Euoplocephalus 94
  Human 219
  Parasaurolophus 98
  Plateosaurus 88
  Stegoceras 101
  Struthiomimus 87
  Triceratops 102
  Tyrannosaurus 84
Ankylosaurs 83, 92, 94-95
Anne's Spot 47
Annual growth ring 125
Annuals 128
Annular river drainage 288
Annular tendon 241
Annulet 460
Annulus
  Fern 121
  Mushroom 115
Annulus of trunk 201
Ant 168
Anta 461
Antarala 490-491
Antarctica
  Cretaceous period 72-73
  Earth's physical features 264-265
  Jurassic period 70
  Late Carboniferous period 66
  Quaternary period 76-77
  Tertiary period 74-75
  Triassic period 68
Antarctic Circle
  Satellite map 265

Surface currents 297
Antarctic circumpolar current 296
Antares 18, 21
Antefixa 461
Antelope 198
Antenna
  Battleship 395
  Crab 172
  Crayfish 173
  Frigate 397
  Insects 168-169
  Malacostraca 172
  Roman corbita 372-373
  Shrimp 172
  Volleyball net 534
Antenna connector 574
Antenna holder 575
Antennule 173
Anterior antebrachial muscle 86
Anterior aorta 170
Anterior arch 222
Anterior brachial muscle
  Brachiosaurus 91
  Gallimimus 86
Anterior branch of spinal nerve 223
Anterior chamber 241
Anterior chamber of cloaca 185
Anterior crural muscle ▪
  Brachiosaurus 90
  Gallimimus 86
Anterior dorsal fin
  Bony fish 181
  Dogfish 179
  Lamprey 178
Anterior fontanelle 220
Anterior horn 223
Anterior median fissure 223, 238
Anterior median vein 253
Anterior nasal spine 220-221
Anterior petal 141
Anterior root 238
Anterior semicircular canal 243
Anterior sepal 141
Anterior tentacle 177
Anterior tibial artery 253
Anterior tibial muscle
  Albertosaurus 84
  Iguanodon 97
Anterior tubercle 222
Anterior wing of shell 176
Antheridium 117
  Fern 121
  Moss 119
Antherozoids 116-117
  Fern 121
  Moss 119
Anthers 140-143, 145
  Dicotyledons 126-127
  Fertilization 146-147
  Pollination process 144-145
Anthozoa 166
Anthracite coal 280
Anthriscus sp. 135
Anthropoids 202
Anthurium andreanum 143
Antibodies 253
Anticlinal fold 60
Anticline 60-61, 62
Anticline trap 280-281
Anticlinorium 61
Anti-collision beacon 422-423
Anti-corrosion paint 413
Anticyclonic storm system
  Cloud features of Neptune 50

Jupiter 44-45
  Structure of Saturn 47
Anti-friction pad 552
Anti-glare lens 553
Antihelix 242
Anti-lift bracing wire
  Avro triplane 403
  Blackburn monoplane 401
  Blériot XI monoplane 401
  LVG CVI fighter 405
Anti-lift wire 399
Antimacassar 329
Antimony 311
Antipodal cell 147
Anti-reverse drive 562
Anti-roll bar
  Renault Clio 350-351
  Volkswagen Beetle 340
Anti-submarine torpedo tube 397
Anti-surge baffle 544
Anti-torque tail rotor 423
Antitragus 242
Anti-turbulence lane lines 588
Anti-vibration engine mount 411
Antler hammer 109
Antler harpoon 109
Antlia 18, 21
Antoniadi 41
Antorbital fenestra
  Baryonyx 83
  Camarasaurus 91
  Diplodocus 90
  Plateosaurus 88
Anura 182
Anus
  Barnacle 173
  Bony fish 181
  Butterfly 169
  Cow 198
  Crayfish 173
  Dolphin 205
  Domestic cat 195
  Elephant 200
  Human 249, 258, 261
  Octopus 176
  Rabbit 196
  Sea urchin 175
  Snail 177
  Spider 170
  Starfish 174
  Tortoise 187
Anvil 242
Aorta
  Anterior 170
  Bony fish 181
  Dogfish 179
  Dolphin 205
  Dorsal 179, 181, 182
  Human 215, 250-251, 252, 255, 256-257
  Posterior 170
  Spider 170
  Ventral 179
Apatite 271
Ape 108, 202-203
Aperture 588
Aperture auto-lock button 589
Aperture/distance index 589
Apex
  Beetle wing 168
  Butterfly wing 169
  Calligraphy characters 445
  Clubmoss shoot 120
  Fern frond 121
  Fern pinnule 121
  Horsetail shoot 120
  Leaf 136-137, 154-155

Lung 255
Moss 119
Pegasus XL SE microlight 426
Pine shoot 125
Snail shell 177
Tongue 244-245
Apex seal 347
Apex wire 426
Aphelion 30-31
Aphrodite Terra 36-37
Apical bud
  Bulb 155
  Pine shoot 125
Apical foramen 247
Apical meristem 134
Apical notch
  Seaweed 116
  Thalloid liverwort 118
Apollo 41
Apomixis 146
Apophysis 119
Apothecium 114
Appalachian mountains
  Late Cretaceous period 67
  Mountain building 62
  Quaternary period 77
  Satellite map 264
  Tertiary period 75
  Triassic period 69
Apparent magnitude 22
Appendix
  Chimpanzee 202
  Human 249
  Rabbit 196
Appendix orifice 249
Apple 148-149
Approach 543
Apse 465, 469, 481
Aquarius 19, 20
Aquatic mammals 104
Aqueduct 256
Aqueous humour 241
Aquiclude 292
Aquifer 292
Aquiferous system 166
Aquila 19, 20
Ara ararauna 190
Ara 20
Arabesque
  Islamic building 488-489
  Neoclassical molding 480
Arabia
  Cretaceous period 72
  Jurassic period 70
Arabian Desert 265
Arabic number system 591
Arachnids 170-171
Arachnoid granulation 237
Arachnoid mater 237, 240
Aral Sea 265
Araneae 170
Araucaria araucana 68
Arcade
  Ancient Roman building 464-465
  Baroque church 479-481
  Gothic building 470-471
  Medieval church 468-469
  Twentieth-century building 495
Arcadia Planitia 43
Arch 484-485
  Ancient Roman building 462, 464-465
  Asian building 490-491
  Baroque church 479, 480
  Calligraphy characters 445
  Cathedral dome 487
  Features of a coastline 295
  French temple 484-485

Gothic church 470-473
High jump 543
Islamic building 488-489
Medieval building 466-469
Nineteenth-century building 492-493
Renaissance building 474-475
Shoe 568
Archaeopteryx 57, 84, 85
Arched brace 473
Arched doorway 474, 475
Arched facade 493
Archegoniophore 118
Archegonium
 Fern 121
 Liverwort 118
 Moss 119
 Scots pine 122
Archery **548-549**
Archery screen 377
Archimedes 40
Architrave
 Ancient Egyptian temple 458-459
 Ancient Greek temple 461
 Ancient Roman building 463, 465
 Baroque church 479-481
 French temple 485
 Gothic building 473
 Neoclassical building 478, 482-483
 Renaissance building 476-477
Archivolt
 Baroque church 479, 481
 French temple 485
 Gothic church 471
 Medieval building 467-468
 Renaissance building 477
Arch of aorta 253
Arch of Titus 463
Arch-plate 493
Archway 493
 Medieval church 469
 Molding 485
Arctic Circle
 Satellite map 265
 Surface currents 297
Arctic Ocean 265
Arcturus 18, 21
 Hertzsprung-Russell diagram 23
Area measurements 590
Areola 160
Areole 156
Arête 286-287
Argentina 331
Argon
 Atmospheric composition 301
 Mars' atmosphere 43
 Mercury's atmosphere 35
 Periodic table 311
 Venus' atmosphere 37
Argyre Planitia 43
Ariel 48
Aries 19, 20
Aril
 Lychee fruit 148
 Yew seed 123
A ring 46-47
Aristarchus 40
Aristillus 40
Aristoteles 40
Arkab Prior 21
Arkansas hone-stone 452
Arm
 74-gun ship 380

Calligraphy characters 445
Chair 576
Gorilla 203
Human 210
Lion 194
Roman anchor 372
Starfish 174
Volkswagen Beetle 341
Armature
 Power drill motor 566
 Sculpture 452, 454-455
Armature spindle 566
Arm bud 260
Arm coupling 573
Armed sports 556-557
Armor
 Battleship 394
 Gun turret 396
 Ironclad 393
Armored dinosaurs 92
Armored seat back 409
Armpit 211, 234
Armpit bight 388
Arm rail 576
Armrest 329, 407
Arms of Brazil 394
Armstand dive 558-559
Arrector pili muscle 235
Arricio 454
Arrow head 109
Arse 382
Arsenic 311
Arsia Mons 43
Arsinoitherium 57, 75, 104-105
Art deco style 495
 Twentieth-century building 494, 495
Artemon 372
Arterial system
 Brain 252
 Kidney 256
Arteriole 252
Artery
 Abdominal 173
 Alveolar 247
 Anterior tibial 253
 Axillary 253
 Basilar 252
 Brachial 253
 Central retinal 240
 Common carotid 215, 251, 253
 Common iliac 215, 253, 257
 Coronary 250-251, 253
 Digital 231, 253
 Dorsal metatarsal 253
 Epibranchial 179
 External iliac 215, 225, 253
 Femoral 225, 253
 Gastric 253
 Hepatic 248, 252-253
 Interlobular 256
 Internal carotid 243, 252
 Internal iliac 215, 253
 Lateral plantar 253
 Orbital 179
 Peroneal 253
 Popliteal 253
 Posterior cerebral 252
 Posterior tibial 253
 Pulmonary 182, 251, 253, 254-255
 Pulp 247
 Radial 231, 253
 Renal 256-257
 Splenic 253
 Sternal 173
 Subclavian 215, 251, 253
 Superior mesenteric 253, 256
 Superior thyroid 244

Testicular 257
Ulnar 231, 253
Umbilical 260
Vertebral 223, 252
Artesian water 292
Arthropoda 168, 170, 172, 278
Articular capsule 232
Articular cavity
 Hip joint 225
 Metatarsophalangeal joint 232
Artificial elements 310
Artificial fly 562-563
Artificial light 319
Artificial lure 563
Artillery loop 389
Artillery wheel 354
Artiodactyla 104, 198-199
Artist's easel 437
Artist's signature 437, 445
Art nouveau style 495
Arundinaria nitida 131
ARV Super 2 light aircraft 424-425
Arzachel 40
Ascender 445
Ascending aorta 251
Ascending colon 249
Ascraeus Mons 43
Asexual reproduction 154
Ash
 Mountain building 62
 Rock cycle 266
 Volcano 272-273
Ash chute 395
Ash-cinder volcano 272
Ash eruptions 272
Ash head 540
Ashlar 464, 486
Asia
 Cretaceous period 72-73
 Earth's physical features 264-265
 Himalaya formation 62-63
 Hominids 108
 Jurassic period 70
 Middle Ordovician period 64
 Quaternary period 76-77
 Tertiary period 74-75
 Triassic period 68
Asian buildings **490-491**
Asian elephant 200-201
Asparagus setaceous 64
Ass 198
Association football 524-525
Astatine 311
Asterias rubens 175
Asterina gibbosa 175
Asteroids **52-53**
 Solar System 30
Asteroxylon 78-79
Asthenosphere 58-59
Astragal
 Church of the Sorbonne 486
 Ship's shield 395
Astragalus 183
Astrolabe 376, 377
Astronavigation dome 408
Asymmetric ridge 283
Atacama Desert 264
Atalanta Planitia 36
Atherstone girth 583
Atlantic Ocean 264-265
 Quaternary period 77
 Tertiary period 75
Atlas
 Baroque building 482
 Horse 199
 Human 222
 Moon 40

Atlas mountains
 Earth's external features 39
 Quaternary period 77
 Satellite map 265
Atmosphere
 Earth 38-39, 64, **300-301**
 Jupiter 45
 Mars 43
 Mercury 34-35
 Neptune 51
 Pluto 51
 Saturn 47
 Uranus 49
 Venus 37
 Water cycle 288
Atoll 298-299
Atoll development 299
Atomic mass 309, 310
Atomic number 310
Atomic weight 310
Atoms 306, **508-509**
 Chemical properties 310
 Chemical reactions 312
 Periodic table 310
Atrial diastole 250
Atrial systole 251
Atrium
 Hong Kong and Shang-hai Bank 498
 Human 215, 250-251
 Sponge 166
Attached column
 Ancient Roman building 465
 Baroque church 480
 Gothic building 473
 Medieval building 468-469
 Neoclassical building 479
Attachment-bracket 424
Attachment lug 404
Attachment plate 424
Attack line 554
Attack radar 420
Attic
 Baroque church 480-481
 Cathedral dome 487
 Neoclassical building 478, 483
Attic vase 372
Attraction 316-317
"A" turret 394
Auda 491
Auditorium 479
Auditory canal 242
Auditory meatus
 Chimpanzee 202
 Seal 204
Auger 374
Augusta National Golf course 546
Aureole 471
Auricle 242
Auricular surface 223
Auriga 18, 21
Aurora 38, 301
Australasia 264-265
Australia
 Cretaceous period 72-73
 Jurassic period 70
 Late Carboniferous period 66
 Middle Ordovician period 64
 Quaternary period 76-77
 Railroad track gauge 331
 Satellite map 265
 Tertiary period 74-75
 Triassic period 68
Australian Desert 265
Australian rules football 524, **528-529**
Australopithecus 77, 108

Lower jaw 107
Tertiary period 74
Autofeather unit 419
Autogiro 422
Automatic cylinder lubricator 342
Automatic direction-finding aerial 423
Automatic door 328-329
Automatic Train Protection (ATP) 330
Automobile freight car 327
Autopilot 412
Autumn wood xylem 134
Auxiliary air intake 420-421
Auxiliary generator 327
Auxiliary power unit 417
Auxiliary power unit inlet 415
Aves 188
Avimimus 87
Avogadro 41
Avro triplane IV 402-403
Avro Tutor biplane 402-403
Away swing bowler 338
Awning 499
Axe 109, 374
Axial gland 175
Axial tilt
 Earth 38
 Jupiter 44
 Mars 42
 Mercury 34
 Moon 40
 Neptune 50
 Pluto 51
 Saturn 46
 Uranus 48
 Venus 36
Axilla 211
Axillary artery 253
Axillary bud 134
 Dicotyledon stem 127
 Durmast oak 131
 Leaf scars 154
Axillary vein 253
Axinite 270
Axis
 Azolla sp. 158
 Horse 199
 Human 222
 Seed 152-153
 Pine cone 122
Axis of rotation
 Jupiter 44
 Mars 42
 Mercury 34
 Moon 40
 Neptune 50
 Pluto 51
 Pulsar 28
 Saturn 46
 Uranus 48
 Venus 36
Axle
 Avro triplane 402-403
 Blackburn monoplane 400
 Bus 333
 Curtiss biplane 399
 Honda VF750 365
 Lockheed Electra airliner 407
 LVG CVI fighter 405
 Steam locomotive 324
Axle bolt 425
Axle brush 328
Axon 239
Aythya fuligula 188
Azimuthal map projection 265
Azo yellow 442
Azurite 306

B

B-17G Flying Fortress bomber 408
Baboon 202
Bach 35
Back
 Acoustic guitar 512
 Block and tackle 383
 Elephant 200
 Horse 198
 Human 210
 Lion 195
 Saddle 583
Backboard 552
Backbone 222
Back box 571
Back button 585
Back-check 514
Back cover 588
Back cover board
 Half-bound book 587
 Leather-bound book 587
Background radiation 10
Back judge 526
Back leg 576-577
Back line 555
Back plate 571
Back rail 576
Backrest
 ARV light aircraft 425
 Lockheed Electra passenger seat 407
Backs
 Handball 535
 Hockey 540
 Soccer 524
 Volleyball 554
Back sight 549
Backstay 378, 379, 380
Backstay stool 381
Back strap 560, 561
Backstroke 558-559
Backward defensive stroke 558
Backward dive 558
Backwash 294
Back zones 534
Bacteria 56
Bactrian camel 199
Baculum 144
Badger 194
Badminton **544-545**
BAe-146 jetliner components 412-415
Baffin Island 264
Baffle 341
Baffle plate 347
Bage, C. 492
Baggage compartment door 425
Bagneux Church 468-469
Bahada 282
Bail 558
Bail arm 562
Bailey 466
Bail handle 336
Bailly 40
Baird's beaked whale 205
Bait fishing 562
Balaenoptera musculus 205
Balance 232
Balance and muscle coordination 237
Balance weight
 Jaguar V12 engine 345
 Mid West rotary engine 411
Balancing drilling
 Mid West rotary engine 411
 Wankel rotary engine 347
Balanophyllia regia 167

Balata surface 546
Balcony 493
  Islamic tomb 489
  Nineteenth-century building 493
  Renaissance theater 477
  Rococo style 478, 482
  Sailing ship 378, 379, 381
Baleen whale 204
Ball
  Australian rules football 528
  Baseball 537
  Basketball 553
  Cricket 538
  Football 526
  Gaelic football 528-529
  Golf 546
  Handball 535
  Hockey 540
  Hurling 541
  Lacrosse 541
  Netball 535
  Racketball 545
  Rugby 524, 530-531
  Soccer 524
  Squash 545
  Tennis 544
  Volleyball 534
Ballast 324
Ball bearings 358-359
Ballflowers 470-471
Ball marker 547
Ball size number 525
Baltica 65
Baltimore oriole 193
Baluster
  Asian building 490
  Gothic building 473
  Neoclassical building 483
Balustrade
  Asian building 490
  Baroque church 479-480
  Cathedral dome 487
  Gothic church 472-473
  Neoclassical building 478, 483
  Nineteenth-century building 493
  Renaissance theatre 477
  Twentieth-century building 495
Balzac 35
Bamboo 131
Banana 146
Banded ironstone 277
Banded milk snake 184
Bandy 540
Bank of England 482
Banner 375
Bar
  Musical notation 502
  Relief-printing press 449
Barb
  Angling 562
  Cnidocyte 167
Barberry 130-131
Barbette
  Battleship 394
  Gun turret 396
Bare end
  Reef knot 388
  Single sheet bend 387
Barium 310
Bark
  Bishop pine stem 125
  Epiphyte 162
  Lichen 114
  Perennials 130-131
  Stem 134
  Woody plants 130-131
Bar keel 392
Barkhan dune 283
Bar leather 583

Bar line 502
Barnacle 172-173
Barnard's Star 23
Baroque style 478-483
Barosaurus 82
Barrel
  Gun turret 397
  Wood capstan 387
Barrel arbor hook 570
Barrel joint 508
Barrel pivot hole 570
Barrel vault 484-485
  Ancient Roman building 463-464
  Baroque church 479
  Medieval church 468
  Nineteenth-century building 493
Barrier beach 294
Barrier reef 299
Barry, C. 493
Bars 516-517
Bar swivel 562
Baryonyx 83, 84-85
Baryte 270
Basal disk 167
Basal scale 114
Basalt 274-275
Basaltic lava 272
Bascule 493
Base
  Ancient Greek temple 461
  Ancient Roman building 463, 465
  Asian building 491
  Baroque church 479, 481
  Dome 484, 486, 487
  French temple 485
  Gothic church 470, 472
  Medieval church 469
  Neoclassical building 478, 483
  Renaissance theater 477
  Sheet lead 383
  Twentieth-century building 494
  Twin bollards 386
Baseball 536-537
Baseline
  Calligraphy lettering 445
  Tennis 544
Basement 483
Basement membrane of Bowman's capsule 257
Base of phalanx 230
Base plate 552
Bases 556
Basic movements 237
Basic shield volcano 272
Basidium 115
Basilar artery 252
Basilar membrane 243
Basilican system 468
Basilica of St. Madeleine 468
Basilic vein 253
Basket
  Basketball 532
  Ski pole 552-553
Basket arch 472, 484
Basketball 532-533
Basket star 174
Basking shark 179
Bas-relief carving 491
Bass angling 562
Bass bridge
  Concert grand piano 515
  Upright piano 514
Bass clarinet 504
Bass clef 502
Bass drum 504-505, 518-519
Bass formation 277
Bass joint 508

Bass notes 512
Bassoon 503, 504-505, 508
Bass voice 502
Bastille 466
Bat
  Baseball 537
  Cricket 539
Bat (animal) 105
Batholiths 274-275
Batsman 538-539
Batten
  74-gun ship 381
  Junk 376
Batter 536-537
Battery
  Bell-47 helicopter 422
  Bersey electric cab 342
  Camera 588
  Kirby BSA racing sidecar 369
  Lawnmower 580-581
Battery box 527, 424
Battery carrier 338
Battery case lid 574
Battery chamber cap 588
Battery compartment 407, 574
Battery connection 581
Battery contact 574
Battery overspill 422
Battery retainer 581
Battery strap 339
Batting gloves
  Baseball 537
  Cricket 539
Battlemented cornice 471
Battlements 466-467
Battleship 394-395
Bauxite 268
Bay
  Building 468, 469, 494
  Coastline features 295
  River features 291
Bay-head beach 294
Bay-leaf garland 480
Bayonet fixing 352
Bay window 477
BE 2B bomber 404-405
Beach
  Coastline 294-295
  River development 289
Beacon 407, 422-423
Beaded edge tire 336
Beadlet anemone 166
Bead molding 459
Beak
  Ankylosaurus 94
  Attic vase 372
  Bird 188-190
  Ceratopsian 100
  Chelonian 186
  Dolphin 204
  Euoplocephalus 94
  Hatching chick 192-193
  Iguanodon 97
  Moss 119
  Octopus 176
  Ornithopod 96
  Panoplosaurus 94
  Protoceratops 102
  Psittacosaurus 103
  Stegosaurus 92
"Beaked lizards" 68
Beaked whale 204
Beaker 312
Beam
  BAe-146 jetliner 414
  Gothic church 473
  High-tension 496
  Iron paddlesteamer 393
  Mini-television 574
  Modern building 497-499
  Nineteenth-century building 492
  Single skull 560

Bean
  Black 153
  Broad 152
Bear 104, 106, 194-195
Bearing
  Electric generator 317
  Jaguar V12 engine 345
  Motorcycle gearbox 366
  Rotary engine output shaft 411
Bearing assembly 425
Bearing housing 344
Bearing mount 411
Bearing seal 359
Bearing sleeve 338
"Beast feet" 84
Beaten gold 432
Beats 502
Beaver 196-197
Becket 583
Becket Chapel 467
Bed
  Relief printing press 449
  Sedimentary rocks 276
Bedding plane
  Cave system 285
  Coastline 294-295
Bedford cord upholstery 336
Bedplate 390
Bedrock 298
  Delta formation 291
Bee 168, 379
Bee hummingbird 193
Bee pollination 144-145
Beeswax 384, 583
Beethoven 35
Beetle 168
Begonia 129, 155
Begonia x tuberhybrida 129, 155
Behavior 108, 237
Belaying pin 582
Belemnites 71, 278-279
Belfry
  74-gun ship 380
  Church of St. George in the East 481
Bell 508
Bell 206 Jetranger 423
Bell 47G-3B1 422-423
Bellatrix 18
Bell chamber 493
Bell crank 391
Bell housing 347
Bell joint 508
Bello 35
Bell Regio 36, 37
Belly
  Bird 188
  Caiman 186
  Dolphin 204
  Elephant 201
  Horse 198
  Lion 195
  Lizard 184
  Sail 384
  Viola 511
  Violin 510
Belly-band 555
Belly nail 582-583
Belt
  Jupiter 44-45
  Structure of Saturn 47
Belt armor 394
Belt color 556
Belt drive 366
Belt guard 580
Belt pulley 345
Belt tensioner 344
Belvedere 476
Bench officials
  Ice hockey 550
  Lacrosse 541
Bending 318

Bends 387
Benguela current 297
  Satellite map 264
Benz, Karl 334
Benz Motorwagen 335
Benz six-cylinder engine 405
Berardius bairdi 205
Berberis sp. 130-131
Berkelium 311
Berries 148-149
Bersey electric cab 342
Berthing ropes 387
Beryl 270
Beryllium 310
Betelgeuse 18, 21
  Hertzsprung-Russell diagram 23
  Orion 18
  Universe 10-11
Betula grossa 74
Betula lenta 76
Betulites 74
Bevel gear 335
Bevel pinion 338
Beverley Minster 484
Bhagirathi Parbat 62
Bianco di San Giovanni 434-435
Biathlon rifle 549
Bib 557
Bi-block engine 337
Biceps brachii muscle 226
Biceps femoris muscle 227
Bicycle 360-361
Bicycle anatomy 358-359
Bicycle riding 315
Biennials 128
Biflagellate cell 116
Bifurcate ligament 232
"Big Ben" 493
Bigbore rifle shooting 548-549
Big end
  Flat-four cylinder arrangement 340
  Four-stroke cycle 343
  Jaguar straight six engine 344
  Mid West engine 410
  Trojan engine 342
Big-end bearing 335
Bight 388
Big toe 232-233
Bile duct 189, 249
Bilge keel 395, 397
Bilge keelson 393
Bill
  Danforth anchor 386
  Running block 383
  Sail hook 384
Bilobed leaves 123
Binder 464
Binder bolt 361
Binder clip 430
Binding 383
  Acoustic guitar 512
  Iron paddlesteamer 392
Binding medium 440
Binnacle box 378
Biology symbols 591
Bipedal dinosaur 84, 96, 100
Bipinnate leaf 137
Biplane elevator 398-399
Biplanes 402-403, 408
Bipolar neuron 239
Birch 74, 76
Bird 84, 188-191
  Beak 190
  Earth's evolution 57

Feathers 191
Feet 190
  Fossil record 279
  Wing 191
"Bird feet" 96
Bird-hipped dinosaur 82, 92, 96
Bird of prey 188
Bird pollination 144
Bishop pine 124-125
Bismuth 281, 311
Bit 567
Biternate leaves 137
Bit-guard 555
Bitt
  74-gun ship 380-381
  Roman corbita 373
Bitter end, Hawser 387
Bituminous coal 280
Bivalves 79, 176, 278-279
Blackbacked gull 193
Black bean 153
Black belt 556
Blackberry 130, 146-147
Blackburn monoplane 400-401
Blackburn, Robert 400
Black dwarf 24-25
Blackheaded gull 189
Black holes 28-29
  Galaxies 12
  Massive stars 26-27
Black Mesa 277
Black rhinoceros 199
Black Sea 265
Blackstonia perfoliata 144
Black walnut 137
Black widow spider 171
Bladder
  Bony fish 181
  Chimpanzee 202
  Dolphin 205
  Domestic cat 195
  Elephant 200
  Human 215, 257, 258-259, 261
  Lizard 185
  Rabbit 196
  Soccer ball 525
  Swim 178, 180-181
  Tortoise 187
  Urinary 181
Bladder wrack 117
Blade
  Butterwort 161
  Calligraphy drawing board 445
  Danforth anchor 386
  Dicotyledon leaf 127
  Fencing foil 557
  Golf clubs 547
  Hockey stick 540
  Kayak paddle 560
  Lawnmower 580-581
  Leaf surfaces 136, 138
  Monocotyledon leaf 127
  Propeller 390
  Roman rudder 373
  Sculling oar 560
  Seaweed 116-117
  Vegetative reproduction 154
  Venus fly trap 160
  Volkswagen Beetle 341
  Wetland plants 158-159
Blade bolt 581
Blade counterweight 406, 422
Blade cover 580
Blade retainer 581
Blade-root attachment 422-423
Blade tip sealing shroud 419
Blanking plate 411

Blast bag 396
Blast-pipe 325
Blending 440
Blériot XI monoplane 401
Blériot, Louis
  Early monoplane 400
  Pioneers of flight 398
Blindage 377
Blind arch
  Asian building 491
  Cathedral dome 487
  Gothic church 470
Blind door 478
Blind pull 336-337
Blind release bar 552
Blind spot 241
Blind tracery 493
Blind trefoil 473
Blind window 478
Block and tackle 382-383
Block carving 470
Block cube 270
Block disintegration 282
Block-fault lake 293
Block-fault mountain 62
Block flap 582-583
Blocking pad 550
Blocks 310
Blood cells 253
Blood clotting 253
Blower control 325
Blower isolator valve 325
Blower shroud 580
Blow hole 508
Blowhole 205
Blubber 204
Blue-and-yellow macaw 190
Blue-green alga 56, 78
Blue light 318
Blue line 550
Blue supergiant star
  Hertzsprung-Russell diagram 23
  Stellar black hole 29
Blue whale 204-205
Bluff 289
Blunt button 556-557
BMW R/60 motorcycle 362
Board
  Ice hockey rink 550
  Modeling 455
  Pastels 441
Boarding 464
Board mounting 450-451
Board paper 586-587
Boat boom 395
Boat builder's tools 374
Boat handling derrick 395
Boat slide 378
Boat winch 394
Bobstay 379
Body
  Anchisaurus 89
  Discus 542
  Dunkeld wet fly 563
  Motorcycle 364-365
  Sauropodomorpha 88
  Stringed instruments 510
Body-bag 426
Body cells 216-217
Body covering 588
Body cradle 398
Body drop 556
Body joint
  Flute 508
  Piccolo 508
Body mount 338
Body organs 214-215
Body padding 526
Body sections
  Insect 168
  Scorpion 170
  Spider 170-171

Body-shell 518-519
Bodyshell
  Renault Clio 348-349
  Volkswagen Beetle 341
Body tackles 528
Body temperature regulation
  Dinosaurs 92
  Mammals 104
Body wire 557
Bodywork 548-349
  Racing cars 356
  Volkswagen Beetle 341
Bodywork mounting point 364
Boeing 747-400 412
Bogie axle 326
Bogie frame 325
Bogie main landing gear 416
Boiler
  Box boiler 392
  Donkey boiler 392
  Steamboat with paddle wheels 391
  Steam locomotives 324-325
Boiler pressure gauge 325
Boiler water level 525
Bole base 432-433
Bollard
  Battleship 395
  Frigate 397
  Mooring and anchoring 386-387
Bolson 282
Bolster 378
Bolt
  Church of St. Pierre 499
  Lawnmower 580
  Lower deadeye 383
  Shackle 386
  Toaster 578
Bolted anchor 425
Bolt hole
  Drum brake 365
  Mid West rotary engine 411
  Twin bollards 387
Bolt rest 548
Bolt rope 372, 384
Bolts 548-549
Bomb 404, 408
Bomb aimer's viewing panel 408
Bomb door 408
Bomber
  Modern military aircraft 420
  World War I aircraft 404-405
  World War II aircraft 408-409
Bomb rack 404
Bonaventure mast 377
Bonaventure topcastle 377
Bonaventure topmast 377
Bonaventure yard 377
Bonded brick wall 492
Bonding
  Chemical reactions 312
  Covalent 309
  English bond 485
  Gases 307
  Ionic 308
  Liquids 307
Bone cell 217, 225
Bone marrow smear 225
Bones
  Fossil 278
  Human 224-225, 230, 232
Bone structure 108
Bone surface 80
Bonnet
  1906 Renault 337

Ford Model T 339
Renault Clio 348
Volkswagen Beetle 340-341
Bonnet catch 336, 349
Bonnet clip 339
Bonnet hinge 349, 341
Bonnet-release cable 349
Bonnet-release handle 341
Bonnet stay 337
Bony crest
  Baryonyx 83
  Corythosaurus 98
  Lambeosaurus 99
  Parasaurolophus 99
Bony dorsal shield 78
Bony frill 100
Bony nodule
  Pachycephalosaurus 100
  Prenocephale 100
Bony ridge 100
Bony shelf 100, 101
Bony spike 100
Bony strut 83
Bony studs 92
Bony tendons 96
Bookbinding 586
Books 586-587
Boom
  Battleship 394-395
  Curtiss Model-D pusher 599
  Double topsail schooner 385
  Guest boat boom 394
  Hong Kong and Shang-hai Bank 498
  Longboat 380
  Rigging 382
  Sailing dinghy 561
Boom guy block 382
Boomkin 380
Boötes 18, 21
Boots
  Riding 554
  Sailing 560
  Ski 552
Bordino Steam Carriage 334-335
Borealis Planitia 35
Borneo 265
Boron 311
Boss
  Church roof 468-469
  Hurley 541
  Viking karv 374
Bothriolepis 65
Botryoidal habit 270-271
Bottom ballast 377
Bottom bracket 358
Bottom bracket axle 358
Bottom cover assembly 588
Bottom filler 568-569
Bottom hose 551
Bottom lining 577
Bottom plate 590, 392-593
Bottom race 559
Bottomset strata 283
Bottom splat 576
Boudin 60-61
Boulder beach 295
Boulder clay 286
Bounce pass 535
Boundary
  Cricket 558
  Mantle-crust 39
  Outer core-mantle 39
Boundary line
  Australian rules football 528
  Badminton 545
  Cricket 558
  Squash 545

Bow
  74-gun ship 381
  Kayak 560
  Sailing dinghy 561
  Stringed instruments 510
  Wooden sailing ship 378
Bowball 561
Bow drill 109
Bower anchor
  Battleship 395
  Sailing warship 377
  Wooden sailing ship 379
Bowclip 561
Bow front 483
Bowl 445
Bowler 538
Bowline 388, 389
Bowling crease 538
Bowman's capsule 256
Bowman's space 257
Bow ornament 375
Bow section 392
Bow-side oar 560
Bowsprit
  Iron paddlesteamer 393
  Longboat 380
  Rigging 382
  Sailing warship 376
  Tea clipper 392
  Wooden sailing ship 378-379
Bowsprit cap 382
Bowtell molding 475
Box 477
Box boiler 392
Box fold 61
Box freight car 327
Boxing 556
Box-leaved milkwort 144
Box-section swingarm fork 364
Box-section tubular cradle frame 364
Box sister keelson 393
Boxwood staff 377
Brace
  Asian building 490
  Barrel vault 485
  Dome 486
  Double topsail schooner 385
  "Ellerman Lines" steam locomotive 324
  Gothic building 473
  Neoclassical building 479
  Nineteenth-century building 493
  Roman corbita 372
  Sailing warship 377
  Trombone 506
  Wooden sailing ship 378
Brace-and-bit 566-567
Brace block 373
Bracer 548
Brachial artery 253
Brachialis muscle 226
Brachial plexus 238
Brachial valve 278
Brachiocephalic trunk 251
Brachiocephalic vein 253
Brachiopods 278-279
Brachioradialis muscle 226
Brachiosaurus 88, 90-91
Brachylophosaurus 98
Bracing 513
Bracing cable 427
Bracing strut 401-402, 423
Bracing tube 364
Bracing wire
  Blériot XI monoplane 401
  LVG CVI fighter 405
  Wright Flyer 599

Bracken 121
Bracket
  Baroque church 479
  Cathedral dome 484
  Gothic building 473
  Islamic tomb 489
  Medieval building 466
  Neoclassical building 478
  Renaissance building 475
Bracket shell 58
Bracteoles
  Dehiscent fruit 151
  Ice-plant 129
  Live-for-ever 129
Bracts 141-143
  Bromeliad 113
  Dicotyledon flower 127
  Durmast oak 131
  Florists' chrysanthemum 129
  Guzmania lingulata 163
  Ice-plant 129
  Indehiscent fruit 150
  Live-for-ever 129
  Peruvian lily 129
  Rose 131
  Slender thistle 129
  Wind-pollinated plant 144
Bract scales 122
Braided polyester 388
Braided stream 286
Braiding
  Dragon prowhead 374
  River features 290
Brailing rope 372
Brail line 372
Brain
  Bird 189
  Bony fish 181
  Butterfly 169
  Chimpanzee 202
  Crayfish 173
  Dogfish 179
  Dolphin 205
  Domestic cat 195
  Elephant 200
  Hominid 108
  Human 236-237
  Lizard 185
  Octopus 176
  Rabbit 196
  Spider 170
Braincase 108
Brain cavity 100
Brainstem 236
Brake 332, 350
Brake actuating chain 327
Brake arm 552
Brake back plate 340, 350
Brake block 360
Brake bridge 361
Brake cable 365
Brake calliper
  ARV light aircraft 424
  Disc brake 365
  Harley-Davidson FLHS Electra Glide 363
  Honda VF750 364-365
  Husqvarna Motocross TC610 368
  Renault Clio 351
  Suzuki RGV500 368-369
  Wagon bogie 331
Brake cylinder 327, 350-351
Brake disc
  ARV light aircraft 424
  Renault Clio 351
  Wagon bogie 331
Brake drum 339-340, 342
Brake duct 356-357
Brake fluid 365

Brake hose 351
Brakeless wheel hub 369
Brake lever
  ARV light aircraft 425
  Benz Motorwagen 335
  Bicycle 359
  Eddy Merckx racing bicycle 361
  Harley-Davidson FLHS Electra Glide 363
  Kirby BSA 369
  Suzuki RGV500 369
  White Steam Car 342
  Windcheetah racing HPV bicycle 361
Brake master cylinder
  Harley-Davidson FLHS Electra Glide 363
  Honda VF750 364
  Suzuki RGV500 368
Brake mount 424
Brake pad
  Disc brake 365
  Eddy Merckx racing bicycle 361
  Renault Clio 351
  Wagon bogie 331
Brake pedal
  Harley-Davidson FLHS Electra Glide 363
  Honda VF750 364
  Oldsmobile bodywork 337
  Renault Clio 350
  Steam-powered Cugnot 334
  Suzuki RGV500 368
Brake pipe
  ARV light aircraft 424
  BAe-146 components 414
  Formula One racing car 357
  Lockheed Electra airliner 406-407
Brake pivot bolt 361
Brake plate 365
Brake quadrant 335
Brake rigging
  British Rail Class 20 diesel engine 327
  "Ellerman Lines" steam locomotive 324-325
Brake rod 337, 339
Brake servo 351
Brake shield 351
Brake shoe 365
  "Deltic" diesel electric locomotive 327
  Drum brake 365
  "Ellerman Lines" steam locomotive 325
  Renault Clio 350
Brake slip 395
Brake torque arm 364
Brake vacuum pump 324
Braking
  Motorcycle 364
  Train 330
Braking control system 330
Braking distance 331
Bramante 35
Bramble 130, 146-147
Branched leaf venation 127
Branches
  Bishop pine 124
  Clubmoss 120
  Crab cactus 129
  Dicotyledons 127
  Horsetail 120
  Perennials 130-131
  Seaweed 117
  Sporophore 114
  Woody plants 130-131

Branchial heart 176
Branching bracteole 151
Branchiostegal ray 181
Branchlet 114
Branch trace 125
Brassavola nodosa 162
Brass bevel 336-337
Brass housing for ignition cable 343
Brassica sp. 132
Brass instruments 504-505, **506-507**
Brazil 331
Brazilian battleship 394-395
Brazilian current 296
Brazilian Highlands 264
Bread 578
Breakfast room 483
Breakwater
  Battleship 395
  Frigate 397
  Single scull 561
Breast
  Bird 188
  Horse 199
  Human 211
Breast auger 374
Breast bone 218
Breast stroke 558-559
Breastwork 380
Breather pipe 422
Breccia 276-277
Breech 396
Breech block 396
Breeches 557
Breech wheel 396
Breve rest 502
Brick arch 324
Brick pier 495
Brick vault 492
Brick wall 492
Bridge
  Acoustic guitar 512-513
  Battleship 394-395
  Cello 511
  Clock 571
  Double bass 511
  Electric guitar 513
  Frigate 397
  Golf course 546
  London Bridge 466-467
  Medieval castle 467
  Modern building 498
  Viola 511
  Violin 510
Bridge pin 512
Bridges 330
Bridle 555
Bright Angel shale 277
B ring 46-47
Britain 331
Brittle stars 174-175
Broad axe 374
Broad bean 133, 152
Broadcast transmitter 574
Broad disk 79
Broad lace trim 336-337
Broadside 378
Broken pediment 481
Bromeliads 112-113
  Epiphytic 162-163
Bromine 311
Bronchi 254
Bronchial nerve 254
Bronchial tree 254
Bronchial vein 254
Bronchiole and alveoli 254
Bronchus
  Frog 182
  Human 215, 255
Bronze casting 452
Bronze finishing tools 454
Bronze mast truck 372
Bronze statue 455

Broomrape 163
Browband 554-555
Brow horn 102
Brow horn core 103
Brown alga 116
Brown scales 121
Brown seaweed 116-117
Brow ridge
  Australopithecus 108
  Gorilla 203
  Homo Sapiens 108
Brush 432, 444, 566
Brush holder 566
Brushing boot 554
Brush lettering equipment 444
Bryce Canyon 276
Bryophytes 112, 118-119
Bryozoans 279
Bryum sp. 112
Buccal cavity
  Bird 189
  Chimpanzee 202
  Dolphin 205
  Domestic cat 195
  Elephant 200
  Pachycephalosaurus 100
  Rabbit 196
  Tortoise 187
Buccal mass 176
Buccinator muscle 229
Bucket seat 361
Bucket tappet 344
Buckle guard 583
Buckram corner piece 586-587
Bud
  Adventitious 154
  Aechmea miniata 162
  Apical meristem 154
  Begonia 129
  Bishop pine 124
  Broomrape 163
  Clematis flower 131
  Dicotyledons 127
  Durmast oak 131
  Florists' chrysanthemum 129
  Horse chestnut 130
  Larkspur 141
  Lily 140
  Lime 143
  London plane 134
  Moss 119
  Oxalis sp. 121
  Pine needle 125
  Rhizome 155
  Root tuber 154-155
  Rose 131
  Rowan twig 131
  Stolon 154
  Water lily 159
Buddhist style 490
Budh Planitia 35
Bud scale
  Bishop pine 124
  Dicotyledon stem 127
  London plane 134
  Pine shoot apex 125
Buffer
  "Deltic" diesel electric locomotive 327
  "Ellerman Lines" steam locomotive 324-325
  Italian State Railways Class 402 328
  "Rocket" steam locomotive 324
Buffing pad 328
Bugatti Type 57S 356
Bugle 506
Bulb
  Renault Clio 352
  Vegetative reproduction **154-155**

Bulb horn
  1906 Renault 337
  Ford Model T 338
Bulbil 154-155
Bulbourethral gland 259
Bulkhead
  ARV Super 2 425
  Flat freight car 327
Bulkhead stiffener 393
Bulkhead trim 407
Bullet 397, 549
Bullet block 373
Bullet-shaped guard 278
Bull-head rail 331
Bullnose chisel 452
Bull's-eye 549
Bulwark
  74-gun ship 380
  Ironclad 393
Bumblebee 168
Bumper
  Bus 332-333
  Pinzgauer Turbo D 355
  Renault Clio 348-349
  Volkswagen Beetle 341
Bunkers 546-547
Bunk space 397
Bun lamp burner 339
Buntline 372
Buon fresco 434-435
Buoy 379
Buoyant wetland plants 158
Burmese pagoda 490
Burning reaction 312, 313, 315
Burnishing 432, 446
Bursting charge 397
Buses **332-333**
Bushes 130-131
Bushing
  Hydroelectric power station 314
  Lamp 572-573
Butt
  Bassoon 508
  Lacrosse crosse 541
  Tennis racket 544
Butt cap 563
Butte
  Igneous rock structures 274
  Weathering and erosion 283
Buttercup 127, 132-133
Butterfly 168
Butterfly knot 389
Butterfly plate 582
Butterfly swimming stroke 558-559
Butterwort 160-161
Butt extension 563
Buttock 198, 210
Button head rivet 392
Button-quilted upholstery 336
Buttress 484
  Baroque church 478-481
  Dome 486
  Gothic church 470-473
  Medieval building 466, 468-469
  Nineteenth-century building 493
Butt section 562

C

3C275 (quasar) 11
Cab 324, 327
Cabane strut 404
Cabbage 132
Cab-end bogie 327

Cabin
  74-gun ship 380-381
  Iron paddlesteamer 392-393
  Wooden sailing ship 379
Cabin air-discharge aperture 414
Cabin air duct 417
Cabin air-pressure discharge valve 413
Cabinet rasp 452
Cabin trim 406-407
Cable 397, 549
Cable entry point 578
Cable guide 358-359, 360
Cable holder 395
Cable retaining gland 578
Cable stop 565
Cable support bracket 581
Cacti
  Desert survivors 112
  Dryland adaptation 156
  Herbaceous flowering plants 129
Caddy cover flap 584
Cadmium 311
Cadmium red 436
Cadmium yellow 438
Caecum
  Bird 189
  Brachiosaurus 90
  Chimpanzee 202
  Cow 198
  Digestive 176, 173
  Gut 170
  Human 249
  Octopus 176
  Pyloric 181-174
  Rabbit 196
  Rectal 174
Caelum 18
Caernarvon Castle 466
Caesium 310
Caiman 186-187
Calamus 191
Calcanean tendon 232-233
Calcaneum 183, 199
Calcareous ooze 299
Calcareous plates 172
Calcareous tufa 284
Calcite (calcium carbonate)
  Blue chalk 430
  Carbonates 269
  Cave 284-285
  Fossils 278
  Mohs scale 271
  Sedimentary rocks 277
  Testing candle wax 313
Calcite curtain 285
Calcite ossicle 174
Calcite ridge 284-285
Calcium 310
  Earth's composition 39
  Earth's crust 58
  Seawater salt content 296
Calcium line 23
Caldera
  Igneous rock structures 275
  Lake formation 293
  Volcano 272
Caledonian mountains
  Late Carboniferous period 67
  Triassic period 69
Calf 210
Calico 576-577
Californian purple sea urchin 175
Californium 311
Calliactis parasitica 166
Calligraphy **444-445**
Calliper assembly 365

Callipers 452
Callisto 44
Caloris Basin 34-35
Caloris Montes 35
Calypte helenae 193
Calyptra 119
Calyx 140
  Allium sp. 143
  Centaury 144
  Human 256
  Simple succulent berry 149
Cam 344
Camarasaurus 91
Cambium 126
Cambrian period
  Fossil record 279
  Geological timescale 56
Cam cover
  Jaguar straight six engine 344
  Jaguar V12 engine 345
  Renault VS10 RS1 engine 356
Camellia 137
Camels 198-199
Camera **588-589**
Camera pouch 426
Cam follower
  Ford diesel engine 547
  Jaguar straight six engine 344
  Jaguar V12 engine 345
  Velocette OHV engine 367
Cam lobe 344
Camouflage 409
Camouflage coloration 192
Campaniform capital 458
Campanile 477
Camptosaurus 70, 97
Camshaft 344-345
Camshaft gear 367
Camshaft sprocket 345
Camshaft timing gear 344
Canada 331
Canadian football 524, **526-527**
Canadian pond weed 158-159
Canal
  Sea urchin 175
  Starfish 174
Canals 42
Canaries current 296
Cancellous bone 224
Cancer 18, 21
Candelabrum 476
Candle lamp 335
Candle wax 312-313
Canes Venatici 18, 21
Canine tooth
  Bear 106, 194
  Chimpanzee 202
  Human 246
  Hyaenodon 107
  Lion 194
  Opossum 106
  Smilodon 107
  Toxodon 106
Canis familiaris 195
Canis Major 18, 21
Canis Minor 18, 21
Canister 394
Cannon 376, 394
Cannon bone 198-199
Cannondale bicycle 361
Cannon pinion 571
Canoeing **560-561**
Canopus 15
Canopy
  1906 Renault 336-337
  ARV light aircraft 424-425

Bell-47 helicopter 422
Daimler engine 343
Ford Model T 339
Hawker Tempest components 409
Oldsmobile engine 336
Schleicher glider 426
Schweizer helicopter 423
Canopy latch 425
Canopy rail 409
Canson paper 441
Cant frame 381
Cantilever beam 494
Cantilever brake 358, 361
Cantilever brake boss 359
Cantilevered shade 495
Cantle
  English saddle 582
  Racing saddle 555
  Show-jumping saddle 554
Canvas
  Acrylic paint 442
  Oil paint 436
  Preparation 437
Canvas shroud 362
Canvas support 437
Canyon
  Sedimentary rocks 276-277
  Weathering and erosion 282-283
Cap
  Alga 116
  Fungus 114-115
  Lamp 572
  Lawnmower 580
  Radicle tip 153
  Wood capstan 387
  Wooden sailing ship 378-379
Capacitor 575
Capacity measurements 590
Cape gooseberry 149
Capella 18, 21
Cape Royal 277
Capillary fringe 293
Capillary network 254
Capital
  Ancient Egyptian building 458-459
  Ancient Greek building 458, 460-461
  Ancient Roman building 458, 463, 465
  Asian building 490, 491
  Baroque church 479, 481
  Cathedral dome 487
  Domed roof 486
  French temple 485
  Islamic mosque 488
  Medieval building 467-469
  Neoclassical building 478, 483
  Ptolemaic-Roman period 459
  Renaissance building 476-477
  Romanesque style 468
Capitate bone 230
Capitulum 129, 142
Cap line 445
Cap nut 572
Capricornus 19, 20
Capstan 387
  74-gun ship 380
  Iron paddlesteamer 393
  Wooden sailing ship 379
Capstan screw 514
Capsule
  Dry fruit 150-151
  Moss 112, 119
Captain's cabin 379, 381

Captain's seat 416
Captain's shelter 394
Capybara 196-197
Carapace 172-173, 187
Carbon
  Atomic mass 310
  Bows 548
  Candle wax 312-313
  Coal formation 280
  Minerals 268
  Periodic table 311
  Small stars 24-25
  Structure of red
    supergiant 26
Carbonates 269
Carbon atom 138
Carbon dioxide
  Earth's atmosphere 300
  Gas 312-313
  Mars' atmosphere 43
  Photosynthesis 138
  Respiratory system 255
  Scrubber compartment
    397
  Structure of comet 53
  Venus' atmosphere 37
Carbon graphite racket
  544
Carbonic acid 284
Carboniferous period 56-
  57, 66-67
  Reptiles 80
Carbon ink stick 444
Carbonized wood 430
Carbon monoxide
  Mars' atmosphere 43
  Venus' atmosphere 37
Carbon powder 311
Carbon-rich earth layers
  66
Carburettor
  ARV light aircraft 425
  Mid West twin-rotor
    engine 411
  Pegasus Quasar
    microlight 427
  Two-stroke engine 366
Carburettor cover 369
Carburettor hot-air intake
  pipe 422
Carburettor hot air lever
  425
Cardiac notch 248
Cardiac region of stomach
  179
Cardiac stomach 174
Cardiac vein 250
Carduus tenuiflorus 129
Cargo-carrying boat
  Dhow 376
  Junk 376
  Liberty ship 392
  Roman corbita 372-373
  Tea clipper 392
Cargo derrick 592
Cargo hatch 376
Cargo hold 372, 592
Caribbean plate 59
Caribbean Sea 264
Carina 21
Carinal canal 120
Carina plate 173
Carling 380
Carmel formation 276
Carnallite 271
Carnassial teeth 194
Carnivores 104, **194-195**
  Jurassic period 70
  Theropod 84
  Triassic period 68
Carnivorous plants **160-
  161**
  Pitcher plant 113
Carotid canal 220
Carp 180

Carpals
  Bird 189
  Bird's wing 191
  Domestic cat 195
  Elephant 201
  Frog 183
  Hare 197
  Horse 199
  Kangaroo 206
  Lizard 184
  Platypus 206
  Rhesus monkey 202
  Seal 204
Carp angling 562
Carpathian mountains 77,
  265
Carpels 140-141
  Dehiscent fruit 151
  Fertilization 146-147
  Fruit development 148-
    149
  Insect-pollinated plant
    144
  Lemon fruit 148
  Ovary 140
  Stigma 140
  Style 140
Carpel wall 148, 151
Carpophore 151
Carpus
  Crab 172
  Crayfish 173
  Human 218
Carrara white marble 453
Carriage 413
Carrick bend 387, 389
Carrion crow 193
Carrot 128, 132
Carrying fork 334
Carrying wheel 324
Cartilage
  Auricle 242
  Bony fish 180
  Meatus 242
  Wrist 230
Cartilaginous fish 178-179,
  180
Cartouche 458
Cartridge starter 408
Caruncle 213
Carved sculpture 452, 453
Carved stone 488
Carvel-built hull 376, 391
Carvel planking 376, 377
Carving
  Asian building 490-491
  Gothic building 470
  Sculpture 452
Carving mallet 452
Caryopses 113, 150
Casa de las Conchas 476
Casa del Fascio 495
Caspian Sea 265
Cassini Division 46, 47
Cassiopeia 19
Cassowaries 188
Cast alloy wheel 346
Cast aluminum wheel
  spider 336
Castanea sativa 136, 150
Castanets 504, 517
Casting 452, 454
Cast-iron 492-493
Cast-iron chair 331
Cast iron cylinder barrel
  363
Castle-deck gunport 376-
  377
Castles, 374, **466-467**
Castor 18, 21
Castor canadensis 197
Cast-steel 497
Cat 104, 194-195
Catalytic converter 344,
  350

Catamaran 560
Cataphoresic coating 348
Cataphyll 152
Cat block 581
Catcher's mask 536
Catch glove 550
Catena 372
Catenary 328, 330
Caterpillar 168, 169
  Eggs 192
Catharina 40
Cathead
  74-gun ship 380
  Battleship 395
Cathedral of St. Lazare
  468
Cathode ray tube 574
Cations 308
Catkin 144
Catted anchor 381
Cattle 104, 198
Caucasus 265
Caudal fin 178, 179, 180-
  181
Caudal musculature 90, 95
Caudal plate 92-93
Caudal spike 92-93
Caudal vertebrae
  Ankylosaurus 95
  Archaeopteryx 85
  Crocodile 186
  Diplodocus 90
  Domestic cat 195
  Elephant 201
  Eryops 81
  Euoplocephalus 95
  Gallimimus 86
  Hare 197
  Horse 199
  Iguanodon 96
  Kangaroo 206
  Kentrosaurus 93
  Lizard 184-185
  Parasaurolophus 98
  Plateosaurus 89
  Platypus 206
  Rhesus monkey 202
  Seal 204
  Stegoceras 101
  Stegosaurus 93
  Struthiomimus 87
  Triceratops 102
  Tuojiangosaurus 93
  Tyrannosaurus 84-85
  Westlothiana 81
Caudate nucleus 237
Caudex 113
Caudo-femoral muscle 97
Cauliculus 460
Caulophryne jordani 180
Cave bear skull 77
Caves **284-285**
  Coastline 294-295
  Glacier 286
Cavetto molding
  Ancient Egyptian
    building 458-459
  Baroque church 479
  French temple 485
  Gothic building 472
  Renaissance building
    477
Cavies 196
Cayley, Sir George 398
C clef 502
CD-ROM **584-585**
Cedar-tree laccolith 274
Ceilings 463, 484
Celestial equator
  Stars of northern skies
    18-19
  Stars of southern skies
    20-21
Celestial poles 18
Celestial sphere 18

Cell
  Alga 116-117
  Body 217
  Building 469, 485
  Chusan palm leaf 130
  Clubmoss stem 120
  Collar 166
  Dicotyledon 126-127
  Epidermal 166
  Epiphytic orchid 162
  Fern rachis 121
  Horsetail stem 120
  Leaf 126, 139
  Marram grass 113
  Monocotyledon 126-127
  Moss 119
  Mushroom 115
  Photosynthesis 138-139
  Pine 124-125
  Pore 166
  Root 132-133
  Root tip 152
  Sinus 112
  Spirogyra sp. 117
  Stem 154-155
  Wetland plants 158-159
Cella 461, 463, 485
Cell body 239
Cell membrane 217
Cell nuclear membrane
  216
Cell nucleus 217
Cell nucleus residue 234
Cello 505-505, 510
Cell wall
  Alga 112, 116
  Leaf 139
  Palisade mesophyll 139
  Root 132
  Spirogyra sp. 117
  Stem surface 156
Celsius temperature scale
  590
Cement-based adhesive
  450
Cement gland 173
Cement-rendered wall 494
Cenozoic era 57, 74, 76
  Fossil record 279
Censer 488
Centaurium erythraea 144
Centaurus 18, 21
Centaurus A (radio
  galaxy) 13
Centaurus and Crux 21
Central Asia 64
Central bulge 12, 14
Central canal 238
Central computer control
  528
Central electrode 306
Central nervous system
  238
Central peak
  Degas and Brönte 34
  Venus' craters 36
Central retinal artery 240
Central retinal vein 240
Central shield 187
Central sulcus 236-237
Center
  Australian football 528
  Basketball 532
  Canadian football 526
  Football 526
  Lacrosse 541
  Netball 535
  Rugby 530
Center-board 561
Center buck-eye coupler
  326
Center circle
  Australian rules football
    528
  Basketball 532

Ice hockey 550
Netball 535
Soccer 524
Center console 353
Center court 545
Centered rudder 375
Center element 579
Center field 536
Center flag 529
Center forward 540
Center gangway 329
Centre Georges Pompidou
  496-497
Center girder 393
Center half 540
Center half-back 528, 529
Center half-forward 528,
  529
Center hole 571
Centerline 413, 415
  Fencing piste 557
  Ice hockey 550
  Soccer 524
Centerline beam 426-427
Centerline keelson 393
Center wheel 570
Centrifugal brake 562
Centrifugal compressor
  418
Centrifugal effect 297
Centering magnet 574
Centriole 217
Centripetal river drainage
  288
Centrum 187
Cephalapsis 65
Cephalic groove 173
Cephalic vein
  Human 253
  Octopus 176
Cephalopods 176, 279
Cephalothorax
  Crayfish 173
  Malacostraca 172
  Scorpion 170
  Shrimp 172
  Spider 170-171
Cepheus 19
Ceramic end-piece 319
Ceratopsia 83, 103
Ceratosauria 83
Ceraunius Tholus 43
Cercidyphyllum sp. 72
Cerebellum 212, 236-237,
  238
Cerebral areas 237
Cerebral ganglion 169,
  177
Cerebral vessel 237
Cerebrum 212, 236-237,
  238
Cereoid cactus 129
Cerium 310
Ceropegia woodii 157
Ceruchi 372
Cerussite 269
Cervical musculature
  Euoplocephalus 94
  Gallimimus 86
Cervical nerves 238
Cervical plate 92-93
Cervical rib 84, 96, 100-
  101, 103
Cervical vertebrae
  Archaeopteryx 85
  Arsinoitherium 104
  Bird 189
  Brachiosaurus 91
  Crocodile 186
  Domestic cat 195
  Elephant 201
  Eryops 80
  Hare 197
  Horse 199
  Human 212, 222, 245

Iguanodon 96
Kangaroo 206
Kentrosaurus 93
Lizard 184
Parasaurolophus 99
Plateosaurus 88
Platypus 206
Rhesus monkey 202
Seal 204
Stegoceras 101
Stegosaurus 93
Struthiomimus 87
Toxodon 106
Tuojiangosaurus 93
Tyrannosaurus 84
Cervix 258-259
Cervus elephas 199
Cetaceans 204-205
Cetiosaurus 91
Cetorhinus maximus 179
Cetus 19, 20
Chaffinch 193
Chain
  Bicycle 358-359, 360-361
  Drum kit 518
  Motorcycle 366
  Wheel and axle 320
  Wooden sailing ship 378
Chain bobstay 382
Chain drive
  Motorcycle clutch 362
  Werner motorcycle 366
  Wright Flyer 398-399
Chain drive-belt 580
Chain locker 393
Chain motif 491
Chain plate 382
Chain swivel 386
Chain wale 376-377
Chair 576-577
  Bull-head rail 331
Chajya 489
Chalcedony 271
Chalk 430
  Tempera 432
  Gesso 434
  Pastel making 440
  Fresco 434
  Sedimentary rocks 277
Chamber
  Building 465, 491
  Gun turret 396
Chambers
  Seaweed 116
  Stomach 198
  Substomatal 139
Chamfered corner 485,
  488, 494
Championship golf
  courses 546
Change 321
Chang Jiang 265
Channel
  74-gun ship 381
  Sailing warship 376-377
  Temple of Neptune 460
  Wooden sailing ship 378
Channeled wrack 116
Chape 583
Chapel
  Baroque church 479
  Gothic church 470
  Medieval church 469
Chapel pier 467
Chaplet 454
Chapter-house 472
Charcoal drawing 430-431
Charentais melon 149
Charge
  Four-stroke cycle 343
  Modern engines 344
Charged atom 306, 308
Charged particle 316
Charging with ball 533
Charon 50

598

Chart house 394
Chase 395
Chassis
First cars 354-355
Ford Model T 358
Kirby BSA sidecar 369
Monocoque 363
Motorcycle 362, **364-365**
Oldsmobile chassis 337
Panhard-system
Pinzgauer Turbo D 354
Volkswagen Beetle 340
White Steam Car 342
Chassis electrical plug 357
Chassis frame 358
Chassis number 327
Chataya arch 491
Châteaux 474, 476-477
Chattra 491
Chattravali 490-491
Chauffeur's seat 334
Checkerbloom 136
Check pawl 562
Cheek
74-gun ship 381
Dunkeld wet fly 563
Horse 199
Human 212
Running block 383
Sailmaker's mallet 384
Stegosaurus 92
Cheek horn 103
Cheek piece
Harness racer 555
Show-jumper 554
Cheek pouch 98, 196
Cheek teeth
Ankylosaurs 92
Carnivores 194
Ornithopods 96
Tetralophodon 104
Theropods 84
Cheese 382, 388-389
Cheese head screw 573
Cheiracanthus 65
Cheirolepis 65
Chekhov 35
Chela 170, 172, 173
Chelicera 79
Chelicerae 170-171
Chelicerates 279
Cheliped
Crab 172
Crayfish 173
Chelonia 186
Chemical bond 307
Chemical change 280-281
Chemical energy 314-315
Chemical equations 312
Chemical properties
Electrons 308, 310
Substances 306
Chemical reactions **312-313**
Chemical sedimentary
rocks 276
Chemical symbols 312, 591
Periodic table 310-311
Chemical weathering 282
Chemise 466-467
Cherry 148
Cherry wood 512
Chert 277
Cherub 472
Chervil 135
Chest
Gorilla 203
Human 211, 214
Lion 194
Chestnut 198
Chest padding 551
Chest pass 532, 535
Chest protector 527
Chevet 469

Chevron 81, 85, 87, 89, 93, 95-96, 98, 101-102
Chevron fold 61
Chevron-tread tire 336
Chi₁ Orionis 18
Chi₂ Orionis 18
Chiastolite hornfels 275
Chihuahuan Desert 264
Chile 331
Chimney
Bordino Steam Carriage 354
"Ellerman Lines" steam locomotive 325
Iron paddlesteamer 393
"Rocket" steam locomotive 324
Chimney-shaft 467
Chimney-stack 476, 483
Chimpanzee 202-203
Chin
Bird 188
Human 211, 212
China
Ball games 524
Late Carboniferous period 66-67
Middle Ordovician period 64-65
Ornithopod 96
Railroad track gauge 331
Thyreophorans 92
Chinese characters 445
Chinese junk 376
Chinese white 438
Chin groove 199
Chin guard 553
Chin gun turret 408
Chinle formation 276
Chin rest 510-511
Chin spoiler 346
Chipmunk 196
Chirostenotes 87
Chisel 452-453
Chlamydomonas sp. 116
Chlorenchyma 120
Chloride 296
Chlorine 311
Chlorophyll 138
Chloroplast 139
Photosynthesis pigment 116, 138, 162
Chlorophyta 116
Chloroplast 138-139
Alga 112
Chlamydomonas sp. 116
Envelope 139
Epiphytic orchid 162
Internal view 139
Spirogyra sp. 117
Choanocyte 166
Choir 468-469, 470, 472
Choir manual 514
Choir-screen 470
Choir-stall 470
Choir stop 514
Choke 575
Chondrichthyes 178
Chondrostean fish 69
Chong Ch'ol 35
Chordae tendineae 251
Chorioallantoic mem-
brane 192
Chorion 260
Choroid 240
Christian architecture 468
Christmas rose 139
Chromate ion 312
Chrome passivation 348
Chrome plating 347
Chrome trim strip 341
Chromium
Mineralization zones 281
Oxide 312
Periodic table 310

Chromosphere 32-33
Chrysalis 168
Chrysanthemum morifolium 129
Chryse Planitia 43
Chrysler Building 495
Chrysocyon brachyurus 195
Chuck 567
Chuck key 567
"Chuffs" 324
Chung-ta-wei 376
Church
Santa Sophia 487
Sorbonne 486
St. Botolph 473
St. Eustache 477
St. George in the East 478, 481
St. Maclou 470, 472
St. Maria della Salute 478
St. Maria della Vittoria 478
St. Paul-St. Louis 478-479
St. Pierre de Libreville 496, 499
St. Serge 469
Church-roof boss 468
Chusan palm 127, 130
Ciconia ciconia 188
Ciliary body 241
Cincture 477
Cinder 272
Cinder cone
Igneous rock structures 274
Volcanic structure 273
Cinnabar 271
Cinquefoil molding 471
Circle 479
Circle area measurement 590
Circuit 316
Circuit breaker 314
Circular mountain lake 293
Cirque 286-287
Cirque formation 287
Cirque Napoleon 478-479
Cirri 172
Cirrocumulus cloud 502
Cirrostratus cloud 502
Cirrus 173
Cirrus cloud
Neptune 50
Structure of Mars 43
Weather 302-303
Citrus limon 148
City bus 332
Civet 194
Cladding 494, 496, 498-499
Cladode 129
Cladonia floerkeana 114
Cladonia portentosa 114
Clam 176
Clamp
Cross-stave 377
Intaglio printing 313
Lamp 573
U-tube 446
Clarinet 503-504, 508
Classical-style architecture 474, 478, 482
Clastic sedimentary rocks 276
Claves 517
Clavicle
Bird 189
Bony fish 181
Eryops 80
Human 211, 218

Kangaroo 206
Rhesus monkey 202
Clavius 40
Clavus 573
Claw
Albertosaurus 84
Anchisaurus 89
Archaeopteryx 85
Beetle 168
Bird 188
Bumblebee 168
Caiman 187
Chick 193
Crab 172
Crayfish 173
Dinosaur 83
Herrerasaurus 86
Kangaroo 207
Lizard 184
Marble sculpture 452
Pachycephalosaurus 100
Psittacosaurus 103
Scorpion 170
Spider 171
Stegoceras 101
Terrapin 187
Tyrannosaurus 84
Clawed feet 190, 206
Clay 298
Clay daub 465
Clay model 455
Clay modeling 452, 455
Clay mounds 286
Clear space 534
Cleavage 270
Clef 502
Cleithrolepis granulatus 69
Cleithrum 80
Clematis 130-131, 137
Clench nail 375
Cleomedes 40
Cleopatra Patera 37
Clerestory 459, 472, 479
Clew 373
Clewline 379, 385
Click wheel 570
Cliffs
Coastlines 294-295
River's stages 289
Sedimentary rocks 276-277
Climate
Carboniferous period 66
Geological time 56
Oceans and seas 296
Weather 302
Climatic change
Coastline 294
Geological time 56
Clincher wheel 339
Clinker-built hull 375
Clinker-built oak planking 375
Clints 284-285
Clitoris 258
Cloaca
Bird 189
Brachiosaurus 90
Dogfish 179
Euoplocephalus 95
Frog 182
Gallimimus 87
Lizard 185
Spider 170
Tortoise 187
Cloacal opening 185
Clock **570-571**
Clock operator 532
Clock tower 493
Clock train 570
Cloister 472
Close-stowing anchor 386
Cloud deck 50-51
Cloud features
Neptune 50

Saturn 46
Venus 36
Clouds
Earth's atmosphere 301
Jupiter 44-45
Mars 42-43
Neptune 50-51
Saturn 46-47
Uranus 48-49
Venus 36-37
Water cycle 288
Weather 302-303
Cloud shadow 50
Clouds of dust and gas
Life of massive star 24
Milky Way 14-15
Nebulae and star clusters 16-17
Origin and expansion of Universe 11
Small stars 24
Cloud-top temperature
Structure of Jupiter 45
Structure of Neptune 51
Structure of Saturn 47
Structure of Uranus 49
Clove hitch 388
Cloven hoof 198
Clubmosses 64, 66, **120-121**
Clump cathead 395
Clustered column 469
Clutch 364, 366
Clutch and flywheel 340
Clutch cable 550, 363, 365
Clutch center plate 351
Clutch cover 363
Clutch lever 363, 369
Clutch pedal 350
Clutch pressure plate 351
Clutch release bearing 351
Clypeaster 279
Cnidocytes 166-167
CNS 258
Coal
Earth's evolution 57
Mineral resources 280-281
Power stations 314
Sedimentary rocks 276
Steam locomotive 324
Coal-forming forests 57
Coal measures 61
Coaming 381
Coastal spring 292
Coaster 374-375
Coastlines **294-295**
Cave 284
Cobalt
Mineralization zones 281
Periodic table 311
Cobra lily 160-161
Coccosteus 65
Coccygeal cornu 223
Coccygeal vertebrae 222
Coccyx 218, 222
Cochlea 242-243
Cocked indicator 589
Cocking lever 549
Cockpit
Avro biplane 403
Kayak 560
LVG CVI fighter 405
Modern military aircraft 420-421
Sailing dinghy 561
Schleicher glider 426
Cockpit canopy 409
Cockpit coaming 425
Cock screw 571
Cocoa 148
Coconino sandstone 276
Cocos nucifera 135
Cocos plate 59

Cod 180
Codiaeum variegatum 136
Coelenterata 166
Coeliac trunk 256-257
Coelodonta 76-77, 104
Coelophysids 68
Coelurus 87
Coenobium 116
Coffer 463, 485
Coffered vault 485
Coffering 475
Cogged drive belt 344
Coil 574-575
Coil spring
"Ellerman Lines" steam locomotive 324
Motorcycle 364
Coil suspension spring
"Deltic" diesel-electric locomotive 327
"Eurostar" multi-voltage electric train 529
Wagon bogie 331
Coil tension spring 573
Coke hopper 334
Cold air intake 420
Cold-air unit 417
Cold front 302-303
Cold occlusion 302
Cold-water pipe 405
Cold-water upwelling 296
Coleoptera 168
Coleus sp. 134
Collagen and elastic fibers 252
Collapsed crater 293
Collar
Cathedral of Notre Dame de Paris 473
Sea anemone 167
Snail 177
Collar-beam 473
Collar bone 211, 218
Collar cell 166
Collar of horsetail 120
Collecting duct 256
Collecting tubule 256
Collective lever 422
Collenchyma 126, **134-135**
Colliding plates 272
Colloids 306
Colon
Butterfly 169
Cow 198
Human 215, 249, 259
Rabbit 196
Colonette
Gothic church 473
Islamic building 488
Medieval building 467-469
Neoclassical building 479
Renaissance building 474
Colonnade
Ancient Greek building 460-461
Ancient Roman building 462-463
Cathedral dome 484, 487
Neoclassical building 483
Colonnaded storey 494
Color 270
Colorado River
Earth's evolution 57
Grand Canyon 277
Valley 290
Color changes 312-313
Colorless gas 311
Color light signals 330
Color wheel 459
Colosseum 462, 464-465
Colpus 144

Columba 18, 21
Columella 119, 145
Column
  Ancient Egyptian
    building 458-459
  Ancient Greek building
    458, 460
  Ancient Roman building
    458, 462-463, 465
  Baroque church 480-481
  Cathedral dome 487
  Cave system 285
  French temple 485
  Gothic church 473
  Islamic mosque 488
  Medieval church 468-469
  Modern building 496-498
  Monocotyledonous
    flower 126
  Neoclassical building
    478-479, 483
  Nineteenth-century
    building 492-493
  Renaissance building
    477
Coma 52-53
Coma Berenices 18, 21
Combat sports 556-557
Combination lever 325
Combustion 326
Combustion chamber
  Capacity 366-367
  Iron paddlesteamer 393
  Jaguar straight six
    engine 344
  Jet engines 418-419
Combustion cycle 410
Comets 30, 52-53
Common bile duct 252
Common blackheaded
  gull 189
Common brittle star
  175
Common carotid artery
  215, 251, 253
Common centaury 144
Common crus 243
Common digital extensor
  muscle 84, 97
Common elder 143
Common English ivy 131
Common horse chestnut
  130
Common horsetail 120
Common Iguana 82
Common iliac artery 215,
  253, 257
Common iliac vein 215,
  253, 257
Common ivy 137
Common lime 143
Common link 386
Common mulberry 130
Common peroneal nerve
  238
Common rafter 473, 486
Common starfish 175
Common tern 193
Common time 502
Communication 108
Communications aerial
  424
Commutator 566
Commuters 363
Compact bone 224-225
Compact disc 584
Companion cells 132-134
Companion ladder 381
Companion way 380
Compass
  Battleship 394
  Vault decoration 485
Compass and rangefinder
  platform 394
Competent bed rock 61

Competition motorcycles
  568-569
Competitions
  Archery 548
  Diving 558
  Judo 556
  Rowing 560
  Skiing 552-553
Complete mesentery 167
Composite capital 478
Composite column 478
Composite pilaster 478
Composite volcano 272
Compound eye
  Beetle 168
  Bumblebee 168
  Butterfly 169
  Crab 172
  Crayfish 173
  Damselfly 168
  Malacostraca 172
  Shrimp 172
Compound inflorescence
  131, 142
Compound leaf 130-131,
  136
Compound pier 468-469
Compound pulleys 320
Compounds 268, 306, 308
Compound succulent fruit
  148-149
Compound umbel 143
Compressible gas 365
Compression
  Faults and folds 60
  Glacier 286
  Igneous and metamor-
    phic rocks 274
  Mineral resources 280
  Mountain building 62
  Rock cycle 266
Compression ring
  Ford diesel engine 347
  Jaguar straight six
    engine 344
Compression stroke 343
Compressor 418
Compressor piston 344
Compsognathus 70
Computer
  CD-ROM 584
  Electronic instruments
    520
  Modern bodywork 348
  System 584-585
Computerized ignition
  system 344
Concave brace 477
Concave molding 482
Concave wall 478, 481
Conceptacles 116-117
Concert grand piano 515
Concha
  Ear 242
  Nasal 221, 241
Conchoidal fracture
  Extrusive igneous rocks
    275
  Fracture 270
  Sedimentary rocks 277
Concorde 416-417
Concrete 492, 494, 496-
  499
Concrete shielding 314
Concrete shoe 499
Concrete track 524
Concrete wall 463, 465,
  496
Condensation 307
  Nuclear power station
    314
  Testing candle wax 313
Condensation level 302
Condenser 342
Conducting tissue 119

Conductor
  Electrical circuit 316
  Generating magnetism
    317
  Orchestra 504
Condylactis sp. 166
Condyle
  Carnivore 194
  Human 220
Cones
  Bishop pine 124
  Gymnosperms 122
  Igneous and metamor-
    phic rocks 274
  Pine 122
  Scots pine 122
  Smooth cypress 123
  Volcanoes 272-273
  Welwitschia 123
  Yew 123
Cone sheet 274
Cone stalk 124
Cone surface area
  measurement 590
Cone volume measure-
  ment 590
Congas 519
Congo Basin 39
Conical bore 507
Conical dome 476
Conical map projection
  265
Conical spire 466, 476
Conical volcano 272
Conifer
  Cretaceous period 72
  Earth's evolution 57
  Fossil record 279
  Gymnosperm 122-125
  Jurassic period 70
  Triassic period 68
Coniferophyta 122
Conjugation 117
Conjunctiva 241
Connecting pin 574
Connecting rod
  Bordino Steam Carriage
    334
  Flat-four cylinder
    arrangement 340
  Four-stroke cycle 343
  Iron paddlesteamer 392
  Jaguar straight six
    engine 344
  Jaguar V12 engine 345
  Mid West two-stroke
    engine 410
  Steamboat with paddle
    wheels 391
Connecting wire
  Light bulb 572
  Toaster 578
Connective tissue cells
  217, 254
Conning tower 394, 397
Conocephalum conicum
  118
Con-rod 540, 543-345
Conservation of Energy
  Law 314
Constant velocity joint
  cover 356
Constellations 18-21
Constratum 373
Constrictor snakes 184
Construction sculpture
  452
Contact 552
Contact metamorphism
  274
Contant d'Ivry, P. 478
Contest area 556
Contests
  Head-butting 100
  Shooting 548

Continental crust 58-59
  Mineralization zones 281
  Mountain building 62-63
  Ocean floor 298
Continental drift 58
Continental margin
  sediments 299
Continental rise 298
Continental Sea 73, 75
Continental shelf
  Ocean floor 298
  Prehistoric Earth 69, 71
  Rock cycle 267
Continental slope
  Ocean floor 298
  Offshore currents 296
  Rock cycle stages 267
Continents
  Formation of the Earth
    38, 56
  Earth's physical features
    264-265
  Geological time 56
Contrabassoon 504-505
Contractile vacuole 116
Contrast control 521
Control cabinet 396
Control circuit 328
Control column
  ARV light aircraft 425
  BE 2B bomber 404
  Curtiss biplane 398-399
Control-column aperture
  425
Control flag 552
Controller 332
Control lever 581
Control line 561
Control panel 581
Control platform 390
Control reservoir drain
  326
Control rod 314, 424
Control room 397
Control stalk 353
Convection cell 33
Convection current 38
Convective zone 24, 33
Converging plates 63
Conversion 530
Convex portico 483
Cooking 108
Cooking equipment 354
Cooksonia 56
Cooksonia hemispherica
  64
Coolant 314
Coolant inlet 424
Coolant jacket 410-411
Coolant outlet
  ARV light aircraft 424
  Jaguar V12 engine 345
  Mid West two-stroke
    engine 410
Coolant passage 346
Coolant pump 410
Coolant rail 345
Cooling fan 345
Cooling fin
  Drum brake 365
  Mid West rotary engine
    411
  Two-stroke motorcycle
    engine 366
  Velocette OHV engine
    367
Cooling tank 335
Cooling tower
  Centre Georges
    Pompidou 496-497
  Nuclear power station
    314
Cooling water tank 335
Co-orbital moons 46
Coping-stone 495

Copper
  Mineral resources 280-
    281
  Minerals 268
  Periodic table 311-312
Copper body-shell 519
Copper conductor 572
Copper face 384
Copper nitrate solution
  312
Copper ore 306
Copper plate nib 444
Copper sheathing 392
Copper sulfate 313
Coprates Chasma 43
Copulatory bursa
  Butterfly 169
  Snail 177
Coracoid
  Bird 189
  Diplodocus 90
  Euoplocephalus 94
  Gallimimus 86
  Triceratops 102
  Turtle 187
  Tyrannosaurus 84
Coral 78, 166-167
  Atoll development 299
  Fossil record 279
Corallina officinalis 117
Coral reef
  Earth's evolution 56
  Ocean floor 298
Cor Anglais 504-505, 508
Corbel
  Cathedral dome 487
  Medieval building 467,
    469
  Neoclassical building
    482
  Nineteenth-century
    building 493
  Renaissance building
    477
  Rococo style 478
Corbita 372-373
Cor Caroli 18, 21
Cordaites 67
Cordate leaf bases 136-137
Cordite case 396
Cordite handling room
  396
Cordite supply shuttle 396
Core
  Earth 38-39
  Helix Nebula 17
  Massive stars 26-27
  Moon 40
  Neutron stars and black
    holes 28-29
  Small stars 24-25
  Structure of comet 53
  Structure of Earth 63
  Structure of Jupiter 45
  Structure of Mars 43
  Structure of Mercury 35
  Structure of Neptune 51
  Structure of Pluto 51
  Structure of Saturn 47
  Structure of Uranus 49
  Structure of Venus 37
Core-engine jet pipe 412,
  415
Core jet pipe 419
Core temperature
  Structure of Earth 39
  Structure of Jupiter 45
  Structure of main
    sequence star 24
  Structure of red giant 25
  Structure of red
    supergiant 26
  Structure of Saturn 47
  Structure of Sun 33
  Structure of Uranus 49

Corinthian capital 460,
  463, 479, 481
Corinthian column 463-
  464, 479-480
Corinthian entablature
  463
Corinthian order 460, 462
Corinthian pilaster 463-
  464, 480-481
Coriolis force 296-297, 300
Cork
  Oboe 508
  Stems 134-135
  Woody dicotyledons 127
Corms 154-155
Corn 112
Cornea 241
Corner arc 524
Corner piece 586
Corner seal 347
Cornet 506
Cornice
  Ancient Egyptian temple
    458-459
  Ancient Greek building
    460-461
  Ancient Roman building
    462-465
  Asian building 491
  Baroque church 479-481
  Dome 484, 486
  French temple 485
  Gothic church 470-473
  Islamic tomb 489
  Medieval building 466-
    467, 469
  Neoclassical building
    478-479, 482-483
  Nineteenth-century
    building 493
  Renaissance building
    474-477
  Twentieth-century
    building 494
Cornucopia 480
Corolla 140, 142-143
Corona
  Earth's atmosphere 300
  Palazzo Strozzi 475
  Sun's atmosphere 32-33
Corona Australis 19
Corona Borealis 18, 21
Coronal section through
  brain 236-237
Coronal suture 220
Coronary artery 250-251,
  253
Coronary sinus 250
Corona temperature 33
Coronet 198, 554
Coronoid process 96, 106,
  194, 220
Corpus albicans 258
Corpus callosum 236-237
Corpus cavernosum 259
Corpus luteum 258
Corpus spongiosum 259
Corridor 465
Corries 286-287
Corrugator supercilii
  muscle 228-229
Cortex
  Apical meristem 134
  Canadian pond weed
    158-159
  Clubmoss stem 120
  Dicotyledon 127
  Epiphytic orchid 162
  Hair 234
  Horsetail stem 120
  Kidney 256
  Lichen 114
  Monocotyledon 127
  Moss 119
  Pine 125

Radicle 152
Rhizome 155
Root 132-133
Stems 134-135
Water hyacinth 158
Water lily 159
Corundum 271
Corvus 18, 21
Corvus corone 193
Corynactis viridis 166
Corythosaurus 96, 98
Cosmic background
  radiation 10
Cosmic ray 301
Costal cartilage 218
Costal facet 223
Costal margin 168, 169
Costal shield 187
Cotter pin 383
Cotton duck canvas 437,
  443
Cotyledon 126, 152-153
  Development 132
  Dicotyledon 126
  Dry fruit seed 150-151
  Embryo development
    147
  Epigeal germination 153
  Hypogeal germination
    152
  Monocotyledon 126
  Pine 122
  Root development 132
  Seed 152-153
  Succulent fruit seed 148-
    149
Couch grass 113
Coucy-le-Château 466-467
Coulomb 316
Counter
  Calligraphy lettering 445
  Shoe 568-569
Counter backer 569
Counterbalancing weight
  506
Counter dial housing 589
Counter rail 381
Counter stiffener 569
Counter timber 381
Counterweight
  Flat-four cylinder
    arrangement 340
  Four-stroke cycle 343
  Hong Kong and
    Shanghai Bank 498
  Jaguar V12 engine 345
  Output shaft 347
  Relief printing press 449
  Rotary engine output
    shaft 410
  Trojan engine 342
  V12 cylinder arrange-
    ment 345
Coupling
  Conventional hook-
    screw 328
  "Ellerman Lines" steam
    locomotive 324
Coupling rod 325
Couronnement 472
Course
  Asian building 491
  Medieval building 466-
    467
  Neoclassical building
    483
  Nineteenth-century
    building 492-493
Court referee 535
Court
  Basketball 532
  Handball 535
  Netball 535
  Volleyball 534
Court seal 375

Courtship display 188
Courtyard 465, 466
Coussinet 460
Covalent bonding 308-309
Cove 381
Coved dome 478, 485
Cover 586
Cover board 586
Cover frame 589
Cover point 541
Coverts 188, 191
Cow 198
Cowhide face 384
Cowling fastener 408
Cowling panel 407, 412
Coxa
  Beetle 168
  Crayfish 173
  Scorpion 170
Coxswain 560
CQR anchor 386
Crab 172
Crab apple 126
Crab cactus 129
Crab Nebula 28
Cracks 284-285
Cradle frame
  Honda VF750 364
  Weslake Speedway 369
Cradling 541
Crane 498
Cranial nerves 238
Cranium
  Ankylosaurus 94
  Archaeopteryx 85
  Australopithecus 108
  Bat 105
  Camarasaurus 91
  Diplodocus 90
  Elephant 201
  Eryops 80
  Euoplocephalus 94
  Homo sapiens 108
  Hyaenodon 107
  Iguanodon 96
  Kentrosaurus 93
  Lambeosaurus 99
  Moeritherium 105
  Opossum 106
  Pachycephalosaurus 100
  Panoplosaurus 94
  Parasaurolophus 99
  Plateosaurus 88
  Prenocephale 100
  Protoceratops 102
  Stegoceras 100
  Stegosaurus 93
  Struthiomimus 87
  Styracosaurus 102
  Toxodon 106
  Triceratops 103
  Tuojiangosaurus 93
  Tyrannosaurus 84
Crank 520
  Brace-and-bit 567
  Eddy Merckx racing
    bicycle 360
  "Ellerman Lines" steam
    locomotive 325
Crank bolt 358, 360
Crankcase
  BE 2B bomber 404
  British Rail Class 20
    diesel engine 327
  Humber engine 343
  Jaguar straight six
    engine 344
  Jaguar V12 engine 345
  Mid West two-stroke
    engine 410
  Oldsmobile engine 336
  Trojan engine 342
  Velocette OHV engine
    367
  Werner motorcycle 362

Crankcase breather pipe
  402
Crank handle 339
Crankpin 343
Crankshaft
  Benz Motorwagen 335
  Flat-four cylinder
    arrangement 340
  Four-stroke cycle 343
  Iron paddlesteamer 392
  Mid West two-stroke
    engine 410
  Oldsmobile engine 336
  Oscillating steam engine
    391
  Straight four cylinder
    arrangement 345
  Two-stroke engine 366
  Velocette OHV engine
    367
Crankshaft counterweight
  344
Crankshaft pulley 344
Crash bar 362-363
Crash cymbal 518
Crash helmet 552
Crater
  Mercury's North Pole 35
  Northern stars 18
  Oceanus Procellarum 40
  Southern stars 21
  Surface features of Mars
    42
Crayfish 172-173
Crayon 448
Creeping stems 154
  Clubmoss 120
  Strawberry 128
Cremasteric fascia 259
Cremocarp 150-151
Crenellation 466
Crenulation 466
Crepidoma 461, 481
Crescent-shaped dune 283
Crest
  Building 479, 488, 493
  Fold formation 60
  Horse 199
  Lizard 184
  Ship's shield 395
Crested porcupine 197
Cretaceous period 72-73
  Fossil record 279
  Geological time 56-57
Crevasse 287
Crevice 284
Crew's seat 416
Cricket (animal) 168
Cricket (game) **538-539**
Cricoid cartilage 255
Cricothyroid ligament 244
Cricothyroid muscle 229,
  244-245
C ring 46-47
Cringle 384
Crista 242
Crocket 471-472
Crocodile clip connector
  316
Crocodiles 68, 73, **186-187**
Crocodylus niloticus 186
Crocoite 271
Cronaca 474
Crook 508
Crop
  Bird 189
  Butterfly 169
  Octopus 176
  Snail 177
Crop-duster 410
Crops 315
Crop-sprayer 410, 422
Cross
  Baroque church 480
  Dome 486-487
  Motif 472

Crossandra nilotica 145
Crossbar
  Calligraphy characters
    445
  Eddy Merckx racing
    bicycle 360
  Gaelic football 529
  Handball 535
  Hurling 540
  Rugby 530
Cross-bed set 283
Crossbow 548
Cross-bracing 497-499
Cross-country skiing 548
Crosse 540-541
Crossing 469-470, 477
Crossing tower 468
Cross-member 338-339
Cross-piece 376-377, 387
Cross-pollination 144
Cross-stave 376-377
Cross stick 576
Cross tube 423
Cross wall of hypha 115
Crosswise strut 512
Crotchet rest 502-503
Croton 136
Crouch 543
Croup 198
Crow 193
Crown
  Bird 188
  Building 484, 490
  Danforth anchor 386
  Harp 511
  Head 212
  Relief-printing press 449
  Rigging 382-383
  Roman anchor 372
  Sail hook 384
  Shackle 386
  Teeth 247
  Timpanum 519
Crowning cornice
Crowning cornice
  Ancient Roman building
    464, 465
  Baroque church 479
  Renaissance building
    474-475
Crown wheel
  Benz Motorwagen 335
  Ford Model T 338
CRT 574
Cruciform column 492
Cruciform pedestal 481,
  487
Cruck frame 466
Crumb tray 578-579
Crupper 555
Crusafontia 56
Crus cerebri of midbrain
  237
Crus of diaphragm 255
Crust
  Moon 41
  Ocean floor 298
  Pulsar 28
  Regional metamorphism
    274
  Structure of comet 53
  Structure of Earth 38-39
  Structure of Mars 43
  Structure of Mercury 35
  Structure of Venus 37
Crustaceans **172-173**
  Arthropoda 170
  Cretaceous period 72-73
  Fossil 279
Crustal movement
  Coastline 294
  Faults and folds 60
  Mineralization zones 280
  Mountain building 62
  Rock cycle 266
  Volcano 272

Crustal plate boundary 39
Crustal plates 58-59, 60
Crustose lichen 114
Crutch
  Pendulum assembly 570
  Viking karv 375
Crux-Centaurus Arm 14
Crypt 467
Crypt-window 481
Crystalline external crust
  28
Crystalline stalagmitic
  floor 284
Crystallisation 307
Crystal Palace Exhibition
  Hall 492-493
Crystals
  Faults 60
  Intrusive igneous rocks
    275
  Mineral features 270-271
  Minerals 268-269
  Solids 307
Crystal systems 270
Ctenidium 176
CT scan 214
Cubic crystal 270
Cubic system 270
Cubital fossa 211
Cuboid bone 232
Cucumis melo 149
Cud 198
Cuesta 283
Cuff 568
Culm 131
Cumulonimbus cloud 302
Cumulus cloud 302
Cuneate leaf base 136-137
Cuneus 465
Cup 509
Cup mute 507
Cupola 466, 479, 493
Cup-shaped mouthpiece
  506-507
Cup surrounding stomata
  157
Cupula 242
Cupule 150
Curium 311
Current 296-297
Current electricity 316
Curtain 477, 497
Curtain wall 466, 496, 498
Curtiss, Glenn 398
Curtiss Model-D Pusher
  398-399
Curved buttress 478-481
Curved cornice 462
Curvilinear tracery 470,
  472
Cuscuta europaea 163
Cushion
  Doric capital 460
  Rowing positions 373
Cushion star 175
Cusp
  Asian building 488
  Gothic building 472-473
  Structure of a tooth 247
Cuspate fold 61
Cuspate foreland 294
Cusped arch 489
Cuspidate leaf apex 137
Cutaneous nerve 238
Cuticle
  Bishop pine needle 124
  Dryland plants 156
  Golden barrel cactus 156
  Hair 234
  Haworthia truncata 157
  Leaf 159
  Lithops bromfieldii 157
  Marram grass 113
  Monocotyledon leaf 126

Nail 231
Rose stem 135
Rush stem 135
Wetland plants 158
Cuttlefish 176
Cutty Sark 392
Cyanotrichite 269
Cycadophyta 122
Cycads 68, 122-123, 279
Cycas revoluta 68, 123
Cycas sp. 68
Cyclic-pitch lever 422-423
Cyclonic storm
  Structure of Earth 39
  Structure of Mars 43
  Structure of Neptune 50
Cyclostomata 178
Cygnus 19, 20
Cylinder
  Diesel train 526
  Early engines 342-343
  "Ellerman Lines" steam
    locomotive 325
  Iron paddlesteamer 392
  Mini-television 574
  Modern piston aero-
    engines 410
  Motorcycle 362, 366
  Oldsmobile engine 336
  "Rocket" steam
    locomotive 324
Cylinder barrel
  Mid West two-stroke
    engine 410
  Werner motorcycle 362
Cylinder block 339
Cylinder-cooling gills 407
Cylinder cover 591
Cylinder drain cock lever
  325
Cylinder head
  ARV light aircraft 425
  British Rail Class 20
    diesel engine 327
  Daimler engine 343
  Jaguar straight six
    engine 344
  Jaguar V12 engine 345
  Mid West two-stroke
    engine 410
  Oldsmobile engine 336
  Renault V10 RS1 engine
    356
  Two-stroke motorcycle
    engine 366
  Velocette OHV engine
    367
Cylinder liner
  Jaguar Straight six
    engine 344
  Mid West two-stroke
    engine 410
Cylinder surface area
  measurement 590
Cylinder volume measure-
  ment 590
Cylinder wall 343
Cylindrical fault 61
Cylindrical map projection
  264
Cyma recta 475
Cyma reversa 460, 472
Cymatium 475
Cymbals 504-505, 516-517
  Drum kit 518
Cyme 129, 143
Cypress 123
Cypselas 150
Cyrillus 40
Cystic duct 248
Cytoplasm
  Chlamydomonas sp. 116
  Diatom 116
  Human 217
  Palisade mesophyll 139

Root cell 132
Thalassiosira sp. 116
Cytosine 216

D

Dacron 548
Dacron sailcloth 384
Dacron skin 426
Dactylus 172-173
Dado
  Baroque church 481
  French temple 485
  Neoclassical building 479
  Renaissance building 476
Dagger 472
Dagoba stupa 490-491
Daimler double-sleeve valve engine 343
Daimler, Gottlieb 334
Daisy gypsum 269
Dakota sandstone 276
D'Alembert 41
Dalmatian coastline 295
Da Maiano, B. 474
Damper
  Piano 514
  TGV electric high-speed train 329
  Wagon bogie 331
Damper bar 516
Damper body 365
Damper pedal
  Concert grand piano 515
  Tubular bells 516
  Upright piano 514
  Vibraphone 517
Damper unit 425
Damp lime-plaster 454
Damselfly 168
Dancette-pattern mosaic 489
Dandelion 150
Danforth anchor 386
Danger area 556
Danilova 36
Dark mica 274
Dark nebulae 16
Darlingtonia californica 160-161
Dart sac 177
Darwin 43
Da Sangallo, G. 474
Dash 353
Dashboard
  1906 Renault 337
  Bordino Steam Carriage 335
  Ford Model T 338
Dashboard radiator 336-337
Dash panel 353
Dash radio speaker 353
Data entry key pad
  Digital sampler 521
  Synthesizer 520
  Wind synthesizer 521
Data increment control 521
Daucus carota 128, 132
Daughter bulbs 154
Daughter plants 154
Davit 395
D-block 310-311
DC current 328
Dead-ball line 530
Deadeye
  74-gun ship 380
  Longboat 380
  Rigging 382-383
  Roman corbita 373
  Sailing warship 377

Deadnettle 135
Dead organisms 278
Dead plant encrustations 284
Dead Sea 292-293
Deadwood 381
Debris
  Glacier 286-287
  Mountain building 62
  Ray crater 34
Debris guard 356
Decathlon 542
Decidual plate 260
Deciduous plants 130-131
Deciduous teeth 246
Deciduous trees 72
Deck
  Greek trireme 373
  Roman corbita 373
Deck beam
  74-gun ship 380
  Ironclad 393
  Paddle steamer 390, 393
  Roman corbita 372
Deck house 373, 376
Deck lantern 392
Deck planking 393
Deck rail 373
Dee 582-583
Deep cracks 284-285
Deep current systems 296-297
Deepened valley 295
Deep floor 393
Deep mid wicket 538
Deep-ocean floor 298
Deep-ocean floor sediments 299
Deep peroneal nerve 238
Deep relief carving 453
Deep square leg 538
Deer 104, 198-199
Deer hopper dry fly 563
Deoxyribonucleic acid strand 139
Deperdussin, Armand 400
Depressed arch
  Ancient Roman building 462
  Islamic building 488-489
Depressions 302
Depressor anguli oris muscle 228-229
Depressor labii inferioris muscle 229
Depth charge 394
Depth-of-field guide 589
Derailleur cage plate 358
Deranged river drainage 288
Dermal armor 95
Dermal papilla 235
Dermis 234-235
Derrick 392, 395
Descender 445
Descending colon 249
Desert 39, 57
  Carboniferous to Permian period 66
  Earth's physical features 264-265
  Rock cycle 266
  Weathering and erosion 282-283
Desertification 57, 76
Desiccated clay 283
Design
  Fresco 434-435
  Modeled sculpture 452
  Mosaic 449
Deslandres 40
Destination screen 332
Detachable bud 154
Detachable ink reservoir 444

Deltoid leaf 137
Deltoid ligament 232
Deltoid muscle 226-227
Demountable wheel 338-339
Dendrite 239
Dendritic copper 268
Dendritic gold 268
Dendritic river drainage 288
Deneb 19, 20
  Hertzsprung-Russell diagram 23
Deneb Algedi 19, 20
Deneb Kaitos 19, 20
Denebola 18, 21
Density
  Formation of black hole 29
  Massive stars 26-27
  Small stars 24-25
  Stellar black hole 29
Dentary 181
Dentary bone 96, 102, 107
Dentate leaf margin
  Hogweed 129
  Ice-plant 129
  Live-for-ever 129
  Mulberry 130
  Rock stonecrop 128
Dentil
  Ancient Roman building 462
  Baroque church 479, 481
  Cathedral dome 487
  French temple 485
  Neoclassical building 478
  Renaissance building 475
Dentine 247
Deoxyribonucleic acid strand 139
Deperdussin, Armand 400
Dekla Tessera 37
de la Cierva, Juan 422
Delphinium 150
Delphinium orientalis 141
Delphinium sp. 151
Delphinus 19, 20
Delta
  Coastline 294
  River features 290
  River 288-289
  Rock cycle 266-267
Delta Andromedae 19
Delta Crucis 21
Delta formation 291
Delta Hydri 20
Delta ring 48
Deltavjatia vjatkensis 81
"Deltic" diesel-electric locomotive 326-327

Detachable rim 339
Deuterium nucleus 22
Deutscher Werkbund style 495
Devonian fish 65
Devonian period 64-65, 80
  Fossil record 279
  Geological time 56
  Primitive life 78
Devon minnow 563
Dewlap 184
Dextral strike-slip fault 61
Dhow 376
Diabase sill 277
Diagonal bracing 401
Diagonal reinforcement 374
Diagonal strut 399
Diagonal turn 388
Dial
  Clockface 571
  Clocktower 493
  Sundial 377
Dial foot hole 571
Dial pointer 574
Dial washer 571
Diameter
  Atoms 308
  Earth 30
  Jupiter 26, 44
  Jupiter's moons 44
  Life of massive star 26-27
  Life of small star 21-26
  Mars 30
  Mars' moons 42
  Mercury 30
  Moon 40
  Neptune 31
  Neptune's moons 50
  Planets 30-31
  Pluto 31
  Saturn 27, 46
  Saturn's moons 46
  Stars 22
  Sun 32
  Uranus 27, 48
  Uranus' moons 48
  Venus 30
Diamond 311
  Chair frame 576
  Mineral features 270-271
  Native elements 268
Diamond-shaped painting knife 436
Diamond whetstone 452
Diaphragm
  ARV Super 2 424
  Camera 588
  Chimpanzee 202
  Domestic cat 195
  Elephant 200
  Human 215, 254-255
  Rabbit 196
Diaphragm blade 589
Diastema 106
Diatom 116
Diceros bicornis 199
Dichasial cyme 143
Dicksonia antarctica 70, 112-113
Dicloelosia bilobata 65
Dicotyledon 126-127, 141-143
Dicyothyris 278
Didelphis 106
Didelphis virginiana 207
Diesel-electric train 326
Diesel fuel injection 326
Diesel motor compartment 397
Diesel, Rudolph 326
Diesel train 324, 326-327

Differential housing 338
Diffuser 356
Digestive caecum 173, 176
Digestive enzymes 160
Digestive gland
  Snail 177
  Spider 170
Digestive glands/zones
  Butterwort 161
  Monkey cup 161
  Venus fly trap 160
Digestive system
  Cow 198
  Human 248-249
Digit 105
Digital artery 231, 253
Digital extensor muscle 94
Digital flexor muscle 84
Digitally recorded data 584
Digital nerve 231
Digital sampler 520-521
Digital vein 253
Digitate leaf 137
Digits
  Bird 189
  Bird's wing 191
  Frog 182
  Kangaroo 207
  Rabbit 196-197
  Rat 196
  Salamander 182
  Seal 204
Dilator muscle 241
Dilsea carnosa 117
Dimetrodon loomisi 67
Dinghy 560
Dining chair 576
Dinosaur cladogram 83
Dinosaur 56-57, 80, 82-83
  Fossil record 279
Dionaea muscipula 160
Dione 46
Dip 61
Diplodocus 70, 88, 90-91
Dip pen 430
Dipping bed rock 60-61
Dipping lug foresail 385
Diprotodon 76
Dip-slip fault 61
Dipstick tube 346, 356
Dipterus valenciennesi 81
Direct current 328
Direct current jack 574
Direction bar 414
Direction-finding-aerial fairing 408
Direct method mosaic creation 450
Direct-vision panel
  ARV light aircraft 425
  Bell-47 helicopter 422
Dirt track motorcycle racing 368
Disc brake
  Harley-Davidson FLHS Electra Glide 362-363
  Honda CB750 363
  Honda VF750 364
  Husqvarna Motocross TC610 368
  Lockheed Electra airliner 407
  Motorcycle 364-365
  Suzuki RGV500 368-369
Disc brake calliper 364, 368-369
Disc drive 584
Disc florets 129, 142, 145
Disconformity 276
Discovery Rupes 35
Discus 542-543
Disk
  Basal 167
  Crab 166-167

Liverwort 118
Pedal 167
Sea anemone 166-167
Starfish 174
Starfish fossil 79
Disk drag 562-563
Displacement reactions 312
Display monitor 585
Distal convoluted tubule 256-257
Distal end of radius 231
Distal interphalangeal joint 231
Distal phalanx 219, 230, 232
Distal tarsal 183
Distance lines
  Gaelic football 529
  Rugby 530
Distance running 542
Distance scale 589
Distance signaling 330
Distilled water 444
Distiller 397
Distributary
  River features 290-291
  Rivers 288-289
Distributor
  Hawker Tempest Mark V 408
  Jaguar straight six engine 344
  Jaguar V12 engine 345
  Renault Clio 351
Distributor drive shaft 345
Distributor fixing point 346
Diving 558-559
DNA 139, 216
Dobro resonator 513
Dock 554
Document panel 407
Dodder 163
Dog 104, 194-195
Dogfish 178-179, 192
Dog-leg hole 546
Dog-leg staircase 481
Doline 284-285
Dolomedes fimbriatus 171
Dolphins 204-205
Dolphin striker 382
Dome 484, 486-487, 572
  Ancient Roman building 462
  Asian building 490-491
  Baroque church 480-481
  French temple 485
  Islamic building 488
  Medieval building 467, 469
  Neoclassical building 478
  Renaissance building 475-477
Domed receptacle 142
Domed roof 489
Domed topdeck 401
Domed turret 493
Dome metalling 486
Dome of the Rock 487
Dome timbering 486
Dome volcano 62, 272
Donjon 466-467
Donkey boiler 392
Door
  Ancient Egyptian tomb 458-459
  Ancient Roman building 463
  Baroque church 479
  Bell 206 jetliner 423
  Double-decker touring bus 333

Gatwick express "People Mover" 328
Lawnmower 580
MCW Metrobus 332-333
Neoclassical building 478
Renaissance theatre 477
Renault Clio 349
Single-decker bus 333
TGV electric high-speed train 529
Door catch 341
Door discharge 581
Door frame 412
Door glass 348
Door handle 341, 348
Door jamb 478
Door key and lock 348
Door molding 353
Door trim panel 353
Doorway 474-475, 479, 481, 495
Doppler 41
Dorado 21
Doric capital 460
Doric column 460, 464
Doric order 460
Dormancy
  Horse chestnut bud 130
  Seed 152
Dormant volcano 272
Dormer head 493
Dormer window 476, 493, 495
Dorsal abdominal artery 173
Dorsal aorta
  Bony fish 181
  Dogfish 179
  Frog 182
Dorsal blood vessel 169
Dorsal fin
  ARV light aircraft 424
  Bony fish 181
  Concorde 416
  Dogfish 179
  Dolphin 205
  Lamprey 178
  World War II aircraft 408-409
Dorsal fin ray 181
Dorsal interosseous muscle 233
Dorsal lobe 158
Dorsal mantle cavity 176
Dorsal margin of shell 176
Dorsal metatarsal artery 253
Dorsal plate 78, 92-93
Dorsal scale 184, 186
Dorsal scute 95
Dorsal spine base 78
Dorsal venous arch 253
Dorsal vertebrae
  Archaeopteryx 85
  Brachiosaurus 90
  Diplodocus 90
  Eryops 80
  Euoplocephalus 94
  Gallimimus 86
  Iguanodon 96
  Kentrosaurus 93
  Parasaurolophus 99
  Pareiasaur 81
  Plateosaurus 88
  Stegoceras 101
  Stegosaurus 93
  Struthiomimus 87
  Tuojiangosaurus 93
  Tyrannosaurus 84
Dorsum 213
Double-arm pantograph 328
Double bass 503-505, 510, 511

Double bassoon 504-505
Double-decker bus 332-333
Double decomposition reaction 312-313
Double-dipper palette attachment 436
Double-ended hull 375
Double flat 502
Double halyard 373
Double helix 216
Double-planet system
  Earth 38
  Pluto 50
Double-pyramid crystal 270
Double reed 508
Double rope becket 383
Doubles 544
Double samaras
  Dry fruit 150-151
  Sycamore 151
Double scull 561
Double sharp 502
Double topsail schooner 385
Dowel
  Chair frame 576
  Mid West single rotor engine 410
  Mortice-and-tenon fastening 373
Dowel hole
  Chair frame 576-577
  Mid West single rotor engine 410-411
Dowel screw 576-577
Downfolds 60
Downhaul 385
Downhill skiing 552
"Downs" 526
Downthrow 60
Down tube 360
Dox formation 277
Draco 19, 20
Draft mark
  Frigate 397
  Wooden sailing ship 379
Draft tube 314
Drag
  Biplanes and triplanes 402
  Cycling 360
  Early monoplane 400
  Early passenger aircraft 406
Drag knob 563
Drag link
  19th century paddlesteamer 391
  Ford Model T 339
  White Steam Car 342
Dragon prowhead 374
Drag spindle 562
Drag washer 562
Drainage systems divide 289
Drain mast 412, 415
Drain-pipe 492
Drain plug 339
Drakensberg 265
Dravidian finial 491
Dravidian style 490
Drawbridge 493
Drawbridge windlass 467
Drawing 430-431
Drawing board 430, 444-445
Drawing instruments 430
Drawing materials 430
Dreadnought-type battleship 394
Dressing-room 477
Dribbling
  Basketball 532

Gaelic football 528
Handball 534-535
Soccer 524
Drill 566-567
D ring 46-47
Drip-cap 482
Drive 543
Drive belt 335, 344, 362
Drive bracket 405
Drive chain 368
Drive end 317
Drive gear 411
Drive-handle 581
Drive motor 584
Driven gear 410
Driven pulley 335
Drive pillar 424
Drive plate 545
Drive point 346
Driver 547
Driverless train 328
Driver's platform 324
Driver's radio aerial 357
Driver's seat
  Bordino Steam Carriage 335
  "Deltic" diesel-electric locomotive 327
  "Mallard" express steam locomotive 325
  Paris RATP Metro 328
Drive shaft
  Jet engine 419
  Renault Clio 351
  Volkswagen Beetle 340
Drive sprocket mounting spline 366
Drive-wheel 567
Driving band 397
Driving chain 335
Driving pulley 335
Driving rein 555
Driving saddle 555
Driving sprocket 335
Driving wheel 324-325
Drizzle 302
Dromiceiomimus 86
Droop nose 416
Droop stop 422-423
Drop 581
Drop arm
  Ford Model T 339
  White Steam Car 342
Drop-down window 334
Drop glass 341
Drop goal 530
Drop handlebar 361
Drop-kick 530
Drop tank 408
Drop window 332
Drowned coastline 294-295
Drowned valley 295
Drum 486
  Ancient Greek building 460
  Baroque church 481
  Cathedral dome 487
  Relief printing press 449
Drum brake
  BMW R/60 362
  Motorcycle 364-365
  Vespa Grand Sport 160
  Mark 1 563
  Windcheetah racing HPV bicycle 361
Drumhead 387
Drumlins 286
Drums 518-519, 520
Drupelets 146-149
Drupes 151, 148-149
Dry air 303
Dry brush 438-439
Dry capacity measurements 590

Dry fresco 434-435
Dry fruits 150-151
  Couch grass 113
  Durmast oak 131
  Sycamore 131
Dry gallery 284-285
Drying agent 313
Dry lake bed 283
Dryland plants 156-157
Dryopteris filix-mas 120-121
Dryosaurus 70
Dry pericarps 150
Dry season 293
Dry wash 283
Dual click gear 562
Dual ignition plug 427
Dual seat 364
Dubhe 18
  The Plow 19
Dubika 490
Duck 188
Duck-billed platypus 206-207
"Duckbills" 96
Duct 496, 497
Duct of Bellini 256
Ductus deferens 259
Dugout 593
Dumb iron 336, 342
Dummy front door 339
Dunkeld wet fly 563
Duodenum
  Bird 189
  Cow 198
  Elephant 200
  Frog 182
  Human 215, 248-249
  Rabbit 196
  Tortoise 187
Duplex tubular cradle frame 363
Duradon 384
Dura mater 223, 237, 240
Durmast oak 131
Dust
  Asteroids, comets, and meteoroids 52-53
  Mars 42-43
  Moon 41
  Nebulae and star clusters 16-17
  NGC 2997 (spiral galaxy) 12
  Overhead view of our galaxy 14
  Solar system 30
  Venus' atmosphere 37
Dust cap 359
Dust cloud
  Geological time 56
  Large Magellanic Cloud 12
  Mars 42-43
  Milky Way 14-15
  Nebulae and star clusters 16-17
  Origin and expansion of Universe 11
  Volcano 272
Dust lane
  Centaurus A 13
  Horsehead Nebula 16
  NGC 2997 (spiral galaxy) 12
  Optical image of Rings and dust lanes 48
  Trifid Nebula 16
Dust particles 53
Dust shroud 340
Dust storm 43
Dust tail 52-53
Dust trap 354
Dutch cubist style 495
Dutch shoe 377

Dutch triple fiddle block 383
Dwarf crocodile 82
Dwarf shoot 124-125
Dyke 274
Dyke swarm 274
Dynastes hercules 12
Dysprosium 311
Dzus fastener 356

E

Ear
  Calligraphy characters 445
  Elephant 200
  Gorilla 203
  Hare 196
  Horse 198
  Human 210, 212, 242-243
  Kangaroo 207
  Rabbit 196
  Rat 196
Eardrum
  Chick 193
  Frog 182
  Human 243
  Lizard 184
Earles forks 362
Early desertification 57
Early engines 542-543
Early English
  Perpendicular-style tracery 472
Early English-style window 472
Early monoplanes 400-401
Early passenger aircraft 406-407
Early tram 332
Early voyagers 374-375
Earphone jack 574
Earplug 558
Earth 38-39
  Cretaceous period 73
  Energy emission from Sun 22
  Jurassic period 71
  Objects in Universe 11
  Phases of the Moon 41
  Primitive life 78-79
  Quaternary period 77
  Solar eclipse 32
  Solar System 30
  Tertiary period 75
  Tides 297
  Triassic period 69
Earth-ball fungus 115
Earth connection 578, 584
Earth formation 56-57
Earth pigments 434
Earthquake anatomy 63
Earthquake region 39
Earthquakes
  Crustal movement 58
  Faults and folds 60
  Mountain building 62-63
Earth's atmosphere 38-39, 78, 300-301
Earth's composition 39
Earth's core 38-39, 63
Earth's crust 38-39, 58-59
  Igneous and meta-morphic rocks 274
  Lake formation 292
  Volcano 272
Earth's crustal plates 62, 64
Earth's energy 314
Earth's evolution 56-57
Earth's external features 59

Earth's interior
  Ocean floor 298
  Rock cycle 266
  Structure 39
Earth's layers 38
Earth's magnetic field 38
Earth's mantle 38-39, 58-59
Earth's orbit 297
Earth's physical features 264-265
Earth's rotation 38
  Atmospheric circulation and winds 300
  Oceans and seas 296
  Satellite mapping 264
Earth's satellite 38
Earth's surface
  Atmosphere 300-301
  Earth's physical features 264
  Formation of the Earth 38-39
  Geological time 56
  Mineral resources 280
  Mountain building 62
  Oceans and seas 296
  Precambrian to Devonian period 64
  Rock cycle 266
Earth's tilt 58
Earwig 168
East Africa 331
East Asian buildings 490-491
East Australian current 297
East Greenland current 296
Eaves
  Ancient Greek building 461
  Ancient Roman building 462, 464
  Islamic tomb 489
  Modern building 499
  Neoclassical building 482
  Renaissance building 477
Eaves board 490
Eccentric 392
Eccentric rod 391
Eccentric rotor journal 347
Eccentric shaft 347, 411
Eccentric-shaft bearing 410
Echidna nebulosa 180
Echidnas 206
Echinocactus grusonii 156
Echinoderms 174, 279
Echinus 460
Echinus esculentus 175
Echo-sounding 298
Ecliptic
  Inclination of planetary orbits 31
  Stars of northern skies 18-19
  Stars of southern skies 20-21
Ecphora 75
Ectoderm 167
Eddy Merckx racing bicycle 360-361
Edible sea urchin 175
Edmontonia 95
Eel 180
Efferent arteriole 256-257
Effervescence 312
Effort 320-321
Eggs 192-193
  Amphibian 78, 80
  Baltimore oriole 193

Bee hummingbird 193
Bird 188
Butterfly 168
Capsule 192
Carrion crow 193
Case 192
Chaffinch 193
Chicken 192
Common tern 193
Dinosaur 82
Dogfish 192
Frog 182-183, 192
Giant stick insect 192
Greater backbacked gull 193
Hatching 192-193
Human 258, 260
Indian stick insect 192
Leaf insect 192
Maiasaura 98
Membrane 193
Ostrich 193
Quail 192-193
Reptile 66, 184
Titanosaurid 91
Willow grouse 193
Egg tempera 432
Egg-tooth 192-193
Egg white 192
Egg yolk binding medium 432
Egyptian building **458-459**
Eichhornia crassipes 158
Eighteenth-century building 492
Baroque 481
Neoclassical 478, 482-483
Eighth-century building 490-491
Einsteinium 311
Eisila Regio 36-37
Ejaculatory duct 259
Ejecta
Degas and Brönte 34
Features of supernova 27
Ray crater 34
Venusian craters 32
Ejector assembly 579
Ejector exhaust 408
Ejector knob 579
Ejector-seat roof hatches 421
Ekeing 381
Ekman spiral 296-297
El-Ainyi Mosque 488
Elasmobranchs 178
Elastic fiber 252, 254
Elastic rocks 60
Elbow
Anchisaurus 89
Corythosaurus 98
Edmontonia 95
Gorilla 203
Horse 199
Human 210
Iguanodon 97
Lion 194
Psittacosaurus 103
Stegoceras 101
Stegosaurus 92
Triceratops 102
Elbow guard 553
Elbow joint
Brachiosaurus 91
Diplodocus 90
Eryops 80
Euoplocephalus 94
Human 218
Parasaurolophus 99
Plateosaurus 88
Stegoceras 101
Triceratops 102
Tyrannosaurus 84
Elbow pad 527, 551

Elder 130-131, 140 143
Electrical braking 330
Electrical cells 316-317
Electrical charge imbalance 316
Electrical circuit 316
Toaster 578
Electrical contact 319
Electrical effects 316
Electrical energy 314-315
Electrical harness 414
Electrical inverter 422
Electrical plant 496
Electrical relay box 330
Electrical service compartment 407
Electrical supply 316
Electrical wiring harness 418
Electric bass guitars 512
Electric cable 517
Electric car 342
Electric charge 308
Electric coil 317
Electric current 316-317, 328
Electric equipment compartment 329
Electric fuel pump 422
Electric generator 317
Electric guitar 512-513
Electric ignition control 362
Electricity **316-317**
Electricity generation
Diesel train 326
Electric train 326
Magnetism 317
Electric locomotive 324, 328-329
Electric motor
Diesel train 326
Electric train 328
Trolley 332
Electric power line 328, 402
Electric power socket 422
Electric scoring system 556-557
Electric street trolleyway 332
Electric toaster 578
Electric train 328-329
Electric trolley 332
Electric transmission 326
Electric window motor 349
Electrode 306
Electrolytic capacitor 574
Electromagnet 317, 578
Electromagnetic induction capacitor 566
Electromagnetic radiation 314-315, 318
Electromagnetic spectrum 318-319
Electron 308, 316
Atomic number 310
Lithium-19 309
Electron gun 574
Electronic control signals 330
Electronic control-unit connector 356
Electronic engine control (EEC) unit 418-419
Electronic ignition unit 351
Electronic impulses 584
Electronic instruments **520-521**
Electronic signals 512
Electronic warfare mast 397

Electron shell 308-309, 310
Electron transfer 308
Electrostatic forces 308, 316
Electrostatic generator 316
Electrothermal de-icing panel 416
Element retaining stop 579
Elements 306, 308
Atomic mass 310
Minerals 268
Periodic table 310-311
Elephant 90, 104, **200-201**
Elephas maximus 200
Elevated green 546
Elevating wheel 396
Elevation 498
Elevator
ARV light aircraft 424
BAe-146 components 415
Bell-47 helicopter 423
Biplanes and triplanes 402-403
Centre Georges Pompidou 497
Curtiss biplane 399
Early monoplanes 400-401
Hawker Tempest components 409
Schleicher glider 426
World War I aircraft 405
Wright Flyer 599
Elevator arm 425
Elevator chassis box 415
Elevator control cable 399, 403
Elevator control rod 409
Elevator control wire
Bell-47 helicopter 47
Blériot XI monoplane 401
Curtiss biplane 399
LVG CVI fighter 405
Elevator drive wheel 399
Elevator hinge
BAe-146 components 415
BE 2B tail 405
Blackburn monoplane 400
Hawker Tempest components 409
Elevator operating arm 599
Elevator-operating bracket 401
Elevator push-rod 424-425
Elevator rocking arm 404
Elevator trimtab 424, 409
Elevator wire 398
Eleventh-century building 466, 468
Elevon 416-417, 421
Elevon-jack fairing 416
Elevon power control unit 417
"Ellerman Lines" steam locomotive 324-325
Elliott steering knuckle 336
Ellipsoid orb 486
Elliptical galaxy 11-12
Elliptical orbit 30
Elliptic leaf 137
Elm 144, 150
El Nath 18, 21
Elodea canadensis 158-159
Elodea sp. 159
Elongating root 133, 153
Elrathia 64
Eltanin 19
Elytra 168

Elytron 168
Emarginate apex 136
Embellisher 353
Embolos 372
Embrasure 466-467, 469
Embryo
Cotyledon 152-153
Dry fruit seed 150-151
Fertilization 146-147
Germination 152-153
Human 260
Reptile 80
Seed leaf 152
Succulent fruit seed 148-149
Embryonic root 150, 152-153
Embryonic shoot 147
Epigeal germination 153
Hypogeal germination 152
Pea seed 150
Pine 122
Seed axis 152-153
Embryo sac 146-147
Emergency air hose 357
Emergency canopy release handle 420
Emergency door control 332-333
Emergency electricity cut-off 357
Emergency escape hatch 406
Emergency exit 416-417
Emergency oxygen cylinder 417
Emergent coastlines 294-295
Emission nebula 11-12, 14, 16-17
Empire State Building 494
Enamel
Islamic buildings 488, 489
Teeth 247
Enceladus 46
Encke 40
Encke Division 46-47
Enclosed bridge 397
Encroachment 527
End 388-389
End baffle plate 578-579
End block 512
End cap 572-573
End element 578-579
End-grain wood block 449
End-line
Basketball 532
Football 526
Men's Lacrosse 540
Volleyball 534
End link 586
Endocardium 250
Endocarp 146-147, 148-149
Endoderm 167
Endodermis
Bishop pine needle 124
Canadian pond weed stem 158-159
Dicotyledon 127
Epiphytic orchid 162
Fern rachis 121
Horsetail stem 120
Mare's tail stem 135
Monocotyledon 127
Pine root 125
Root 132-133
Water hyacinth root 158
Endomysium 228
Endoperidium 115
Endoplasmic reticulum 259
Endopod 172

Endoscopic view
Alimentary canal 248
Vocal cords 245
Endoskeleton 174
Endosperm 147
Endosteum 225
Endothecium 144
Endothelium 252
Endpaper 586-587
End-pin 510
End-plate
Formula One racing car 356-357
Modern piston aero-engine 410-411
End-plate aerodynamic skirt 357
End zone 526
En échelon fractures 60-61
Energy **314-315**
Chemical reactions 312
Electron shells 310
Light 318
Energy conversion 138
Energy emission from Sun 22
Engaged column 469
Engaged pediment 462-463
Engine **342-347, 410-411, 418-419**
1906 Renault 337
ARV light aircraft 425
BAe-146 jetliner 415
BMW R/60 362
Bordino Steam Carriage 334
Diesel 326
Early monoplane 400-401
Hawker Tempest components 408
Helicopter 422-423
Honda CB750 363
Honda VF750 364
Kirby BSA 369
Lawnmower 580
Lockheed Electra airliner 406-407
Motorcycles 362, 364, **366-367**
Oldsmobile engine 336
Pegasus Quasar microlight 427
Pioneers of flight 398-399
Renault Clio 350-351
Renault V10 RS1 356
Velocette Overhead valve (OHV) 367
Volkswagen Beetle 340
Engine aft bulkhead 421
Engine air intake
BE 2B bomber 404
Concorde 416
Formula One racing car 357
Hawker Tempest fighter 409
Schweizer helicopter 423
Tornado 420
Engine and propeller thrust frame 398
Engine and recoil assembly 580
Engine bearer 343
Engine block 347
Engine cooling radiator 357
Engine cover
Honda VF750 374
Oldsmobile bodywork 337
Two-stroke engine 366

Vespa Grand Sport 160
Mark 1 363
Volkswagen Beetle 341
Engine cowling
ARV light aircraft 424-425
Avro biplane 403
Concorde 416
Formula One racing car 356
Hawker Tempest components 408
Lockheed Electra airliner 407
Pegasus Quasar microlight 427
Engine crankcase 327
Engineering 496
Engine front mount 418-419
Engine front support link 417
Engine fuel pump 417
Engine instruments 425
Engine lifting eye 347
Engine mounting
ARV light aircraft 425
Blackburn monoplane 401
Honda VF750 364
Modern piston aero-engine 411
Pegasus Quasar microlight 427
Velocette OHV engine 367
Engine pulley 580
Engine pylon 412
Engine rear mount
Pegasus Quasar microlight 427
Turboprop engine 419
Engine room 326
Engine timing gear 336
Englacial moraine 287
Englacial stream 286
England 92
English baroque style 480-481
English bond brickwork 485
English Decorated style 470
English ivy 131
English Perpendicular style 470, 472
English saddle 582
Engraving 446
Enif 19, 20
Pegasus and Andromeda 19
Ensign staff 396
Entablature
Ancient Greek building 460
Ancient Roman building 462-465
Baroque church 480-481
Cathedral dome 487
French temple 485
Neoclassical building 478-479, 482-483
Entasis 461
Enteromorpha linza 117
Entomophilous pollination 144
Entrance
Islamic tomb 489
Medieval building 466-467
Modern building 496-499
Neoclassical building 483
Nineteenth-century building 493

Twentieth-century building 494
Entrenched meander 290
Entresol 467
Enzyme 160
Eocene epoch
  Fossil record 279
  Geological timescale 57
Eon
  Fossil record 279
  Geological time 56-57
Epée 556-557
Epibranchial artery 179
Epicardium 250
Epicenter 63
Epicotyl 152-153
Epicranial aponeurosis 237
Epidermal cell 166
Epidermis
  Apical meristem 134
  Canadian pond weed stem 159
  Clubmoss stem 120
  Dicotyledon 126-127
  Epiphytic orchid 162
  Fern rachis 121
  Flower 142
  Horsetail stem 120
  Human 234-235
  Leaf 139
  Marram grass 113
  Monocotyledon 126-127
  Moss 119
  Multi-layered 162
  Pine needle 124
  Pine stem 125
  Prickle 135
  Radicle 152
  Rhizome 155
  Root 132-133
  Stem 134-135
  Water hyacinth 158
  Water lily 159
Epididymis 259
Epidote 269
Epigeal germination 152-153
Epiglottis
  Elephant 200
  Human 212, 244-245, 248, 255
Epiphysis 230
Epiphytes 112, 162-163
Epithelial cell 217
Epithelium 254
Epoccipital bone 102
Epoch
  Fossil record 279
  Geological time 56-57
Epsilon Centauri 21
Epsilon Crucis 21
Epsilon Hydri 20
Epsilon ring 48-49
Equal-shock intensity lines 63
Equator
  Atmosphere 300
  Quaternary period 76
  Saturn 47
  Satellite map 265
  Surface currents 297
Equatorial air 300
Equatorial current 296-297
Equatorial furrow 144
Equatorial Zone 45
Equestrian sports 554-555
Equisetites sp. 66
Equisetum arvense 70, 120
Equuleus 19, 20
Era
  Fossil record 279
  Geological time 56-57
Eraser 430

Erasing stick 448
Erbium 311
Erect limb stance 82
Erh-wei 376
Eridanus 19, 20
E ring 46
Erosion 282-283
  Coastline 294-295
  Lake formation 293
  Ocean floor 298
  River features 290-291
  Rock cycle 267
  Sedimentary rocks 276
Eryops 80-81
Escalator 497-498
Escape wheel 570
Esker 286
Esophagus
  Barnacle 173
  Bird 189
  Brachiosaurus 91
  Butterfly 169
  Chimpanzee 202
  Cow 198
  Dogfish 179
  Dolphin 205
  Domestic cat 195
  Elephant 200
  Human 212, 215, 245, 248
  Lizard 185
  Rabbit 196
  Snail 177
  Spider 170
  Starfish 174
  Tortoise 187
Estonioceras perforatum 65
Estuarine mud-flat 295
Estuary 288, 290-294
Eta Centauri 21
Eta Mensae 20
Eta Orionis 18
Eta ring 48
Eta Sagittarii 21
Etching 446
Euathlus emilia 170
Euoplocephalus 94-95
Eurasia 76
Eurasian plate 59
Europa 44
Europe
  Cretaceous period 72-73
  Earth's physical features 264-265
  Electric train 328
  Electric trolley 332
  Jurassic period 70
  Loading gauge 331
  Middle Ordovician period 64
  Quaternary period 76
  Railroad track gauge 331
  Tertiary period 74-75
  Triassic period 68
European field elm 144
European hard-screw-coupling 328, 402
Europium 311
"Eurostar" multi-voltage electric train 328-329
Eurypterid fossil 79
Eustachian tube 243
Eustreptospondylus 85
Euthynteria 460
Evaporation 307
Event horizon 28-29
Evergreens 130-131
Everlasting pea 129
Evolute shell 278
Evolution
  Earth 56-57
  Living things 278
Excretory pore 177
Excurrent pore 166

Exfoliation 282
Exhaust
  Ford diesel engine 347
  Formula One racing car 357
  Modern mechanics 350-351
  Paddlesteamer 391
Exhaust clamp 362
Exhaust collector ring 403, 406
Exhaust connection 427
Exhaust cone 419
Exhaust diffuser 418
Exhaust downpipe 350
Exhaust fairing 419
Exhaust gas recirculation valve 344
Exhaust heat shield 345
Exhaust manifold
  1906 Renault 357
  ARV light aircraft 425
  Jaguar V12 engine 345
  Mid West two-stroke engine 410
  Renault Clio 351
Exhaust nozzle 418
Exhaust pipe
  Avro biplane 403
  Bell-47 helicopter 422
  BMW R/60 562
  Brazilian battleship 395
  Harley-Davidson FLHS Electra Glide 363
  Hawker Tempest fighter 409
  Honda CB750 363
  Honda VF750 364
  Kirby BSA 369
  Lockheed Electra airliner 406-407
  Oldsmobile engine 336
  Pegasus Quasar microlight 427
  Suzuki RGV500 368
  White Steam Car 342
  World War I aircraft 404-405
Exhaust pipe flange 411
Exhaust port
  "Deltic" diesel-electric locomotive 326
  Four-stroke cycle 343
  Mid West 75-HP engine 410
  Two-stroke engine 367
  Velocettes OHV engine 367
  Wankel engine 347
  Wankel rotary cycle 346
Exhaust silencer 423, 427
Exhaust stack 405
Exhaust steam water injector control 325
Exhaust stroke 343
Exhaust system 368
Exhaust tract 410
Exhaust valve 343-345
Exhaust valve push-rod 400
Exhaust vent
  British Rail Class 20 diesel engine 327
  Drill 567
  "Union Pacific" locomotive 326
Exine 144-145
Exit door 333
Exocarp 146-149
Exoccipital bone 183
Exocet missile launcher 397
Exodermis 162
Exoperidium 115
Exopod 172

Exoskeleton
  Insect 168
  Malacostraca 172
  Spider 171
Exosphere 300
Exothermic reactions 312
Expander bolt 359
Expandible sponge 448
Expansile jaw 85
Expansion lever 325
Expansion of sail 378-379
Expelling plate 397
Expiration 255
Exploding shell 396, 397
Exposure 588-589
Expressionist style 495
Extended cave system 285
Extended port air-brake 421
Extensor digitorum brevis muscle 233
Extensor digitorum longus tendon 233
Extensor digitorum tendon 233
Extensor hallucis brevis muscle 233
Extensor hallucis longus tendon 233
Extensors of hand 227
External anatomy
  Body 210-211
  Brain 237
  Ear 242-243
  Foot 233
  Hand 231
  Sperm 259
External auditory meatus
  Homo erectus 108
  Homo sapiens 108, 220, 242
External crust 28
External elastic lamina 252
External iliac artery 215, 225, 253
External iliac vein 215, 253
External nostril 184
External oblique muscle 226
External occipital crest 220
External pubo-ischio-femoral muscle 97
External skeleton
  Insect 168
  Malacostraca 172
  Spider 171
External spermatic fascia 259
External step 355
External urinary meatus 258
Extinct geyser 275
Extinction
  Dinosaur 56, 74, 82, 104
  Life 66
  Pleistocene mammals 76
Extinct volcano 62, 272
  Igneous rock structures 275
  Mountain building 62
  Ocean floor 298
Extrados 484-485
Extra period 532
Extrusive rocks 274, 275
Eye
  Allosaurus 85
  Amphibian 182
  Anchisaurus 89
  Angling hook 562
  Beetle 168
  Bird 188
  Bony fish 181

Brachiosaurus 91
Bumblebee 168
Butterfly 169
Caiman 186
Carnivore 194
Chick 192-193
Corythosaurus 98
Crab 172
Crayfish 173
Crocodilian 186
Deer hopper dry fly 563
Devon minnow 563
Dhow 376
Dogfish 178
Dolphin 204
Elephant 201
Figurehead 374
Forward-facing 194
Frog 182
Gallimimus 86
Gorilla 203
Greek and Roman ships 372
Herrerasaurus 86
Horse 198
Human 211, 212, 240-241
Iguanodon 97
Kangaroo 207
Knot 388
Lamprey 178
Lion 194
Lizard 184
Median 170
Octopus 177
Pachycephalosaurus 100
Psittacosaurus 103
Rabbit 196
Rat 196
Rattlesnake 185
Rigging 382-383
Salamander 182
Scallop 176
Scorpion 170
Seal 204
Shrimp 172
Simple 170-171
Snail 177
Snake 185
Spider 171
Stegoceras 101
Stegosaurus 92
Terrapin 187
Triceratops 102
Trilobite fossil 78
Tyrannosaurus 84
Westlothiana 87
Eyeball 241
Eye bolt 381
Eyebrow
  74-gun ship 381
  Human 212
Eyelash 212
Eyelet 568-569
Eyelid
  Caiman 186
  Human 213
  Snake 184
  Terrapin 187
Eye plate lug 382
Eyespot 116

F

F-14 Tomcat fighter 420
Fabric 384
Fabric covering
  Aluminum and steel wing 403
  BE 2B tail 405
  Blériot XI monoplane 401
  Steel-tube fuselage 403
Fabric lacing 405
Fabric skin 401
Fabry 41

Facade
  Ancient Greek building 461
  Ancient Roman building 465
  Baroque church 480-481
  Gothic church 470-472
  Modern building 496-499
  Neoclassical building 478, 483
  Nineteenth-century building 493
  Renaissance building 474
Facade pediment 481
Facade wall 470
Face
  Deadeye 383
  Human 211
  Sailmaker's mallet 384
Face mask
  Fencing 557
  Football 526
  Hockey goalkeeper 540
  Ice hockey goalkeeper 550
  Lacrosse goalkeeper 541
  Slalom skiing 553
Facet 222-223
"Facing off" 550
Faering 374-375
Fag end 387, 388
Fahrenheit temperature scale 590
Fairing 364, 369
Fairing of landing gear 413
Fairing panel 415
Fairing stay 369
Fairlead
  Battleship 395
  Frigate 397
  Rigging 383
  Roman corbita 373
Fairway 546
Falciform ligament 248
Falco tinnunculus 189
Falkland current 296
Fall 582
Fallopian tube 258-259, 261
False acacia 136
False anthers 141
False door 458-459
False fruit 148-149
False ram bow 394
"False ribs" 218
False septum 151
Falx cerebri 237
Fan
  Jaguar straight six engine 344
  Jet engines 418-419
  Power drill 566
Fan blade
  Renault Clio 353
  Turbofan 419
Fancase 418
Fan drive shaft 345
Fan duct nozzle 412
Fan fold 61
Fang 170
Fan motor 351
Fan vault 484-485
Farming axe 109
Fascia
  Ancient Roman building 463-464
  Baroque church 479, 481
  Dome 486
  French temple 485
  Gothic building 472
  Medieval building 467, 469
  Modern building 498

Neoclassical building 482
Renaissance building 476-477
Renault Clio 353
Fat
  Cells 217
  Tissue 215, 235
Faultline
  Lake formation 292
  Mountain building 62-63
  Weathering and erosion 283
Fault plane 60
Faults **60-61**, 292
  Mineral resources 280
  Mountain building 62
  Oil and gas traps 281
  Show-jumping competitions 554
Fault spring 292
Fault structure 60
Fault trap 281
F-block 311
F clef 502
Feather 188, 191
Feathered float 391
Feathering 440-441
Feather shuttlecock 544-545
Feather star 174
Feed bilge pump 391
Feeder station 328
Feet
  Human **252-233**
  Theropods 84
Feldspar 267, 269, 275
Felloe 390
Felt blanket 447
Felt-covered mallet 516, 518-519
Felt-tip pen 444
Female
  Body 210, 211
  Pelvis 218, 258
  Reproductive organs 259
Female apex 119
Female cones
  Bishop pine 124
  Gymnosperm 122
  Pine 122, 124
  Smooth cypress 123
  Yew 123
Female flower organs 140-143
Female flower remains 148
Female flowers 143, 144, 148
Female gametes
  Fertilization 146-147
  Gymnosperm 122
  Scots pine 122
  Seaweed 116-117
  Yew 123
Female receptacles 117
Female reproductive organs
  Fern 121
  Fruit 148
  Moss 119
  Plants 144
Femoral artery 225, 253
Femoral musculature 86
Femoral nerve 238
Femoral vein 253
Femoro-tibial muscle 84
Femur
  Albertosaurus 84
  Archaeopteryx 85
  Beetle 168
  Bird 189
  Brachiosaurus 90
  Butterfly 169
  Crocodile 186

Dinosaur 82
Domestic cat 195
Elephant 201
Eryops 81
Euoplocephalus 94
Frog 183
Gallimimus 86
Hare 197
Horse 199
Human 218-219, 224-225
Iguanodon 96-97
Kangaroo 206
Kentrosaurus 93
Lizard 184
Parasaurolophus 98
Pareiasaur 81
Plateosaurus 88
Platypus 206
Rhesus monkey 202
Scorpion 170
Seal 204
Spider 171
Stegoceras 101
Stegosaurus 93
Struthiomimus 87
Toxodon 107
Triceratops 102
Tuojiangosaurus 93
Turtle 187
Tyrannosaurus 84
Fencing **556-557**
Fender
  1906 Renault 336-337
  BMW R/60 with Steib chair 362
  Cannondale ST 1000 touring bicycle 361
  Ford Model T 338-339
  Harley-Davidson FLHS Electra Glide 363
  Honda VF750 364
  Husqvarna Motocross TC610 368
  Kirby BSA 369
  Lockheed Electra 406
  Motorcycle 364
  Suzuki RGV500 369
  Volkswagen Beetle 341
  Weslake Speedway bike 369
Fender eye bolt 339
Fender jazz bass guitar 513
Fender stay 337, 362, 363
Fender stratocaster guitar 513
Fenestration 474, 494
Fermentation 313
Fermium 311
Fern **120-121**
  Fossil 66, 279
  Life-cycle 121
  Prehistoric Earth 68, 70, 72
  Tree fern 112-113
Ferrel cell 300
Fertile horsetail stem 120
Fertile oasis 283
Fertilization **146-147**
  Fern 121
  Gymnosperm 122
  Scots pine 122
  Seaweed 117
Festoon
  Ancient Roman building 462-463
  Cathedral dome 487
  Neoclassical building 478-479
Fetal skull 220
Fetlock 199, 554
Fetus 260-261
Fiber 154-135
Fiberglass 548
Bow 548

Bucket seat 361
Canopy frame 425
Fuel tank 425
Racket 544
Reinforced plastic cover 329
Wheel guard 369
Fiber plate 366
Fibrils 32
Fibrin 253
Fibrous capsule 256
Fibrous habit 271
Fibrous pericardium 250
Fibrous septum 245
Fibula
  Albertosaurus 84
  Brachiosaurus 90
  Crocodile 186
  Diplodocus 90
  Domestic cat 195
  Elephant 201
  Eryops 81
  Euoplocephalus 94
  Gallimimus 87
  Hare 197
  Horse 199
  Human 219, 232-233
  Iguanodon 96-97
  Kangaroo 206
  Lizard 184
  Parasaurolophus 99
  Plateosaurus 88
  Platypus 206
  Rhesus monkey 202
  Seal 204
  Stegoceras 101
  Stegosaurus 93
  Struthiomimus 87
  Toxodon 107
  Triceratops 102
  Turtle 187
  Tyrannosaurus 84
Fibulare 183
Ficus carica 148
Ficus sp. 137
Fid 383, 384
Fiddle block 378, 383
Field arrow 549
Field coil 566
Fielder's glove 537
Field events 542
Field goal 526-527
Fielding 558
Fielding team 536
Field judge 526
Field positions 538
Field umpire 528
Fifteenth century
  Mihrab 488
  Renaissance building 474-475
  Style 462, 470
  Terrace 490
  Tracery 472
Fig 137, 148
Fighters 404-405, 408-409, 420
Fighting 556
Fighting platform 374
Figurehead
  74-gun ship 380-381
  Wooden sailing ship 379
Figure of eight turns 387
Filament
  Alga 116
  Dicotyledon flower 126-127
  Fern 121
  Fertilization 146-147
  Flowers 140-141, 143
  Fungal 114-115
  Jellyfish 167
  Lightbulb 319, 572
  Nebulae and star clusters 16-17

Sun 32-33
Moss 119
Pollination 144
Filbert bristle brush 436
Filicinophyta 120
Filiform papilla 244
Filing 455
Filled shell element 310-311
Fillet
  Ancient Greek temple 461
  Dome 486
  French temple 485
  Gothic building 470
  Neoclassical molding 480
  Renaissance building 475, 477
Filling transom 381
Film 588
Film chamber 588
Film guide rail 588
Film pressure plate 588
Film rewind crank 588-589
Film roller 588
Film speed indicator 589
Film sprocket spool 588
Film strip connector 584
Film take-up spool 588
Film wind lever 589
Filter 575
Fimbria 258-259
Fin
  Anal 178, 181
  ARV light aircraft 424
  Avro biplane 402
  BAe-146 components 415
  Blackburn monoplane 401
  Caudal 178-181
  Concorde 416
  Devon minnow 563
  Dorsal 178-179, 181, 205
  Helicopter 423
  Lockheed Electra airliner 407
  Lungfish 81
  LVG CVI fighter 405
  Pectoral 178, 180-181
  Pelvic 179-181
  Schleicher glider 426
  Tornado 421
  Ventral 179
  World War II aircraft 408-409
Final drive and gearbox 340
Final-drive sprocket 335
Fin-attachment skin 415
Fine leg 538
Fine linen canvas 437
Fine-toothed marble claw 453
Finger
  Anchisaurus 89
  Gorilla 203
  Human 211
  Iguanodon 97
  Pachycephalosaurus 100
  Psittacosaurus 103
  Stegoceras 101
  Theropod 84
Fingerboard 510-511, 513
Finger-claw 83, 85
Finger hole 508
Finger key 507
Fingerless glove 527
Fingernail 231
Finger tab 548
Finial
  Asian building 490-491
  Baroque church 479, 481
  Gothic church 470-471

Islamic building 488-489
Medieval building 468
Neoclassical building 478
Nineteenth-century building 493
Renaissance building 476
Finish line 542, 554-555
Fin leading-edge attachment 415
Fin-root aerial fairing 421
Fin tip 415
Fin tip fairing 421, 424
Fin trailing edge 415
Fir 66
Fire 108
Fireball 10
Firebox 324-325
Fire extinguisher 328
Fire-extinguisher discharge indicator 412
Fire-hole 325
Fire-making tools 109
Fireman's seat 325
Fire opal 270
Fireplace 466-467
Fire-resistant clay 454
Fire-resistant curtain 497
Fire-resistant panel 496
Fire safety 576
Fire-tube boiler 334
Fire tubes 324-325
Firewall 406, 425
Firing 452
Firing pin 549
Firn 287
First century 462-464
"First down" 526- 527
First pilot's seat 408
First quarter 41
First rate ship 378
First slip 538
First transition metals 310
First violin 503, 504-505
First wheel set 329
Fish
  Bony 180-181
  Breathing 180
  Cartilaginous 178
  Fossil 279
  Holostean 73
  Jawless 178-179
Fish davit 379
Fisherman's schooner 385
Fishing tackle 109
Fish-scale tile 476-477, 486
Fishtail nectaries 160
Fissure 247
Fissures 157
Fissure volcano 272
Five-line stave 502
Five yard mark 540
Fixative 430, 440
Fixed float 390
Fixed gear 346-347, 411
Fixed lug 383
Fixed-spool reel 562
Fixing screw 579
Fjord 294-295
Flagella 166
Flagellum
  Beetle 168
  Chlamydomonas sp. 116
  Moss 119
  Seaweed gametes 117
  Snail 177
  Sperm 259
Flag halyard 380
Flagmast 395
Flag pin 547
Flagpole 495

Flaking rock 282
Flamboyant tracery 472
Flame 312-313
Flame regulator 354
Flamingo 188, 190
Flamsteed 40
Flange 492, 498
Flanged plate 425
Flank
  Bird 188
  Cow 198
Flanker
  Canadian football 526
  Rugby 530
Flank spike 95
Flap
  ARV light aircraft 425
  Hawker Tempest components 409
  Lockheed Electra airliner 406
  Racing saddle 555
  Show-jumping saddle 554
  Tornado 421
Flap drive screw 413
Flap lever 425
Flap seal 413, 414
Flap tip 414
Flap torque tube 424
Flap track 413
Flap-track fairing 413, 415
Flared bell
  Brass instruments 506-507
  Woodwind instruments 508-509
Flashgun 588
Flash steam generator 342
Flash tube 397
Flask 312-313
Flat
  Musical notation 502
  Twin bollards 386
Flatboard 384
Flat bottom 391
Flat-bottomed rail 331
Flat chisel 452
Flat cone 272
Flatfish angling 562
Flat-four engine 540
Flat freight car 327
Flat horse-races 554
Flat laminae 138
Flat roof
  Ancient Egyptian building 458
  Neoclassical building 483
  Twentieth-century building 494-495
Flat seam 384
Flat seizing 383, 389
Flat soffit 464
Flattened pericarp 151
Flattened petiole 160
Flattened stem 129
Flat-topped plateau 275, 282
Flat-topped seamount 298
Flat wire seizing 383
Flavian amphitheatre 464
Flax-spinning mill 492
Fleet number 333
Flesh-eaters 194
Flesh-eating dinosaur 70
Flesh tones 433
Fleshy aril 148
Fleshy axis 143
Fleshy fruit 146-147
Fleshy hair 140
Fleshy infolded receptacle 148
Fleshy scale leaf 155
Fletch 548

Flexor digitorum longus
muscle 233
Flexor digitorum tendon
231
Flexor hallucis longus
muscle 233
Flexor pollicis brevis
muscle 231
Flexor retinaculum
muscle 231
Flexors of forearm 226
Flexors of hand 227
Flexor tubercle 85
Flight 543
Flight-control hydraulic
jack 416
Flight-control mixing unit
417
Flight-control rod 423
Flight controls 412
Flight feathers 188, 191
Flight instruments 425
Flight refuelling recepta-
cle 421
Flint 277
Flint tools 108-109
Flipper 204
Flitch-plated wooden
chassis 342
Float 390-391
Floating disc brake 364-
365
"Floating" rib 218
Flocked pastel board 441
Flock stuffing 582
Flood-plain 289-291
Floods 290
Floor
  Gun turret 396
  Ironclad 393
  Longboat 380
  Modern building 496-498
  Nineteenth-century
  building 492
  Twentieth-century
  building 494-495
Floor anchor 407
Floorboard 464, 486
Floor-joist 464
Floor of gun house 396
Floor pan 340
Floor tom 518-519
Floppy disk drive 521
Florence Cathedral 475,
487
Florets 142
  Florists' chrysanthemum
  129
  Ultraviolet light 145
Florida current 296
Florists' chrysanthemum
129
Flower bud
  Aechmea miniata 162
  Broomrape 163
  Bulb 155
  Clematis 131
  Florists' chrysanthemum
  129
  Hibiscus 127
  Ice-plant 129
  Live-for-ever 129
  Oxalis sp. 157
  Peruvian lily 129
  Rose 131
  Water lily 159
  Wind pollination 144
Flowering plant 57, 70, 72
Flowering shoot 155
Flowers 140-143
  Brassavola nodosa 162
  Bromeliad 113
  Broomrape 163
  Buds 140-141, 143
  Clematis 131

Color 140, 144-145
Dicotyledons 126-127,
141-143
Dodder 163
Epiphytes 162-163
Everlasting pea 129
Florists' chrysanthemum
129
Guzmania lingulata 163
Ice-plant 129
Involucre 129
Monocotyledons 126,
140-141, 143
Peruvian lily 129
Pollination 144-145
Rose 131
Russian vine 131
Scented 144
Stem arrangements 143
Ultraviolet light 145
Vegetative reproduction
154
Water lily 159
Yew 123
Flower scars 154
Flower spike 143, 155
Flower stalk
  Brassavola nodosa 162
  Bulbil 154
  Clematis 131
  Dry fruit 150-151
  Fertilization 146-147
  Florists' chrysanthemum
  129
  Fruit development 146-
  147
  Monocotyledons 140-
  141, 143
  Oxalis sp. 157
  Rose 131
  Rowan 131
  Russian vine 131
  Succulent fruit 148-149
  Sycamore 131
  Water lily 159
Flow splitter 418
Fluid 306
Fluke
  74-gun ship 380
  Danforth anchor 386
Fluorescent light 318-319
Fluorine 308-309, 311
Fluorite 271
  Halides 269
Flush-riveted aluminum
fuselage 423
Flush-riveted metal-
skinned wing 406
Flush window 494
Flute 503, 504-505, 508
Fluted pilaster 462
Fluted pinnacle 481
Fluted shaft 478
Fluting 461, 463
Flutter kick 559
Fly 168
Fly back transformer 575
Fly fishing 562
Fly-half 530
Flying boat 406
Flying buttress
  Gothic building 470-473
  Medieval building 466,
  468-469
  Nineteenth-century
  building 493
Flying Fortress bomber
408
Flying helmet 404
Flying jib 385
Flying reptile 70
Flying tackle 531
Flyleaf 587
Fly rod 562-563

Flywheel
  Benz Motorwagen 335
  Early engines 342-343
  Etching press 447
  Lawnmower 580
  Mid West rotary engine
  411
  Oldsmobile engine 336
  Renault Clio 351
  Steamboat 391
Flywheel retaining thread
411
Flywheel with balance
weight 347
Foam stuffing 576-577
Focal length scale 589
Focker, Anthony 404
Fo'c'sle 380
Focus 63
Focus control 575
Focusing ring 589
Fog 42-43
Fog-lamp 349, 353
Fog light 332, 363
Foil 556-557
Foilist 557
Foil pommel 557
Folded rock 60, 266
  Impermeable rock 281
  Mineral resources 280
  Strata 60-61
Folded schist 274
Folding mountain range
274
Folding step 326
Fold mountains 62
Fold of mucous mem-
brane 249
Folds 60-61
Foliage leaf
  Bishop pine 124
  Bud 124
  Bulb 155
  Germination 152-153
  Monocotyledon 126
  Parasitic plant 162
  Pine 124-125
  Rhizome 155
  Seedling 152-153
  Stem bulbil 155
  Yew 123
Foliated capital 469
Foliated frieze 469, 479
Foliated panel 479
Foliated scrollwork 472
Foliated volute 476
Foliate papilla 244
Foliose lichen 114
Foliose thallus 114
Follicle
  Dehiscent dry fruit 150-
  151
  Hair 235
  Ovary 258
Fomalhaut 19, 20
Fontanelle 220
Food storage
  Bulb 155
  Corm 155
  Embryo 147
  Rhizome 155
  Root tuber 155
  Scale leaf 155
  Seed 152
  Succulent 156-157
  Swollen stem 113, 155
Foot
  Anchisaurus 89
  Bird 190
  Caiman 186-187
  Corythosaurus 98
  Cow 198
  Diplodocus 90
  Duck 188
  Elephant 90

Gorilla 203
Harp 511
Herrerasaurus 86
Horse 198
Human 210
Iguanodon 96
Kangaroo 207
Lizard 184
Pachycephalosaurus 100
Relief-printing press 449
Sails 374, 385
Slug 176
Snail 177
Stegoceras 101
Stegosaurus 92
Toaster 578-579
Tube 174
Webbed 188
Westlothiana 81
Football 524-525, 527
Footboard 335, 363
Foot brake 363
Footbridge 493
Foot-fault judge 544
Foot mat 363
Foot pedal 366, 514
Footplate 324
Footrest
  Curtiss biplane 598-599
  Roman corbita 372
  Suzuki RGV500 568
  Weslake Speedway bike
  369
Footrest hanger 364
Foot rope 378-379, 382,
385
Foot throttle 427
Foramen caecum 244
Foramen magnum 220
Foraminiferans 279
Force 520-521
"Force play" 536
Ford Cosworth V6 12-
valve engine 344
Ford Cosworth V6 24-
valve engine 344
Ford, Henry 338
Ford Model T 338-339
Ford turbocharged diesel
engine 347
Fore-and-aft rigged lateen
sails 376
Fore-and-aft sails 384
Fore-and-aft schooner 385
Forearm
  Gorilla 203
  Horse 199
  Human 210
  Movement 227
Forearm guard 548
Forearm pass 534
Fore bitt 380
Fore breast rope 387
Forecarriage 335
Forecastle
  74-gun ship 380
  Sailing warship 376
  Square-rigged ship 375
Forecastle castle-deck
gunport 376
Fore-edge 586-587
Forefoot
  Caiman 186
  Diplodocus 90
  Edmontonia 95
  Elephant 90
  Iron paddlesteamer 393
  Stegosaurus 92
Fore hatch tackle 379
Forehead
  Bird 188
  Dolphin 204
  Elephant 200-201
  Horse 199
  Human 211, 212

Foreleg
  Caiman 186
  Elephant 201
  Lizard 184
  Terrapin 187
Forelimb
  Anchisaurus 89
  Bird 188
  Corythosaurus 98
  Edmontonia 95
  Frog 182
  Hare 196
  Herrerasaurus 86
  Iguanodon 97
  Kangaroo 207
  Pachycephalosaurus 100
  Psittacosaurus 103
  Rabbit 196
  Rat 196
  Salamander 182
  Stegoceras 101
  Stegosaurus 92
  Thyreophorans 92
  Triceratops 102
  Tyrannosaurus 84
Forelock 199
Fore lower topsail 385
Fore mast
  Iron paddlesteamer 392
  Roman corbita 372
  Sailing warship 376
  Square-rigged ship 375
  Wooden sailing ship 379
Fore mast course 379
Fore mast hole 380
Fore mast topgallant sail
379
Fore mast topsail 379
Forepeak 393
Forepiece 583
Fore royal stay 383
Fore sail 372, 385
Fore sail halyard 380
Foreset strata 283
Fore shroud 379
Foresight
  Rifle 549
  Target pistol 549
Foreskin 259
Fore spring rope 387
Fore stay
  Rigging 382
  Roman corbita 372
  Sailing warship 376
  Wooden sailing ship 379
Fore staysail 379, 385
Forest-dwelling mammals
74
Fore throat halyard 385
Fore top 379
Fore topcastle 376
Fore topgallant mast 379
Fore topmast 376, 379
Fore topmast stay 376,
379
Fore topmast staysail 385
Fore topmast staysail tack
382
Fore topsail 379
Fore upper topsail 385
Forewing 169
Fore yard 376, 379
Forged iron anchor 392
Fork
  ARV Super 2 425
  Eddy Merckx racing
  bicycle 361
  Harley-Davidson FLHS
  Electra Glide 363
  Honda CB750 363
  Motorcycle 364
  Vespa Grand Sport 160
  Mark 1 363
Fork blade 559
Forked beam 380

Forked connecting-rod
342
Fork end 383
Fork slide 365
Fork stanchion 365
Fork yolk 365
Formeret 469, 479
Fornax 19, 20
Fornix 236-237
Fortifications 466
Forum of Trajan 463
Forward 532, 534-555
Forward bulkhead panel
406
Forward deck 561
Forward defensive stroke
538
Forward dive 558
Forward door 415, 417
Forward-facing eyes 194
Forward fairing 415
Forward-firing machine-
gun 405
Forward funnel 393, 395
Forward fuselage
structure 401
Forward galley 416
Forward hydroplane 397
Forward main door 412
Forward ramp drive 417
Forward short leg 538
Forward spar 415
Fossa ovalis 251
Fossil fuel 280-281, 314-
315
Fossilization 278
Fossil record 279
Fossils 278-279
  Acanthostega skull 80
  Ankylosaurus tail club 95
  Birch leaf 74, 76
  Blue-green algae 78
  Brachiopod 65
  Clubmoss 66
  Eurypterid 79
  Fern 66
  Graptolite 65
  Horsetail 66
  Hyaenodon skull 107
  Jawless fish 78
  Land plant 64
  Lungfish 81
  Nautiloid 65
  Palm bark 74
  Shark teeth 67
  Starfish 79
  Swamp plant 64
  Sweetgum leaf 76
  Titanosaurid egg 91
  Trilobite 78
Fossil skeleton
  Archaeopteryx 85
  Bat 105
  Parasaurolophus 98
  Pareiasaur 81
  Struthiomimus 87
  Westlothiana 81
Foster, N. 496, 498
Foul lines 536
Fouls 552
Foul tackle 524
Foul tip 537
Foundation
  Ancient Roman building
  464
  Iron paddlesteamer 392
  Modern building 496
  Nineteenth-century
  building 492
Foundry plug 387
Fountain pen 444
Four-aspect color light
signal 330
Four-chambered heart
104

Four-cylinder 12-HP engine 399
Four-cylinder motorcycle 363
Four-footed dinosaur 88, 92, 96, 100
Four-pulley system 320
Four-stroke combustion engine 366
Four-stroke cycle 343
Fourteenth century 474
  Arch 488
  Gothic building 471-473
  Medieval building 466-467
  Roof 490
  Style 470
Fourth mast 376
Four-wheel bogie 417
Four-wheel-drive 354
Fovea 224
Fowler flap 413, 414
Foxes 194
Fracastorius 40
Fracture 270
Fractured rock 34
Fragaria x *ananassa* 128, 150
Fra Mauro 40
Frame
  74-gun ship 381
  ARV light aircraft 424
  Bicycle 358-359
  Cannondale SH 600 hybrid bicycle 361
  Concert grand piano 515
  Concorde 416
  Harley-Davidson FLHS Electra Glide 363
  Honda VF750 364
  Ironclad 393
  Longboat 380
  Medieval house 466
  Modeled sculpture 452
  Modern building 496
  Motorcycle 364
  Oscillating steam engine 390
  Racing bicycle 360
  Racket 544-545
  Relief-printing press 449
  Single scull 560
  Steam-powered Cugnot 335
  Steel 494
  Upright piano 514
  Weslake Speedway bike 369
Frame angle 360
Frame drum 518
Frame head 340
Frame mounted-fairing 364
Fram Rupes 35
Francis turbine 314
Francium 310
Frapped turn 389
Free nerve ending 235, 239
Freestyle swimming stroke 558
Free-throw line 532-533, 535
Freewheel 361
Freewheel locknut 358
Freewheel sprocket 360
Freezing 307
Freezing level 302
Freight car 327
Freight locomotive 326
French baroque style 479, 482
French bowline 388
French Flamboyant style 470

French TGV train 528-529
French trotter 554
Fresco **434-435**
Freshwater bay 291
Freshwater angling 562
Freshwater lake
  Lakes and groundwater 292
  Weathering and erosion 283
Freshwater turtle 186
Fret 512-513
Fret-pattern mosaic 488-489
Fretwork 461, 491
Frieze
  Ancient Egyptian building 459
  Ancient Greek building 461
  Ancient Roman building 463, 465
  Baroque church 479, 481
  Cathedral dome 487
  French temple 485
  Medieval church 469
  Neoclassical building 478-479, 482
  Renaissance building 476
  Twentieth-century building 495
Frigate **596-597**
F ring 46-47
Fringed crumble cap 115
Fringilla coelebs 193
Fringing reef 299
Frog 182-183
  Double bass bow 511
  Eggs 183, 192
  Fossil 278
  Violin bow 510
Frog kick 559
Frond
  Fern 120-121
  Seaweed 116-117
  Tree fern 112-113
Frontal bone
  Bony fish 181
  Chimpanzee 202
  Human 212-213, 220-221
Frontalis muscle 226, 228-229
Frontal lobe 236-237
Frontal notch 213
Frontal process 221
Frontal rib 161
Frontal sinus 212, 245
Front axle
  1906 Renault 336-337
  Ford Model T 338
  Honda VF750 365
  Husqvarna Motocross TC610 368
  Kirby BSA 369
Front bezel 584
Front board assembly 588
Front brake cable
  Bicycle 359
  Eddy Merckx racing bicycle 361
Front brake lever 363
Front bumper 332
Front cabinet 575
Front cantilever brake 359
Front cover board 586-587
Front crawl 558-559
Front cylinder exhaust pipe 368
Front derailleur 358-360
Frontispiece 587
Front leg 168-169
Front lens group 588
Front light
  Bicycle 360

Paris RATP Metro 328
Italian State Railways Class 402 328
Frontoparietal bone 183
Frontozygomatic suture 220
Front plate 570
Front rail 576
Front spring 337
Front tire 580
Front wheel
  Bicycle 359
  Lawnmower 580-581
Front wing 168
Frost wedging 282, 286-287
Froude's early test propeller 391
Frozen rubber puck 550-551
Fruit
  Bramble 130
  Couch grass 113
  Development 146-147
  Dry 150-151
  Durmast oak 131
  Peach 131
  Pitcher plant 113
  Rowan 131
  Succulent 148-149
  Sycamore 131
Fruit wall 148-149, 150-151
Fruticose lichen 114
Fruticose thallus 114
"F" turret 594
Fucoxanthin 116
Fucus spiralis 116
Fucus vesiculosus 116, 117
Fuel/air intake pipe 337
Fuel and oil heat ex-changer 418
Fuel and oil tank 398-399
Fuel breather 357
Fuel cap 348, 369
Fuel contents indicator 413
Fuel-cooled oil cooler 419
Fuel drip tray 411
Fuel filler 357
Fuel filler and vent 403
Fuel filler cap
  Curtiss biplane 398
  Volkswagen Beetle 340
Fuel filler neck 340
Fuel filter 419
Fuel heater 419
Fuel hose 425
Fuel injection 344, 356
Fuel inlet 419
Fuel-jettison pipe 417
Fuel-jettison valve 406
Fuel manifold 418-419
Fuel nozzle 418-419
Fuel pipe
  Concorde 417
  Curtiss biplane 398
  Jaguar V12 345
Fuel reservoir 368
Fuel sediment bowl 339
Fuel shut-off valve cable 419
Fuel sprayer 418
Fuel supply pump 327
Fuel tank
  Avro triplane 402
  Benz Motorwagen 335
  BMW R/60 362
  Concorde 417
  "Deltic" diesel-electric locomotive 326
  Harley-Davidson FLHS Electra Glide 363
  Helicopter 422-423
  Honda VF750 364

Lawnmower 580
Lockheed Electra airliner 407
LVG CVI fighter 405
Pegasus XL SE microlight 426
Pinzgauer Turbo D 354
Renault Clio 350
Suzuki RGV500 369
Volkswagen Beetle 340
Werner motorcycle 362
Weslake Speedway bike 369
White Steam Car 342
Wright Flyer 398
Fuel tank breather 369
Fuel tank cap 581
Fuel tank cradle 422
Fuel tank filler cap 369
Fuel tank filler neck 350
Fuel tank filler nozzle 427
Fuel tank sender unit 340
Fuel tank top skin 425
Fuel tap 366
Fuel vent pipe 422
Fulcrum 320-321
Fullback
  Australian rules football 527
  Canadian football 526
  Football 526
  Gaelic football 529
  Rugby 530
Fullback line 529
Full-elliptic leaf spring 334-335
Full-elliptic steering spring 337
Full forward 528-529
Fumaroles 272-273
Funaria hygrometrica 119
Funaria sp. 119
Functionalism 496
Function display 520-521
Fundus 258
Fungal filament 114-115
Fungi 114, **114-115**, 133
Fungia fungites 167
Fungiform papilla 244
Fungoid-structure encrustations 284
Funicle 150
Funnel
  Battleship 595
  Frigate 397
  Iron paddlesteamer 392-393
  Lizard 185
  Octopus 176-177
  Steamboat with paddle wheels 391
Funnel guide 126
Funnel stay 595
Furcula 189
Furled forecourse sail 375
Furled lateen main sail 376
Furled lateen mizzen sail 375, 376
Furnerius 40
Furrow 282
Furud 21
Fused carpels 140, 144, 151
Fused petals 142, 145
Fused receptacles 149
Fusee 570
Fusee chain 570
Fuse enclosure 572
Fusee pivot hole 570
Fusee stop 570
Fuselage 401, 409, 424
Fuselage bottom skin 424
Fuselage bracing wire 403, 426

Fuselage mid-section 412
Fuselage nose-section 412
Fuselage skin 402
Fuselage spine fairing 414
Fuselage tail-section 415
Fuselage top skin 424
Fusion crust 52
Futtock shroud 378

G

Gabbro 267, 274
Gable
  Gothic building 470-473
  Medieval building 467, 469
  Nineteenth-century building 492-493
  Renaissance building 476
Gabled arch 471
Gacrux 21
Gadolium 311
Gaelic football **528-529**
Gaff 380, 385
Gagarin 41
Gait 554
Galactic center 14, 18, 20
Galactic nucleus 12-13
Galactic plane 14-15
Galaxy 10-15
Galena 268
Galeocerdo cuvier 179
Galilean moons 44
Galium aparine 150
Gallbladder
  Domestic cat 195
  Human 248, 252
  Rabbit 196
  Tortoise 187
Galle ring 50-51
Gallery
  74-gun ship 381
  Ancient Roman building 465
  Baroque church 479-480
  Cathedral dome 487
  Frigate 397
  Medieval building 466-468
  Modern building 496-497
  Renaissance theater 477
  Wooden sailing ship 378-379
Galley 372-397
Gallimimus 82, 84, 86-87
Gallium 311
Gallop 582
Galois 41
Galvanized "D" shackle 386
Gambrel roof 490
Game target shooting 548
Gamete 154
  Brown seaweed 116-117
  Bryophyte 118-119
  Fern 120-121
  Fertilization 146-147
  Gymnosperm 122
  Moss 112
  Pine 122
  Vegetative reproduction 154
  Yew 123
Gametophyte
  Bryophyte 118-119
  Fern 120-121
  Liverwort 118
  Moss 112, 119
Gamma 18, 21
Gamma Centauri 21
Gamma Hydri 20
Gamma Mensae 20
Gamma radiation 10

Gamma ray 22, 318-319
Gamma ring 48
Ganges plain 63
Ganges River delta 288
Ganglion 173, 177
Gangway
  74-gun ship 580
  Colosseum 464
  Sailing warship 377
Ganymede 44
Gape
  Angling hook 562
  Dolphin 204
Garboard strake 393
Gargoyle 473
Garnet 267
Garnet-mica schist 267
Garnierite 270
Garudimimus 86
Gas 306-307
  Asteroids, comets, and meteoroids 52-53
  Chemical reactions 313
  Massive stars 26-27
  Mineral resources 280-281
  NGC 2997 (spiral galaxy) 12
  Small stars 24-25
  Stellar black hole 29
Gas blanket 300
Gas cloud
  Earth's formation 56
  Milky Way 14
  Nebulae and star clusters 16-17
  Origin and expansion of Universe 10-11
Gas current 29
Gas deposit 57, 281
Gaseous exchange in alveolus 255
Gaseous water 49
Gas exchange 134
  Leaf 138-139
  Photosynthesis process 138
  Root 132
  Sunken stoma 156-157
  Wetland plants 158
Gas formation 280-281
Gas giants
  Jupiter 44-45
  Neptune 50-51
  Saturn 46-47
  Solar System 30-31
  Uranus 48-49
Gaskin 198, 554
Gas loop 32-33
Gas molecule 53
Gassendi 40
Gas shell 16-17, 25
Gas tail 52-53
Gastralia 85, 87
Gas traps 281
Gastric artery 253
Gastrocnemius muscle
  Albertosaurus 84
  Euoplocephalus 94
  Human 226-227
  Iguanodon 97
Gastroepiploic vein 253
Gastropod mollusc 75
Gastropods 176, 279
Gastrovascular cavity 167
Gas turbine 418
Gate
  Building 467, 490-491
  Canoeing 560
  Downhill skiing 552
  Hydroelectric power station 314
Gate clamp 560
Gate-house 467
Gateway 460

Gatwick express "People Mover" 328
Gauge 330-331
Gauge class 525
Gauged arch 492
Gauntlet 540, 557
Gavialis gangeticus 186
G clef 502
Gear band 536
Gearbox
  ARV light aircraft 425
  Ford Model T 339
  Harley-Davidson FLHS Electra Glide 363
  Motorcycle 364, 366
  Renault Clio 351
  Volkswagen Beetle 340
Gearbox bevel drive 418
Gearbox case 410
Gearbox drive spline 410
Gearbox fixing stud 356
Gearbox mount 413
Gearbox oil scavenge line 419
Gearbox unit 413
Gear cable 359
Gearcase 567
Gearcase assembly 580
Gearcase position 566
Gear change 363
Gear-change rod 351
Gearing mechanism 584
Gear lever
  1906 Renault 337
  Husqvarna Motocross TC610 368
  Renault Clio 350
  Two-stroke engine 366
Gear lever knob 340
Gear lever surround 352
Gear ratios 361
Gear retainer 562
Gear shift 359
Gear system 358, 366
Gears
  Clock 570
  Drills 566
  Lawnmower 580
  Motorcycle 366
Gelatine roller 447
Gemini 18
Gemma 118
Generative nucleus 147
Generator
  British rail class 20 diesel engine 327
  Diesel train 326
  Electric train 326
  Nuclear power station 314
  Van de Graaff 316
Generator cooling fan 327
Generator housing 411
Generator rotor
  Hydroelectric power station 314
  Mid West engine 410
Generator unit 314
Genioglossus muscle 245
Geniohyoid muscle 245
Genital plate 175
Gentlemen's room 477
Geographic pole 38
Geological time 56-57, 279
Geranium pratense 144
Gerberette 497
Gerbil 196
Germanium 311
German-style baroque 482
Germany 326
Germinal epithelium 258
Germination 152-153
  Cabbage seed 132
  Epigeal 152-153
  Fern spore 121

Hypogeal 152-153
Mushroom spore 115
Pine 122
Pollen grain 146-147
Gesso 452, 453
Geyser 272-273, 275
Gharial 186
Ghost anemone 166
Giant redwood 112
Giant slalom 552
Giant stars 22-23, 26
Gibbon 202
Gibson Les Paul guitar 513
Gig 395
Gilded band 490
Gilded cross 487
Gilded orb 487
Gilded rib 487
Gilded truck 378-379
Gilding materials 431, 432
Gill
  Bivalves 176
  Bony fish 180-181
  Dogfish 178-179
  Fungi 114-115
  Lamprey 178
  Newt 182
  Salamander 182
  Tadpole 183
Gill filament 180
Gill opening 178
Gill raker 180
Gill slit 178-180
Gilt ironwork 482, 490
Ginger 155
Gingiva 247
Ginkgo 68, 70, 72, 122-123, 279
Ginkgo biloba 68, 123
Ginkgophyta 122
Ginkgo pluripartita 72
Giornate 434-435
Giraffa camelopardalis 199
Giraffe 198-199
Girder 493
Girdle 116
Girdle scar 123
Girth
  English saddle 582
  Harness racer 555
  Show-jumper 554
Gizzard
  Bird 189
  Brachiosaurus 91
  Euoplocephalus 94
  Gallimimus 86
Glabella
  Human skull 213, 221
  Trilobite fossil 78
Glacial deposits 286-287, 292-293
Glacial periods 56-57, 76
Glacial sediments 299
Glacial streams 286
Glacier Bay 286
Glacier features 286-287
Glaciers 286-287
  Prehistoric Earth 66, 76
  River's stages 289
  Rock cycle 266-267
  Weathering and erosion 282
Glacier snout 286, 289
Gladiolus 154-155
Gland
  19th century paddlesteamer 391
  Axial 175
  Butterwort 161
  Cement 173
  Green 173
  Monkey cup 161
  Mucous 177

Pedal 177
Poison 170, 176
Rectal 179
Salivary 177
Silk 170
Venus fly trap 160
Glans penis 259
Glass 307
  Buildings 492, 494
  Tesserae 450
Glass bulb 319
Glass circle 535, 541
Glass curtain 497
Glass deflector 325
Glass enamel 450
Glass envelope 572
Glass flask 312
Glass mosaic 489
Glass muller 436, 440
Glass pane 494
Glass paper 441
Glass prism 318
Glass slab 436, 440
Glass tube 319
Glass wall 496, 499
Glazing
  Acrylic paints 442
  Modern building 496-499
  Twentieth-century building 494
Glazing bar 499
Gleba 114-115
Glechoma hederacea 154
Gleditsia triacanthos 137
Glenoid cavity 80
Gliders 426-427
Global warming 301
Globe 264
Globe Theatre 477
Globular cluster 12, 16, 21
Globule 24, 26
Glomerulus 256-257
Gloriosa superba 143
Glory lily 143
Gloss finish
  Acrylics 442
  Oil painting 436
Glossopteris 67
Gloster Meteor fighter 408
Glove box 425
Gloves
  Baseball fielder 537
  Cricket batsman 539
  Cricket wicket-keeper 539
  Fencing 556-557
  Football 527
  Ice hockey 551
  Lacrosse goalkeeper 541
  Racketball 545
  Sailing 560
  Skiing 552-553
  Soccer goalkeeper 525
Glucose 158
Glue 575-576, 586
Glulam wall-plate 499
Gluon 309
Gluteal fold 210
Gluteus maximus muscle 227
Gluteus medius muscle 225
Gluteus minimus muscle 225
Glyph 460
Gnathostomata 178, 180
Gneiss 274
Gnetophytes 122
Gnome seven-cylinder rotary engine 400
Gnomon 377
Goal
  Australian rules football 528
  Gaelic football 529
  Hockey 540

Hurling 541
Ice hockey 550
Lacrosse 541
Rugby 530-531
Soccer 524
Goal area
  Gaelic football 529
  Handball 535
  Soccer 524
Goal attack 535
Goal circle 535, 541
Goal crease 541, 550
Goal defense 535
Goal judge 550
Goalkeeper
  Australian rules football 528
  Football rules 524
  Gaelic football 529
  Handball 534-535
  Hockey 540
  Ice hockey 550
  Lacrosse 541
  Netball 535
  Soccer 525
Goalkeeper's equipment 540
Goalkeeper's gloves 525
Goalkeeper's helmet 550-551
Goalkeeper's kicker 540
Goalkeeper's pad 550
Goalkeeper's shirt 525, 550
Goalkeeper's stick 550
Goal line
  Australian rules football 528
  Football 526
  Handball 535
  Hockey 540
  Ice hockey 550
  Rugby 530
  Soccer 524
Goal line referee 535
Goal net 524, 534, 550
Goalposts
  Australian rules football 528
  Football 526
  Gaelic football 529
  Netball 535
  Rugby 530
Goal shooter 535
Goal square 528
Goal third 535
Goal umpire 528-529
Goat 198
Goat hair brush 438, 442
  Calligraphy 444
Goat hake wash brush 438
Gobi Desert 265
Goggles
  Harness racing 555
  Skiing 552-553
  Swimming 558
Gold 31, 268, 280-281, 438
Gold chalcopyrite 271
Gold embossing 586-587
Golden barrel cactus 156
Golden lion tamarin 203
Gold leaf 452
  Fresco 435
  Illumination 444-445
  Smalti 450
  Vitreous glass 451
  Wood sculpture highlighting 453
Golf 546-547
Golgi complex 217
Gomphoi 373
Gonad
  Jellyfish 167
  Octopus 176
  Sea anemone 167

Sea urchin 175
Starfish 174
Gondwanaland
  Cretaceous period 72
  Jurassic period 70-71
  Late Carboniferous period 66-67
  Middle Ordovician period 64-65
Gong 504, 516
Goniastrea aspera 167
Gonopore
  Barnacle 173
  Sea urchin 175
  Snail 177
  Starfish 174
Goose-feather quill 444
Goosegrass 150
Goose neck 388
Gopher 196
Gopuram finial 491
Gorge
  Cave 284-285
  River features 290
Gorilla 202-203
Gothic architecture 468, 470-473
Gothic book script lettering 445
Gothic stone arch 467
Gothic torus 470
Gouge
  Relief printing 446, 449
  Woodcarving 454-455
Gour 284-285
Goya 35
Grab handle 355, 362
Graben 61
Graben lake 293
Gracilis muscle 226-227
Graded wash 439
Graffian follicle 258
Graffias 21
Gran Chaco 264
Grand Canyon 57, 226-227
Grand piano 514-515
"Grand Prix" world championships 368
Grandstand 555
Granite-aggregate slab 499
Granite cladding 494
Granular stalk 114
Granum 139
Grape hyacinth 155
Graphite 268, 311
Graphite pencil 430
Graphite stick 430
Grapnel-type anchor 376
Grasping tail 202
Grass 113
Grass bag 581
Grate 324
Grating 380-381
Graver 449
Gravitation (gravity)
  Atmosphere 300
  Force and motion 320
  Neutron stars and black holes 28
  Oceans and seas 296-297
  Universe 10
Gravitational pull 296-297
Gravity-feed fuel tank 405
Gray Cliffs 276
Gray matter 236-237, 238
Gray squirrel 197
Gray whale 204
Grease 446
Greaser 339
Great Bear Lake 264
Great cabin 379, 381
Great Dark Spot 50-51
Greater blackbacked gull 193

Greater flamingo 190
Greater omentum 214
Greater palatine foramen 220
Greater trochanter of femur 224-225
Greater wing coverts 188
Greater wing of sphenoid bone 220-221
Great Lakes 264
Great manual 514
Great Mosque 484
Great Red Spot 44-45
Great Rift Valley 60
Great saphenous vein 253
Great stop 514
Greek ship 372-373
Greek-style fret ornament 483
Green (golf) 547
Green alga 112, 116-117
Green calc-silicate mineral 275
Green chlorophyll pigment 116, 138
Green earth 434-435
Green fluorite 269
Green gland 173
Greenhouse effect 36, 300-301
"Greenhouse gas" 301
Greenland
  Cretaceous period 73
  Late Carboniferous period 66
  Middle Ordovician period 64
  Satellite map 264
Green light 318, 530-531
Green marble 275
Green seaweed 117
Green snakelock anemone 166
Green starboard navigation light 406
Greenwich Meridian
  Satellite map 264-265
  Surface currents 296
Grid lines 445
Griffon 461
Grikes 284
Grille
  MCW Metrobus 332
  "Eurostar" warning horn 329
  Roman Mill 464
Grimaldi 40
Grip
  Sailmaker's fid 384
  Sailmaker's mallet 384
Gripe 379
Groin
  Arches and vaults 485
  Human body 211
Groin pad 527
Groin vault 479, 484-485
Grommet 373, 375, 384, 426
Groove
  Chair 576
  Rope starter 335
  Serving mallet 384
Grooving 383
Grotesque figure 476
Ground handling wheel 422
Ground ivy 154
Ground-mapping radar 420
Groundmass 268-269
Ground roller 447
Ground speed control knob 581
Groundwater 273, 292-293
Grout 450-451

Growing point 153
Growing tip 79
Growth line
  Fossilized jawless fish 78
  Snail 177
Groyne 294
Grundtvig Church 495
Gruppo Seven Cubist 495
Grus 19, 20
Gryphon 461
Gryposaurus 96, 99
Guanine 216
Guard
  All-terrain vehicles 354
  Basketball 532
  Fencing foil 557
  Football 526
Guard cell 138-139
Guardrail 591-392, 395
Guardstop 541
Gubernator 373
Gudgeon 375
Gudgeon pin 345
Gudgeon strap 378
Guest boat boom 394
Guiana Highlands 264
Guide hair 126
Guide mark 535
Guidepost 584
Guide wheel 328
Guinevere Planitia 36, 37
Guitars 510, **512-513**
Gula Mons 37
Gulf of Mexico 264
Gulf Stream 296
Gull 189, 193
Gullet 582
Gulley 538
Gully 289
Gum 247
Gum arabic 458
  Lithographic printing 446, 448
  Pastel making 440
Gun
  1.3 kg gun 395
  3 pound gun 395
  4.5 in gun 397
  4.7 in gun 394
  11 cm gun 397
  12 cm gun 394
  12 in gun 394
  30 cm gun 394
  Battleship 394
  Frigate 397
  Measurements 394
  Sailing warship 376
  Wooden sailing ship 378, 379
Gun battery 395
Gun carriage 377
Gun deck 380
Gun loading cage 396
Gunnery control radar dish 397
Gunnery spotting top 394
Gunport 381
  Sailing warship 376-377
  Wooden sailing ship 379
Gun position 397
Gun section 392
Gunship 422
Gun turret 396-397
  Battleship 394
  Frigate 397
  World War II aircraft 408
Gut caecum 170
Gutenberg discontinuity 39
Gutter 486, 492
Guyot 298
Guzmania lingulata 162-163
Gymnosperm **122-125**
Gynoecium 140

Gypsum 271
Gyroscopic gunsight 409

H

Habit 270-271
Habitat 112
  Dryland plants 156-157
  Wetland plants 158-159
Hackle 563
Hackly fracture 270
Hadar 21
Hadley cell 300
Hadrosaur 96, 98-99
Hadrosaurus 96, 99
Haemal spine 180
Haematite 268
Hafnium 310
Hagfish 178
Hail 302
Hair **254-235**
  Cobra lily 160
  Golden barrel cactus 156
  Inflorescence 140, 142
  Insulating 104, 107
  Mammal 104
  Marram grass 113
  Monocotyledon 126
  Pitcher plant 113
  Root 152
  Venus fly trap 160
  Water fern leaf 158
Hair bulb 235
Hair cell 242-243
Hairdryer 315
Hairlike sepal 142
Hair follicle 254-235
Hair gel 306
Hair shaft 235
Hakatai shale 277
Halfback 526, 529
Halfback flank 528
Half-bound book 586
Half-column 464, 468-469
Half-court line 545
Half-forward 529
Half-forward flank 528
Half-fruit 151
Half hitch 388
Half pulley 580
Half-shaft
  Ford Model T 338
  Formula One racing car 356
  Half turn 543
Halide 269
Halite crystal 277
Hall
  Asian building 491
  Hypostyle 458
  Medieval building 466-467
  Modern building 496, 499
  Neoclassical building 483
Halleflinta 275
Halley's Comet 52
"Hall-keeps" 466
Hallux
  Anchisaurus 89
  Archaeopteryx 85
  Herrerasaurus 86
  Human 232
  Tyrannosaurus 84
Halo 14
Halogen headlamp bulb 352
Halogens 311
Halo ring 44
Halyard
  Double topsail schooner 385
  Junk 376

Longboat 380
Rigging 382
  Roman corbita 372, 373
  Viking karv 374
Hamada 282-283
Hamal 19, 20
Hamate bone 230
Hammer 242, 285
  Antler 109
  Athletics 542
  Concert grand piano 515
  Mosaic 450
  Target pistol 549
  Upright piano 514
Hammer actuator 566-567
Hammer-beam roof 470, 473
Hammerhead shark 179
Hammer throw 543
Hand
  Anchisaurus 89
  Human 210
  Iguanodon 97
  Pachycephalosaurus 100
  Primate 203
  Stegoceras 101
  Tyrannosaurus 84
Handball **534-535**
Hand-bound book 586
Handbrake 337, 339-340, 350
Handbrake control shaft 338
Handbrake quadrant 339
Hand brake wheel 331
Hand collet 571
Hand drill 566-567
Hand-held gun 408
Handle
  Belaying pin 382
  Brace-and-bit 567
  Lawnmower 581
Handle and traction control assembly 581
Handlebars
  Bicycle 358-359
  BMW R/60 362
  Cannondale SH 600 hybrid bicycle 361
  Cannondale ST 1000 touring bicycle 361
  Eddy Merckx racing bicycle 361
  Suzuki RGV500 368
Handling
  Motorcycle 360
  Touring bicycle 364
Hand protector 368
Hand rail
  "Ellerman Lines" steam locomotive 324
  Modern building 498
  Renaissance building 477
  Sailmaker's mallet 384
  Serving mallet 384, 388
  Ship's wheel 390
  TGV electric high-speed train 329
  Twentieth-century building 494
Hands **250 -231**
Handstand 543
Hand throttle 427
Hand winch 354
Handy Billy 582-583
"Handy man" 108
Hanger 498
Hang-gliders **426-427**
Hanging valley 286-287
Hapteron 116-117
Hardback book 586
Hard disk drive 521
Hard endocarp 146-147, 149

Hard granite 283
Hard hat 554
Hard-headed mallet 516, 518-519
Hard metals 310
Hardness 270-271
Hard palate 212, 245
Hard rock 60
  Faults and folds 60
  Glacier 286
  River features 290-291
  Weathering and erosion 282
Hard trim 352
Hardwood implements 452
Hardwood laminate limb 548
Hardwood panels 432
Hardwood sticks 517
Hardy 450
Hare 196-197
Harley-Davidson FLHS Electra Glide 362-363
Harmika 491
Harmon, A.L. 494
Harmonically-tuned exhaust pipe 356
Harmony
  Drums 518
  Percussion instruments 516
Harness
  Avro triplane IV 402
  Equestrian sports 555
Harness racing 554
Harness strap 409
Harp 504, 510-511
Harpoon point 109
Harpsichord score 521
Hash mark 541
Hastate leaf 128
Hatch
  Cargo 376
  Iron paddlesteamer 393
  Single scull 561
Hatch board 372
Hatch coaming 381
Hatching egg 192-193
Hatchling 98
Hathor Mons 37
Haunch 484
Haustoria 163
Haustration of colon 249
Haversian system 225
Hawker Tempest 408-409
Hawksmoor, N. 478, 481
Haworthia truncata 157
Hawse hole
  74-gun ship 381
  Sailing warship 376
  Wooden sailing ship 378
Hawse piece 381
Hawse pipe 393, 395
Hawser 386-387
Hawser fairlead 395
Hawthorne 35
Haystack boiler 334
Haze 37, 47
Head
  74-gun ship 380
  Allosaurus 85
  Beetle 168
  Brace-and-bit 567
  Bumblebee 168
  Butterfly 169
  Caterpillar 169
  Ceratopsian 100
  Chair 576-577
  Deer hopper dry fly 563
  Double bass bow 511
  Double topsail schooner 385
  Dunkeld wet fly 563
  Femur 224-225

Frog 182
Hammer 542
Human 211, **212-213**
Insect 168
Lacrosse crosse 541
Lamprey 178
Pachycephalosaurus 100
Phalanx 230
Prosauropod 88
Racing bike 360
Racing saddle 554
Rattlesnake 185
Sail 375, 384
Sauropodomorph 88
Serving mallet 388
Snail 177
Sperm 259
Stegoceras 101
Stegosaurus 92
Thyreophoran 92
Ulna 231
Violin bow 510
Headband 544
Head beam 380
Headboard 381
Head-butting contest 100
Head crest 96
Head cringle 384
Head earing 375
Headers
  Brickwork 485
  Nineteenth-century building 492
Head horn 94
Head joint 508
Headlamp
  Bordino Steam Carriage 335
  Bulbs 352
  "Eurostar" multi-voltage electric train 329
  Ford Model T 338-339
  Italian State Railways Class 402 328
  Pinzgauer Turbo D 355
  Renault Clio 349, 353
  "Union Pacific" locomotive 326
  Volkswagen Beetle 341
Headland 294
Head light
  BMW R/60 362
  Harley-Davidson FLHS Electra Glide 363
  MCW Metrobus 332
  Single-decker bus 333
  Vespa Grand Sport 160
  Mark 1 363
Head linesman 526
Head rail 380-381
Headrest
  ARV light aircraft 425
  Hawker Tempest fighter 409
  Mazda RX-7 346
  Renault Clio 349, 352
  TGV electric high-speed train 329
  Windcheetah racing HPV bicycle 361
Head rope 387
Headset 361
Headstock
  Acoustic guitar 512-513
  Electric guitar 513
  Honda VF750 364
Head tube 559-361
Headward erosion 290
Headwaters 288
Hearing 237, 242
Heart
  Bird 189
  Bony fish 181
  Branchial 176

Butterfly 169
Chimpanzee 202
Crayfish 173
Dogfish 179
Dolphin 205
Domestic cat 195
Elephant 200
Euoplocephalus 94
Frog 182
Gallimimus 86
Human 214-215, **250-251**
Lizard 185
Mammal 104
Octopus 176
Rabbit 196
Snail 177
Spider 170
Systemic 176
Tortoise 187
Heartbeat sequence 250-251
Heart bulge 260
Heartwood 125
Heat 314-315
  Chemical reactions 312
  Global warming 300-301
  Igneous and metamorphic rocks 274
Heat absorption 92
Heated filament 319
Heater element contacts 548
Heater unit 353
Heat exchanger
  Concorde 417
  Nuclear power station 314
  Volkswagen Beetle 340
Heat exchanger air intake 421
Heat exchanger exhaust duct 420
Heat exchanger hot-air exhaust 421
Heat radiation 92
Heat shield
  Formula One racing car 356
  Jet engine 419
  Motorcycle 363
Heat trapping 300
Heaver for wire serving 383
Heaving line 389
Heavy chemical elements 27
Hedera colchica 137
Hedera helix 131, 137
Heel
  Horse 198
  Human 210
  Rudder post 392
  Shoe 568-569
Heel grip 568
Heel nail 569
Height adjuster 580
Heine 35
Heka 18
Helen Planitia 36
Helianthus annulus 142
Heliconia peruviana 143
Helicoprion bessonowi 67
Helicopter landing-pad 498
Helicopters 396, 410, **422-423**
Helium
  Jupiter 44-45
  Massive stars 26
  Mercury's atmosphere 35
  Neptune's atmosphere 51
  Pluto's atmosphere 51
  Periodic table 311

Saturn 46-47
Small stars 24-25
Sun 32
Uranus' atmosphere 49
Helium-3 nucleus 22
Helium-4 nucleus 22
Helium line 23
Helix 242
Helix Nebula 17
Helleborus niger 139
Hellenic plate 59
Helmet
  Baseball batter 536
  Bicycle 360
  Cricket 559
  Football 526-527
  Hockey goal keeper 540
  Hurling 541
  Ice hockey 550-551
  Lacrosse goalkeeper 541
  Skiing 542
Helmsman 372-373
Hemicyclapsis 56
Hemispherical dome 477,
  486-487, 490-491
Hen coop 395
Hepaticae 118
Hepatic artery 248, 252-
  253
Hepatic portal vein 253
Heptathlon 542
Heracleum sp. 151
Heracleum sphondylium
  129
Heraldic device 372
Herbaceous plants 126,
  128-129
  Structure 112-113
  Woody 130-131
Herbaceous stems 154
Herbivores
  Carnivora 194
  Jurassic period 70
  Marginocephalian 100
  Ornithopodian 96
  Prosauropods 88-89
  Sauropodomorphian 88
  Triassic period 68
Hercules 19, 20, 40
Herds 88
Hermaphrodite duct 177
Hermit shale 276
Herodotus 40
Herrerasaurids 68, 86
Herring-bone pattern 488
Hertzsprung 41
Hertzsprung-Russell
  diagram 22-23
Hesperidium 148
Hestia Rupes 37
*Heterocentrotus
  mammillatus* 175
Heterodontosaurus 83
Heteropoda venatoria 171
Hexagonal system 270
Hexagon nut 573
HF radio aerial 408
HF radio aerials fairing
  417
Hibiscus 126-127
Hide 105
Hide grip 384
Hieroglyphs 458-459
High altar 470
High-altitude cloud 45, 50
Highboard diving 558
High-density minerals
  280
High-energy particle 301
High-energy radiation 22
High-explosive projectile
  396
High-jump 542
Highland coastline 295
High-level jet streams 300

High-pressure areas 302-
  303
High-pressure bleed
  venturi connector 419
High-pressure compressor
  418
High-pressure cylinder
  342
High-pressure turbine 418
High-pressure zone 300
High-speed trains **528-529**
High Spring tide 296-297
High temperature gas 306
High-tension beam 496
High-tension ignition lead
  344
High tension wire 315
High tide 296-297
High-velocity air duct 420
High voltage cable 314
Hi-hat cymbal 518
Hilbert 41
Hillman anti-kink weight
  562
Hilum
  Dehiscent fruit seed 151
  Epigeal germination 153
  Hypogeal germination
  152
  Succulent fruit seed 148-
  149
Himalayas
  Earth's physical features
  264-265
  Geological time 56-57
  Formation 60, 62-62
  Mountain building 62-63
  Quaternary period 77
  Tertiary period 74
Himeji Castle 490
Hind foot
  Caiman 187
  Stegosaurus 92
Hindgut 173
Hind leg
  Amphibian 182
  Beetle 168
  Bumblebee 168
  Butterfly 169
  Caiman 187
  Elephant 200
  Frog 182
  Hare 196
  Iguanodon 97
  Lizard 185
  Rabbit 196
  Terrapin 187
Hind limb
  Anchisaurus 89
  Corythosaurus 98
  Edmontonia 95
  Frog 182
  Iguanodon 96
  Kangaroo 207
  Pachycephalosaurus 100
  Prosauropod 88
  Psittacosaurus 103
  Rabbit 197
  Rat 196
  Salamander 182
  Stegoceras 101
  Stegosaurus 92
  Theropods 84
  Thyreophoran 92
  Triceratops 102
  Tyrannosaurus 84
Hindlimb bone 105
Hind wing 168-169
Hinge 569
  ARV light aircraft 425
  BAe-146 components
  412-415
Hinge bracket 414
Hinge cell 113, 160
Hinged brass bezel 571

Hingeless bivalve shell 79
Hingeline 60
Hip
  Anchisaurus 89
  Human 211
  Kangaroo 207
  Lion 195
  Midway Gardens 495
  Stegosaurus 92
Hip girdle 80
Hip joint 218, 224-225
  Brachiosaurus 90
  Diplodocus 90
  Gallimimus 86
  Parasaurolophus 98
  Plateosaurus 88
  Stegoceras 101
  Struthiomimus 87
Hip pad 527
Hippeastrum sp. 155
Hipped roof 476-477
Hippocampus kuda 180
Hippophae rhamnoides
  136
Hippopotamus 198
Hippopotamus amphibus
  77
Hippuris vulgaris 135
Hip-rafter 490
Hispano Mark V 20-mm
  cannon 409
Historiated boss 469
Historiated keystone 469
Hitched hauling end 383
Hitch-kick 543
Hitch pin
  Concert grand piano 515
  Upright piano 514
Hittorff, J.I. 479
Hobbles 554
Hock 195, 198
Hock joint 554
Hog hair brush 432, 434
Hog's-back 283
Hog's back jump 554
Hogweed 129, 150-151
Hohenbuehelia petaloides
  115
Hoisting cage 396
Holden 43
Holdfast 116-117
Holding 527
Holding timekeeper 556
Hold pillar 393
Hole 589
Hole and peg joint 373
Hollow disc wheel 361
Hollow pith cavity 120
Holmium 311
Holocene epoch
  Fossil record 279
  Geological timescale 57
Holostean fish 73
Homarus sp. 172
Home computer system
  520-521
Homeosaurus pulchellus
  71
Home plate 536
Home run 536
"Home" signal 330
Hominid 74-75, **108-109**,
  202
Homocephale 101
Homo erectus 108
Homo habilis 108
Homo sapiens 57, 76, 108-
  109
Honda CB750 362-363
Honda VF750 364-365
Hone-stone 452
Honesty 150-151
Honeycomb coral 167
Honey guides 140-141, 145

Honey locust 137
Hong Kong and Shanghai
  Bank 496, 498
Honshu 265
Hood
  Battleship 394
  Ford Model T 339
  Gun turret 396
  Jellyfish 167
  Pitcher plant 160
Hood bag 346
Hood end 374
Hood frame 339
Hood iron 334
Hood-mold 479, 481, 486
Hoof 198, 554
Hoofbone 105, 198
Hoof-like nail 36-37
Hook
  Angling 562
  Cricket 538
  Deer hopper dry fly 563
  Devon minnow 563
  Rigging 383
  Sail 384
Hooked beak 190
Hooked pericarps 150
Hooked riffler 454
Hooker 550
Hoop 580, 425
Hoover Factory 495
Hop 543
Hopper freight car 327
Horizon 376
Horizontal bed rock 61
Horizontal cleavage 270
Horizontal damper 329
Horizontal fissure 255
Horizontal frequency
  adjustment 575
Horizontally opposed
  engine 362
Horizontal movement 60
Horizontal stabilizer 423
Horn
  Ford Model T 339
  Glacier 286-287
  Mooring 387
  Musical instrument 503,
  504
  "Union Pacific" locomo-
  tive 326
  Vespa Grand Sport 160
  Mark 1 363
Horn balance 414, 415
Horn bulb 339
"Horned faces" 100
Horny beak 96
Horse 104-105, 198-199
Horse chestnut 130, 137
Horse-drawn vehicle 332
Horsehair bow 510-511
Horsehead Nebula 16
Horse riding 554-555
Horseshoe arch 484
Horsetail **120-121**
Horsley Church 473
Horst 61
Horu Geyser 272
Host plants 162-163
Hot-air de-icing duct 414
Hot mineral springs 272
Hot shoe 589
Hot spot
  Black holes 29
  CD-ROM 584-585
  Earth's crust 58
  Ocean floor 298
Hot water jet 273
Hound 378
Hour hand 571
Hour line 377
Hour marker 571
Hour wheel 571
Household appliances 315

Housing
  Alpine skiing 552
  Electric motor 342
  Lawnmower 580-581
House spider 171
Howe 36
Howea forsteriana 126
Howler monkey 202
Hti 490
Huang He 265
Huayangosaurus 93
Hub
  1906 Renault 336
  ARV light aircraft 424
  Benz Motorwagen 335
  Bicycle wheels 358-359
  Blackburn monoplane
  400-401
  Bordino Steam Carriage
  334
  Eddy Merckx racing
  bicycle 361
  Paddle wheel 390-391
  Pegasus Quasar
  microlight 427
  Propellers 390
  Renault Clio 351
  Wright Flyer 399
Hub and brake drum 350
Hub bearing 351
Hub bolt 338
Hub brake shoe 338
Hub cap
  1906 Renault 336
  Ford Model T 339
  Renault Clio 350
Hub carrier 351
Hub nut 350
Hub quick release lever
  361
Hub seal 350
Hudson Bay 264
Hull
  Carvel-built 376, 391
  Clinker-built 375
  Cross-section 378
  Double-ended 375
  Greek and Roman ships
  372-373
  Iron and wood 392
Hull plank 373
Human body **210-211**
Human classification 108
Human Powered Vehicles
  (HPV) 358, 360
Humans 57, 76, 108, 202,
  315
Humber engine 343
Humboldt current 296
Humerus
  Archaeopteryx 85
  Arsinoitherium 104
  Bird 189, 191
  Brachiosaurus 91
  Crocodile 186
  Diplodocus 90
  Domestic cat 195
  Elephant 201
  Eryops 80
  Euoplocephalus 94
  Frog 183
  Gallimimus 86
  Hare 197
  Horse 199
  Human 218
  Iguanodon 96
  Kangaroo 206
  Kentrosaurus 93
  Pareiasaur 81
  Plateosaurus 88
  Stegoceras 100
  Struthiomimus 87
  Toxodon 106
  Triceratops 102
  Tyrannosaurus 84

Humic acid 284
Hunter-killer submarine
  396-397
Hunter's bend 388
Hunting 108, 548
Huntsman spider 171
Hurdle races 554
Hurdling 542
Hurling **540-541**
Hurricane 302-303
Husk 150
Husqvarna Motocross
  TC610 368
Hyaenodon 74, 107
Hyaline cartilage 225
Hybrid bicycle 360-361
Hydra 18, 21
Hydrated copper sulfate
  313
Hydraulic actuator
  attachment 413, 414
Hydraulic brake calliper
  424
Hydraulic brake hose 369
Hydraulic brake pipe 414
Hydraulic fluid
  Disc brake 365
  Spring/damper unit 365
Hydraulic grab 396
Hydraulic hand-pump 421
Hydraulic hose 369
Hydrocarbon 313
Hydrochloric acid 312
*Hydrochoerus
  hydrochaeris* 197
Hydroelectric power
  station 314
Hydrogen 308, 310
  Candle wax 312-313
  Covalent bonding 309
  Jupiter's atmosphere 45
  Massive stars 26
  Mercury's atmosphere
  35
  Nebulae and star
  clusters 16-17
  Neptune's atmosphere
  51
  Nuclear fusion in Sun 22
  Salt formation 312
  Saturn's atmosphere 47
  Small stars 24-25
  Sun 32
  Uranus' atmosphere 49
Hydrogen alpha line 23
Hydrogen atom 138
Hydrogen beta line 23
Hydrogen fluoride 308-309
Hydrogen gamma line 23
Hydrogen gas 312
Hydrogen nucleus 22
Hydrogen requirement
  138
Hydrogen sulfide 51
Hydroplane 396-397
Hydroxide 268
Hydrus 20
Hyena 194
Hymenoptera 168
Hyoglossus muscle 244
Hyoid bone 244-245, 255
Hypacrosaurus 99
Hypaethral temple 460-
  461
Hyperesion 373
Hyphae
  Fungus 114-115
  Mycorrhizal association
  133
Hypocotyl 152-153
Hypodermis
  Gynosperm 125
  Human 235
Hypogeal germination
  152-153

Hypoglossal nerve 244
Hypogymnia physodes 114
Hypostyle hall 458-459
Hypothalamus 236
Hypsilophodon 72, 82
Hypural 180
Hystrix africaeaustralis 197

I

I bar 393
Ice 66, 307
  Glacier 286-287
  Weathering and erosion 282
Ice age 56
Ice-age mammals 76
Ice block
  Ice-fall 287
  Lake formation 293
Ice-cap 287
Ice crystal 302
Ice cube 307
Ice erosion 287
Ice-fall 287
Ice hockey **550-551**
Ice margin lake 286
Ice-plant 128-129
Ice sheet 76
Ichthyosaur 70-71
Ichthyostega 56, 80
Icterus galbula 193
Idle control valve 344
Idocrase 270
Igneous intrusion 274
Igneous rock 266-267, **274-275**
Igniter 418
Igniter plug 419
Ignition amplifier 345
Ignition control 362
Ignition lever 338
Ignition lock 362
Ignition switch 337
Ignition trigger housing 410
Iguana iguana 82
Iguanodon 73, 96-97
Ileocaecal fold 249
Ileum
  Bird 189
  Frog 182
  Human 226, 249
  Rabbit 196
Iliac crest 224-225
Iliac fossa 224
Iliac spine 224
Iliacus muscle 225
Ilio-femoral muscle 84, 97
Ilio-fibular muscle 84, 97
Ilio-ischial joint 82
Iliopsoas muscle 226
Ilio-pubic joint 82
Ilio-tibial muscle
  Albertosaurus 84
  Euoplocephalus 94
  Iguanodon 97
Ilium
  Archaeopteryx 85
  Bird 189
  Diplodocus 90
  Eryops 81
  Euoplocephalus 94
  Frog 183
  Gallimimus 86
  Human 218
  Iguanodon 96-97
  Kentrosaurus 93
  Ornithischian 82
  Parasaurolophus 98
  Plateosaurus 88
  Saurischian 82
  Stegoceras 100-101

Stegosaurus 93
Struthiomimus 87
Toxodon 107
Tuojiangosaurus 93
Tyrannosaurus 84
Illuminated manuscript 432
Illumination 444-445
Imaging the body 214
Imago 168
Immature pitcher 161
Immature spur 141
Impasto 436-437, 442
Impeller 347
Imperial-Metric conversions 591
Imperial unit measurements 590
Impermeable clay 292
Impermeable mudstone 292
Impermeable rock
  Cave 284-285
  Lake 292
  Mineral resources 280-281
  River's stages 289
Impermeable salt dome 281
Impermeable shale 292
Impost
  Ancient Roman building 465
  Cathedral dome 484
  Gothic building 473
  Islamic building 488
  Medieval building 466, 469
In-board 561
Inboard elevon 417, 421
Inboard elevon-jack fairing 416
Inboard end 387
Inboard engine 415
Inboard lift spoilers 413
Inboard trimtab 413
Inbound line 526
Incandescent light 318-319
Incident laser light 319
Incisive canal 245
Incisor teeth
  Bear 194
  Chimpanzee 202
  Elephant 201
  Human 245, 246
  Lion 194
  Rabbit 196
  Rodent 196
  Toxodon 106
Incline 468
Incompetent bed rock 61
Incomplete mesentery 167
Incurrent pore 166
Incus 242
Indehiscent fruit 150
Independent portal swing axle 355
Index button 585
Index finger 230-231
India
  Cretaceous period 72-73
  Jurassic period 70
  Himalaya formation 62-63
  Late Carboniferous period 66
  Middle Ordovician period 64
  Mountain building 62-63
  Quaternary period 76-77
  Railroad track gauge 331
  Tertiary period 74-75
  Thyreophorans 92
  Triassic period 68

Indian handmade paper 445
Indian ocean 73, 75, 77, 265
Indian stick insect 192
Indicator
  "Deltic" diesel-electric locomotive 327
  Double-decker tour bus 333
  Harley-Davidson FLHS Electra Glide 363
  Honda CB750 363
  MCW Metrobus 332
  Pinzgauer Turbo D 355
  Single-decker bus 333
  Volkswagen Beetle 340
Indicator assembly 352
Indicator board 542
Indicator lamp 353
Indicator lens 341
Indirect method mosaic creation 450-451
Indium 311
Indo-Australian plate 59
Inducer 418
Induction stroke 343
Indus 20
Indusium 121
Industrial Revolution 492
Inert gas 311
Inferior articular process 223
Inferior concha 212, 241
Inferior extensor retinaculum 233
Inferior meatus 245
Inferior mesenteric vein 253
Inferior nasal concha 221, 241, 245
Inferior oblique muscle 241
Inferior orbital fissure 221
Inferior rectus muscle 241
Inferior vena cava 215, 252-253, 257
Infertile swamp 288
Infield 556-557
Infilled swamp 291
Inflated petiole 158
Inflation valve 403
Inflorescences 140
  Aechmea miniata 162
  Bromeliad 113
  Catkin 144
  Compound 142-143
  Couch grass 113
  Dodder 163
  Stem arrangements 143
Inflorescence stalk 140-143
  Aechmea miniata 162
  Brassavola nodosa 162
  Everlasting pea 129
  Indehiscent fruit 150
  Peach 131
  Peruvian lily 129
  Rowan 131
  Russian vine 131
  Succulent fruit 148
  Vegetative reproduction 154-155
  Wind-pollinated plant 144
Inflorescence types
  Capitulum 129, 142
  Compound umbel 143
  Dichasial cyme 143
  Raceme 129
  Single flower 143
  Spadix 143
  Spherical umbel 143
  Spike 143, 155, 162
Infraorbital foramen 221

Infraorbital margin 213, 221
Infra-red radiation 318-319
  Energy emission from Sun 22
  Infra-red map of our galaxy 15
Infraspinatus muscle 227
Infratemporal fenestra
  Baryonyx 85
  Camarasaurus 91
  Diplodocus 90
  Heterodontosaurus 83
  Lambeosaurus 99
  Panoplosaurus 94
  Parasaurolophus 99
  Plateosaurus 88
  Protoceratops 102
  Triceratops 103
Infratemporal foramen 106-107
Ingres paper 441
Initial cave 285
Ink 430, 444
Ink dabber 446
Inked-up copper plate 447
Ink pad 445
Ink reservoir 444
Ink roller 448, 449
Ink sac 176
Ink stick 444
Ink stone 444
Inlay 488-489
Inlet 295
Inlet cone 418
Inlet manifold
  Daimler engine 343
  Jaguar V12 engine 345
  Mid West single-rotor engine 411
Inlet manifold tract 345
Inlet-over-exhaust (IOE) engine 362
Inlet port 343, 367
Inlet rotor 347
Inlet tract 410
Inlet valve 343, 345, 362
Inner bud scales 134
Inner cage assembly 579
Inner clutch drum 366
Inner core 38-39, 41
Inner counter 445
Inner dome 484
Inner floret 129, 142
Inner jib downhaul 385
Inner jib halyard 385
Inner jib stay 382
Inner jib tack 582
Inner layer of cortex
  Dicotyledon 127
  Epiphytic orchid 162
  Monocotyledon 127
  Wetland plants 158-159
Inner mantle 44-47
Inner martingale stay 383
Inner membrane 139
Inner planetary orbits 31
Inner posts 528
Inner sock 568-569
Inner tepal 126, 140, 143
Innertube 359, 424, 507
Inner vane 191
Innings 536, 538
Inorganic substances 280
Inscription 488
Insectivorous plants 113, **160-161**
Insects **168-169**, 279
  Cretaceous 72-73
  Plant food 160-161
  Pollinators 144-145
Inselberg 283
Insole 568-569
Insoluble solids 312

Inspection cover
  Avro biplane 403
  Lockheed Electra airliner 407
Inspection door 407
Inspection panel 417
Inspiration 255
Installing ring 589
Installing ring retainer plate 588
Instep 211
Instructor's cockpit 403
Instrument console 420
Instrument landing system aerial 420-421
Instrument panel
  ARV light aircraft 425
  Bell-47 helicopter 422
  Renault Clio 353
  Schweizer helicopter 426
Insulating column 316, 584
Insulating hair 104, 107
Insulation
  Atmosphere 300
  Lamp 572
Insulator
  Electric circuit 316
  Generating magnetism 317
  Hydroelectric power station 314
Intaglio printing 446-447, 448
Intake manifold 351
Intake pipe 335
Intake port 346
Integral ink reservoir 444
Integrated circuit 584
Integrated transportation system 332
Integument
  Ovule 147
  Scots pine 122
Intentional foul 533
Interalveolar septum 254
Intercellular leaf space 139
Interception 526
Inter-City travel 332
Intercolumniation 461, 485
Intercompressor bleed valve 419
Intercompressor diffuser pipe 419
Intercostal muscle 91, 255
Interdental papilla 247
Interdental septum 247
Interglacial period 76
Interior light 353
Interlobular artery 256
Interlobular vein 256
Interlocking spur 289
Intermediate frequency coil 575
Intermediate housing 346
Intermediate lamella 225
Intermediate ring 563
Internal capsule 237
Internal carotid artery 243, 252
Internal combustion engine
  First cars 534
  Motorbike engine 366
  Pioneers of flight 398
Internal crust 28
Internal elastic lamina 252
Internal iliac artery 215, 253
Internal jugular vein 253
Internal skeleton 174
Internal spermatic fascia 259

Internal urethral orifice 257
Internal urethral sphincter muscle 257
International referees signals 533
International rules 532
International squash 544-545
International track gauge 331
Internode
  Canadian pond weed 158-159
  Horsetail 120
  Ice-plant 129
  Live-for-ever 129
  London plane 134
  Rhizome 155
  Rock stonecrop 128
  Rose stem 130
  Stem 134
  Stolon 154
Interopercular bone 181
Interosseous ligament 252
Interphalangeal joint
  Baryonyx 85
  Human 231, 233
Interplane strut 399, 404-405
Interradicular septum 247
Interrupter gear 404
Intertragic notch 242
Intertrochanteric line 225
Intertropical convergence zone 300
Interventricular septum 251
Intervertebral disk 212, 218, 223, 245, 261
Intestinal muscle 226
Intestine
  Bony fish 181
  Butterfly 169
  Chimpanzee 202
  Cow 198
  Crayfish 173
  Dogfish 179
  Dolphin 205
  Elephant 200
  Frog 182
  Gallimimus 86
  Human 214
  Large 195, 202
  Lizard 185
  Sea urchin 175
  Small 182, 185, 187, 195, 198, 200, 202
  Spider 170
  Tortoise 187
Intrados 469, 484
Introitus 258
Intrusive rocks 26, 275
Invasion stripes 409
Invertebrates
  Earth's evolution 56
  Fossil record 279
  Insects 168-169
  Marine 65
Inverted ovolo 486
Inward dive 558, 559
Io 44
Iodine 311
Ion 308
Ionic bonding 308
Ionic capital 460
  Baroque church 481
  French temple 485
  Renaissance building 476
Ionic column
  Baroque church 481
  French temple 485
  Neoclassical building 483

Ionic half-column 464
Ionic order 460
Iota Centauri 21
Iota Pegasi 19
Iota Sagittarii 21
Ipomoea batatas 154
Ireland 331
Iridium 311
Iridocorneal angle 241
Iris
 Human 213, 226, 241
 Linear leaf 137
 Octopus 177
Iris lazica 137
Iron 311
 Earth's composition 39
 Earth's crust 58
 Golf club 547
 Magnetic domains 317
 Meteorite 52
 Nineteenth-century
 buildings 492
 Structure of Mercury 35
 Structure of Venus 37
Iron armature support 455
Ironclad 392-393
Iron club 546-547
Iron filings 517
Iron hull 392-393
Iron oxide
 Earth pigments 434
 Flesh-colored pigments
 433
 Sanguine crayon 430
 Sedimentary rocks 267,
 277
Iron oxide dust 42
Iron paddlesteamer 392-
 393
Iron pyrite 79, 270
Iron railing 493
Iron roof 479
Iron ship **392-393**
Iron tracery 493
Iron tire 334
Ironwork 478, 482
Irregular galaxy 10-12, 15
Irreversible reactions 312
Ischial tuberosity 224
Ischium
 Archaeopteryx 85
 Bird 189
 Crayfish 173
 Diplodocus 90
 Eryops 81
 Euoplocephalus 94
 Frog 185
 Human 218, 224
 Iguanodon 96
 Ornithischian 82
 Parasaurolophus 98
 Plateosaurus 88
 Saurischian 82
 Stegoceras 100-101
 Stegosaurus 93
 Struthiomimus 87
 Triceratops 102
 Tyrannosaurus 84
Ishtar Terra 36-37
Islamic buildings **488-489**,
Islamic mosaic 489
Islands 291, 294
Isocline 61
Isolated single boulders
 286
Isolated steep-sided hill
 283
Isolator valve 325, 327
Isoseismal lines 63
Isotopes 310
Israel 293
Isthmus
 Reproductive system
 258-259

Water hyacinth 158
Italian State Railways
 Class 402 328
Italic Roman lettering 445
Itonaco 434
Ivy 130-131, 137

J

Jack 514
Jacket-wall 466
Jack-locating hole 569
Jack-rafter 473
Jack staff
 Battleship 394
 Frigate 397
 Square-rigged ship 375
 Wooden sailing ship 379
Jacob's ladder 378
Jagged fracture 270
Jaguar straight six engine
 344
Jaguar V12 engine 345
Jali 488-489
Jamb
 Ancient Roman temple
 463
 Baroque church 479
 Medieval church 468
 Neoclassical building
 478, 482-483
 Nineteenth-century
 building 492
Jami Masjid 488
Javelin 542-543
Jaw
 Brace-and-bit 567
 Hand drill 567
 Human 212, 220-221
 Power drill 567
 Rope 389
Jawbone
 Allosaurus 85
 Australopithecus 107-108
 Ceratopsian 100
 Dolphin 204
 Horse 105
 Human 220, 247
 Ornithopod 96
 Shark 178
 Snake 184
 Theropods 84
Jawless fish 78, **178-179**,
 180
Jeep 354
Jeer 377
Jejunum 249
Jelly 192
Jellyfish 78, **166-167**
 Earth's evolution 56
 Fossil record 279
Jerrycan 354-355
Jet engine 412, **418-419**
Jetliners **412-415**
Jet pipe 418-419, 423
Jet pipe connection 419
Jetstream 300, 418
Jewel anemone 166
Jewel Box 11
Jibboom 379, 382
Jib fairhead 561
Jib halyard 380
Jibsail 378, 379, 385
Jib sheet 385
Jib stay 382
Jib tack 382, 383
Jockey 554-555
Jockey wheel 358
Jodhpurs 554
Joint
 Cave 284-285
 Chair 576
 Coastline 295
 Faults and folds 61

Jointed plug 19
Leather-bound book
 586-587
 Weathering and erosion
 282
Jointed leg 79, 168
Jointed pincer 79
Jointed solidified lava 292
Jointed stem 131
Joints **224-225**
Joist 464, 486
Jones, H. 493
Jordan 293
Joule 314, 316
Journal 347
Joystick 361, 520
Judo **556-557**
Jugal bar 201
Jugal bone 96, 102-103
Jugal plate 94
Juglans nigra 137
Jugular vein 215
Juice sac 148
"Jumbo jet" 412
Jumps 552, 554
Jump seat 337
Jump shot 532, 535
Junction
 Electrical circuit 516
 Giornata 434-435
Juncus sp. 135
Junior ratings' mess 397
Junk 376
Junk ring 343
Jupiter 30-31, **44-45**
Jurassic period **70-71**
 Fossil record 279
 Geological time 57
Jury mast knot 389
Justicia aurea 144
Juvenile volcano 275

K

Kabe 375
Kaibab limestone 276
Kaibab Plateau 277
Kaiparowits formation 276
Kaiparowits Plateau 277
Kalahari Desert 265
*Kalanchoe
 daigremontiana* 154
Kalasa finial 489
Kalos 372
Kame delta 286
Kame terrace 286
Kangaroo 206-207
Kappa Pegasi 19
Kara Kum 265
Karv 374
Kasugado Shrine of Enjoi
 490
Kasuga-style roof 490
Katastroma 373
Kaus Australis 19, 20
 Sagittarius 21
Kaus Borealis 21
Kaus Meridionalis 21
Kawana House 496
Kayak 560
Kayenta formation 276
Kazakstania 65
Keel
 Battleship 395
 Bird 189
 Frigate 397
 Ironclad 393
 Iron paddlesteamer 392
 Longboat 380
 Sailing warship 377
 Viking ship 374-375
 Wooden sailing ship 378
Keel boat 560

Keeled lesene 486
Keeler 41
Keelson (Kelson) 560
 19th century paddle
 steamer 391
Ironclad 393
Keep 466
Keeper ring 562
Kelvin temperature scale
 590
Kendo 556
Kentrosaurus 92-93
Kepler 40
Keraia 372
Keratin 234
Kestrel 189
Ketch 384, 385
Kettle 286
Kettle drum 519
Kettle lake 295
 Post-glacial valley 286
Kevlar 384, 388
Key
 Concert grand piano 515
 Home keyboard 520
 Motorcycle clutch 366
 Musical notation 502
 Steel lock 360
 Synthesizer 520
 Upright piano 514
 Woodwind instruments
 508-509
Keyboard 585
Keyboard instruments
 514-515, 520
Key guard 509
Key rod 509
Key signature 502
Keystone 484
 Ancient Roman building
 463, 465
 Baroque church 479, 481
 French temple 485
 Medieval church 469
 Neoclassical building
 478, 482
 Renaissance building
 476-477
Keystone amplifier
 integrated circuit 574
Keyway 590
Kick-stand 363
Kick-starter 363, 366
Kidney
 Bird 189
 Bony fish 181
 Brachiosaurus 90
 Dogfish 179
 Dolphin 205
 Domestic cat 195
 Elephant 200
 Frog 182
 Gallimimus 86
 Human 215, 256-257
 Lizard 185
 Octopus 176
 Rabbit 196
 Snail 177
 Tortoise 187
Kidney ore haematite 268
Kidney-shaped palette 436
Killer whale 205
Killick 386
Kiln 452
Kimberlite 268, 275
Kinetic energy 314-315
Kinetic sculpture 452
King pin 338
King-post 473, 479
 Early monoplane 400-
 401
 Pegasus Quasar
 microlight 427
 Pegasus XL SE
 microlight 426

King-post strut 401
King spoke handle 390
King strut 464
King vulture 190
Kirby BSA racing sidecar
 369
Kittiwake 190
Kiwis 188
Kneaded eraser 430, 440
Knee
 Anchisaurus 89
 Corythosaurus 98
 Faering 375
 Gorilla 203
 Horse 199
 Human 211
 Iguanodon 96
 Kangaroo 207
 Lion 195
 Pachycephalosaurus 100
 Psittacosaurus 103
 Rabbit 197
 Stegoceras 101
 Stegosaurus 92
 Tyrannosaurus 84
Knee cover 582
Knee joint
 Brachiosaurus 90
 Diplodocus 90
 Euoplocephalus 94
 Human 219
 Parasaurolophus 98
 Plateosaurus 88
 Stegoceras 101
 Struthiomimus 87
 Toxodon 107
 Triceratops 102
 Tyrannosaurus 84
Knee of the head 378
Knee pad 527, 534
Knee roll
 Cricket pad 539
 Saddle 554, 582
Knife
 Palette 436
 Relief printing 446, 449
Knighthead 380
Knots **388-389**
Knuckle 210
Koala 207
Kochab 18
Kope 572-573
Korolev 41
Kubernetes 372
Kunzite 271
Kuan Han-ch'ing 35
Krypton 311
Kuroshio current 297

L

Labellum 126, 145
Label mold 481
Labia 258
Labial palp 168
Labrum 168
Laburnum x *watereri* 137
Laccolith 273-275
Lacerta 19, 20
Lacertilia 184
Lacing thread 583
Lacrimal apparatus 241
Lacrimal bone
 Bony fish 181
 Human 221
 Protoceratops 102
Lacrimal canaliculus 241
Lacrimal gland 241
Lacrimal punctum 241
Lacrimal sac 241
Lacrosse **540-541**
Lacuna
 Bones and joints 225

Clubmoss 120
Mare's tail 155
Wetland plants 158-159
Lacustrine terrace 286
Lada Terra 36, 37
Ladder
 74-gun ship 381
 Battleship 394
 Frigate 396
 Iron paddlesteamer 392,
 393
 Roman corbita 372-373
 Train equipment 330
 Wooden sailing ship 378
Ladder way 395-396
Lady Chapel, Salisbury
 Cathedral 470
Lagomorpha 196
Lagoon
 Atoll development 299
 Coastline 294-295
 River features 290-291
Lagoon Nebula 21
Lagopus lagopus 193
Lagostomus maximus
 197
Lake Baikal 265
Lake Erie 264
Lake Huron 264
Lake Michigan 264
Lake Nyasa 265
Lake Ontario 264
Lakes **292-293**
 Glacier 286-287
 Groundwater system 293
 Igneous rock structures
 275
 River features 290
 River's stages 289
 Rock cycle 266-267
 Weathering and erosion
 283
Lake Superior 264
Lake Tanganyika 265
Lake Victoria 265
Lakshmi Planum 37
Lambda Andromedae 19
Lambda Pegasi 19
Lambdoid suture 220
Lambeosaurus 96, 98-99
Lamb, T. 494
Lamella 139
Lamina 136
 Butterwort 161
 Couch grass 113
 Dicotyledon leaf 127
 Human 222-223
 Leaf 138
 Monocotyledon leaf 127
 Seaweed 116-117
 Succulent 113
 Vegetative reproduction
 154
 Water hyacinth leaf 158
 Water lily leaf 159
Laminaria digitata 116-
 117
Laminated windshield 355
Laminates 548
Lamium sp. 135
Lamp **572-573**
Lamp bracket 336, 342
Lamp cluster 341
Lamp guard 355
Lampland 43
Lamprey 178
Lampropeltis ruthveni 184
*Lampropeltis triangulum
 annulata* 184
Lamp shield 330
Lanceolate leaf 120, 131,
 136
Lancet 471
Lancet arch 473, 484
Lancet window 470-472

Land 39
  Amphibians 80
  Animals 64
  Atmosphere 301
  Plants 56, 64
  Rivers 288
  Vertebrates 82
Landau body 334
Landau iron 334
Landing 477
Landing and taxiing light 414
Landing gear 406-407, 424-425
Landing-gear damper 423
Landing gear door
  BAe-146 components 414
  Concorde 416
  Hawker Tempest components 409
  Lockheed Electra airliner 406-407
Landing gear drag strut 401
Landing gear fork 407
Landing gear front strut 400, 404
Landing gear hydraulics 417
Landing gear leg 424
Landing gear rear cross-member 400
Landing gear rear strut 400-401
Landing light
  BAe-146 jetliner components 414-415
  Bell-47 helicopter 422
  Lockheed Electra airliner 407
  Schweizer helicopter 423
Landing skid
  Avro triplane 403
  Blackburn monoplane 400-401
  Helicopter 422-423
  Wright Flyer 399
Land movement 59
Land plants 56, 78
Land Rover 354
Landscape features 290-291, 294
Land surface removal 282
Land turtle 186
Lane
  Athletic track 542
  Swimming pool 558
Lane timekeeper 558
Langrenus 40
Language 108
Langur 202
Lantern 486
  Baroque church 480-481
  French temple 485
  Neoclassical building 478-479
  Twentieth-century building 494
  Wooden sailing ship 379
Lanthanides 310
Lanthanum 310
Lanyard
  Lifejacket 561
  Oar 373
  Rigging 382-383
  Roman corbita 373
Lap 542
Lapilli 272
Lap strap
  ARV light aircraft 425
  Curtiss biplane 398
  Lockheed Electra passenger seat 407
  Pegasus Quasar microlight 427

Large intestine
  Brachiosaurus 90
  Chimpanzee 202
  Domestic cat 195
  Euoplocephalus 94
  Human 214
Large Magellanic Cloud
  Hydrus and Mensa 20
  Our galaxy and nearby galaxies 15
  Stars of southern skies 20-21
Large mammals 57
Larkspur 141, 151
Larus marinus 193
Larus ridibundus 193
Larva 168
Laryngeal prominence 212, 244-245
Larynx
  Amphibian 182
  Human 214-215, 244
Laser 584
Laser ranger 420
Lasso 582
Latch handle 581
Lateen sail 375, 376, 384
Lateral angle 213
Lateral bracing strut 402-403, 416
Lateral branch
  Adventitious roots 158-159
  Horsetail 120
  Vegetative reproduction 154
Lateral bud 134
  Begonia 129
  Dicotyledon 127
  Horse chestnut 130
  Leaf scars 154
  London plane tree 134
  Rhizome 155
  Rowan twig 131
  Stem bulbil 155
  Stolon 154
Lateral canal
  Human 247
  Starfish 174
Lateral caudal muscula-ture 87
Lateral column 223
Lateral control wheel 401
Lateral control wire 404
Lateral dorsal aorta 179
Lateral epicondyle 225
Lateral fault 61
Lateral fault lake 293
Lateral lacuna 237
Lateral line 181
Lateral malleolus 233
Lateral mass 222
Lateral moraine 286-287
Lateral plantar artery 253
Lateral plate 78
Lateral rectus muscle 240-241
Lateral root 133
  Broomrape host 163
  Carrot 128
  Dicotyledon 127
  Germination 152-153
  Horse chestnut 130
  Seedling 152-153
  Strawberry 128
  Sweet pea 128
Lateral root scar 128
Lateral sepal 141
Lateral shield 187
Lateral shoot 156
Lateral strike-slip fault 61
Lateral sulcus 237
Lateral tepal 126
Lateral vein 136, 159
Lateral ventricle 237

Lath 464
Lathyrus latifolius 129
Lathyrus odoratus 128
Latissimus dorsi muscle 227
Latrodectus mactans 171
Lattice-beam 496-497
Latticed screen 488-489
Latticed shade 495
Lattice-truss 499
Lattice window 492
Lattice-work 493
Laurasia
  Cretaceous period 62
  Jurassic period 70-71
  Late Carboniferous period 66-67
Laurentia 65
Laurentian Library 474-475
Lava 62
  Igneous and metamorphic rocks 274-275
  Mountain building 62
  Rock cycle 266
  Volcano 272-273
Lava eruptions 272
Lava flow 273
  Contact metamorphism 274-275
  Mars 42
  Rock cycle 266
Lava fragments 272
Lavatera arborea 131
Lava types 273
Lavinia Planitia 36-37
Lawnmower 580-581
Lawrencium 311
Layering
  Fresco 434-435
  Pastel colors 440
Lay-up shot 552
Leach 374, 384
Lead
  Mineralization zones 281
  Minerals 268
  Periodic table 311
Lead covering 487
Leading block 394
Leading edge
  Avro biplane 403
  Avro triplane 403
  BAe-146 components 413, 414-415
  BE 2B tail 405
  BE 2B wings 404
  Blackburn monoplane 401
  Concorde 416-417
  Hawker Tempest components 409
  Lockheed Electra airliner 406
  Northrop B-2 bomber 421
  Pegasus Quasar microlight 427
  Wright Flyer 399
Leading-edge aerial 421
Leading-edge fairing 425
Lead-in wire 319
Lead iodide 313
Lead nitrate 313
Lead shot 517
Lead tin yellow 433
Lead wash 433
Lead wire 566
Leaf axis 137
Leaf bases 128, 136-137
  Aechmea miniata 162
  Couch grass 113
  Dicotyledon 127
  Florists' chrysanthemum 129

Guzmania lingulata 162-163
Hogweed 129
Monocotyledon 126-127
Sago palm 123
Seedling leaf 152
Water hyacinth 158
Leaf blade
  Butterwort 161
  Dicotyledon 127
  Leaf surface 136, 138
  Monocotyledon 127
  Vegetative reproduction 154
  Venus fly trap 160
  Wetland plants 158-159
Leaf insect 192
Leaflets 136-137
  Everlasting pea 129
  Fern 120-121
  Horse chestnut leaf 130
  Mahonia 130-131
  Monocotyledon 126
  Pinna 121, 136-137
  Rose 131
  Rowan 130
  Sago palm 123
  Tree fern 112-113
Leaflet stalk 137
Leaf-like structures 141-143
  Dehiscent fruit 151
  Dicotyledon flower 127
  Guzmania lingulata 163
  Ice-plant 129
  Live-for-ever 129
  Peruvian lily 129
  Slender thistle 129
  Wind pollination 144
Leaf margin 129
  Aechmea miniata 162
  Slender thistle 129
  Vegetative reproduction 154
Leaf notch 154
Leaf primordium 134
Leaf scar
  Begonia 129
  Elder 130
  Horse chestnut 130
  Ice-plant 128-129
  London plane 134
  Rock stonecrop 128
Leaf shape 136-137
Leaf sheath 129
Leaf spring 338
Leaf spring suspension 327
Leaf stalk 128, 136-137
  Chusan palm 130
  Clematis 131
  Cobra lily 160
  Common horse chestnut 130
  Dicotyledon 127
  Everlasting pea 129
  Florists' chrysanthemum 129
  Kedrostis africana 113
  Maidenhair tree 123
  Monocotyledon 126-127
  Mulberry 130
  Oxalis sp. 157
  Passion flower 130
  Peach 131
  Seedling 153
  Strawberry 128
  String of hearts 157
  Tree fern 112
  Tree mallow 131
  Vegetative reproduction 154-155
  Venus fly trap 160
  Water lily 159
  Wind pollination 144

Leaf succulents
  Haworthia truncata 157
  Lithops bromfieldii 157
  Lithops sp. 156
Leaf trace 127
Leafy liverwort 118
Leafy thallus 114
Lean-to roof 468-470, 472
Leather
  Books 586-587
  Saddle 582-583
  Shoes 568
Leather ball making 525
Leather belly 585
Leather grommet 373
Leather hood 354
Leather ink dabber 446
Leather pad 557
Leather seat 582-583
Leather upholstery 337
Leather valance 337
Leathery exocarps 148
Leaves 136-157
  Abaxial surface 123, 130
  Adaxial surface 123, 130
  Aechmea miniata 162
  Apex 136-137
  Apical meristem 134
  Barberry 130-131
  Bishop pine 124
  Brassavola nodosa 162
  Bromeliad 112-113
  Broomrape 163
  Butterwort 161
  Canadian pond weed 158-159
  Carnivorous plants 160-161
  Checkerbloom 136
  Chusan palm 130
  Classification 136-137
  Clematis 130-131
  Clubmoss 120
  Cobra lily 160
  Couch grass 113
  Dicotyledon 126-127
  Dryland plants 156-157
  Durmast oak 131
  Epiphyte 162-163
  Fern 120-121
  Florists' chrysanthemum 129
  Germination 152-153
  Guzmania lingulata 162-163
  Haworthia truncata 157
  Hinge cell 113
  Hogweed 129
  Horsetail 120
  Intercellular space 139
  Ivy 131
  Kedrostis africana 113
  Lamina 136
  Lithops bromfieldii 157
  Liverwort 118
  London plane tree 134
  Maidenhair tree 123
  Margin 136
  Marram grass 113
  Midrib 136
  Monkey cup 161
  Monocotyledon 126-127
  Moss 112, 119
  Mulberry 130
  Orange lily 154
  Oxalis sp. 157
  Parasite host 163
  Passion flower 130
  Peach 131
  Photosynthesis 154, 138-139
  Pine 122, 124-125
  Pitcher development 161
  Pitcher plant 113, 160-161

Primordia 134
Rock stonecrop 128
Rose 130-131
Rosettes 162-163
Rowan 130
Sago palm 123
Scots pine 122
Seedling 152-153
Slender thistle 129
Smooth cypress 123
Stomata 139
Strawberry 128
Tendrils 161
Toadflax 129
Tree fern 112-113
Tree mallow 131
Vegetative reproduction 154-155
Veins 136, 138-139
Venus fly trap 160
Water fern 158
Water hyacinth 158
Water lily 159
Welwitschia 122-123
Xerophyte 156-157
Yew 123
Le Corbusier 494
Leda Planitia 36, 37
Ledge 381
Leech 374, 384
Leechline 375
Leg
  Amphibian 182
  Caiman 186-187
  Chair 576-577
  Crab 172
  Crayfish 172-173
  Crocodilian 186
  Elephant 200
  Frog 182
  Gorilla 203
  Human 210
  Kangaroo 207
  Lizard 184-185
  Relief-printing press 449
  Salamander 182
  Scorpion 170
  Shrimp 172
  Spider 170-171
  Tadpole 183
  Terrapin 187
  Tripod congas stand 519
"Leg before wicket" 538
Leg bud 260
Leg pad 539, 551
Leg protector 551
Leg slip 538
Legumes 150
Leibnitz 41
Lemercier, J. 486
Lemming 196
Lemon 148
Lemur 202-203
Lemur catta 203
Lenoir, Etienne
  Early engines 342
  First cars 334
Lens
  Camera 588
  Human body 241
Lens alignment node 589
Lens barrel assembly 588
Lens lock release lever 588-589
Lenticels 130-131, 134
Lenticular bob 570
Lentiform nucleus 237
Leo 18, 21
Leo Minor 18, 21
Leonaspsis 279
Leonid meteor shower 52
Leontopithecus rosalia 203
Lepidodendron 66-67
Lepidoptera 168
Lepidotes maximus 73

Leptoceratops 103
Lepus 21
Lesbian leaf pattern 460
Lesene
  Ancient Roman building 462, 465
  Baroque church 480-481
  Dome 486
  French temple 485
  Gothic church 473
  Renaissance building 476-477
Lesser trochanter of femur 225
Lesser wing covert 188
Lesser wing of sphenoid bone 221
Letronne 40
Lettering 444-445
Levator anguli oris muscle 229
Levator labii superioris muscle 229
Levator palpebrae superioris muscle 241
Levee 289-291
Level-wind system 562
Lever 320-321
Le Verrier ring 50-51
Liang K'ai 35
Libellulium longialatum 73
Liberty ship 392
Libra 18, 21
Library 483, 496
Lichens **114-115**
Lid
  Moss 119
  Pitchers 161
  Ships for war and trade 377
Lierne 469
Life 56, **78-79**, 300
Lifeboat 394
Lifeboat davit 395
Life buoy 395
Life-cycle
  Brown seaweed 117
  Fern 121
  Insect 168
  Moss 119
  Mushroom 115
  Plants 112
  Scots pine 122
Lifeguard 532
Life of massive star 26-27
Life of small star 24-25
Life-raft 416
Liferaft cylinder 397
Lift
  Double topsail schooner 385
  Roman corbita 372
  Sailing warship 376-377
  Track and field 543
  Wooden sailing ship 378
Lift bracing wire
  Biplanes and triplanes 403
  Early monoplane 400-401
  Pegasus Quasar microlight 427
  World War I aircraft 404-405
Lifting handle 336
Lifting hook 357
Lifting lug 330
Lift spoiler 413, 414
Lift wire 399
Ligament
  Bifurcate 232
  Cricothyroid 244
  Deltoid 232
  Falciform 248

Foot 232
Hip joint 224
Iliofemoral 224
Interosseus 232
Ovarian 258
Periodontal 247
Plantar calcaneonavicular 232
Posterior cuneonavicular 232
Posterior tarsometatarsal 232
Pubofemoral 224
Talonavicular 232
Zonular 241
Ligature 508, 509
Light 314-315, **318-319**
  Chemical reactions 312
  Photography 588
  Renaissance building 474
  Seed germination 152
  Translucent "window" 157
  Twentieth-century building 495
  Ultraviolet 145
Light aircraft 410, **424-425**
Light bulb 572
Light Emitting Diode 584
Lighterman's hitch 389
Light hour 14
Lighting hole 393
Lightning 45, 316
Lights
  Bicycle 360
  MCW Metrobus 332
Light screen 394
Light switch 339
Light-well 487
Light year 14
Lignite 280
Lignum vitae bearing 387
Ligulate ray floret 129
Lilienthal, Otto 398
Lilium bulbiferum 154
Lilium sp. 133, 138, 140-141, 155
Lily
  Bulbil 154-155
  Flower 140-141
  Leaf surface 138
Limb
  Mammal 104
  Paddlesteamer 390
  Reptile 80
  Structure of a fold 60
Limber hole 393
Lime 143
Lime-resistant pigment 454
Limestone
  Cave 284
  Contact metamorphism 274
  Faults and folds 60
  Fossilized blue-green alga 78
  Lower Carboniferous 60
Limestone block 470
Limestone cladding 494
Limestone false door 459
Limestone spring 292
Limestone strata 284
Lime water 313
Limonite groundmass 268-269
Limpet 176
Linaria sp. 129
Line 562
Linea alba 226
Linear dune 283
Linear leaf 129, 137
Linebacker 526
Line guide 563

Line judge 526
Linen thread 583
Line of sight 41
Linesman
  Badminton 545
  Gaelic football 529
  Ice hockey 550
  Rugby 550
  Soccer 524
  Tennis 544
  Volleyball 534
Lingual nerve 244
Lingual tonsil 245
Lining
  Half-bound book 586
  Leather-bound book 587
  Saddle 582
  Shoes 568
Link 386
Linocut 446
Linoleum block 446, 449
Linseed oil 436
Lintel
  Building 459, 494
  Coastline 295
Lintel course 483
Lion 194-195
Lion crest 395
Lionfish 180
Lip
  Flower 126, 145
  Human 212-213
  Lamprey 178
  Pollination 145
Lip of trunk 200-201
Lip plate 508, 508
Lip tension 506
Liquidambar styraciflua 76
Liquid capacity measurements 590
Liquid helium 45
Liquid hydrogen 44-47
Liquid ink 444
Liquids 306-307
Litchi chinensis 148
Lithification 266
Lithium 308, 310
Lithium fluoride molecule 308
Lithographic ink 446
Lithographic printing 446
Lithographic printing equipment 448
Lithops bromfieldii 157
Lithops sp. 156
Lithosphere 58-59
Little finger 230 -231
Little grebe 190
Little toe 232-233
Live-for-ever 128-129
Liver
  Bird 189
  Bony fish 181
  Chimpanzee 202
  Dogfish 179
  Dolphin 205
  Domestic cat 195
  Euoplocephalus 94
  Frog 182
  Gallimimus 86
  Human 214, 248, 252
  Lizard 185
  Rabbit 196
  Tortoise 187
Liverworts 112, **118-119**
Livestock freight car 327
Living organisms 306
Lizard 184-185, 382
"Lizard-feet forms" 88
Lizard-hipped dinosaurs 82, 88-89
Llama 198
Load 320-321
Loading arm 396

Loading gauge 330-331
Load space 334
Lobby 498
Lobe
  Liverwort 118
  Venus fly trap 160
Lobed leaf 129, 131
Lobsters 172
Lobule 242
Local Arm 14
Local control cabinet 396
Lock button 566
Lock forward 530
Lockheed Electra airliner 406-407
Locking differential 355
Locking fuel filler cap 354
Locking nut 573
Lock nut 351, 359
Locks 360
Lock washer 358-359
Locomotion 104
Locomotives 524-329
Lodging knee 381
Loft 477
Log basket 334
Loin
  Horse 198
  Human 210
London Bridge 466-467
London plane tree 134
Longboat 380
Long bridge 515
Long-distance cycling 360
Long-distance running 542
Longeron 403, 424
Longitudinal channels 120
Longitudinal fissure 236-237
Long jump 542-543
Long leading-link fork 362
Long leg 538
Long off 538
Long on 538
Long pass 532
Long radius turns 552
Longrod stabilizer 549
Longship 374-375
Longshore drift 294-295
Long-travel suspension 368
Long-wave radio 318
Look out periscope 396
Loom 560
Loop 588-589
Looped prominence 32-33
Loophole
  Medieval building 466-469
  Renaissance building 477
Loop of Henlé 256
Loose forward 530
Loose-head prop 530
Lopolith 274
Lora 127, 130
Lorises 202
Lost-wax casting method 454
Lotus flower 488
Lotus petal 489
Loudspeaker 520
Lounge 392
Louvre 493, 498
Love-in-a-mist 150-151
Lowell 45
Lower Carboniferous Limestone 60
Lower crankcase 410
Lower crux of antihelix 242
Lower deadeye 382-383
Lower deck 393
Lower-energy radiation 22

Lower epidermis 139, 159
Lower eyelid 213
Lower fin 423
Lower haze 37
Lower lobe of lung 215, 254-255
Lower saloon window 33
Lower seed axis 152-153
Lower topsail 385
Lower-wing attachment 404
Lower yard 395
Lowland coastline 295
Low Neap tide 297
Low pressure areas 300, 302-303
Low pressure gases 306
Low tides 296-297
Loxodonta africana 200
Lozenge 471, 485
Lubricant 366
Lucarne window 480-481, 486
Lufengosaurus 89
Luff 384-385
Luff 382, 386
Lugger 384
Lug sail
  Junk 376
  Sail types 384
Lumbar nerves 238
Lumbar vertebrae
  Crocodile 186
  Domestic cat 195
  Hare 197
  Horse 199
  Human 222-223
  Kangaroo 206
  Platypus 206
  Rhesus monkey 202
  Seal 204
Lumbrical muscle 231
Lump hammer 452-453
Lunae Planum 43
Lunaria annua 151
Lunate bone 230
Lunette 480
Lung
  Amphibian 182
  Bird 189
  Brachiosaurus 91
  Chimpanzee 202
  Dolphin 205
  Domestic cat 195
  Elephant 200
  Euoplocephalus 94
  Frog 182
  Gallimimus 86
  Human 214-215, 252, 254-255
  Lizard 184-185
  Rabbit 196
  Snail 177
  Snake 184
  Spider 170
  Tortoise 187
Lungfish 80, 81
Lunule 251
Lures 562-563
Lutetium 311
LVG CVI fighter 405
Lychee 148
Lycoming four-cylinder engine 423
Lycoming six-cylinder engine 422
Lycopodiophyta 64, 120
Lymphocytes 253
Lynx 18, 21
Lynx helicopter 396
Lyra 19, 20
Lysosome 217

M

M22 (globular cluster) 21
Macaques 202
Macaws 190
Mach 41
Machine-gun 404-405
Machine heads 512-513
Mackenzie-Peace River 264
Mackerel angling 562
Maquette 455
Macrobius 40
Macrofibril 254
Macrospicule 33
Macula 240-241
Madagascar 265
Madreporite 174, 175
Madrillus sphinx 203
Maenianum summum 465
Magazine 548-549
Magellanic Cloud 15, 20
Maginus 40
Magma
  Igneous and metamorphic rocks 26
  Mountain building 63
  Ocean floor 298-299
  Rock cycle 266
  Volcanoes 272
Magma reservoir
  Igneous rock structures 275
  Volcanic structure 273
Magnesium 310
  Earth's composition 39
  Earth's crust 58
  Seawater salt content 296
Magnesium riser 548
Magnet
  Mini-television 574
  Toaster 578
Magnetic axis 28
Magnetic compass 423
Magnetic field 38
Magnetism **316-317**
Magneto
  Avro triplane 402
  Hawker Tempest components 408
  Wright Flyer 399
Magneto drive 367
Magnetosphere 38
Magnitude 22
Magnolia 57, 72
Mahonia 130-131
Maidenhair tree 122-123
Maillot 386
Main-line signaling system 330-331
Mainplane 356-357
Mainrail head 379
Main sail
  Dhow 376
  Roman corbita 373
  Sailing rigs 385
  Square-rigged ship 375
Main sequence star
  Massive stars 26
  Objects in Universe 11
  Small stars 24
  Stars 22-23
Main sheer strake 393
Main sheet
  Longboat 380
  Roman corbita 373
  Sailing dinghy 561
  Viking karv 375
Main shroud 378
Mains lead 572-573, 578
Main spar bridge 413
Mainspring 570
Main stay 377, 379
Main topcastle 377

615

Main topgallant mast 377, 378
Main topgallant sail 379
Main topgallant stay 379
Main topmast 377, 379
Main topmast preventer stay 379
Main topmast topcastle 377
Main topsail 379
Main topsail halyard 385
Main topsail yard 379
Main top yard 377
Main turbine 397
Main wale 381
Main wheel 426
Main wing bracing-strut 401
Main wing-strut 427
Main yard
  Dhow 376
  Sailing warship 377
  Wooden sailing ship 379
Maize 127
Major calyx 256
Major coverts 188, 191
Malachite 433
Malacostraca 172
Malaysia 331
Male
  Bladder 257
  Body 210, 211
  Pelvis 259
  Reproductive organs 259
  Urinary tract 257
Male apex 119
Male catkin 144
Male cone 122-123, 24
Male fern 120-121
Male flower organs 140-143
Male flowers
  Fertilization 146-147
  Gymnosperms 122
  Painter's palette 143
  Seaweed 116-117
  Succulent fruit 148
  Wind-pollinated plant 144
"Mallard" express steam locomotive 324-325
Mallet
  Drums 518-519
  Marble carving 452
  Ships and sailing 383, 384, 388
  Tubular bells 516
Malleus 242
Malpighian tubule
  Butterfly 169
  Spider 170
Malus 373
Malus sp. 126
Malus sylvestris 149
Mammals **104-107**
  Carnivora 194
  Cetacea 204
  Cretaceous period 72
  Earth's evolution 56-57
  Fossil record 279
  Jurassic period 70
  Lagomorpha 196
  Large 57
  Marsupalia 206
  Monotremata 206
  Pinnipedia 204
  Primates 202
  Proboscidea 200
  Rodentia 196
  Shrewlike 70
  Small 56
  Tertiary period 74-75
  Ungulates 198
Mammoth 107
Mammut 75

Mammuthus 76, 77, 104
Mandapa 491
Mandarinfish 180
Mandible
  Acanthostega 80
  Ankylosaurus 94
  Arsinoitherium 104
  Baryonyx 83
  Bat 105
  Bear 194
  Beetle 168
  Bird 188-189
  Bony fish 181
  Camarasaurus 91
  Chimpanzee 202
  Crayfish 173
  Crocodile 186
  Diplodocus 90
  Elephant 201
  Eryops 80
  Euoplocephalus 94
  Hare 197
  Heterodontosaurus 83
  Horse 199
  Human 220-221, 244-245
  Hyaenodon 107
  Iguanodon 96
  Kangaroo 206
  Lambeosaurus 99
  Lion 194
  Moeritherium 105
  Panoplosaurus 94
  Parasaurolophus 99
  Phiomia 105
  Plateosaurus 88
  Protoceratops 102
  Rattlesnake 185
  Rhesus monkey 202
  Seal 204
  Stegoceras 100-101
  Styracosaurus 102
  Toxodon 106
  Triceratops 103
  Turtle 187
  Tyrannosaurus 84
Mandrills 202-203
Mane 194, 199
Manganese 281, 310
Manharness knot 389
Manila 586
Manilla rope 589
Man-of-war 378
Mansard roof 490
Mantle
  Earth 38-39, 58-59, 63
  Mars 43
  Mercury 35
  Moon 41
  Molluscs 176-177
  Neptune 51
  Pluto 51
  Regional metamorphism 274
  Uranus 49
  Venus 37
Maple 127
Map projections 264-265
Maracas 504, 516-517
Marble 274
Marble block 453
Marble breaking equipment 450
Marbled paper 586-587
Marble mosaic 489
Marble sculpture 452
Marble tessera 450
Marble veneer 462
Marchantia polymorpha 118
Mare Crisium 40
Mare Fecunditatis 40
Mare Frigoris 40
Mare Humorum 40
Mare Imbrium 40
Mare Ingenii 41

Mare Moscoviense 41
Mare Nectaris 40
Mare Nubium 40
Mare Orientale 41
Mareotis Fossae 43
Mare Serenitatis 40
Mare Smithii 41
Mare's tail 135
Mare Tranquillitatis 40
Mare Vaporum 40
Margaritifer Sinus 43
Margin
  Lamina 116-117, 161
  Leaf 129, 136-137
  Needle 124
  Water lily leaf 159
Marginal shield 187
"Margined heads" 100
Marginocephalians 83, **100-103**
Maria 40
Marine invertebrates 65
Marine plants 56
Marine reptiles 57, 70
Marine sediments 280
Marine turtles 186
Mariopteris 66
Markab 19, 20
Markeb 21
Marlin 388
Marlinspike 383, 389
Marmosets 202
Marram grass 113
Mars 30, **42-43**
Marsh 293
Marsupials 104, **206-207**
Martellange, E. 479
Martingale 382, 557
Martingale stay 383
Mary Rose 376
Mascaron 487
Mask 460, 487, 536
  Ancient Roman building 465
  Cathedral dome 484
  Neoclassical building 482
Masonry apron 487
Mason's mark 470
Mason's tools 485
Mass
  Atoms and molecules 309, 320
  Earth 30
  Jupiter 26, 44
  Mars 30
  Mercury 30
  Neptune 31
  Planets 30-31
  Pluto 31
  Saturn 31
  Stars 22
  Uranus 31
  Venus 30
Massive habit 270-271
Massive stars **26-27**
Mass measurements 590
Massospondylus 89
Mass-production **558-559**, 492
Mass transportation 332
Mast
  Battleship 394
  Frigate 397
  Greek galley 372
  Iron paddlesteamer 392
  Junk 376
  Longboat 380
  Roman corbita 373
  Sailing 561
  Sailing warship 376-377
  Submarine 397
  Tea clipper 375
  Three-masted square-rigged ship 375

Viking karv 375
Wooden sailing ship 378-379
Mast band 382
Master cylinder
  Disc brake 365
  Harley-Davidson FLHS Electra Glide 363
  Honda VF750 364
Master shipwright 574
Master's sea cabin 381
Masthead
  Roman corbita 373
  Viking karv 375
  Wooden sailing ship 378
Mast head bend 389
Masthead pulley for tye halyard 375
Mast hoop 585
Mastoid fontanelle 220
Mastoid process 220, 242
Mast partner 381
Mast step 592
Mast truck 372
Matar 19
Match play 546
Maternal blood pool 260
Maternal blood vessel 260
Mathematics symbols 591
Mato Grosso 264
Matter **506-507**
  Electrical charge 316
  Identification 312
Mature ruptured follicle 258
Mawsonites spriggi 65
Maxilla
  Ankylosaurus 94
  Baryonyx 83
  Bear 194
  Bony fish 181
  Camarasaurus 91
  Chimpanzee 202
  Diplodocus 90
  Elephant 201
  Eryops 80
  Euoplocephalus 94
  Frog 183
  Horse 105
  Human 212, 220-221, 244-245, 246, 248
  Iguanodon 96
  Lion 194
  Pachycephalosaurus 100
  Prenocephale 100
  Stegoceras 100
  Toxodon 106
Maxillary fenestra 90
Maxilliped 173
Maxwellian diagram 318
Maxwell Montes 36, 37
Mazda RX-7 346
MCW Metrobus 332-333
ME 262 fighter 408
Meadow cranesbill 144
Meadow rue 137
Meadow sage 145
Meanders 288-289, 290, 461
Measurement units 590
Meatus 242-243
Mechanical semaphore signal 330
Mechanical weathering 282
Mechanics **350-351**
Mechanism of respiration 255
Medial epicondyle 225
Medial malleolus 233
Medial moraine
  Glaciers 286-287
  River's stages 289
Medial rectus muscle 240-241

Median canal 243
Median cubital vein 253
Median eye 170
Median glossoepiglottic fold 244
Median nerve 238
Median sulcus 244
Median wing coverts 188
Medieval castles **466-467**
Medieval churches **468-469**
Medieval houses **466-467**
Medinet Habu, Egypt 459
Mediterranean Sea 74, 265
Mediterranean sea anemone 166
Medium-wave radio 318
Medulla 114, 234, 256
Medulla oblongata 212, 236-237
Medullary cavity 224
Medullary pyramid 256
Medullary ray 125
Medullosa 66
Megaspores 122
Megazostrodon 104
Megrez 19
Meiolania 77
Meissner's corpuscle 234-235, 239
Melanin 234
Melanosaurus 68, 88-89
Melon 149, 205
Melting glacier 286, 289
Meltwater 287, 289
Meltwater pool 286
Membrane
  Chloroplasts 139
  Chorioallantoic 192
  Egg 193
  Shell 192
  Thylakoid 139
Mendel 41
Mendeleev 41
Mendelevium 311
Meninges 237
Menkalinan 21
Menkar 19, 20
Menkent 21
Mensa 20, 21
Mental foramen 213, 220-221
Mentalis muscle 229
Mental protuberance 221
Mental symphysis 220
Mentolabial sulcus 213
Merak 19
Merchants' Exchange, U.S.A 493
Mercury 30, **54-55**
Mercury (metal) 281, 311, 519
Mericarp 151
Meristematic cells 154
Merlon 466
Mermaid's purses 192
Mersenius 40
Merus 172, 173
Merycoidodon 75
Mesa 275, 277, 282
Mesentery 167, 182
Mesocarp 146-147,148, 148-149
Mesoglea 167
Mesohyal 166
Mesophyll 135
  Bishop pine needle 124
  Dicotyledon leaf 126
  Marram grass 113
  Monocotyledon leaf 126
  Palisade layer 139
  Spongy layer 139
Mesosphere 300
Mesothorax 168

Cretaceous period 72
  Dinosaurs 82
  Fossil record 279
  Geological timescale 57
  Jurassic period 70
  Reptiles 80
  Triassic period 68
Mess 397
Metacarpals
  Archaeopteryx 85
  Arsinoitherium 104
  Baryonyx 85
  Bird 189, 91
  Brachiosaurus 91
  Cow 198
  Diplodocus 90
  Domestic cat 195
  Elephant 90, 201
  Eryops 80
  Euoplocephalus 94
  Frog 183
  Gallimimus 86
  Hare 197
  Horse 198-199
  Human 218-219, 230
  Kangaroo 206
  Lizard 184
  Parasaurolophus 99
  Plateosaurus 88
  Platypus 206
  Rhesus monkey 202
  Seal 204
  Stegoceras 100
  Toxodon 106
  Triceratops 103
  Tyrannosaurus 84
Metacarpophalangeal joint 85
Metalliferous muds 299
Metalling 486
Metal modeling implements 452
Metal needle pad 584
Metal nib 444
Metal riser 455
Metal runner 455
Metals 310
Metal shade 572-573
Metal tire 324
Metal wire conductor 316-317
Metamorphic aureole 26
Metamorphic rocks 26, **274-275**, 266-267
Metamorphosis
  Amphibian 182
  Frog 183
  Insect 168
Metasoma 170
Metatarsals
  Albertosaurus 84
  Archaeopteryx 85
  Brachiosaurus 90
  Crocodile 186
  Domestic cat 195
  Elephant 201
  Eryops 81
  Euoplocephalus 94
  Frog 183
  Gallimimus 87
  Hare 197
  Horse 199
  Human 218-219, 252
  Iguanodon 96-97
  Kangaroo 206
  Lizard 184
  Parasaurolophus 98
  Plateosaurus 88
  Platypus 206
  Rhesus monkey 202
  Scorpion 170
  Seal 204
  Spider 171
  Stegoceras 100-101
  Struthiomimus 87

Toxodon 107
Triceratops 102
Metathorax 168
Metaxylem 127, 132-133
Meteor 52, 301
Meteorite
  Asteroids, comets, and
  meteoroids 52
  Earth's atmosphere 38
  Moon 41
  Ray crater 34
Meteorite impact 34, 40
Meteoroids **52-53**
  Solar System 30
Methane
  Jupiter 45
  Neptune and Pluto 50-51
  Saturn 47
  Uranus 48-49
Methane cirrus clouds 50-51
Metis Regio 36
Metope 460
Metric-Imperial conversions 591
Metric unit measurements 590
Metridium senile 166
Metrobus 332-333
Metrolink trolley 332
Mexican hat plant 154
Mexican mountain king snake 184
Mexican true red-legged tarantula 170
Mexico 331
Mezzanine 467, 496
Miaplacidus 21
Mica 26, 270
Mice 104, 196
Michelangelo 35
Micrasterias sp. 112
Microfilament 217
Microlights 410, **426-427**
Micro-organisms 38, 78
Microsporangium 122
Microspores 122
Microsporophyll 122
Microtubule 217, 239
Microwave oven 315
Microwave radiation 10
Microwaves 318
Midbrain 236
Middle ear ossicles 242
Middle finger 230-231
Middle leg
  Beetle 168
  Bumblebee 168
  Butterfly 169
Middle lobe of lung 215, 254-255
Middle meatus 241, 245
Middle nasal concha 212, 221, 241, 245
Middle phalanx 219, 230, 232
Middle rail 381
Midfielders
  Gaelic football 529
  Lacrosse 541
  Soccer 524
Midgut 173
Mid-latitude band 36
Mid-latitude cyclones 302
Mid-ocean ridge 281, 298-299
Mid-off 538
Mid-on 538
Midrib
  Dicotyledon leaf 126-127
  Durmast oak leaf 131
  Fern fronds 121
  Hogweed leaf 129
  Ice-plant leaf 129
  Live-for-ever leaf 129

Liverwort 118
Monkey cup 161
Moss leaf 119
Spiral wrack 116
Sweet chestnut leaf 136
Tree fern 113
Venus fly trap 160
Water lily leaf 159
Midships fence 373
Midships section 392
Midwater current 297
Midway Gardens 495
Mid West single-rotor engine 411
Mid West twin-rotor engine 411
Mid West two-stroke engine 410
Mihrab 488
Milan Cathedral 473
Milankovic 43
Milk snake 184
Milk teeth 246
Milky quartz 268, 271
Milky Way **14-15**
  Northern stars 18
  Solar System 30
  Stars of southern skies 20
Mill 462, 464, 492
Millstone grit 60-61
Milne 41
Milton 35
Mimas 46
Mimosa 21
Mimulopsis solmsii 145
Minaret 488-489
Mineral-filled fault 60-61
Mineral-rich deposits 298
Minerals **268-269**
  Carnivorous plants 160
  Epiphytes 162
  Fossils 278
  Mineral features 270-271
  Mineral resources 280-281
  Photosynthesis 138-139
  Wetland plants 158
  Xylem vessel 134
Mineral spicules 166
Mineral spring 273
Minim 502
Mini-television **574-575**
Minmi 95
Minor calyx 256
Minor coverts 188, 191
Mint 109
Mintaka 18
Minute hand 571
Miocene epoch
  Fossil record 279
  Geological timescale 57
Mira 19, 20
Mirach 19, 20
Miranda 48
Mirfak 19, 20
Mirzam 18, 21
Missile launcher 397
Mississipian period 56
Mississippi Delta 290-291
Mississippi-Missouri River 264
Mississippi River 291
Mist 306
Mistle thrush 190
Mistletoe 162
Mitochondrial crista 217
Mitochondrial sheath 259
Mitochondrion 217, 239
Mitral valve 251
Mixosaurus 57
Mizar 19
Mizzen backstay 378
Mizzen bitt 381
Mizzen course 379

Mizzen mast
  Dhow 376
  Iron paddlesteamer 392
  Junk 376
  Sailing warship 377
  Square-rigged ship 375
  Wooden sailing ship 378
Mizzen sail 375, 385
Mizzen shroud 378
Mizzen stay 378
Mizzen top 378
Mizzen topcastle 377
Mizzen topgallant sail 379
Mizzen topmast 377, 378
Mizzen topsail 379
Mizzen yard 376-377, 378
Moat 466-467
Mobile sculpture 452
Modeling 452
Modeling tools 454
Moderator 314
Modern buildings **496-499**
Modern engines **544-545**
Modern humans 57
Modern jetliners **412-415**
Modern military aircraft **420-421**
Modern piston aero-engines **410-411**
Modified lateral shoots 156
Modified leaflets 129
Modified leaves
  Barberry 130-131
  Cobra lily 160
  Dryland plants 156-157
  Everlasting pea 129
  Golden barrel cactus 156
  Pitcher development 161
  Spines 156
  Strawberry 128
Modified shoots 156
Modified stipules 128-129
Modillion
  Baroque church 479
  Neoclassical building 478
  Renaissance building 475
Moenave formation 276
Moenkopi formation 276
Moeritherium 104
Mohorovic discontinuity 39
Mohs scale 270-271
Molar tooth
  Arsinoitherium 104
  Australopithecus 107
  Bear 106, 194
  Chimpanzee 202
  Elephant 201
  Horse 105
  Human 246
  Hyaenodon 107
  Moeritherium 105
  Opossum 106
  Phiomia 105
  Toxodon 106
Mold 114, 278
Molded bracket 484
Molded corbel 493
Molding 485
  Ancient Egyptian temple 458-459
  Asian building 490
  Baroque church 480-481
  Dome 486-487
  Gothic church 471-472
  Medieval building 466, 469
  Neoclassical building 479-480, 482
  Renaissance building 475-477
  Ship's shield 395

Molding tool 454
Molds 114
Molecular orbitals 308
Molecules 306, **308-309**
Molluscs **176-177**
  - Belemnite 71
  Nautiloid 69
Molten bronze 454
Molten core 39
Molten rock
  Igneous and metamorphic rocks 274
  Matter 306
  Ocean floor 298
  Plate movements 58
  Rock cycle 266
  Volcanoes 272
Molting 171
Molybdate 269
Molybdenum 310
Mongooses 194
Monkey cup 161
Monkeys 202-203
Monoceros 18, 21
Monoclinal fold 60
Monocline 61
Monoclinic system 270
Monocoque chassis 363
Monocoque shell 348
Monocotyledonous petals 140, 143
Monocotyledonous sepals 126, 140, 143
Monocotyledons **126-127**, 140-141, 143
Monodon monoceros 205
Monograptus convolutus 65
Monolithic shaft 463
Monoplanes **400-401**, 402, 406
Monotremes **206-207**
Montes Apenninus 40
Montes Cordillera 41
Montes Jura 40
Montes Rook 41
Monteverdi 35
Montgolfier brothers 398
Monument 470
Moon **40-41**
  Objects in Universe 11
  Solar eclipse 52
  Tides 296-297
Moonquake region 41
Moons
  Jupiter 44
  Mars 42
  Neptune 50
  Saturn 46
  Solar System 30
  Uranus 48
Mooring **386-387**
Moorish arch 484
Moraine 286-287, 292-293
Moray eel 180
Mortar 432
Mortice 373, 576-577
Mortise 486, 492
Morus nigra 130
Mosaic **450-451**
  Islamic building 488-489
Mosque 484, 488
Mosquito netting 354
Mosses 112, 114, **118-119**
  Epiphytic 162
  Life-cycle 119
  Structure 119
Moth 168
Motion **520-521**
Motocross motorcycle racing 368
Motorcycle chassis 362, **364-365**
Motorcycle engines **366-567**

Motorcycle racing 368
Motorcycles **362-363**
Motorcycle sidecar 362, 369
Motor-driven bogie axle 326
Motor end plate 228, 239
Motorized buses 332
Motor neuron 228, 239
Motor operating signal 330
Motor whaler 397
Motte 466
Mouchette 472
Mounds 286
Mount 588
Mountain bikes 358, 360
Mountain building 56, 58, **62-63**
Mountain hollows 286
Mountain lake 288
Mountain ranges
  Earth's physical features 264
  Faults and folds 60
  Geological time 56
  Igneous and metamorphic rocks 26
  Mountain building 62
  Ocean floor 298
  Plate movements 59
Mountain ridge 295
Mountain ring 34
Mountain spring 288
Mounting bush 365
Mounting splines 366
Mouse 521, 584-585
Mouse and collar 379
Mouse pad 521, 584-585
Mouth
  Barnacle 173
  Bony fish 180-181
  Cobra lily 160
  Cow 198
  Crayfish 173
  Dogfish 179
  Dolphin 204
  Elephant 200
  Frog 182
  Gorilla 203
  Horse 199
  Human 211, 212, **244-245**, 248
  Jellyfish 167
  Kangaroo 204
  Lamprey 178
  Lizard 184
  Pitcher plant 161
  Rabbit 196
  Rat 196
  Sea anemone 166-167
  Seal 204
  Sea urchin 175
  Snail 177
  Spider 170
  Starfish 174-175
Mouth diffuser 430, 440
Mouthpiece
  Brass instruments 506
  Clarinet 508
  Tenor saxophone 509
  Trumpet 506
  Wind synthesizer 521
Movement
  Gas particles 307
  Objects 320
Moving picture 574
MRI scan
  Head 214
  Brain 236
Mt. Everest 264
Mu Andromedae 19
Muav limestone 277
Muccini brush 434

Mucosa 248
Mucosal gland 254
Mucous gland 177
Mucronate leaf apex 137
Mucus-secreting duodenal cells 217
Mud 267, 273
Mud crab 279
Mudflap 355
Mud-flat 295
Mud pools 272-273
Mud river 298
Muffler 580
Mulberry 130
Muliphen 21
Mull 586, 587
Mullion
  Gothic church 470, 472-473
  Modern building 497-499
  Renaissance building 476
  Small-scale rock formation 60-61
  Twentieth-century building 494
Multicellular animals 56
Multicellular organisms 78
Multicellular soft-bodied animals 56
Multifoil 472
Multi-gabled roof 492
Multi-layered information 585
Multiplait nylon 388
Multiplate clutch 364, 366
Multiple fruits 148-149
Multiplier reel 562
Multi-ply tire 416
Multipolar neuron 239
Mu Orionis 18
Mu Pegasi 19
Musa 'lacatan' 146
Muscari sp. 155
Musci 118
Muscle **226-229**
  Abductor digiti minimus 231, 233
  Adductor longus 225
  Adductor magnus 227
  Adductor pollicis 231
  Abductor pollicis brevis 231
  Anal sphincter 249
  Arrector pili 235
  Cricothyroid 244-245
  Dilator 241
  Dorsal interosseous 233
  Energy system 315
  Extensor digitorum brevis 233
  Extensor hallucis brevis 233
  Flexor digitorum longus 233
  Flexor hallucis longus 233
  Flexor pollicis brevis 231
  Flexor retinaculum 231
  Genioglossus 245
  Geniohyoid 245
  Gluteus medius 225
  Gluteus minimus 225
  Hyoglossus 244
  Iliacus 225
  Inferior oblique 241
  Inferior rectus 241
  Intercostal 255
  Internal urethral sphincter 257
  Lateral rectus 240-241
  Levator palpebrae superioris 241
  Lumbrical 231

Medial rectus 240-241
Myohyoid 245
Opponens digiti minimi 251
Opponens pollicis 251
Orbicularis oris 245
Papillary 251
Pectineus 225
Peroneus brevis 233
Peroneus longus 233
Psoas major 225, 257
Pyloric sphincter 249
Soleus 233
Sphincter 241
Styloglossus 244
Superior longitudinal 245
Superior oblique 241
Superior rectus 241
Tensor tympani 243
Thyrohyoid 244
Tibialis anterior 233
Tibialis posterior 233
Urethral sphincter 257
Vastus lateralis 225
Vastus medialis 225
Muscovite 269
Muscular septum 176
Mushroom anchor 386
Mushroom coral 167
Mushrooms 114, 115
Music 514
Musical Instrument
  Digital Interface (MIDI)
  system 520-521
Musical manuscript 502-503
Musical notation **502-503**
Musical score 502-503, 505
Music gallery 477
Musicians 504
Music sequencing software 521
Music software 520
Mussels 176
Mussosaurus 68
Mutes 506-507
Muttaburrasaurus 97
Muzzle 199, 397
Mycelium 114-115
Mycorrhizal association 133
Myelin sheath 239
Mylar 384
Myocardium 250-251
Myofibril 228
Myohyoid muscle 245
Myometrium 260

N

Nail
  Corythosaurus 98
  Edmontonia 95
  Elephant 90
  Human 231
  Iguanodon 96-97
  Shoes 568
  Stegosaurus 92
  Triceratops 102
Nair Al Zaurak 19, 20
Naismith, James 552
Nameplate 583
Namib Desert 265
Naos 461, 463, 485
Nape 188, 210
Napier Sabre 24-cylinder engine 408
Naris
  Anchisaurus 89
  Ankylosaurus 94
  Arsinoitherium 104
  Australopithecus 108

Baryonyx 83
Brachiosaurus 91
Camarasaurus 91
Corythosaurus 98
Edmontonia 95
Eryops 80
Euoplocephalus 94
Homo erectus 108
Homo habilis 108
Homo sapiens 108
Hyaenodon 107
Iguanodon 96
Lambeosaurus 99
Moeritherium 105
Opossum 106
Panoplosaurus 94
Parasaurolophus 99
Plateosaurus 88
Protoceratops 102
Smilodon 107
Stegoceras 100-101
Stegosaurus 92
Styracosaurus 102
Triceratops 102-103
Tyrannosaurus 84
Narrow gauge track 331
Narwhal 205
Nasal bone
  Ankylosaurus 94
  Bear 194
  Frog 183
  Human 220-221
  Lion 194
  Panoplosaurus 94
  Protoceratops 102
  Toxodon 106
Nasal cavity
  Chimpanzee 202
  Domestic cat 195
  Elephant 200
  Human 245, 248
  Rabbit 196
Nasal horn 104
Nasalis 229
Nasal passage 200
Nasal plug 205
Nasal septum 213, 221, 241
Nasal tusk 105
Nash 21
Nasion 221
Nasolacrimal duct 241
Nasopharynx 245
Natal cleft 210
Natal cocoon 24, 26
Native elements 268
Natural bridge 290
Natural elements 310
Natural fly 562
Natural forces 314
Natural glass 306
Natural gut strings 544
Natural lakes 292
Natural satellites 40
Natural sponge 438
Nautiloid mollusc 69, 65
Navajo Mountain 277
Navajo sandstone 276
Nave
  Ancient Egyptian temple 458-459
  Baroque church 479
  Cathedral dome 484
  Gothic church 470-473
  Medieval church 468-469
  Ship's wheel 390
Navel 211, 260
Nave plate 390
Navicular bone 232
Navigating bridge 394
Navigational aerial 423-424
Navigational panel 584-585
Navigator's cockpit 420

Navigator's seat 408
Navka 37
Nazca plate 59
Neanderthals 108
Neap tides 296-297
Nebulae **16-17**
  Galaxies 12-13
  Life of massive star 26
  Milky Way 14-15
  NGC 1566 (Seyfert galaxy) 13
  Small stars 24
  Structure of nebula 24
Neck
  Acoustic guitar 512-513
  Anchisaurus 89
  Calligraphy character 445
  Corythosaurus 98
  Electric guitar 513
  Golf club 547
  Harp 511
  Horse 199
  Human 211, 224-225, 247, 258-259
  Iguanodon 97
  Pachycephalosaurus 100
  Rat 196
  Sauropodomorpha 88
  Sculling oar 560
  Stegoceras 101
  Stegosaurus 92
  Stringed instruments 510
  Tenor saxophone 509
  Theropod 84
  Violin 510
Necking 381
Nectar 142, 160-161
Nectaries 141, 144-145 160-161
Needles
  Bishop pine 124
  Pine 124-125
  Scots pine 122
  Yew 123
Nefertiti Corona 37
Negative electric charge 316
Negative fluorine atom 308
Negative ions 308, 310
Negative pole 574
Neo-Baroque style 492-493
Neo-Byzantine style 492-493
Neoclassical style **478-483**, 496
Neodymium 310
Neo-Gothic style 492-493
Neo-Greek style 492-493
Neon 35, 311
Nepenthes mirabilis 161
Nephron 256
Neptune 31, **50-51**
Neptunides polychromus 12
Neptunium 311
Nerve
  Ampullar 242
  Bronchial 254
  Cervical 238
  Cochlear 243
  Common peroneal 238
  Cranial 238
  Cutaneous 238
  Deep peroneal 238
  Digital 231
  Femoral 238
  Hypoglossal 244
  Lingual 244
  Lumbar 238
  Median 238
  Optic 240
  Posterior tibial 238

Pudendal 238
Pulp 247
Radial 238
Sacral 238
Sciatic 238
Spinal 223, 238
Superficial peroneal 238
Superior laryngeal 244
Thoracic 238
Ulnar 231, 258
Vestibular 243
Vestibulocochlear 243
Nerve cell 217, 237, 239
Nerve cord 173
Nerve fiber 255
Nerve ring 175
Nervous system 176, **238-239**
Nervous tissue 166
Netball **534-535**
Neural spine
  Arsinoitherium 104
  Bony fish 180
  Brachiosaurus 90
  Eryops 81
  Euoplocephalus 95
  Gallimimus 87
  Iguanodon 96
  Parasaurolophus 98
  Plateosaurus 89
  Stegoceras 100-101
  Stegosaurus 93
  Toxodon 106
  Triceratops 102
  Tuojiangosaurus 93
  Tyrannosaurus 85
Neurofilament 239
Neuron 239
Neurotransmitter 239
Neutral fluorine atom 308
Neutralization 312
Neutral lithium atom 308
Neutrino 22
Neutron 22, 28
Neutrons 308, 309, 310
Neutron stars **28-29**, 26-27
New Guinea 265
New Moon 41
New State Paper Office 482
Newton (N) 520
Newton, Isaac 320
Newton meter 320-321
Newton's Motion laws 320-321
Newts 182
New World monkeys 202-203
New Zealand 265, 272
NGC 1566 (Seyfert galaxy) 13
NGC 2997 (spiral galaxy) 12
NGC 4406 (elliptical galaxy) 11
NGC 4486 (elliptical galaxy) 12
NGC 5236 (spiral galaxy) 11
NGC 5754 (colliding galaxies) 9
NGC 6656 (globular cluster) 21
NGC 6822 (irregular galaxy) 11
Nib types 444
Niche
  Ancient Roman building 462
  Asian temple 491
  Baroque church 480
  Cathedral dome 487
  Gothic church 471-472
  Islamic building 488
  Medieval building 467

Neoclassical building 482
Renaissance building 476
Nickel 37, 49, 281, 311
Nickel-iron 270
Nigella damascena 151
Nile crocodile 186
Nimbostratus cloud 302
Nimbus cloud 302
Nineteenth-century buildings 479, 482, **492-493**, 494
Ninth-century building 490
Niobe Planitia 36, 37
Niobium 310
Nippers 450
Nipple
  Cathode ray tube 574
  Human 211
  Marsupials 206
Nissl body 239
Nitrate ions 312
Nitrates 160
Nitrogen
  Atmospheric composition 301
  Helix Nebula 17
  Mars' atmosphere 43
  Periodic table 311
  Pluto's atmosphere 51
  Venus' atmosphere 37
Nitrogen dioxide gas 312
Nobelium 311
Noble gases 310-311
Nock 548
Noctis Labyrinthus 42, 43
Nocturnal mammals 104
Node
  Bamboo 131
  Brassavola nodosa 162
  Canadian pond weed 158-159
  Couch grass 113
  Dicotyledons 127
  Horsetail 120
  Ice-plant 129
  Live-for-ever 129
  Modern buildings 497
  Rhizome 155
  Rock stonecrop 128
  Rose stem 130
  Stems 134
  Stolon 154
  Strawberry 128
Node of Ranvier 228, 239
Nodule fields 299
Nodules 128
Nonconformity 276
Non-drive end 317
Non-explosive eruptions 272
Non-flowering plants 68
Non-metals 310
Non-return valve 367
Non-skid tire 337
North America
  Appalachian Mountains 62
  Cretaceous period 72-73
  Earth's physical features 264
  Jurassic period 70
  Late Carboniferous period 66
  Middle Ordovician period 64
  Quaternary period 76-77
  Tertiary period 74-75
  Triassic period 68
North American Cordillera 71
North American period 56

North American plate 59
North Atlantic current 296
North Atlantic Gyre 296
North Atlantic Ocean 39, 71, 73
North East Africa 64
North-easterly wind 303
North-east monsoon 297
North-east trade winds 300
North Equatorial Belt 45
North Equatorial current 296-297
Northern Hemisphere 296-297
North Galactic Pole 15
North magnetic polar region 28
North Pacific current 296
North Pacific Gyre 296
North polar aurora 45
North polar ice-cap 43
North Pole
  Atmospheric circulation and winds 300
  Coriolis force 297
  Jupiter 44
  Mars 42
  Mercury 34
  The Moon 40
  Neptune 50
  Pluto 51
  Pulsar 28
  Saturn 46
  Uranus 48
  Venus 36
North rim 277
North Temperate Zone 45
North Tropical Zone 45
North-westerly wind 303
Nose
  B-17 bomber 408
  Concorde 416-417
  Horse 198
  Human 211-212, 244-245
  Lion 194
  Lockheed Electra airliner 406
  Rabbit 196
  Rat 196
Noseband 554, 555
Nose clip 558
Nose cone 418, 560
Nose cowling 412
Nose-end bogie 327
Nose-gear
  ARV light aircraft 424-425
  Concorde 417
  Tornado 420
Nose horn 102, 103
Nose-ring
  Avro biplane 403
  Blackburn monoplane 400
Nose-wheel
  ARV light aircraft 425
  Curtiss biplane 398
  Pegasus XL SE microlight 426
  Tornado 420
Nostril
  Bird 188
  Chick 193
  Crocodilians 186
  Dolphin 205
  Domestic cat 195
  Elephant 200
  Frog 182
  Gorilla 203
  Horse 198
  Human 213
  Kangaroo 207
  Lion 194
  Lizard 184

Monkey 202
Rat 196
Rattlesnake 185
Seal 204
Nostril pocket 80
Notes 502, 506
Nothosaurian reptile 69
Notre Dame de Paris 470, 473
Nozzle
Concorde 416-417
Jet engines 418-419
Tornado 421
NPT 301 turbojet 418
Nu Andromedae 19
Nucellus 147
Nuchal plate 187
Nuchal ring 95
Nuchal shield 187
Nuclear energy 314
Nuclear fusion
Massive stars 26
Small stars 24
Stars 22
Sun 32
Nuclear "hunter-killer" submarine 396-397
Nuclear power station 314
Nuclear reactions 315
Nucleolus 216, 239
Nucleoplasm 216
Nucleus
Asteroids, comets, and meteoroids 52-53
Atoms and molecules 308, 309
Chlamydomonas sp. 116
Cnidocytes 167
Endosperm 147
Fungal cell 115
Galaxies 12-13
Generalized human cell 216
Muscle cell 228
Neuron 239
Overhead view of our galaxy 14
Palisade mesophyll cell 139
Pollen 122
Pollen tube 147
Roots 132
Scots pine pollen 122
Side view of our galaxy 14
Synergid 147
Thalassiosira sp. 116
Nuctenea umbratica 171
Number systems 591
Nunki 19, 20-21
Nu Orionis 18
Nut
Deadeye 383
Dry fruit 150
Durmast oak 131
Lamp 573
Toaster 578
Nutcrackers 321
Nutlets 150
Nutrients
Carnivorous plants 160
Epiphyte supply 162
Phloem sieve tube 134
Plant transport 139
Nylon and silicon cloth 384
Nylon rope 582
Nymphaea sp. 159
Nyssa sylvatica 137

O

Oak 74
Oar
Greek and Roman ships 372-373
Junk 376
Longboat 380
Viking ships 374-375
Oarweed 116-117
Oasis 283
Oberon 48
Object mass 320
Oblique-slip fault 61
Oboe 504-505, 508
Obovate leaves 137
Observer's cockpit 405
Observer's windshield 404
Obsidian 275, 306
Obturator canal 224
Obturator membrane 224
Occipital bone 202, 220
Occipital condyle 107, 194, 220
Occipital lobe 236-237
Occipital region 106
Occluded fronts 502-503
Ocean currents 296-297
Ocean floor **298-299**, 266-267
Oceanic crust
Earth's crust 58-59
Mineralization zones 281
Mountain building 62-63
Ocean floor 298
Oceanic seahorse 180
Ocean ridges 58-59
Oceans 9, **296-297**, 301
Ocean trenches
Ocean floor features 299
Offshore currents 296
Plate movements 58
Oceanus Procellarum 40
Ocellus 176
Octafoil 471
Octastyle portico 462
Octave 557
Octopus 176-177
Ocular end 377
Oculus
Ancient Roman building 462-463
Gothic church 472-473
Medieval building 466, 469
Neoclassical building 483
Roman corbita 372
Odd-toed ungulates 198-199
Odontoblast 247
Oeil-de-boeuf window
Baroque church 479, 481
Cathedral dome 487
Oerlikon gun position 397
Off-road motorcycle racing 368
Off-road tire 355
Offshore deposits 294
Ogee 395
Ogee arch 488
Ogee-arched motif 490
Ogee curve 472
Ogee-curved dome 486
Ogee-curved roof 489
Ogee molding 475-477, 481
Ogee tracery 493
Ohms 316
Oil
Clutches 366
Diesel trains 526
Energy storage 315
Mineral resources 280-281

Oil bottle dripfeed 336
Oil cooler 347, 364
Oil-cooler duct 415
Oil cooler matrix 347
Oil damper 364
Oil deposit formation 57
Oil deposits 281
Oil dipstick 344, 580
Oil duct 151
Oil feed 411
Oil feed pipe 345, 366, 367
Oil filter
Ford diesel engine 347
Jaguar V12 engine 345
Turbofan engine 418
Turboprop engine 419
Oil-fired power station 315
Oil formation 280-281
Oil paints 436-437
Oil pipe banjo 345
Oil-pressure regulating valve 419
Oil pump
Humber engine 343
Mid West single-rotor engine 411
Velocette OHV engine 367
Weslake speedway bike 369
Oil rig 315
Oil side lamp 336-337
Oil sump
Honda VF750 364
Humber engine 343
Modern engines 344-345
Velocette OHV engine 367
Oil tank
Bell-47 helicopter components 422
Formula One racing car 356
Harley-Davidson FLHS Electra Glide 363
Lockheed Electra airliner 406
Turbofan engine 418
Turboprop engine 419
Oil traps 281
Oldsmobile 336-337
Old World monkeys 202-203
Olecranon 85
Olenellus 64
Oleo lock-jack 414
Olfactory bulb 181
Oligocene epoch
Fossil record 279
Geological timescale 57
Olivine
Igneous rock 267
Meteorites 52
Silicates 269
Olivine gabbro 275
Olympus Mons 42-43
Omasum 198
Omega Centauri 21
Omicron Andromedae 19
Omicron₁ Canis Majoris 21
Omicron₂ Canis Majoris 21
Omicron Orionis 18
Omicron Sagittarii 21
Omnivores 84
Omohyoid muscle 229
One-toed ungulates 198
Onion dome 467, 486-488
Onion-skin weathering 282
Onyx 268
Oocyte 258
Oogonium 117
Oort Cloud 52

Oospheres 116-117
Fern 121
Moss 119
Ooze 298
Open cluster 16
Open gun mounting 394
Opera House, Paris 493
Opera House, Sydney 496, 499
Opercula 180
Opercular bone 181
Operculum
Bony fish 180-181
Cnidocyte 167
Giant stick insect eggs 192
Indian stick insect eggs 192
Leaf insect eggs 192
Moss 119
Ophidia 184
Ophiothrix fragilis 175
Ophiuchus 19, 20
Ophthalmos 372
Opisthodomos 461
Opisthosoma 170-171
Opossums 206, 207
Opponens digiti minimi muscle 251
Opponens pollicis muscle 251
Optical map of our galaxy 14-15
Optic chiasma 236
Optic disk 240-241
Optic nerve 240
Opus incertum 463, 465
Opus quadratum 465
Opus sectile mosaic 488-489
Oral arm 167
Oral cavity 248
Oral disk 166-167
Oral surface 175
Orange citrine 271
Orange halite 269, 277
Orange light 318
Orangutans 202
Ora serrata 241
Orb 488
Baroque church 480
Cathedral dome 487
Gothic church 471
Neoclassical building 479
Nineteenth-century building 493
Renaissance building 477
Orbicularis oculi muscle 226, 229
Orbicularis oris muscle 228-229, 245
Orbicular lamina 158
Orbicular leaves 137
Orbit
Acanthostega 80
Ankylosaurus 94
Archaeopteryx 85
Arsinoitherium 104
Australopithecus 108
Baryonyx 83
Bear 194
Bird 189
Bony fish 181
Camarasaurus 91
Chimpanzee 202
Diplodocus 90
Elephant 201
Eryops 80
Euoplocephalus 94
Heterodontosaurus 83
Homo erectus 108
Homo habilis 108
Homo sapiens 108

Horse 199
Hyaenodon 107
Iguanodon 96
Inner planetary 30
Lambeosaurus 99
Lion 194
Lizard 184
Opossum 106
Outer planetary 31
Pachycephalosaurus 100
Panoplosaurus 99
Parasaurolophus 99
Plateosaurus 88
Platypus 206
Prenocephale 100
Protoceratops 102
Rattlesnake 185
Rhesus monkey 202
Smilodon 107
Stars of northern skies 18
Stars of southern skies 20
Stegoceras 100-101
Styracosaurus 102
Toxodon 106
Triceratops 103
Tyrannosaurus 84
Orbital artery 179
Orbital cavity 220
Orbital motion 31, 52
Orbital plane
Earth 38
Jupiter 44
Mars 42
Mercury 34
Neptune 50
Pluto 51
Saturn 46
The Moon 40
Uranus 48
Venus 36
Orbitals 308-309, 310
Orbital speed (velocity)
Mercury 34
Solar System 30-31
Orb spider 171
Orchestra layout 504-505
Orchestral instruments 504-505
Musical notation 502-503
Orchestras **504-505**
Orchestra shell 495
Orchids 126, 133, 162
Orcinus orca 205
Ordovician period 64-65
Fossil record 279
Geological time 56
Primitive life 78
Organ 514, 502-503
Organic compound 313
Organic material deposition 281
Organic remains 276-277, 280
Organ of Corti 243
Oriel window 467
"O Ring" drive chain 366
Orion 18, 21, 24
Orion Arm 14
Orion Nebula 15, 17, 18
Orion's belt 15-16
Ornament
Asian building 491
Baroque church 479, 481
Cathedral dome 487
Islamic building 488
Neoclassical building 483
Ornithischians 68-69, 82-83
Marginocephalians 100
Ornithopods 96
Stegosaurs 92-93
Thyreophorans 92

Ornithomimosaurs 86-87
Ornithopoda 83
Ornithopods **96-7, 98-99**
Ornithorhynchus anatinus 207
Orobanche sp. 163
Orogenesis 62-63
Oropharynx 245
Orpiment 270-271
Orthoclase 269, 271
Orthorhombic system 270
Os 258-259
Oscillating cylinder 390
Oscillating electric field 318
Oscillating magnetic field 318
Oscillating steam engine 390-391
Osculum 166
Osmium 311
Ossicles 79, 174
Ossicles of middle ear 242
Osteichthyes 180
Osteocyte 225
Osteolaemus tetraspis 82
Osteon 225
Ostiole 117
Ostium
Crayfish 173
Sea anemone 167
Spider 170
Sponge 166
Ostrich 188, 193
Otters 194
Otto cycle 542
Otto, Nikolaus 342
Ouranosaurus 97
Outboard ammunition-feed blister 409
Outboard elevon 421
Outer bud scale 134
Outer core 38-39, 41
Outer ear
Brachiosaurus 91
Stegoceras 101
Stegosaurus 92
Outer electrons 510-511
Outer envelope 25-26
Outer fertilized floret 142
Outer jib downhaul 385
Outer jib halyard 385
Outer jib sheet 385
Outer jib stay 382
Outer jib tack 383
Outer lamella 225
Outer mantle
Jupiter 44-45
Saturn 46-47
Outer tepals
Glory lily 143
Lily 140
Monocotyledons 126
Outfield 536
Outlet manifold 411
Outrigger 573, 377
Outsole 568-569
Outside quarter 568-569
Outwash plain 287
Outwash terrace 286
Ovary
Barnacle 173
Bony fish 181
Brachiosaurus 90
Butterfly 169
Chimpanzee 202
Crayfish 173
Dogfish 179
Epigeal germination 153
Fertilization 146-147
Flower 140-143
Gallimimus 86
Human 258-259
Hypogeal germination 152

Insect pollination 144
Lizard 185
Rose 131
Spider 170
Succulent fruit 148-149
Tortoise 188
Ovate leaf
Ice-plant 129
Live-for-ever 129
Strawberry 128
Ovda Regio 36, 57
Overarm pass 535
Overhand knot 388
Overhand serve 554
Overhead camshaft
engine 368
Overhead pass 532
Overhead valve engine
(OHV) 367, 369
Overhead view of our
galaxy 14
Over-reach boot 555
Overs 538
Oversailing fascia 477,
482, 486
Overthrust fold 61
Overturned fold 61
Oviduct
Barnacle 173
Brachiosaurus 90
Butterfly 169
Crayfish 173
Dogfish 179
Lizard 185
Spider 170
Tortoise 187
Ovolo 486
Ovolo molding
Cathedral dome 487
Gothic church 472
Neoclassical building
480
Ovotestis 177
Ovules 140-143
Bishop pine 124
Dehiscent fruit 151
Fertilization 146
Pine 122
Scots pine 122
Smooth cypress 123
Yew 123
Ovuliferous scales
Bishop pine 124
Pine 122
Scots pine 122
Smooth cypress 123
Yew 123
Ovum
Ancient Roman building
462
Fertilization 146-147
Scots pine 122
Oxalis sp. 157
Oxbow lake 293
River features 290
River's stages 289
"Ox-eye" window
Baroque church 479, 481
Cathedral dome 487
Oxides 268
Oxygen
Atmospheric
composition 301
Early micro-organisms
78
Earth's composition 39
Earth's crust 58
Earth's formation 38, 64
Helix Nebula 17
Mars' atmosphere 43
Mercury's atmosphere
35
Periodic table 311
Photosynthesis 138
Seed germination 152

Structure of red
supergiant 26
Respiration 255
Oxygenated blood 255
Oxygen bottle 408
Oxygen group 311
Oyashio current 297
Oyster fungus 114
Oysters 176
Ozone 64
Ozone layer 300

P

Pachycephalosaurus 69,
83, 100
Pachypteris sp. 68
Pachyrhinosaurus 103
Pacific coastline 295
Pacific Ocean 264-265, 272
Pacific plate 59
Pacing races 554
Pacing sulky 554-555
Pacinian corpuscle 234-
235
Pack-ice 296
Packing tissue
Dicotyledon leaf 126
Fern rachis 121
Golden barrel cactus 156
Haworthia truncata 157
Horsetail stem 120
Leaf succulents 157
Lithops bromfieldii 157
Monocotyledon leaf 126
Roots 132-133
Stem 134-135
String of hearts 157
Water lily leaf 159
Padded coaming
Avro biplane 403
BE 2B bomber 404
Paddle
Eurypterid fossil 79
Kayak 560
Paddlesteamer
19th century 390-391
Iron 392-393
Paddle wheels 390-391,
392
Padmakosa 489
Page 586
Pagoda 490
Pahoehoe 272
Painted Desert 277
Painting knives 436, 442
Painting tools 436
Pair-cast cylinder 343
Paired cylinder 342
Palace of Westminster
492-493
Palaeocene epoch
Fossil record 279
Geological timescale 57
Palaeontology 278
Palaeozoic era
Fossil record 279
Geological time 56
Palais de Fontainebleau
476
Palais de Versailles 482
Palatine Chapel, Aix-le-
Chapelle 484
Palatine tonsil 212, 244-
245
Palatoglossal arch 244
Palazzo Stanga 482
Palazzo Strozzi 474-475
Pale calcite 26
Pale feldspar 26
Palette 143, 436
Palette knife 436
Paling 466, 477

Palisade mesophyll 126,
159
Palladium 311
Pallet 570
Palm
Danforth anchor 386
Hand 211
Roman anchor 372
Sailmaker's 384
Tertiary plant 74
Palmar arch 253
Palmar vein 253
Palmate leaves 130, 136
Palmate venation 129
Palmette 460-461, 479-480
Palmoxylon 74
Pamirs 265
Pampas 264
Panavia Tornado GR1A
420-421
Pancreas
Bird 189
Bony fish 181
Chimpanzee 202
Dogfish 179
Domestic cat 195
Frog 182
Human 215, 249
Rabbit 196
Tortoise 187
Pandas 194
Panduriform leaves 136
Pane 494
Panel 485
Asian building 491
Baroque church 479-481
Cathedral dome 487
Gothic building 473
Islamic building 488
Medieval building 466,
469
Modern building 496-498
Neoclassical building
478-479
Nineteenth-century
building 493
Renaissance building
475
Twentieth-century
building 494
Pangaea 66, 68-69, 70
Panicle 131
Panniers 360, 361, 362
Panoplosaurus 94
Pantheon 462-463
Pantile 464, 482
Pantograph 328, 330
Pan troglodytes 202
Paper
Acrylic paint 442
Books 586
Calligraphy 444, 445
Pastels 440
Printing processes 446,
447
Watercolors 438
Paper stumps 440
Papilla
Flower 140
Hair 235
Renal 256
Tongue 244
Papillary muscle 251
Pappus 142
Papyriform column 459
Parabellum machine-gun
405
Parabolic dune 283
Paraboloid roof 496, 499
Parachute seed dispersal
150
Paradise palm 126
Paragaster 166

Parallel dunes 283
Parallel river drainage 288
Parallel shaft 382
Parallel venation 126
Parana River 264
Parapet
Ancient Roman building
465
Asian building 491
Baroque church 481
Dome 486
Gothic church 470-472
Islamic tomb 489
Medieval building 467
Neoclassical building
478, 483
Nineteenth-century
building 493
Twentieth-century
building 494
Parapet rail 483
Paraphysis 117, 119
Parasaurolophus 98-99
Parasitic anemone 166
Parasitic cone 272-273
Parasitic plants 162-163
Parasitic volcano 275
Paraxeiresia 373
Parceling 388
Parchment
Gilding 432
Imitation 445
Parenchyma
Dicotyledon leaf 126
Dryland plants 156-157
Fern rachis 121
Golden barrel cactus 156
Horsetail stem 120
Monocotyledon leaf 126
Pine stem 125
Roots 132
Stems 134-135
Water lily leaf 159
Parent plant 154
Parietal bone
Bony fish 181
Chimpanzee 202
Human 220-221
Parietal fenestra 102
Parietal lobe 236-237
Parieto-occipital sulcus
236-237
Parietosquamosal frill
102-103
Paris RATP Metro 328
Paripteris 66
Paris RATP Metro 328
Paroccipital process
Iguanodon 96
Plateosaurus 88
Parrel
Dhow 376
Longboat 380
Sailing warship 377
Viking karv 375
Parrel beads 384
Parrel tackle 376
Parthenon 461
Partial solar eclipse 32
Partial veil 115
Particle attraction 307
Particle properties 318
Passiflora caerulea 130
Passing brace 473
Passion flower 130
Pastels 440-441
Pastern 198-199, 554
Pasteur 41
Patagonia 264
Patella
Domestic cat 195
Elephant 201
Hare 197
Horse 199
Human 219

Platypus 206
Rhesus monkey 202
Scorpion 170
Spider 171
Patellar surface 225
Patera
Neoclassical building
480
Renaissance building
476
Paved floor 492
Pavilion 489, 495
Paving slab 499
Pavlova 37
Pavlova 278
Pavo 20
Pavonis Mons 43
Paw 195
Pawl 580
Pawl slot 387
Paxton, J. 492-493
Pazzi Chapel 475
Pea
Dry fruit 150
Danforth anchor 386
Peach 131, 148
Peacock 20
Peak halyard 380
Peat 280
Peccaries 198
Pecopteris 66
Pectineus muscle 225-226
Pectoral fin
Bony fish 180-181
Lamprey 178
Pectoral fin ray 181
Pectoralis major muscle
226
Pedal board 514
Pedal cluster 340
Pedal-damper bar
mechanism 516
Pedal disk 167
Pedal-driven bicycle 358
Pedal gland 177
Pedalia 372
Pedals
Bass drum 518
Bicycle 320, 358-359
Eddy Merckx racing
bicycle 360
Harp 511
Hi-hat cymbal 518
Piano 514
Rossin Italian time-trial
bicycle 361
Pedal stop 514
Pedestal
Ancient Roman building
462
Baroque church 480-481
Dome 484, 486-487
French temple 485
Harp 511
Neoclassical building
479
Renaissance building
476
Pedice 168
Pedicel
Brassavola nodosa 162
Clematis 131
Dicotyledon flower 127
Dry fruit 150-151
Fertilization 146-147
Florists' chrysanthemum
129
Flowers 140-141, 143
Fruit development 146-
147
Oxalis sp. 157
Pitcher plant 113
Rose 131
Rowan 131
Russian vine 131

Succulent fruit 148-149
Sycamore 131
Vegetative reproduction
154
Water lily 159
Pedicle of vertebra 223
Pedicle valve 278
Pediment
Ancient Greek building
460
Ancient Roman building
462-463
Baroque church 480-481
Neo-Baroque building
493
Neoclassical building
478
Renaissance building
476
Pedipalp 170-171
Peduncle 140, 142-143
Aechmea miniata 162
Brassavola nodosa 162
Everlasting pea 129
Florists' chrysanthemum
129
Indehiscent fruit 150
Peach 131
Peruvian lily 129
Rowan 131
Russian vine 131
Succulent fruit 148-149
Toadflax 129
Vegetative reproduction
154
Wind-pollinated plant
144
Peephole 412, 414
Pegasus 19, 20
Pegasus Quasar
microlight 426-427
Pegasus XL SE microlight
427
Peg-box 510-511
Pegmatite 26
Peg of vertebra 222
Pelagic clay 299
Pelecypoda 176
Peloneustes philarcus 71
Pelota 540
Pelvetia canaliculata 116
Pelvic fin
Bony fish 180-181
Dogfish 179
Pelvis
Bird 189
Bony fish 181
Dinosaur 81
Domestic cat 195
Elephant 201
Hare 197
Horse 199
Human 256, 258, 259
Kangaroo 206
Lizard 184
Platypus 206
Rhesus monkey 202
Seal 204
Turtle 187
Penalty area 524
Penalty box 524
Penalty kick 530
Penalty spot 529, 540
Pencils 430
Pencil sharpener 430
Pencil slate sea urchin 175
Pendentive 479, 484, 488
Pendulum 570
Penguins 188
Penis
Barnacle 173
Dolphin 205
Human 211, 259
Snail 177
Pennant number 397

Pennsylvanian period 56
Penny washer 383
Pens 430
Penstock 314
Pentaprism 589
Pentaradiate symmetry 174
Pentroof 490
Penumbra 32
Pepo 149
Pepper-pot lantern 481
Perch 180
Percolation 280
Percussion instruments 516-517
  Drums 518-519
  Electronic 520
  Orchestral arrangement 504-505
Perennials 128, 130-131
Pereopod 172-173
Perforated wing cap 568
Perianth 140
Pericardial cavity 250
Pericarp 148
  Dry fruit 150-151
  Embryo development 147
  Fruit development 146-147
  Succulent fruit 148-149
  Sycamore 131
Pericranium 237
Pericycle 127, 132
Periderm 125
Peridium 115
Perihelion 30-31
Perineum 258
Periodic table 310-311
Periodontal ligament 247
Periodontium 247
Periosteum 225
Peripheral nervous system 238
Peripteral temple 460-461
Periscope 396, 397
Perissodactyla 104, 198-199
Peristome tooth 119
Peristyle 461
Peritoneum 249, 257
Permeable limestone
  Caves 284-285
  Lake formation 292
Permeable rock 292
Permeable sandstone 292
Permian period 66-67
  Fossil record 279
  Geological time 57
Permit holder 332
Peroneal artery 253
Peroneus brevis muscle 227, 233
Peroneus brevis tendon 233
Peroneus longus muscle 253
Peroxisome 217
Perseus 19, 20
Perseus Arm 14-15
Persian ivy 137
Personal flotation device 561
Perspective drawing 431
Peru current 296
Peruvian lily 129
Petal molding 480
Petals 140-143
  Clematis 131
  Color 140, 144-145
  Dicotyledons 126-127
  Everlasting pea 129
  Fertilization 146
  Insect pollination 145
  Monocotyledons 126

Peruvian lily 129
Rose 131
Water lily 159
Petavius 40
Petiole 128, 136-137
  Chusan palm 130
  Clematis 131
  Cobra lily 160
  Dicotyledons 127
  Everlasting pea 129
  Florists' chrysanthemum 129
  Horse chestnut 130
  Kedrostis africana 113
  Maidenhair tree 123
  Monocotyledons 126-127
  Mulberry 130
  Oxalis sp. 157
  Passion flower 130
  Peach 131
  Rock stonecrop 128
  Seedling 153
  Strawberry 128
  String of hearts 157
  Tree fern 112
  Tree mallow 131
  Vegetative reproduction 154
  Venus fly trap 160
  Water hyacinth 158
  Water lily 159
  Wind-pollinated plant 144
Petiolule 137
Petrol 315
Peugeot, Armand 334
Phacops 64
Phaeophyta 16
Phaet 21
Phalaenopsis sp. 126
Phalanges
  Cow 198
  Crocodile 186
  Domestic cat 195
  Elephant 90
  Eryops 80-81
  Frog 183
  Hare 197
  Horse 198-199
  Kangaroo 206
  Lizard 184
  Parasaurolophus 99
  Plateosaurus 88
  Platypus 206
  Rhesus monkey 202
  Seal 204
  Stegoceras 100-101
  Triceratops 102-103
  Turtle 187
  Tyrannosaurus 84
Phalanx
  African elephant 201
  Archaeopteryx 85
  Arsinoitherium 104
  Baryonyx 85
  Gallimimus 87
  Horse 105
  Human 219, 230
  Plateosaurus 88
  Stegoceras 100
  Struthiomimus 87
  Toxodon 107
Phallus impudicus 114
Phanerozoic eon 279
Pharyngeal tubercle 220
Pharynx
  Bony fish 180-181
  Dogfish 179
  Human 212, 244
  Sea anemone 167
  Sea urchin 175
Phascolarctos cinereus 207
Phaseolus sp. 153
Phases of the Moon 41

Phekda 19
Phellem
  Pine root 125
  Stem 134-135
  Woody dicotyledon 127
Phi Andromedae 19
Phidias 35
Philippine plate 59
Phillips, Horatio 402
Philoxenus 35
Philtral ridge 213
Philtrum 213
Phiomia 104
Phloem 138
  Bishop pine 124-125
  Clubmoss stem 120
  Dicotyledons 126-127
  Dodder host 163
  Epiphytic orchid 162
  Fern rachis 121
  Horsetail stem 120
  Marram grass 113
  Monocotyledons 126-127
  Parasite host 163
  Photosynthesis 138
  Pine root/stem 125
  Radicle 152
  Root 132-133
  Sieve tube 134
  Stem 134-135
  Water hyacinth root 158
  Water lily leaf 159
Phloem fibers 134-135
Phobos 42
Phoebe Regio 36
Phoenicopterus ruber 190
Phoenix 19, 20
Phorusrhacus 74
Phosphates 269
Phosphate/sugar band 216
Phosphor 574
Phosphorus 311
Photographic film 588
Photomicrographs of skin and hair 235
Photons 318
Photosphere 32-33
Photosynthesis 112, 116, 134, 136, 138-139
  Carnivorous plants 160-161
  Organelle 116, 139
Photosynthetic cells 139
  Bishop pine 124
  Coconut palm stem 135
  Water lily leaf 159
Photosynthetic region 157
Photosynthetic tissue
  Cacti 156
  Dicotyledon leaf 126
  Horsetail stem 120
  Marram grass 113
  Monocotyledon leaf 126
  Rush stem 135
Phyla 116
Phyllode 160
Phylum 116
Physalis peruviana 149
Physeter catodon 205
Physical weathering 282
Physics symbols 591
Pi2 Orionis 18
Pi3 Orionis 18
Pi4 Orionis 18
Pi5 Orionis 18
Pi6 Orionis 18
Pia mater 257, 240
Piano 503, 514
Piano nobile 474, 494
Piano, R. 496
Piazza 474
Pi Canis Majoris 21
Piccolo 504, 508
Picon 585
Pictor 21

Pier 484
Ancient Egyptian temple 459
Ancient Roman building 465
  Baroque church 480
  Gothic church 470
  Medieval building 467-469
  Renaissance building 476-477
  Twentieth-century building 494-495
Pier buttress 469-471, 486
Pietra dura inlay 489
Pigments 433, 434, 436
Pigs 104, 198
Pilaster
  74-gun ship 381
  Ancient Greek building 461
  Ancient Roman building 465-465
  Asian temple 490-491
  Baroque church 479-481
  Cathedral dome 484, 487
  Gothic church 471
  Neoclassical building 478, 483
  Renaissance building 476
Pileus 114-115
Pillar
  Asian buildings 490-491
  Clock case 570
  Domed roof 486
  Gothic church 472
  Ironclad 393
  Renaissance building 477
  Twin bollards 387
Pillow lava 298
Pilotis 494
Pilot's cockpit
  LVG CVI fighter 405
  Tornado 420
Pilot's cradle 398-399
Pilot's seat
  Avro biplane 402
  Curtiss biplane 398
  Pegasus Quasar microlight 427
Pin
  Capstan 387
  Clock 571
  Dome timbering 486
Pinacocyte 166
Pineal body 212, 236
Pine hull 373
Pines 122, 124-125
Pinguicula caudata 161
Pinion
  Benz Motorwagen 335
  Clock 570
  Ford Model T 338
  Hand drill 567
Pinna
  Elephant 201
  Everlasting pea 129
  Fern 121
  Gorilla 203
  Human 242-243
  Kangaroo 207
  Leaves 136-137
  Rabbit 196
  Rat 196
  Sago palm 123
  Tree fern 112-113
Pinnacle
  Baroque church 479, 481
  Gothic church 470, 472-473
  Medieval church 469
  Nineteenth-century building 493

Renaissance building 476
Pinnate leaves 136-137
  Mahonia 130-131
  Rowan 130
  Sago palm 123
Pinned sheepshank 389
Pinnipedia 204
Pinnule 121, 137
Pinocytotic vesicle 217
Pintle strap 378
Pinus muricata 72, 124-125
Pinus sp. 122, 124-125
Pinus sylvestris 122
Pinzgauer Turbo D 355-356
Pi Pegasi 19
Pipette 312
Pips 148-149
Pi Sagittarii 21
Pisanosaurus 68
Pisces 19, 20
Pisces Austrinus 19, 20
Pisiform bone 230
Piste 556, 557
Pistol shooting 548
Piston
  Disc brake 365
  Early engines 342-343
  "Ellerman Lines" steam locomotive 325
  Ford diesel engine 347
  Mid West two-stroke engine 410
  Modern engines 344-345
  Relief-printing press 449
  Steam locomotive 324
  Two-stroke engine 366
  Velocette OHV engine 367
  Volkswagen Beetle 340
Piston engines 410-411, 424
Piston rod 324, 334, 390
Piston valves
  Brass instruments 506
  Cornet 507
  "Ellerman Lines" steam locomotive 325
  Flugelhorn 507
  Stringed instruments 510
  Trumpet 506
  Tuba 507
Pisum sativum 150
Pitatus 40
Pitch
  Brass instruments 506
  Drums 518
  Musical notation 502
  Percussion instruments 516
  Propeller action 390
  Screw thread angle 320
  Woodwind instruments 508
Pitched roof
  Ancient Roman building 462, 464
  Gothic church 471-472
  Medieval building 466-468
  Nineteenth-century building 492
  Renaissance building 476-477
  Twentieth-century building 495
Pitcher 536
Pitcher plants 113, 160-161
Pitches
  Australian rules football 528
  Cricket 538

Gaelic football 529
Lacrosse 540
Pitching wedge 547
Pitfall traps 160
Pith
  Apical meristem 134
  Bishop pine stem 125
  Dicotyledons 127
  Epiphytic orchid 162
  Horsetail stem 120
  Monocotyledon root 127
  Pine stem 125
  Stems 134-135
Pith cavity 135
Pitot head
  ARV light aircraft 425
  BAe-146 jetliner components 412
  Bell-47 helicopter 422
  Concorde 416-417
  Hawker Tempest fighter 409
  LVG CVI fighter 405
  Schweizer helicopter 423
  Tornado 420
Pitot mast 407
Pituitary gland 212, 236
Pivot
  Astrolabe 377
  BAe-146 jetliner components 414
  Drum brake 365
  Lamp 573
  Sundial 377
  Viking ships 374-375
Pivot plate 572-573
Place kick 550
Placenta
  Dry fruit 150-151
  Fern pinnule 121
  Human 260
  Succulent fruit 148-149
Placental mammals 74, 104
Placer deposits 280
Plagioclase feldspar 275
Plains viscacha 197
Planck 41
Planetary nebula
  Nebulae and star clusters 17
  Small stars 24-25
Planetary orbits 30-31
Planetary rotation 30
Planets
  Jupiter 44-45
  Mars 42-43
  Mercury 34-35
  Neptune 50-51
  Pluto 50-51
  Saturn 46-47
  Solar System 30-31
  Uranus 48-49
  Venus 36-37
Planking
  Ironclad 393
  Longboat 380
  Roman corbita 373
  Sailing warship 377
  Tea clipper 392
Plantar calcaneonavicular ligament 232
Plant bodies 116
Plant capital 459
Plant-eating dinosaurs 68, 70
Plant matter 280
Plant remains
  Fossils 278-279
  Mineral resources 280
  Sedimentary rocks 276
Plants 56, 66
  Electromagnetic radiation 314
  Flowering 57, 70, 72

Fossil record 279
Non-flowering 68
Plant variety **112-113**
Plasma 306
Plaster 452, 464-465
Plastic fletch 548
Plastic insulator 316, 317
Plastic rackets 544
Plastic sheath 575
Plastid 116
Platanus x acerifolia 154
Platband 481
Plate
  Etching press 477
  Motorcycle clutch 366
  "O Ring" drive chain 366
Plateau
  Neptune's rings 50
  Structure of Neptune 51
Plateaus 276-277
Plate boundaries 62, 273
Platelets 253
Plate movements 58-59
  Faults and folds 60
  Mountain building 62-63
Platen 449
Plateosaurus 69, 88-89
Plate tectonics 58-59
Platform
  Cathedral dome 487
  Medieval building 467-468
  Modern building 498
Platform diving 558
Platform stage 477
Platinum 311
Plat lesene 480
Plato 40
Platypus 206-207
Platysma 229
Playa 283
Player's bench
  Basketball 532
  Football 526
  Handball 535
  Ice hockey 550
  Volleyball 534
Plaza 498
Pleiades 14, 16, 19, 20
Pleistocene epoch
  Fossil record 279
  Geological timescale 57
Pleistocene period 76
Plenum chamber 344-345
Plenum ring 418
Pleopod 172
Plesiochelys latiscutata 73
Plesiosaurs 70-71
Pleurotus pulmonarius 114
Plica circulare 249
Plicate lamina 127
Pliers 321
Plinth
  Baroque church 480
  French temple 485
  Islamic tomb 489
  Modern building 499
  Neoclassical building 479, 483
  Renaissance building 476
  Twentieth-century building 494-495
Pliocene epoch
  Fossil record 279
  Geological timescale 57
Plough anchor 386
Plug lead conduit 337
Plugs 272-273
  Igneous rock structures 274
Plumage 188
Plume 45
Plumose anemone 166
Plumule 147, 152-153

Plunge 60
Plunge pool 289, 291
Plunger contact 572
Pluto 31, **50-51**
Plutonium 310-311
Plywood skin 404
Pneumatic tires 358, 555
Podetium 114
Podium 463, 499
Point
  Angling hook 562
  Cricket 538
  Double bass bow 511
  Sailmaker's fid 384
  Sculpting tool 452-453
  Violin bow 510
Point bar
  Mississippi Delta 291
  River's stages 289
Point cover 582
Pointed arch 466, 467, 469, 472
Pointed bristle brush 434
Pointed riffler 454
Pointed sable brush 444
Pointing 383
Point pocket 582
Poison duct 170
Poison gland
  Octopus 176
  Spider 170
Polacanthus 95
Polar band 36
Polar bottom water 296
Polar easterlies 300
Polar fronts 302
Polar hood 36
Polaris 14, 18-19
Polar jet stream 300
Polar nuclei 146
Poles 297, 300
Pole star 14, 18
Pole vault 542
Polian vesicle 175
Poll 199
Pollen 140, 142, 144-145
  Dicotyledon flower 126
  Fertilization 146-147
Pollen-forming structures 122
Pollen grains 144-145
  Fertilization 146-147
  Pine 122
  Scots pine 122
Pollen sac wall 144
Pollen tubes
  Fertilization 146-147
  Scots pine 122
Pollination **144-145**, 122
Pollution 328
Pollux 18, 21
Polonium 311
Polyester 388
Polygala chamaebuxus 144
Polygnotus 35
Polygonum baldschuanicum 131
Polyhedral dome 486-487
Polypropylene rope 388
Polythene 306
Polytrichum commune 119
Pome 131, 149
Pommel 554, 582
Pond weeds 158
Pons 212, 236-237
Poop break 373
Poop deck
  74-gun ship 381
  Iron paddlesteamer 392
  Roman corbita 373
Poop rail
  74-gun ship 381
  Wooden sailing ship 378
Poor metals 310-311

Popchu-Sa Temple 490
Popliteal artery 253
Popliteal fossa 210
Porch 470-471
Porcupines 196-197
Pore
  Bishop pine needle 124
  Blackberry 147
  Dryland plants 156-157
  Elder stem 130
  Epigeal germination 153
  False fruit 148
  Gas exchange 138, 158
  Golden barrel cactus 156
  Haworthia truncata 157
  Leaf 138-139
  Liverwort 118
  Monocotyledon leaf 126
  Nuclear membrane 217
  Perennial bark 130-131
  Pollen grain 144-145
  Seed 153
  Sponge 166
  Water absorption 150, 153
  Wetland plants 158
  Woody plants 130-131
  Woody stems 134
Porifera 166
Porocyte 166
Porous limestone 284
Porous stipe 114
Porphyritic andesite 275
Porpoises 204
Porrima 21
Porsche, Ferdinand 340
Port
  Trojan two-stroke engine 342
  Wooden sailing ship 379
Portal 476, 480
Portal vein 252
Porta Nigra 462, 465
Port bower anchor 377, 395
Port foremast 376
Porthole
  Battleship 394
  Dome 487
  Frigate 397
Portico
  Ancient Greek building 460-461
  Ancient Roman building 462-463
  Neoclassical building 482-483
  Renaissance building 475
Port-side oar 560
Portugal 331
Portuguese bowline 388
Position guide 447
Positive electric charge 316
Positive ions 308, 310
Positive lithium atom 308
Positive metal comb 316
Positive pole 574
Positive terminal 316, 317
Positron 22
Post 481, 486
Postabdominal spine 169
Postacetabular process 82
Postcentral gyrus 237
Post-crural musculature 90
Posterior antebrachial musculature 86, 91
Posterior aorta 170
Posterior arch 222
Posterior border of vomer 220
Posterior brachial muscle 86, 91

Posterior branch of spinal nerve 223
Posterior cerebral artery 252
Posterior chamber 241
Posterior chamber of cloaca 185
Posterior column 223
Posterior crural muscle 87
Posterior cuneonavicular ligament 252
Posterior dorsal fin
  Bony fish 181
  Dogfish 179
  Lamprey 178
Posterior horn 223
Posterior nasal aperture 220
Posterior nasal spine 220
Posterior part of tongue 245
Posterior petal 141
Posterior root 223, 238
Posterior semicircular canal 243
Posterior sepal 141
Posterior tarsometatarsal ligament 232
Posterior tentacle 177
Posterior tibial artery 253
Posterior tibial nerve 238
Posterior tubercle 222
Posterior vena cava 182
Posterior wing of shell 176
Posterolateral horn 94
Post-glacial stream 286
Post-glacial valley 286
Post-modernism 296, 496
Potassium 35, 58, 286, 310
Potassium chromate solution 312
Potassium dichromate ions 312
Potassium iodide 312-313
Potassium nitrate 313
Potassium permanganate 306
Potato 128
Potential energy 314, 315
Potholes 284
Pouch 206
Power bar 552
Power drill 566-567
Power knob 575
Power output 360, 366
Power stations 314, 315
Power steering belt 351
Power steering pump 344, 351
Power stroke 343
Power-to-weight ratio 328
Practice projectile 396
Pradakshina 491
Praesepe 18
Prairie style 495
Praseodynium 310
Pratt & Whitney Canada turbofan engine 418-419
Pratt & Whitney Canada turboprop engine 419
Pratt & Whitney radial engine 406-407
Praxiteles 35
Preacetabular process 82
Precambrian period 56, **64-65**, 279
Precambrian seas 78
Precentral gyrus 237
Precious metals 311
Precipitate 312
Precipitation 288, 302-303
Predatory dinosaurs 84
Predatory theropods 88
Predentary bone
  Arsinoitherium 104

Iguanodon 96
Lambeosaurus 99
Moeritherium 105
Protoceratops 102
Triceratops 103
Prehensile tail 202
Prehistoric foods 109
Pre-load adjustor 365
Premaxilla
  Baryonyx 83
  Bony fish 181
  Chimpanzee 202
  Elephant 201
  Frog 183
  Iguanodon 96
  Lambeosaurus 99
Premolars
  Australopithecus 107
  Bear 106, 194
  Chimpanzee 202
  Horse 105
  Human 246
  Lion 194
Prenocephale 100-101
Preopercular bone 181
Preoperculum 181
Preparatory drawing 430-431
Prepubic process
  Iguanodon 96
  Parasaurolophus 98
  Stegosaurus 93
Prepubis
  Ornithischian 82
  Stegoceras 100-101
Prepuce 259
Preserved remains 278
Press
  Book 586
  Etching 447
  Lithographic printing 446
  Relief-printing 449
Pressed steel wheel 340
Pressure
  Formation of black hole 29
  Igneous and metamorphic rocks 274
  Mineral resources 280
  Stellar black hole 29
  Volcanic features 273
Pressure gauge 325, 354
Pressure line 418
Pressure plate 366
Pressurized cabin 406
Pressurized keel box 417
Pressurized strut 425
Pressurized water reactor 314
Presta valve 561
Presynaptic axon 239
Presynaptic membrane 239
Prickers 383
Prickle
  Blackberry 147
  Bramble stem 130
  Rose stem 130
  Slender thistle 129
Primary bronchus 215
Primary colors 439
Primary-drive gear 366
Primary flight feathers 188, 191
Primary follicle 258
Primary leaf 121
Primary mycelium 115
Primary remiges 188, 191
Primary root 152-133
  Germination 152-153
  Seedling 152-153
Primary teeth 246
Primary thallus 114
Primary xylem 125, 135
Primates 108, **202-203**, 279

Primer 348, 436
Primitive crocodilians 68
Primitive life-forms 64
Primitive mammals 206
Principal arteries and veins 253
Principal rafter
  Ancient Roman mill 464
  Dome 486
  Gothic building 473
Printed circuit board 575
Printing block 449
Printing papers 447
Print making 446-447, **448-449**
Prism 318
Prismatic habit 271
Prism retainer plate 589
Prism retainer spring 589
Privy 380
Probactosaurus 97
Proboscidea 104
Proboscis 169, 201
Procambial strand 134
Procerus muscle 229
Processional path 470
Procompsognathus 87
Procyon 8, 21
Procyon lotor 195
Production line
  Mass-production 338
  Modern bodywork 348
  Modern trim 352
Projectile 396
Prokaryotes 78
Prolegs 169
Promethium 311
Prominence 32-33
Pronaos 461
Pro-otic bone 183
Propagative structures 154-155
Propellant 396
Propeller **390-391**
  ARV light aircraft 425
  Battleship 395
  Biplanes and triplanes 402-403
  Early monoplanes 400-401
  Ford diesel engine 347
  Frigate 396
  Hawker Tempest components 408
  Lockheed Electra airliner 406-407
  Pegasus Quasar microlight 427
  Pioneers of flight 398-399
  Submarine 396
  World War I aircraft 404-405
Propeller-bolt collar 411
Propeller brake pad 419
Propeller drive flange
  ARV light aircraft 425
  Modern piston aero-engines 410-411
Propeller drive gearbox 427
Propeller drive shaft 408
Propeller-hub spinner 407
Propeller shaft
  Brazilian battleship 395
  Wright Flyer 399
Propeller shaft boss 395
Propeller-shaft bracing strut 398-399
Propeller shaft rear bearing 410
Propeller speed probe 419
Propeller spinner 408, 409
Propodus 172, 173

Propylaeum 460
Prosauropoda 83
Prosauropods 88
Proscapular process 187
Prosimians 203
Prosimii 202
Prostate gland 257, 259
Prostyle colonnade 483
Protactinium 310
Protective clothing
  Cricket 559
  Football 528
  Ice hockey 550-551
Protective eyewear 544
Protective gaiter 422
Protective outer layer 125
Protective root covering
  153
Protective scale 134
Protective scale leaf 155
Protein body 112
Protein fibers 166
Protein matrix 166
Protein synthesis site 139
Proterozoic eon 279
Proteus 50
Prothallus 121
Prothorax 168
Protista 112, 116
Protoceratops 102-103
Protogalaxies 10-11
Proton 308, 316
  Atomic mass 310
  Atomic number 310
  Lithium-19 309
  Nuclear fusion 22
Protonema 119
Protostar 24, 26
Protoxylem
  Dicotyledon root 127
  Monocotyledon root 127
  Root 132-133
Proventriculus
  Bird 189
  Crayfish 173
Prow 372, 375
Prowhead 374
Proxima Centauri 18
Proximal convoluted
  tubule 256-257
Proximal interphalangeal
  joint 231
Proximal phalanx 230 ,
  232
Prunus persica 131
Psathyrella candolleana
  115
Pseudocarps 148-149
Pseudo-Corinthian capital
  476
Psi Sagittarii 21
Psittacosaurus 100, 103
Psoas major muscle 225,
  257
Pterapsis 65
Pterichthyodes 65
Pteridium aquilinum 121
Pterois volitans 180
Pteron 460-461, 463
Pterosaurs 70-71
Pterygoid bone 183
Pterygoid hamulus 220
Pterygoid plate 220
Ptolemaeus 40
Ptolemaic-Roman period
  459
"P" turret 395
Pubic bone 261
Pubic ramus 257
Pubic symphysis 258
Pubis
  Archaeopteryx 85
  Bird 189
  Diplodocus 90

Eryops 81
Gallimimus 86
Human 218, 224, 259
Iguanodon 96
Ornithischian 82
Plateosaurus 88
Saurischian 82
Stegosaurus 93
Struthiomimus 87
Tyrannosaurus 84
Pubofemoral ligament 224
Pudenda 211
Pudendal nerve 238
Puffballs 114
Pugin, A.W.N. 493
Pulley bolt 360
Pulley rim rear brake 362
Pulley wheel
  Simple pulleys 320
  Van de Graaff generator
  316
Pulmonary artery
  Frog 182
  Human 251, 253, 254-255
Pulmonary semilunar
  valve 251
Pulmonary trunk 251, 255
Pulmonary vein 251, 253,
  254
Pulp artery and vein 247
Pulp chamber 247
Pulp horn 247
Pulp nerve 247
Pulsar 28
  Marble carving 453
Pump
  Nuclear power station
  314
  Testing candle wax 313
Pump drive belt 410
Pump drive shaft 411
Pump piston 391
Punchhole 568
Pupa 168
Pupil
  Caiman 186
  Human 213, 226, 241
Pupil's cockpit 403
Puppis 18, 21
Purchase 382-383
Purchase wire 394
Pure substances 306
Purfling 510, 511
Purkinje's cells 237
Purlin 473
Pusher propeller
  Pegasus Quasar
  microlight 426
  Pioneers of flight 398-
  399
Push moraine 286
Push-rod 365, 367
Push-rod adjuster 357
Push switch 572
Putter 547
Putting green 546
Putto 476
"P" wave 63
Pygal shield 187
Pygostyle 189
Pylon 314
Pylon fairing 427
Pylon strut 427
Pyloric caecum
  Bony fish 181
  Starfish 174
Pyloric duct 174
Pyloric region of stomach
  179
Pyloric sphincter muscle
  249
Pyloric stomach 174
Pyramid 458
Pyrenees 77, 265

Pyrenoid 112, 116
Pyrites 268
  Intrusive igneous rocks
  275
Pyroclasts 272
Pyromorphite 269
Pyroxene 52, 267
Pyxis 18

Q

Quadrant arch 468
Quadrate bone 181
Quadratojugal bone
  Frog 183
  Heterodontosaurus 83
Quadrilateral 489
Quadripartite vault 469
Quadrupedal dinosaurs
  88, 92, 96, 100
Quadruplanes 402
Quark 309
Quarter and counter
  lining 569
Quarterback 526
Quarter backer 568-569
Quarterdeck 380-381
Quarterdeck house 376
Quarter gallery 381
Quarter glass 548
Quarter light 340-341
Quarter lining 568
Quarter panel molding
  352
Quarter tip 569
Quarter trim panel 352
Quartz
  Color 271
  Metamorphic rock 267
  Oxides/hydroxides 268
Quasar (quasi-stellar
  object)
  Galaxies 12
  Objects in Universe 11
  Origin and expansion of
  Universe 10-11
Quasar nucleus 13
Quaternary period 57, 76-
  77
  Fossil record 279
Quatrefoil 471-473
Quaver 502
Quayside 587
Queen-post 473
Quercus palustris 74
Quercus petraea 131
Quick-release mechanism
  425
Quick release strap 360
Quill
  Drill 567
  Feather 191
  Writing tool 444
Quinacridone red 442
Quiver 548
Quoin
  Baroque church 481
  Medieval building 466
  Nineteenth-century
  building 492
  Renaissance building
  476

R

Rabbit line 380
Rabbits **196-197**
Raccoons 194-195
Raceme 129
Rachilla 137
Rachis 136-137
  Bipinnate leaf 137
  Couch grass 113

Everlasting pea 129
Feather 191
Fern 121
Hogweed 129
Pinnate leaf 136-137
Rowan leaf 130
Tree fern 112
Tripinnate leaf 137
Racing bike 360
Racing car 356-357
Racing chain 361
Racing colors 554-555
Racing saddle 554
Racing sidecar 368-369
Racing "silks" 554-555
Racing tire 365
  Formula One racing car
  357
  Suzuki RGV500 368-369
Racketball 544-545
Racket sports 544-545
Radar
  Modern jetliners 412
  Modern military aircraft
  420-421
  World War II aircraft 408
RADAR antenna 397
RADAR for gunnery and
  missile control 397
Radial artery 231, 253
Radial canal
  Jellyfish 167
  Sea urchin 175
  Starfish 174
Radial cartilage 180
Radial diffuser 418
Radial engine
  Curtiss biplane 398-399
  Lockheed Electra
  airliner 406-407
Radial groove 365
Radial nerve
  Human 238
  Sea urchin 175
Radial river drainage 288
Radial spoke 47
Radial studio easel 457
Radial wall 465
Radiation 38
  Electromagnetic 314
  Energy emission from
  Sun 22
  Galaxies 12-13
  Nebulae and star
  clusters 16
  Ozone formation 64
  Universe 10
Radiative zone
  Structure of main
  sequence star 24
  Structure of Sun 33
Radiator
  1906 Renault 336-337
  ARV light aircraft 424
  Ford Model T 338-339
  Formula One racing car
  357
  Hawker Tempest fighter
  409
  Honda VF750 364
  Kirby BSA 369
  Renault Clio 351
  Wright Flyer 399
Radiator-access cowling
  408
Radiator air vent 368
Radiator apron 339
Radiator coolant 326
Radiator fan 326
Radiator filler cap 339
Radiator filler neck 339
Radiator grill 355
Radiator header tank 408
Radiator hose 339
Radiator outlet 409

Radiator pipe 364
Radicle
  Dry fruit 150
  Embryo development
  147
  Epigeal germination 153
  Hypogeal germination
  152
Radio
  Bell-47 helicopter 422
  Renault Clio 353
Radio aerial
  Pinzgauer Turbo D 355
  Schleicher K23 glider
  426
Radio antenna 395
Radio galaxies 12-13
Radio image 13
Radio lobe 13
Radio map of our galaxy
  15
Radio mast 494
Radio operator's seat 408
Radio plugs 425
Radio speaker 353
Radio-ulna 185
Radio wave beam 28
Radio-wave emission 15
Radio waves
  Electromagnetic
  spectrum 318
  Pulsar 28
  Radio image of
  Centaurus A 13
Radium 310
Radius
  Archaeopteryx 85
  Arsinoitherium 104
  Baryonyx 85
  Bird 189
  Bird's wing 191
  Crocodile 186
  Diplodocus 90
  Domestic cat 195
  Elephant 90, 201
  Eryops 80
  Euoplocephalus 94
  Hare 197
  Horse 199
  Human 218,
  230-231
  Iguanodon 96
  Kangaroo 206
  Lizard 184
  Parasaurolophus 99
  Pareiasaur 81
  Plateosaurus 88
  Platypus 206
  Rhesus monkey 202
  Seal 204
  Stegoceras 100-101
  Struthiomimus 87
  Toxodon 106
  Triceratops 102
  Turtle 187
Radius rod
  Avro Tutor biplane 403
  Ford Model T 338-339
Radome
  BAe-146 jetliner 415
  Concorde 416-417
  Tornado 420
Radon 311
Radula 176-177
RAF Central Flying School
  badge 402
RAF roundels 403, 409
Raft 496
Rafter
  Ancient Roman mill 464
  Dome 486
  Gothic building 473
  Modern building 499
  Nineteenth-century
  building 492

Raft spider 171
Rail
  Electric trolley 332
  Kayak 560
  Neoclassical building
  483
  Relief-printing press 449
  Train 330-331
  Wooden sailing ship 379
Rail chair 324
Railing
  Asian building 490-491
  Cathedral dome 487
  Medieval building 467
  Nineteenth-century
  building 493
  Renaissance theater 477
Railroad crest 326
Railroad system 324
Rain 302
Rain erosion 294
Rain gutter 412, 415
Rainwater
  Caves 284
  Weathering and erosion
  282
Raised beach 295
Raja clavata 179
Raked windshield 333
Raking cornice
  Ancient Greek building
  460-461
  Ancient Roman building
  462-463
  Baroque church 480-481
  Neoclassical building
  478
Raking stempost 376
Ram 372
Ramaria formosa 114
Ramentum 112, 121
Rammer 396
Ramp 467, 494
Ram scoop
  BE 2B bomber 404
  Tornado 420-421
Rangefinder
  Battleship 394
  Gun turret 396
Ranks 514
Ranunculus sp. 127, 132-
  133
Raphe 153
Rapid-fire pistols 548
Rapids
  River features 290
  River's stages 289
Rare earths 310
Rare gases 311
Ras Algethi 20
Ras Alhague 19, 20
Rasp 452
Raspberry 149
Rat 104, 196
Ratchet
  Brace-and-bit 567
  Fixed-spool reel 562
  Ratchet mechanism 567
Ratchet pawl 570
Ratchet wheel 334
Rating 378
Rating nut 570
Ratings' mess 397
Ratline 376, 379
Rat's tail 584
Rat tail 389
Rattlesnake 185
Raw sienna 454
Raw umber 434
Ray
  Branchiostegal 181
  Caudal fin 180
  Dorsal fin 181
  Jawless fish 178
  Liverwort 118

Mercury 34
Near side of the Moon 40
Parenchyma cells 134
Pectoral fin 181
Ray crater 34
Ray florets
  Florists' chrysanthemum 129
  Sunflower 142, 145
Reactants 312
Reactive metals 310-311
Reactor core 314
Reactor space 397
Read Only Memory (ROM) 584-585
Rear axle 338
Rear axle adjustor 364, 368
Rear bearing 411
Rear brake 362
Rear-brake cable 359, 360
Rear brake calliper 368
Rear brake pedal 368
Rear bulkhead 417
Rear cabinet 574
Rear cantilever brake 358
Rear cylinder exhaust pipe 368
Rear derailleur 358, 360
Rear door 359
Rear drop-outs 358
Rear hatch 349
Rear hub quick-release spindle 358
Rear indicator 362
Rear lamp
  Oldsmobile trim 337
  Volkswagen Beetle 340
Rear lamp cluster 355
Rear leaf spring 338
Rear lens group 589
Rear light
  Bicycle 360
  Italian State Railways Class 402 328
  Paris RATP Metro 328
Rear limit line 557
Rear-mounted propeller
  Pegasus Quasar microlight 426
  Pioneers of flight 398-399
Rear oil lamp 336
Rear shelf 352
Rear shock absorber 340
Rear sub-frame 364
Rear taillight 329
Rear tire 580
Rear-view mirror
  1906 Renault 336
  Formula One racing car 357
  Pinzgauer Turbo D 355
  Renault Clio 353
Rebate 576
Receiver
  American squash 545
  Badminton 545
  International squash 545
  Racketball 545
  Tennis 544
Receiving line 545
Receptacles
  Algae 116
  Dicotyledon flower 127
  Dry fruit 150-151
  Fertilization 147
  Flower 140-36
  Rose 131
  Seaweed 116-117
  Succulent fruit 148-149
Recessed arch 488
Recessed hinge 414, 415
Recharge area 292
Recoil case 580-581

Recoil cylinder 396
Reconnaissance camera 420
Record trigger 521
Rectal caecum 174
Rectal gland 179
Rectangle measurements 590
Rectangular cross-band 374
Rectangular pier 465, 467, 480
Rectangular river drainage 288
Rectangular window
  Ancient Roman building 465
  Asian building 490
  Baroque church 481
  Medieval building 466
  Renaissance building 474, 476
Rectum
  Bird 189
  Butterfly 169
  Chimpanzee 202
  Cow 198
  Dogfish 179
  Dolphin 205
  Elephant 200
  Frog 182
  Human 215, 248-249, 258-259, 261
  Lizard 185
  Rabbit 196
  Starfish 174
  Tortoise 187
Rectus abdominis muscle 226
Rectus femoris muscle 226
Recumbent fold 61
Red algae 116
Red blood cells 217, 253
Red-brown crocoite 271
Red card 524
Red deer 199
Red dwarf 23
Red earth 433, 434-435
Red filter signal light 407
Red giant
  Small stars 24-25
  Stars 22-23
Red howler monkey 203
Red light 318
  Main-line signaling system 330, 331
  Red light photon 318
Red marble 450
Red port navigation light 406
Red sandstone 277
Red seaweeds 117
Red spot 44-45
Red supergiant
  Massive stars 26-27
  Stars 22-23
Reduction gearbox
  Early piston aero-engines 410-411
  Jet engines 419
  Turboprop engine 419
Redwall limestone 277
Red warning light
  Italian State Railways Class 402 328
  Paris RATP Metro 328
Redwood trees 70
Reed pen 444
Reef knot 388
Reef point 385
Reel
  Angling equipment 562-563
  Fencing piste 557
  Frigate 397

Reel foot 562-563
Reel scoop 562-563
Reel seat 563
Re-entrant angle 485
Re-entrant corner 479
Referee
  Basketball 532
  Football 526
  Gaelic football 529
  Ice hockey 550
  Judo 556
  Lacrosse 541
  Rugby 530
  Soccer 524
  Swimming 558
  Volleyball 534
Referee's crease 550
Referee's equipment 524
Referee's signals
  Basketball 533
  Football 527
Reflection 318
Reflection nebula 16
Reflector
  Ford Model T 339
  Oldsmobile trim 337
Refraction 318-319
Refractory (heat-resistant) skin 421
Refrigerator freight car 527
Regency-style carver 576
Régie Autonome des Transports Parisien 328
Regional metamorphism 274
Regional weather 302
Registers 514
Regolith (soil) 41
Regula 461
Regulator
  "Mallard" express steam locomotive 325
  "Rocket" steam locomotive 324
Regulator valve 325
Regulus 18, 21
Rein 554
Reinforce 395
Reinforced concrete 494, 497
  Sleepers 330
Reinforced plinth 499
Rein terret 555
Relative atomic mass 310
Relay baton 543
Relay running 542
Release 537, 543
Release adjustment screw 552
Release button 425
Release lever 563
Release spring 563
Relief 458
Relief printing 446
Relief printing equipment 449
Relieving arch
  Ancient Roman building 462, 465
  Medieval building 466-467
Remiges 188, 191
Removable archery screen 377
Renaissance buildings 474-477
Renal artery 256-257
Renal column 256
Renal papilla 256
Renal pelvis 256
Renal sinus 256
Renal vein 256-257
Renault (1906) 336-337
Renault Clio 348-353

Renault logo 348
Renault V10 RS1 engine 356
Renoir 35
Repeater indicator 333
Repeating pattern 307
Replum 151
Reproduction
  Algae 116-117
  Fertilization 146-147
  Flowering plants 140
  Liverwort 118
  Moss 118-119
  Vegetative 154-155
Reproductive canal 94
Reproductive chamber 116
Reproductive organs 259
Reproductive structures
  Flower 140-143
  Pollination 144
Reproductive system 258-259
Reptiles 80-81, 184-187
  Carboniferous period 66
  Dinosaurs 82-83
  Fossil record 279
  Jurassic period 70
  Present-day 82
  Rhynchosaurian 71
  Synapsid skull 67
  Triassic period 68
Reptilia 184, 186
Repulsion 316-317
"Request identification" aerial 421
Re-radiated heat 300-301
Reredos 470
Rescue strap 561
Reservoir 314
Resin canal
  Bishop pine needle 124
  Pine root/stem 125
Resistance 316
Resonator 513
Respiration 255
Respiratory system 254-255
Rest
  Musical notation 502
  Newton's first motion law 321
Resurgence 284-285
Retaining screw 588-589
Retaining bolt hole 366
Retaining screw 562, 563
Reticulum
  Digestive system of a cow 198
  Southern stars 20
Retina 240-241
Retraction jack 417
Retractor muscle 167
Retreating glacier 286
Retrices 188
Retroarticular process 83
Return 486-487
Rev counter 369
Reversed bend hook 562
Reversed dive piked 559
Reverse dip-slip fault 61
Reverse dive 558
Reverse-flow combustion chamber 418
Reverse lever 342
Reverser handle 325
Reverse shock wave 27
Reversible reactions 312
Reversing shaft lock control 325
Reversing wheel 392
Revivalist style 493-494
Rewind shaft 589
Rewind shaft collar 589
Rhamphodopsis 65
Rhamphorhynchus sp. 71

Rheas 188
Rhenium 310
Rhesus monkey 202
Rhinoceroses 198-199
Rhizine 114
Rhizoids 118-119
  Alga 116
  Fern 121
  Liverwort 118
  Moss 119
Rhizomes 154-155
  Fern 121
  Herbaceous flowering plants 128
  Horsetail 120
  Water hyacinth 158
  Water lily 159
Rhizophore 120
Rho1 Sagittarii 21
Rhodium 311
Rhodophyta 116
Rhomboideus major muscle 227
Rhomboid leaves 137
Rhombus 471
Rhopalium 167
Rhynchosaurian reptile 71
Rhynchosaurs 68-69, 71
Rhyolite 274-275
Rhyolitic lava 272
Rhythm
  Drums 518
  Percussion instruments 516
Rhythm pattern selector 520
Rib
  Acoustic guitar 512
  Archaeopteryx 85
  Avro triplane 403
  Baroque church 479
  BE 2B tail 405
  BE 2B wings 404
  Bird 189
  Blackburn monoplane 401
  Bony fish 181
  Brachiosaurus 90
  Concorde 417
  Crocodile 186
  Diplodocus 90
  Dome 486-487
  Domestic cat 195
  Double bass 511
  Elephant 201
  Eryops 80
  Euoplocephalus 94
  Gallimimus 86
  Hare 197
  Herbaceous flowering plant 128
  Horse 199
  Kangaroo 206
  Leather-bound book 586-587
  Lizard 184
  Medieval church 469
  Modern building 499
  Pareiasaur 81
  Pegasus Quasar microlight 426-427
  Pegasus XL SE microlight 426
  Plateosaurus 88
  Platypus 206
  Rhesus monkey 202
  Seal 204
  Snake 185
  Stegoceras 101
  Struthiomimus 87
  Toxodon 107
  Triceratops 102
  Tyrannosaurus 84
  Violin 510
  Westlothiana 81

Riband 381
Ribbing 568
Ribbon 586-587
Ribbon Lake 287
Ribbon window 499
Rib cage
  Carnivores 195
  Human 218
Ribosome
  Chloroplast 139
  Human cell 217
Rib vault 469, 484-485
  Gothic building 470
  Medieval building 467
  Renaissance building 477
Rice paper 445
Ride cymbal 519
Ridge
  Epigeal germination 153
  False septum 151
  Gothic building 473
  Modern building 499
  Nineteenth-century building 492
  Seed 153
  Twentieth-century building 495
Ridge and furrow roof 492
Ridge-board 473
Ridge-rib 469, 485
Ridges 286-287
Ridge tile 464, 476
Riding bitt 372
Riding boot 554
Riding jacket 554
Riffler 452, 453, 454
Rifle 548-549
Rift valley 58
  Lake formation 292-293
Rig 384-385
Riga brush 434
Rigel
  Northern stars 18
  Orion 18
  Southern stars 21
  Star magnitudes 22
Rigger 560
Rigger's gauge 382
Rigging 382-383
  Iron 392
  Sailing dinghy 561
  Wooden sailing ship 378-379
Rigging rail 376
Rigging tools 382-383
Right whales 204
Rigid rock 60
Rigol 381
Rim
  Bicycle wheel 358-359
  Kayak paddle 560
  Paddle wheel 391
  Tam-tam 516
  Twin bollards 386
Rim brake 330
Rim clamp 337
Rim of pitcher 161
Rim plate 390
Rim section 390
Rind 149
Ring
  74-gun ship 380
  Mushroom 115
  Roman corbita 372
Ring 1986 U1R 48
Ring 1986 U2R 48
Ring 6 48
Ring bolt 373
Ring canal
  Sea urchin 175
  Starfish 174
Ring dyke 26
Ring finger 230 -231
"Ring of Fire" 272

Ring of trunk 201
Rings
  Jupiter 44-45
  Neptune 50-51
  Saturn 46-47
  Uranus 48-49
Rings 4 and 5 48
Ring scar 130,131
Ring-tailed lemur 203
Rink corner 550
Riojasaurus 89
Ripple finish 451
Riser
  Bronze casting 454, 455
  Staircase 477
Rising air
  Atmospheric circulation and winds 300
  Precipitation 302
Rising land 294
Risorius muscle 229
Rissa tridactyla 190
Ritchey 43
River Amur 265
Riverbanks 289, 290
Riverbed 289
River capture 288
River cliff 289, 290
River Congo 265
River course 288
River development 289
River drainage patterns 288
River features 290-291
River flow 290
River Ganges 288
River Jordan 293
River Lena 265
River Mekong 265
River-mouth 290
River Nile 264-265
River Ob-Irtysh 265
Rivers **288-289**
  Earth's physical features 264
  River features 290-291
  River source 288, 290
  Rock cycle 266-267
  Weathering and erosion 282
River's stages 288-289
River terrace 290-291
River valley 288, 289, 290
Rivet
  Saddle 582
  Shoes 568
Rivetted plates 392
Road spring 340
Roband 372, 374
Robie House 495
Robinia pseudoacacia 136
Roche 41
Roches moutonnées 286
Rock compression 60
Rock crystal 271
Rock cycle **266-267**
Rock debris 295
Rock deformations 60, 61
Rocker 446
Rocker arm 366
Rocker-beam 496-497
Rocker cover 547
Rock erosion 282
Rocking beam 334
Rocking elevator arm 424
Rocking lever 342
Rock layer
  Caves 284
  Faults and folds 60

Rock lip
  Cirque formation 287
  Tarn lake 293
Rock mounds 286
Rock particles 266-267
Rock pavement 282-283
Rock pedestal 282-283
Rock prisms 61
Rocks
  Faults and folds 60-61
  Fossils 278-279
  Igneous and metamorphic rocks 274-275
  Mineral resources 280
  Minerals 268
  Rock cycle 266-267
  Sedimentary rocks 276
  Weathering and erosion 282
Rock salt
  Halides 269
  Sedimentary rocks 276-277
Rock scar 284
Rock stonecrop 128
Rock strata 60, 61
  Fossils 278
Rock stress 60, 61
Rock tension 60, 61
Rocky Mountains 73, 75, 77, 264
Rocky planets
  Mars 42-43
  Mercury 34-35
  Solar System 30-31
  Venus 36-37
Rococo style 478
Rod 562-563
Rodentia 104, 196
Rodents 196-197
Rod-shaped structure 144
Rogers, R. 496
Roll 400
Roller
  Mid West single-rotor engine 410
  "O Ring" drive chain 366
  Painting tool 442
  Printing equipment 447, 449
  Tenor saxophone 509
Roller bearing 584
Roller-bearing axle box 527
Roller-blind 497
Roller path 596
Rolling hitch 388
Roll spoiler 414
Roll-spoiler hydraulic actuator attachment 414
Rolls-Royce Olympus
  Mark 610 turbojet 417
Roman anchor 372
Roman architecture **462-465**
Roman corbita 372-373
Romanesque style 468, 470
Roman mill 464
Roman number system 591
Roman numeral 571
Roman ships **372-373**
Roof boss 468
Roof dome 552, 553
Roofed space 479
Roofing tile 482
Roofless temple 460
Roof molding 552
Roof-rack 554-555
Roofs 484
  Ancient Egyptian temple 458-459
  Ancient Roman building 462

Asian building 490
Baroque church 481
  Dome 486
Gothic building 470-473
Hammer-beam 470, 473
Islamic building 488-489
Medieval building 467, 468
Modern building 496-499
Neoclassical building 479, 483
Nineteenth-century building 492
Renaissance building 476-477
Twentieth-century building 494-495
Rooftop tent 554
Root
  BAe-146 jetliner components 413, 415
  BE 2B wings 404
  Tooth 247
Root canal 247
Root cap
  Broad bean 133
  Radicle 153
Root growth 282
Root hairs 132
Root nodule 128
Root of tail 198
Root parasite 163
Root rib 413
Roots 132-133
  Adventitious 112-113
  Amaryllis 155
  Begonia 155
  Brassavola nodosa 162
  Broomrape host 163
  Carrot 128
  Cell division 135
  Clubmoss 120
  Couch grass 113
  Dehiscent fruit 150
  Dicotyledons 127
  Elongation region 133
  Embryo 147
  Epigeal germination 153
  Epiphytes 162-163
  Fern 121
  Germination 152-153
  Ginger 155
  Gladiolus 155
  Golden barrel cactus 156
  Grape hyacinth 155
  Horse chestnut 130
  Horsetail 120
  Hypogeal germination 152
  Ivy 131
  Kedrostis africana 113
  Lily 155
  Monocotyledons 126-127
  Mycorrhizal association 133
  Oxalis sp. 157
  Pine seedling 122
  Potato 128
  Rock stonecrop 128
  Seedling 152-153
  String of hearts 157
  Sweet pea 128
  Sweet potato 155
  Vegetative reproduction 154-155
  Water hyacinth 158
  Water transport 138
Root scar 128
Root succulents 157
Root tip 132-133
  Radicle 152-153
Root tubers 154-155, 157
Rope and paterae decoration 459
Rope band 372

Rope hole 386
Rope molding 395
Rope parrel 373
Rope preventer 378
Ropes **388-389**
Rope serving mallet 383
Rope strand 384
Rope wooling 379
Ropework 388
Rorquals 204
Rosa sp. 130-131, 135
Rose 130-131, 513
Rose quartz 271
Rosette
  Epiphytic plants 162-163
  Neoclassical building 480
Rosette Nebula 11
Rosewood head beater 516
Rossby waves 300
Rossin Italian time-trial bicycle 361
Rostellum 16
Rostral bone 102, 103
Rostrum
  Crayfish 173
  Dolphin 204
Rotary engine 346-347
  Blackburn monoplane 400
  Modern piston aero-engines 410-411
Rotary valves 507
Rotating beacon 407
Rotating table top 455
Rotational period 36
Rotor
  Mid West rotary engine 411
Rotor and seals 347
Rotor blade 423
Rotor chamber
  Mid West single-rotor engine 410
  Wankel rotary engine 346
Rotor gear 346-347
Rotor gear teeth 411
Rotor house 314
Rotor hub
  Bell-47 helicopter 422
  Schweizer helicopter 423
Rotor journal 347
Rotor mast 422-423
Rotring pen 444
Rotunda 462-463, 482
Rough 546
Rough endoplasmic reticulum 217
Rough terrain motorcycle racing 368
Rough-textured paper 439, 441
Roulette 446
Rounce 449
Round arch
  Ancient Roman building 464-465
  Baroque church 479-480
  Dome 484, 486-487
  French temple 485
  Gothic church 473
  Medieval building 467-469
  Nineteenth-century building 493
  Renaissance building 474-475
Round-arched window
  Ancient Roman building 465
  Baroque church 481
  Dome 486
  Medieval building 466, 468-469

Neoclassical building 478
Round ball 524
Round-corner single limousine coachwork 336
Roundel
  Avro biplane 403
  Hawker Tempest fighter 409
Roundhead nib 444
Roundhouse 380
Round pin 335
Round shot 378
Round thimble 384
Route information 532
Rover 528
Rowan 130-131
Rowing 560-561
Rowing boat 375
Rowing positions on a Greek trireme 373
Rowing shoe 560
Rubber 568
Rubber bungee shock absorber 425
Rubber cord suspension 402-403
Rubber guide wheel 328
Rubber mounting bush 365
Rubber puck 550-551
Rubber roller 449
Rubber sealing strip 413
Rubber seat 583
Rubber-sprung wheel 400-401
Rubber tire 402
Rubber-tired running wheel 328
Rubber wheel-guard 328
Rubber wheels
  Paris RATP Metro 328
  "People Mover" 328
Rubbing
  Charcoal drawing 431
  Relief printing 446
Rubbing ink 448
Rubbing strake
  Mazda RX-7 346
  Pinzgauer Turbo D 554-355
  Roman corbita 372
Rubbing strip
  Pinzgauer Turbo D 554-355
  Renault Clio 353
Rubens 35
Rubidium 310
Rubus fruticosus 130, 146-147
Rubus idaeus 149
Ruckstell axle 339
Rudder
  ARV light aircraft 424
  Avro biplane 402
  Avro triplane 403
  BAe-146 jetliner 415
  Battleship 395
  BE 2B bomber 405
  Blackburn monoplane 401
  Blériot XI 401
  Concorde 416-417
  Curtiss biplane 399
  Dhow 376
  Frigate 396
  Greek and Roman ships 372-373
  Iron paddlesteamer 392
  Junk 376
  Lockheed Electra airliner 407
  Longboat 380
  LVG CVI fighter 405

Northrop B-2 bomber 421
Sailing dinghy 561
Sailing warship 377
Schleicher glider 426
Submarine 396
Tornado 421
Viking boats 374-375
Wooden sailing ship 378
World War II aircraft 408-409
Wright Flyer 399
Rudder cable
  ARV light aircraft 424
  Avro biplane 402
Rudder chain 378
Rudder head 376
Rudder hinge
  Avro biplane 402
  Blériot XI monoplane 401
Rudder mass balance 424
Rudder pedal 425
Rudder post
  BE 2B bomber 405
  Blackburn monoplane 401
  Iron paddlesteamer 392
Rudder power control unit 417
Rudder strut 399
Rudder tip fairing 424
Rudder trimtab 409
Ruden 372
Rudimentary ear 260
Rudimentary eye 260
Rudimentary liver 260
Rudimentary mouth 260
Rudimentary vertebra 260
Ruellia grandiflora 145
Ruffini corpuscle 235, 239
Ruga 481
Rugby 524, 530-531
Rugby League 530-531
Rugby Union 530
Rumen 198
Ruminants 198
Rumpler monoplane 400
Run 536
Runners
  Bronze casting 454-455
  Rock stonecrop 128
  Strawberry 128
  Vegetative reproduction 154
Running 542
Running back 526
Running block 583
Running board
  Ford Model T 339
  1906 Renault 337
  Volkswagen Beetle 341
Running martingale 554
Running part 382
Running rail 328
Running rigging 382-383, 585
Running shoe 543
Running track 542
Running wheel 328
Runs 558
Rupes 34
Rupes Altai 40
Rush 135
Russian vine 131
Rustication
  Neoclassical building 479, 482-483
  Renaissance building 474-475
Rusts 114
Ruthenium 311

S

62 Sagittarii 21
Sabik 20
Sable brushes
  Acrylics 442
  Calligraphy 444
  Oil paints 436
  Tempera 432
  Watercolors 438
Sabres 556-557
Sabreur 557
Sabre warning line 557
Sacajawea 37
Saccule 243
Sacral foramen 223
Sacral nerves 238
Sacral plexus 258
Sacral promontory 223
Sacral vertebra 183
Sacral vertebrae
  Diplodocus 90
  Eryops 81
  Human 223
  Iguanodon 96
  Parasaurolophus 98
  Plateosaurus 88
  Stegoceras 101
Sacristy 470
Sacrum
  Crocodile 186
  Domestic cat 195
  Elephant 201
  Hare 197
  Horse 199
  Human 218, 223, 259
  Kangaroo 206
  Lizard 184
  Rhesus monkey 202
  Seal 204
Saddle 582-583
  Acoustic guitar 512
  Bicycle 358-359
  Cannondale SH 600
  hybrid bicycle 361
  Eddy Merckx racing
  bicycle 360
  Horse racing 555
  Show-jumping 554
  Werner motorcycle 362
Saddle clamp 360
Saddle lining 582
Safety area 556
Safety barrier 552
Safety belt 356
Safety binding 552
Safety harness 357
Safety valve
  Bordino steam carriage
  334
  Steamboat 391
Safe working load mark
  383
Sagartia elegans 166
Sagitta 20
Sagittal crest 107, 194
Sagittal section through
brain 236
Sagittarius 19-21
Sagittarius Arm 14
Sago palm 123
Sahara 39, 264-265
Sail
  Roman corbita 372-373
  Square-rigged ship 375
  Types 384-385
  Viking karv 374
Sail batten 376
Sailcloths 384
Sail foot control line 375
Sail hook 384
Sailing 560-561
Sailing rigs 384-385
Sailing warship 376-377
Sailmaker's whipping 382

Sailmaking tools 384
Sail patterns 379, 384
Saiph 18
Salamanders 182
Salient 466
Salisbury Cathedral 470-
471
Saliva 244
Salivary gland
  Butterfly 169
  Snail 177
Salmon 109, 180
Salmon angling 562
Salmon bend gouge 452
Salmson radial engine
398-399
Salt
  Dead Sea 293
  Seawater salt content
  296
Saltasaurus 72, 91
Salt-dome trap 281
Salt formation 312
Salt groundmass 277
Salt lakes 292
Samaras
  Dry fruit 150
  Sycamore 131, 150
Samarium 311
Sambucus nigra 130-131,
143
Samotherium 74
San Andreas fault 58, 62-
63
Sand-bars 290
Sand box 326, 327
Sand dunes
  Rock cycle 267
  Weathering and erosion
  282-283
Sand groundmass 277
Sanding pipe 329
Sand-pits 546
Sandstone
  Marble tomb of Itimad-
  Ud-Daula 489
  Sedimentary rocks 276
Sand wave 299
Sand wedge 547
Sandy deposits 298
Sandy spit 295
Sanguine crayon 430
Sankey diagram 314
Sappho Patera 37
Sapwood 125
Saratoga Race Course 555
Sarcolemma 24
Sarcomere 24
Sarcophilus harrisii 207
Sarcoplasmic reticulum 24
Sarcorhamphus papa 190
Sarracenia purpurea 113
Sartorius muscle 226
Satellite 264
Satellite map 264-265
Saturated zone 292-293
Saturn 46-47
  Solar System 31
Saucer dome 486-487
  Ancient Roman building
  462
Saurischia 82-83, 84, 88
Sauropoda 83
Sauropodomorpha 83, 88
Sauropodomorphs 88-91
Sauropods 70, 88
Savannah 74
Saxboard 561
Saxophone 504, 508-509
Scala 372-373
Scale (musical) 502
Scale leaf scar 124, 155
Scale leaves
  Bishop pine 124
  Bulb 155

Corm 155
Epiphytic orchid 162
Hypogeal germination
152
Pine 122, 125
Plumule 152
Rhizome 155
Sago palm 123
Stem bulbil 155
Scalenus medius muscle
229
Scale of degrees 377
Scales
  Asteroxylon 79
  Bishop pine 124
  Bony fish 180
  Bract 122
  Brassavola nodosa 162
  Caiman 186
  Cartilaginous fish 178
  Crocodilians 186
  Dicotyledons 127
  False fruit 148
  Fern fronds 121
  Insects 168
  Lepidoptera wings 168
  Lizard 184
  Mushroom 115
  Ovuliferous 122-124
  Pine cone 122
  Pine shoot apex 125
  Rattlesnake 185
  Sago palm 122
  Tree fern 112
  Yew 123
Scallop 176
  Fossil 278
Scalloped hammerhead
shark 179
Scalp 234, 236-237
Scaly lichens 114
Scaly skin
  Anchisaurus 89
  Corythosaurus 98
  Dinosaurs 82
  Edmontonia 95
  Gallimimus 87
  Ichthyostega 80
  Iguanodon 97
  Pachycephalosaurus 100
  Psittacosaurus 103
  Reptile 80
  Snake 184
  Stegosaurus 92
  Triceratops 102
  Tyrannosaurus 84
  Westlothiana 81
Scan coil clamp 574
Scan coil deflection yoke
574
Scandinavia 64, 69
Scandium 310
Scapania undulata 118
Scape 168
Scaphoid bone 230
Scaphoid fossa 242
Scaphonyx fischeri 69
Scapula
  Archaeopteryx 85
  Arsinoitherium 104
  Bird 189
  Bony fish 181
  Brachiosaurus 91
  Crocodile 186
  Diplodocus 90
  Domestic cat 195
  Elephant 201
  Eryops 80
  Euoplocephalus 94
  Gallimimus 86
  Hare 197
  Horse 199
  Human 210, 218
  Iguanodon 96
  Kangaroo 206

Lizard 184
Parasaurolophus 99
Pareiasaur 81
Plateosaurus 88
Platypus 206
Rhesus monkey 202
Seal 204
Stegoceras 101
Struthiomimus 87
Toxodon 106
Triceratops 102
Tuojiangosaurus 93
Turtle 187
Tyrannosaurus 84
Scapular muscle 91
Scarlet star 162-163
Scarph 395
Scars
  Horse chestnut 130
  Leaf 128-30, 134
  Rowan twig 131
Scavenge oil line 419
Scelidosaridae 83
Scelidosaurids 71
Scelidosaurus 71
Scent 144
Scheat 19,20
Schedar 19
Schickard 40
Schist 26
Schizocarpic dry fruits
150-151
Schleicher K23 glider 426
Schlumbergera truncata
129
Schooner 384-385
Schrödinger 41
Schubert 35
Schwann cell 228, 239
Schweizer 300c 423
Sciatic nerve 258
Scientific units 591
Scintigram 214
Scissor brace 473
Sciurus carolinensis 197
Sclera 213, 240
Sclereid 159
Sclerenchyma
  Fern rachis 121
  Horsetail stem 120
  Marram grass 113
  Monocotyledon leaf 126
  Stems 134-135
Sclerenchyma fibers 135
Scleroderma citrinum 115
Sclerotic ring 90, 99
Scooter 50-51
Score 388
Scorecard 547
Scorer
  Basketball 532
  Fencing contest 557
  Judo contest 556
  Lacrosse 541
  Netball 535
  Volleyball 534
Scoria 273
Scoring
  Australian rules football
  528
  Badminton 544
  Baseball 536
  Basketball 532
  Cricket 538
  Gaelic football 529
  Hockey 540
  Hurling 540-541
  Netball 534
  Rugby 530-531
  Tennis 544
  Volleyball 534
Scorper 449
Scorpion 170, 278
Scorpiones 170
Scorpius 19, 20

Scotia 463, 485
Scots pine 122
Scraper 46
Scraper ring 344
Scratchplate 513
Scree 282-283
Screen
  French baroque building
  482
  Hydroelectric power
  station 314
  Islamic building 488-489
  Mini television 574
  Screen printing 448
  Twentieth-century
  building 494
Screen bulkhead 381
Screen panel 581
Screen printing 446, 448
Screw 320
  Acoustic guitar 513
  Chair 576-577
  Double bass bow 511
  Lawnmower 580-581
  Mini-television 574
  Power drill 566
  Saddle 582
  Toaster 578
  Violin bow 510
Screw and locknut tappet
adjustor 367
Screw coupling 325
Screwdown greaser 336
Screw fitting 319
Screw hole
  Clock 571
  Power drill 566
Screw joint 413
Screw link 386
Screw locking nut 563
Screw pressure adjustor
447
Scriber 446
Scroll
  Cello 511
  Double bass 511
  Viola 511
  Violin 510
Scrolled buttress 478
Scrolling button 584-585
Scrolling figure 585
Scroll motif 470, 491
Scroll molding 466
Scroll ornament 476, 479,
485
Scroll-shaped corbel 482,
487
Scrollwork 472
Scrotum 211, 259
Scrum-half 530
Scrummages 530
Scrums 530
SCSI 584
Scull 561
Sculling 560
Scull oar 560
Sculptor 19, 20
Sculptural decoration 467
Sculpture 452-455, 493,
495
Sculptured testa 151
Scumbling 440-441
Scupper 393
Scute 186
Scutellum 168
Scutum 19
Scutum plate 173
Scyphozoa 166
Sea
  Anticline trap 281
  Fossils 278
  Hurricane structure 303
  River features 290-291
Sea anemone 166-167
Sea angling 562

Seabed
  Fossils 278
  Ocean floor 298
  River features 290
  Rivers 288
Seabed profile 299
Sea buckthorn 136
Seacat missile launcher
397
Sea-cave 295
Sea-cliff 294-295
  River features 291
Sea creature remains 298
Sea cucumber 174
Sea daisies 174
Sea-dwelling organic
structures 78
Sea-floor spread 58
Seahorse 180
Sea level 66
Sea-level variations 294
Sea lilies 174
Sea lion 204
Seals 204-205
Seam
  Rivetted plates 392
  Sail 384
Seaming twine 384
Seamounts 298
Sea of Japan 265
Searchlight 394-395
Seas 296-297
  Igneous and
  metamorphic rocks 275
  Rivers 288
  Satellite map 265
Seasons 72
Seat
  1906 Renault 337
  Driver's 325, 328
  Faering 375
  Fireman's 325
  First cars 334-335
  Ford Model T 339
  Greek trireme 373
  Harley-Davidson FLHS
  Electra Glide 363
  Honda CB750 363
  Honda VF750 364
  Husqvarna Motocross
  TC610 368
  Kayak 560
  Longboat 380
  Motorcycle 364
  Racing sulky 555
  Renault Clio 352-353
  Show-jumping saddle
  554
  Suzuki RGV500 368
  TGV electric high-speed
  train 329
  Vespa Grand Sport 160
  Mark 1 363
  Weslake Speedway bike
  369
Seat angle 360
Seat assembly 425, 353
Seat back rest frame 337,
352-353
Seat beam 399
Seat belt catch 352
Seat cushion 407, 425
Sea temperature 303
Seat frame
  Chair 577
  Renault Clio 353
Seating 465
Seat lift 568-569
Seat mount 340
Seatpad 576
Seat pan 409
Seat post 358, 360
Seat post quick-release
bolt 358
Seat rail 577

Seat spring 335
Seat squab 335, 337
Seat stay 358, 360
Seat support strut 398
Seat tube 358, 360, 361
Seat upholstery 577
Sea urchins 174-175
Seawater
  River features 290
  Salt content 296
Seaweeds **116-117**
Seaworm 78
Sebaceous gland 234-235
Secondary bronchus 215
Secondary colors 439
Secondary conduit 272-273
  Rock cycle 266
Secondary crater 34
Secondary flight feathers 188, 191
Secondary follicle 258
Secondary mycelium 115
Secondary phloem 134-135
Secondary remiges 188, 191
Secondary rotor 317
Secondary suspension 327
Secondary thallus 114
Secondary vascular tissue 134
Secondary xylem 125, 134-135
Second-century building 462
Second electron shell 309
Second mast 376
Second-row forward 530
Second slip 538
Second toe 232
Second violins 503, 504-505
Second wheel set 329
Secretory gland 161
Secretory thyroid gland cells 217
Secretory vesicle 216
Section 586, 587
Secure anchor 386
Security chain 355
Sediment
  Coastlines 294-295
  Fossils 278
  Glaciers 286-287
  Lakes 292
  Mineral resources 280
  Mountain building 62-63
  Ocean floor 298-299
  River features 290-291
  Rivers 288
  Rock cycle 266-267
Sedimentary rocks **276-277**
  Igneous and metamorphic rocks 274
  Rock cycle 266-267
Sedna Planitia 36-37
Sedum rupestre 128
Sedum spectabile 128-129
Seed
  Apomixis 146
  Apple 149
  Cape gooseberry 149
  Dehydration 152
  Dispersal 148-151
  Dormancy 152
  Dry fruit 150-151
  Embryo development 147
  Fig 148
  Germination 152, 152-153
  Goosegrass 150
  Gymnosperms 122

Hilum 148-149, 151-153
Hogweed 151
Honesty 151
Larkspur 151
Lemon 148
Love-in-a-mist 151
Lychee 148
Melon 149
Parts 152-153
Pea 150
Pine 122
Raspberry 149
Root development 152
Scots pine 122
Smooth cypress 123
Strawberry 150
Succulent fruit 148-149
Sweet chestnut 150
Sycamore 151, 151
Wind dispersal 150
Wings 150-151
Yew 123
Seed axis 152-153
Seed coat 132, 152-153
  Dry fruit 150-151
  Embryo development 147
  Epigeal germination 153
  Hypogeal germination 152
  Succulent fruit 148-149
Seed fern 278
Seed leaves 126, 152-153
  Dry fruit 150-151
  Embryo development 147
  Epigeal germination 153
  Hypogeal germination 152
  Pine 122
  Succulent fruit 148-149
Seedlings
  Epigeal germination 153
  Hypogeal germination 152
  Pine 122
Seed-producing organs 148-149
Seed scar 122
Seed stalks 150
Seed wings 151
Segmental arch 492
Segmental pediment 462, 478
Segnosauria 83
Seif dune 283
Seismic activity 58
Seizing 383, 384, 387, 388-389
Selaginella sp. 120
Selector fork 366
Selector switch 578-579
Selenite 270
Selenium 311
Self-pollination 144
Semaphore signal 330
Semen 217
Semi-arch 470-471
Semibreve 502-503
Semi-bulkhead 425
Semi-circle 532
Semicircular barrel vault 493
Semicircular canals 243
Semicircular tower 465
Semi-conductor 506
Semi-dome 484, 482, 488
Semi-elliptical arch 484
Semi-elliptic leaf spring 342
Semilunar fold 249
Semi-metals 310-311
Seminal receptacle 169
  Spider 170
Seminal vesicle 259

Semiquaver 502
Semi-solid core 37
Semi-solid outer core 41
Semi-sprawling stance 82
  Westlothiana 81
Semitendinosus muscle 227
Senior ratings' mess 397
Sensory antenna 168
Sensory hinge 160
Sensory tentacle 176
Sepal 140-143
  Clematis 151
  Dicotyledons 126-127
  Dry fruit 150-151
  Everlasting pea 129
  Fertilization 146-147
  Monocotyledons 126
  Peruvian lily 129
  Pitcher plant 113
  Pollination 145
  Rose 151
  Succulent fruit 149
Sepal remains 146-147
Sepal sheath 141
Separated carpels 151
Septime 557
Septum 115
  False 151
  Interventricular 251
  Nasal 213, 241
  Placenta 260
Sequoiadendron sp. 70
Series electrical circuit 316
Serif 445
Serous pericardium 250
Serpens Caput 18, 21
Serpens Cauda 19, 20
Serpentes 184
Serpentine neck 374
Serrated tooth 84, 85, 88
Serrate leaf margins 129
Serratus anterior muscle 226
Server 534, 544, 545
Service 544
Service area 534
Service box line 545
Service court 544, 545
Service door 415
Service judge 544, 545
Service line 544, 545
Service shaft 498
Service zone 545
Serving 388
Serving mallet 383, 384, 388
Servo control-unit fairing 417
Servo-tab 414, 415
Sesamoid bone 198
Seta 112, 119
Set-back buttress 481
Set square 445
Seven Sisters 14
Seventeenth century 474
  Building 479-481, 488
  Capital 490
  Dome 486-487
  Roof 490
  Style 478
  Tomb 489
Seventh century
  Building 491
Sevier fault 276
Sex cells 154
  Fertilization 146-147
  Gametophyte plants 120
  Gymnosperms 122
  Liverwort 118
  Moss 118-119
Sextans 21
Sexual reproduction
  Algae 116-117

Bryophytes 119
Flowering plants 140-147
Mosses 118-119
Seaweed 116-117
Spirogyra sp. 117
Seyfert 41
Seyfert galaxies 12-13
Shackle 382, 386
Shackle pin 382
Shade coupling 573
Shaft
  Ancient Egyptian column 459
  Ancient Greek temple 461
  Ancient Roman building 465, 465
  Arrow 548
  Asian building 490-491
  Badminton racket 545
  Electric generator 317
  Feather 191
  Femur 225
  French temple 485
  Golf club 547
  Harness racer 555
  Hydroelectric power station 314
  Javelin 542
  Kayak paddle 560
  Medieval church 468-469
  Modern building 498
  Neoclassical building 478, 483
  Nineteenth-century building 493
  Phalanx 250
  Power drill 566
  Roman Corbita 373
  Sculling oar 560
  Ski pole 553
  Squash racket 545
Shaft drive 366
Shale
  Contact metamorphism 274
  Grand Canyon 277
Shallow carvel-built hull 391
Shallow flats 293
Shank
  Anatomy of a hook 562
  Danforth anchor 386
  Hook 383
  Roman anchor 372
  Sail hook 384
  Shackle pin 382
  Shoes 568-569
Shannon bone 198
Shape
  Chemical reactants 512
  Matter 306-307
  Periodic table 310
Sharks **178-179**, 180
  Fossil teeth 67
Sharp 502
Sharpey's fiber 225
Shaula 19, 20
Shave 374
Shaving foam 306
Shearing 61
Sheave 383
Sheave for cat tackle 380
Sheep 198
Sheepskin numnah 554
Sheer 374
Sheerplank 380
Sheer pole 373
Sheer strake 375, 393
Sheet 372, 375, 382
Sheet anchor 395
Sheet bend 389
Sheet-iron louvre 493
Sheet lead 383
Shelf formation 282

Shell
  379 cm shell 397
  6 in shell 397
  Bicycle helmet 360
  Building 464, 476
  Chelonians 186
  Crab 172
  Dorsal margin 176
  Egg 192-193
  Exploding 394, 396-397
  Fossil 278
  Massive stars 26
  Mollusc 176-177
  Octopus 176
  Rib 176
  Rudiment 176
  Scallop 176
  Small stars 24-25
  Snail 177
  Standing block 382
  Terrapin 187
  Ventral margin 176
Shell bogie 396
Shell case 397
Shelled invertebrates 56
Shelley 35
Shell-like fracture 270
Shell room 396
Shelly limestone 267
"Shiaijo" 556
Shield 394-395
"Shield bearers" 92
Shield volcano 42
Shin
  Herrerasaurus 86
  Human 211
Shinarump member 276
Shin guard 525, 553
Shinty 540
Shinumo quartzite 277
Ship 387
  74-gun ship 379, 380-381
Ship of the line **380-381**
Ship's cannon 376, 394
Ships of Greece and Rome **372-373**
Ship's shield 394-395
Ship's wheel 378, 390, 394
Shipwright 374
Shiv 383
Shiver 383
Shock absorber
  1906 Renault 336
  ARV light aircraft 425
  Football helmet 527
  Honda CB750 363
  Honda VF750 364
  Renault Clio 350
  Suzuki RGV500 368
  Vespa Grand Sport 160
  Mark 1 563
  Volkswagen Beetle 340
Shock-absorbing spring 401, 405
Shock-strut 401
Shock waves 27
  Path 63
Shoes **568-569**
  Baseball 537
  Basketball 533
  Football 527
  Golf 547
  Handball 535
  Hurling 541
  Rowing 560
  Rugby 531
  Soccer 525
  Track and field 543
Shoot
  Broomrape 163
  Embryo 147
  Horsetail 120
  Hypogeal germination 152
  Pine 125

Vegetative reproduction 155
Shoot apex 125
Shooting 548-549
Shooting circle 540
Shooting positions 548
Shoreline
  Coastlines 294
  Continental-shelf floor 298
Short line 545
Shorts
  Australian rules football 529
  Hurling 541
  Soccer 525
  Volleyball 534
Short saphenous vein 253
Shortstop 556
Short-wave radio 318
Shot
  Field events equipment 542
  Gun 378
Shot garland 381
Shot put 543
Shot-put circle 542
Shot-put fan 542
Shoulder
  Anchisaurus 89
  Cello 511
  Corythosaurus 98
  Double bass 511
  Gorilla 203
  Harp 511
  Horse 199
  Human 210
  Iguanodon 97
  Rabbit 196
  Rigging 382-383
  Stegoceras 101
  Stegosaurus 92
  Viola 511
  Violin 510
Shoulderblade 210, 218
Shoulder cowling 412
Shoulder girdle 80
Shoulder joint
  Brachiosaurus 91
  Gallimimus 86
  Human 218
  Parasaurolophus 99
  Plateosaurus 88
  Triceratops 102
  Tyrannosaurus 84
Shoulder pad 426
Shoulder padding 551
Shoulder pass 535
Shoulder spikes
  Edmontonia 95
  Euoplocephalus 94
Shoulder strap 426
Shoulder wheel throw 556
Show-jumping 554
Shreve, R.H. 494
Shrewlike mammals 70
Shrimp 172
  Fossil 79
Shrine 490-491
Shroud
  Dhow 376
  Longboat 380
  Rigging 383
  Roman corbita 373
  Sailing dinghy 561
  Sailing warship 376
Shrubs 130-131
Shutter 588
Shutter for gun 394
Shutter release button 588-589
Shutter speed dial 588-589
Shuttlecock 544-545
Sickle motif 491
Sidalcea malviflora 136

Side aisle
  Cathedral dome 484
  Gothic church 472-473
  Medieval church 469
Side bench 380
Side brace and retraction
  jack trunnions 414
Sidecar
  BMW R/60 362
  Motorcycle racing 368-369
Side chapel 469-470, 479
Side counter timber 381
Side-cowling 408
Side drum 504-505
Side fairing
  BAe-146 jetliner 415
  Formula One racing car 357
Side forequarter hold 556
Side gear 347
Side housing 346-347
Side lamp 338-339
Side light 332, 333, 362
Sideline
  Badminton 545
  Basketball 532
  Football 526
  Handball 535
  Hockey 540
  Men's lacrosse 540
  Netball 535
  Tennis 541
  Volleyball 534
Side marker lamp 346, 349
Side-mounted engine 398
Side plate 562
Side reflector 362, 363
Siderite band 277
Side rudder 374-375
Side-shooting 541
Side vent 329
Side view of our galaxy 14
Side wall 545, 558
Side-wall line 545
Sideways erosion
  River features 290
  Rivers 288
Sierra Madre 264
Sierra Nevada 57, 75
Sieve tubes 134
Sieving beak 188
Sif Mons 37
Sight 394
Sight pin 549
Sight screen 538
Sighting hood
  Battleship 394
  Gun turret 396
Sighting rule 376-377
Sights 548-549
Sigma Canis Majoris 21
Sigmoid colon 249
Signal 574
Signal flag compartment 397
Signal gear 395
Signaling systems 330-331
Signature 586, 587
Sikorsky, Igor 422
Silence 502
Silencer
  Harley-Davidson FLHS
    Electra Glide 362
  Renault Clio 350
  Suzuki RGV500 368
  Vespa Grand Sport 160
    Mark 1 363
  Weslake Speedway bike 369
Silencing heat exchanger 404
Silicate core 51
Silicate dust 53
Silicate material 39

Silicate rock 39
Silicates 269
Siliceous ooze 299
Silicon 26
  Earth's composition 39
  Earth's crust 58
  Periodic table 311
  Variety of matter 306
Siliquas 150-151
Silk gland 170
Sill 26
  Ancient Roman mill 464
  Renaissance building 475
  Twentieth-century building 494
Sill trim 353
Silly mid-off 538
Silly mid-on 538
Silurian period
  Fossil record 279
  Geological time 56
Silver
  Mineral resources 280-281
  Minerals 268
  Periodic table 311-312
  Streak 271
Silver lines 430-431
Silver molybdenite 271
Silver nitrate solution 312
Silverpoint 430, 431
Silver wire 430
Silvery metals 310
Simple electrical circuit 316
Simple eye 170-171
Simple leaves 136-137
  Entire 130
  Hastate 128
  Herbaceous flowering plants 128-129
  Lanceolate 131
  Lobed 131
Simple machines 320
Simple Machines Law 320
Simple pulleys 320
Simple succulent fruits 148-149
Simulated sound 520
Single bass note string 515
Single-celled micro-organisms 78
Single clump block 373
Single cylinder 335
Single-decker bus 332, 333
Single flowers 140-141, 143
Single front driving wheel 334
Single-leg main landing gear 407
Single overhead cam engine 363
Single-piece skin 413
Single-pulley system 320
Single reed 508, 509
Singles 544
Single scull 560, 561
Single sheet bend 387
Single-sided trailing-link fork 363
Single wing hold 556
Singularity
  Formation of black hole 29
  Stellar black hole 29
Sinistral strike-slip fault 61
Sink-holes 284-285
Sinking land 294
Sinopia 434, 435
Sinous venosus sclerae 241
Sinuous cell wall 156

Sinus
  Frontal, 212, 245
  Green alga 112
  Renal 256
  Superior sagittal 212
Sinus Borealis 69
Sinus Iridum 40
Siphon
  Octopus 176-177
  Sea urchin 175
Siphonoglyph 167
Sirius
  Canis Major 21
  Northern stars 18
  Our galaxy and nearby galaxies 15
  Southern stars 21
  Spectral absroption lines 23
  Star magnitudes 22
Sirius A 23
Sirius B 23
Sixteenth century
  Building 476-477
  Staircase 472
  Style 462, 470
Size (glue) 431, 432, 436
Skarn 26
Skate
  Chondrichthyes 178
  Ice hockey 550, 551
Skeletal muscle 228
Skeletal muscle fiber 228
Skeleton
  Archaeopteryx 85
  Arsinoitherium 104-105
  Baryonyx hand 85
  Bat 105
  Bird 189
  Bony fish 180-181
  Cow's foot 198
  Crocodile 186
  Diplodocus 90
  Domestic cat 195
  Elephant 201
  Eryops 80-81
  Frog 183
  Hare 197
  Horse 199
  Human 218-219
  Iguanodon 96
  Kangaroo 206
  Kentrosaurus 93
  Lizard 184
  Parasaurolophus 98-99
  Pareiasaur 81
  Plateosaurus 88-89
  Platypus 206
  Rhesus monkey 202
  Seal 204
  Snake 185
  Spider 171
  Sponge 166
  Stegoceras 100-101
  Stegosaurus 93
  Struthiomimus 87
  Toxodon 106
  Triceratops 102-103
  Tuojiangosaurus 93
  Turtle 187
  Tyrannosaurus 84-85
  Westlothiana 81
Sketch book 430
Ski boot 552
Skid 402, 404
Skid beam 580
Ski goggles 552, 553
Skiing 552, 553
Skilled movements 237
Skin
  Amphibian 80, 182
  Drumhead 518
  Lizard 184
  Reptile 80
  Snake 184

Succulent fruits 148-149
  Waterproof 81
Skin and hair 234-235
"Skin-grip" pin 424-425
Skin lap-joint 413, 414, 415
Skin tones 441
Ski pole 552
Skirt
  Lamp 572
  Saddle 583
Skis 552
Skull
  Acanthostega 80
  Alligator 186
  Ankylosaurus 94
  Australopithecus 108
  Baryonyx 83
  Bear 194
  Bird 189
  Camarasaurus 91
  Chimpanzee 202
  Crocodilians 186
  Diplodocus 90
  Domestic cat 195
  Elephant 201
  Euoplocephalus 94
  Fetal 220
  Gharial 186
  Hadrosaurs 96
  Hare 197
  Heterodontosaurus 83
  Homo erectus 108
  Homo habilis 108
  Horse 199
  Human 108, 212, 218, 220-221, 222, 236-237
  Hyaenodon 107
  Iguanodon 96
  Kangaroo 206
  Lambeosaurus 99
  Lion 194
  Lizard 184
  Marginocephalian 100
  Moeritherium 105
  Octopus 176
  Opossum 106
  Pachycephalosaurs 100
  Pachycephalosaurus 100
  Phiomia 105
  Plateosaurus 88
  Platypus 206
  Prenocephale 100
  Protoceratops 102
  Rattlesnake 185
  Rhesus monkey 202
  Seal 204
  Smilodon 107
  Stegoceras 100
  Styracosaurus 102
  Synapsid reptile 67
  Tortoise 77
  Turtle 187
Skull bones 81
Skullcap 555
Skunks 194
Skylight
  Battleship 394
  Building 493, 494
  Iron paddlesteamer 392-393
Skyscraper 494
Slab
  Ancient Egyptian building 458-459
  Modern building 499
  Twentieth-century building 494
Slaked lime 434
Slalom
  Kayaking 560
  Skiing 552
Slalom clothing 553
Slalom equipment 553
Slalom gate 552

Slat 421
Slate 274, 275
Sleeper 324, 331
Sleeve port 343
Sleeve valve 343
Slender thistle 129
Slick racing tire 365
  Formula One racing car 357
  Kirby BSA 369
  Suzuki RCV500 369
Slide 396
Slide bar 325
Slide brace 507
Slide locking lever 396
Slide track 561
Slide valve 390
Sliding bed 447
Sliding curtain 329
Sliding seat 561
Sliding window 333
Sling fixing point 549
Slip face 285
Slip faults 61
Slipher 43
Slope structure 60
Sloping roof 486
Slot 356
Slug 176
Slumped cliff 295
Slur 503
Smallbore rifle shooting 548
Smallbore rifle target 549
Small Computer System
  Interface (SCSI) 584
Small intestine
  Brachiosaurus 90
  Chimpanzee 202
  Cow 198
  Domestic cat 195
  Elephant 200
  Euoplocephalus 94
  Frog 182
  Human 214, 249
  Lizard 185
  Tortoise 187
Small Magellanic Cloud
  Hydrus and Mensa 20
  Our galaxy and nearby galaxies 15
  Stars of southern skies 20
Small stars 24-25
Small theropods 87
Small-scale rock deformi-ties 61
Smalti 450
Smalti mosaic 450
Smash 534
Smell 244
Smilodon 107
Smokebox 324, 325
Smoky quartz 268
Smooth cypress 123
Smooth endoplasmic reticulum 216
Smudging 430, 431
Smuts 114
Snail 176-177
Snake-head ornament 375
Snakes 184-185
Snap head 392
Snare 518
Snare drum 518
Snort mast 397
Snout
  Anchisaurus 89
  Caiman 186
  Crocodilians 186
  Dogfish 178
  Edmontonia 95
  Herrerasaurus 86
  Iguanodonts 96
  Jawless fish fossil 78

Pachycephalosaurus 100
  Rat 196
Snow
  Glaciers 286-287
  Weather 302
Snowflake moray eel 180
Snowflakes 302
Soane, J. 478, 482-483
Sobkou Planitia 35
Soccer 524-525
Soccer uniform 525
Socket 573
Socle
  Ancient Egyptian temple 458
  Baroque church 479
  Cathedral dome 487
  Gothic church 472
  Medieval church 469
  Neoclassical building 478-479
  Renaissance building 474
Sodalite 269
Sodium 35, 58
  Periodic table 310
  Seawater salt content 296
Sodium hydroxide 312
Sodium lines 23
Soffit 464, 484, 498
Soft eye 382
Soft hair brush 436, 438, 440
Soft-headed mallet 516, 517, 519
Soft metals 310
Soft palate 212, 245
Soft pastels 440
Soft pedal 514, 515
Soft rock
  River features 290
  Weathering and erosion 282
Solanum tuberosum 128
Solar day 34
Solar eclipse 32
Solar flare 32-33
Solar panel 496
Solar radiation 300-301
Solar system 38, 30-31
Solar wind
  Earth's magnetosphere 38
  Structure of comet 53
  Sun 32
Solarium 494
Solar Wings Pegasus
  Quasar microlight 427
Sole 568
Sole of foot 234
Soleus muscle 227, 233
Solfataras 272-273
Solid body 512, 513
Solid crystals 306
Solid heart thimble 383
Solidified lava
  Lake formation 292
  Volcanoes 272-273
Solid ink stick 444
Solid rubber tire 335
Solids 306-307
  Chemical reactions 312
Solutions 306, 312
Sombrero 529
Somites 79
SONAR bulge 397
SONAR torpedo decoy 396
SONAR transducer array 397
Sonic boom 416
Sonoran Desert 264
Soot particles 313
Sophocles 35
Soralium 114

Sorbus aucuparia 130-131
Soredia 114
Sori 120-121
Sostenuto pedal 514, 515
Sound 314-315
  Coastline 295
  Electronic instruments 520
  Musical notation 502
Soundboard
  Acoustic guitar 513
  Concert grand piano 515
  Harp 511
  Upright piano 514
  Viola 511
  Violin 510
Sound hole
  Acoustic guitar 512-513
  Cello 511
  Double bass 511
  Viola 511
  Violin 510
Sound module 521
Sound selection control 520
South Africa 64
South America 264
  Cretaceous period 72-73
  Jurassic period 70
  Late Carboniferous period 66
  Middle Ordovician period 64
  Quaternary period 76-77
  Tertiary period 74-75
  Triassic period 68
South American plate 59
South Asian buildings **490-491**
South Atlantic Gyre 296
  Satellite map 265
South Atlantic Ocean 39, 73
South-east trade winds 300
South-easterly wind 303
South Equatorial Belt 45
South equatorial current 296-297
Southerly wind 303
Southern Hemisphere 296-297
South Galactic Pole 15
South Indian Gyre 297
South magnetic polar region 28
South Pacific Gyre 296
South Pacific Ocean 39
South polar ice-cap
  Structure of Mars 43
  Surface of Mars 42
South Pole
  Atmospheric circulation and winds 300
  Coriolis force 297
  Earth 38
  Jupiter 44
  Mars 42
  Mercury 34
  The Moon 40
  Neptune 50
  Pluto 51
  Pulsar 28
  Saturn 46
  Uranus 48-49
  Venus 36
South rim 277
South seeking pole 317
South Temperate Belt 45
South Temperate Zone 45
South Tropical Zone 45
Space 300-301
Spadix 143
Span 484

Spandrel
  Gothic church 471
  Islamic building 488-489
  Neoclassical building 482
  Nineteenth-century building 493
  Renaissance building 474
Spanish bowline 389
Spar
  BAe-146 jetliner components 415
  BE 2B tail 405
  Concorde 417
  Pegasus Quasar microlight 427
Spare tire 337, 339
Spare wheel 355
Spare wheel well 341
Spark plug 342-343, 410
Spark plug cap 366
Spark plug hole 346
Spark plug lead 344
Spar trunnion 409
Spat 426-427
Spathe 143
  Horsetails 120
Spawn 182-183, 192
Speaker 521, 575, 585
Spear 382
Spear head 109
Spectral absorption lines 22-23
Spectral type 22-23
Specular haematite 268
Speech 237
Speed
  Forces 320
  Gearbox 366
Speedball nib 444
Speedometer 362
Speedometer drive 365
Speedway motorcycle racing 368
Sperm 258-259
Spermatheca
  Snail 177
  Spider 170
Sperm cell 217
Sperm duct 195
Spermoviduct 177
Sperm whale 204-205
Sperry-ball gun turret 408
Sphenethmoid bone 183
Sphenoidal fontanelle 220
Sphenoidal sinus 212, 245
Sphenoid bone 220
Sphenopsids 279
Sphenopteris latiloba 72
Spherical umbel 143
Sphincter muscle
  Anal 249
  Iris 241
  Pyloric 249
  Sea anemone 167
  Urethral 257
Sphyrna lewini 179
Spica 18, 21
Spicule 32, 33
Spicules 166
Spider
  Arachnid 170-171
  Bicycle 358, 360
Spigot
  Capstan 387
  Lamp 573
Spike
  Aechmea miniata 162
  Dodder 163
  Double bass 511
  Flower 143
  Grape hyacinth 155
  Thyreophorans 92-93
  Volleyball 554

Spiked sole 547, 543
Spiky cupule 150
Spinal column 238
Spinal cord
  Bird 189
  Bony fish 181
  Chimpanzee 202
  Dogfish 179
  Dolphin 205
  Domestic cat 195
  Elephant 200
  Human 212, 217, 223, 236, 238, 261
  Lizard 185
  Rabbit 196
Spinal ganglion 223, 238, 243
Spinal nerve 223, 238
Spindle 567
Spine
  Aechmea miniata 162
  Barberry 130-131
  Book 586-587
  Bromeliad 113
  Calligraphy character 445
  Cnidocyte 167
  Diatom 116
  Dryland plants 156
  Golden barrel cactus 156
  Haemal 180
  Herbaceous flowering plants 128-129
  Human 218, 222-223
  Mahonia 130-131
  Modern jetliners 413, 415
  Neural 180
  Sea urchin 174
  Starfish 174
Spine end fairing 421
Spinner
  ARV light aircraft 424-425
  Hawker Tempest components 408
  Hawker Tempest fighter 409
  Lockheed Electra airliner 407
  Turbofan engine 418
Spinneret 170-171
Spinner mounting disk 406
Spinning lure 562
Spinose-dentate margin 129
Spinous process 222-223
Spiny anteaters 206
Spiny leaflets 130-131
Spiracle
  Acanthostega 80
  Caterpillar 169
  Spider 170
Spiral arm
  Galaxies 12-13
  Milky Way 14
Spiral galaxy
  Galaxies 12-13
  Milky Way 14-15
  Objects in Universe 11
  Origin and expansion of Universe 10-11
Spiral ganglion 243
Spiraling clouds 302
Spiraling low-pressure cells 302
Spiraling rain 303
Spiraling winds 302-303
Spiral scroll 460
Spiral spring 449
Spiral staircase 472, 476
Spiral tubes 542
Spiral valve 179
Spiral wrack 116

Spire
  Asian building 490-491
  Gothic church 470-471, 473
  Medieval building 466, 468
  Nineteenth-century building 493
  Renaissance building 476-477
Spirketting 381
Spirogyra sp. 117
Spit 291
Splat 576
Splat mortice 576-577
Splayed window-sill 475, 482
Spleen
  Bony fish 181
  Chimpanzee 202
  Domestic cat 195
  Elephant 200
  Frog 182
  Human 215, 249
Splenic artery 253
Splicing fid 383
Splint bone 198
Splinter bar 335
Splintery fracture 270
Split flap 406
Split line 151
Split-open pollen sac 144
Split rudder 421
Spoiler 346, 349
Spoiler anchorage 413
Spoiler arm 414
Spoke
  Bicycle wheel 358-359
  Bordino Steam Carriage 335
  Eddy Merckx racing bicycle 361
  Etching press 447
  Paddle wheel 391
  Ship's wheel 390
Spoked wheel
  Bicycle 358-359
  Pacing sulky 555
Spoke guard 358
Spoke nipple 361
Sponge roller 442
Sponges **166-167**
  Fossils 279
Spongocoel 166
Spongy bone 224
Spongy mesophyll 126, 139
Spongy tissues 156
Spool 562
Spoon 560
Spoon-shaped tooth 91
Sporangia 120-121
Sporangiophore 120
Sporangium 79
Spore-case 79
Spore-producing structures
  Fern 121
  Fungi 114-115
  Lichen 114
  Moss 112
Spores
  Clubmoss 120
  Fern 120-121
  Fungi 114-115
  Horsetail 120
  Lichen 114
  Liverworts 118
  Mosses 118-119
  Mushroom 115
Sporophores 114-115
Sporophytes
  Clubmoss 120
  Fern 120-121
  Horsetail 120

Liverworts 118
  Moss 112, 118-119
Sports tire 365
Sports wheel 340
Sprag clutch 410
Spreader 561
Spring
  Lakes and Groundwater 292
  Lawnmower 580
  Motorbike 366
  Power drill 566
  Toaster 579
Spring and chassis unit 337
Spring attachment 573
Spring balance 320
Springboard diving 558
Spring line 292
Spring perch 338
Spring petiole 160
Spring shock absorber 338-339
Spring tides 296-297
Spring-trap mechanism 160
Spring tree 582
Spring washer 567
Spring wood xylem 134
Sprint races 560
Sprinting 542
Spritsail 578
Sprit yard 576
Sprocket 358, 366
Spruce 513
Spruce beam 560
Sprung chassis 334
Spunyarn 388
Spun yarn serving 383
Spur 169
Spurious wing 191
Squadron code 409
Squamata 184
Squamosal bone 183
Squamous suture 220
Squamulose lichens 114
Squamulose thallus 114
Square 485
Square brass line 576
Square cut 538
Square knot 388
Square leg 538
Square-leg umpire 538
Square masonry 465
Square rib 486
Square-rigged ship 375
Square sail 374, 378, 384
Square-section steel tubing 364
Square section tire 362, 369
Squash 544, 545
Squeegee 448
Squid 176
Squinch 466
Squirrel 196-197
Squirrel hair brush 438
Squirrel mop wash brush 438
SST 416-417
St. John's wort 145
St. Basil's Cathedral 487
St. Paul's Cathedral
  Arch 484
  Baroque style 478, 480-481
  Dome 480, 486-487
  Old 470, 472
Stabilizer 397, 548
Stabilizer-bar weight 422
Stabilizer fin 396
Stable elements 310, 311

Stack 295
Staff 577, 396
Stage 477, 495
Stained glass 470
Stainless steel cover 579
Staircase
  Ancient Roman building 465
  Baroque church 481
  Gothic church 470, 472
  Medieval building 466
  Modern building 496-497, 499
  Neoclassical building 483
  Renaissance building 474-477
Staircase turret 468
Stairs 477
Stairway 489
Stalactites 284-285
Stalagmites 284-285
Stalagmitic boss 284
Stalagmitic floor 284
Stalk
  Algae 116
  Barnacle 173
  Dicotyledons 127
  Flower 140
  Fungi 114-115
  Liverwort 118
  Monocotyledons 128
  Moss 112, 119
  Pitcher plant 113
  Seaweed 117
  Stem succulent 113
  Water lily 159
Stalked barnacle 173
Stalked secretory glands 161
Stalk scar 123
Stall warning vane 412
Stamen remains 146-147, 150
Stamens 140-143
  Anther 140-143
  Dicotyledon flower 126-127
  Fertilization 146-147
  Filament 140-143
  Insect-pollination 144
  Monocotyledon flower 126
  Rose 131
Stamp 445
Stance
  Dinosaurs 82
  Hominids 108
  Westlothiana 81
Stanchion 373, 393
Standard 554
Standard-bred horse 554, 555
Standard European paper 445
Standard knee 381
Standby pitot head 416-417
Standing block 382
Standing lug mizzen 385
Standing part
  Hawser bend 387
  Knots 388, 389
  Rigging 382-383
  Single sheet bend 387
Standing position 548
Standing rigging 382-383
Stand-off half 530
Stapes 242
Staple 449
Starbirth region 16
Starboard side 374, 560
Starch grains 139
  Chlamydomonas sp. 116
  Orchid root 133

Star clusters 16-17
 Objects in Universe 11
 Our galaxy and nearby
 galaxies 14
Star coral 167
Star drag 562
Star dune 283
Starfish 174-175
 Fossil 79
Star formation in Orion 24
Starling 467
Star magnitudes 22
Stars 22-23
 Massive stars 26-27
 Milky Way 14-15
 Neutron stars and black
 holes 28-29
 Small stars 24-25
 Star clusters 16
 Sun 32-33
Star-shaped parenchyma
 135
Star-shaped sclereids 159
Stars of northern skies 18-
 19
Stars of southern skies 20-
 21
Starter 339, 558
Starter cog 336
Starter cup 580
Starter motor
 Hawker Tempest
 components 408
 Mid West twin-rotor
 engine 411
 Renault Clio 351
 Volkswagen Beetle 340
Starter ring 345
Starting block 558
Starting handle 336-337,
 338, 343
Starting line (100m) 542
State room 392
Static air-pressure plate
 412
Static discharge wick 406
Static electricity 316
Stationary gear 346-347,
 411
Stator 410
Stator electricity generator
 317
Statue 472, 478
Statue creation 455
Statuette 476, 481
Staurikosaurids 69
Staurikosaurus 69
Stay 325, 392
Staysail 378, 385
Steady pin hole 570
"Stealth" bomber 420-421
Steam 273, 307
 Locomotives 324, 325
 Nuclear power station
 314
 Oil-fired power station
 315
Steamboat with paddle
 wheels 391
Steam car 334, 342
Steam chest 334
Steam chest pressure
 gauge 325
Steam condenser 397
Steam dome 325
Steam engine 390-391
Steam generator 314
Steam grating 380
Steam launch 394
Steam locomotive 324, 325
Steam pipe 334-335
Steam pipework 397
Steam-powered Cugnot
 "Fardier" 334
Steam whistle 392

Steel 492
Steel and concrete floor
 498
Steel and titanium skin
 416
Steel body 354
Steel brace 493
Steel column 497-498
Steel floor-plate 497
Steel frame 360, 364
Steel girder framework
 314
Steel lattice-beam 497
Steel lock 360
Steel mallet 517
Steel mullion 494
Steel point 452
Steel rails 330
Steel-reinforced concrete
 494
Steel sleeper 330
Steel wheel 340, 350-351
Steeple 471, 481
Steeplechase 554
Steep ridge 283
Steerboard side 374
Steerer tube 359
Steering 350, 364
Steering actuator 416
Steering arm 338-339
Steering box assembly 340
Steering column
 Benz Motorwagen 335
 Ford Model T 339
 Renault Clio 350
 Volkswagen Beetle 341
Steering gear 392
Steering gearbox 339
Steering head 335
Steering idler 340
Steering knuckle 338
Steering link 335, 357
Steering oar 374
Steering pump pulley 344
Steering rack 335, 350
Steering spindle 336
Steering stop 425
Steering tie-rod 340
Steering tiller 334-335, 337
Steering track-rod 337
Steering wheel
 1906 Renault 337
 Ford Model T 338-339
 Renault Clio 350, 353
 White Steam Car 342
Steering wiffletree 337
Steersman 560
Stegoceras 100-101
Stegosauria 83
Stegosaurus 71, 92
Steib chair 362
Stela 459
Stele
 Dicotyledons 127
 Monocotyledons 127
 Root 132-133
Stellar core 17
Stellar spectral absorption
 lines 22-23
Stellate parenchyma 135
Stem 134-135
 Aechmea miniata 162
 Asteroxylon 79
 Bamboo 131
 Barberry 130-131
 Battleship 394
 Begonia 129
 Bishop pine 124-125
 Brassavola nodosa 162
 Bromeliad 113
 Broomrape 163
 Calligraphy character
 445
 Canadian pond weed
 158-159

Chusan palm 130
Clubmoss 120
Corallina officinalis 117
Couch grass 113
Crab cactus 129
Dicotyledons 126-127
Dodder 163
Eddy Merckx racing
 bicycle 561
Epiphytes 162-163
Everlasting pea 129
Florists' chrysanthemum
 129
Flower arrangements
 143
Golden barrel cactus 156
Guzmania lingulata 162-
 163
Hogweed 129
Horsetail 120
Ice-plant 128-129
Iron paddlesteamer 393
Ivy 131
Kedrostis africana 113
Live-for-ever 128-129
Liverwort 118
Maidenhair tree 123
Maple 127
Monocotyledons 126-127
Moss 119
Parasitic plants 163
Passion flower 130
Peach 131
Perennials 130-131
Sago palm 123
Strawberry 128
String of hearts 157
Vegetative reproduction
 154-155
Water fern 158
Welwitschia 123
Woody plants 130-131
Woody stem 134
Yew 123
Stem bases
 Bulbil 155
 Gazmania lingulata 162-
 163
Stem branch 129
Stem bulbils 155
Stem cambium 126
Stem head 376
Stempost
 74-gun ship 381
 Dhow 376
 Longboat 380
 Sailing warship 376
 Viking ships 374-375
Stem projections 156
Stem segments 129
Stem succulents 113, 156-
 157
Stem tubers 128, 154
Stencil 446
Step
 74-gun ship 381
 ARV light aircraft 424
 BE 2B bomber 404
 Blériot XI monoplane
 401
 Medieval building 467
 Modern building 499
 Neoclassical building
 483
 Steam-powered Cugnot
 334
 Twentieth-century
 building 495
 Wooden sailing ship 378
Stephenson, Robert 324
Stepped roof 481
Stepped stempost 375
Stepped sternpost 375
Sterile hairs 117, 119
Sterile ray 119

Sterile ray floret 142
Sterile shoot 120
Sterile whorl 116
Stern
 74-gun ship 381
 Iron paddlesteamer 392
 Kayak 560
 Sailing dinghy 561
 Wooden sailing ship 378-
 379
Sterna hirundo 193
Sternal artery 173
Sternal bone 96, 102
Stern balustrade 373
Stern carving 381
Stern framing 392
Stern gallery 397
Stern lantern 379
Sternocleidomastoid
 muscle 226-227, 229
Sternohyoid muscle 229
Sternpost
 Greek galley 372
 Roman corbita 373
 Sailing warship 377
 Single scull 560
 Viking ships 374-375
 Wooden sailing ship 378
Stern quarter gallery 379
Stern rope 387
Stern section 392
Sternum
 Bird 189
 Domestic cat 195
 Elephant 201
 Hare 197
 Horse 199
 Human 218
 Kangaroo 206
 Seal 204
Stern walk 395
Stibnite 268
Stick insect 192
Stiff brush 436
Stifle 198
Stigma
 Damselfly 168
 Dicotyledon flower 126-
 127
 Fertilization 146-147
 Flower 140-143
 Pollination 144-145
Stigma remains 146-147,
 150-151
Stilt 494
Stilted arch 468
Sting 170
Stinging cells 166
Stinkhorn 114
Stipe 114-115, 116-117
Stippled effect 442
Stipule
 Begonia 129
 Everlasting pea 129
 Passion flower 130
 Rose 131
 Seedling leaf 152
 St. John's wort 145
 Strawberry 128
Stirrup
 Crossbow 548
 Ossicles of middle ear
 242
 Saddle 555, 582
Stoa 460
 Ancient Roman building
 463, 465
 Islamic building 488
Stock
 74-gun ship 380
 Danforth anchor 386
 Roman anchor 372
 Stockless anchor 386
 Stöfler 40
 Stoker's seat 334

Stolons 154
Stomach
 Barnacle 173
 Bird 189
 Bony fish 181
 Chimpanzee 202
 Cow 198
 Crayfish 173
 Dogfish 179
 Dolphin 205
 Domestic cat 195
 Elephant 200
 Frog 182
 Human 214, 248
 Jellyfish 167
 Lizard 185
 Octopus 176
 Rabbit 196
 Ruminants 198
 Snail 177
 Starfish 174
 Tortoise 187
Stomach throw 556
Stomata
 Dryland plants 156-157
 Golden barrel cactus 156
 Haworthia truncata 157
 Monocotyledon leaf 126
 Photosynthesis role 138-
 139
 Pine needle 124
 Wetland plants 158
Stone
 Succulent fruits 148
 Lithographic printing
 446, 448
 Sculpture 452
Stone canal 174, 175
Stone plate 446, 448
Stony-iron meteorite 52
Stony meteorite 52
Stop lamp assembly 352
Stopper 313, 560
Stop signal 330
Stopwatch 524
Storage organs
 Bulb 155
 Corm 155
 Rhizome 155
 Scale leaf 155
 Seed 152
 Succulent tissue 156-157
 Swollen stem 113, 155
 Tubers 128, 154
 Underground 154-155
Store button 521
Stores pylon 420-421
Stork 188
Storm 303
Straddle wire 358, 359
Straight 555
Straight four cylinder
 arrangement 345
Straight gouge 452
Straight handlebar 361
Strake
 Concorde 416-417
 Ironclad 393
 Roman corbita 372
 Viking ships 374-375
Strap bearing 582
Strap lug 588-589
Strapontin 337
Strap-shaped leaf 162
Strata 276
 Faults and folds 60-61
 Sedimentary rocks 276
Stratocumulus cloud 302
Stratosphere
 Earth's atmosphere 300-
 301
 Jupiter's atmosphere 45
 Mars' atmosphere 43
 Saturn's atmosphere 47
Stratum basale 235

Stratum corneum 235
Stratum granulosum 235
Stratum spinosum 235
Stratus cloud 302
Strawberry 128, 150
Straw butt 549
Streak 270-271
Stream
 Glaciers 286-287
 Groundwater system 293
 Spring examples 292
Streamlined spinner 407
Strengthening tissue
 Fern rachis 121
 Horsetail stem 120
 Marram grass 113
 Monocotyledon leaf 126
 Stems 134-135
 Water lily leaf 159
Stress 61
Stressed cylinder block
 356
Stretcher
 Brickwork 485
 Nineteenth-century
 building 492
 Single scull 560
Stretches 555
Striated effect 442
Striation 46
Strike
 Baseball 536
 Baseball umpire signal
 537
 Slope structure 60
Striker 524
Strike-slip fault 61
Strike-slip fault lake 293
Strike zone 536
Strindberg 35
String
 Acoustic guitar 512-513
 Cello 511
 Concert grand piano 515
 Double bass 511
 Electric guitar 513
 Harp 511
 Upright piano 514
 Viola 511
String arm 511
String course
 Ancient Roman building
 465
 Cathedral dome 487
 Medieval building 466-
 467
 Nineteenth-century
 building 493
Stringed instruments 510,
 511
 Guitar 512, 513
 Orchestral arrangement
 504, 505
Strings
 Guitar 512-513
 Racket 544
 Violin 510
Strix aluco 190
Strobili 120
Stroke judge 558
Stroke play 546
Strokes 546
Stroma 139
Stroma thylakoid 139
Strongylocentrotus
 purpuratus 175
Strontium 310
Strop 583
Strut
 Dome 484, 486
 Gothic building 473
 Marble sculpture
 support 453
 Neoclassical building
 479

Paddlesteamer 390
Timpanum 519
Strut insert 340
Struthio camelus 188
Egg 193
Struthiolaria 279
Struthiomimus 84, 87
Stub axle 424
Stud
 Ancient Roman mill 464
 Gothic building 473
 Mid West single rotor engine 410
Studding sail boom 378
Studding sail yard 378
Studio Elvira 495
Study 477
Stuffing box 390
Stuffing hole 582
Stump
 Coastline 295
 Wicket 558
Stupa 490-491
Stupica 491
Sturgeon 180
Style 140-143
 Fertilization 146-147
 Monocotyledon flower 126
 Pitcher plant 113
 Pollination 144-145
 Rowan fruit 131
Style of the gnomon 377
Style remains
 Dry fruit 150-151
 Fruit development 146-147
 Succulent fruit 148-149
Stylet 167
Stylobate 460
Styloglossus muscle 244
Styloid process 220, 243
Styracosaurus 102, 103
Subacute leaf apex 136-137
Subarachnoid space 237
Subclavian artery 215, 251, 253
Subclavian vein 253
Subduction 58
Subduction zone 281
Subframe 351
Subgenital pit 167
Subglacial stream 287
Sublimation 307
Sublingual fold 245
Sublingual gland 244-245
Submandibular gland 244
Submarine 396-397
Submarine canyon 298
Submerged atoll 299
Submerged glacial valleys 294-295
Submerged river valleys 294
Subopercular bone 181
Substitutions 532, 550
Substomatal chamber 139
Substrate 112
Substratum 115
Subsurface current 297
Subtropical jet stream 300
Succulent fruits 148-149, 150
 Bramble 130
 Development 146-147
 Peach 131
 Rowan 131
Succulent leaves 128, 157
Succulent plants 156-157
Succulents 112
 Leaf 157
 Stem 156-157
 Stem and root 157
 Trailing stem 157

Succulent stem 129
Sucker 176, 178
Sucking stomach 170
Sudan 331
Sugar
 Fermentation 312
 Formation 138
 Photosynthesis 315
 Transport 139
Sulcus terminalis 244
Sulky 554-555
Sulfates 269, 296
Sulfides 268
Sulfur 59, 268
 Periodic table 311
Sulfur dioxide 37
Sulfuric acid 36-37
Sulfurous gases 273
Sumatra 265
Sumigi 490
Summer petiole 160
Summit caldera 42
Sump 543, 344-345
Sun 32-33, 38
 Atmosphere 301
 Comet tails 48
 Earth's energy 314
 Electromagnetic radiation 314-315
 Energy emission from Sun 22
 Light 318
 Milky Way 14
 Objects in Universe 11
 Oceans and seas 296-297
 Ozone formation 64
 Solar eclipse 32
 Solar System 30-31
 Stars 22-23
Sundew 160
Sundial 376, 377
Sunflower 140, 142, 145
Sunken stoma 157
Sunlight and photosynthesis 138
Sun roof 341
Sun scoop 498
Sunspots 32-33
Sun visor 350, 353
Supai group 277
Superclusters 10
Supercooling 307
Supercool liquid 306-307
Superficial peroneal nerve 238
Superficial skeletal muscles 226-227
Superfluid neutrons 28
Super-giant slalom (Super-G) skiing 552
Supergiant stars
 Massive stars 26
 Stars 22-23
 Stellar black hole 29
Supergranule 33
Superheater 325
Superior articular facet 222
Superior articular process 222-223
Superior concha 212
Superior laryngeal nerve 244
Superior longitudinal muscle 245
Superior meatus 245
Superior mesenteric artery 253, 256
Superior mesenteric trunk 257
Superior mesenteric vein 253
Superior nasal concha 245
Superior oblique muscle 241

Superior orbital fissure 221
Superior ramus of pubis 224, 257
Superior rectus muscle 241
Superior sagittal sinus 212, 257
Superior thyroid artery 244
Superior vena cava 215, 251, 252-253, 255
Supernova
 Massive stars 26-27
 Nebulae and star clusters 16
 Neutron stars and black holes 29
Supernova remnant
 Nebulae and star clusters 16-17
 X-ray image of Crab Nebula 28
Supersonic flight 416
Supersonic jetliners 416-417
Supersonic transportation 416-417
Support arm assembly 573
Supporter 381
Supporter ring 589
Supporting tissue
 Bishop pine stem 125
 Dicotyledon leaf 126
 Stems 134-135
Supraoccipital bone 181
Supraoccipital crest 84
Supraoesophageal ganglion 173
Supraorbital fissure 221
Supraorbital foramen 221
Supraorbital margin 213, 220, 221
Supraorbital notch 213
Supraorbital ridge
 Chimpanzee 202
 Stegaceras 100
 Styracosaurus 102
Suprarenal gland 257
Suprarenal vein 257
Suprascapula 183
Suprasternal notch 211
Surangular bone 102
Surcingle 582-583
Surcingle loop 555
Surface currents 296-297
Surface deposits 273
Surface layer 293
Surface ocean current 296
Surface streams 284
Surface temperature 39
 Stars 22
Structure of main sequence star 24
Structure of Mars 43
Structure of Mercury 35
Structure of Neptune 51
Structure of red giant 25
Structure of red supergiant 26
Structure of Venus 37
Sun 33
Surface terrain 284
Surface vegetation 282
Surface winds 300
Surveillance RADAR 397
Suspended erratic 286
Suspension
 "Deltic" diesel-electric locomotive 327
 Microlight 426
 Motocross racing 368
 Motorcycle 364
Suspension arm 350-351
Suspension linkage 362

Suspension spring
 Clock 570
 Renault Clio 350
Suspension strut 340, 351
Suspension top mount 340
Sustaining pedal 514, 515
Suture 202
Su-wei 376
Suzuki RGV500 368, 369
Swab hitch 387, 389
Swallow 383
Swallow-hole 284
Swamp 290-291
Swan neck ornament 373
Swash plate 344
Swash zone 294
S waves 63
Sweat duct 235
Sweat gland 234-235
Sweat pore 234-235
Sweep rowing 560
Sweep-rowing boat 561
Sweeping low throw 556
Sweet chestnut 136, 144, 150
Sweetgum 76
Sweet pea 128
Sweet potato 154
Swell manual 514
Swell of muzzle 395
Swell pedal 514
Swell stop 514
Swifting tackle 377
Swim bladder 178, 180-181
Swimmeret 172
Swimming 558, 559
Swimming pool 558
Swimwear 558
Swingarm fork 364, 368
"Swing-wings" 420
Switch 316
Switchboard room 397
Switch enclosure 572
Switch end casting 578-579
Switch gear 314
Swivel becket 382
Swivels
 Mooring and anchoring 386
 Angling 562, 563
 Swivel suspension ring 377
Swollen leaf base 154-155
Swollen stem base
 Guzmania lingulata 163
 Kedrostis africana 113
 Oxalis sp. 157
Swollen stem 154-155
Sword 556-557
Sycamore 131, 150-151
Sycamore beam 560
Syconium 148
Syenite 275
Symbiosis
 Lichens 114
 Mycorrhizal association 133
Symbols
 Biology 591
 Chemistry 591
 Communication 108
 Mathematics 591
 Music 502, 503
 Physics 591
Symphony orchestra 504, 505
Synapsid reptile skull 67
Synaptic knob 228, 239
Synaptic vesicle 259
Syncarpous gynoecium 140
Synchiropus splendidus 180

Synchronized elevator 423
Syncline 60, 61, 62
Synclinorium 61
Synergid nucleus 147
Synsacrum 189
Synthesizer 520
Synthetic brush 436, 438
Synthetic flax 384
Synthetic bristle brush 442
Synthetic materials 306
Synthetic polymer 306
Synthetic resin 442
Synthetic ropes 388
Synthetic sable brush 442
Synthetic strings 544, 545
Synthetic wash brush 438, 442
Syria Planum 42, 43
Systems connector 413

T

Tabernacle 463, 474, 476
Tab hinge 415
Table clamp 573
Tablet flower 488, 491
Tabling 372, 384
Tabular habit 271
Tacan aerial 420
Tachybaptus ruficollis 190
Tack
 Chair 577
 Saddle 582
 Viking karv 375
Tackling
 Australian rules football 528, 529
 Football 526
 Rugby 531
 Soccer 524
Tactical air navigation (Tacan) aerial 420
Tadpoles 182-183, 192
Taenia 460
Taenia colica 249
Taffrail 378, 381
Tag 569
Tail
 Amphibian 182
 Anchisaurus 89
 BE 2B bomber 404
 Caiman 187
 Calligraphy character 445
 Corythosaurus 98
 Crocodilians 186
 Deer hopper dry fly 563
 Dolphin 205
 Dunkeld wet fly 563
 Gallimimus 87
 Half-bound book 586
 Hare 196
 Hawker Tempest components 409
 Horse 198
 Ichthyostega 80
 Iguanodon 96
 Iguanodonts 96
 Kangaroo 206
 Leather-bound book 586
 Lion 195
 Lizard 184-185
 Lungfish 81
 Monkey 202
 Ornithopods 96
 Pachycephalosaurus 100
 Prehensile 202
 Rabbit 196-197
 Rat 196
 Rattlesnake 185
 Rigging 382-383
 Salamander 182
 Sauropodomorpha 88

Schweizer helicopter 423
Scorpion 170
Ski 552-553
Stegoceras 101
Stegosaurus 93
Tadpole 183
Triceratops 102
Tyrannosaurus 84
Westlothiana 81
Tailband 586-587
Tail boom 423
Tail bud 260
Tail bumper 417
Tail club 95
Tail cone 416-417, 418
Tail crest 187
Taileron 420-421
Tail fairing 409
Tail feathers 188
Tail fluke 205
Tail-gate 348
Tail gunner's compartment 408
Tail-gun turret 408
Taillight
 BMW R/60 362
 Harley-Davidson FLHS Electra Glide 362
 Honda CB750 363
 Vespa Grand Sport 160 Mark 1 363
Tailpiece 510, 511
Tail-pin 510
Tail pipe 340, 356
Tailplane
 ARV light aircraft 424
 BAe-146 jetliner 415
 BE 2B tail 405
 Biplanes and triplanes 402-403
 Blackburn monoplane 401
 Blériot XI monoplane 401
 Curtiss biplane 399
 Hawker Tempest 409
 Lockheed Electra airliner 407
 Schleicher glider 426
Tailplane fairing 415
Tailplane root 409
Tailplane tip 407, 415
Tailrace 314
Tail rod 390
Tail rotor 422-423
Tail-rotor drive shaft 422, 423
Tail rotor gearbox 423
Tail shield 78
Tailskid
 ARV light aircraft 424
 Avro triplane 403
 BE 2B bomber 405
 Blackburn monoplane 400-401
 LVG CVI fighter 405
Tail spike 92
Tail spine 79
Tail unit 368
Tailwheel
 Avro biplane 402
 B-17 bomber 408
 Hawker Tempest fighter 409
 Lockheed Electra airliner 407
 Schleicher glider 426
Tailwheel leg 401
Take-off and landing skid 398
Takla Makan Desert 265
Talc 270-271
Tallow coating 379
Talonavicular ligament 232

631

Talons 188
Talus 282-283
Talus bone 232
Tamarins 202, 203
Tambourine 504, 518
Tam-tam 504, 516
Tandem wings 402
Tank 392
Tank drain tap 407
Tank inspection access 417
Tank support 339
Tantalum 310
Tantalus Fossae 43
Tape
  Book 586-587
  Mini-television 574
Tapeats sandstone 277
Tapir 198
Tappet 343
Tappet adjustor 367
Tap root 128
Tarantula Nebula 26-27
  Large Magellanic Cloud 12
Tarantulas 170-171
Target areas 556, 557
Target hole 546
Target pistol 548, 549
Target shooting 548, 549
Tarn 293
  U-shaped valley formation 287
Tarsal bone
  Albertosaurus 84
  Gallimimus 87
  Iguanodon 97
Tarsals
  Crocodile 186
  Domestic cat 195
  Elephant 201
  Frog 183
  Hare 197
  Horse 199
  Kangaroo 206
  Lizard 184
  Platypus 206
  Rhesus monkey 202
  Seal 204
Tarsiers 202
Tarsomere 13
Tarsometatarsus 189
Tarsus
  Beetle 168
  Bird 188
  Human 219
  Scorpion 170
  Spider 171
Tas-de-charge 469
Tasmanian devil 207
Taste 244
Taste bud 244
Tau Orionis 18
Taurus 19, 20
Taurus mountains 77
Tau Sagittarii 21
Tawny owl 190
Taxiing light 414, 420
Taxus baccata 70, 123
Tea clipper 392
Team crest 551
Team jersey 529
Team name 533
Tear fault 61
Technetium 310
Technosaurus 69
Tee 546
Teeing ground 546
Tee peg 547
Teeth
  Ankylosaurus 92
  Bear 106
  Caiman 186
  Canine 194, 202
  Carnassial 194

Carnivores 194
Ceratopsian 100
Cheek 194
Chimpanzee 202
Crocodilians 186
Extinct shark 67
Hadrosaur 96
Hominid 108
Horse 105
Human **246-247**
Iguanodont 96
Incisor 194, 196, 201, 202
Lamprey 178
Leaf-shaped 88-89
Molar 194, 201, 202
Ornithopod 96
Premolar 194, 202
Rabbit 196
Rodents 196
Theropod 84
Thyreophoran 92
Venus fly-trap 160
Teeth development 246
Tegenaria gigantea 171
Telescopic damper 326, 329
Telescopic fork
  Harley-Davidson FLHS Electra Glide 363
  Honda CB750 363
  Honda VF750 364
  Husqvarna Motocross TC610 368
  Motorcycle 364
  Suzuki RGV500 368
  Weslake Speedway bike 369
Telescopic sight 548, 549
Telescopic strut 416
Telltale 545
Tellurium 311
Tellus Regio 36, 37
Tellus Tessera 37
Telson 172
  Fossil 79
Tempe Fossae 43
Tempera 432, 433
Temperate latitudes 302
Temperature
  Atmosphere 300-301
  Chemical reactions 306-307
  Formation of black hole 29
  Germination 152
  Matter 312
  Mineral resources 280
  Oceans and seas 296
  Stellar black hole 29
  Weather 302-303
Temperature and pressure sensor 418
Temperature changes
  Atmosphere 301
  Oceans and seas 296
  Weathering and erosion 282
Temperature conversions 590
Temperature scales 590
Tempered pigment 432
Temple 484-485
  Ancient Egyptian 458
  Ancient Greek 460-461
  Ancient Roman 462-463
  Asian 490
  Building 490
  Style 468
Temple blocks 516
Temple Butte limestone 277
Temple Cap sandstone 276
Temple of Amon-Re 458-459

Temple of Aphaia 461
Temple of Athena Polias 460
Temple of Heaven 490
Temple of Isis 459
Temple of Mallikarjuna 491
Temple of Neptune 460-461
Temple of Vesta 462-463
Temple of Virupaksha 490-491
Tempo 504
Temporal bone
  Chimpanzee 202
  Human 220-221, 242
Temporal lobe 237
Temporalis muscle 226-227, 229
Tendon
  Achilles 232-233
  Annular 241
  Calcanean 252-233
  Extensor digitorum longus 233
  Extensor digitorum 251
  Extensor hallucis longus 233
  Flexor digitorum 251
  Gallimimus 87
  Palmaris longus 231
  Peroneus brevis 233
Tendril
  Arabesque 480
  Clematis 130
  Dogfish egg 192
  Everlasting pea 129
  Monkey cup 161
  Passion flower 130
Tennis 544
Tennis racket 544
Tenon
  Chair 576-577
  Flax spinning mill 492
  Hull plank fastening 373
Tenon tongue 576
Tenor drum 518-519
Tenor joint 508
Tenor mute 507
Tenor note strings 515
Tenor saxophone 509
Tenor voice 502
Tension
  Drums 518
  Faults and folds 60-61
  Mountain building 62
Tension-column 497
Tension control 552
Tension key 518, 519
Tension member 499
Tension pulley 360
Tension rod 518, 519
Tension screw 518
Tension spring 570
Tensor fasciae latae muscle 226
Tensor tympani muscle 243
Tentacle
  Coelentrates 166
  Jellyfish 167
  Molluscs 176-177
  Scallop 176
  Sea anemone 166-167
  Snail 177
Tenth century
  Building 490
  Style 468
Tepal scar 140
Tepal
  Flower parts 140, 143
  Monocotyledons 126
  Peruvian lily 129
Terbium 311
Teres major muscle 227

Teres minor muscle 227
Tergum plate 173
  Egg 193
Terminal box 317
Terminal bronchiole 254
Terminal bud
  Bishop pine 124
  Horse chestnut 130
  London plane 134
  Rhizome 155
  Root tuber 154-155
  Stems 134
  Stolon 154
Terminal ileum 249
Terminal lake 286
Terminal moraine 286, 289
Terminal pinna 136
Terminal ring 259
Terminal screw 572
Terminus 286
Terrace
  Asian building 490-491
  Modern building 497-499
  Twentieth-century building 494-495
Terracotta clay 455
Terrain-following radar 420
Terrapin 186-187
Terrestrial animal 74
Terrestrial mammal 104
Terrigenous sediment 299
Tertiary bronchus 215
Tertiary period 57, 74, 75
  Fossil record 279
Tessellation 489
Tessera 450, 489
Test 174-175
Testa 132
  Dry fruit 150-151
  Embryo development 147
  Epigeal germination 153
  Hypogeal germination 152
  Succulent fruit seed 148-149
Testicle 259
Testicular artery 257
Testicular vein 257
Testis
  Barnacle 173
  Dolphin 205
  Domestic cat 195
  Human 259
  Rabbit 196
Test tube 313
Tetanurae 83
Tethus Regio 36
Tethys 46
Tethys Sea
  Cretaceous period 73
  Jurassic period 71
  Tertiary period 74, 75
  Triassic period 69
Tetragonal system 270
Tetralophodon 75, 104
Text 444, 584
Textured papers 441
TGV electric high-speed train 329
Thalamian 373
Thalamus 236-237
Thalassiosira sp. 116
Thalictrum delavayi 137
Thallium 311
Thalloid liverwort 118
Thallus
  Algae 116-117
  Lichen 114
  Liverwort 118
  Seaweed 116-117
T-handle auger 374
Thar Desert 265

Tharsis Tholus 43
Thatched roof 477
Thaumasia Fossae 43
Themis Regio 36
Theobroma cacao 148
Therapsids 104
Thermals 426
Thermocouple bus-bar 419
Thermogram 214
Thermosphere
  Earth's atmosphere 300
  Mars' atmosphere 43
  Venus' atmosphere 37
Thermostat 411
Theropods **84-87**
Thesium alpinium 145
Theta1 Sagittarii 21
Theta Andromedae 19
Theta Pegasi 19
Thetis Regio 36
Thick skull 46
Thigh
  Anchisaurus 89
  Bird 188
  Corythosaurus 98
  Gorilla 203
  Horse 198
  Human 211
  Iguanodon 96
  Kangaroo 207
  Lion 195
  Psittacosaurus 103
  Stegoceras 101
  Stegosaurus 92
  Triceratops 102
  Tyrannosaurus 84
Thigh musculature 90
Thigh pad 527
Thimble
  Harness racing 555
  Last 569
  Rigging 383, 384
Third-century building 465
Third home 541
Third man 538, 541
Third rail 528
Third wheel 570
Thirteenth century
  Building 467, 469-471
  Style 470
Thistle funnel 313
Thole pin 380
Thoracic cavity 255
Thoracic leg 169
Thoracic nerve 238
Thoracic pleurae 78
Thoracic segment 79
Thoracic vertebrae
  Crocodile 186
  Domestic cat 195
  Hare 197
  Horse 199
  Human 222
  Kangaroo 206
  Platypus 206
  Rhesus monkey 202
  Seal 204
Thoracolumbar vertebrae
  Elephant 201
  Lizard 184
Thorax
  Cirripedia 172
  Human 211
  Insects 168-169
Thorium 310
Thornback ray 179
Thoroughbred horse 554
Thranite 373
Thread
  Leather-bound book 587
  Shoes 569
  Structure of a Cnidocyte 167

Threaded rod 573
Three-blade main rotor 423
Three-cylinder Anzani engine 401
Three-cylinder engine 425
Three-lobed stigma 143
Three-masted square-rigged ship 375
Three-point line 532
Three pounder 395
Three-toed ungulates 198
Threshold 463
Throat
  Angling hook 562
  Bird 188
  Danforth anchor 386
  Human 212, **244-245**
  Lacrosse crosse 541
  Racketball racket 545
  Squash racket 545
  Tennis racket 544
Throatlatch 199
Throttle
  Avro triplane 402
  Curtiss biplane 398
  "Rocket" steam locomotive 324
  Suzuki RGV500 363
  Vespa Grand Sport 160
  Mark1 363
  Weslake Speedway bike 369
Throttle butterfly 345
Throttle cable 350
  Harley-Davidson FLHS Electra Glide 363
  Husqvarna Motocross TC610 368
  Kirby BSA racing sidecar 369
  Suzuki RGV500 369
  Weslake Speedway bike 369
Throttle control knob 581
Throttle guard 580
Throttle lever 419, 425
Throttle linkage
  Ford Model T 338
  Jaguar V12 engine 345
  Oldsmobile trim 337
  Renault Clio 350
Throttle wheel 342
Throw
  Judo 556
  Structure of a fault 60
Thrower 394
Throw-in 532
Thrushes 188
Thrust 543
Thrust fault 61
Thrust plate 567
Thrust-reverser 421
Thulium 311
Thumb 211, 230-231
Thumb-claw
  Anchisaurus 89
  Apatosaurus 83
  Baryonyx 83, 85
  Massospondylus 85, 89
  Plateosaurus 88
Thumb knot 389
Thumb piston 514
Thumb-spike 96-97
Thwart 375, 375, 380
Thylakoid 139
Thymine 216
Thyreophora 83
Thyreophorans **92-93, 94-95**
Thyrister converter 328
Thyrohyoid membrane 244
Thyrohyoid muscle 229, 244

Thyroid cartilage 245, 255
Thyroid gland 214-215, 217, 244-245, 255
Tibetan plateau 63
Tibia
  Archaeopteryx 85
  Beetle 168
  Butterfly 169
  Crocodile 186
  Diplodocus 90
  Domestic cat 195
  Elephant 201
  Eryops 81
  Gallimimus 86
  Hare 197
  Horse 199
  Human 219, 252-253
  Iguanodon 96-97
  Kangaroo 206
  Lizard 184
  Parasaurolophus 99
  Plateosaurus 88
  Platypus 206
  Rhesus monkey 202
  Scorpion 170
  Seal 204
  Spider 171
  Stegoceras 101
  Stegosaurus 95
  Struthiomimus 87
  Toxodon 107
  Triceratops 102
  Turtle 187
  Tyrannosaurus 84
Tibiale 183
Tibial flexor muscle 97
Tibialis anterior muscle 226, 233
Tibialis posterior muscle 233
Tibiofibula 183
Tibiotarsus 189
Tidal bulge 297
Tidal currents 296-297, 298
Tidal flow 296
Tidal levels 295
Tidal river mouth 295
Tidal scour 298
Tidal waves 58
Tides 294, 297
Tie
  Basketball match 552
  Bordino Steam Carriage 334
  Musical notation 502, 503
  Pinzgauer Turbo D 354
Tie-beam
  Ancient Roman mill 464
  Dome 486
  Gothic church 473
  Neoclassical building 479
Tie plate 393
Tierceron 485
Tie rod 334, 340
Tiger seat 334
Tiger shark 178-179
Tight end 526
Tight-head prop 530
Tile
  Dome 486
  Islamic mosque 488
  Modern building 499
  Neoclassical building 482
  Renaissance building 476-477
Tiled roof 495
Tilia sp. 154
Tilia x *europaea* 143
Tiller
  Dhow 376
  First cars 334-335

Longboat 380
Oldsmobile trim 337
Roman corbita 373
Sailing dinghy 561
Steamboat with paddle wheels 391
Viking ships 374-375
Tilt and rotation
  Jupiter 44
  Mars 42
  Mercury 34
  The Moon 40
  Neptune 50
  Pluto 51
  Saturn 46
  Uranus 48
  Venus 36
Timber 516
Timber frame
  Ancient Roman building 462, 464-465
  Dome 486
  Medieval building 466-467
  Renaissance building 477
Timber head 380
Timber rafter 492
Time interval signal 330
Timekeeper
  Basketball 552
  Fencing contest 557
  Handball 535
  Judo contest 556
  Lacrosse 541
  Netball 535
  Swimming 558
Time signature 502
Time switch 578
Time-trial bike 360
Timing chain 343, 345
Timing chest 343
Timing gear 367
Timpani 503, 504, 505, 518
Timpanum 519
Tin 311
  Mineralization zones 281
  Squash 545
Tinatin Planitia 37
Tinted paper 441
Tip of dodder stem 163
Tip ring 563
Tip section 563
Titania 48
Titanium 310
Titanohyrax 74
Toad 182
Toadflax 129
Toaster **578-579**
Toe
  Albertosaurus 84
  Anchisaurus 89
  Archaeopteryx 85
  Bird 188
  Caiman 186-187
  Corythosaurus 98
  Golf club 547
  Gorilla 203
  Herrerasaurus 86
  Human 211, 232-233
  Iguanodon 96-97
  Lion 194
  Lizard 184
  Pachycephalosaurus 100
  Psittacosaurus 103
  Stegoceras 101
  Tyrannosaurus 84
Toe clip 360
Toenail
  Elephant 200
  Gorilla 203
  Human 233
Toe piston 514
Toe puff 568
Toe strap 558-559

Toggle switch 513
Toilet 416, 483
Tolstoj 35
Tomb 458-459, 489
Tomb of Itimad-ud-daula 489
Tomb of King Tjetji 459
Tombolo 294
Tom-toms 518-519
Tondo brush 434
Tone editor control 520
Tonehole 509
Tone pattern selector 520
Tongs 321
Tongue
  Allosaurus 85
  Caiman 186
  Chimpanzee 202
  Corythosaurus 98
  Cow 198
  Dolphin 205
  Domestic cat 195
  Elephant 200
  Human 212, 226, 244, 248
  Iguanodon 97
  Lamprey 178
  Lion 194
  Rabbit 196
  Rattlesnake 185
  Shoe 568
  Ski boot 552
Tongue lining 568
T'on-wei 376
Tool and battery box 335
Tools
  Rigging 382-383
  Sailmaking 384
  Viking boat building 374
Tooth
  Acanthostega 80
  Anchisaurus 89
  Ankylosaurus 94
  Arsinoitherium 104
  Australopithecus 108
  Baryonyx 83
  Camarasaurus 91
  Diplodocus 90
  Dragon prowhead 374
  Eryops 80
  Euoplocephalus 94
  Heterodontosaurus 83
  Homo habilis 108
  Human 108, 246-247, 248
  Iguanodon 96
  Lambeosaurus 99
  Moeritherium 105
  Pastels application 440
  Phiomia 105
  Plateosaurus 88
  Protoceratops 102
  Smilodon 107
  Triceratops 103
  Tyrannosaurus 84
Toothless beak
  Ankylosaurs 92
  Corythosaurus 98
  Euoplocephalus 94
  Gallimimus 86
  Theropods 84
  Triceratops 102
Topaz 271
Topcastle 375, 377
Top cover 589
Topgallant mast
  Battleship 395
  Sailing warship 377
  Wooden sailing ship 378-379
Top hose 351
Top leather 582
Topmast 377, 378
Topping lift 380
Topping-up valve 561
Top-plate 464

Top race 359
Topsail
  74-gun ship 379
  Double topsail schooner 385
  Junk 376
Topset strata 283
Topside strake 393
Top sliding block 437
Top splat 576
Tornado GR1A 420-421
Torosaurus 73
Toroweap formation 276
Torpedo 394-397
Torque arm 364, 365
Torquemeter mount 419
Torque tube 338-339
Torque tube assembly 425
Torrential rain 302
Torsional vibration damper 410-411
Torsion bar 350
Tortillon 440, 441
Tortoise 186
Tortoise skull 77
Torus
  Ancient Roman building 463
  Asian building 490
  Dome 486
  Gothic building 470
  Medieval building 467-469
  Renaissance building 475, 477
Total solar eclipse 32
Tote board 555
Touchdown 526
Touch-in goal line 530
Touch line
  Rugby 530
  Soccer 524
Touchpiece 509
Tour buses 353
Tour de César 466
Touring bicycle 360, 361
Tourmaline 269
Tower
  Ancient Roman building 465
  Asian building 490-491
  Clock 493
  Gothic church 472
  Islamic building 488
  Medieval building 466-467, 468-469
  Modern building 496-497
  Nineteenth-century building 492-493
  Renaissance building 476
  Twentieth-century building 495
Tower Bridge 492-493
Tower vault 469
Towing fairlead 395
Towing hook 355, 426
Towing pintle 355
Town Hall 495
Tow strap 555
Toxodon 76, 106, 107
Trabecula 250-251
Trace fossils 278
Tracery
  Gothic building 470-473
  Nineteenth-century building 493
Trachea
  Bird 189
  Brachiosaurus 91
  Chimpanzee 202
  Dolphin 205
  Domestic cat 195
  Elephant 200
  Gallimimus 86

Human 212, 215, 244-245, 248, 255
Lizard 185
Rabbit 196
Spider 170
Tortoise 187
Trachelion 460
Trachycarpus fortunei 127, 130
Track 413
Track and Field **542-543**
Track control arm 540
Track events 542, 543
Track gauge 330, 331
Track rod
  Elegance and utility 336-337
  Ford Model T 338-339
  Renault Clio 351
Track shoe 543
Traction cable 581
Traction lever 581
Traction motor 328
Trade winds 300
Traffic congestion 332
Traffic surveillance 422
Tragus 242
Trailboard 379
Trailing arm 340
Trailing edge
  BAe-146 jetliner components 413, 414, 415
  BE 2B tail 405
  BE 2B wings 404
  Hawker Tempest components 409
  Pegasus Quasar microlight 426-427
Trailing-link arm 414
Trailing wheel 324
Train equipment **330-331**
Training gear 396
Trains
  Diesel **526-527**
  Electric **328-329**
  High-speed **328-329**
  Steam **324-325**
Transaxle 340
Transept
  Gothic church 470, 473
  Medieval church 468-469
Transfer port 342
Transformation 168
Transformer 314, 328
Transform fault 59
Transistor 584
Transitional cell mucosa 257
Transition metals 310, 311
Transit plug 397
Translucent crystal 271
Translucent impasto glaze 443
Translucent white marble 453
Translucent "window" 157
Transmission 350-351
Transmission adaptor plate 344
Transmission system 326, 366
Transom
  74-gun ship 381
  Junk 376
  Longboat 380
  North wing, Chateau de Montal 476
  Sailing warship 377
Transparent glassy crystal 271
Transparent lower drumhead 518
Transparent tissue 160
Transparent wash 439

Transpiration 136
Transponder aerial 423
Transport system 332
Transport tissue
  Golden barrel cactus 156
  Monocotyledons 126
  Photosynthesis 138-139
Transversary 377
Transverse arch 485
  Baroque church 479
  Medieval church 468-469
Transverse colon 249
Transverse dune 283
Transverse foramen 222
Transverse leaf spring 338
Transverse line 535
Transverse process
  Human 222-223
  Plateosaurus 89
  Tyrannosaurus 85
Transverse rib 485
Transverse strut 512
Trapezium 17
Trapezium bone 230
Trapezius muscle 226-227, 229
Trapezoid bone 230
Traps
  Butterwort 161
  Cobra lily 160
  Monkey cup 161
  Pitcher plant 113, 160-161
  Sundew 160
  Venus fly trap 160
Traveler 380
Travertine shell 464
Tread 477
Tread pattern 365
Tread plate 355
Treasury of Atreus 461
Treble bridge 514
Treble clef 502
Treble hook 562-563
Treble note strings 515
Treble voice 502
Tree 66-67, 130-131
  Energy storage 315
  English saddle 582
  Epiphytes 162-163
  Gymnosperms 122-125
Tree fern 112-113
Tree mallow 131
Treenail (trenail) 387
Trefoil
  Gothic church 470-473
  Nineteenth-century building 493
Trefoil arch 473, 484
Trellis window 459
Trellised river drainage 288
Trembler coil box 335
Trestle trees 378
Trevithick, Richard 324
Triac device 566
Trials tire 365
Triangle
  Area measurement 590
  Musical instrument 504, 517
  Steamboat with paddle wheels 391
Triangle mosaic 489
Triangular buttress 484
Triangular fossa 242
Triangular horn 85
Triangular lesene 481
Triangular pediment 462
Triangular-section fuselage
  Avro triplane 403
  Bell-47 helicopter 423
  Blackburn monoplane 401

Triangulum 19, 20
Triangulum Australe 21
Triassic period **68-69**
　Fossil record 279
　Geological time 57
Triatic stay 385
Tribune 467-468
Tributary
　Coastlines 295
　Rivers 288
Tributary moraine 287
Tributary stream 289
Triceps brachii muscle 227
Triceratops 100, 102-103
Trichome 156
　Marram grass 113
Triclinic system 270
Tricolpate pollen grain 145
Tricuspid valve 251
Triere 373
Trifid Nebula 16
Trifoliate leaves 128, 130
　Laburnum 137
　Oxalis sp. 157
Triforium 469
Trigger
　Air pistol 549
　Biathlon smallbore rifle 549
　Cnidocyte structure 167
Trigger hair 160
Trigger mechanism 566
Trigger position 566
Triglyph 460
Trigon 488
Trigonal system 270
Trigone 257
Trike nacelle 426-427
Trilete mark 145
Trilobate rotor 346
Tri-lobed tail 81
Trilobites 64, 78
　Earth's evolution 56
　Fossil record 279
Trim **352-353**
　1906 Renault 336-337
　Oldsmobile trim 337
　Renault Clio **350-351**
　Volkswagen Beetle 341
Trimala 491
Trimming 586
Trimtab 407, 414, 415
Trim tank 416-417
Trinity Chapel, Salisbury Cathedral 470
Tripinnate leaves 137
Triplanes 402-403
Triple bar jump 554
Triple jump 542
Triple spine 130-131
Tripod mast 394
Tripod socket hole 588
Tripod stand
　Congas 519
　Drum kit 518
　Electronic drums 520
　Modeling stand 455
　Radial studio easel 437
Tripping palm 586
Tripping ring 372
Triquetral bone 230
Trireme 372-373
Tri-spoke wheel 361, 368, 369
Triton 50
Trochanter
　Beetle 168
　Scorpion 170
　Spider 171
Trochlea
　Baryonyx 85
　Human 241
Trochoid housing 410

Trojan two-stroke engine 342
Trolleys 332-333
Trombone 504, 505, 506, 507
Tropeter 373
Trophoblast 260
Tropical cyclone 302
Tropical orchids 162
Tropical rain forest 39, 66
Tropic formation 276
Tropic of Cancer
　Satellite map 265
　Surface currents 297
Tropic of Capricorn
　Satellite map 265
　Surface currents 297
Troposphere
　Earth's atmosphere 300
　Jupiter's atmosphere 45
　Mars' atmosphere 43
　Saturn's atmosphere 47
　Venus' atmosphere 37
Trout 180
Trout angling 562
Truck
　Early trolley 332
　Greek galley 372
　Longboat 380
　Wooden sailing ship 378-379
Trumpet 504, 506, 503
Truncate leaf base 137
Trunk
　Elephant 200-201
　Mammoth 107
　Phiomia 105
　Tree fern 112
　Woody flowering plant 130-131
Trunnion 395
Truss
　Gothic church 473
　Modern building 497-499
　Steam boat with paddle wheels 391
Truss rod 513
Try 530, 531
T-section beam 492
Tsiolkovsky 41
T-type cantilevered fin 426
Tu-144 416
Tuba 504, 505
Tube feet 174, 175
Tubeless sports tire 365
Tuber
　Broomrape 145
　Dryland plants 157
　Horsetail 120
　Potato 128
　Vegetative reproduction 155
Tubercle
　Corythosaurus 98
　Golden barrel cactus 156
　Sea urchins 174
　Starfish 174
　Stem projections 156
Tubular bells 504, 516
Tubular chassis 335
Tubular drums 518
Tubular open cradle frame 369
Tubular petioles 160
Tuck 381
Tudor arch 484
Tufted duck 188
Tug propeller 391
Tulip mount 563
Tuner 574
Tungsten
　Mineralization zones 281
　Periodic table 310
Tungsten carbide tip 450

Tungsten filament 319
Tunica adventitia 252
Tunica intima 252
Tunica media 252
Tuning adjustor 510-511
Tuning drive gear 574
Tuning pedal 519
Tuning peg 510, 511
Tuning pin 514, 515
Tuning printed circuit board 574
Tuning slide 506
Tunnel
　Cave 285
　Trains 330
Tunnel vault 485
Tuojiangosaurus 92
Tupelo 137
Turbine
　Energy 314-315
　Jet engines 418-419
　Nuclear "Hunter-Killer" submarine 397
Turbocharger 356
Turbofan engine 418-419
　Landing gear 412
Turbo impeller 347
Turbojet engine 418-419
　Landing gear 412
　Supersonic jetliner 416
Turbo propeller 347
Turboprop engine 418-419
Turdus viscivorus 190
Turgai strait 71
Turkish crescent finial 488
Turk's head 383
Turnbuckle
　Avro triplane 402
　Blackburn monoplane 401
　Curtiss biplane 398
　LVG CVI fighter 405
　Rigging screw 383
Turn indicator 558
Turning force 320
Turning indicator 332, 333
Turning judge 558
Turns 555
Turpentine 436
Turret 486
　Baroque church 481
　Battleship 394-395
　Gothic church 470-471
　Gun turret 396
　Medieval building 466, 468
　Nineteenth-century building 493
　Renaissance building 476-477
Turtle 72-73, 186-187
Tuscan capital 465
Tuscan pilaster 465, 483
Tusche 446
Tusche pen 448
Tusche stick 448
Tusk
　Elephant 200-201
　Mammoth 107
　Phiomia 105
Twelfth century
　Building 466-467
　Church 469, 473
　Roof 490
　Style 468, 470
Twentieth-century buildings **494-495**
Twin-blade main rotor 423
Twin carbon-fiber disc brake 369
Twin carburettors 427

Twin-cylinder engine
　Harley-Davidson 362
　Pegasus Quasar microlight 427
　Steam-powered Cugnot 334
Twin-domed forehead 200
Twine 384
Twin-lobed leaf blade 160
Twin nose-wheel 420
Twin rate spring 365
Twin rear axle 333
Twin rudder 372
Twin-wheel main landing gear 414
Twin-wheel nose-gear 417, 420
Twist dive 558, 559
Twisted wire habit 271
Two-burner alcohol stove 354
Two-lobed stigma 142
Two-pulley system 320
Two-seater cockpit 421
Two-stroke combustion engine 366
Two-toed ungulates 198
Two-towered gate 467
Tyagaraja 35
Tycho 40
Tye 377
Tye halyard 374
Tympan 449
Tympanic bulla 194
Tympanic canal 243
Tympanic membrane 243
Tympanum
　Frog 182
　Quail chick 193
Typhoon 302
Tyrannosaurus 73, 84-85
Tyre
　1906 Renault 336-337
　ARV light aircraft 424
　Avro triplane 402
　BAe-146 jetliner components 414
　Bicycle 358-359
　Blériot XI monoplane 401
　BMW R/60 362
　Cannondale SH 600 hybrid bicycle 361
　Curtiss biplane 398
　Double-decker tour bus 333
　Eddy Merckx racing bike 360
　First cars 334-335
　General use 365
　Lockheed Electra airliner 407
　MCW Metrobus 333
　Metal 324
　Motocross racing 368
　Motorcycle 365
　Pacing sulky 555
　Pinzgauer Turbo D 355
　Pneumatic 358, 555
　Racing car 356-357
　Renault Clio 352-353
　"Rocket" steam locomotive 324
　Rossin Italian time-trial bicycle 361
　Single-decker bus 333
　Slick racing 365
　Suzuki RGV500 368-369
　Trials 365
　Tubeless sports 365
　Volkswagen Beetle 340
　Weslake Speedway bike 369
　World War I aircraft 404-405

Tyre carrier 337
Tyre lever 354
Tyre tread 360, 365, 368
Tyre wall 360
Tyringham House 483

U

UHF aerial 420
UK loading gauges 331
Ulmus minor 144
Ulna
　Archaeopteryx 85
　Arsinoitherium 104
　Baryonyx 85
　Bird 189, 191
　Brachiosaurus 91
　Crocodile 186
　Diplodocus 90
　Domestic cat 195
　Elephant 90, 201
　Eryops 80
　Euoplocephalus 94
　Gallimimus 86
　Hare 197
　Horse 199
　Human 218, 230
　Iguanodon 96
　Kangaroo 206
　Kentrosaurus 93
　Lizard 184
　Parasaurolophus 99
　Pareiasaur 81
　Plateosaurus 88
　Platypus 206
　Rhesus monkey 202
　Seal 204
　Stegoceras 100, 101
　Stegosaurus 93
　Struthiomimus 87
　Toxodon 106
　Triceratops 102
　Tuojiangosaurus 93
　Turtle 187
　Tyrannosaurus 84
Ulnar artery 251, 253
Ulnar nerve 231, 238
Ultramarine lapis lazuli 433
Ultrasound scan 214
Ultraviolet light 145, 319
Ultraviolet radiation 22, 319
Ultraviolet solar radiation 300
Umbels 143
Umbilical artery and vein 260
Umbilical cord 260-261
Umbilicus 211, 260
Umbo 176
Umbra 32
Umbrella 491
Umbriel 48
Umpire
　Badminton 545
　Baseball 536
　Cricket 538
　Football 526
　Hockey 540
　Lacrosse 541
　Netball 535
　Tennis 544
　Volleyball 534
Umpire signals 537
Una corda pedal 514, 515
Unarmed combat 556
Underarm pass 535
Underframe 332
Underground mycelium 115
Underground stem 154
Underground storage organs 154-155

Underground stream 284-285
Underground water
　Lake formation 292
　Rivers 288
Underhand serve 534
Under plastron 557
Underwater mountains 298
Underwing fairing 425
Ungulates **198-199**
Unicellular organisms 56
Unified leaf pair 157
Uniform motion 321
Uniform tone 442
Union Pacific diesel train 326
Unipolar neuron 239
Unison 503
Unit number 328
Universal veil 114-115
Universe **10-11**
Unmapped region
　Degas and Brönte 34
　Structure of Mercury 35
Unnilennium 311
Unnilhexium 310
Unniloctium 311
Unnilpentium 310
Unnilquandium 310
Unnilseptium 310
Unreactive gas mixture 319
Unreactive metals 311
Unstable elements 310
Unukalhai 21
Upcurved edge 191
Upfold 60
Upfold trap 280
Upholstery 336-337
Uplifted block fault mountain 62
Upper arm 210
Upper Belvedere 482
Upper Carboniferous Coal Measures 61
Upper Carboniferous Millstone Grit 60-61
Upper crankcase 410
Upper crux of antihelix 242
Upper deadeye 382-383
Upper deck 380
Upper epidermis 159
Upper eyelid 213
Upper fin 423
Upper finishing 381
Upper Frater 473
Upper gallery 379
Upper gear case 580
Upper head 387
Upper jaw 212, 220-221, 244-245, 246, 248
Upper joint
　Clarinet 508
　Cor Anglais 508
　Oboe 508
Upper lobe of lung 215, 254-255
Upper octave key 509
Upper rudder 416-417
Uppers 568
Upper seed axis 152-153
Upper sheer strake 393
Upper topsail 385
Upper wireless and telegraphy yard 395
Upright man 108
Upright piano 514
Upright planks jump 554
Upright poles jump 554
Upsilon Sagittarii 21
Upstream gates 560
Upthrow 60
Urachus 257

Ural mountains
  Cretaceous period 73
  Earth's physical features 265
  Jurassic period 71
  Late Carboniferous period 67
  Triassic period 69
Uranium 310
Uranium fuel 314
Uranius Tholus 43
Uranus 48-49
  Solar System 31
Ureter
  Bird 189
  Bony fish 181
  Domestic cat 195
  Elephant 200
  Frog 182
  Human 215, 256-259
  Lizard 185
  Rabbit 196
  Snail 177
Ureteric orifice 257
Urethra
  Chimpanzee 202
  Domestic cat 195
  Human 256-257, 259, 261
  Rabbit 196
Urethral opening 259
Urethral sphincter muscle 257
Urinary bladder 181
Urinary system 256-257
Urinogenital opening
  Bony fish 181
  Dolphin 205
Urn 478, 481, 487
Urodela 182
Uropod 172
Urostyle 183
Ursa Major 18, 19
Ursa Minor 18, 21
Ursus americanus 195
Ursus spelaeus 77, 106
U-shaped gouge 449
U-shaped valley 286-287
Uterine wall 260-261
Uterus
  Chimpanzee 202
  Elephant 200
  Human 258-259
Utricle 243
U-tube 313
Utzon, J. 499
Uvula 212, 245, 248

V

V1 "flying bomb" 408
V12 cylinder arrangement 345
V4 engine unit
  British Rail Class 20 diesel 327
  Honda VF750 364
Vacuole
  Chlamydomonas sp. 116
  Diatom 116
  Human cell 216
  Palisade mesophyll 139
Vacuum brake lever 325
Vacuum circuit braker 328
Vacuum operated inlet valve 362
Vacuum reservoir 324
Vagina
  Chimpanzee 202
  Elephant 200
  Human 258-259, 261
  Snail 177
  Spider 170
Valance
  1906 Renault 337

Ford Model T 339
Volkswagen Beetle 341
Valency electrons 310
Vallate papillae 244
Vallecular canal 120
Valles Marineris 43
Valley
  Coastline 294
  Glacier 286-287
  Grand Canyon 277
  Mountain 62
  River features 290
  River 288-289
  Rock cycle stages 267
Valley floor erosion 267
Valley head 289
Valley rafter 473
Valley spring 292
Vālmiki 35
Valve 359
Valve chest 324
Valve cusp 252
Valve lifter 367
Valve return spring 347
Valve rocker 344, 402
Valves
  Bivalves 176
  Dehiscent fruit 151
  Indehiscent fruit 150
  Scallop 176
Valve slide 506, 507
Valve spring 343, 344
Valve system 506
Vamp 568
Vamp backer 569
Vanadium 310
Van Allen radiation belt 38
Van de Graaff 41
Van de Graaff generator 316
Vane 191
Van Eyck 35
Vang 378
Vanishing point 431
Variable incidence air intake 420
Variable incidence gust-alleviator 421
Variable nozzle 416-417
Variable pitch aluminum-alloy blade 408
Variable pitch propeller 396
Variable time control knob 578-579
Variegated lamina 131, 137
Varnish 548, 436
Vasa recta 256
Vascular cambium 134-135
Vascular plants 279
Vascular plexus 235
Vascular strand 149
Vascular system 162-163
Vascular tissue 130
  Aerial shoot 155
  Apical meristem 134
  Bishop pine 124
  Canadian pond weed 159
  Clubmoss stem 120
  Corm 155
  Dicotyledon 127
  Dodder 163
  Epiphytic orchid 162
  Fern rachis 121
  Higher plants 118-119
  Horsetail stem 120
  Marram grass 113
  Monocotyledon 126-127
  Parasite host 163
  Perennials 130-131
  Pine needle 124
  Pine root/stem 125
  Radicle 152

Rhizome 155
Root 132-133
Stem 134-135
  Water hyacinth root 158
  Water lily leaf 159
  Woody plants 130-131
Vas deferens
  Domestic cat 195
  Human 259
  Rabbit 196
Vastitas Borealis 43
Vastus lateralis muscle 225-226
Vastus medialis muscle 225-226
Vault 484-485, 496
  Ancient Roman building 462-464
  Baroque church 479
  Gothic building 470
  Medieval building 467-469
  Modern building 496, 499
  Nineteenth-century building 492-493
  Renaissance building 477
Vaulting shaft 468-469
V-belt pulley 347
Vedette boat 395
Vega 19, 20
  Our galaxy and nearby galaxies 15
Vegetable oil 436
Vegetative reproduction 154-155
Veil 114-115
Vein
  Alveolar 247
  Anterior median 253
  Axillary 253
  Basilic 253
  Brachiocephalic 253
  Bronchial 254
  Cardiac 250
  Central retinal 240
  Cephalic 176, 253
  Common iliac 215, 253, 257
  Dicotyledon leaf 126-127
  Digital 253
  External iliac 215, 253
  Femoral 253
  Gastroepiploic 253
  Great saphenous 253
  Hepatic portal 253
  Hogweed leaf 129
  Inferior mesenteric 253
  Inferior vena cava 215, 252-253, 257
  Internal iliac 253
  Internal jugular 253
  Jugular 215
  Leaf 136, 138-139
  Median cubital 253
  Monocotyledon leaf 126
  Palmar 253
  Portal 252
  Pulmonary 251, 253, 254
  Pulp 247
  Renal 256-257
  Short saphenous 253
  Subclavian 253
  Superior mesenteric 253
  Superior vena cava 215, 251, 252-253, 255
Vertex
  Building 495
  Human body 212
Vertical air current 302
Vertical cleavage 270
Vertical damper 329
Vertical frame ladder 392

Vela 18, 21
Velamen 162
Velarium 464
Velar scale 115
Vela Supernova Remnant 17
Vellum 432
Velocette overhead valve (OHV) engine 367
Velum 373
Vena cava
  Frog 182
  Inferior 215, 252-253, 257
  Superior 215, 251, 252-253, 255
Vendelinus 40
Veneer 462
Venomous snake 184
Vent
  Frigate 397
  Igneous rock structures 275
  Mountain building 62
  Rock cycle 266
  Suzuki RGV500 368
  Volcano 272-273
Ventilation 462
Ventilation grille 329
Ventilator 422, 423
Ventilator exit 406-407
Ventral abdominal artery 173
Ventral antebrachial muscle 94
Ventral aorta 179
Ventral fin 179
Ventral margin of shell 176
Ventral nerve cord 169, 173
Ventral scale 184, 186
Ventricle
  Brain 236-237
  Heart 215, 250-251, 252
Ventricular diastole 251
Ventricular systole 251
Venturi 424
Venus 36-37
  Solar System 30
Venus fly trap 160
Verdaccio 433
Verge 464, 492
Vermiculated rustication 482
Vermilion 433
Vermilion border of lip 213
Vermilion Cliffs 277
Versal lettering 445
Vertebra 261
  Bony fish 180
  Cervical 212, 222
  Frog 183
  Lumbar 222-223
  Rattlesnake 185
  Rudimentary 260
  Thoracic 222-223
  Turtle 187
  Westlothiana 81
Vertebral artery 223, 252
Vertebral body 223
Vertebral column 218, 222, 257
Vertebral foramen 222-223
Vertebral shield 187
Vertebrates 56, 64, 104
  Fossil record 279

Vertical movement
  Faults and folds 60
  Lake formation 292
Vertical pupil 186
Vertical ridge 129
Vertical spindle 387
Vertical stroke 445
Very high-frequency (VHF) radio 318
Vesicle 148
Vespa Grand Sport 160 Mark 1 363
Vespa scooter 362, 363
Vessel
  Baroque church 479
  Gothic church 470
  Medieval church 468-469
Vesta Rupes 37
Vestibular canal 243
Vestibular membrane 243
Vestibular nerve 243
Vestibule
  Ancient Greek temple 461
  Baroque church 481
  Human body 212, 245
  Medieval church 469
  Neoclassical building 483
Vestibulocochlear nerve 243
VHF aerial
  B-17 bomber 408-409
  BAe-146 jetliner 415
  Bell Jetranger helicopter 423
  Concorde 416-417
  VHF radio 318
VHF omni-range aerial
  Bell-47 helicopter 422
  Concorde 417
VHF omni-range and instrument-landing-system aerial 412
Vibraphone 504, 516, 517
Vibrations
  Brass instruments 506
  Stringed instruments 510
Vibrato arm 513
Vibrato effect 516, 517
Vibrissa
  Lion 194
  Rabbit 196
  Rat 196
  Seal 204
Vicia faba 133, 152
Viewfinder eyepiece 588-589
Viewing area 584, 585
Viking ships 574-575
Villa Rotunda 475
Villa Savoye 494
Villi of mucosa 248
Viola 503, 504, 505, 510, 511
Violent eruptions 272
Violet light 318
Violin 503, 504, 505, 510
Violoncello 510-511
Virginia opossum 207
Virgo 18, 21
Visceral cartilage 254
Visceral hump 177
Visceral pericardium 250
Viscous coupling 344-345
Visible light 318-319
Vision 237
Visor 416-417
Visual Display Unit 521
Visual recognition 237
Vitreous glass mosaic 451
Vitreous glass tessera 450, 451
Vitreous humour 240
Vitta 151

Vivaldi 35
Vocal cords 245
Voices 503
Volans 21
Volcanic activity
  Mineralization zones 280
  Rock cycle 266
Volcanic eruption 26
Volcanic gases 64
Volcanic island 58, 299
Volcanic lake 293
Volcanic lava
  Jupiter 44
  Mars 42
  The Moon 40
  Venus 36
Volcanic mountain 62
Volcanic rock 298, 306
Volcano 58, 63, 272-273
  Jupiter 44
  Locations 273
  Mars 42
  Mineralization zones 281
  Mountain building 62-63
  Ocean floor 298
  Vent 62
  Venus 36
Volkmann's canal 247
Volkmann's vessel 225
Volkswagen Beetle 540-541
Volleyball 534-535
Voltage 306, 316
Volume 306, 307
Volume control 520, 521
Volume measurements 590
Volute
  Ancient Greek building 460-461
  Baroque church 479, 481
  Dome 486
  Islamic building 488
  Neoclassical building 478, 480
  Renaissance building 476-477
Volva 114-115
Volvox sp. 116
Vomer 221
Von Kármàn 41
Voussoir 484-485
  Ancient Roman building 465
  Neoclassical building 482
  Renaissance building 474
V-shaped gouge 449
V-shaped valley
  River features 290
  Rivers 288-289
V-strut 404-405
V-twin engine 362, 363
Vulpecula 19
Vulture 190
Vulva 204
Vyāsa 35
Vyne 482

W

Wadi 283
Wagner 35
Wagon 324
Wagon bogie 330
Wagon vault 485
Wahweap sandstone 276
Waist
  74-gun ship 380-381
  Human 210
  Stringed instruments 510-511
Waistband 548

Waist gun 408
Wale
  74-gun ship 381
  Roman corbita 373
  Sailing warship 376-377
Walkway 497
Wall
  Ancient Greek temple 461
  Ancient Roman building 462, 465
  Baroque building 478-479, 481
  Carpel 148, 151
  Cell 112, 117, 132, 139
  Concrete 496
  Fruit 148-151
  Fungal tissue 115
  Glass 496
  Gothic church 470
  Islamic building 488
  Medieval building 466-467, 469
  Modern building 498-499
  Neoclassical building 479, 482
  Nineteenth-century mill 492
  Ovary 140, 150
  Renaissance building 476-477
  Twentieth-century building 494
Wall anchor 407
Wall panel 406-407
Wall painting 434
Walrus 204
Wankel, Felix 546
Wankel rotary engine 346-347
Wannanosaurus 101
Wardrobe 416
Wardroom 381
Warhead 394
Warm air 300, 302-303
Warm blood
  Mammals 104
  Theropods 84
Warm front 302-303
Warm occlusion 302
Warm periods 56
Warning horn 327, 329
Warning light 328
Warship
  74-gun ship 379, 380-381
  Battleship 394-395
  Frigate 396-397
  Ironclad 392-393
  Man-of-war 378-379, Sailing warship 376-377
  Submarine 396-397
Wasatch formation 276
Wash cant 378
Wash over dry brush 439
Washburn twelve-string guitar 513
Washer 567
  Bicycle 358
  Camera 588-589
  Chair 576
  Lamp 573
  Lawnmower 581
  Power drill 566-567
  Toaster 578-579
Washer jet 353
Washes 438, 439
Washing machine 315
Wasp 168
Waste heat 314-315
Water 38, 66
  Absorption 150
  Amphibian 80
  Changing states 307
  "Deltic" diesel electric-locomotive 326

Energy generation 314-315
Epiphyte supply 162
Fermentation 313
Lithographic printing 446
Mars 42
Molecule 138
Oceans and seas 296
Photosynthesis 138
Pollination 144
Reversible reactions 312
Seed germination 152-153
Solutions 306
Storage organs 156-157
Transport 134, 139
Waterborne sports 560-561
Water-closet 483
Watercolor 438-459
Watercolor paint pan 438
Watercolor paper 439, 441
Watercolor-style acrylic painting 442, 443
Water connection 342
Water-cooled engine 366
Water cycle 288
Water density 296
Water distribution 264
Water droplets 45
Waterfall 291
  Glacier 286
  River 289-290
  Rock cycle 267
Water fern 158
Water float 324
Water hyacinth 158
Water ice
  Jupiter's atmosphere 45
  Mercury's atmosphere 47
  Structure of comet 53
  Structure of Mars 43
  Structure of Neptune 51
Water-ice fog 42
Water-ice permafrost 43
Water jacket
  Daimler engine 343
  Ford diesel engine 347
  Humber engine 343
  Jaguar straight six engine 344
Water key 506, 507
Water lily 158-159
Waterline 380
Water obstacle 546
Water outlet 356, 425
Water passage 346
Water pipe
  1906 Renault 337
  Humber engine 343
  Wright Flyer 399
Water pressurizer 514
Waterproof acrylic paint 442
Waterproof covering
  Bishop pine needles 124
  Golden barrel cactus 156
  Haworthia truncata 157
  Lithops bromfieldii 157
  Monocotyledon leaf 126
  Rush stem 135
  Wetland plants 158
Waterproof shell 80
Waterproof ski clothing 553
Waterproof skin 81
Waterproof stowage box 427
Water pump
  Jaguar V12 engine 345
  Renault Clio 351
  White Steam Car 342
Water pump pulley 347

Water rail
  Jaguar V12 engine 345
  Formula One racing car 357
Water reactor 314
Water-retaining cuticle 78
Water salinity 296
Water-saturated permeable rock
  Lakes and groundwater 292
  Mineral resources 280-281
Watershed 289
Water shoot 560
Water-soluble glue 450
Water storage tank 497
Water-storing parenchyma 156-157
Water supply
  Gun turret 396
  Steam locomotive 324
Water table 284, 292
Water tank
  Bordino Steam Carriage 334
  "Ellerman Lines" steam locomotive 324
  White Steam Car 342
Water vapor
  Chemical reactions 312-313
  Hurricane structure 303
  Jupiter's atmosphere 45
  Mars' atmosphere 43
  Saturn's atmosphere 47
  Venus' atmosphere 37
  Water cycle 288
Water vascular system 174
Waterway 380, 393
Wattle-and-daub
  Ancient Roman building 462, 464-465
  Medieval house 466
Wave 294, 298
  Erosion 294
  Features 294
  Properties 518
Wave-cut platform 295
Wavelength 518
Wavellite 269
Wavering pitch 516, 517
Wavy foliation 267
Wax modeling 452
Wax riser 454
Wax runner 454
Waxy cuticle 156, 157
Waxy fruit skin 149
Waxy laminae 159
Waxy zone 161
Weapon-bay bulkhead 421
Weaponry 375
Weasel 194
Weather 302-303
Weathercock 486
Weathering 282-283
  Gothic church 471-472
  Medieval church 469
  Mineral deposits 280
  Renaissance building 477
  Rock cycle 266
  Sedimentary rocks 276
Weather radar 416
Weather shutter for gun 394
Weather-vane 471, 477
Web
  English saddle 582
  Frog 182
Webbed feet 188, 190
Webbing
  Chair 576-577
Saddle 583

Weight
  Arch 484
  All-purpose bicycle 360
  Bolts 548
  Measurement 320, 590
  Motorcycle engine 366
  Newton meters 320
Weights 562
Wei-wei 376
Weld line 392
Welt
  Saddle 583
  Shoes 568-569
Welwitschia gymnosperm 122-123
Welwitschia mirabilis 122-123
Werner motorcycle 362
Weslake Speedway bike 369
West Australian current 297
Westerlies 300
Western saddle 582
Westlothiana 67, 80-81
Westminster Abbey 484
Westminster Cathedral 493
Wet-in-wet wash 438, 439
Wetland plants 158-159
Wet season 293
Wet wash 438
Wezen 18
  Canis Major 21
Whaler 395
Whales 204-205
Wheat 109, 150
Wheel
  1906 Renault 337
  Bicycle 358-359
  Diesel motor output 326
  First cars 334-335
  Force/motion 320
  Ford Model T 358-359
  Harley-Davidson FLHS Electra Glide 363
  Mazda RX-7 346
  Motorcycle 364
  Pacing sulky 555
  Paddle 390-391
  Renault Clio 350-351
  Rossin Italian time-trial bicycle 361
  Ship 378, 390, 394
  Single scull 561
  Volkswagen Beetle 340
  Weslake Speedway bike 369
Wheel axle
  BAe-146 jetliner 414
  Touring bicycle 360
Wheelbase 360
Wheel bolt 580-581
Wheelchair access 333
Wheel fairing
  Blackburn monoplane 400
  Pegasus Quasar microlight 427
  Pegasus XL SE microlight 426
Wheel fork 335
Wheel guard 324, 369
Wheel hub 414
Wheel sets 327, 329
Wheel spacer 561
Whelp 387
Whetstone 452
Whip 555
Whipping 384, 388
Whisker
  Lion 194
  Rabbit 196
  Rat 196
  Seal 204

Whisker boom 382
"Whispering Gallery" 484
Whistle
  Iron paddlesteamer 392
  Life jacket 561
  Referee 524
Whistle lever 325
White belt 556
White blood cells 217, 253
White Cliffs 276
White diamond 268
White dwarfs
  Small stars 24-25
  Stars 22-23
White feldspar 275
White-gray crystal 271
White light 318
White matter
  Cerebrum 236-237
  Spinal cord 238
White of eye 213
White oval
  Jupiter 44-45
  Saturn 46
White Steam Car 342
White stork 188
White warning light 328
White whale 204
Whorls
  Flower 140
  Green alga cell 116
  Sepals 144, 149
Wick 554
Wicket 538
Wicket-keeper 538
Wide receiver 526
Wiener 41
Williams 1990 Formula One racing car 356-357
Willow charcoal 430
Willow grouse 193
Wind
  Atmosphere 300
  Ekman spiral 297
  Energy generation 314
  Oceans and seas 296-297
  Rock cycle 266-267
  Water cycle 288
  Weather 302
Weathering and erosion 282-283
Windspeed 303
Windcheetah SL Mark VI "Speedy" racing HPV Bicycle 361
Wind chest 514
Wind controller 521
Wind deflector 341
Wind-dispersed seeds 150-151
Wind erosion 282-283
  Coastline 294
Winding cornice 472
Winding hole 571
Winding key 570
Wind instruments 508, 509
  Brass 506, 507
  Electronic 520
  Woodwind 508, 509
Windlass
  Buildings 467, 477
  Roman corbita 372
Windlass bar 380
Wind lever collar 589
Window
  Ancient Egyptian building 459
  Ancient Roman building 463, 465
  Asian building 490-491
  Baroque church 479-481
  Dome 486-487
  Dormer 495
  Double-decker tour bus 333

"Eurostar" multi-voltage electric train 329
  Gothic building 470-473
  MCW Metrobus 333
  Medieval building 466-469
  Modern building 498, 499
  Neoclassical building 478, 482-483
  Nineteenth-century building 492-493
  Renaissance building 474, 476
  Rococo style 482
  Single-decker bus 333
  TGV electric high-speed train 329
  Twentieth-century building 494-495
Window blind 336
Window-frame 486
Window glass 348
Window jamb 479, 482, 483
Windowsill
  Baroque church 479
  Neoclassical building 482-483
  Twentieth-century building 494
Window stage 477
Wind-pollinated plants 144
Windshield
  BAe-146 jetliner components 412
  BE 2B bomber 404
  BMW R/60 sidecar 362
  Concorde 416-417
  "Deltic" diesel-electric locomotive 327
  Double-decker tour bus 333
  Ford Model T 339
  Harley-Davidson FLHS Electra Glide 363
  Hawker Tempest components 409
  Kirby BSA racing sidecar 362
  Lockheed Electra airliner 406-407
  Tornado 420
Windshield wiper
  "Deltic" diesel-electric locomotive 327
  "Eurostar" multi-voltage electric train 329
  Italian State Railways Class 402 528
  MCW Metrobus 332
  Paris RATP Metro 328
  TGV electric high-speed train 329
  Union Pacific locomotive 326
  Volkswagen Beetle 341
Windsor green 458
Windspeed 303
Wind synthesizer 521
Wind-up 537
Windvane 375
Windward face 283
Wing
  1906 Renault 336
  Alula 191
  ARV light aircraft 424-425
  Australian rules football 528
  Avro biplane 403
  BAe-146 jetliner components 413, 414
  BE 2B wings 404

Beetle 168
Biplanes and triplanes 402
Bird 188, 191
Blackburn monoplane 401
Bones 191
Bumblebee 168
Butterfly 169
Cobra lily 160
Coverts 188
Curtiss biplane 398
Deer hopper dry fly 563
Developing 192
Dry fruit 150-151
Early monoplanes 400
Feather 188, 191
Ford Model T 338
Formula One racing car 357
Gliders, hang-gliders, and microlights 426
Handball 535
Hawker Tempest components 409
Hockey 540
Ice hockey 550
Lockheed Electra airliner 406
Pine seed 122
Pitcher plant 113
Rugby 530
Scots pine seed 122
Show-jumping fence 554
Ski boot safety binding 552
Spurious 191
Sycamore 151
Wing assembly 413
Wing attack 535, 541
Wing cap 568
Wing case 168
Wing defense
  Lacrosse 541
  Netball 535
Winged seeds
  Scots pine 122
  Sycamore 131, 151
Winged stem 129
Wing end-plate 357
Wing-feather impression 85
Wing fillet panel 409
Wingframe 427
Wing nut 572-573
Wing piping 341
Wing-protecting skid 398-399
Wing-root glove fairing 420-421

Wing-root mount 413
Wing scar 122
Wing stay 339
Wing strut
  ARV light aircraft 424-425
  Avro triplane 402-403
  Curtiss biplane 398
Wingtip
  ARV light aircraft 424
  BE 2B wings 404
  Hawker Tempest components 409
  Schleicher glider 426
Wingtip aerial fairing 421
Wing transom 381
Wing warping 400
Wire armature 454, 455
Wire bristle brush 519
Wire-ended cutting tool 454
Wire-end tools 452
Wire gauze pad 542
Wireless and telegraphy yard 395
Wireless office 397
Wires 518
Wire wheel 402
Wishbone
  Bird 189
  Formula One racing car 357
Withdrawal stride 543
Withdrawing-room 483
Withers 199
Wolf 195
Wolffian duct 179
Wolf hair brush 444
Wollastonite 271
Womb 258-259
Women's lacrosse field 540, 541
Women's shot 542
Wood
  Golf club 547
  Sculpture 454
Wood block 446, 449
Wood capstan 387
Woodcarving 452, 453
Woodcut 446
Wooden arrow 109
Wooden artillery wheel 337
Wooden bar 516
Wooden bezel 571
Wooden body 510
Wooden body-shell 519
Wooden buffer 324
Wooden case 514, 515
Wooden-domed deck 403

Wooden driving wheel 324
Wooden frame
  Chair 576
  Harp 511
  Printing mesh 446, 448
  Sculpture 452
  Steam-powered Cugnot "Fardier" 334
Wooden golf clubs 546, 547
Wood engraving 446, 447
Wood engraving print 449
Wooden grip 549
Wooden hearth 109
Wooden "key" 331
Wooden mold 568
Wooden packing 397
Wooden panel 473
Wooden peg 570-571
Wooden sailing ship 378-379
Wooden sleeper 324, 331
Wooden spoke 334
Wooden-spoked wheel 339
Wooden stands 554
Wooden wheel 334
Woodwind instruments 504, 505, 508, 509
Woodwork 467
Woody flowering plants 126, 130-131
Woody pericarps 150
Woody plants 126
Woody scales 123, 124
Woody stem 134-135
Woolding 376
Work 314
Working chamber 396
Working saddle 582
Worklamp 572
World War I aircraft 404-405
World War II aircraft 408-409
Worming 388
Worms
  Earth's evolution 56
  Fossil record 279
Woven dacron 384
Wrack 116-117
Wren, C. 478
  Baroque church 480
  Cathedral dome 484, 487
Wrest plank
  Concert grand piano 515
  Upright piano 514
Wright brothers
  Modern piston aero-engines 410

Pioneers of flight 398-399
Wright, F. L. 495
Wright Flyer 398-399
Wrist
  Corythosaurus 98
  Elephant 90
  Human 211, 230-231
  Iguanodon 97
  Stegosaurus 92
  Triceratops 102
Wrist joint
  Baryonyx 85
  Brachiosaurus 91
  Diplodocus 90
  Euoplocephalus 94
  Human 218
  Parasaurolophus 99
  Plateosaurus 88
  Stegoceras 100, 101
  Tyrannosaurus 84
Wrist pin 390
Wrist position 444
Wrist protection 551
Wrist strap 552, 553
Wrist thong 545
Writing surface 444
Writing tools 444
Wuerhosaurus 93
Wulfenite 269

X

X-contact 589
Xerophytes 156-157
X-flash sync terminal 588
Xi2 Sagittarii 21
Xi Orionis 18
Xi Pegasi 19
X line 445
X ray 318-319
  Colon 214
  Gallbladder 214
  Hand 230
X-ray emission 28
X-ray image of Crab Nebula 28
"X" turret 395
Xylem
  Bishop pine 124
  Clubmoss stem 120
  Dicotyledons 126-127
  Dodder host 163
  Epiphytic orchid 162
  Fern rachis 121
  Higher plants 118-119
  Horsetail stem 120
  Marram grass 113

Monocotyledons 126-127
Pine needle 124
Pine root/stem 125
Radicle 152
Root 132
Stem 134-135
Water hyacinth root 158
Water lily leaf 159
Xylem fibers 134-135

Y

Yacht racing 560
Yangchuanosaurus 85
Yangtze River 265
Yard 382
  Battleship 395
  Double topsail schooner 385
  Greek and Roman ships 372, 373
  Steel 392
  Tea clipper 392
  Viking karv 375
Yardang 282
Yardarm 379
Yardsman 526
Yasti 490, 491
Year
  Earth 30
  Jupiter 30
  Mars 30
  Mercury 26, 34
  Neptune 31
  Planets 30-31
  Pluto 31
  Saturn 31
  Uranus 31
  Venus 30
Yeast
  Fermentation 313
  Fungi 114
Yellow card 524
Yellow light 318, 331
Yellow ochre 442
Yellow orpiment 271
Yellow River 265
Yellow warning arm 330
Yellow-wort 144
Yew 123
Y.M.C.A. 532
Yoke 574
Yolk 192
Yolk sac 192
Ytterbium 311
Yttrium 310
"Y" turret 395
Yucca 126
Yucca sp. 126

Z

Zagros Mountains 75
Zaire 265
Zea mays 127
Zeami 35
Zebra 198
Zeeman 41
Zeilleria frenzlii 66
Zeta Centauri 21
Zeta Sagittarii 21
Zeugen 282
Ziggurat-style step-back 494
Zinc 281, 312
Zinc phosphating 348
Zinc plating 477
Zingiber officinale 155
Zion Canyon 276
Zipper 354
Zirconium 310
Zone
  Jupiter 44-45
  Structure of Saturn 47
Zone defenses 533
Zonular ligament 241
Zooming-in 585
Zoomorphic head 374
Zosteres 372
Zosterophyllum llanoveranum 64
Zubenelgenubi 18, 21
Zubeneschamali 18, 21
Zugon 373
Zygian 373
Zygomatic arch
  Bear 194
  Chimpanzee 202
  Human 213, 220
  Lion 194
  Smilodon 106
  Toxodon 107
Zygomatic bone 220-221
Zygomaticus major muscle 228-229
Zygote
  Bryophyte 118-119
  Fertilization 146-147
  Plant formation 146
  Primitive land plants 120
  Seaweed 116-117

Acknowledgments

Dorling Kindersley would like to thank (in order of sections):

The Universe
(consultant editors – Sue Becklake, Gevorkyan Tatyana Alekseyevna):
John Becklake; the Memorial Museum of Cosmonautics, Moscow; The Cosmos Pavilion, Moscow; The United States Space and Rocket Center, Alabama; Broadhurst, Clarkson and Fuller Ltd; Susannah Massey

Prehistoric Earth
(consultant editors – William Lindsay, Martyn Bramwell, Dr. Ralph E. Molnar, David Lambert):
Dr. Monty Reid, Andrew Neuman, and the staff of the Royal Tyrrell Museum of Palaeontology, Drumheller, Alberta; Dr. Angela Milner and the staff of the Department of Palaeontology, the Natural History Museum, London; Professor W. Ziegler and the staff, in particular Michael Loderstaedt, of the Naturmuseum Senckenburg, Frankfurt; Dr. Alexander Liebau, Axel Hunghrebüller, Reiner Schoch, and the staff of the Institut und Museum für Geologie und Paläontologie der Universität, Tübingen; Rupert Wild of the Institut für Paläontologie, Staatliches Museum für Naturkunde, Stuttgart; Dr. Scheiber of the Stadtmuseum, Nördlingen; Professor Dr. Dietrich Herm of Staatssammlung für Paläontologie und Historische Geologie, München; Dr. Michael Keith-Lucas of the Department of Botany, University of Reading; Richard Walker; American Museum of Natural History, New York

Plants
(consultant editor – Richard Walker):
Diana Miller; Lawrie Springate; Karen Sidwell; Chris Thody; Michelle End; Susan Barnes and Chris Jones of the EMU Unit of the Natural History Museum, London; Jenny Evans of Kew Gardens, London; Kate Biggs of the Royal Horticultural Society Gardens, Wisley, Surrey; Spike Walker of Microworld Services; Neil Fletcher; John Bryant of Bedgebury Pinetum, Kent; Dean Franklin

Animals
(consultant editor – Richard Walker):
David Manning's Animal Ark; Intellectual Animals; Howletts Zoo, Canterbury; John Dunlop; Alexander O'Donnell; Sue Evans of the Royal Veterinary College, London; Dr. Geoff Potts and Fred Frettsome of the Marine Biological Association of the United Kingdom, Plymouth; Jeremy Adams of the Booth Museum of Natural History, Brighton; Derek Telling of the Department of Anatomy, University of Bristol; the Natural History Museum, London; Andy Highfield of the Tortoise Trust; Brian Harris of the Aquarium, London Zoo; the Invertebrate Department, London Zoo; Dr. Harold McClure of the Yerkes Regional Primate Research Center, Emory University, Atlanta, Georgia; Nielson Lausen of the Harvard Medical School, New England Regional Primates Research Center, Southborough, Massachusetts; Dr. Paul Hopwood of the Department of Veterinary Anatomy, University of Sydney; Dean Franklin

The Human Body
(consultant editors – Dr. Frances Williams, Dr. Fiona Payne, Richard Cummins FRCS):
Derek Edwards and Dr Martin Collins, British School of Osteopathy; Dr. M.C.E. Hutchinson of the Department of Anatomy, United Medical and Dental Schools of Guy's and St. Thomas' Hospitals, London. Models – Barry O'Rorke (Bodyline Agency) and Pauline Swaine (MOT Model Agency)

Geology, Geography, and Meteorology
(consultant editor – Martyn Bramwell):
Dr. John Nudds of the Manchester Museum, Manchester; Dr. Alan Wooley and Dr. Andrew Clark of the Natural History Museum, London; Graham Bartlett of the National Meteorological Library and Archive, Bracknell; Tony Drake of BP Exploration, Uxbridge; Jane Davies of the Royal Society of Chemistry, Cambridge; Dr. Tony Waltham of Nottingham Trent University, Nottingham; staff of the Smithsonian Institute, Washington; staff of the United States Geological Survey, Washington; staff of the National Geographic Society, Washington; staff of Edward Lawrence Associates (Export Ltd), Midhurst; John Farndon; David Lambert

Rail and Road
Rail (consultant editor – John Coiley)
Michael Ashworth of the London Transport Museum

Road (consultant editors – David Burgess-Wise, Hugo Wilson)
The National Motor Museum, Beaulieu; Alf Newell of Renault UK Ltd; David Suter of Cheltenham Cutaway Exhibits Ltd; Francesca Riccini of the Science Museum, London. Signore Amadelli of the Museo dell' Automobile Carlo Biscaretti di Ruffia; Paul Bolton of the Mazda MCL Group; Duncan Bradford of Reg Mills Wire Wheels; John and Leslie Brewster of Autocavan; David Burgess-Wise; Trevor Cass of Garrett Turbo Service; John Corbett of The Patrick Collection; Gary Crumpler of Williams Grand Prix Engineering Ltd; Mollie Easterbrooke and Duncan Gough of Overland Ltd; Arthur Fairley of the Vauxhall Motor Co; Paul Foulkes-Halbard of Filching Manor Motor Museum; Frank Gilbert of I. Wilkinson and Son Ltd; Paolo Gratton of Gratton Museum; Colvin Gunn of Gunn and Son; Judy Hogg of Ecurie Bertelli; Milton Holman of Dream Cars; Ian Matthews of IMAT Electronics; Eric Neal of Jaguar Cars Ltd; Paul Niblett, Keith Davidson, Mark Reumel, and David Woolf of Michelin Tyre plc; Doug Nye; Kevin O'Keefe of O'Keefe Cars; Seat UK; Roger Smith; Jim Stirling of Ironbridge Gorge Museum, Stafford-shire; Jon Taylor; Doug Thompson; Martyn Watkins of Ford Motor Co Ltd; John Cattermole, Customer Services Manager, at London Northern Buses; F. W. Evans Cycles Ltd; Trek UK Ltd (Bicycle); Sam Grimmer

Physics and Chemistry
(consultant editor – Jack Challoner)

Sea and Air
Sea (consultant editors – Geoff Hales and Harvey B. Loomis):
David Spence, Gillian Hutchinson, David Topliss, Simon Stephens, Robert Baldwin, Jonathan Betts, all of the National Maritime Museum, London; Ian Friel; Simon Turnage of Captain O.M. Watts of London Ltd; Davey and Co Ltd, Great Dunmow; Avon Inflatables Ltd, Llanelli; Musto Ltd, Benfleet; Peter Martin of Spencer Rigging Ltd, Southampton; Peter Rowson of Ratseys Sailmakers, Southampton; Swiftech Ltd, Wallingford; Colin Scattergood of the Barrow Boat Co Ltd, Colchester; Professor J.S. Morrison of the Trireme Trust, Cambridge; The Cutty Sark Maritime Trust; Adrian Daniels of Kelvin Hughes Marine Instruments, London; Arthur Credland of Hull City Council Museums and Art Galleries; The Hull Maritime Society; Gerald Clark; Peter Fitzgerald of the Science Museum, London; Alec Michael of HMB Subwork Ltd, Great Yarmouth, and Ray Ward of the OSEL Group, Great Yarmouth; Richard Bird of UWI, Weybridge; Walker Marine Instruments, Birmingham; The International Sailing Craft Association; The Exeter Maritime Museum; Jane Wilson of the Trinity Lighthouse Co, London; The Imperial War Museum Collections; Thorn Security Ltd; Michael Bach

Air (consultant editor – Bill Gunston):
Aeromega Helicopters, Stapleford; Aero Shopping, London; Avionics Mobile Services Ltd, Watford; Roy Barber and John Chapman of the RAF Museum, Hendon; Mitch Barnes Aviation, London; Mike Beach; British Caledonian Flight Training Ltd; Fred Coates of Helitech (Luton) Ltd; Michael Cuttell and CSE Aviation Ltd, Oxford; Dowty Aerospace Landing Gear, Gloucester; Guy Hartcup of the Airship Association; Anthony Hooley, Chris Walsh, and David Cord of British Aerospace Regional Aircraft Ltd; Ken Huntley of Mid-West Aero Engines Ltd; Imperial War Museum, Duxford; The London Gliding Club, Dunstable; Musée des Ballons, Calvados; Noel Penny Turbines Ltd; Andy Pavey of Aviation Scotland Ltd; Tony Pavey of Thermal Aircraft Developments, London; the Commanding Officer and personnel of RAF St Athan; the Commanding Officer and personnel of RAF Wittering; The Science Museum, London; Ross Sharp of the Science Museum, Wroughton; The Shuttleworth Collection; Skysport Engineering; Mike Smith; Solar Wings Ltd, Marlborough; Julian Temple of Brooklands Museum Trust Ltd; Kelvin Wilson of Flying Start

Architecture
(consultant editor – Alexandra Kennedy):
Stephen Cutler for advice and text; Gavin Morgan of the Museum of London, London; Chris Zeuner of the Weald and Downland Museum, Singleton, Sussex; Alan Hills and James Putnam of the British Museum, London; Dr. Simon Penn and Michael Thomas of the Avoncroft Museum of Buildings, Bromsgrove,

Worcestershire; Christina Scull of Sir John Soane's Museum, London; Paul Kennedy and John Williamson of the London Door Co, London; Lou Davis of The Original Box Sash Window Co, Windsor; Goddard and Gibbs Studios Ltd, London, for access to stained glass windows; The Royal Courts of Justice, Strand, London; Charles Brooking and Peter Dalton for access to the doors and windows in the Charles Brooking Collection, University of Greenwich, Dartford, Kent; Clare O'Brien of the Shakespeare Globe Trust, Shakespeare's Globe Museum, Bear Gardens, Southwark, London; Ken Teague of the Horniman Museum, London; Canon Haliburton, Mike Payton, Ken Stones, and Anthony Webb of St. Paul's Cathedral, London; Roy Spring of Salisbury Cathedral; Reverend Gillean Craig of the Church of St. George in the East, London; the Science Museum, London; Dr. Neil Bingham; Lin Kennedy of Historic Royal Palaces; Katy Harris of Sir Norman Foster and Partners; Production Design, Thames Television plc, London, for supplying models; Dominique Reynier of Le Centre Georges Pompidou, Paris; Denis Roche of Le Musée National des Monuments Français, Paris; Franck Gioria and students of Les Compagnons du Devoir, Paris, for access to construction models; Frank Folliot of Le Musée Carnavalet, Paris; Dr Martina Harms of Hessische Landesmuseums, Darmstadt; Jefferson Chapman of the University of Tennessee, Knoxville, for access to the model of the Hypostyle Hall, Temple of Amon-Re; staff of the Palazzo Strozzi, Florence; staff of the Sydney Opera House, Sydney; staff of the Empire State Building, New York; Nick Jackson; Ann Terrell

The Visual Arts
(consultant editor – Pip Seymour):
Rosemary Simmons; Michael Taylor of Paupers Press, London; Tessa Hunkin and Emma Biggs of Mosaic Workshop, London; John Tiranti, Jonathan Lyons of Alec Tiranti Ltd, London; Chris Hough; Dr. Ashok Roy; Satwinder Sehmi of Alphabet Soup, London; Phillip Poole of Cornelissens, London; George Weil and Sons Ltd, London; The National Gallery, London; Chris Webster of the Tate Gallery, London; China Art Cultural Centre, London; London Graphic Centre, London; A.P. Fitzpatrick, London; Flowers Graphics, London; Intaglio Printmaker, London; Falkiner Papers, London; Edgar Udny and Co, London; John Green

Music
(consultant editor – Susan Sturrock):
Boosey and Hawkes Music Publishers Ltd, London, for permission to reproduce extract from The Prodigal Son by Arthur Sullivan; The Bass and Drum Cellar, London; Empire Drums and Percussion, London; Argents (part of World of Music), London; Bill Lewington Ltd, London; Frobenius organ at Kingston Parish Church, Kingston-upon-Thames, Surrey; Yamaha-Kemble Music (UK) Ltd, Tilbrook, Milton Keynes; Yamaha Atelier, London; Akai (UK) Ltd, Hounslow, Middlesex; Casio Electronics Co Ltd, London; Roland (UK) Ltd, Fleet, Hampshire; Richard Schulman

Sports
The Sports Council Information Centre, London; The British Olympic Games Committee; Brian Crennell of Black's Leisure Group (First Sport); Lillywhites of Piccadilly, London; Mitre Sports International Ltd, Huddersfield; David Bloomfield of the Football Association; Denver Athletics Ltd, Norfolk; Greg Everest and Keith Birley of the British League of Australian Rules Football; Peter McNally of the Gaelic Athletic Association; Rex King of the Rugby Football Union, Twickenham; Neil Tunnicliffe of the Rugby Football League, Leeds; Wayne Patterson of the Basketball Hall of Fame, Springfield, Connecticut; Brian Coleman of the English Basketball Association; All American Imports, Northampton; George Bulman of the English Volleyball Association; Julie Longdon of Mizuno Mallory (UK) Ltd; Juliet Stanford of the All-England Netball Association; Jeff Rowland of the British Handball Association; Cally Melin of Adidas UK Ltd; Patrick Donnely of the Baseball Hall of Fame, Cooperstown, New York; Ian Lepage and Stephen Barlow of the Hockey Association, Milton Keynes; Alison Taylor and Anita Mason of the All England Women's Lacrosse Association, Birmingham; David Shuttleworth of the English Lacrosse Union; Les Barnett and Jock Bentley of the British Athletic Federation Ltd, Birmingham; Mike Gilks of the Badminton Association of England; Gurinder Purewall for advice on archery; Chris McCartney of the US Archery Association; Geoff Doe of the National Smallbore Rifle Association, Bisley, Surrey, for information and reference material on shooting; Fagan Sports Goods Distributors, Surrey; Konrad Bartelski for advice on skiing; The British Ski Federation, Edinburgh; Mike Barnett of Snow and Rock of London; Sally Spurway of Mast-Co. Ltd, Reading; Sarah Morgan for advice on equestrian sports; Steve Brown and the New York Racing Association Inc, New York; Danrho of London; Alan Skipp and James Chambers of the Amateur Fencing Association, London; Carla Richards of the US Fencing Association; Hamilton Bland and John Dryer of the Amateur Swimming Association, Loughborough; Cotswold Camping Ltd, London; Tim Spalton of Glyn Locke (Racing Shells) Ltd, Chalgrove; Terry Friel of the US Rowing Association; House of Hardy; Leeda Fishing Tackle

Everyday Things
City Clocks (Clocks); Christopher Cullen of Babber Electronics; Sony UK Ltd (Mini-television); Black and Decker Ltd (Drills); British Footwear Manufacturing Federation; Grenson Shoes Ltd (Shoes); The Folio Society; R S Bookbinders (Books); Pentax UK Ltd (Camera); F E Murdin of the Decorative Lighting Association; Habitat (Lamp); Chingford Reproductions Ltd (Chair); Dualit Ltd (Toaster); J B Dove; Toro Wheelhorse UK Ltd (Lawnmower); WandH Gidden Ltd (Saddle)

PHOTOGRAPHY:
M. Alexander; Peter Anderson; Charles Brooks; Jane Burton; Peter Chadwick; Simon Clay; John Coiley; Andy Crawford; Geoff Dann; Philip Dowell; John Downs; Mike Dunning; Torla Evans; David Exton; Robert and Anthony Fretwell of Fretwell Photography Ltd.; Philip Gatward; Anna Hodgson; Gary Kevin; J. Heseltine; Cyril Laubscher; John Lepine; Lynton Gardiner (American Museum of Natural History, New York); Steve Gorton; Michelangelo Gratton; Judith Harrington; Peter Hayman; Anna Hodgson; Colin Keates; Gary Kevin; Dave King; Bob Langrish; Brian D.Morgan; Nick Nicholls; Nick Parfitt; Tim Parmenter and Colin Keates (Natural History Museum, London); Tim Ridley; Dave Rudkin; Philippe Sebert; James Stevenson; Clive Streeter; Harry Taylor; Matthew Ward; Jerry Young

PHOTOGRAPHIC ASSISTANCE:
Kevin Zak; Gary Ombler

ILLUSTRATORS:
Julian Baum; Rick Blakeley; Kuo Kang Chen; Karen Cochrane; Simone End; Ian Fleming; Roy Flooks; Mark Franklin; David Gardner; Will Giles; Mick Gillah; David Hopkins; Selwyn Hutchinson; Mei Lim; Linden Artists; Nick Loates; Chris Lyon; Kathleen McDougall; Coral Mula; Sandra Pond; Dave Pugh; Colin Rose; Graham Rosewarne; John Temperton; John Woodcock; Chris Woolmer

MODEL MAKERS:
Roby Braun; David Donkin; Morrison Frederick; Gordon Models; John Holmes; Graham High and Jeremy Hunt of Centaur Studios; Richard Kemp; Kelvin Thatcher; Paul Wilkinson

ADDITIONAL DESIGN ASSISTANCE:
Stefan Morris; Ulysses Santos; Suchada Smith

ADDITIONAL EDITORIAL ASSISTANCE:
Helen Castle; Colette Connolly; Camela Decaire; Nick Harris; Andrea Horth; Stewart McEwen; Damien Moore; Melanie Tham;

INDEX: Kay Wright

Picture credits:

Action Plus 530tc; Anglo Australian Telescope Board 11cl, 11cra, 11cbl, 12tr, 12bc, 13tl, 13bl, 14tl, 16b, 17tc, 17bl, 22tl/D.Malin 16tl, 26tr, 27tl; Austin Brown and the Aviation Picture Library 426tl; Baptistery, Florence/Alison Harris 453r; Biophoto Associates 217ca, 217cra, 228cbc, 228cbc 230tr; Paul Brierley 311bra; British Aerospace/Anthony Hooley 412tl, 415tl; British Aerospace (Commercial Aircraft) Ltd 416tl; by permission of the British Library 432tl; British Museum 459tl, 459tr, 460tr, 460tc, 460tb, 489b; BP Exploration 299; Duncan Brown 25tl; Frank Lloyd Wright, American, 1867-1959, Model of Midway Gardens, 1914, executed by Richard Tickner, mixed media, 1987, 41.9 x 81.3 x 76.2, 1989.48. view 1. Photography courtesy of the Art Intitute of Chicago 495t; J.A. Coiley 331cr; Bruce Coleman Ltd/Andy Price 272tl; Courtesy of the Board of Trustees of the Victoria and Albert Museum, London 454-455b; European Passenger Services 329tl; ESA /PLV 11bl; French Railways 329c; Geoscience Features 311cla; Robert Harding Picture Library 62tl; Michael Holford /British Museum 372bl, Michael Holford 374tr; Hutchison Picture Library 60cl; The Image Bank/Edward Bower 306tr; Jet Propulsion Laboratory 11cbr; 30bc; 31bc; 31bcr; 38tl; 42crb; 44cb; 44cbr; 44bc; 44br; 46tl; 46cr; 46cb; 46bc; 46br; 50tl; 50cra; 50cl; 50c; 50cr; 50br; KeyMed Ltd 248bl, 249bl, 249bcl; Department of Prints and Drawings, Uffizi, Florence/Philip Gatward 431tc/Uffizi, Florence/Philip Gatward 433tl; Dr. D.N. Landon (Institute of Neurology) 228bl,br; Life Science Images/Ron Boardman 244bl, 244br; The Lund Observatory 15bc; Brian Morrison 329tl, 329tr; © The Henry Moore Foundation 455tl, 455tr; Musée d'Orsay, Paris/Philippe Sebert 437tc, 441tc; Musée du Louvre, Paris/Philippe Sebert 453tl, 453r; NASA/AUI 13tr; NASA/JPL 11 cbr, 11br, 30tl, 30bl, 30br, 30bc, 31bc, 31bcr, 31bl, 34cr, 38tl, 40tl, 40cr, 42cr, 44tl, 44cb, 44cbr, 44bc, 44br, 44cr, 46crb, 46tl, 46cr, 46cb, 46bc, 46br, 48tl, 48cra, 48bca, 48bc, 48br, 50tl, 50bc, 50bc, 50cbr, 50br, 50cr, 52cr; National Maritime Museum 373br, 392-393b; National Medical Slide Bank 217cr; Nature Photographers/Paul Sterry 286tl; Newage International 317bl; Oxford Scientific Films/Breck P. Kent 166tl; Planet Earth 274tr; Quadrant 326tr; Margaret Robinson 332tl, 453br; Giotto The Expulsion of the Merchants from the Temple Scala 435tc, 435bl, 435br; Science Photo Library 10bl, 13tr, 28tr, 214bcr, 214bl, 236tr/Michael Abbey 225tc/ Agema Infrared Systems 318tl/AGFA 220tl/ Biophoto Associates: 217crb/Dr. Jeremy Burgess/Science Photo Library 132tr; Dr. Jeremy Burgess 235bcl/CNRI 214tl, 214cl, 214c, 214cr, 214bl, 214clb, 214crb, 214blc, 214br, 217cb, 235bcr, 238tl, 249bcr, 253tr, 253cra, 256tl; Science Photo library /Earth Satellite Corporation 288cl, 293br/Dr. Brian Eyden 228cbr/Professor C. Ferlaud 245bl/Vaughan Fleming 311tl/Simon Fraser/U.S. Dept.of Energy 214bcl, 266tl/Eric Grave 217br/Hale Observatories 32br/Max Planck Institute for Radio Astronomy 15tl/Jan Hinsch 225tc/Jodrell Bank 11 tr, 13c /Manfred Kage 217c, 235br, 237br/Dr. William C. Keel 13br/Keith Kent 316tl/Russ Lappa 310bra/Astrid & Hans-Freider Michler 217tr/Dennis Milon 52bl/NASA 11cla, 12tl, 15tr, 30c, 31br, 32tl, 35tl, 36tl, 36cl, 36cr, 36bc, 42br, 42tr, 44tl 52tl, 291tr, 300tl/National Optical Astro Observatory 52tr/NIBSC 253crb/ Novosti Press Agency 42bc/Omikron 244bc/ David Parker 63bl, 304-305, 308br/Philippe Plailly 308tl, Roussel-UCLAF/CNRI 217tc/Rev Ronald Royer 32cr/Royal Observatory, Edinburgh/D Malin 11 tl, 11cr,12c, 16cl, 16cr, 17br/ David Scharf 235bl/Dr. Kaus Schiller 248bcl, 248bcr, 248br/Secchi-Lecaque/Roussel-UCLAF/CNRI 253br/H. Sochurek 214cb/ Stammers/Thompson 230tl/Sheila Terry 234tl/ US Department of Energy 310bc/US Geological Survey/Science Photo Library 8-9, 30bcr, 42tl, 42bl/Tom Van Sant/Geosphere Project, Santa Monica/Science Photo Library 273tr, 281tr, 296tr, 297tl/Dr. Christopher B. Williams/(Saint Marks Hospital)249br; Oxford Scientific Films/ Animals Animals/Breck P. Kent 167tl; Pratt & Whitney Canada 418-419b, 419t; Science Museum 306bl, 306bcl, 306 bcr, 324t, 326-327b, 330tr, 331ct, 331 cb; Sporting Pictures 524tl, 544cr; Tony Stone Worldwide 280tl; David Bomberg St. Pauls and River 1945/Dinora Davies-Rees/Tate Gallery 431bc; David Hockney A Bigger Splash 1967/ © David Hockney/Tate Gallery 443tc; J.M.W. Turner The Burning of the Houses of Parliament Tate Gallery 439tc; Vision 26tr, 27c; Jerry Young 306tl; Dr. Robert Youngson 241cr; Zefa 217bc/ Janicek 276tl/H. Sochurek 210tl, 250tl, 254tl,/ G. Steenmans 292tl

(t=top, b=bottom, a=above, l-left, r=right, c=center)

Every effort has been made to trace the copyright holders. Dorling Kindersley apologises for any unintentional omissions and would be pleased, in any such cases, to add an acknowledgment in future editions.

Some pages in this book previously appeared in the *Visual Dictionary* series published by Dorling Kindersley. Contributors to this series include:

Project Art Editors:
Duncan Brown, Ross George, Nicola Liddiard, Andrew Nash, Clare Shedden, Bryn Walls

Designers:
Lesley Betts, Paul Calver, Simone End, Ellen Woodward

Additional design assistance:
Sandra Archer, Christina Betts, Alexandra Brown, Nick Jackson, Susan Knight

Project Editors:
Fiona Courtney-Thompson, Paul Docherty, Tim Fraser, Stephanie Jackson, Mary Lindsay

Editorial Assistant:
Emily Hill

Additional editorial assistance:
Susan Bosanko, Edward Bunting, Candace Burch, Deirdre Clark, Jeanette Cossar, Danièle Guitton, Jacqui Hand, David Harding, Nicholas Jackson, Edwina Johnson, David Lambert, Gail Lawther, David Learmount, Paul Jackson, Christine Murdock, Bob Ogden, Cathy Rubinstein, Louise Tucker, Dr. Robert Youngson

Picture Researchers:
Vere Dodds, Danièle Guitton, Anna Lord, Catherine O'Rourke, Christine Rista, Sandra Schneider, Vanessa Smith, Clive Webster

Series Editor:
Martyn Page

Series Art Editor:
Paul Wilkinson

Managing Art Editors
Philip Gilderdale, Steve Knowlden

Art Director
Chez Picthall

Managing Editor
Ruth Midgley

Production:
Jayne Simpson